A TEXTBOOK OF BACTERIOLOGY

This book is made in full compliance with
Government Directive L 120 limiting the
bulk of paper.

A TEXTBOOK OF
BACTERIOLOGY

THE APPLICATION OF BACTERIOLOGY AND IMMUNOLOGY TO THE
ETIOLOGY, DIAGNOSIS, SPECIFIC THERAPY AND PREVENTION OF
INFECTIOUS DISEASES FOR STUDENTS AND PRACTITIONERS
OF MEDICINE AND PUBLIC HEALTH

BY

THE LATE HANS ZINSSER, M.D.
FORMERLY PROFESSOR OF BACTERIOLOGY AND IMMUNOLOGY,
HARVARD UNIVERSITY MEDICAL SCHOOL
FORMERLY CONSULTING BACTERIOLOGIST TO THE PETER BENT BRIGHAM
HOSPITAL AND THE CHILDREN'S HOSPITAL, BOSTON

AND

STANHOPE BAYNE-JONES, M.D.
PROFESSOR OF BACTERIOLOGY, YALE UNIVERSITY SCHOOL OF MEDICINE,
NEW HAVEN, CONNECTICUT

EIGHTH EDITION, REVISED AND RESET

D. APPLETON–CENTURY COMPANY
INCORPORATED

NEW YORK   LONDON

Dedicated
to the memory of
PHILIP HANSON HISS, Jr., M.D.

PREFACE TO THE EIGHTH EDITION

INTENDED for students of medicine and public health this *Textbook* presents the fundamentals of bacteriology and immunology and the application of this knowledge to the understanding and control of infectious diseases. A primarily medical point of view has led naturally to a selection of material for inclusion in the book. The conception of medicine, however, as a division of biological and social sciences, in relation to other sciences, gives scope for both a general and practical treatise. A large amount of space has been devoted to the biology of bacteria and other infectious agents and to the physiology and chemistry of states of susceptibility and immunity in man and animals. We have attempted in this edition, as in previous editions, to coördinate the knowledge provided by the basic sciences with technical and practical information.

Rapid advances in bacteriology and immunology have been made during the past few years. To mention only a few of these: Systematic studies of genera and species of bacteria have disclosed new relationships and added new types. There is now a general acceptance of the main facts of bacterial variability, although the relation of forms to possible life-cycles is still uncertain. Many variants have been newly recognized. This is somewhat confusing and troublesome to the technician with the limited objective of tagging organisms but it is the breath of biological life in the body of the science. Studies of bacterial metabolism have resulted in the isolation of substances requisite for growth and of substances produced by growth of bacteria. Increased knowledge has been gained concerning the enzyme-systems of bacterial respiration and the relation of oxidation-reduction potentials to growth and activity. The toxins of diphtheria and tetanus have been highly purified. Improvements have been made in the serum treatment of pneumonia and in the methods for recognition of types of pneumococci. The serological grouping of streptococci has brought order into a chaotic field of knowledge. Certain antigens have been characterized chemically. New methods are available for the selection and preservation of strains of organisms bearing the so-called "Vi" antigen, essential for immunization against infection. Intensive investigation of the *Rickettsiae* has yielded improved methods of cultivation, the preparation of antigens and antiserums through the use of these cultures, and a correlation of knowledge of relationships among the types of typhus fever and spotted fevers. Ultramicroscopic viruses have been recognized and handled with sharper precision. Chemical studies have indicated that certain viruses may be crystallizable proteins of large molecular size and weight, endowed with autocatalytic properties. Influenza has been recognized as a virus disease. The epidemiology of many virus diseases has been extended through methods of recognition and control. Vitamins and hormones have been brought into relation with states of susceptibility and immunity. Increased attention has been paid to the bearing of the hereditary constitution of animals upon their resistance to infection and intoxication. Bacterial chemotherapy, in the doldrums until recently, has been revived by the discovery and use of sulfanilamide. Technical methods have been improved and new procedures devised.

The text of the seventh edition, published in 1934, contained much new material drawn from modern bacteriology and immunology. Corrections and partial revisions were made in 1935 and in 1937. For the eighth edition we have made many changes throughout the book and have rewritten large sections, in order to incorporate in this volume much of the newer knowledge which has been gained along the lines mentioned above and, in fact, in almost every division of the field.

The section on pathogenic protozoa has been omitted. Neither of us is competent to deal with protozoology. Furthermore, it seemed inappropriate to include that subject in a textbook concerned primarily with bacteria and related organisms. Redundant and obsolete material in other sections also has been deleted. The index has been shortened to provide better workability. A few new illustrations have been added. The eighth edition, therefore, is more compact and somewhat reduced in size.

We are deeply indebted to many colleagues, students and friendly critics for advice and help in the preparation of this text. In addition to references to authors, acknowledgments for special assistance are noted in appropriate places in the book. To these investigators and to others to whom we have offered thanks personally we wish to express our gratitude.

H. ZINSSER
S. BAYNE-JONES

PREFACE TO THE FIRST EDITION

THE volume here presented is primarily a treatise on the fundamental laws and technic of bacteriology, as illustrated by their application to the study of pathogenic bacteria.

So ubiquitous are the bacteria and so manifold their activities that bacteriology, although one of the youngest of sciences, has already been divided into special fields —medical, sanitary, agricultural and industrial—having little in common, except problems of general bacterial physiology and certain fundamental technical procedures.

From no other point of approach, however, is such a breadth of conception attainable, as through the study of bacteria in their relation to disease processes in man and animals. Through such a study one must become familiar not only with the growth characteristics and products of the bacteria apart from the animal body, thus gaining a knowledge of methods and procedures common to the study of pathogenic and nonpathogenic organisms, but also with those complicated reactions taking place between the bacteria and their products on the one hand and the cells and fluids of the animal body on the other—reactions which often manifest themselves as symptoms and lesions of disease or by visible changes in the test tube.

Through a study and comprehension of the processes underlying these reactions, our knowledge of cell physiology has been broadened, and facts of inestimable value have been discovered, which have thrown light upon some of the most obscure problems of infection and immunity and have led to hitherto unsuspected methods of treatment and diagnosis. Thus, through medical bacteriology—that highly specialized offshoot of general biology and pathology—have been given back to the parent sciences and to medicine in general methods and knowledge of the widest application.

It has been our endeavor, therefore, to present this phase of our subject in as broad and critical a manner as possible in the sections dealing with infection and immunity and with methods of biological diagnosis and treatment of disease, so that the student and practitioner of medicine, by becoming familiar with underlying laws and principles, may not only be in a position to realize the meaning and scope of some of these newer discoveries and methods, but may be in better position to decide for themselves their proper application and limitations.

We have not hesitated, whenever necessary for a proper understanding of processes of bacterial nutrition or physiology, or for breadth of view in considering problems of the relation of bacteria to our food supply and environment, to make free use of illustrations from the more special fields of agricultural and sanitary bacteriology, and some special methods of the bacteriology of sanitation are given in the last division of the book, dealing with the bacteria in relation to our food and environment.

In conclusion it may be said that the scope and arrangement of subjects treated of in this book are the direct outcome of many years of experience in the instruction of students in medical and in advanced university courses in bacteriology, and that it is our hope that this volume may not only meet the needs of such students but may prove of value to the practitioner of medicine for whom it has also been written.

It is a pleasure to acknowledge the courtesy of those who furnished us with illustrations for use in the text, and our indebtedness to Dr. Gardner Hopkins and Professor Francis Carter Wood for a number of the photomicrographs taken especially for this work.

P. H. H., JR.
H. Z.

CONTENTS

THE GENERAL BIOLOGY OF BACTERIA AND THE GENERAL METHODS OF BACTERIOLOGY

CONTENTS

PATHOGENIC MICRO-ORGANISMS

CONTENTS

xix

MEDICAL MYCOLOGY, THE MOLDS, YEASTS, ACTINOMYCETES
AND PATHOGENIC FUNGI

DISEASES CAUSED BY ULTRAMICROSCOPIC VIRUSES, THE EXANTHEMATA AND DISEASES OF UNCERTAIN ETIOLOGY

TECHNICAL METHODS OF BACTERIOLOGY, IMMUNOLOGY AND SEROLOGY

A TEXTBOOK OF BACTERIOLOGY

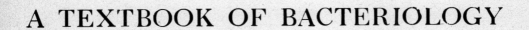

SECTION I

THE GENERAL BIOLOGY OF BACTERIA AND THE GENERAL METHODS OF BACTERIOLOGY

CHAPTER I

OUTLINE OF THE HISTORY AND SCOPE OF BACTERIOLOGY

The history of many general concepts now embodied in the doctrines of bacteriology is an account of attempts to solve the problems of the origin of life and the nature of communicable changes in the bodies of living men and animals and in dead organic materials. The visible aspects of these phenomena were as apparent and as interesting to ancient observers as they are to modern biologists. Their hidden causes were no less provocative of philosophical inquiry and speculation. The early history of what has become the science of microbiology is to be found, therefore, in the writings of the priests, philosophers and scientists who sought to explain the invisible mechanisms of the generation of animals, of fermentation and putrefaction, and the causes of communicable disease.

In the past, as at present, notions of ultimate causes of these phenomena were colored by the theological and philosophical tenets of the time and by the available factual knowledge. Throughout centuries, one group of "theurgical theories" of vital processes and of pestilences has profoundly influenced the thoughts and behavior of people. These ideas, arising from religious beliefs and superstitions, have had and retain practical importance for individuals and society in efforts to control infectious disease. Their influence upon the development of bacteriology has been detrimental in so far as it has inhibited experimentation, and beneficial to the extent to which it has provoked scientific testing of the validity of theological dogma. The other group of conceptions, springing from a basis of knowledge available at one time, was projected into the future by the force of admirable reasoning and keen foresight. It is among these interesting speculations, which were given significance by the later discovery of micro-organisms, that the important early doctrines of the genesis of life from life, the vital elements in fermentation and putrefaction, and the living cause of contagion are to be found.

In this historical outline we shall review only the theories and investigations which appear to have exerted the greatest influence upon the development of medical bacteriology. For many years the chief source book of information on these subjects was Löffler's lectures on the history of bacteriology. Since then the literature has been enlarged by the publication of many papers and books on the history of science and notably the history of biology and medicine. Fortunately for the students of bacteriology, Bulloch published in 1930 the results of his scholarly investigations. This is now the most reliable and valuable account of the history of bacteriology from its beginning to the end of the nineteenth century. We acknowledge

1

a great debt to Bulloch's *History of Bacteriology*, which has served us as a guide to information and which has directed our studies to many of the most important sources.

In order to understand the course taken by the development of bacteriology it is necessary to know something about the theories of fermentation, putrefaction, origin of animals and nature of contagion as they existed before the discovery of bacteria.

The rising of bread and the transformation of grape juice into wine have always excited wonderment. The Biblical proverb: "a little leaven leaveneth the whole lump" (I Corinthians, 5:6) is an indication of the early recognition of a communicable element in the changes which were later called fermentations. Before the discovery of bacteria, there appears to have been no definite supposition that the ferment was a living organism. The closest approach to a chemical explanation of the process was the opinion expressed by Thomas Willis in 1659, which Bulloch [1] summarizes as "the conception of fermentation as an internal commotion of the particles of the fermentable substance." This conception influenced chemistry and bacteriology throughout the next two hundred years. About this time, Robert Boyle stated quite clearly that an insight into the nature of disease would be gained through the study of fermentation. In 1663, in an essay "Offering some particulars relating to the pathologicall part of physick" he wrote: "And let me adde, that he that throughly understands the nature of Ferments and Fermentations, shall probably be much better able then he that ignores them, to give a fair account of divers *phænomena* of severall diseases (as well Feavers as others) which will perhaps be never thoroughly understood, without an insight into the doctrine of Fermentation." [2] This prophecy was fulfilled by Pasteur.

Saint Paul's reference to leaven conveyed to his hearers a sense of communicable corruption. In addition to this there are many figurative as well as explicit ancient statements relating to the transmissibility of decay. The material transferred from a decomposing body to other bodies, both living and dead, was commonly supposed to be a sort of poisonous exhalation. It was noted that epidemics accompanied wars and a relationship was conceived to exist between vapors given off by putrefying bodies and the spread of disease. These notions crystallized in a doctrine of miasms. The miasmatic diseases were recognized as communicable maladies, transmitted chiefly through the air and contracted by inhalation. Miasms were supposed to come not only from putrefying materials but also from changes in the atmosphere and mysterious emanations from the earth. The doctrine of miasms has persisted throughout centuries. It still shows its vitality in such medical words as "influenza" and "malaria," and continues to play an expensive rôle in modern plumbing and sanitary arrangements. Investigations on the actual causes of putrefaction and the nature of miasmatic diseases became immensely important in the development of bacteriology.

Side by side with theories of the divine causes of disease there have been since

---

[1] W. Bulloch, *History of Bacteriology*, in A System of Bacteriology in Relation to Medicine, Medical Research Council, London, 1930, p. 23.

[2] Robert Boyle, *The Usefulness of Experimental Philosophy*, Oxford, 1663. Part II, Essay II, p. 44. This title is listed as No. 50 in *A Bibliography of the Honourable Robert Boyle*. Oxford, 1932, p. 43, by J. F. Fulton. We are indebted to Dr. Fulton for having located this statement and for the transcription of it which we have quoted.

ancient times shrewd guesses that the agents of communicable diseases were living. It is said that Varro and Columella, in the first century B.C., expressed the opinion that disease was caused by invisible living things, "animalia minuta," taken into the body with food or breathed in with the air. Unsupported by any proof of the existence of invisible organisms, these ideas had little or no influence. It appears to have been recognized in the reign of Justinian that bubonic plague was contagious. The devastating epidemics of the Middle Ages repeatedly demonstrated that disease was contagious, since it was so often seen that a new case of pestilential disease arose from more or less close contact with a previous case. The establishment of quarantine by Marseilles and Venice in the fourteenth century was a practical application of this belief. It is probable that the epidemic spread of syphilis in Europe in the late fifteenth and early sixteenth centuries "had the greatest influence," as Ford [3] states, "in teaching the world that disease can pass from individual to individual." "Here the mechanism of transmission was almost self-evident." Certainly, a knowledge of the natural history of syphilis influenced Fracastorius, who most clearly stated the theory that the agent of communicable disease was living, a "contagium vivum." In his book on contagious diseases, published in 1546, Fracastorius described the transmission of disease by direct contact, by intermediary inanimate fomites, and through the air "ad distans." He called the agents of disease "seminaria morbi," living germs, and he expressed the opinion that the seeds of these agents, passing from one infected animal, produced the same disease in another which received them. These essentially true statements were unconvincing because they were not based upon a demonstration of the physical reality of the hypothetical invisible organisms. Even after the discovery of bacteria confirmation of the theories of Fracastorius was long delayed.

The generation of animals has been a fruitful source of speculation and controversy since antiquity. It was supposed that animals and plants whose forbears or seeds could not be seen were produced by spontaneous combinations of elements and ethereal principles. Backed by Aristotle's authority, this conception of spontaneous generation, or abiogenesis, dominated thought throughout the Middle Ages. Samson's riddle relating to the production of bees and honey from the carcass of a lion (Judges 14: 8, 14) was matched in 1652 by van Helmont's directions for generating mice from pieces of dirty cloth and fermenting grain. What appeared to be particularly astonishing to van Helmont was that the mice generating from rags and grain were sexually mature and capable of copulating with mice descended from natural parents. Similar fanciful notions of the generation of insects were put to experimental test by Francesco Redi shortly after the middle of the seventeenth century. Redi proved conclusively that the maggots which appeared in decomposing meat were developed from the eggs of flies and showed by experiments that when meat was screened by gauze so that flies could not deposit their eggs in it no visible worms or insects were generated from it, although the meat putrefied. Redi's conclusion that life comes from life, supported by experiments which any one could repeat, should have decided the issue. As a matter of fact Redi seems to have retained a belief in the spontaneous generation of some insects. About this time William Harvey gave new currency to the Aristotelian notion of form and principle in the statement of his belief

3 W. W. Ford, *Text-book of Bacteriology*, W. B. Saunders Co., Philadelphia, 1927, p. 24.

that an "incorperal" something fertilized the ovum. Credulity persisted in spite of the knowledge gained by Redi's experiments. After bacteria were discovered, the doctrine of spontaneous generation took on a vitality in proportion to the great novelty and totally obscure origins of these minute creatures. Much of the foundation of bacteriology was laid in the experimental work done to prove that bacteria were not generated spontaneously.

One piece of apparatus was essential to the discovery of bacteria. This was a magnifying glass of sufficient power. Simple spherical or biconvex magnifying glasses had been in use for a long time and there had been a considerable amount of microscopic observation of mites, insects, lichens and other objects before the middle of the seventeenth century. Singer has shown that by the year 1661, the importance of microscopy was becoming more generally appreciated. But since the discoverer of the bacteria, and of many other micro-organisms, made with his own hands the superior simple magnifying glasses through which he first saw these previously unseen animalcules, and since he appears to have known nothing about the learned works of his predecessors and contemporaries in microscopy, it is misleading to set forth the history of the invention and development of the compound microscope as a prelude to the opening scenes of bacteriology. According to Singer and Disney the compound microscope was invented independently by two men at about the same time. The compound microscope appears to have been the result of a fortuitous combination of lenses placed in a tube by Zaccharias Jansen in Holland in the first decade of the seventeenth century and the rational invention of Galileo, who made an instrument according to the principles of optics in Italy in 1609. The microscope has been improved repeatedly. Each major improvement has opened new vistas and made possible new discoveries in microbiology.

From this brief review of older theories and observations, it is apparent that before 1676 the doctrine of spontaneous generation had been rendered doubtful if not untenable, that a relationship between fermentation, putrefaction and disease had been foreseen, that a living agent of disease, transmissible by contact, fomites and through the air had been forecast and that microscopy had reached a stage capable of displaying at least some of the minute agents of these communicable changes and of disease. It might be supposed that only the discovery of micro-organisms was needed to advance the solution of a host of problems. It will be seen that the course of advancement was by no means so logical as this. The discovery of the bacteria had little influence, through more than a century, on the solution of the problems of infectious disease. The discovery was unappreciated, overlooked or served to revive superstitions. Progress was made not by a direct study of the bacteria or by the application of previous knowledge to new investigations of disease, but along a circuitous route of what now seem to be almost irrelevant controversies.

It was necessary for the early microscopists to invent a terminology for the strange small creatures they saw. They called them "little animals," "little worms" or "little insects." It is certain that these terms were applied to microscopic tissue débris and other inanimate objects. By interpreting these vague descriptions in modern language, claims have been made that a number of men saw bacteria before Leeuwenhoek. The honor of priority has been urged by Singer [4] in behalf of two men: Pierre Borel

4 C. Singer, *J. Roy Microscop. Soc.*, 1915, pp. 335-338, 338-340.

(1620-1671) and Athanasius Kircher (1602-1680). We have not examined Borel's book, *Historiarum et Observationum Medicophysicarum*, published in 1653, from which Singer quotes a passage describing "animals of the shape of whales or dolphins swimming in the human blood as in a red ocean." It may be true that Borel saw blood corpuscles, small clots, vinegar eels, tissue fragments and small larvae of insects, but we are not convinced that it is even "probable that he caught a glimpse of infusoria and possibly bacteria." An indirect claim that Kircher saw bacteria about 1650 was made by Löffler in the opening chapter of his *Vorlesungen,* where he states that Kircher announced the discovery of a new world of living beings. Nevertheless, Löffler admits that Kircher's microscope gave only a 32-fold linear magnification and that Kircher could not have seen the bacterial cause of plague. Singer grants that the "small worms" described by Kircher were probably blood corpuscles and rouleaux of red cells, but echoes the old supposition that he "had perhaps seen infusoria." We have examined the passages referred to, and others, in Kircher's book on plague and have not found any recognizable description of bacteria in these parts of the writings of this learned Jesuit. Both Borel and Kircher definitely suggested that the microscopic forms they saw in blood and pus and in putrefying flesh were the living agents of plague. In fact, Kircher supports the theories of Fracastorius with microscopic observations. While the claims for priority in the discovery of bacteria by Borel and Kircher can be dismissed, it seems certain that both of these men, particularly Kircher, had some insight into the living nature of the agents of contagion, and influenced favorably the spread of the doctrine of *contagium vivum.*

The bacteria were discovered by Antony van Leeuwenhoek (1632-1723) in the year 1676. This statement seems to have been placed beyond the reach of refutation through available historical records by the great biography of van Leeuwenhoek published by Dobell in 1932. In addition to translations from the "Nether-Dutch" of all of the important parts of the letters of Leeuwenhoek in which bacteria and protozoa are described, this book contains completely convincing evidence that Leeuwenhoek was in fact the "father of protozoölogy and bacteriology."

For the details of Leeuwenhoek's life and of what is known of how he made his magnifying glasses and observed the thousands of minute things he saw, the reader is referred to Dobell's biography. We shall present only the briefest summary of the true and objective observations made on bacteria by this indefatigable and remarkable man. The "microscope" with which he saw bacteria was a simple biconvex lens, of short focal length, clamped between two metal plates. The preparation under examination in a drop of fluid or thin glass tube was fixed upon a metal point and moved into focus by means of screws. One type of the instrument is shown in Figure 1, copied from a drawing made by Dobell. It is probable that Leeuwenhoek's best glasses gave a magnification of 300 diameters. He never disclosed the secrets of all his methods and it is not known with certainty how he obtained the necessary illumination of his preparations. Dobell suggests that Leeuwenhoek probably hit upon some simple means of dark ground illumination. The first written descriptions of bacteria are in his letter to the Royal Society of London, dated October 9, 1676 (Dobell's No. 18). Here he gives recognizable descriptions of bacteria in various waters and in "pepper water" in which he was searching with his magnifying glass for the cause of the hotness of pepper. Clearer descriptions of several forms of bacteria are given in his letter to the Royal Society, dated September 17, 1683 (Dobell's No. 39). In this he described the animalcules he found in the feces of man and animals and in the tartar from his teeth. A drawing of bacteria accompanied this letter. The original has been lost, but the record has been preserved in the plate illustrating the Latin translation of this letter published in 1695. We reproduce a photograph of this famous drawing here, as Figure 2. It shows beyond question that Leeuwenhoek saw the chief forms of bacteria—cocci, rods, filaments and spirochetes. When Dobell nominated Leeuwenhoek the first and greatest of all microbiologists, he gave him first place among all bacteriologists because in 1675 Leeuwenhoek discovered the bacteria in various waters, in 1680 he discovered anaerobic bacteria in pepper infusions, in 1680 he described yeast in beer, and in 1681 he discovered bacteria and spiro-

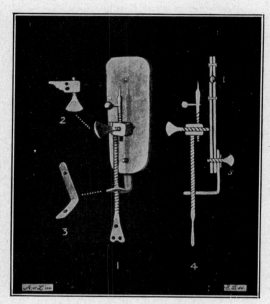

FIG. 1.—LEEUWENHOEK'S "MICROSCOPE."

Plate XXI, from *Antony van Leeuwenhoek and His "Little Animals,"* by C. Dobell, 1932. Reproduced with the permission of the publishers, Harcourt, Brace and Co., New York.

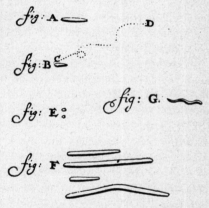

FIG. 2.—LEEUWENHOEK'S PICTURE OF BACTERIA FROM THE HUMAN MOUTH.

From *Arcana Naturae*, 1695. Dobell's identifications are as follows: *A*, a motile *Bacillus; B, Selenomonas sputigena; E*, Micrococci; *F, Leptothrix buccalis; G*, probably *Spirochaeta buccalis.*

chetes in the mouth and in the intestines.

After Leeuwenhoek's discovery of the bacteria, two main directions of investigation were indicated: the study of the nature and the classification of these organisms and the study of the relation of the bacteria to fermentation, putrefaction and disease.

In 1678 Hooke confirmed Leeuwenhoek's discovery and during the early part of the eighteenth century, the "little animals" were seen and described by a number of microscopists. The difficulties of assigning them a place and giving them a name are exemplified in Linnaeus' creation in 1758 of a genus of *Vermes* which he called "Chaos." A few years later, Wrisberg named these organisms *Infusoria.* No doubt this helped Linnaeus to give them a name, for in the eleventh edition of his *Systema naturae*, in 1767, according to Bulloch he formed a class called *Chaos infusorium.* That he was still confused as to the nature of bacteria and protozoa is indicated by his listing them with "the ethereal nimbus floating in the month of flowering." In some respects the classification of bacteria is chaotic even now.

The first important classification of the *Infusoria* was made by O. F. Müller in 1773 and 1786. The terms *Vibrio* and *Monas* were introduced by Müller. Some fifty years later, Ehrenberg, without really understanding the nature of bacteria, began to publish classifications of them. In 1829 he established the genus *Bacterium*, using a term formed from the Greek word βάκτηριον, the diminutive of βάκτρον, signifying a staff. The whole subject of bacteriology has taken its common name from the prominence of the rod forms. In his huge book on the infusion animals, published in 1838, Ehrenberg established more firmly the generic terms *Bacterium* and *Vibrio* and introduced others which are used to-day, notably *Spirillum* and *Spirochaeta*. Ehrenberg regarded the bacteria as complete animals, classing them with the polygastric protozoa. The transference of the bacteria to the plant kingdom was first proposed by Ferdinand Cohn in 1854. Cohn's publications after 1872 marked a great advance in the systematic study of the bacteria. His classical papers had an enormous influence. His personal influence as a teacher and director of investigators was equally great. Under Cohn's guidance, the botanical point of view became dominant in bacteriology. In 1857, Nägeli had noted the relationship of bacteria to fungi and had introduced the term *Schizomycetes*, which has remained the scientific designation of these organisms.

It is certain that the analogies to fungi suggested in this term conveyed more than the facts warranted. About the middle of the nineteenth century it was found that one and the same fungus could appear in several vegetative forms and in various fructifying forms. Knowledge of the demonstrated life cycles of fungi was extended by supposition to the bacteria in which no relationship of form to developmental stage, other than that of spore formation, had been demonstrated. At this time, no one knew with certainty that a culture of bacteria consisted of only one organism. There were no pure cultures, except those obtained by accident, and these were liable to uncontrollable contamination. The most complex and variable life cycles were described by Hallier, Nägeli and Billroth. Billroth's "cocco-bacteria septica" may be regarded as a type species of these polymorphic hypothetical organisms. It was evident that a corrective was needed to stop increasing confusion. Pasteur believed in the constancy of form, and Koch, after his introduction of solid media for the cultivation of bacteria, enforced a strict conception of monomorphism. Nevertheless, the biologically sound notions that bacteria were as variable as other organisms and perhaps had a life cycle never died out. The corrective influences went too far. Many true variants of bacteria were discarded as contaminations. Interest in the variations of bacteria, studies of the variants and investigations of possible life cycles have been actively revived within the past quarter-century. We shall discuss these phases of bacteriology more fully in our chapters on classification and bacterial variation.

Leeuwenhoek did not appreciate the significance of his discovery, nor did any one else for a long time. Dobell has said that the notions and knowledge were there, but they were premature. In the eighteenth century, however, there were several definite statements of the germ theory of disease, based in part upon what was known of Leeuwenhoek's "little animals." One of the earliest of these was Benjamin Marten's book on consumptions, published in 1720. Marten refers to Leeuwenhoek's discoveries and definitely states the theory that "the original and essential cause of consumption may possibly be some certain species of Animalcula or wonderfully minute living creatures," [5] which, lodging and growing in the lungs, produce the disorders of consumption. He did not believe in spontaneous generation and had a notion of the specificity of microbes, as expressed in his statement: "the ova or seed of animalculae that cause consumption [are] different from those that cause smallpox." Marten's writing is in a distinctly modern vein, but his book had no basis in demonstrated fact and Marten himself did not apply his theory. The most remarkably clear statement of the germ theory of disease in the eighteenth century was that of Plenciz in 1762. Plenciz referred to Leeuwenhoek's discoveries of animalcules, discussed transmission of disease according to the Fracastorian methods, by contact, by fomites and through the air, stated his belief in the doctrine of *contagium vivum*, and explained his conception of the specificity of the living agents of infectious disease. There was truth in these ideas, but they were not accompanied by any experimental proof.

The conception of a *contagium vivum* was thus practically established with the work of Plenciz and many others who followed in his train, but the astonishingly slight impression which the acute reasoning of these men left upon the medical thought of their day is illustrative of the futility of the most penetrating speculation when unsupported by experimental data.

Almost a hundred and fifty years passed after Leeuwenhoek's discovery of bacteria and protozoa before any definite applications of this new knowledge were made. In a remarkable series of investigations during the first quarter of the nineteenth century, Agostino Bassi proved almost conclusively that a fungus, later named in his honor *Botrytis bassiana*, was the cause of a disease of silkworms called "mal segno" in Italy and "muscardine" in France. Bassi's biographer, Calandruccio, called Bassi the founder of the theory of parasitism, and Bulloch states that "Bassi can justly be claimed as the real founder of the doctrine of pathogenic micro-organisms of vegetable origin—a man of great originality, and the forerunner of Schwann, Pasteur, Koch and Lister."

Bassi's work was confirmed and extended. In 1839 Schoenlein found the causative fungus in the lesions of favus, and in 1846 Eichstedt discovered a fungus in the skin-scrapings from patients with pityriasis versicolor and noted the contagiousness of the disease, since his patients were bedfellows. In 1837 Donné found bacteria and spirochetes in secretions of the genital tract of men and women, and described a spirochete, probably *Spirochaeta refringens*, in fluid from syphilitic lesions. Rayer and Davaine had seen rod-shaped organisms in the blood of animals dead of anthrax in 1850. Rayer recalled experiments made by Barthélemy in 1825 showing that anthrax was inoculable in series in sheep. By 1863 Davaine had proved by experiment that the disease could be transmitted by blood and the sediment of laked blood containing these rods and could not be transmitted by blood from which these rods were absent. This work was important in the influence it had upon the development of a bacterial doctrine of infection in contrast to the prevailing notion that fungi were the chief agents of contagion. Between 1868 and 1873 Obermeier at the Charité in Berlin, under Virchow's eye, was carefully confirming his discovery of

5 B. Marten, *A New Theory of Consumptions*, London, 1720, pp. 50, 51, 55, 79 and 83.

the relationship of a spirillum to relapsing fever. He demonstrated the first case in which a pathogenic microörganism was found in the blood of man.

It must be remembered that during these early years of etiological research investigators had pure cultures to work with only by accident and did not know when contaminating growths occurred in the materials they used. There was much speculation and loose thinking and a considerable amount of equivocal work that hindered the development of an essentially true doctrine. A firm corrective of this tendency was the expression of a logical and critical point of view by Jacob Henle in 1840. In his theoretical discussion of miasmatic and contagious diseases, Henle, the future teacher of Robert Koch, affirmed his belief in the animate nature and specific action of the agents of contagion. Referring particularly to the investigations of Jenner, Bassi, Audouin, Schoenlein and Ricord, he anticipated Koch's postulates by insisting that the proof that an organism causes a disease must be brought by demonstration of the constant presence of the micro-organism in the lesions, the isolation of this micro-organism and the reproduction of the disease by inoculation. With much the same point of view Villemin proved by experiments on rabbits in 1865 that tubercle was inoculable. Villemin interpreted his experiments as evidence that tuberculosis was the effect of a virus. He thought that the virus must be present in the morbid products and when introduced into a susceptible animal must be able to reproduce itself and at the same time reproduce the disease.

While these experiments and others carried out between 1807 and 1868 seem to indicate that bacteriology was advancing along the course it was to follow to its great accomplishments through the school of Cohn and Koch, the actual path proved to be not so straight. A most important and clarifying progress was being made along other lines, through studies on fermentation, spontaneous generation and, again, the diseases of silkworms. The great advance to be considered next was led by Pasteur.

In 1837, Schwann, a botanist, showed that the yeasts, found in fermenting substances, were living beings, which bore a causal relationship to the process of fermentation. At almost the same time, similar observations were made by a French physicist, Cagniard-Latour. The opinions advanced by these men on the nature of fermentation aroused much interest and discussion, since, at that time and for a long period thereafter, fermentation was ascribed universally to protein decomposition, a process which was entirely obscure but firmly believed to be of a purely chemical nature. These observations, however, signalled the approaching solution of the problem.

Although belief in the discovery of Schwann did not master the field until after Pasteur had completed his classical studies upon the fermentations occurring in beer and wine, yet the conception of a "fermentum vivum" aroused much speculation, and the attention of physicians and scientists was attracted to the many analogies existing between phenomena of fermentation and those of disease. The fulfilment of the prophecy of Robert Boyle had begun.

It was during this period also that one of the most fundamental questions, namely, that of the origin of these minute living beings, was being discussed with much passion by the scientific world. It was held by the conservative majority that the micro-organisms described by Leeuwenhoek and others after him were produced by spontaneous generation. The doctrine of spontaneous generation, shaken by Redi, was still solidly established and sanctified by tradition. And it must not be forgotten that without the aid of our modern methods of study, satisfactory proof for or against such a process was not easily brought.

Needham, who published in 1749, had spent much time in fortifying his opinions in favor of spontaneous generation by extensive experimentation. He had placed putrefying material and vegetable infusions in sealed flasks, exposing them for a short time to heat, by immersing them in a vessel of boiling water, and had later shown them to be teeming with micro-organisms. He was supported in his views by no less an authority than Buffon. The work of Needham, however, showed a number of experimental inaccuracies which were thoroughly sifted by the Abbé Spallanzani. This investigator repeated the experiments of Needham, employing, however, greater care in sealing his flasks, and subjecting them to a more thorough exposure to heat. His results did not support the views of Needham, but were answered by the latter with the argument that by excessive heating he had produced chemical changes in his solutions which had made spontaneous generation impossible.

The experiments of Schulze, in 1836, who failed to find living organisms in infusions which had been boiled, and to which air had been admitted only after passage through strongly acid solutions, and similar results obtained by Schwann, who had passed the air through highly heated tubes, were open to criticism by their opponents, who claimed that chemical alteration of the air subjected to such drastic influences had been responsible for the absence of bacteria in the infusion. Similar experiments by Schröder and Dusch, who had stoppered their flasks with cotton plugs, were not open to this objection, but had also failed to convince. The question was not definitely settled until the years immediately following 1860, when Pasteur conducted a series of experiments which were not only important in incontrovertibly refuting the doctrine of spontaneous generation of bacteria, but in establishing the principles of scientific investigation which have influenced bacteriological research since his time.

Pasteur attacked the problem from two points of view. In the first place he demonstrated that when air was filtered through cotton wool innumerable micro-organisms were deposited upon the filter. A single shred of such a contaminated filter dropped into a flask of previously sterilized nutritive fluid sufficed to bring about a rapid and luxuriant growth of micro-organisms. In the second place, he succeeded in showing that similar, sterilized "putrescible" liquids, if left in contact with air, would remain uncontaminated provided that the entrance of dust particles was prohibited. This he succeeded in doing by devising flasks, the necks of which had been drawn out into fine tubes bent in the form of a U. The ends of these U-tubes, being left open, permitted the sedimentation of dust from the air as far as the lowest angle of the tube, but, in the absence of an air current, no dust was carried up the second arm into the liquid. In such flasks, he showed that no contamination took place but could be immediately induced by slanting the entire apparatus until the liquid was allowed to run into the bent arm of the U-tube. Finally, by exposing a series of flasks containing sterile yeast infusion at different atmospheric levels, in places in which the air was subject to varying degrees of dust contamination, he showed an inverse relationship between the purity of the air and the contamination of his flasks with micro-organisms.

The doctrine of spontaneous generation of bacteria had thus received its final refutation, except in one particular. It was not yet clear why complete sterility was not always obtained by the application of definite degrees of heat. This final link in the chain of evidence was supplied, some ten years later, by Cohn, who, in 1871, was the first to observe and correctly interpret bacterial spores and to demonstrate their high powers of resistance against heat and other deleterious influences.

Meanwhile, Pasteur, while investigating spontaneous generation, had been carrying on experiments upon the subject of fermentation along the lines suggested by Cagniard-Latour. As a consequence of these experiments, he not only confirmed the opinions both of this author and of Schwann concerning the fermentation of beer and wine by yeast, but was able to show that a number of other fermentations, such as those of lactic and butyric acid, as well as the decomposition of organic matter by putrefaction, were directly due to the action of micro-organisms.

The proof that putrefaction was caused by living agents linked old theories with new knowledge and exerted a most active influence upon the medical research in the middle of the nineteenth century. This is illustrated by the work of Lister who was a bacteriologist in his own right as well as a great surgeon. The suppurative processes occurring in wounds had long been regarded as a species of putrefaction. The futility of older notions and the fruitfulness of Pasteur's discoveries are clearly summed up by Lister in the introduction to his paper "On the Antiseptic Principle in the Practice of Surgery." After citing unsuccessful attempts to prevent the occurrence of suppuration by methods designed to exclude air from wounds, Lister wrote: "But when it had been shown by the researches of Pasteur that the septic property of the atmosphere depended, not on the oxygen or any gaseous constituent, but on minute organisms suspended in it, which owed their energy to their vitality, it occurred to me that decomposition in the injured part might be avoided without excluding the air, by applying as a dressing some material capable of destroying the life of the floating particles." [6] He then recounted his extraordinary success in preventing suppuration by the use of carbolic acid. Thus, through bacteriology, were instituted the antiseptic principles, later largely replaced by aseptic methods, which have made modern surgery possible.

The controversy over spontaneous generation was raging in England, after 1850, almost as intensely as in France. In England, as in France, the chief opponent of the doctrine was a man of ideas, great experimental skill, keen insight and exact method. This was John Tyndall, who, starting from experiments to remove motes from air, made many important discoveries in bacteriology. He discovered independently the great heat-resistance of spores, devised a method of fractional sterilization and confirmed many of Pasteur's findings. By means of lectures and demonstrations, and by a notable book published in 1882, Tyndall, as Bulloch states, "gave the final blow to the doctrine of spontaneous generation" and opened the road for the progress of the germ theory of disease.

In 1865 and 1866 there was a devastating epidemic of cholera in Europe. The disaster forced a review of what was known and spurred attempts to gain new knowledge by applying new ideas and new methods. The most conspicuous move along the new line of the germ theory of disease, announced with a flourish of long papers and drawings, proved to be a false lead. This was the work of Hallier, the professor

[6] J. Lister, "On the Antiseptic Principle in the Practice of Surgery," *Brit. M. J.* 1867. 2:246.

of botany in Jena, who thought that he had discovered the cause of cholera in a polymorphous fungus. Hallier cultivated *Mucor, Penicillium*, and other organisms of whose presence he was not aware, under a bell jar. The glass cover kept out organisms from the air, but the materials put into the apparatus were not sterile before they were inoculated with cholera feces. As a result, Hallier was able to see in juxtapositions of cocci and bacteria with the mycelium and spores of fungi all the evidences that he interpreted as indicating transformation of one form into the other. Hallier's work enjoyed a brief period of influence. Even Lister published pictures showing the metamorphosis of fungi into bacteria. There were, however, competent critics of mixed cultures even at that time. The most outspoken of these was de Bary, who pointed out clearly that Hallier's cultures were of no value since it was highly probable that the bacterial forms thought to be derived from fungi were the progeny of germs present in the original substrate. He argued that the cause of cholera could not be established by such means.

Amid a conflict of opinion there was naturally much confusion. The state of mind in 1867 is well illustrated by the title and contents of a long review published that year in the Virchow-Hirsch *Jahresbericht*. This article is entitled "Acute Infectionskrankheiten." Among the acute infectious diseases listed in it are snake-bite, hay fever, cholera, influenza, meningitis and other diseases of bacterial origin. This was an etymologically correct usage of the word, but it shows that the term had not yet been set apart from its older general meaning of "staining or tainting with morbid matter" and given its modern significance as a term for diseases caused by living parasitic agents.

The time was approaching when bacteriology was to enter its great period of contribution to the knowledge of the causes of communicable disease. In France, Pasteur and his associates had completed their studies of spontaneous generation, fermentation, putrefaction, the diseases of silkworms and the disorders of beer. Much had been learned about bacteria in general and there had been important medical and industrial applications of bacteriology. Technical methods of sterilization of media and apparatus had been devised, methods for limiting contaminations by organisms from the air were in use, and concepts of bacterial specificity were being established. But the exact technic of the study of bacteria had not been sufficiently advanced to yield systematically conclusive results. Pasteur, approaching his sixtieth year, was about to undertake those studies which became the foundation of a new science of immunology. Etiological investigations continued in France, but the great successes in the search for the bacterial causes of disease were soon to be achieved in Germany, through the school of Ferdinand Cohn and Robert Koch. The date of the beginning of this new development was 1876.

In 1876, Robert Koch, who had been a pupil of Jacob Henle, came to Breslau at the invitation of Cohn to demonstrate the results of his studies on anthrax. In Cohn's laboratory, Koch exhibited his culture methods, showed the life cycle of the anthrax bacillus from spore to spore, and proved beyond doubt the ability of cultures of this organism to produce the disease. Koch's classical paper on the etiology of anthrax, published in 1876, was the first of a great series of enlightening contributions by him and his pupils. It inaugurated a new era of exact research in bacteriology.

Koch realized the importance of method and technic and was not long in introducing many of the procedures which are now everyday, indispensable practices in laboratories of bacteriology. From Weigert, Ehrlich and Salomonsen he learned methods of staining bacteria with aniline dyes. In his work on anthrax his chief culture medium had been sterile aqueous humor from the eyes of animals. He had seen the advantages of the older opaque solid media made from potato, beets, starch, bread, egg-white and flesh, but realized that they were uncertain and incapable of giving all the desired information about bacterial colonies. In order to separate one species of bacterium from another, Koch devised a transparent solid medium in 1881 by mixing gelatin with Löffler's peptone solution. During a period of thirteen years, from about 1870 to 1883, and especially during the seven years after 1876, fundamental discoveries went hand in hand with the advance of technic, and improvements in apparatus.

The background and chronology of discoveries in the period of fifteen years from 1876 to 1890, which Bulloch has called "the heyday of bacteriological aetiological discovery" [7] would make a longer account than we have space for here. As examples of the accomplishments of those years we shall mention only a few. In 1876, Koch established the etiology of anthrax; in 1880, Koch discovered the causes of several wound infections; in 1881, Koch discovered the cholera vibrio; in 1882, Koch discovered the tubercle bacillus, and in the paper reporting that discovery he announced his famous postulates. In the same year, Löffler and Schütz isolated the glanders bacillus. In 1884, Gaffky isolated the typhoid bacillus and Löffler isolated and studied the diphtheria bacillus. Weichselbaum discovered the meningococcus in 1887 and in 1889, Kitasato cultivated the tetanus bacillus. In England, France, Malta and in the United States, as in other countries, etiological discoveries were being made rapidly during this period. In our chapters on specific diseases we shall present a more detailed account of these discoveries and, by inclusion of accounts of discoveries of pathogenic viruses, bring the narrative up to the present time.

The period of great technical advance, 1871 to 1884, saw the gradual introduction of methods of filtration of fluids containing bacteria. It was desirable to test the possible toxicity of filtrates, freed from cells of the organisms. When it became apparent that filter papers, porous clay cups and packed asbestos fibers would not retain bacteria, the logical step of making tighter filters was taken. Chamberland devised a successful filter from a cup of unglazed porcelain in 1884. The Berkefeld type of filter, made of *Kieselguhr*, was introduced by Nordtmeyer in 1891. The Chamberland-Pasteur filters made possible the immediately realized discovery of bacterial toxins. There seems to have been no suspicion at that time that these filters would later appear to be sieves capable of separating visible from invisible forms of life and to be a sort of dividing partition between biological concepts.

It was found, unexpectedly, that the agents of some of the communicable diseases passed through these filters in invisible forms. In 1892, Iwanowski showed that the ultramicroscopic agent of mosaic disease of tobacco plants was present in the filtered juice of diseased leaves. In 1899, Beijerinck independently confirmed this discovery. He conceived of the invisible self-perpetuating agent of mosaic disease as a *contagium fluidum vivum*. A few years later, Löffler and Frosch showed that foot and mouth disease also was due to a filtrable virus. Since then many diseases of animals and

7 W. Bulloch, *J. Path. & Bacteriol.*, 1925, 28:684.

plants have been added to this list by the demonstration of the filtrability of their etiological agents.

By means of filters a remarkable material having the property of causing transmissible lysis of bacteria was discovered by Twort in 1915 and independently by d'Herelle in 1917. This material, called "bacteriophage" by d'Herelle, has many properties analogous to those of the ultramicroscopic viruses. It has been extensively investigated and its use is having important consequences for the modern development of bacteriology.

Investigations since 1900 have proved that viruses are particulate bodies with diameters ranging from 10 to 300 mμ. But it has not been determined whether they are living organisms in the usual sense of the word. Stanley's crystallization of the virus protein of tobacco mosaic in 1935 has revived Beijerinck's conception. The debate over the nature of viruses again involves a definition of life itself. As Gratia notes in his chapter in the volume on ultraviruses edited by Levaditi and Lépine, the doctrine of spontaneous generation is reappearing under the guise of the process of autocatalysis.

Immunology, like bacteriology from which it was an offspring, has an ancient history, a preliminary period of approximate realization and, after a lapse of many years, a rapid advancement through scientific experimentation upon animals.

It is recorded that primitive peoples since ancient times have tried to gain resistance to snake poisoning by treatment with venom. Mithridates VI, King of Pontus, 63 B.C., practised a sort of oral immunization when he attempted to increase his tolerance to many poisons by repeated ingestion of small doses of them. Variolization, the inoculation against smallpox with material from smallpox was an old practice in the Orient which Lady Montagu introduced into England about 1721. Variolization was applied on a considerable scale in this country during the colonial period. The results of some of these efforts to produce protection in advance of infection were occasionally as disastrous as the disease from which escape was being sought, and these attempts were not based upon scientific conceptions.

It is the achievement of Edward Jenner that a practice of the people was converted by controlled observations into a scientific principle of prophylaxis. About 1778, Jenner began his study of the immunity to smallpox which seemed to exist in milkmaids who had been infected with cowpox. He published his observations and experiments in 1798, establishing a method of protection against smallpox and a generally applicable principle of active immunization by the use of attenuated virus.

Almost a hundred years passed between the period of Jenner's investigations and the effective foundation of the science of immunology by Pasteur. In 1877 Pasteur began to be interested in the recovery of animals from infection. At about this time, Pasteur found that fowls inoculated with old cultures of the bacterium of chicken cholera recovered after a mild illness and were subsequently refractory to infection with a virulent culture. He penetrated at once to the core of the phenomenon. He called these old cultures "attenuated virus." Recognizing the relationship of his discovery to the immunity against smallpox consequent upon jennerian vaccination, he gave the general term "vaccine" to the various attenuated organisms he used later to induce immunity to a number of bacterial diseases.

After his studies on chicken cholera Pasteur took up the investigation of anthrax.

As a prophylactic against anthrax he used a vaccine made from cultures of the anthrax bacillus attenuated by growth at 42° to 43° C. At the dramatic demonstration of the power of his vaccine to protect sheep against anthrax at Pouilly-le-Fort in 1881 Pasteur gained an extraordinary triumph.

Living, attenuated virus, however, was not without its dangers. A new advance upon a safer, but possibly less effectual line, was made between 1884 and 1886 in this country by Theobald Smith and D. E. Salmon who showed that immunity could be produced by injections of heat-killed cultures of the hog cholera bacillus. Upon this has been based the great development of vaccine prophylaxis and therapy for man and animals.

From successes in immunization against bacterial diseases Pasteur transferred his interest to the study of rabies. After a slight diversion, during which he incidentally discovered the pneumococcus, he recognized that rabies was due to an ultramicroscopic virus. He discovered that this virus could be attenuated for man by passage through rabbits and could be generally attenuated by desiccation of the spinal cords of experimentally infected animals. Results were achieved rapidly and by 1886 several thousand victims of the bites of dogs and wolves had received the Pasteur treatment. In commemoration of this triumph, the Pasteur Institute was erected in Paris in 1888.

During these years Pasteur had noted the differences in resistance exhibited by different species of animals, had seen that lowering the body temperature decreased the resistance of an animal to infection, and had conceived of immunity as being a sort of exhaustion process, which by depletion of certain essential materials rendered the body unfavorable as a medium for the growth of micro-organisms. But not much had been accomplished in the search for a specific explanation of the mechanism of immunity.

Two schools of immunological doctrine grew up. In one, protection was attributed wholly to the action of the blood and tissue fluids. In the other, certain cells of the body were regarded as the agents of defense against infection. It is apparent now that there was much truth in both points of view and that since blood and tissue fluids are the products of cells the distinctions drawn were somewhat artificial. The controversy, however, was sharply defined and for years was fertile in causing an advancement of knowledge through the ingenious experiments of the partisans of one or the other opinion.

The humoral theory of immunity and much subsequent serum therapy were founded upon Nuttall's convincing demonstration of the bactericidal action of the blood in 1888. Two years after this, Behring showed that animals could be protected against diphtheria by injections of diphtheria toxin and Behring and Kitasato produced immunization against tetanus by injections of the toxin. In both cases they showed that the serum of the immunized animals contained substances which neutralized toxin specifically and that protection could be conferred upon normal animals by injecting them with antitoxic serum. The application of these methods of passive immunization to human beings was immediately successful. Following these accomplishments a great variety of antitoxic and antibacterial sera were produced and used. Much of scientific value has been gained from the study of the reactions of these sera with the antigens that caused their production. These serological reactions have been very serviceable for diagnosis, for bacterial identifications and for immunochemical research. Their clinical uses have been attended with strikingly beneficial results in some instances, but with disappointing results in others. Research in serum therapy is entering upon a new period, from which more effective products are to be expected.

The growth of immunology out of a study of defensive mechanisms into a discipline of its own is epitomized in the controversies between Bordet and Ehrlich in the latter part of the last century. In the course of this argument the interest shifted from a study of how an animal protects itself against infection to an investigation of the mechanisms of specific serological reactions, the reactions between antigens and antibodies. Many new reactions were discovered; agglutinins, cytolysins, complements and amboceptors, and their interactions with homologous antigens were found and studied during the course of this debate. Bordet appears to have supplied most of the new and original observations. Ehrlich and his associates made many useful discoveries by elaboration and exact research. Bordet concluded that serological reactions were most clearly explained in terms of physical chemistry. Ehrlich was led by his analysis to adopt a chemical explanation of both the immunizing process and the mechanism of reactions of antigens with the products of immunization. This viewpoint, stated by Ehrlich in 1897 as his famous side-chain or receptor theory, dominated immunological thought during the next twenty-five years.

During this time, attention was directed to the significance of the finding of bacteria in various stages of degeneration in leukocytes seen in exudates and in sections of lesions. The cellular school of immunologists had their common focus of interest in observations of this type. About 1881, Metchnikoff, a zoölogist, observed that the fate of the water flea, *Daphnia*, in its struggle with an invading fungus depended entirely upon whether or not certain mobile cells in the transparent body of this little animal were able to engulf and digest the micro-organism. He discovered cells with a similar function in inflammatory exudates of higher animals and to all cells with this characteristic he gave the name phagocyte. The cellular theories of immunity thus had their origin in observation on phagocytosis. These opinions came into sharp conflict with the humoral theories. They have become established as a true explanation of a general, fundamental and most effectual defensive mechanism of the animal body against the invasion of many kinds of germs.

A third important path for immunology was opened during this period by observations on states of specific hypersensitivity, or, as they have been called, anaphylaxis and allergy. Flexner's report in 1894 that "animals that had withstood one dose of dog serum would succumb to a second dose after the lapse of some days or weeks, even when the dose was sublethal for a control animal" [8] described a clear-cut instance of anaphylaxis. Many years before this, in 1837, Magendie, a physiologist, had described the sudden death of dogs which had been repeatedly injected with egg albumin. Beginning in 1902 Richet and Portier carried out the first systematic and purposeful studies of anaphylaxis. The publication of Arthus in 1903 and the "phenomenon of Theobald Smith" communicated to Ehrlich in 1904 served again to focus the attention of investigators upon the curious state of hypersensitiveness which followed after an interval the injection of proteins. The study of the manifestations of hypersensitivity in man actually began with Jenner's note on the

8 S. Flexner, *Med. News*, 1894, 65:116.

accelerated vaccinal reaction which he saw in the skin of certain previously vaccinated persons. The next increase in the interest in human hypersensitivity came
through Koch's observation on the tuberculin reaction. But the effective development
of this field of investigation in relation to man took place after 1905, when von
Pirquet and Schick published their observations on serum sickness. Since that time
there has been an enormous accumulation of knowledge on the subjects of the numerous causes of hypersensitiveness, the protean manifestations of hypersensitiveness,
and the relationship of allergy and anaphylaxis to immunity and other features of
infection.

The history of immunology has been summarized briefly here because this science
sprang from bacteriology and is still intimately connected with bacteriology. It is
becoming more and more apparent, however, that immunology and serology have an
independent status. While they are inseparably associated with bacteriology, they are
important subdivisions of the field of biochemistry and physiology. One direction of
this independent destiny has been clearly indicated in Landsteiner's work on the chemical basis of the specificity of immune reactions.

Many of the most beneficial applications of bacteriology have been made in
public health and hygiene. The aim of these activities has been the control and
eradication of infectious diseases. Except for those diseases transmitted through the
respiratory tract, most of the pestilential afflictions of mankind have been brought
under control by application of the principles of bacteriology and immunology. It is
not an exaggeration to state that modern ways of life owe their security to the
guardianship of bacteriologists.

In this historical outline, we have traced the growth of bacteriology chiefly in relation to medicine. Our interest here is in medical bacteriology and it cannot be denied
that most of the discoveries of greatest importance for human welfare have come
from investigations of bacteria as the causes of diseases of man and domesticated
animals. It is unfortunate, however, that the medical bacteriologist has been ignorant
or neglectful of the fundamentally important developments of bacteriology which
have taken place in other fields. Some of the most profound investigations of bacterial
metabolism, systematic relationships of bacteria and general biological studies of the
bacteria have been made by those who had no immediate interest in medicine or any
other art. In addition, those concerned in the applications of bacteriology to agriculture and the industries have made discoveries of great value not only to their
specialties but to the whole of bacteriology and to biology. There is an increasing
recognition of bacteriology as a field of knowledge worthy of cultivation on its own
account, for, as Theobald Smith wrote in 1893: "In the study of the microscopic
forms known as bacteria we have what might be fitly called the focal point of the
various branches of biological science." [9]

The scope of bacteriology is thus a wide one, and none of its various fields has, as
yet, been fully explored. The future of the science is rich in allurement of interest,
in promise of result, and in possible benefit to mankind.

9 T. Smith, *The Wilder Quarter-Century Book, Ithaca*, 1893, 187.

18 TEXTBOOK OF BACTERIOLOGY

REFERENCES

ARTHUS, M. M. Compt. rend. Soc. de biol., 1903, 55:817.

BARON, J. The Life of Edward Jenner, M.D., London, 1827.

BAYNE-JONES, S. Science, 1931, 73:599.

BEHRING, E. Deutsche med. Wchnschr., 1890, 16:1145.

BEHRING, E., AND KITASATO. Deutsche med. Wchnschr., 1890, 16:1113.

BEIJERINCK, M. W. Centralbl. f. Bakteriol., 1899, 5:29.

BILLROTH, T. Untersuchungen über die Vegetationsformen von Coccobacteria Septica, Berlin, 1874.

BORDET, J. Studies in Immunity. Translated by F. P. Gay, New York, 1909.

BOREL, P. Historiarum et Observationum Medicophysicarum, 1653.

BULLOCH, W. History of Bacteriology, Medical Research Council, London, 1930.

CAGNIARD-LATOUR. Compt. rend. Acad. d. sc., 1837, 4:905.

CALANDRUCCIO, S. Agostino Bassi, di Lodi, Il Fondatore della Teoria Parasitaria, Catania, 1892.

CHAMBERLAND, C. Compt. rend. Acad. d. sc., 1884, 99:247.

COHEN, B. The Leeuwenhoek Letter. A photographic copy of the letter of the 9th of October, 1676 sent by Antony van Leeuwenhoek to Henry Oldenberg, Secretary of the Royal Society of London. Published by the Society of American Bacteriologists, Baltimore, 1937.

COHN, F. Beitr. z. Biol. d. Pflanz., 1872, 1, 2: 127–224; 1876, 2, 2:249.

DAVAINE, C. J. L'Œuvre de C.-J. Davaine, Paris, 1889, 1–93, 490–575.

DE BARY, A. Jahresb. ü. d. Leistung. d. ges. Med., ed. by R. Virchow and A. Hirsch, 1868, 2:244.

D'HERELLE, F. Compt. rend. Acad. d. sc., 1917, 165: 373.

DISNEY, A. N. Origin and Development of the Microscope, London, 1928.

DOBELL, C. Parasitology, 1923, 15: 308–319.

———— Antony van Leeuwenhoek and His "Little Animals," New York, 1932.

DONNÉ, A. Recherches microscopiques sur la nature des mucus, Paris, 1837.

DUCLAUX, E. Pasteur, the History of a Mind. Translated by Erwin F. Smith, Philadelphia, 1920.

EHRLICH, P. Klin. Jahrb., 1897, 6:299.

———— Collected Studies on Immunity. Translated by C. Bolduan, New York, 1906.

EHRENBERG, C. G. Die Infusionsthierchen als volkommene Organismen, Leipzig, 1838.

EICHSTEDT. Neue Notiz. a. d. geb. d. Natur. u. Heilkunde, 1846, 39:270.

FORD, W. W. Johns Hopkins Hosp. Bull., 1911, 22:415.

FRACASTORIUS, H. De contagionibus et contagiosis morbis et eorum curatione, libri tres, Venice, 1546. Consulted in the German translation by Viktor Fossel, in the Klassiker der Medizin series, 1910.

GAGE, S. H. The Microscope, 15th ed., Ithaca, 1932.

GODLEE, J. Lord Lister, London, 1917.

HALLIER, E. Gahrungserscheinungen, Leipzig, 1867.

HENLE, J. Pathologische Untersuchungen, Berlin, 1840.

IWANOWSKI, D. Bull. d. Acad. imp. d. Sci. d. St. Petersbourg, 1892, 13:237. Quoted from Centralbl. f. Bakteriol., 1899, 5:250.

JENNER, E. An Inquiry into the Causes and Effects of the Variolae Vaccinae, London, 1798, p. 13.

KIRCHER, A. Scrutinium physico-medicum Contagiosae Luis, quae Pestis dicitur, Rome, 1658, 42, 141–142.

KOCH, R. Beitr. z. Biol. d. Pflanz., 1876, 2, 2:277–308.

———— Gesammelte Werke, ed. by G. Gaffky and E. Pfuhl, Leipzig, 1912.

———— Zur Zuchtung von pathogenen Mikroorganismen, Mitt. a. d. Kaiserlichen Gesundheitsamte, 1881, 1:1–48.

LEVADITI, C. and LÉPINE, P. Les ultravirus des maladies humaines, Paris, 1938.

LINNAEUS, C. Systema naturae, 10th ed., Holmiae, 1758, 820–821.

LISTER, J. The Collected Papers of Joseph, Baron Lister, 2 vols., Oxford, 1909.

LÖFFLER, F. Vorlesungen über die geschichtliche Entwickelung der Lehre von Bacterien, Leipzig, 1887.

LÖFFLER, F., and FROSCH. Centralbl. f. Bakteriol., 1898, 23:371.

MAGENDIE, F. Lectures on the Blood. Translation. Philadelphia, 1839.

METCHNIKOFF, E. L'Immunité dans les maladies infectieuses, Paris, 1901. Translated by F. G. Binnie, Cambridge, 1905.

MÜLLER, O. F. Animalcula infusoria, Hauniae, 1786.

NEEDHAM, T. Philosoph. Trans., 1749, 490: 615. Quoted by Bulloch.

NORDTMEYER, H. Ztschr. f. Hyg., 1891, 10:145.

NUTTALL, G. H. F. Parasitology, 1924, 16:214.

——— Ztschr. f. Hyg., 1888, 4:353.

OBERMEIER, O. H. F. Centralbl. f. d. med. Wissensch. 1873, 11:145.

OTTO, R. Gedenkschrift f. R. von Leuthold, 1906, 1:153.

PASTEUR, L. Ann. de chim. et phys., 1862, 64:5–110.

——— Œuvres de Pasteur, Paris, 1922–1928.

PLENCIZ, M. A. Opera medico-physica, Vindobonae, 1762, 13–35.

PORTIER, and RICHET, C. Compt. rend. Soc. de biol., 1902, 54:170.

RAYER. Compt. rend. Soc. de biol., 1850, 2:141–144.

REDI, F. Esperienze intorno alla generazione degl'insetti, 5th ed., Florence, 1688. A translation of this book was published by M. Bigelow, Chicago, 1909.

RODDIS, L. H. Edward Jenner and the Discovery of Smallpox Vaccination, Menasha, Wisconsin, 1930.

SALMON, D. E., and SMITH, T. Proc. Biol. Soc., Washington, 1886, 3:29.

SCHOENLEIN. Arch. f. Anat., Physiol. u. Wissenchftl. Med., 1839, 82.

SCHRÖDER, H., and VON DUSCH, T. Ann. d. Chem. u. Pharmacie, 1854, 89:232.

SCHULZE, F. Ann. d. Phys. u. Chem., 1836, 39:487.

SCHWANN, T. Ann. d. Phys. u. Chem., 837, 41:184.

SINGER, C. Janus, 1911, 16:81–98.

——— Studies in the History and Method of Science, Oxford, 1921, Vol. 2, 385, 408.

——— "The Dawn of Microscopical Discovery," J. Roy. Micr. Soc., 1915, 317–340.

SPALLANZANI, L. Saggio di osservazioni microscopiche, Modena, 1765. This reference is quoted from Bulloch.

STANLEY, W. M. The isolation and properties of tobacco mosaic and other virus proteins. The Harvey Lectures, 1938, Ser. XXXIII, p. 170.

TWORT, F. W. Lancet, 1915, 2:1241.

TYNDALL, J. Essays on the Floating-Matter of the Air in Relation to Putrefaction and Infection, New York, 1882.

VALLERY-RADOT, R. The Life of Pasteur. Translated by R. L. Devonshire, New York, 1926.

VAN HELMONT, J. B. Ortus medicinae id est initia physicae inaudita, Tract 21, Imago fermenti impraegnat massam semine, Elzivir, Amsterdam, 1648, Part 9, p. 113.

VAN LEEUWENHOEK, Anton. Arcana naturae detecta, Delft, 1695, 42.

VILLEMIN, J. A. Compt. rend. Acad. d. sc., 1865, 61:1012–1015.

VON PIRQUET, C. F., and SCHICK, B. Die Serumkrankheit, Leipzig, 1905.

WRISBERG, H. A. Observationum de animalculis infusoriis, Goettingen, 1765, 82.

ZEISS, H. Arch. f. Gesch. d. Med., 1923, 15:161.

——— Otto Obermeier: Die Entdeckung von fadenförmigen Gebilden im Blut von Ruckfallfieberkranken, Vol. 31, 1926.

CHAPTER II

GENERAL MORPHOLOGY AND REPRODUCTION OF THE BACTERIA

Bacteria are minute, unicellular plant-like organisms, without chlorophyl. They usually multiply by binary fission. They may occur free or singular, or in aggregations, forming multicellular groups or colonies. The individual cells in colonies are physiologically independent, although they are influenced by environmental changes produced by neighboring cells.

The cells have a number of basic or ground shapes which may be roughly considered in three main classes: the cocci or spheres, the bacilli or straight rods, and the spirilla or curved rod forms.

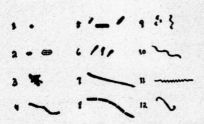

Fig. 3.—Types of Shapes and Arrangements of Bacteria, Spirilla and Spirochetes.

1, coccus; *2,* diplococci; *3,* staphylococci; *4,* streptococcus; *5,* bacilli; *6,* club-shaped bacilli; *7,* filament, leptothrix type; *8,* chain of bacilli; *9,* vibrio, single and in chain; *10,* spirillium; *11,* spirochete; *12,* leptospira.

The cocci are, when fully developed and free, perfectly spherical. When two or more are in apposition, they may be slightly flattened along the tangential surface, giving an oval appearance.

The bacilli, or rod-shaped forms, consist of elongated cells whose long diameter may be from two to ten times as great as their width, with ends squarely cut off, as in the case of *Bacillus anthracis,* or gently rounded as in the case of the typhoid bacillus.

The spirilla may vary from small comma-shaped micro-organisms, containing but a single curve, to longer or more sinuous forms which may roughly be compared to a corkscrew, being made up of five, six or more curves. The turns in the typical micro-organisms of this class are always in three planes and are spiral rather than simply curved.

Among the known micro-organisms, the bacilli by far outnumber other forms, and are probably the most common variety of bacteria in existence.

Many variations from these fundamental types may occur even under normal conditions. The significance of these variations will be discussed in other chapters.

The size of bacteria is subject to considerable variation. Cocci may vary from .15 μ to 2 μ in diameter. The average size of the ordinary pus coccus varies from .8 μ to 1.2 μ in diameter. A graphic illustration of the size of a staphylococcus is obtained by calculating that two billion micrococci could easily be contained in a drop having a volume of 1 c. mm. Among the bacilli the range of size is subject to even greater variations. Probably the smallest of the common bacilli is the bacillus of influenza, which measures about .5 μ in length by .2 μ in thickness. The limit of the optical possibilities of the modern microscope is almost reached by some of the known micro-organisms, and there are some diseases which are caused by filtrable, ultramicroscopic, viruses.

Many details of the finer structure of micro-organisms can be seen through modern microscopes by transmitted visible light or by oblique illumination. By the use of radiation of shorter wave-length even smaller structures are resolvable. These methods, using invisible radiations, require photography for the registration of the images. Very small structures, including some of the virus particles, have been photographed by ultraviolet light. The latest advance, since 1937, is the development of the *electron microscope,* first applied to the study of bacteria by Marton, von Borries and Ruska, and by Krause. Magnifications up to 21,000 have been obtained and particles as small as 10 mμ have been photographed. This new instrument makes it possible to explore a new region in the realm of molecular morphology.

Morphology of the Bacterial Cell.—When unstained, most bacteria are transparent, colorless, homogeneous or granular bodies with a low refractive index, approximately that of water.

The cells consist of a mass of protoplasm, surrounded, in most instances, by a delicate cell membrane.

The presence of a *nucleus* in bacterial cells, though denied by the earlier writers, has been demonstrated beyond question by Zettnow, Nakanishi and others. The original opinion of Zettnow was that the entire bacterial body consisted of nuclear material intimately intermingled with the cytoplasm. The opinion now held by most observers who have studied this phase of the subject favors the existence of an ectoplasmic zone which includes cell membrane and flagella, but is definitely a part of the cytoplasm, and an endoplasm in which is concentrated the nuclear material. Buetschli claims to have demonstrated within this endoplasmic substance a reticular meshwork, between the spaces of which lie granules of chromophilic or nuclear material. Confirmation of this opinion has been brought by Zettnow and others. Nakanishi, working with a special staining method, asserts that some micro-organisms show within the endoplasmic zone a well-defined, minute, round or oval nucleus, which possesses a definitely characteristic staining reaction. A review of the older work and a report on new evidence on the existence of nuclei in bacteria was published by Gutstein in 1925. The fine photomicrographs of living bacteria made by Barnard with dark field illumination and the fluorescent image from ultraviolet light show structures in resting and dividing cells that clearly suggest that the bacterial cell possesses a nucleus.

In the bodies of a large number of bacteria, notably in those of the diphtheria group, Ernst, Babes, and others have demonstrated granular, deeply staining bodies now spoken of as *metachromatic granules,* or *Babes-Ernst granules,* or, because of their frequent position at the ends of bacilli, as *polar bodies.* These structures are irregular in size and number, and have a strong affinity for dyes. They are stained distinctly dark in contrast to the rest of the bacterial cell with methylene-blue, and may be demonstrated by the special methods of Neisser and of Roux. Their interpretation has been a matter of much difficulty and of varied opinion. Those who first observed them held that they were a part of the nuclear material of the cell. Others have regarded them as an early stage in spore formation, or as arthrospores. Again, they have been interpreted as structures comparable to the centrosomes of other unicellular forms. As a matter of fact, the true nature of these bodies is by no means certain. It is probable that granules composed of different substances, glycogen, lecithin, nucleic acid compounds and unidentified products of degeneration have been called metachromatic granules. Dobell, who has studied bacterial nuclei, has expressed the opinion that these granules are not chromatin, but are a reserve material composed of nucleic acid and an organic base. They are present most regularly in micro-organisms taken from young and vigorous cultures or in those taken directly from the lesions of disease. It is unlikely that they represent structures in any way comparable to spores, since cultures containing individuals showing metachromatic granules are not more resistant to deleterious influences than are others. Their abundant presence in young vigorous cultures may indicate a relationship between them and the growth energy of the micro-organisms. There is no proof, however, that these bodies are related to the virulence of the bacteria.

Cell Membrane and Capsule.—Actual proof of the existence of a cell membrane has been brought in the cases of both the larger and smaller forms. The presence of such envelopes may be inferred for most bacteria by their behavior during plasmolysis, where definite retraction of the protoplasm from a well-designed cell outline has been repeatedly observed. The occurrence, furthermore, of so-called "shadow forms" which appear as empty capsules, and of a well-outlined cell body, after the vegetative form has entirely degenerated in the course of sporulation, make the assumption of the presence of a cell membrane appear extremely well founded. Differing from the cell membranes of plant cells, cellulose has not been demonstrable for bacteria, nor has chitin, which occurs in fungi, been found in bacteria; and the membrane is possibly to be regarded rather as a peripheral protoplasmic zone, which remains unstained by the usual manipulations.

The membrane and ectoplasmic layer are devoid of chromatin and are not stained in the usual manipulations. Special structures, such as flagella and capsules, arise from this region of the cell. The property of retaining the dye in the Gram stain has been shown by Churchman, particularly in the case of the anthrax bacillus, to reside in the ectoplasmic layer. Polysaccharides and other materials of antigenic significance are often concentrated here.

Many bacteria have been shown to possess a mucoid or gelatinous envelope or capsule. According to Migula, such an envelope is present on all bacteria though it is in only a few species that it is sufficiently well developed and stable to be easily demonstrable and of differential value. When stained, the capsule takes the ordinary anilin dyes less deeply than does the bacterial cell-body, and varies greatly in thickness, ranging from a thin, just visible margin of dimensions four or five times exceeding the actual size of the bacterial body itself. This structure is perfectly developed in a limited number of bacteria only in which it then becomes an important aid to identification. Most prominent among such bacteria are *Diplococcus pneumoniae*, *Micrococcus tetragenus*, the bacilli of the Friedländer group, and *B. aërogenes capsulatus*. The development of the capsule depends upon the environment from which the bacteria are taken and upon the phase of dissociation of the culture. By selection of colonies it is possible to demonstrate capsules in many smooth and mucoid variants of species of organisms previously regarded as being noncapsulated. It is most easily demonstrable in preparations of bacteria taken directly from animal tissues and fluids, or from media containing animal serum or milk. If cultivated for a prolonged period upon artificial media, many otherwise capsulated micro-organisms no longer show this characteristic structure.

Capsules may be demonstrated on bacteria taken from artificial media most successfully when albuminous substances, such as ascitic fluid or blood serum, are present in the culture-media, or when the bacteria are smeared upon cover slip or slide in a drop of beef or other serum (Hiss). Most observers believe that the capsule represents a swelling of the ectoplasmic zone of bacteria. By others it is regarded as an evidence of the formation of a mucoid intercellular substance, some of which remains adherent to the individual bacteria when removed from cultures. It is noticeable, indeed, that some of the capsulated bacteria, especially *Streptococcus mucosus* and *B. mucosus capsulatus*, develop such slimy and gelatinous colonies that, when these are touched with a platinum wire, mucoid threads and strings adhere to the loop.

There is reason to believe that there is a relation between virulence and capsulation; capsulated bacteria are less easily phagocyted than are the noncapsulated. Capsulated organisms are not easily amenable to the agglutinating action of immune sera. Many bacteria (plague, anthrax) habitually uncapsulated on media acquire capsules within the infected animal body. Also in some species (pneumococci), loss of capsule formation is accompanied by a diminution of virulence. The capsular material consists largely of the carbohydrate "residue" material studied by Heidelberger, Avery and ourselves. The capsular polysaccharides are specifically antigenic, stimulating the production of antibodies and also functioning as haptenes.

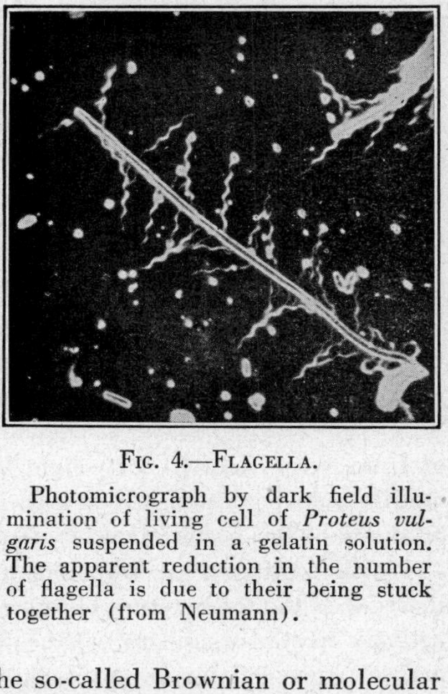

FIG. 4.—FLAGELLA.

Photomicrograph by dark field illumination of living cell of *Proteus vulgaris* suspended in a gelatin solution. The apparent reduction in the number of flagella is due to their being stuck together (from Neumann).

Organs of Locomotion.—When suspended in a drop of fluid many bacteria are seen to be actively motile. It is important, however, in all cases to distinguish between actual motility and the so-called Brownian or molecular movement which takes place whenever small particles are held in suspension in a fluid.

Brownian or molecular movement is a phenomenon entirely explained by molecular bombardment and has absolutely no relation to independent motility. It may be seen when particles of carmine or any other insoluble substance are suspended in water, and consists in a rapid to and fro vacillation during which there is actually no permanent change in position of the moving particle except inasmuch as this is influenced by currents in the drop.

The true motility of bacteria, on the other hand, is active motion due to impulses originating in the bacteria themselves, where the actual position of the bacterium in the field is permanently changed.

The ability to move in this way is, so far as we know, limited almost entirely to the bacilli and spirilla, there being but few instances where members of the coccus group show active motility. In all cases, with the exception of the spirochetes, bacterial motility is due to hair-like organs known as *flagella*. Unstained flagella cannot be seen by ordinary transmitted light. They can be seen and have been photographed in motion by the use of dark field illumination (Neumann). For their recognition, enumeration and study in fixed preparations, special staining procedures must be used.

In such stained preparations the bacterial cell bodies often appear thicker than when ordinary dyes are used, and the flagella apparently are seen to arise from the thickened ectoplasmic zone.

The flagella are long filaments, averaging in thickness from one-tenth to one-thirtieth that of the bacterial body, which often are delicately waved and undulating, and, judging from the positions in which they become fixed in preparations, move by a wavy or screw-like motion. In length they are subject to much variation, but are supposed to be generally longer in old than in young cultures.

As to the finer structures of flagella, little can be made out except that they possess a higher refractive index than the cell body itself, and that they can be stained only with those dyes which bring clearly into view the supposedly true cytoplasm of the cell. Whether they penetrate this cytoplasmic membrane or whether they are a direct continuation of this peripheral zone of the bacterial body, cannot be decided.

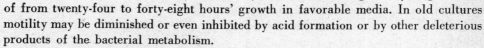

FIG. 5.—ARRANGEMENT OF BACTERIAL FLAGELLA.

The manner in which bacteria move is naturally subject to some variation depending upon the number and position of the flagella possessed by them. Whether bacteria exercise or not the power of motility depends to a large extent upon their present or previous environment. They are usually most motile in vigorous young cultures of from twenty-four to forty-eight hours' growth in favorable media. In old cultures motility may be diminished or even inhibited by acid formation or by other deleterious products of the bacterial metabolism.

At the optimum growth-temperature motility is most active, and a diminution or increase of the temperature to any considerable degree diminishes or inhibits it. Thus actively motile organisms, in the fluid drop, may be seen to diminish distinctly in activity when left for any prolonged time in a cold room, or when the preparation is chilled. Any influence, in other words, chemical or physical, which tends to injure or depress physiologically the bacteria in any way, at the same time tends to inhibit their motility.

Messea has proposed a classification of bacteria which is based upon the arrangement of their organs of motility, as follows:

I. Gymnobacteria, possessing no flagella
II. Trichobacteria, with flagella

    1. Monotricha, having a single flagellum at one pole
    2. Lophotricha, having a tuft of flagella at one pole
    3. Amphitricha, with flagella at both poles
    4. Peritricha, with flagella completely surrounding the bacterial body

Bacterial Spores.—Among the rod-shaped bacteria about one hundred species of aerobes and some fifty species of anaerobes are known to have the capacity to develop

a sort of encysted or resting stage by a process known as sporulation or spore formation. The body thus formed in the bacterial cell is called an endospore. The spherical
bacteria and the spirochetes do not produce endospores. Endospore formation,
therefore, is a distinguishing feature of the organisms of the family *Bacillaceae*,
of which the aerobic genus is called *Bacillus* and the anaerobic genus, *Clostridium*.
Organisms is these groups occur chiefly in the intestinal contents of man and
animals, in soil, water and air. Most of them are saprophytic. Others capable
of causing disease are not strictly parasitic, and, in fact, produce their effects only
when a medium of dead or injured tissue affords them a nidus for growth in the
animal body. As we have seen, organisms having the ability to form spores played a
prominent part in the phenomena investigated during the controversy over spontaneous generation. They continue to be of very great importance in industrial bacteriology as well as in medical and veterinary bacteriology. In this place we shall
consider chiefly the biological aspects of endospores.

A variety of refractile bodies in bacteria have been supposed to be different sorts
of spores. The Babes-Ernst metachromatic granules, once thought to have the properties of spores, are now recognized to be reserve material or products of degeneration.
It has not been established that arthrospores occur in the true bacteria. Certainly the
cells containing bodies regarded as arthrospores have not been shown to be unusually
resistant to heat or other deleterious agents. Tests of germination, however, may
serve to give more information than tests of resistance to heat on the possible spore-
like properties of some of these granules.

The true endospore is a highly refractile body formed within the bacterial cell
at a certain stage of growth. The size, shape
and position of the spore are relatively constant characteristics of species and are therefore of some value in distinguishing one kind
of bacillus from another. The position of the
spore in the cell may be central, subterminal or
terminal. It may be of the same diameter as that

FIG. 6.—VARIOUS POSITIONS OF SPORES IN
BACTERIAL CELLS.

of the cell or smaller, or may be larger, causing a swelling of the cell. Several typical
arrangements are shown in Figure 6.

The old cell or sporangium envelops the spore for several hours or days, according to conditions. It eventually disintegrates, freeing the spore.

Spores of the bacilli are notably resistant to heat, drying and disinfectants. According to the age and previous history of the spores they may survive boiling in
water or alkaline fluids more than an hour and may resist dry heat at 150° C. for
an hour or more. The periods of heating and temperatures applied in practical
sterilizing methods used in bacteriology, surgery and canning are determined by the
thermal resistance of spores. Spores are relatively impenetrable to dyes and when
once stained are difficult to decolorize. In general, spores are resistant to physical and
chemical environmental conditions which would be fatal to the vegetative forms of
the same or other species of organisms.

This resistance to unfavorable conditions serves to tide the organism over periods
of hardship in the air or soil. It has been held, therefore, that bacteria form spores
for the purpose of surviving unfavorable conditions. This is a teleological point of

view, which, as we shall show, appears to be incorrect, or at least inadequate to give a genuine insight into spore formation.

Since the early observations of de Bary it has been said that a small granule in the cell grows into the large endospore. We have shown by motion photomicrography that in *Bacillus megatherium* there is no precedent granule for the spore, but that a large block of cytoplasm appears to become more solid than the rest of the cytoplasm and actually shrinks into the final spore. We have seen the same process in *Bacillus anthracis*. Wyckoff and Ter Louw who studied the process by means of ultraviolet photomicrographs, are in agreement with us in failing to find any granule as the origin of the spore. From what we have seen we are inclined to support Darányi's dehydration hypothesis as an explanation of the shrinkage of material within the cell into the spore, although there are phases not explained by this or any other theory.

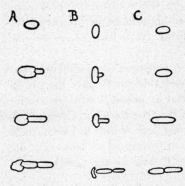

FIG. 7.—DIAGRAM OF TYPES OF GER-
MINATION OF SPORES.

A, polar; *B*, equatorial; *C*, germination by stretching and absorption of
spore membrane.

We have not seen the formation of the spore membrane, but do not doubt that one is developed. The membrane or case can be plainly seen as a shriveled capsule after the dehiscence of the spore at the time of germination.

A number of observers have noted that the bacterial nucleus takes part in spore formation, being condensed with other materials in the sporogeneous area.

The conditions influencing spore formation are diverse. These differences, however, are to be cor-related with species differences and do not indi-cate that spore formation in any one species occurs in response to the influences exerted by a heterogeneous group of unfavorable conditions. Spore formation does not occur if the organism is exposed to unfavorable conditions at the start of growth. As Pasteur discovered, nonsporing anthrax bacilli can be produced by growing the culture at a temperature of 42°–43° C. At the start of growth, lack of oxygen for aerobes or too much oxygen for anaerobes, too little moisture, the presence of injurious substances, acids or disinfectants, sublethal radia-tions, in fact, any growth impeding factor will inhibit spore formation. A long series of optimum conditions must be provided to permit the development of the endospore. Hence the spore could not have been developed primarily as an adaptation to un-favorable environment.

When the period of growth appropriate for spore formation has been reached, shortly after the end of the so-called period of logarithmic increase, as Henrici has shown, then accumulation of waste products, exhaustion of nutriment, a slight amount of oxygen in cultures of anaerobes (Zinsser) and a number of other factors may serve to precipitate the formation of the endospore. We have seen, however, organisms in the prespore stage proceed to the completion of the spore even when they were trans-ferred from an old medium to a fresh nutritive substrate. This indicates that there is an inertia in the process.

The function of the endospore is not a multiplicative one, as one bacillus forms one spore from which only one bacillus arises by germination. Occasionally two spores are formed in a rod and there are a few disporous species. But this is a rare occurrence and the numbers of cells are not unusually increased by sporulation of bacteria. The spores, however, may have some reproductive significance. The cycle from bacillus to bacillus through the spore is of the nature of a life cycle, as established by Cohn and Koch themselves. Since the beginning, however, the spore has been regarded as a resting stage, a form of the cell resistant to deleterious conditions. In our chapter on variation in bacteria we shall discuss the evidence presented by those who regard the spore as either a product of sexual conjugation or as a nonsexual mechanism of bacterial rejuvenation. Although such questions as these are matters of dispute, we are convinced from our observations of the process that the formation of the endospore has a significance in the bacterial life cycle greater than its obviously advantageous production of a temporarily resistant form.

Since 1876, many papers have been published on spore formation and on the germination of spores. A useful summary of the older material with a report of more recent investigations, expressing a point of view with which we are largely in sympathy, was published in 1932 by R. P. Cook.

Whenever the spores of any micro-organism are brought into an environment suitable for bacterial growth as to temperature, moisture, and nutrition, the spores develop into vegetative forms. This process differs according to species. In general it consists of an elongation of the spore body with a loss of its highly refractile character and resistance to staining fluids. The developing vegetative cell may now rupture and slip out of the spore membrane at one of its poles, leaving the empty spore capsule still visible and attached to the bacillary body. Again, a similar process may take place equatorially instead of at the pole. In other species, there may be no rupture of the spore membrane at all, the vegetative form arising by gradual elongation of the spore and an absorption or solution of the membrane which is indicated by change in staining reaction. Division by fission in the ordinary way then ensues.

Reproduction of Bacteria.—Binary fission into two equal parts is the usual and predominant mode of reproduction and multiplication of bacteria under standardized conditions of cultivation in the laboratory and in natural environment. Whether or not binary fission is the exclusive mode of bacterial reproduction has been debatable since the early days of bacteriology. There is a great mass of evidence, summarized chiefly by Löhnis in 1922, and increased by others since then, indicating that bacteria reproduce in other ways in addition to simple fission and that they exhibit pleomorphism in reproduction. In this section we shall consider and attempt to evaluate the different bacterial forms to which reproductive significance has been ascribed by various investigators. In Chapter IX we shall discuss these observations in connection with the general subject of bacterial variation.

General biological considerations and the probable relationship of the bacteria to the blue-green algae and the fungi suggest that bacteria may reproduce and multiply in several ways and that each mode of reproduction may have a distinctive morphological expression. As it is well established that many unicellular organisms have diverse reproductive forms, it is logical to suppose that the bacteria may not be exceptions to what appears to be a general biological law.

These analogies, however, are only suggestive, and cannot take the place of experiment and observation in establishing the facts of bacterial life cycles. It seems to us that the test to be applied to a supposedly reproductive form is the direct observation of its germination or its transition into a new form. All transitional forms or stabilized reproductive forms, except those which may be ultramicroscopic, should be observed continuously under the microscope. The validity of any series of reproductive forms and their progeny can be finally established only through serial visual or photographic microscopical observations. Data on these points, obtained by cultures not under microscopic view, by animal passage, by filtration and other methods in which the form passes out of direct observation for a period of time, have strong suggestive and confirmatory force. But as other organisms may enter the material unobserved, these methods cannot give conclusive results. The reconstruction of a life cycle from forms taken from cultures and animals is apt to be a patchwork of observations whose necessary connections are lacking.

Nuclear changes have been described in connection with the reproduction of bacterial cells. Thus far the difficulties of differentiating the minute parts of the very small organized or distributed chromidial nucleus of a bacterial cell have been almost insurmountable. Nakanishi, Enderlein, and Mellon have described chromosomal changes in the nuclei of reproducing bacterial cells. Since some of these nuclear particles are on the border line of microscopic visibility and since there is opportunity to confuse them with other granules in the cell there is need for further confirmation of these observations before they can be accepted.

The modes of bacterial reproduction which have been described may be listed as follows:

A. *Asexual reproduction by:*
   1. Binary fission
   2. Budding
   3. Branching
   4. Filamentous growth with unequal segmentation
   5. Formation of conidia
   6. Production of gonidia
   7. Formation of arthrospores and microcysts
   8. Formation of endospores
   9. Formation of a symplasm

B. *Sexual reproduction by:*
   1. Conjugation of two individuals
   2. Conjunction of several individuals
   After the fusion of the cells it is supposed that the zygote may reproduce asexually or sexually.

Although we are unable in this place to review all the evidence on these described modes of bacterial reproduction, we think that the following comments are pertinent:

Binary Fission.—Simple fission is the common mode of reproduction of bacteria. When reproducing in this way the bacterial cell enlarges until it attains an adult size and then divides into two approximately equal parts by formation of a constriction or membrane at a right angle to its long axis. The size of the adult is related to the age of the culture. Spherical cells may or may not elongate slightly before division. Transverse fission occurs in the cocci, bacilli, spirilla and spirochetes, and has been seen to be a subsequent mode of reproduction of some of the specialized reproductive forms.

The planes of cleavage of spherical forms determine the conformations of the aggregate of cells. Division in one plane produces diplococci or cocci in chains (streptococci). Cleavage in two or more planes produces a grape-like cluster (staphylococci) or an arrangement in packets or cubes (sarcinae). The cylindrical or curved forms may adhere, end to end, in chains or spirals. These arrangements of cells are of differential value.

Budding.—Lateral protrusions or buds have been seen on young and old bacterial cells by many observers. These buds may enlarge and segment by fission while still attached to cells or may grow and multiply by segmentation after detachment from the cells. These stages have been followed in serial continuous observations by Hort in cultures of *B. typhosus* and other members of the typhoid-dysentery group. Many less complete observations made by others support the opinion that under certain conditions bacteria reproduce by budding.

Branching.—As a branching type of reproduction begins by the formation of a bud it may be regarded as a specialized type of budding. True branching has been observed in more than seventy species of bacteria. In 1902, Hill saw branching and the development of individual rods from the branches in hanging agar block cultures of *B. diphtheriae.* In 1920, Hort observed branching growth in *B. typhosus,* and in 1925, Gardner independently saw branching reproduction in members of the typhoid, dysentery and cholera groups. Gardner called this type of reproduction the Y-form or "three point multiplication." After simple or multiple branching, the extended branches may segment, giving rise to cells which reproduce by fission. In other cases, curved, rounded, budding or branching forms are developed from the original branched elements. Branched forms have been found most frequently in older cultures. They have been seen in young cultures on ordinary media, in acid media and can be obtained in greater abundance by selection of colonies.

Filamentous Growth.—Long unsegmented filaments or filaments showing unequal segmentation occur under conditions of ordinary cultivation in many organisms. Certain strains of the influenza bacillus, the typhoid bacillus and aerobic spore forming organisms produce filaments in abundance during rapid growth on moist media. Walker and Murray observed these and other forms in cultures of typhoid bacilli, but did not arrive at a definite conclusion regarding their significance in the life cycle of the organism.

Conidia.—A conidium is an asexual spore produced by constriction or abstriction of the terminal portion of a rod or structure called a conidiophore. Bacteriologists seem to have used this term loosely, often making it appear to be synonymous with gonidium. Rods and spiral forms occasionally have granules at their ends, suggesting that they have been produced by the cell after the manner of conidia. Small lateral, terminal or median buds or "gemmules" have been likened to conidia. The formation of true conidia by bacteria seems altogether unproven.

Gonidia.—Gonidia are formed by the contraction and segmentation of the protoplasm within the bacterial cell. Two, four or more gonidia may be formed in a cell. They escape from the cell by penetration of the cell wall or are freed by disintegration of the enclosing membrane. These bodies are usually round, measuring 0.1 μ to 0.13 μ in diameter. The chief evidence for the existence of gonidia in bacteria has been supplied by Löhnis and Smith, Thornton and Gangulee, Hort, Mellon and Hadley. Evidence that these bodies can reproduce themselves or give rise to the ordinary forms of the respective bacteria is partly direct and largely indirect. Growth of these very small granules into normal bacterial forms or by further segmentation into granules of the "gonidial type" has been followed by Kahn in direct microscopical observations of single tubercle bacilli in hanging drops. On the other hand Wyckoff has never seen growth of micrococcal forms "split from" the Shiga type of dysentery bacillus. Gonidia are said to be filtrable. The growth of bacterial forms in filtrates from Chamberland and Berkefeld filters has been interpreted as evidence in the unfiltered culture of very small and even ultramicroscopic viable bacterial elements. The filtrable forms of bacteria have been supposed by some, on entirely inadequate grounds, to be identical with or closely related to the ultramicroscopic viruses. Our own observations are opposed to these views. We agree that filtrable forms of bacteria exist. Their place in the life cycle of bacteria, however, has not yet been established. We shall discuss these questions in greater detail in appropriate sections elsewhere in this book.

Arthrospores and Microcysts.—Parts of bacterial bodies appear to be enclosed in membranes at times, and some observations indicate that the whole cell may develop a membrane less permeable than usual. These forms, found chiefly in old cultures, may be endowed with increased resistance to drying and age. They have no increased resistance to heat. Their reproductive properties have not been clearly demonstrated.

Endospores.—The mode of formation and reproductive significance of endospores in the life cycle of the bacilli have been described in the section on bacterial spores.

Symplasm.—Löhnis has described an amorphous stage in the cycle of bacterial reproduction. In this stage, the bacterial forms disintegrate and the living matter of numerous cells becomes thoroughly mixed. Under suitable conditions, regenerative bodies appear in this symplasm. From these regenerative bodies new bacterial forms are developed. It is obvious that a mass of disintegrated dead bacterial substance, slime and other intercellular material might conceal either normal vegetative cells or small forms, possibly gonidia, capable of growth. In view of this probability, the available evidence is not convincing that bacteria can be regenerated from a totally amorphous mass of indeterminate material.

Sexual Modes of Reproduction.—Conjugation of two individuals or conjunction of several individuals has been described by Löhnis, Mellon, Potthoff, Broadhurst and others. We have seen some of the cellular arrangements which have been interpreted as evidence of conjugation. These appearances could be equally well explained as attachments due to post fission bridges, entanglements of flagella, retention of a small organism within the surface film of a larger one and accidental juxtapositions fixed by mucoid material. On the whole, the evidence for a sexual phase in the life cycles of bacteria is unconvincing.

Morphology of Colonies of Bacteria.—A group of bacteria growing in one place is called a colony. Colonies of nonmotile organisms can be formed in undisturbed fluid media. Colony formation occurs most characteristically in the depths of or on the surface of solid media. The usual solid substrate is composed of agar or gelatin.

Other firm substances, however, may be used to support colonies of bacteria. Chief among these are potato, bread, coagulated serum, silica gel, and tissues of animals.

Under ideal conditions a colony is composed of the descendants of a single cell. This possibility is the rationale of all plate culture methods which since Koch's introduction of solid media in 1881 have been used to separate one kind of bacterium from another and thereby obtain "pure cultures." Even with the most careful dilution and distribution of material, however, it cannot be assumed always that a colony is the resultant of the multiplication of one organism. A clump of cells may give rise to one colony. The clump may be composed of cells of the same species or may include cells of different species. Overgrowth of one type may hide the others. Sometimes the colony may be seen to be obviously the product of several species. In other instances, frequent replating is required to separate the components of a mixed colony.

After incubation of the culture for twelve to twenty-four hours at an appropriate temperature, the colony usually becomes visible to the eye. It should be examined both by the naked eye and by low-power magnification. The discovery of minute colonies requires the use of a magnifying glass.

Colonies of bacteria differ in configuration, texture, size, shape, color and in their degree of adherence to the medium. There are so many combinations of characteristics of colonies that it would be unprofitable to list them here. They will be described in connection with specific micro-organisms. It is to be emphasized here that the characteristics of colonies are fairly constant properties of groups and even of species of bacteria. They are, therefore, valuable aids in the differentiation of bacteria.

The morphology of a colony is related primarily to the post-fission movements of the bacteria composing it. These movements have been classified by Graham-Smith as loop-forming, folding, snapping and slipping. Colonies of organisms of the loop-forming group usually have wavy edges (*B. anthracis*). Those of the folding and snapping groups (*B. pestis* and *B. diphtheriae*) may have serrated, indented, crenated or angular edges, and those of the slipping group (*B. coli, Proteus vulgaris*) may have smooth or lobose edges with a spreading growth.

Many other conditions affect the morphology of colonies. The nature of the nutriment, the degree of moisture of the medium, the production of intercellular substance by the bacteria, the age of the culture, and other physical and chemical factors influence the configuration, texture and color of colonies.

There are four general characteristics of colonies which should receive the closest attention because of their relation to bacterial variation. These are:

Smooth and Rough Types.—A single species of bacterium is capable of giving rise to two distinct types of colonies. One of these, having in general a dome shape with a more or less smoothly curved edge and a homogeneous consistency, has been called the smooth or S-type of colony. The other, having a more sharply angular edge, roughened surface and granular consistency, has been called the rough or R-type of colony. Between these extremes there are many transitional or intermediary types and subtle differences. One type of colony can be seen to arise from the other. Smoothness and roughness of colonies also are variable according to species. Properties of morphology, virulence, biochemical activities and antigenic composition of organisms are correlated with the S and R types of colonies. On the basis of these differences, bacterial species have been dissociated and the studies of such dissociated species have been the basis of a remarkable advance in the investigation of variation in bacteria. In Figure 8 the photographs *A, B* and *C* show smooth, rough and the rough-to-smooth transformation colonies of an acid-fast bacterium.

Secondary or Daughter Colonies.—After relatively prolonged incubation, secondary growth may appear at the edges or upon the surfaces of colonies. These new colonies, called daughter colonies, are formed by the multiplication of cells often somewhat different from the cells which produced the original colony. These cells differ in larger or smaller degree from their probable parents and are evidence of variation within a species. Daughter colonies of the cholera vibrio are shown in Figure 8, *D*.

Plaques. — Occasionally colonies may have a moth-eaten appearance or contain clear spots or clear circular zones. This is usually evidence of a lytic process occurring in the colony and is often an indication of the presence of bacteriophage.

Organization of a Colony.—It is usually said that the cells composing a bacterial colony are physiologically independent. This may be true as far as structural continuity is concerned, but it is probably an inexact statement in view of the fact that cells in different parts of a colony are subject to different environments created by the growth of neighboring cells. These differences no doubt exert an effect upon the organism. In addition, cells in direct contact with the medium have a different food supply from those growing on the surface or at the edge of the colony. These relationships are usually destroyed by the method of examining organisms taken from a colony with a platinum loop. "Histological" studies can be made by means of sections of colonies fixed *in situ*. The chief description of the organized state of the colonies of the cholera vibrio has been published by Legroux and Magrou. Similar studies of the colonies of the tubercle bacillus by Kahn, and of colonies of various bacteria by Mackenzie indicate that colonies have an organization and that different forms of micro-organisms occur in different parts of the colonies.

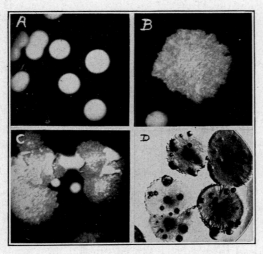

FIG. 8.—TYPES OF BACTERIAL COLONIES.

A, smooth; *B,* rough; *C,* smooth developing from rough colonies. *A, B,* and *C* are from a culture of an acid-fast bacterium. *D,* colonies of the cholera vibrio with secondary daughter colonies (after Eisenberg).

REFERENCES

BABES, V. Ztschr. f. Hyg., 1889, 5:172.
BARNARD, J. E. System of Bacteriology, London, 1930, I:116, Plates I and II.
BAYNE-JONES, S., and PETRILLI, A. J. Bacteriol., 1933, 25:261.
BROADHURST, J. J. Bacteriol., 1933, 25:32; 1934, 27:28.
BUETCHLI. Bau der Bakterien, Leipzig, 1890.
CHURCHMAN, J. W. J. Exper. M., 1927, 4:46.

Cook, R. P.   Biol. Reviews, 1923, 7:1–23.
Darányi, J.   Centralbl. f. Bakteriol., II Abt., 1927, 71:353; I Abt., 1930, 117:543.
De Bary, A.   Lectures on Bacteria, Translation of 2nd German Edition, Oxford, 1887, p. 16.
Dobell, C. Q.   J. Microscop. Sci., 1911, 56:395.
Enderlein, G.   Bakterien-Cyclogenie, Leipzig, 1925.
Ernst, P.   Ztschr. f. Hyg., 1888, 4:25.
Gardner, A. D.   J. Path. & Bacteriol., 1925, 28:189.
Graham-Smith, G. S.   Parasitology, 1910, 3:17.
Gutstein, M.   Centralbl. f. Bakteriol., I Abt., 1925, 95:357.
Hadley, P., Delves, E., and Klimek, J.   J. Infect. Dis., 1931, 48:1.
Henrici, A. T.   Proc. Soc. Exper. Biol. & Med., 1924, 22:197.
Hill, H. W.   J. Med. Research, 1902, 2:115.
Hiss, P.   J. Exper. M., 1905, 6:316.
Hort, E. C.   Proc. Roy. Soc., Lond., B., 1917, 89:468.
———— J. Hyg., 1920, 18:361–369.
Kahn, M.   Am. Rev. Tuberc., 1929, 20:150.
Knaysi, G.   J. Bacteriol., 1930, 19:113.
Krause, F.   Naturwiss., 1937, 25:817.
Legroux, R., and Magrou, J.   Ann. de l'Inst. Pasteur, 1920, 34:417.
Löhnis, F., and Smith, N. R.   J. Agric. Research, 1916, 6:675.
———— Studies upon the Life Cycle of the Bacteria, Memoirs of the National Academy of Sciences, Washington, 1922, 16:2nd mem.
Marton, L.   Bull. Acad. Belg., Classe des Sci., 1937, 23:672.
Mellon, R. R.   Am. Rev. Tuberc., 1929, 19:483.
———— Proc. Soc. Exper. Biol. & Med., 1932, 30:110.
Messea, A.   Riv. d'ig. e san. pubb., 1890, 1:513.
Migula.   System der Bakterien, 1894, 1:56.
Naganishi, K.   Centralbl. f. Bakteriol., I Abt., 1901, 30:97, 145, 193, 225.
———— Centralbl. f. Bakteriol., 1901, 1:30.
———— München. med. Wchnschr., 1900, 47:1.
Neumann, F.   Centralbl. f. Bakteriol., I Abt., 1925, 96:250; 1928, 109:143.
Potthoff, H.   Centralbl. f. Bakteriol., II Abt., 1924, 61:249.
Schaudinn, F.   Archiv f. Protistenk., 1902, 1:306.
Thornton, H. G., and Gangulee, N.   Proc. Roy. Soc., Lond., B., 1926, 99: 427.
Von Borries, B., Ruska, E., and Ruska, H.   Wiss. Veröffentlichungen a.d. Siemens-Werken, 1938, 17:99, 107.
Walker, E. W. A., and Murray, W.   Brit. M. J., 1904, 2:16.
Wyckoff, R. W. G.   Science, 1932, 76: 240.
———— J. Exper. M., 1934, 59:381.
Wyckoff, R. W. G., and Ter Louw, A.   J. Exper. M., 1931, 54:449.
Zettnow.   Ztschr. f. Hyg., 1897, 24:72 and 1918, 85:17.
Zinsser, H.   J. Exper. M., 1906, 8:542.

CHAPTER III

GROWTH AND DEATH OF BACTERIA

Definition and Methods of Measuring Growth.—For biological and practical purposes it is often necessary to measure the growth of single bacterial cells and of a culture composed of thousands of cells. When we use the term "growth" we should mean the progressive development of an organism from its earliest stage to its death or subdivision. From this fundamental process of increase or maintenance of protoplasmic bulk come most of the phenomena of interest to bacteriologists. Unfortunately, it is impossible to measure the actual progression of changes in bulk of a single cell, because the amount of absorbed water, stored fat and other nonvital material cannot be determined. It is impossible to define the beginning and ending of growth, since from the start there is a simultaneous breakdown and building-up of protoplasm. Bacteria, as Rahn has clearly depicted, are like all other cells in this respect that they are disintegrating while they are increasing and renewing their substance even when disintegration is gaining the upper hand. Lacking a measure of this fundamental characteristic of the cell, indirect methods are used to obtain an approximate estimate of growth. Many criteria are used. Rates of multiplication, number of organisms in a given volume, total crop yield, biochemical activity and micro-kjeldahl determinations of nitrogen (Mueller) have been called indices of growth. Each of these is a measure of only one characteristic of growth. It is essential, therefore, to note the distinctions between the different methods used to measure growth in order to understand the meaning of the results obtained by any or all of them.

Growth of a Single Cell.—The volume of the cell can be calculated from measurements of the dimensions. In this way, a number of investigators have followed the progression in volume of a single bacterial cell at intervals during its generation span. By means of a motion photomicrographic apparatus we have studied the volume changes of living cells of yeast, *Bact. coli* and *B. megatherium*. After a period of latency on new medium at 37° C. the single cell begins to grow, reaching a maximum rate of volume increase in about one hour. Adult body volume, large at first, progressively decreases as the culture ages. Under the conditions of our experiment, *B. megatherium* produced 250 times the bulk of the inoculated individuals, while *Bact. coli* produced only 30 times its bulk before reproduction ceased. The generation times, that is, the intervals between fissions, of *Bact. coli* were: Sixty-six to ninety minutes in the first generation, thirteen to twenty-three minutes in the second generation, fifteen to twenty in the third, twenty minutes in the fourth and fifth and thirty-five to forty minutes in the sixth. Thus the generation time after the first generation gradually lengthened. Observations upon single cells disclose a fallacy in the use of enumeration of cells as an exact measure of growth. The cells in cultures after about the fifth hour, as we and others have found, are smaller than those in the earlier

34

hours, and numbers are increased by subdivisions of larger cells with very little increase in total bulk.

Other methods for measuring growth in volume or mass of the single cell are based upon determinations of the volume or weight of numerous cells, sedimented by centrifugation or collected by scraping the growth from the surface of solid medium. The values thus obtained are divided by the total number of cells in the sample. These methods give only crude averages.

Measurements of Growth of Cultures.—In addition to measurements of the volumes of cells packed in a centrifuge tube, or weight of moist or dry masses of bacteria, the progressive development of a culture is determined principally by the enumeration of the number of bacteria present in a given volume. The number of organisms can be determined roughly by comparison of the density of their suspension with a known density standard, previously evaluated in terms of bacterial numbers by direct counts. Density standards are made of barium sulphate, as in the McFarland series. Nephelometers or the simple densitometer of Gates may be used. When the bacteria are few in the fluid, nephelometric methods and density comparisons are inaccurate. As the opacities and light-scattering effects of organisms vary, reliable results can not be obtained by these means, but practically useful approximations can be made by them.

The numbers of bacteria present in a given volume of fluid can be determined by: direct counts in a ruled chamber under the microscope; counts of the number of organisms in a stained film of known volume, by the method of Breed; and by making plate-counts. The first and third methods are the ones usually employed in studies of growth. They give different results at different periods of the incubation of the culture and both are disturbed by the tendency of bacteria to form clumps of cells. The direct count discloses the total number of organisms present. It does not distinguish between living and dead cells. During the first few hours of development of the culture almost all, at least about 95 per cent, of the cells are alive. After that time more and more cells die, so that the discrepancy between the viable and dead cells increases with time. The special staining methods of Benians, and Gay and Clark have been used as a supplementary means of obtaining an estimate of the relative proportions of living and dead cells. In our hands, direct counts have been the most reliable index of the number of active cells in cultures during the first six or eight hours of development.

To obtain plate-counts, properly diluted samples of the culture are mixed with melted nutrient agar medium and poured into a Petri dish. After an appropriate period of incubation at the required temperature, the colonies developed in the medium are counted, and this number, multiplied by the dilution factor, is called the bacterial count. It is usually given an unwarranted precision, as for example, 265,421 bacteria per c.c. Such a statement is based upon the assumptions that each colony represents one bacterium and that every bacterium transferred to the plate multiplied. Neither supposition is true. Clumps of from two to more than fifty cells may give rise to one colony and not all bacteria living in the original sample are able to multiply when transferred to new medium. Much of the investigation of bacterial growth has been based upon plate-counts of viable bacteria without due appreciation of these sources of error and of other irregularities which affect this method of enumeration.

Finally, biochemical activity, rate of fermentation or of decomposition of some substrate have been used as measures of bacterial growth. As some of the changes can be produced by enzymes outside of the cells and as cells which are not reproducing may continue to metabolize, it is obvious that such methods as these can not provide any true information on the actual growth of the cells.

Most of the published growth curves of bacteria are graphs of the results of enumeration of cells in cultures. Although they do not actually represent growth in bulk, they are very useful in permitting an analysis of the progression of changes in a culture. Figure 9 is a schematic reproduction of an enumeration growth curve of a culture during fifty hours. The logarithms of the numbers of bacteria per cubic centimeter are used in place of the actual numbers because they facilitate the display of the different phases of growth and because a graph of actual numbers would be too unwieldy. A graph of logarithms of these numbers has the disadvantage of obscuring irregularities which may be significant. In Figure 9 the solid line is the graph of the number of viable organisms per c.c., the dotted line is the graph of the total number of cells. It is seen at once that the total number of cells increases rapidly at first and then slowly increases during the remaining hours. After a period, the length of which depends upon many factors, reproduction ceases and the total number of cells decreases as the cells disintegrate.

The graph of the number of viable cells per unit volume of the culture can be divided into the following parts (Fig. 9):

1 to A: Initial stationary period
A to B: Period of accelerating multiplication or growth rate
         The period 1 to B is usually designated as the lag period
B to C: Period of maximum multiplication rate, logarithmic period of growth
C to D: Period of decreasing growth rate, negative growth acceleration
D to E: Stationary period
E to F: Period of decline or accelerating death rate
F to G: Period of maximum death rate, logarithmic death rate
G to end: Period of prolonged decline

There are differences of bacterial morphology, staining reactions, intracellular substances, rates of multiplication, biochemical activity, resistance to injurious substances and influences and probably also differences in pathogenicity associated with all the phases of this growth curve.

LAG PHASE.—This is the period of time between the planting of the organism in the medium and the beginning of maximum multiplication rate. It is divisible into a stationary phase and a phase of accelerating rate of cell division. Observations of single cells show that growth, as evidenced by increase in volume, begins within an hour and sometimes within ten minutes. Hence the initial stationary phase of actual growth is probably quite short. During the lag phase (1 to B, Fig. 9) the cells, if the inoculum was from a culture twenty-four hours or more in age, enlarge, lose their granules and become homogeneous. They have been called embryonic cells by Henrici. During this period there occurs apparently an active process of rejuvenation, solution of old reserve material and synthesis of new protoplasm.

The lag period has been a subject of much study by most of those who have investigated the growth of bacteria. It was noticed by Max Müller in 1895, investigated by Rahn in 1906, by Barber in 1908, and since then chiefly by Coplans, Lane-Claypon, Penfold, Chesney, Buchanan and Sherman and Albus. The facts established are that lag lasts longest in organisms from old cultures and can be reduced almost to zero by transferring actively growing bacteria to new medium. The explanations of lag have been several. Chesney explained it as the time required for the bacterium to recover from an injury caused by the accumulation of metabolites in its previous environment. Sherman and Albus present evidence that the cells of later generations in cultures are somewhat resistant to injury and would explain lag as a period occupied by the processes of cellular rejuvenation, during which the physiological

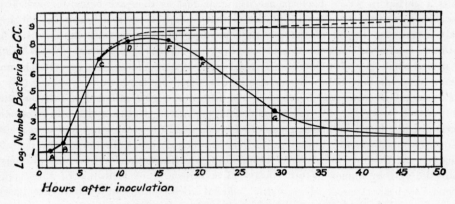

FIG. 9.—SEMIDIAGRAMMATIC GROWTH CURVE OF BACTERIA.
For explanation see text. — — — — Total cells. ——— Viable cells.

youth of the organisms is regained. It is probable that both explanations are correct; they are not contradictory.

During this period, some of the so-called involution forms transferred from old cultures have been seen to enlarge, branch or bud, producing in some cases temporarily branched and irregular forms and in others typical rod forms after the first stages of the Y-type of "three point multiplication."

LOGARITHMIC PERIOD.—This is the period of maximum growth rate. The organisms, multiplying by fission, increase by geometric ratio (2^1, 2^2, 2^3 — — 2^n). Generation times of most of the pathogens growing at 37° C. are reduced to fifteen to twenty minutes. There is a rapid increase in the number of cells. The cells are large and homogeneous. The graph of logarithms of numbers of cells in the culture during this period is a straight line, as shown in Figure 9, B to C. This period may last a few minutes or for one or more hours. The existence of a true logarithmic period is debatable, but there is no question as to the existence of a period of maximum and rapid multiplication. In this phase of the culture the organisms are actively synthesizing new protoplasm. It is difficult to discover changes in the medium from which the organisms are deriving their nutriment, partly because the changes are slight and partly because the buffering action of the medium is capable of compensating for changes in reaction. When organisms growing in the logarithmic phase are transferred to a new medium of the same composition and at the same temperature they continue to multiply and grow without lag. This has been called by Sherman and Albus the period of "physiological youth." The physiologically young bacteria have a greater susceptibility to heat, salt solutions, disinfectants and physical injury than bacteria from a later stage of development of the culture. This has a bearing on comparative tests of disinfectants. The organisms in this phase appear also to have greater pathogenicity or virulence, as shown by Felton. Walker and others have shown that in this period the cells increase greatly in volume and metabolic activity is highest.

STATIONARY STAGE.—After a period of decreasing rate of multiplication the organisms in a culture enter a so-called stationary stage. Plate counts indicate that this is a period in which bacteria are dying as fast as they are being formed. This stage begins ordinarily after about the sixth or tenth hour and continues for five or six hours, the length of the period depending upon numerous conditions. The total number of cells continues to increase slowly, as shown by the direct count. During this period there is a slow increase in total bulk of protoplasm but the cells become progressively smaller. Catabolic metabolism becomes predominant.

Periods of Decline and Death.—At the fifteenth, eighteenth and usually by the twenty-fourth hour, the culture has entered the periods of decline and death. Synthetic processes are reduced, catabolic metabolism has gained the ascendancy and changes in the nutrient medium are conspicuous. The characteristics of the organism declare themselves to the eye in pigment production, gas formation, colony morphology, hemolysis, and in numerous other ways. The threshold of visibility of these phenomena has been crossed. Most of the "official" descriptions of bacteria are based upon the morphological, tinctorial and biochemical properties exhibited by organisms after eighteen to twenty-four hours incubation of the cultures. The forms of bacteria in this phase of the growth cycle were established by Koch and others as the normal forms and the doctrine of monomorphism was based in part upon the selection of a particular time for the examination of a culture. It may be fairly questioned whether these forms have any more validity as species characteristics than the forms appearing earlier or even somewhat later in the cultures. Certainly most cultures have entered the period of senescence at this time. The organisms are smaller and more uniform in size than those which were present in the earlier hours of incubation of the cultures. It is admittedly valuable to have established standardized procedures for the examination of cultures grown in standardized media under standardized conditions of incubation, since bacteria show differences under different conditions. For practical reference, data obtained under standardized conditions are indispensable. But such measures of systematic diagnostic convenience are not altogether suitable for the study of the complete cycle of growth of an organism.

The phase of death has been extensively investigated by Falk and Winslow, Rahn and others. In this period (*F* to *G*, and to the end, Fig. 9), the death rate increases to a logarithmic order and then gradually declines. Granules of various materials accumulate in the cells. The cells become smaller, coccoidal forms may occur, as in *B. coli*, replacing the rods, and long clubbed forms may replace the original coccoidal forms in cultures of certain strains of diphtheroids. Swollen, spindle-shaped, branched and apparently budding forms make their appearance. While the predominant type of cells in most cultures is small and fairly regular in shape in these later stages, bizarre and irregular forms become more frequent. These are the so-called "involution forms," usually regarded as evidence of degeneration. Undoubtedly many of these forms are pathological, the result of changes in the cell membrane or other degenerative processes. These forms are usually discarded as abnormal and insignificant by bacteriologists who regard the forms of bacteria as fairly constant according to species. They are also the forms receiving particular attention by the modern investigators of the possible life cycles of bacteria. We have discussed them in the section on reproduction of bacteria in Chapter II and will consider their significance in relation to bacterial variation in Chapter IX. As some of these irregular forms resume growth when transferred to a new medium they are not all to be classed as nonviable products of degeneration. The problems presented by them are unsolved at present.

Growth and all its associated phenomena are functions dependent upon many conditions. Growth is possible only when the cell can derive energy and structural material from its environment. Bacteria obtain this energy from chemical reactions, unaided by chlorophyl or any photosynthetic mechanism. Energy is utilized in various ways in the exchanges of anabolic and catabolic metabolism. Physical conditions, affecting the environment, rates of chemical reactions and the state of protoplasm exert great influence upon growth. Hereditary factors also play a part in growth. Knowledge of the growth of bacterial cells is useful not only to the bacteriologist, but also to those who study growth of animal and plant cells, to the student of cancer and to the general and specialized biologist. There are similarities between the growth curves of bacterial cultures and the growth curves of animals, plants, fruit flies and human populations. For a more extensive treatment of this subject, with mathematical analyses of growth curves, reference should be made to the publications of Rahn, Buchanan and Fulmer, Winslow, Lane-Claypon, and Ledingham and Penfold.

From the point of view of the medical bacteriologist these investigations have several important consequences. They have afforded evidence of the change of bacterial morphology at different periods of the growth cycle of the organisms, as shown particularly by Clark and Ruehl and later by Henrici in his exposition of cytomorphosis of bacteria based upon measurements of more than 100,000 cells. This is to be taken into consideration in making morphological distinctions between bacteria. It has been shown that bacteria differ in resistance to injurious substances at different phases of the development of a culture. These differences are to be taken into account in making tests of disinfectants and other agents acting upon bacteria. Differences have been noted in the pathogenicity of rapidly growing young bacteria as compared with organisms from older cultures, the younger organisms appearing to be more virulent. Felty and Bloomfield, studying the infectivity of streptococci and pneumococci at various stages of the growth cycle found young cells to be more pathogenic than older ones and suggested a possible relationship between the growth stage of microorganisms and the genesis of epidemics, particularly as regards the pre-epidemic stage.

DORMANCY OF BACTERIAL CELLS.—Aside from properties causing the relatively short period of lag in cultures, a peculiar attribute of the bacterial protoplasm is its ability to lie dormant for long periods within and outside the body. Bacteria, even nonspore-bearing varieties, planted on media and allowed to grow, then put away in hermetically sealed tubes in a cool, dark place, may remain alive for years. A typhoid culture kept sealed in this way by the late Hiss grew when we took it out after twelve years. Plague bacilli kept in the safe at the New York Quarantine station were reported by Wilson as retaining virulence four years later. Pneumococci and strepto-cocci, if frozen and dried, will remain viable and fully virulent for indefinite periods. (See technical section for methods of preserving cultures.) Even within the body such dormant states can be attained by the vegetative cells of non-spore-bearing bacteria. We have observed a hemolytic streptococcus lying dormant in a healed cicatrix after infection, recultivated after an apparently clean secondary operation for mechanical repair eighteen months later. This matter has been studied by Burke, Sprague and Barnes. The ability of bacteria to maintain life in a state of dormancy is important from the biological point of view and may be of considerable practical significance.

REFERENCES

BARBER, M. A.   J. Infect. Dis., 1908, 5:379.
BAYNE-JONES, S., and ADOLPH, E. F.   J. Cellular & Comp. Physiol, 1932, 1:387, 409.
BENIANS, T. H. C.   Brit. M. J., 1916, 2:722.
BREED, R. S.   Standard Methods of Milk Analysis, American Public Health Association, 1927.
BUCHANAN, R. E.   J. Infect. Dis., 1918, 23:109.
———— The Newer Knowledge of Bacteriology and Immunology, Chicago, 1928, Chap. V, 46.
BUCHANAN, R. E. and FULMER, E. I.   Physiology and Biochemistry of Bacteria, Baltimore, 1928, 1:4–62.
BURKE, V., SPRAGUE, A., and BARNES, L.   J. Infect. Dis., 1925, 36:555.
CHESNEY, A. M.   J. Exper. M., 1916, 24:387.
CLARK, P. F., and RUEHL, H.   The Newer Knowledge of Bacteriology and Immunology, Chicago, 1928, Chap. IV, 38.
COPLANS, M.   J. Path. & Bacteriol., 1910, 14:1.
FALK, I. S., and WINSLOW, C.-E. A.   J. Bacteriol., 1926, 11:1.
FELTON, L. D.   Johns Hopkins Hosp. Bull., 1923, 34:262.
FELTON, L. D., and DOUGHERTY, K. M.   J. Exper. M., 1924, 39:137.
FELTY, A. R., and BLOOMFIELD, A. L.   Johns Hopkins Hosp. Bull., 1924, 40:703.
GAY, F. P., and CLARK, A. R.   J. Bacteriol., 1934, 27:175.
HENRICI, A. T.   Morphologic Variation and the Rate of Growth of Bacteria, Springfield, Ill., 1928.
LANE-CLAYPON, J. E.   J. Hyg., 1909, 9:239.
LEDINGHAM, J. C. G., and PENFOLD, W. J.   J. Hyg., 1914, 14:242.
MUELLER, J. H.   J. Bacteriol., 1935, 29:383.
MÜLLER, M.   Ztschr. f. Hyg., 1895, 20:245.
PEARL, R.   Scientific Monthly, 1921, 13:193.
PEARL, R., and REED, L. J.   Proc. Nat. Acad. Sc., 1920, 6:275.
PENFOLD, W. J.   J. Hyg., 1914, 14:215.
RAHN, O.   Physiology of Bacteria, Philadelphia, 1932, Part C, pp. 162–269.
———— Centralbl. f. Bakteriol. II Abt., 1906, 16:417, 609.
REED, H. S., and HOLLAND, R. H.   Proc. Nat. Acad. Sc., 1919, 5:135.
ROBERTSON, T. B.   Arch. f. Entwicklngsmechn., 1908, 25:581.
SHERMAN, J. M., and ALBUS, W. R.   J. Bacteriol., 1922, 8:127; 1924, 9:305.
WALKER, H. H., WINSLOW, C.-E. A., HUNTINGTON, E., and MOONEY, M. G.   J. Bacteriol., 1934, 27:303.
WINSLOW, C.-E. A.   The Newer Knowledge of Bacteriology and Immunology, Chicago, 1928, Chapter IV, p. 38; Chap. VI, 58.

CHAPTER IV

THE CHEMICAL COMPOSITION OF BACTERIA

Bacteria have an extraordinary range of biochemical activity and are capable of synthesizing a great variety of compounds. They provide unique material for the investigation of the chemical constitution and chemical processes of cells. The study of the chemical composition of bacteria gives not only an insight into the nature of these organisms, but also an understanding of the chemistry of the cells of animals and plants through the fundamental unity of vital phenomena. The biochemistry of the cells of other organisms is applicable in turn to the chemistry of the bacteria.

In medical bacteriology, the knowledge of the chemical composition of bacteria aids in the solution of many problems. It is of assistance in the identification of organisms. It facilitates the cultivation of bacteria. It advances the knowledge of staining reactions. It forms a rational basis for the development of disinfectants and of bacterial chemotherapy. It helps to explain phenomena of infection, immunology and serology. It is a means of relating the production of symptoms and lesions to definite bacterial compounds and thereby increases the power to treat and control infectious disease.

On account of the small size of bacteria, the labor and expense of harvesting them in bulk, the complexities of their constitution, and the variations which they exhibit in response to different chemical, physical and hereditary factors, the field of bacterial chemistry is difficult. The conditions necessary for its cultivation, however, and the system and methods to be used to isolate *without change* the constituents of the bacterial cell are being understood more clearly. Great progress has been made, particularly in the chemical analysis of such groups of bacteria as the pneumococci and tubercle bacilli.

Two groups of methods are used: microchemical and gross chemical procedures. Microchemical methods have a certain indicative value and could be developed further with profit. The analyses based upon material in bulk are, of course, indispensable and have given the most valuable information.

Bacterial chemistry is both quantitative and qualitative. Lack of attention to the composition of media and other conditions affecting the synthesis of bacterial protoplasm and products has deprived many of the older quantitative results of their significance. But with the more general use of media of known chemical composition and with greater control of conditions of growth the results of modern quantitative chemical analyses are increasing in value. The qualitative chemical studies, however, yield the most important general and practical information.

In this chapter we shall deal chiefly with the qualitative chemistry of bacterial cells and shall arrange the material under headings of the chief groups of substances. For the manner in which the cells construct these substances and for information on

41

other phases of the biochemical activities of bacteria, the reader is referred to Knight's monograph and to our chapter on bacterial metabolism (Chapter VI).

Elementary and General Composition.—Bacterial substance contains carbon, hydrogen, oxygen, nitrogen, sulphur, phosphorus, iron, calcium, magnesium, silicon, potassium, sodium, chlorine, and, occasionally, other elements. These elements are present in both inorganic and organic combinations. The convenient groups under which these compounds may be considered are: water content, composition of the inorganic ash, constitution of organic compounds (proteins, carbohydrates, fats, waxes) and materials of unknown composition. A useful compilation of the results of numerous chemical analyses, published by Buchanan and Fulmer in 1928, indicates that these constituents are present in bacterial cells in the following variable proportions:

Water content, 75 to 85 per cent; solids, 25 to 15 per cent.

The percentage proportions of the dry weight of the solids for the main groups of compounds are: proteins, 23 to 72, carbohydrates 12 to 28, fats 0.17 to 40. The great variability of these figures is due to differences in species, differences in composition of the media on which the organisms were grown, and differences in handling the bacteria.

The *ash* obtained by incineration has been found to amount to 2 to 30 per cent of the dry weight of the cell. The following variable percentage proportions for elements contained in the ash have been found: Phosphorus as P_2O^5, 10 to 74; potassium as K_2O, 5 to 30; sodium as Na_2O, 28 to 34; calcium as CaO, 0.3 to 14; magnesium as MgO, 0.12 to 8; silicon as SiO_2, 0.6 to 8; sulphur as SO_3, 0.6 to 8; chlorine as Cl, 1.25 to 44. The chief value of these figures is to indicate the range of possible proportions and to emphasize again that characteristics of species and composition of culture media greatly influence the chemical constitution of bacteria.

The nitrogen content has been found to vary between 2 and 14 per cent of the dry weight of the cell, with an average value of about 10 per cent. The proteins of the cell contain the greatest proportion of this nitrogen, but other constituents of the cell also contain nitrogen.

The carbon content is high. Its percentage proportion is generally 45 to 55 per cent of the dry substance. Most of the carbon is contained in the proteins and carbohydrates.

Water.—The amount of water in bacterial cells varies with the age of the culture, the moisture of the medium and with the production of special growth forms. It is very low in endospores, but on an average represents 80 per cent of the weight of the vegetative cell. No one has determined the proportions of free and bound water in bacteria. It is obvious, however, that since water is as essential for the activities of these cells as it is for all other types of cells, it is not to be regarded as an inert constituent. Further study is required to determine the water balance in bacterial cells and the rôle of water in the structure and properties of bacterial protoplasm, as indicated by the investigations of Adolph and Gortner.

Proteins.—The bacterial protein is of several types. A true globulin has been described and coagulable proteins were demonstrated by Buchner in the "Pressaft" or juice obtained by subjecting bacteria to mechanical pressure. Proteins occur in bacterial cells as simple proteins and as compounds of protein with nucleic acid, with carbohydrates and with lipoids. Most of the group and species specific immunological reactions are determined by simple and nucleoproteins. The protein-carbohydrate and protein-lipoid compounds are especially important as the bearers of strict immunological specificities. These protein compounds contain specific "haptenes."

Investigations following those of Ruppel have shown that more than half of the protein of the cell of the tubercle bacillus and other bacteria is combined with or associated with nucleic acid or nucleins, forming a class of indefinite compounds loosely called "nucleoproteins."

Staining reactions and microchemical studies have shown that there is a large proportion of nuclear material in the bacterial cell. Whether this material is organized or diffusely distributed has not been determined with certainty. A review of these questions and the results of the application of a microchemical Feulgen reaction to the bacterial cell have been reported by Pietschamm and Pietschamm and Rippel. They found no morphologically recognizable nucleus in *B. mycoides* and other bacteria. The cells reacted diffusely in the Feulgen fuchsin-aldehyde reaction even after the formation of the endospore. It seems possible that the necessary treatment with HCl may have disturbed the cellular organization. The reaction indicated the presence of thymonucleic acid in bacteria.

It was hoped that the relationship of bacteria to animals or plants might be revealed by a study of the nucleic acid in bacteria. The purines, guanine, adenine, xanthine and hypoxanthine, which have been shown to be present in various bacteria, are common to both animals and plants. In the plant nucleic acid there is a pyrimidine uracile and a pentose, while in the animal nucleic acid these are represented by thymine and a pentose. We found that bacterial nucleic acid did not contain pentose, and Brown and Johnson showed that tuberculinic acid, the nucleic acid of tubercle bacilli, contained a sugar, yielding levulinic acid on hydrolysis. Johnson and Brown and Johnson and Coghill found both thymine and cytosine in tuberculinic acid. It seems likely, therefore, that bacterial nucleic acid is distinctive.

"Nucleoproteins" have been obtained from many types of bacteria. Undoubtedly their chemical and antigenic properties have been altered by the methods used to extract them from the cells. We have presented evidence that the nucleoproteins may be obtained in bacterial autolysates in a less denatured form. Heidelberger and Kendall have isolated a labile nucleoprotein with distinct physical and specific properties by extracting fat-free scarlatinal streptococci with acid phosphate solution in the cold.

A protein resembling Bence-Jones protein has been extracted by us from tubercle bacilli, but this has not been thoroughly studied.

Analysis of bacterial protein by Tamura and others have yielded most of the monamino and diamino acids. Leucine, isoleucine, lysine, arginine, proline, valine, histidine, cystine, phenylalanine, tyrosine, and tryptophane have been recovered from tubercle bacilli, diphtheria bacilli and other organisms. The work of these investigators indicates that the fundamental chemical nature of the protein of bacteria does not differ from protein of other organisms.

By the use of protein-free "synthetic" culture media it has been shown that bacteria can build up the most complex compounds from relatively simple materials, and these compounds can be obtained for examination uncontaminated by the usual protein derivatives incorporated in nutrient media. Eckstein and Soule found that

B. coli can synthesize from alanine or cystine proteins containing numerous amino acids, including those with aromatic nuclei, and can construct also fats and carbohydrates. A most notable progress in the protein chemistry of bacteria, made in this way since 1925, by Seibert and Long, has been the isolation and study of a crystalline albumin-like protein from tuberculin. This is the active principle of tuberculin.

Only a small amount of information is available on the protein or protein-like constitution of some of the structures of the bacterial cells. *Volutin,* and material forming the metachromatic granules of Babes and Ernst appear from the investigations of Zettnow, Meyer and Schumacher to be composed of nucleic acid compounds, but not nucleoproteins. *Flagella,* which have never been obtained free from other parts of the bacterial body, are said by Fischer and Hochberg to be composed chiefly of globulin. Neither nucleic acid nor sulphur was found in the fractions examined by them.

Carbohydrates and Related Substances.—Carbohydrates and carbohydrate compounds form a variable but most important part of the bacterial substances. Many elements of structure, qualities of pathogenicity and specific immunological reactions are due to the carbohydrates and to compounds of carbohydrates with proteins.

Cellulose and Hemicellulose.—The cell walls of bacteria are by no means as well defined as those of plants. In fact, while an ectoplasmic zone can be distinguished from an endoplasmic region, the cell membrane of bacteria is no more definite than that of animal cells. Since bacteria are related to plants, a search for cellulose in them has been made repeatedly. This polymer of cellobiose has not been proved to be present in bacteria. It seems unlikely, moreover, that any of the polysaccharides found in bacteria can be classed as hemicellulose. We agree with the summary of information of these questions as presented by Buchanan and Fulmer, that while it seems certain that bacteria do not contain cellulose, it is very doubtful that hemicellulose forms any part of their cell wall or ectoplasm.

Chitin.—This polymer of glucosamine, which forms the carapace of crustaceans, was said by Iwanoff to be present in bacterial cells. In 1912, Vierhoever found chitin by microchemical tests in a number of bacteria. Neither von Wisselingh nor Aronson was able to obtain positive tests for chitin in bacteria. Glucosamine has been found in micro-organisms and chitin occurs in molds. Whether or not it exists in bacteria remains undetermined.

Starch and Glycogen.—These polysaccharides or compounds closely related to them, having the formula $(C_6H_{10}O_5)N$, occur as granules in bacterial cells. They stain blue or reddish brown with iodine. The granules which stain blue with iodine and are dissolved by amylase have some differences from true starch and have been called *granulose* by Beijerinck, according to Buchanan and Fulmer. On the other hand, Gray regarded granules of this nature in *Bact. coli* as true starch. *Glycogen* has been identified in numerous bacteria by Meyer.

Gums and Slime.—These are indefinite polysaccharides with peculiar viscous properties. They occur in the cells and as thick mucinous material around them and in the media in which certain bacteria are growing. They are classified as dextrans, levulans and cellulans. They have considerable importance in the "ropy" fermentations of milk and beer, but aside from their possible relation to bacterial capsules they are of minor significance in medical bacteriology.

Tamura isolated from tubercle bacilli a polyatomic alcohol of high molecular weight, to which he gave the name "mykol." He related the alkali-fast and acid-fast properties of tubercle bacilli to mykol. Tamura did not find mykol in the nonacid-fast diphtheria bacilli. Later investigations have indicated that the waxy material of tubercle bacilli responsible for their staining reactions is to be classed among the fat-like substances in the cell.

Specific Polysaccharides.—Bacteria have in their cells, and especially in their capsules, polymers of glucose-glucuronic acid, some of which contain nitrogen while others do not contain nitrogen. There is a close correlation between the virulence of organisms, such as pneumococci, and the development of capsules. Since the strictest immunological specificity is mediated by these compounds, they are given the terms "specific polysaccharides," or "soluble specific substance." Their properties have been studied intensively in pneumococci and tubercle bacilli. They appear to occur in all bacteria, however, and are being investigated generally.

The earliest work dealing with substances of this nature in which their immunological relations were considered was published by Pick in 1902. In 1917, Dochez and Avery found substances of this class in the blood stream and urine of pneumonia patients and in broth cultures of pneumococci. In 1921, we reported the presence of a similar substance in tubercle bacillus extracts prepared in a manner calculated to exclude the bacterial proteins. Heidelberger, who in association with Avery and Goebel, has investigated the chemistry and immunology of these polysaccharides, has published two informative reviews of the knowledge of these compounds and we have dealt with them at length in a discussion of the bacterial antigen. Reference to these specific polysaccharides will be found in many sections of this book.

The specific polysaccharides of Type I *Pneumococcus* appears to be made up of carbohydrate units with nitrogen as a part of the molecule. The polysaccharides of Type II and Type III *Pneumococcus* do not contain nitrogen. Heidelberger and Kendall have shown that the polysaccharides derived from Type IV *Pneumococcus* differ markedly from those derived from Types I, II and III. Another species-specific type of polysaccharide containing acetyl nitrogen and called "C-substance," discovered by Tillett and Francis in R-forms as well as S-forms of pneumococci, has been studied chemically by Tillett, Goebel and Avery. Specific polysaccharides have been isolated from tuberculin, from the lipoids of the tubercle bacillus, from dysentery bacilli, yeast and many other organisms. These will be described in sections dealing with those bacteria.

In 1933 it was learned from the researches of Pappenheimer and Enders and Avery and Goebel that the Type I pneumococcus polysaccharide as originally described by Heidelberger and his coworkers represents a chemically incomplete form of the specific carbohydrate. As it exists in the organism, or at least in autolysates, this polysaccharide contains the acetyl group not found in the Heidelberger derivative. This group renders the substance considerably more active in combining with homologous antibody and also confers upon it the capacity to act as a complete antigen when injected into mice.

From the immunological point of view, none of these polysaccharides alone, with the possible exception of the substances described by Wadsworth and Brown, Pappenheimer and Enders, is capable of stimulating the production of antibodies when injected into an animal. They react specifically, however, with antiserum from animals after immunization with the whole bacterial organism. When coupled with proteins these polysaccharides endow the protein complex with antigenic specificity related almost exclusively to the polysaccharide portion of the protein-carbohydrate complex. They are, therefore, typical examples of Landsteiner's "haptenes." A new and most important phase of immunology has been developed upon the recognition that biological specificity, hitherto considered to be an attribute of protein structure alone, is determined also by complex carbohydrates of this type.

Fats, Lipoids and Waxes.—By extraction of bacteria with fat solvents, alcohol, ether, acetone, benzol and chloroform, a large number of fats, lipoids, waxes and related substances is obtained. The total amount and characteristics of these substances vary with the culture medium, age of growth of the culture and type of organism. In some bacteria these extractives make up less than 0.2 per cent of the dry weight; in others, as for example tubercle bacilli, fats and related compounds constitute 40 to 50 per cent of the dry weight of the cells.

The fat in bacteria has been demonstrated microchemically by the use of osmic acid and Sudan III, and naphthol and dimethyl-p-phenylenediamine, by Meyer, Sato and Eisenberg.

Attention has been directed chiefly to the fatty acids, phosphatides and waxes derived from bacteria. Although it is not known in what combinations all of these compounds occur in bacteria, great progress has been made by Anderson in the analysis of acid-fast bacteria and by others who have studied the protein lipoid combinations known as Forssman's "heterophile antigens."

Palmitic, stearic, oleic, butyric, caproic, and arachidic acids have been found as glycerides in bacteria by Goris and Liot and others, as listed by Buchanan and Fulmer.

A liquid saturated fatty acid obtained by Anderson from the phosphatides of tubercle bacilli possesses unusual interest. When this acid is injected into normal animals it acts upon the monocytes and causes the formation of tubercles. For this reason the acid was named *phthioic acid*.

The phosphatide fractions of tubercle bacilli differ from the usual plant and animal phosphatides in their low content of nitrogen and phosphorus, and in their content of a new type of polysaccharide. When injected into animals the phosphatide leads to the formation of massive tuberculous tissue. This phosphatide is said to be antigenic.

As we shall describe in greater detail in the chapter on tuberculosis, chemical studies of this nature are not only enriching biochemistry but are providing a means of relating symptoms and lesions of disease to components of bacterial protoplasm.

The heterophile antigens of Forssman are complex substances composed of proteins united to lipoids. The molecular aggregates of these compounds contain, in some cases, carbohydrates. The lipoidal part of the molecule alone is incapable of stimulating the production of antibodies but it can react with antibodies produced by injection of the protein-lipoid complex. These lipoidal substances, therefore, form another group of haptenes. Heterophile antigens have been found in organisms of the dysentery, paratyphoid, lepisepticum and other groups of bacteria by Rothacker, Iijima, and a number of other investigators as recorded by Jungeblut and Ross.

Heterophile antigens when injected into rabbits cause the production of lysins active against sheep cells, antibodies to the protein component, and also antibodies which react specifically with the lipoidal fraction of the compound. These results have a general bearing upon the determination of biological relationships through immunological reactions and a practical significance in the study of infectious diseases, and in the use of complement-fixation tests and flocculation reactions.

Sterols.—Bacteria do not contain cholesterol. Eckstein and Soule and von Behring failed to find sterols of any sort in *B. coli* and *B. diphtheriae*. Sterols, possibly phytosterol, or mycosterol or ergosterol, such as is found in yeast, may occur in bacteria. A review of the available information on this subject does not permit a definite statement to be made.

Waxes.—The polyatomic alcohol of high molecular weight isolated by Tamura from tubercle bacilli, called by him "mykol," has been referred to. Progress in the study of the large amount of waxy material produced by the tubercle bacillus has been made by Anderson. The crude wax resembles beeswax in appearance but is more brittle. From this a solid wax and a soft wax have been separated. Solid fatty acids, consisting of hexacosinic acid, palmitic and stearic acids, have been obtained from the saponifiable wax, and among other fractions a liquid acid resembling phthioic acid was isolated. The amorphous unsaponifiable powder gave no sterol reactions, had the formula $C_{94}H_{188}O_4$ and was the only compound isolated from the tubercle bacillus which was acid-fast. In this respect it resembled Tamura's "mykol." The unsaponifiable wax does not cause the formation of tuberculous tissue but stimulates the development of connective tissue cells.

Pigments.—There are many kinds of pigments in bacterial cells. Some of these are lipochrome compounds of unknown function. Others appear to be related to bacterial respiration and, in the sulphur bacteria, have photosynthetic capacity.

Buchanan and Fulmer have adequately reviewed the knowledge of the carotinoids, anthocyanins, melanins and miscellaneous pigments produced in or outside of bacterial cells. Many of these have diagnostic value in the identification of species, and some have practical uses as indicators or dyes. The class of yellow pigments known as carotinoids may have significance as sources of carotene or provitamin A. Further investigation of this possibility is needed.

The diffuse pigment, bacteriopurpurin, in the sulphur bacteria is biologically interesting as evidence of the occurrence in certain bacteria of a photo-synthetic pigment, differing from chlorophyl in composition but resembling it in action.

RESPIRATORY PIGMENT.—In 1925 Keilin began to report his investigation of *cytochrome*, which he discovered as a widely distributed respiratory pigment in the cells of animals, plants and aerobic bacteria. He found cytochrome in abundance in *B. subtilis* and other aerobes, and proved its absence in anaerobes. This pigment resembles hemoglobin. It is a mixture of hemochromogen compounds which have an iron-pyrrol nucleus similar to that of hemoglobin. Cytochrome has the function of a thermostable peroxidase and acts as a hydrogen acceptor, playing an important part in the oxidation-reduction processes of the cell.

Locke and Main have presented evidence that copper compounds, in the nature of respiratory catalysts possibly resembling hemocyanine, are important in the respiration of anaerobes and in the production of bacterial toxins.

Pyocyanine, the blue pigment of *B. pyocyaneus,* has been shown by Friedheim to increase the respiration of the cells containing it, and also of cultures of staphylococci, streptococci and pneumococci to which it was added.

Although they are not pigments, there are a number of other compounds in bacterial cells which take part in the respiratory mechanism. On account of their function as respiratory catalysts they may be mentioned conveniently here. *Glutahione,* which occurs conspicuously in yeast, is apparently not contained in bacteria. McLeod and Gordon and Callow and Robinson found that bacteria gave the nitroprusside reaction, but concluded that this was not due to the sulph-hydryl group and that bacteria lacked the glutamic acid, glycine and cysteine tripeptide known as glutathione. *Catalase* is present in many bacteria but is absent in most of the strict anaerobes and in some of the facultative anaerobes. The production of peroxide of hydrogen and its decomposition by catalase is related to the growth processes of numerous micro-organisms, as indicated by the studies of Avery and Neill on peroxide production by pneumococci.

Enzymes.—The great number of various biochemical activities of bacteria are carried on largely through the mediation of enzymes. These catalytic substances occur inside the cells as part of their component substance and after excretion by cells act upon the surrounding nutritive substrates. As each biochemical process appears to be under the control of a specific ferment, the list of enzymes obtained in one way or another from bacteria is a long one. The occurrence of enzymes in bacteria has been reviewed by Waksman and Waksman and Davison. The chemical composition of enzymes is at present largely undetermined. The development of investigations of enzymes was summarized in 1932 by Waldschmitt-Leitz, indicating the direction of chemical attack upon the specific active groups and the colloidal carrier components of these substances. Further knowledge of enzymes may be expected to contribute greatly to the understanding of the pathogenic and biochemical activities of bacteria and viruses.

Among the substances of unknown composition in bacterial cells there are two main groups which should be mentioned here. One of these is the group of toxins, the other is the group of growth-regulating, growth-promoting and vitamin-like substances.

Toxins.—There are two kinds of bacterial poisons more or less closely associated with the constituents of the cell. These are the *endotoxins,* which are liberated only when the bacterial cell is dissolved, and the *exotoxins,* which are found chiefly, if not entirely, in the medium or animal tissues outside the bacterial cell.

Endotoxins appear to be proteins of bacteria, although it must be admitted that they cannot be characterized chemically. The bacterial residues of cultures of the cholera spirillum, the typhoid and paratyphoid and dysentery bacilli, and of other organisms, freed entirely from external products of their growth, are very poisonous for man and animals, producing fever, prostration and destructive effects. The protoplasm of the dysentery bacilli, for example, contains an endotoxin which acts upon the intestine. Since the work of Pfeiffer, and the later work of Vaughan, newer investigations have indicated that many older notions relating to endotoxins require revision. The mode of preparation of bacterial proteins, the hitherto unrecognized effects of specific carbohydrates and lipoids, and the influence of hypersensitivity upon the outcome of a contact between bacterial derivatives and animal cells have to be taken into account.

Exotoxins are poisons easily separated from bacterial cells. They are usually obtained by filtration of liquid media in which toxigenic organisms have grown. The classical types of exotoxins are the heat-labile poisons produced by diphtheria, tetanus and botulinus bacilli. Other organisms, such as streptococci, produce less potent toxins with greater resistance to heat. Neither their general nor specific chemical composition is known. They appear to consist of a relatively small toxic "molecule" attached to or integral with a protein. They may be formed from the medium by bacterial enzymes acting upon the protein substrate, or, as seems more likely, they may be specific secretion products of the cells. If they are secretion products of the cells, then the toxins or their precursors are components of the organisms. For that reason they are referred to in this section on the chemistry of bacterial cells. They will be described in greater detail in chapters dealing with the various organisms which produce toxins.

Vitamins.—The ability of bacteria to synthesize vitamin B has been demonstrated by several investigators, especially by Sunderlin and Werkman. This vitamin occurs within the bacterial substance, as it does in yeast. Its chemical constitution has not yet been determined.

Investigations have indicated that bacteria may contain a growth accessory substance of the nature of Wildiers' "Bios." It is possible that bacteria produce a Bios-like substance in their protoplasm, but the complexities of the interrelationships of micro-organisms in mixed cultures and the problems relating to the effects of bacterial extracts upon the growth of other micro-organisms are still so largely unsolved that a definite answer to the "Bios question" cannot be given here.

REFERENCES

ADOLPH, E. F. Quart. Rev. Biol., 1930, 5:51.

ANDERSON, R. J. J. Biol. Chem., 1929, 83:169.

——— Ann. Rev. Biochem., 1932, 1:89.

ARONSON, H. Arch. f. Kinderhk., 1900, 30:23.

AVERY, O. T., and GOEBEL, W. F. J. Exper. M., 1933, 58:731.

AVERY, O. T., and NEILL, J. M. J. Exper. M., 1924, 39: 347, 357, 543, 745.

BROWN, E. B., and JOHNSON, T. B. J. Am. Chem. Soc., 1923, 45:1823.

BUCHANAN, R. E., and FULMER, E. I. Physiology and Biochemistry of Bacteria, Baltimore, 1928, Vol. I, Chap. III, 63–138.

BUCHNER, H. München. med. Wchnschr., 1897, 44:299.

CALLOW, A. B., and ROBINSON, M. E. Bio-Chem. J., 1925, 19:19.

DOAN, C. A. Tr. Nat. Tuberc. Ass., 1929, 25:182.

DOCHEZ, A. R., and AVERY, O. T. J. Exper. M., 1917, 26:477.

ECKSTEIN, H. C., and SOULE, M. H. J. Biol. Chem., 1931, 91:395.

EISENBERG, P. Centralbl. f. Bakteriol., I Abt. Orig., 1908, 48:257.

FEULGEN, R. Abderhaldens Handbuch d. biol. Arbeitsmeth., 1923, Abt. 5, Teil 2, II, 1055.

——— Ztschr. f. physiol. Chem., 1924, 135: 203, 249; 136: 57.

FISCHER, M. N., and HOCHBERG, R. B. Ztschr. f. Immunitätsforsch., 1930, 68:43.

FORSSMAN, J. Biochem. Ztschr., 1911, 37:78.

FRIEDHEIM, E. A. H. J. Exper. M., 1931, 54:207.

GORIS, A., and LIOT, A. Compt. rend. Acad. d. sc., Paris, 1921, 172:1622.

GORTNER, R. A. Ann. Rev. Biochem., 1932, 1:21.

Gray, E. C.   Biochem. J., 1924, 18:712.

Heidelberger, M.   Chem. Rev., 1927, 3:403.

——— Ann. Rev. Biochem., 1932, 1:659.

Heidelberger, M., and Kendall, F. E.   J. Exper. M., 1931, 53:625; 54:515.

Iijima, T.   J. Path. & Bacteriol., 1923, 26:519.

Iwanhoff, K. S.   Beitr. z. chem. Physiol. u. Pathol., 1902, 1:524.

Johnson, T. B., and Brown, E. B.   J. Biol. Chem., 1922, 54:731.

——— Am. Rev. Tuberc., 1926, 14:164–171.

Johnson, T. B., and Coghill, R. D.   J. Biol. Chem., 1925, 63:225.

Jungeblut, C. W., and Ross, A. T.   J. Immunol., 1929. 16:369.

Keilin, D.   Proc. Roy. Soc., Lond., B., 1925, 98:312; 1926, 100:129; 1929, 104:206.

Knight, B. C. J. G.   Bacterial Nutrition. Medical Research Council, London, Spec. Report Ser. No. 210, 1938.

Landsteiner, K., and Simms, S.   J. Exper. M., 1923, 38:127.

Locke, A., and Main, E. R.   J. Infect. Dis., 1930, 46:393.

Long, E.   The Newer Knowledge of Bacteriology and Immunology, Chicago, 1928, Chap. 76, p. 1020.

McLeod, J. W., and Gordon, J.   Biochem. J., 1924, 18:937.

Meyer, A.   Die Zelle der Bakterien, Jena, 1912.

Pappenheimer, A., and Enders, J. F.   Proc. Soc. Exper. Biol. & Med., 1933, 31:37.

Pick, E. P.   Beitr. z. chem. Physiol. u. Path., 1902, 1:397.

Pietschamm, K.   Arch. f. Mikrobiol., 1931, 2:310.

Pietschamm, K., and Rippel, A.   Arch. f. Mikrobiol., 1932, 3:422.

Pinner, M.   Am. Rev. Tuberc., 1928, 18:497.

Rothacker, A.   Ztschr. f. Immunitätsforsch., 1913, 16:491.

Ruppel, W. G.   Ztschr. f. physiol. Chem., 1898, 26:218.

Sabin, F. R., Doan, C. A., and Forkner, C. E.   J. Exper. M., 1930, 52, Supp. No. 3:1–152.

Sato, Y.   Centralbl. f. Bakteriol. II Abt., 1905, 19:27.

Schaffer, J., Folkoff, C., and Bayne–Jones, S.   Johns Hopkins Hosp. Bull., 1922, 33:151.

Schumacher, J.   Centralbl. f. Bakteriol., I Abt. Orig., 1922, 88:362.

Seibert, F. B.   Science, 1926, 63:619.

Stephenson, M. A.   Bacterial Metabolism, New York, 1930, p. 67.

Sunderling, G., and Werkman, C. H.   J. Bacteriol., 1928, 16:17.

Tamura, S.   Ztschr. f. physiol. Chem., 1913, 87:85; 88:190; 1914, 89:289.

Tanner, F. W.   Chem. Rev., 1925, 1:397.

Tillett, W. S., and Francis.   J. Exper. M., 1930, 52:561.

Tillett, W. S., Goebel, W. F., and Avery, O. T.   J. Exper. M., 1930, 52:895.

Vaughan, V. C.   Protein Split Products in Relation to Immunity and Disease, Philadelphia, 1913.

Vierhoever, A.   Ber. d. deutsch. Bot. Gesellsch., 1912, 30:443.

Von Behring, H.   Ztschr. f. physiol. Chem., 1930, 192:112.

Von Wisselingh, C.   Jahrb. f. wissensch. Bot., 1898, 31:619.

Wadsworth, A., and Brown, R.   J. Immunol., 1931, 21:245.

Waksman, S. A.   Abstr. Bacteriol., 1922, 6:265.

Waksman, S. A., and Davison, W. C.   Enzymes, Baltimore, 1926.

Waldschmitt-Leitz, E.   Ann. Rev. Biochem., 1932, 1:69.

Wells, H. G.   The Chemical Aspects of Immunity, New York, 1929, p. 56.

Zettnow.   Ztschr. f. Hyg. u. Infektionskrankh., 1918, 85:17.

Zinsser, H.   J. Exper. M., 1921, 34:495.

——— Resistance to Infectious Diseases, New York, 1931, p. 100.

Zinsser, H., and Mueller, J. H.   The Newer Knowledge of Bacteriology and Immunology, Chicago, 1928, Chap. 52, p. 721.

CHAPTER V

THE PHYSICAL PROPERTIES OF BACTERIA

The dividing line between physical and chemical properties of bacteria is as ill defined as in any other material, dead or living. We realize that some of the distinctions we shall make will create artificial categories, more convenient than true. Nevertheless, there are certain properties and actions commonly called physical as distinct from chemical for which separate treatment is expedient. In this chapter we shall deal with these physical characteristics and effects, selecting from a large material the information having the most direct bearing upon problems of medical bacteriology.

Bacterial protoplasm consists essentially of a micellar arrangement of colloids in various degrees of dispersion in fluids of complex constitution. In young cells the state of the protoplasm appears to resemble that of a sol, while in older, dying or dead cells it more nearly approaches a gel. Bacterial protoplasm has the physical properties of protoplasm in general. As we shall not undertake to present an inclusive or mathematical description here, we refer the reader for such information to the treatises of Alexander, Buchanan and Fulmer and Heilbrunn.

The physical characteristics of bacteria are manifested as properties of the cell substance and as properties of suspensions of the cell. The individual cells composing the suspensions are, of course, the ultimate sources of all these physical properties and actions. The suspensions as a whole, however, have distinct features, dependent upon the size and number of particles and their relationship to their environment. Both the intracellular colloidal system and the total colloidal system of all the cells in suspension are to be considered.

Spatial Properties.—Most spherical pathogenic bacteria have an average diameter of 1 μ or less. Cylindrical forms have an approximate mean range of length of 1 to 3 μ, with an average width close to 1 μ. Although they are larger than the upper limits of true colloidal particles, they retain some of the properties of very small bodies. They exhibit Brownian movement in suspensions. The ratio of surface to volume or surface to mass is large. Falk has calculated that micrococci with a diameter of 1 μ may have a surface area not less than 60,000 square centimeters per gram of mass. Surface phenomena, therefore, are prominent in bacterial actions. Pathological effects of bacteria due to their size and bulk become noticeable when single cells or small clumps of cells obstruct capillary blood vessels, forming emboli.

Optical Properties.—The *refractive index* of bacteria, as determined by sodium light in media at 15° C. lies between 1.33 and 1.40. Angerer has shown that bacteria are barely visible in 1 per cent NaCl solution and invisible in amyl alcohol. The refractive index of spores is somewhat greater than 1.55.

Bacteria are translucent, transmitting 60 to 70 per cent of visible light. Radiations in the region of the spectrum between wave-length 400 mμ and 186 mμ are almost

completely absorbed. This absorption of light of short wave-length is directly related
to the photochemical germicidal action of ultraviolet light. Bacteria become less
translucent as they grow older or produce pigment. The cells in suspension scatter
light, exhibiting the Tyndall phenomenon. With due regard for variations in opacity,
refractivity and size, advantage is taken of these properties to measure densities of
suspensions and to enumerate bacteria in them by means of suitably calibrated
nephelometers or scales for comparison of densities.

Amann discovered that the bacterial membrane is anisotropic, showing double
refraction in polarized light.

Specific Gravity.—On account of a number of variables, determinations of the
specific gravity of bacteria are somewhat unsatisfactory. The water-content, relative
proportion of light substances, such as fats, to substances such as proteins and carbohydrates, which have a specific gravity greater than that of water, the age of the cells,
the conditions of cultivation—and the procedures used in making the measurements—
cause differences in specific gravity. Rubner, using a capillary method which was not
free from objectionable features, determined that the specific gravity of various bacteria was 1.038 to 1.065. Stigell, by centrifuging bacteria in various concentrations of
NaI, determined that the specific gravity of bacteria from cultures on nutrient agar
was 1.130 to 1.315. Other observers have determined the specific gravity of *B. coli* to
be 1.040. Through differences in specific gravity bacteria can be separated from each
other or from other particles by sedimentation or flotation in solutions of appropriate
density.

Viscosity.—The viscosity of the protoplasm varies with the age and condition of
the cell. In young rapidly growing forms we have seen granules dart from one end of
the cell to the other, suggesting a highly fluid protoplasm of low viscosity. In older
cells, the protoplasm appears to become increasingly viscous, finally preventing all
movements of enclosed granules. There is no absolute measure of the viscosity of
bacterial protoplasm, although it has been estimated to be only 10 to 20 times as
great as that of water. The viscosity of suspensions of bacterial cells varies with proportion of the total volume occupied by the bacterial bodies. A determination of this
value by means of a viscosimeter was used by Bronfenbrenner according to the
method of Kunitz to estimate the sizes of bacteria in cultures with bacteriophage.

The elasticity and relative rigidity of bacteria resides partly in their membranes
and partly in the turgor of the cells. Wámoscher, by microdissection of bacteria,
determined that the cell membrane has enormous elasticity against pulling, stretching
and torsion. Turgor is regulated by osmotic processes.

Osmotic Properties.—Bacterial protoplasm and other constituents of the cell
are enclosed in a *semipermeable membrane*. This membrane, composed of proteins,
lipoids and carbohydrates in an undetermined arrangement, is thin and resembles the
membrane of animal cells more than that of plants. It is readily permeable to water
and has various degrees of permeability to organic and inorganic substances. The
permeability of the surface membrane of bacterial cells varies according to the
species of organism, the composition of the cell, the age of the cell, the nature and
amount of surface tension reducing substances in the medium, the hydrogen-ion
concentration, temperature and many other factors. The characteristics of this semipermeable membrane influence the growth, morphology, staining reactions, composi-

tion and distribution of cell-substance, osmotic phenomena and important electrical properties of the cells.

There appears to be a relationship between permeability of the membrane, size and shape of cells and rates of reproduction by fission. With a membrane of definite permeability the rate of diffusion of nutritive substances into the cell is determined largely by the ratio of volume to surface. Fischer has pointed out this ratio is most constant in cylindrical forms and has correlated this with the preponderance of rod-forms among bacteria.

Bacterial substance enclosed in a semipermeable membrane is a small osmotic unit, susceptible to differences in osmotic pressure existing between the protoplasm and the surrounding medium. The conditions of osmotic equilibrium and osmotic regulation have been analyzed in detail by Rideal, and an extensive review of recorded observations on osmotic phenomena in bacteria was published by Falk in 1923. From these observations it appears that the osmotic pressure of bacterial protoplasm is not known and that notions of isotonicity of salt solutions based upon tests with animal cells may not hold for bacteria. Bacterial species show great differences in their toler-ance or requirements of salt concentrations. Some species grow well in dilute salt solutions, others require concentrations of 15 to 25 per cent NaCl for growth. So-called "normal" or "physiological saline solution" containing 0.85 per cent NaCl is commonly used as an isotonic fluid medium for bacteria, but it should not be forgotten that this solution, because of its simple composition and osmotic pressure adjusted to animal cells, is often toxic or physically injurious to bacteria.

Bacteria are more resistant than commonly supposed to changes in osmotic pressure. Great differences in salt concentration of the environment and periods of exposure from twenty to ninety minutes are required to bring about swelling or shrinkage of the protoplasm. By transferring the usual pathogenic bacteria from a 2 per cent NaCl solution to water, swelling of the cells, extrusion of globules of protoplasm and occasional bursting can be observed, as shown by Fischer, Raichel, and Gotschlich. This effect is called *plasmoptysis*. These and other investigators have shown that the transference of cells from a dilute solution of salts to solutions of higher concentration brings about shrinkage and granulation of the protoplasm within the cell membrane, producing *plasmolysis*. These effects vary with the age and composition of the cells. They must be considered in attempts to interpret the biological significance of unusual bacterial forms. Plasmolysis may not lead to the death of the cell. Plasmoptysis, carried to the point of rupture of the membrane, kills the cell. As a rule, young cells are more susceptible than older ones to the effects of different concentrations of salts in their environment and older cells show marked morphological changes as the result of plasmolysis or plasmoptysis. Spores appear to be less susceptible to osmotic changes than are the vegetative forms.

Adsorption.—It has been pointed out that the ratio of surface to volume of the bacterial cell is large. This large surface area possesses the capacity to adsorb materials from solution. Adsorption has an important influence upon the characteristics of the cell membrane, diffusion through the membrane and is part of the chain of physical effects and properties of bacteria. Morphology, reproduction, and numerous physico-chemical and immunological reactions are conditioned by the ions and other compounds adsorbed by the cell surface. It will be most convenient to deal with adsorption in connection with surface tension, electrical properties and other physical states and actions of bacteria.

The *surface tension* of the bacterial cell in a fluid medium cannot be measured directly, but data obtained by surface tension measurements of solutions at the air liquid interface are applicable in general, and with precautions, to the interfacial tension of bacterial cells suspended in a liquid. Substances such as soaps, bile salts, phenols, etc., which reduce the surface tension of solutions become concentrated in the bacterial surface, affecting the permeability of the membrane, diffusion through the membrane, electrical properties of the surface and numerous cellular phenomena. The importance of this physical characteristic of the cell will become more apparent from our consideration of its relation to disinfection, growth and morphology, filtrability and agglutination. It may be said in general here that as the surface tension of the common peptone solutions used as nutritive media is in the neighborhood of 44 to 55 dynes per centimeter, different bacterial properties and actions may be expected to occur when the organisms are cultivated or suspended in fluids having a greater or less surface tension than this value.

A force of somewhat undefined nature tends to cause one bacterial cell to adhere to another or to the surface of some other substance, such as glass. This is called the *cohesive force*, or "stickiness." Northrop and DeKruif have measured it in terms of the force required to pull apart two pieces of glass coated with bacteria. This attractive force does not vary with the potential difference between the surface of the cells and the fluid around them. It is affected by salts but no valency effect is apparent in their ability to reduce this cohesive force. The cohesive force has an important influence upon agglutination.

Electrical Properties.—Bacteria, like other particles in a suspension, reduce the conductivity of the solution. Bacteria, however, are themselves conductors of electricity. The actual values obtained in different investigations of the *conductance* of bacterial cells are variable, showing the obvious influences of the composition, age, viability and species of the cell. The net conductance, as measured by Brooks, is usually a negative value, showing that the electrical resistance of bacteria is two or three times as great as that of the fluid in which they may be suspended. This was found to be the case by Green and Larson. The resistance decreases somewhat on the death of the cells.

Bacterial cells tend to remain in suspension for long periods. Evidently this *suspension stability* depends upon some force opposing the sedimenting action of gravity. It has been determined that this force is the repulsive force of an electrical charge on the surface of bacterial cells. That bacteria have an electrical charge when suspended in an aqueous medium was demonstrated first by Bechhold in 1904. Numerous investigations since then have proved that in neutral solutions this charge is *negative,* causing bacteria to migrate to the anode under the influence of an electrical current.

The origin of the charge upon the bacterial cell has not been determined. Undoubtedly ionic equilibria on the two sides of the semipermeable membrane, of the nature of the Donnan equilibrium, are at the basis of the membrane potential existing on bacterial cells. Adsorption and other factors affecting the Helmholz double electrical layer on particles play important rôles in determining the sign and potential of this charge. The amphoteric nature of the composition of the cell and its membrane, as pointed out by Stearn, is also significant in the electrical behavior of the cell. The potential of the charge is not greatly affected by the death of the organism.

From our point of view, the most important phenomena in this connection are the relation of charge and potential to spontaneous and specific agglutination, filtration, staining reactions and biological differences between bacteria with respect to virulence and other characteristics. For general reviews of these and related topics the reader is referred to the papers of Falk, Northrop and Harkins.

The motion of bacteria in an external electrical field is known as *cataphoresis* or *electrophoresis*. Measurements of the velocity of migration of the cells can be made macroscopically by noting the movement of the boundary of the suspension in the modified Burton U-tube devised by Northrop, or with greater accuracy microscopically in the electrophoretic cell of Northrop and Kunitz or the capillary apparatus of Falk. The sign of the charge is determined from the direction of the movement, and the potential difference between the bacterial cell and the medium surrounding it can be calculated from the velocity of the migration. The results may be expressed in millivolts or in terms of micra per second of movement.

The potential difference between the bacterial cell and the surrounding fluid can be altered by adsorption of ions by bacteria and by a variety of changes in the cell. Among adsorbed ions, the H^+ ion is extremely important. Other cations have a similar effect. This effect is to bring about a reduction of the potential and sometimes a reversal of the charge on the cell. When the potential difference is reduced to zero, migration in the electrical field ceases. This is the true *isoelectric point* of the cell. When, however, the *potential difference* between the cell and the fluid in which it is suspended is reduced to 15 millivolts, the repulsive force becomes less than the cohesive force (provided the cohesive force has not been affected), and the "stickiness" of the cells then results in their agglutination (Northrop). The clumping of bacteria in this way through the action of the H^+ ion is known as *acid agglutination*. It gives practical and readily determined isoelectric points, which for most bacteria are in the region pH 3.0 to 4.8. By a similar mechanism flocculation of bacteria is produced by various electrolytes. Winslow and Shaughnessy have demonstrated that an alkaline isopotential point of the bacterial cell occurs near pH 13.5.

When bacteria are placed in a solution of protein the cells may become coated with a film of the protein and assume the nature of the added substance. The isoelectric point is shifted to that of added protein. This effect is true of both ordinary proteins and the antibody bearing proteins of antibacterial serums. In the case of the formation of protein films upon bacteria, there is a specific element in the combination between bacterial cell and antibody protein which is not present in the adsorption of ordinary proteins. The actual occurrence of agglutination, however, is governed by the laws we have outlined above, clumping taking place through cohesive force when the electrolytes have reduced the potential difference between the cell and surrounding fluid below 15 millivolts.

Electrophoretic potential differences have been shown by Northrop and DeKruif to be related to virulence in *B. lepisepticum,* by Falk and his associates to be related to virulence of diphtheria bacilli and pneumococci, and by Tittsler and his coworkers to be correlated with agglutinability of cultures of *Salmonolla pullorum* and the ability of *Rhizobium meliloti* to fix nitrogen (Tittsler). Some practical use of electrophoretic methods has been made in the identification of virulent diphtheria bacilli, the selection of strains for various purposes and for the study of bacterial variation.

The electrical charge on the bacterial cell determines in a large measure whether or not it will pass through a capillary pore or become attached to the wall of the tube. This has a direct bearing upon the *filtrability* of bacteria through Berkefeld and Chamberland candles. Mudd has shown that in Berkefeld filters the surface boundary of pores and water is the site of an electrical potential difference—an ordinary Helmholz electric double layer. As many of the pores in these filters are wider than the transverse diameters of bacterial cells, electrical forces influence the progress of bacteria through them. We shall return to a discussion of the physics of filtration in the chapters dealing with bacterial variation and the ultramicroscopic viruses. As a consequence of investigations of these electrical properties of bacteria and of the transport of bacteria along phase boundaries, Mudd has brought together a number of older observations under the suggestion that an electrocapillary mechanism may be an important factor in the penetration of epithelial surfaces by pathogenic bacteria.

A number of physical phenomena, in addition to those we have just considered, are associated with the biochemical activities of bacteria. As some of these are so closely related to bacterial metabolism and are used as measures of metabolism, they will be mentioned briefly here on account of their general physical significance and referred to again in appropriate chapters.

The processes of *oxidation-reduction* may involve the transfer of oxygen, hydrogen, electrons (Clark) or a combination of these chemical species depending upon the substances concerned and the conditions. Reduction is commonly exhibited in bacterial cultures by the transformation of dyes such as indigo carmine, and methylene blue to the respective leuco-compounds, by the reduction of nitrates to nitrites, and by reduction of many other substances. Gillespie, in 1920, found that the electrical potential difference between mercury and certain cultures or between noble metals and these cultures becomes progressively more negative as if it were indicating the development of a progressively more intense reducing environment. Since then, Clark and his collaborators have reported systematic studies both upon the characteristic potentials of dye systems and upon the electrode phenomena in biological systems. These studies and similar studies by other investigators (McLeod) will ultimately give us considerable knowledge of the free energy changes involved in the oxidation-reduction processes of bacterial cultures. However, while several very suggestive uses of the new information are already available, it is almost inherent in the nature of these studies that the more useful applications must await both more extensive development of theory and detailed information upon specific oxidation-reduction systems.

The oxidative processes are controlled in large measure by oxidative enzymes. In certain bacteria these are not active enough to wholly balance the reductive tendencies. In other instances they can do so. The work of Warburg suggests that the oxidative catalysts are complexes of iron and specific porphyrins.

It is an old observation that bacterial metabolism is accompanied by an evolution of *heat*. This heat-production has been investigated as the cause of "spontaneous combustion" of decomposing or fermenting materials by James, Rettger and Thom. Rubner made measurements of heat-production by bacteria as a measure of the energy exchange in the metabolic processes of these organisms. Using a modification of Hill's differential microcalorimeter, we in collaboration with Rhees have correlated heat production with the growth curves of *B. coli* and *Staphylococcus aureus*, and Wetzel has used our data as a basis for analysis of energy exchanges during growth.

Radiations of shorter wave-length than those of heat are produced by bacteria. Some of these are in the spectral region of visible light; others appear to have the nature of ultraviolet light. The luminous bacteria are interesting, but have no direct significance for medical bacteriology since none of the species in this group is pathogenic, although several have intimate, almost symbiotic, relationships with fish and other animals. Harvey has shown that these organisms do not contain luciferin and luciferase, which are responsible for the light produced by *Cypridina* and fireflies. Light-production by these bacteria is dependent upon the presence of free oxygen.

Mitogenetic Rays.—In 1923, Gurwitsch discovered that cell divisions were stimulated when growing plant tissue was exposed to the tip of an onion-root. By appropriate devices he showed that radiations were given off by the root-tip which stimulated mitosis in cells. Gurwitsch has concluded that these radiations which pass through quartz, very thin layers of glass, but are absorbed by films of gelatin and glass more than 140 μ thick, are ultraviolet light radiations of very low intensity with wavelengths of 199 to 237 mμ. It has been claimed that yeast and bacteria emit these radiations. Yeast and bacteria in the lag-phase have been used by Wolff and others to detect these so-called "mitogenetic rays." It has been difficult to prove the existence of these radiations by physical effects upon photographic plates, and electroscopic investigations with very sensitive apparatus (Schreiber, Locher, Hollaender and Claus) have given negative results. On the other hand, the claims for the existence of the effect upon cells seem to have been supported by substantial evidence, and it is possible that it will be necessary to take account of radiations of this nature in connection with studies of the growth-promoting and pathogenic activities of bacteria (Hollaender).

REFERENCES

ALEXANDER, J. Colloid Chemistry, New York, 1928, Vol. 2. Numerous articles by different authors.

AMANN, J. Centralbl. f. Bakteriol., I Abt., Orig., 1893, 13:775.

BAYNE-JONES, S. J. Bacteriol., 1929, 17:105.

BAYNE-JONES, S., and RHEES, H. S. J. Bacteriol., 1929, 17:123.

BECHHOLD, H. Ztschr. f. phys. Chemie., 1904, 48:385.

BRONFENBRENNER, J. Proc. Soc. Exper. Biol. & Med., 1926, 23:633.

BROOKS, S. C. J. Gen. Physiol., 1925, 7:327.

BUCHANAN, R. E., and FULMER, E. I. Physiology and Biochemistry of Bacteria, Baltimore, 1928, Vol. 1, Chaps. IV and V, pp. 139–461.

CANNAN, R. K., COHEN, B., and CLARK, W. M. U. S. Pub. Health Rep., 1926, Supp. No. 55, Paper No. X.

CLARK, W. M. U. S. Pub. Health Rep., 1923, 38:443, 666, 933.

CLARK, W. M., *et al.* Studies on Oxidation-Reduction, U. S. Public Health Service, Hygienic Laboratory Bull., No. 151, 1928.

DONNAN, F. G. Chem. Rev., 1925, 1:73.

—— Bull. Nat. Res. Council, 1929, 69:61–55.

FALK, I. S.   Electrophoresis of Bacteria, etc., in J. Alexander's Colloid Chemistry, New York, 1928, Vol. 2, pp. 731–746.

——— Abstr. Bacteriol., 1923, 7:33, 87, 133, esp. p. 35.

——— The Colloidal Behavior of Bacteria, in J. Alexander's Colloid Chemistry, New York, 1928, Vol. 2, pp. 545–555.

FALK, I. S., et al.   Am. J. Pub. Health, 1926, 16:1102; 1927, 17:714.

——— J. Bacteriol., 1928, 15:367, 413, 421.

——— J. Infect. Dis., 1925, 37:481, 495, 499, 507; 1926, 38:182, 188.

FALK, I. S., JENSON, L. B., and MILLS, J. H.   J. Bacteriol., 1927, 14:421.

FISCHER, A.   Vorlesungen ueber Bakterien, 2nd ed., Jena, 1903, p. 20.

——— Ztschr. f. Hyg. u. Infektionskrankh., 1900, 35:1.

GILLESPIE, L. J.   Soil Science, 1920, 9:199.

GOTSCHLICH, E.   Handb. d. pathog. Mikroorganismen, edited by W. Kolle, R. Kraus, and P. Uhlenhuth, Jena, 1929, Vol. 1, Chap. II, p. 87.

GREEN, R. G., and LARSON, W. P.   J. Infect. Dis., 1922, 30:550.

GURWITSCH, A.   Arch. f. Entwiklungsmech., 1924, 100:11.

——— Protoplasma, 1929, 6:449. See also GURWITSCH, A., and GURWITSCH, L., Die mitogenetische Strahlung, Berlin, 1932.

HARKINS, W. D.   The Newer Knowledge of Bacteriology and Immunology, Chicago, Chap. 10, pp. 136–178.

HARVEY, E. N.   Am. J. Physiol., 1926, 77:548.

——— J. Gen. Physiol., 1928, 11:469.

HEILBRUNN, L. V.   The Colloid Chemistry of Protoplasm, Berlin, 1928.

HOLLAENDER, A.   The Problem of Mitogenetic Rays, Chap. XXVIII, pp. 919–959, in Vol. II, Biological Effects of Radiation, ed. by B. M. Duggar, New York, 1936.

HOLLAENDER, A., and CLAUS, W. D.   An Experimental Study of the Problem of Mitogenetic Radiation. National Research Council, Bull. Ser., No. 100, Washington, 1937.

JAMES, L. H., RETTGER, L. F., and THOM, C.   J. Bacteriol., 1928, 15:117.

KUNITZ, M.   J. Gen. Physiol., 1926, 9:715.

LOCHER, G. L.   Physiol. Rev., 1932, 42:525.

MARSHALL, M. S.   J. Infect. Dis., 1924, 35:526.

McLEOD, J. W.   A System of Bacteriology in Relation to Medicine, London, 1930, 1:282. See also KNIGHT, B. C. J. C., ibid., 1931, 9:165.

MUDD, S.   J. Bacteriol., 1923, 8:459.

MUDD, S., and MUDD, E. B. H.   J. Bacteriol., 1924, 9:151.

NORTHROP, J. H.   The Newer Knowledge of Bacteriology and Immunology, Chicago, 1928, Chap. 58, pp. 782–801.

——— J. Gen. Physiol., 1922, 4:629.

NORTHROP, J. H., and KUNITZ, M.   J. Gen. Physiol., 1925, 7:729.

NORTHROP, J. H., and DeKRUIF, P. H.   J. Gen. Physiol., 1922, 4:639, 655.

RAICHEL, B.   Arch. f. Protistenk., 1928, 63:333.

RIDEAL, E. K.   A System of Bacteriology in Relation to Medicine, London, 1930, Vol. 1, Chap. III, pp. 119–132.

RUBNER, M.   Arch. f. Hyg., 1890, 11:365, esp. 384.

SCHREIBER, H., and FRIEDRICH, W.   Biochem. Ztschr., 1930, 227, 386.

STEARN, E. B., and STEARN, A. E.   J. Bacteriol., 1924, 9:463, 479; 1933, 25:21.

STIGELL, R.   Centralbl. f. Bakteriol., I Abt., Orig., 107, 45:487.

TITTSLER, R. P., and LISSE, M. W.   J. Bacteriol., 1928, 15:105.

TITTSLER, R. P., LISSE, M. W., and FERGUSON, R. L.   J. Bacteriol., 1932, 23:481.

VON ANGERER, K.   Arch. f. Hyg., 1923, 93:14.

WÁMOSCHER, L.   Ztschr. f. Hyg. u. Infektionskrankh., 1930, 111:424.

WETZEL, N. C.   Proc. Soc. Exper. Biol. & Med., 1932, 30:360.

WINSLOW, C.-E. A., and SHAUGHNESSY, H. J.   J. Gen. Physiol., 1924, 6:697.

WOLFF, L. K.   Nederl. Tijdschr. f. Geneesk., 1932, 76:III, 3278.

CHAPTER VI

BACTERIAL METABOLISM

Bacterial metabolism is the sum of the chemical processes in active or "resting" living cells by which energy is obtained for their functions and material from their nutritive surroundings is assimilated to form new protoplasm and repair waste. In this metabolism there is a transformation of energy and an exchange of material with the environment.

It has been apparent for a long time that the bacteria stand at a focal point of the biological sciences. This is so conspicuously true with respect to their biochemical activities that Kluyver is justified in a paper on human cancer in emphasizing the essential unity in metabolism of all organisms and in drawing from examples of bacterial metabolism inferences as to the chemical working of the cells of man. Nevertheless, it should not be overlooked that bacteria differ from animals and plants in several important features. Some of the doctrines derived from the study of metabolism of the higher forms cannot be applied directly to bacterial metabolism. In addition, much remains to be discovered before laws can be enunciated. It is important, therefore, that the bacteria be investigated objectively, as distinctive organisms.

The total metabolic process is divisible into two main phases: *anabolism,* the phase of assimilation or building up of protoplasm and a synthesis of compounds, and *catabolism,* the phase of breakdown, degradation or dissimilation of both the protoplasm of the cells and of material of the environment. Both of these processes go on at the same time. In the early stages of growth cellular construction appears to predominate, but the anabolic phase does not stop here. In the later stages, after the phase of logarithmic growth, catabolic activity is predominant and conspicuous.

Bacterial cells lack chlorophyl. Only the purple sulphur bacteria have a pigment with photosynthetic properties. Hence the vast majority of bacteria cannot use the radiant energy of light to build up chemical compounds. Bacteria obtain the energy they need—and waste—from chemical reactions, chiefly from oxidations. Two main classes of bacteria are now sharply distinguishable on the basis of their ability to obtain energy by the oxidation of different substances. One group, called the *autotrophic bacteria,* obtain energy by the oxidation of the elements of simple compounds of hydrogen, carbon, nitrogen, sulphur and probably ferrous and manganous salts. The other group, the *heterotrophic bacteria,* obtain energy by the oxidation and dissimilation of organic matter. All the organisms concerned in the production of disease are heterotrophs.

The study of the energy exchange in bacterial metabolism began at the commencement of this century with the investigations of Rubner. From time to time since then there have been various calorimetric, chemical and thermodynamical studies of the energetics of bacterial growth. We have referred to our own and other observations in Chapter V in our discussion of heat production as a physical phenomenon of bacterial activity. The whole subject has been treated broadly in relation to the autotrophic bacteria by Baas-Becking and Parks, from the standpoint of the heterotrophic bacteria by Wilson and Peterson, and from a generalized viewpoint by Stephenson, Buchanan and Fulmer and Rahn. An excellent monograph on bacterial nutrition, providing material for a comparative physiology of bacteria, was published by Knight in 1938.

It is apparent from many observations that bacteria have an enormous capacity to produce chemical changes and transform energy. Both of these characteristics are no doubt related to the large ratio of surface area to volume or mass of the bacterial cell. This ratio is 200,000 times greater for bacteria than for man. Only a small part of the energy obtained by bacteria can be accounted for in terms of utilization by the cells. Energy is utilized by bacteria for, (1) cell structure, increase in protoplasmic bulk, reproduction, (2) for motion (calculated by von Angerer and Wilson and Peterson to be infinitesimal), (3) for increase of surface, surface energy, (4) for the performance of osmotic work, (5) for the displacement of equilibrium conditions in the cell, (6) possibly for the maintenance of oxidation-reduction potentials, (7) for temperature increase in the immediate environment. After all these uses are evaluated, the greater part of the liberated energy remains unaccounted for. This is dissipated as heat and no useful work appears to be done with it. Apparently there is little meaning in the term "energy of maintenance" which has been applied to the predominantly catabolic phase of bacterial activity. Stephenson [1] has expressed the opinion that "the greater proportion of the energy liberated by micro-organisms is no measure of their metabolic needs, but is merely the result of unprotected enzymes acting on an appropriate substrate." Nevertheless, the chemical changes associated with this liberation of energy are of the utmost importance.

The study of the results of bacterial metabolism is important, aside from general biological considerations, for the following reasons: (1) It gives an insight into the vital chemical processes of bacteria; (2) it explains some of the cycles of the elements in nature; (3) it discloses the means of obtaining valuable products in industries; (4) it has important applications in agriculture, in food production and food preservation; (5) it permits the identification of micro-organisms morphologically indistinguishable; (6) it is of service in the identification of chemical compounds; (7) it provides an understanding of many of the effects produced by bacteria upon animals and plants and hence is one of the bases for the campaign against infectious disease; (8) it is fundamental to investigations in immunology and serology; and (9) it is the basis for the development of a rational therapy of bacterial disease. We can not deal with all of these matters in this chapter, nor would it be advisable to do so. Metabolic processes will be described in connection with all of the groups of organisms mentioned in this book and in numerous other connections.

Oxygen.—Oxygen is obtained, by the large majority of bacteria, directly from the atmosphere in the form of free oxygen. For many micro-organisms, moreover, the presence of free oxygen is a necessary condition for growth. These are spoken of as the "obligatory aerobes." Among the pathogenic bacteria proper, many, like the *Gonococcus, Bacillus influenzae,* and *Bacillus pestis,* show a marked preference for a

[1] M. Stephenson, *Bacterial Metabolism*, Longmans, Green and Co., London and New York, 1930.

well-oxygenated environment. Probably there is no pathogenic micro-organism which, under certain conditions of nutrition, is entirely *unable* to exist and multiply in the complete absence of this gas. The conditions existing within the infected animal organism cause it to seem likely that all incitants of infection may, at times, thrive in the complete absence of free oxygen.

There is another class of organisms, on the other hand, for whose development the presence of free oxygen is directly injurious. These micro-organisms, known as "obligatory anaerobes," obtain their supply of oxygen indirectly, by enzymatic processes of fermentative and proteolytic cleavage, from carbohydrates and proteins, or by reduction from reducible bodies. Among the pathogenic micro-organisms the class of obligatory anaerobes is represented chiefly by *B. tetani*, the bacillus of malignant edema, the bacillus of symptomatic anthrax, *B. welchii*, and *B. botulinus*.

Intermediate between these two classes is a large group of bacteria which thrive well both under aerobic and anaerobic conditions. Some of these, which have a preference for free oxygen but nevertheless possess the power of thriving under anaerobic conditions, are spoken of as "facultative anaerobes." In others the reverse of this is true; these are spoken of as "facultative aerobes." These varieties of bacteria are by far the most numerous and comprise most of our parasitic and saprophytic bacteria.

The relation of micro-organisms to oxygen is extremely subtle, therefore, and not to be biologically dismissed by a rigid classification into aerobes, facultative anaerobes, and obligatory anaerobes. Cultures in columns of medium in "deep tubes" and cultures under various gaseous mixtures give abundant evidence of the wide range and selective requirements of bacteria in relation to gradations of oxygen tension.

Optimal oxygen tension is an important growth requirement of micro-organisms. Pasteur observed that anaerobic growth is limited to atmospheres which maintain methylene blue in the leuko form. Oxygen tension in culture media may be determined by means of various indicators, such as the series of indophenols and sulfonates studied by Clark and his coworkers, or by electrode measurements. Clark has introduced a convenient scale for recording these oxidation-reduction potentials, using the normal hydrogen electrode as a standard of reference. Methylene blue is half decolorized at Eh $+$ 0.011 (Eo) at pH 7.0. Dyes decolorized at greater oxygen tensions have higher Eo values (indophenol), and those decolorized at lower tensions have lower Eo values (sulfonates). Recent work upon the cultivation of anaerobes has emphasized the importance of a systematic approach to this subject. By means of dyes, Fildes, 1929, observed that tetanus spores failed to germinate if the potential were above Eh $+$ 0.01 volt. The period required for germination in a suitable medium was attributed to the time required for the medium to reach a suitable reducing intensity.

Plotz and Geloso, 1931, found that a rapid multiplication of tetanus, botulinus and other anaerobes can take place only in media with oxidation-reduction potentials between Eh $-$0.006 and $-$0.436 volt. The potential of sterile infusion broth under anaerobic conditions gradually becomes more negative, after several days reaching a value between Eh $-$0.050 and $-$0.198 (Coulter).

While a profuse supply of oxygen absolutely inhibits the growth of most anaerobes, a number of these may, nevertheless, develop when only small quantities of oxygen are present. Minute quantities of free oxygen in culture media do not inhibit the growth of *B. tetani*, and Theobald Smith demonstrated that when suitable nutritive material in the form of fresh liver tissue is added to bouillon, a number of anaerobic bacteria may be induced to grow in indifferently anaerobic environment. Ferrán succeeded in adapting the tetanus bacillus to an aerobic environment. In this case, however, the virulence of the bacillus was lost.

These considerations of oxygen consumption and carbon dioxide production by bacteria, of aerobic and anaerobic life and the relation of bacterial growth comprise only part of the subject of bacterial respiration. In the broad sense in which the term is now used, respiration is "any chemical process, aerobic or anaerobic, by which energy is liberated by the cell."

In Chapter IV we have discussed the pigments such as cytochrome, porphyrin compounds, pyocyanine and the catalases and peroxidases present as constituents of the cell which take part in the oxidative processes of respiration. Gillespie and Rettger have used oxidation-reduction measurements for the differentiation of species of anaerobes, of lactobacilli, and other bacteria. Marked differences were observed in the oxidation-reduction potentials of closely related species or types of bacteria in different genera.

The discovery by Pasteur that certain bacteria develop only in the absence of free oxygen, produced a revolution in conceptions of metabolic processes, since up to that time it was believed that life could be supported only when a free supply of oxygen was obtainable. Pasteur's original explanation for this phenomenon was that anaerobic conditions of life were always associated with some form of carbohydrate fermentation and that oxygen was obtained by these micro-organisms by a splitting of carbohydrates. As a matter of fact, for a large number of micro-organisms, this is actually true, and the presence of readily fermentable carbohydrates not only increases the growth energy of a large number of anaerobic bacteria, but in many cases permits otherwise purely aerobic bacteria to thrive under anaerobic conditions. On the other hand, the basis of anaerobic growth cannot always be found in the fermentation of carbohydrates or in the simple process of reduction. A number of strictly anaerobic bacteria may develop in the entire absence of carbohydrates or reducing substances, obtaining their oxygen supply from other suitable sources, some of which may be the complex proteins. Thus the tetanus bacillus may thrive when the nutritive substances in the media are entirely protein in nature.

The favorable influence of certain actively reducing bodies, like sodium formate or sodium-indigo-sulphate, upon anaerobic cultivation is probably referable to their ability to remove free oxygen from the media and thus perfect the anaerobiosis.

Unlike plants which derive much of their energy for growth from the sun's rays, bacteria, with the exception of the pigmented sulphur bacteria, are dependent upon their food supply as a source of energy. To some extent a simple oxidation of carbohydrates and other substances takes place by means of atmospheric oxygen with the production of carbon dioxide. There is thus a type of true respiration in bacteria with the absorption of oxygen and elimination of carbon dioxide. Not all the absorbed oxygen reappears as carbon dioxide and most of the remainder is probably used up in the formation of water or goes into the structure of the bacterial cell. The production of carbon dioxide has also been shown to occur in anaerobic cultures where the oxygen must have come from some constituent of the medium. It is probable that bacterial respiration is frequently of the anaerobic type in which, for example, such compounds as nitrates are reduced to nitrites and free nitrogen. Energy may be produced, however, by the oxidation of other elements than carbon and hydrogen; thus, certain of the iron bacteria seem to obtain energy from the oxidation of ferrous to ferric compounds in their protoplasm, and the sulphur bacteria oxidize hydrogen sulphide to free sulphur. The colored sulphur bacteria carry out this change under the combined influence of sunlight and their pigment, in this way resembling the green plants, but the unpigmented forms do not require radiant energy.

While processes of oxidation are perhaps the most important source of energy for certain bacteria, for other types and under different conditions chemical reactions of another kind serve to produce energy. Processes of fermentation and perhaps of decay and putrefaction liberate considerable quantities of energy. For example, alcoholic fermentation in which neither oxidation nor reduction is involved produces about thirty-three calories for each gram-molecule of sugar fermented. Since complete oxidation of the same quantity of sugar results in the liberation of about 680 calories it is apparent that relatively large amounts of glucose must be fermented to supply micro-organisms with sufficient energy for their growth and, as a matter of fact, bacteria will ferment many times their weight of carbohydrates. Acid fermentation, such as the lactic fermentation of milk and probably many of the processes of protein cleavage, are exothermic and will supply bacteria with energy. Obviously these reactions are particularly adapted to anaerobic growth since for many of them oxygen is not required.

In Chapter III, we have described in some detail the chemical composition of the bacteria. Their protoplasm differs in no essential way from that of the more highly organized plants and animals, and contains the same elements characteristic of living material in general. For the growth and development of bacteria, therefore, carbon, hydrogen, oxygen, nitrogen, sulphur and phosphorus, as well as certain inorganic salts must be supplied in a form suitable to their needs. The greatest diversity exists, however, among bacterial species, as to the nature of the chemical compounds from which these various elements may be obtained. The autotrophic organism inhabiting the soil and able to build up its protoplasm from NH_3 and CO_2 appears to have little in common with the heterotrophic pathogen adapted to growth within the animal body, and requiring preformed amino acids and sometimes "vitamins" as its foodstuffs.

A detailed consideration of bacterial nutrition as a whole is beyond the scope of this book. We shall consider here very briefly only the general aspects of the nutrition of the heterotrophic organisms concerned with the production of disease. For a more detailed account of the subject in all its aspects, the reader is referred to the excellent monograph of Knight. There are still many gaps in our knowledge of the nutritional requirements of the more strictly pathogenic organisms. These are now rapidly being filled in, and it is reasonable to predict that within a comparatively short time this information will make possible considerable simplification in routine procedures of bacterial cultivation.

Perhaps the most logical view of the whole matter is stated by Knight. He considers the subject from the evolutionary standpoint and believes the autotrophic organism, growing upon strictly inorganic materials, to be the earliest form of bacterial life. Such an organism is independent of plant or animal life, and is equipped with the necessary enzymes to effect synthesis of all the component parts of its protoplasm. As bacterial, plant and animal life and with it the supplies of highly organized carbon and nitrogen compounds became more abundant, many varieties of bacteria began to adapt themselves to growth on this type of material. Here they were no longer forced to build up synthetically the amino acids, for example, of their proteins from ammonia, but obtained them already formed. Certain of their enzyme mechanisms, consequently, no longer needed, were gradually lost, and such bacteria became unable to multiply on simple salts of NH_3.

A measure of proof of the validity of such a conception is provided by the fact that certain bacterial species, for example, of the colon-typhoid group, growing readily, when freshly isolated from fecal material, on amino acids as the sole source of N, but not on ammonium salts, may quite easily regain their ability to utilize the latter by a brief period of "training." This involves subculture on media containing gradually decreasing concentrations of amino acids and increasing amounts of ammonium salts with finally the complete removal of the former. The same may be accomplished for other somewhat more fastidious organisms with an individual amino acid such as tryptophane, the complex molecule of which evidently offers some synthetic difficulty.

With still longer and more complete adaptation of bacteria to the animal host, further synthetic functions are lost, referable often directly to certain enzyme systems. Thus, for example, the pyridine nucleus which appears to be involved in various types of co-enzymes, must be supplied to certain organisms (see below) although readily produced by the more free-living types. Actually, although the observations are still too few to establish the matter definitely, it appears that all bacteria which do not require a given "accessory" substance of this type, produce it by synthetic processes. This, of course, supplies a considerable further support of the validity of Knight's theory.

It follows from these considerations that the more closely adapted an organism becomes to a living host, the greater the number and complexity of materials necessary to its metabolism for which it depends upon the host and becomes unable to build up from simpler materials. From this point of view, the protoplasm of such an organism, lacking numerous synthetic enzymes, is probably considerably simpler than that of the early autotrophic forms. Gradually progressive stages of adaptation may readily be traced through the whole range of known pathogenic micro-organisms up to the *Rickettsia* of Typhus Fever and Rocky Mountain Spotted Fever which have not yet been cultivated in the absence of fresh cellular debris, and the *Treponema pallidum* of syphilis which has probably never been cultivated outside the animal body. Whether a still further regression in synthetic power will explain certain of the filtrable viruses, or whether these agents belong in quite another category, is not yet known.

Although the above discussion has dealt primarily with nitrogenous compounds, similar considerations hold also for carbon- and sulphur-containing materials. The former, as carbohydrates, simple alcohols, organic acids, etc., are utilized over a wide range and in diverse ways by different bacterial species and many of the important differential methods used by the bacteriologist are based on this fact. The exact mechanisms by which such changes are brought about are complex and only partially understood. Their study has in many cases, however, afforded considerable insight into similar processes in animal metabolism. As regards sulphur, it is known that both cystine and methionine are important in the growth of certain pathogenic organisms,—the former, perhaps, through the ease with which its -S-S- linkage is transformed into -SH, has an effect in the regulation of the oxidation-reduction potential of the medium; both, possibly, by supplying essential groupings which the organisms have lost the ability to synthesize. It is worthy of note that the amino acid methionine was first isolated and described in connection with studies of bacterial growth requirements (Mueller).

Inorganic salts are essential to the growth of all varieties of bacteria. It is probable that Na, K, Mg and Ca are all required, although often it is difficult to demonstrate the situation clearly because of the minute amounts required, the difficulty of obtaining reagents of a sufficiently high degree of purity, and the possibility of solution of traces from glassware employed. Phosphate, of course, is essential, and often sulfate and probably chloride. In the case of bacteria giving unusually heavy growth, and therefore requiring salts in concentrations which may be more readily controlled, other elements are also sometimes found to be essential. Thus, Mueller has shown that minute amounts of iron, manganese, copper and zinc all increase the growth of the diphtheria bacillus, and other instances of a similar nature are also known.

Organism or Group	Nitrogen and Accessory Requirements
Colon bacillus	NH_3
Typhoid-paratyphoid dysentery	Amino acids
	(Nicotinic acid)
Anaerobes (sporogenes; botulinus, etc.)	Amino acids
	"Sporogenes vitamine"
Staphylococcus	Amino acids
	Vitamine B₁
	Nicotinic acid
Diphtheria bacillus	Amino acids
	Nicotinic acid
	Beta-alanine
	(Pimelic acid)
Hemolytic Streptococcus	Amino acids
	Glutathione
	Riboflavine
	Thiochrome
	Nicotinic acid
	Betaine
	Glucosamine
	(a nucleotide)
	(an unknown peptide?)
Hemophilic group (B. Influenzae)	Amino acids
	Unidentified extractives
	Hematin
	Warburg's Co-enzyme
Other more fastidious groups	Requirements unknown

The above tabulation will illustrate some of the above statements, and is not intended to be in any sense complete. In general it may be seen that the more strictly parasitic an organism has become, the more fastidious are its growth requirements, or conversely, the fewer are its synthetic abilities.

GENERAL BIOLOGICAL ACTIVITIES OF BACTERIA

While the bacteria pathogenic to man and animals largely usurp the attention of those interested in disease processes, this group of micro-organisms is after all but a small specialized offshoot of the realm of bacteria, and, broadly speaking, actually of minor importance. Surveying the existing scheme of nature, as a whole, it is not an extravagant statement to say that without the bacterial processes which are constantly active in the reduction of complex organic substances to their simple compounds, the chemical interchange between the animal and vegetable kingdoms would fail, and all life on earth would of necessity cease. To understand the full significance of this, it is necessary to consider for a moment the method of the interchange of matter between the animal and vegetable kingdoms.

All animals require for their sustenance organic compounds. They are unable to build up the complex protoplasmic substances which form their body cells from chemical elements or from the simple inorganic salts. They are dependent for the manufacture of their foodstuffs, therefore, directly or indirectly, upon the synthetic or anabolic activities of the green plants.

These plants, by virtue of the chlorophyl contained within the cells of their leaves and stems, and under the influence of sunlight, possess the power of utilizing the carbon of the carbonic acid gas of the atmosphere, and of combining it with water and the nitrogenous salts absorbed by their roots, building up from these simple radicals the highly complex substances carbohydrates, proteins, fats and other compounds, required for animal sustenance.

These products of the synthetic activity of the green plants, then, are ingested by members of the animal kingdom, either directly, in the form of vegetable food, or indirectly, as animal matter. They are utilized in the complex laboratory of the animal body and are again broken down into simpler compounds, which leave the body as excreta and secreta.

The excreta and secreta of animals, however, are, in a small part only, made up of substances simple enough to be directly utilized by plants. The dead bodies, moreover, of both animals and plants would be of little further value as stores of matter unless new factors intervened to reduce them to that simple form in which they may again enter into the synthetic laboratory of the green plant. Agents for further cleavage of these compounds are required, and these are supplied by the varied activities of the bacteria.

On the other hand, bacteria are also important in the process of synthesis. The main supply of nitrogen available for plant life is found in the elementary state in the atmosphere—a condition in which it cannot be utilized as a raw product by the plant. This gap again is bridged by the bacteria found in the root bulbs of the leguminous plants—bacteria which possess the power of assimilating or aiding in the assimilation of atmospheric nitrogen and its preparation for further use by the plant itself. Another bacterial activity which may be classified as an anabolic process is the oxidation of the ammonia, released by decomposition, into nitrites and nitrates.

This is carried on by certain bacteria of the soil. These processes will be discussed in greater detail in another section.

There is a constant circulation, therefore, of nitrogen and carbon compounds, between the plant and the animal kingdoms, by virtue of an anabolic or constructive process in the one, and a catabolic or destructive process in the other, rendering them mutually interdependent and indispensable. The circuit, however, it not by any means a closed one; there are important gaps, both in the process of cleavage and in that of synthesis, which, if left unbridged by the bacteria, would effectually arrest all life-activity of plants and eventually of animals.

Far from being scourges, therefore, these minute micro-organisms are paramount factors in the great cycle of living matter, supplying necessary links in the circulation of both nitrogenous and carbon compounds.

General Catabolic Activities of Bacteria

The catabolic activities of bacteria, then, consist in the fermentation of carbohydrates and in the cleavage of proteins and fats.

Fermentation is carried out to a large extent by the yeasts, but also to no inconsiderable degree by bacteria. Protein decomposition and the cleavage of fats are carried out almost exclusively by bacteria.

For our knowledge of the fundamental laws underlying these phenomena of fermentation and of protein decomposition, we are indebted to the genius of Pasteur, who was the first to prove experimentally the exclusive and specific parts played by various micro-organisms in these processes. While the observations and deductions made by Pasteur have not been greatly modified, a large store of information has been gained since his time, which has thrown additional light upon the chemical details and the more exact manner of action of the factors involved.

The actual work of cleavage in both fermentation and protein cleavage is carried out by substances known as enzymes or ferments, the nature of which we must further discuss before their manner of action can be fully comprehended.

Bacterial Enzymes or Ferments.—A ferment or enzyme is a substance produced by a living cell, which brings about a chemical reaction without entering into the reaction itself. The enzyme itself is not bound to any of the end-products and is not appreciably diminished in quantity after the reaction is over, although its activity may be finally inhibited by one or another of the new products. The action of bacterial enzymes is thus seen to be closely similar to that of the chemical agents technically spoken of as "catalyzers," represented chiefly by dilute acids. Thus, if an aqueous solution of saccharose is brought into contact with a dilute solution of sulphuric acid, the disaccharide is hydrolyzed and is decomposed into levulose and dextrose.

Thus:

$$C_{12}H_{22}O_{11} + H_2O = C_6H_{12}O_6 + C_6H_{12}O_6$$

in contact with   dextrose   levulose

dilute H_2SO_4

During this process, which is known as "inversion," the concentration of the sulphuric acid remains entirely unchanged. While theoretically the changes brought about by enzymes and catalyzers are usually such as would occur spontaneously, the time for the spontaneous occurrence would be, at ordinary temperatures, infinitely long. The definition for enzymes and catalyzers is given by Ostwald, therefore, as "substances which *hasten* a chemical reaction without themselves taking part in it." Exactly the same result which is obtained by the use of dilute sulphuric acid is caused by the ferment "invertase" produced, for instance, by *B. megatherium*. Were a solution of saccharose subjected to heat, without catalyzer or ferment, a similar change would occur, but by the mediation of these substances the inversion is produced without other chemical or physical reinforcement.

This analogy between enzymes and catalyzing agents is very striking. Thus, as stated, both catalyzers and enzymes bring about changes without themselves being used up in the process, both act without the aid of heat, and the reactions brought about by both have occasionally been shown to be *reversible*. While this last phenomenon has been variously shown for catalyzers, the process of reversibility has been demonstrated for bacterial enzyme action only in isolated cases. Thus, it has been found that by the action of the yeast enzyme maltase upon concentrated dextrose solutions, a reformation of maltose may occur. In both cases, moreover, the quantity of enzyme or catalyzer is infinitely small in proportion to the amount of material converted by their action.

There is a close similarity, furthermore, between the bacterial enzymes and the ferments produced by specialized cells of the higher animals and plants. For instance, the action of the ptyalin of the saliva or of the diastase obtained from plants is entirely analogous to the starch-splitting action of the amylase produced by many bacteria.

The action of all enzymes depends most intimately upon environmental conditions. For all of them the presence of moisture is essential. All of them depend for the development of their activity upon the existence of a specifically suitable reaction. Strong acids or alkalies always inhibit, often destroy them. Temperatures of over 70° C. permanently destroy most enzymes, whereas freezing, while temporarily inhibiting their action, causes no permanent injury, so that upon thawing, their activity may be found almost unimpaired. Direct sunlight may injure, but rarely destroys, ferments. Against the weaker disinfectants in common use, enzymes often show a higher resistance than do the bacteria which give rise to them.

The optimum conditions for enzyme action, then, consist in the presence of moisture, the existence of a favorable reaction, weakly acid or alkaline, as the case may be, and a temperature ranging from 35° to 45° C. (Oppenheimer).

Proteolytic Enzymes.—In nature, the decomposition of dead animal and vegetable matter occurs only when the conditions are favorable for bacterial development. Thus, as is well known, freezing, sterilizing by heat, or the addition of disinfectants will prevent the rotting of organic material.

In the laboratory, the presence of proteolytic enzymes is determined chiefly by the power of bacteria to liquefy gelatin, fibrin, or coagulated blood serum. These ferments are not always secretions from the bacterial cell, but in some cases may be closely bound to the cell body and separable only by extraction after death. In such cases they are spoken of as endo-enzymes. Whenever they are true secretory products, however, they can be obtained separate from the micro-organisms which form them by filtration through a Berkefeld candle. From such filtrates they may, in some cases, be obtained in the dry state by precipitation with alcohol. When obtained in this way the precipitated enzyme is usually much more thermostable than when in solution, for while soluble enzymes in filtrates are usually destroyed by 70° C., and even less, the dried powder may occasionally withstand 140° C. for as long as ten minutes (Fuhrmann).

Apart from the general conditions of temperature and moisture, the development of these enzymes seems to depend directly upon the presence of proteins in the culture media. The number of bacterial species which produce proteolytic enzymes is legion. Among those more commonly met with are staphylococci, *B. subtilis*, *B. proteus*, *B. faecalis liquefaciens*, *Spirillum cholerae asiaticae*, *B. anthracis*, *B. tetani*, *B. pyocyaneus*, and a large number of others. The inability of any given micro-organism to liquefy gelatin or fibrin by no means entirely excludes the formation by it of proteolytic enzymes, since these ferments may often be active for one particular class of protein only.

In order to study the qualitative and quantitative powers of any given bacterial proteolyzing enzyme or protease, it is, of course, necessary to study these processes in pure culture in the test tube with media of known composition. In the refuse heap, in sewage, or in rotting excreta, the process is an extremely complicated one, for besides the bacteria which attack the protein molecule itself, there are many other species supplementing these and each other, one species attacking the more or less complex end-products left by the action of the others.

Exactly what the chemical reactions are which take place in these cleavages is not entirely clear. It is believed, however, that most of the cleavages are of an hydrolytic nature.

In general, the action of the protein-splitting ferments is comparable to that of the pancreatic ferment trypsin, and they are most often active in an alkaline environment. They differ, among themselves, in the extent to which they are able to reduce the protein molecule to its simple radicals, some types leading to a relatively mild cleavage, while others, of the proteus type, yield amino-acids. Many species of bacteria which are unable to secrete a proteolytic enzyme, nevertheless produce erepsin-like ferments which readily attack peptones or polypeptids, with the formation of amino-acids.

A distinction is occasionally made between the terms *putrefaction* and *decay*, the former being used to refer to the decomposition taking place under anaerobic conditions, that is, in the absence of oxygen, a process resulting in the production of amino-acids, hydrogen sulphide, indole, skatole, and particularly the mercaptans which cause the highly offensive odor characteristic of this type of decomposition. The gases generated in such decomposition are largely made up of carbon dioxide and hydrogen. The coincident presence, furthermore, of the carbohydrate-splitting bacteria and of denitrifying micro-organisms renders the actual process of putrefaction a chaos of many activities in which the end-products and by-products are qualitatively determinable only with little precision, and which completely defies any attempt at quantitative analysis. *Decay* is the term used to signify decomposition under aerobic conditions, leading primarily to the formation of amino-acids, which are, as a rule, changed further to carbon dioxide, water and ammonia, often together with hydrogen sulphide and less completely decomposed substances, such as indole and various amines. Mercaptans are never formed and the foul odor of putrefaction is not present in this aerobic proteolysis (Rettger and Newell).

Ptomaines.—Very early in the study of the products of bacterial growth, a number of well-defined crystalline basic substances were isolated from protein material which had undergone bacterial putrefaction. These received, as a class, the name of *ptomaines* (from πτωμα, a dead body), and were shown to be toxic when fed to or injected into animals. It was attempted, at the time of their discovery, to explain the action of pathogenic bacteria on the basis of a production of ptomaines or related substances. This soon proved not to be the case, for not only were these bases never toxic in the minute dose sufficient for the true toxins of diphtheria and tetanus, but the anatomical lesions produced were different. Moreover, true bacterial toxins seemed to be formed to a great extent independently of the composition of the media upon which growth was obtained, while, as will be seen, ptomaine production depends directly upon the constitution of the substrate. Finally, nothing in the nature of antitoxin production could be shown, following sublethal injections of the ptomaines. While it is, therefore, not possible to account for the symptoms of bacterial action in the body on the basis of ptomaines, it is not impossible that the ptomaines themselves, if ingested in food which has undergone some putrefactive changes, may occasionally cause sickness. Food poisoning of this variety was formerly believed to be very common, and was described under various names, as creatotoxism (meat poisoning), tyrotoxism (cheese poisoning) and sitotoxism (vegetable poisoning). At present there is much question as to whether food poisoning, wherever met with (excepting botulism and staphylococcal food poisoning which are caused by the ingestion of bacterial toxins), is not caused by the presence of living bacteria of the Gärtner type in the food, and not to ptomaines. It is quite possible, on the other hand, that bacteria present in the intestine may, under certain conditions, set up putrefactive changes in the large bowel, leading to the formation of ptomaines or closely allied substances which can be absorbed directly and cause illness.

Chemically, the ptomaines are bases produced by the splitting out of carbon dioxide from the acid group of the amino-acids. Amines have been isolated resulting from this form of decomposition of practically all the known amino-acids. Of historic interest are putrescine and cadaverine. The former is produced by the decarboxylization of ornithin, thus:

$$CH_2(NH_2)CH_2.CH_2.CH(NH_2)COOH = CH_2(NH_2).CH2_2.CH_2.CH_2.(NH_2) + CO_2$$

Cadaverine is similarly formed from lysin. Both these bases possess relatively slight toxicity. Much more highly toxic is the base histamine, obtained in an entirely analogous manner from histidine. Some light seems to have been shed on the mechanism of this process of decarboxylization by Koessler and Hanke, who found, while investigating the production of histamine by *B. coli*, that it was formed only in cultures in which considerable quantities of acid were being produced at the same time, and they believe that the production of this strongly basic substance offsets to a degree the acid production and enables the organisms to develop further before the hydrogen-ion concentration reaches the point of inhibition. Sepsin, another base of unknown composition, but probably related in structure to the other ptomaines, has been isolated by Faust from putrid yeast, and has been shown to be highly toxic.

In breaking down animal excreta, the task of the bacteria is rather a simpler one than when dealing with the cadavers themselves, for here a part of the cleavage has already been carried out either by the destructive processes accompanying metabolism, or by partial decomposition by bacteria begun within the digestive tract. This material outside of the body is further reduced by bacterial enzymes into still simpler substances, the nitrogen usually being liberated in the form of ammonia. One example of such an ammoniacal fermentation may be found in the case of the urea fermentation by *Micrococcus ureae,* in which the cleavage of the urea takes place by hydrolysis according to the following formula:

$$(NH_2)_2CO + 2H_2O = CO_2 + 2NH_3 + H_2O$$

Similar ammoniacal fermentations are carried out, though perhaps according to less simple formulae, by a large number of micro-organisms. Perhaps the most common species which possesses this power is the group represented by *B. proteus vulgaris* (Hauser).

From what has been said it follows naturally that, so far, the decomposition of the protein molecule from its complex structure to ammonia or simple ammonia compounds is an indispensably important function, not only for agriculture, but for the maintenance of all life processes. It is clear, on the other hand, that a further decomposition of ammonia compounds into forms too simple to be utilized by the green plants would be a decidedly harmful activity. And yet this is brought about by the so-called denitrifying bacteria which will be considered in a subsequent section.

Lab Enzymes.—There are a number of ferments produced by bacteria which, although affecting proteins, cannot properly be classified with the proteolytic enzymes. These are the so-called coagulases or lab enzymes, which have the power of producing coagulation in liquid proteins. Just what chemical process underlies this coagulation is not known. If Hammarsten's conclusions as to the hydrolytic natures of the changes produced by them are true, these enzymes are brought into close relationship to the proteolyzers, although a coagulation can hardly be regarded as a true catabolic process. In milk where the lab action becomes evident by precipitation of casein, a strict differentiation must be made between this coagulation and that brought about by acids or alkalis. In the former case, casein is not only precipitated and converted into paracasein, but is actually changed so that when redissolved it is no longer precipitated by lab (Oppenheimer).

Coagulating enzymes for milk proteins, blood and other protein solutions are produced by a large variety of bacteria. They have been observed in cultures of the cholera vibrio, *B. prodigiosus, B. pyocyaneus,* and several others.

The lab enzymes are easily destroyed at temperatures of 70° C. and over, and are very susceptible to excessive acidity or alkalinity.

Fat-splitting Enzymes (*Lipase*).—The fat-splitting powers of bacteria have been less studied than some of the other bacterial functions and are correspondingly more obscure. It is known, nevertheless, that the process is due to an enzyme and that it is probably hydrolytic in nature. The following formula represents the simplest method in which some of the molds and bacteria produce cleavage of fats into glycerin and fatty acid:

$$C_3H_5(C_nH_{2n-1}O_2) + 3H_2O = C_3H_5(OH_3) + 3C_nH_{2n}O_2$$
$$\text{glycerin} \qquad \text{fatty acid}$$

Some of the bacteria endowed with the power of producing lipase are the cholera spirillum, *B. fluorescens liquefaciens*, *B. prodigiosus*, *B. pyocyaneus*, *Staphylococcus pyogenes aureus*, and some members of the streptothrix family. The method of investigating this function of bacteria, originated by Eijkmann, consists in covering the bottom of a Petri dish with tallow and pouring over this a thin layer of agar. Upon this the bacteria are planted. Any diffusion of lipase from the bacterial colonies becomes evident by a formation of white, opaque spots in the tallow. For the study of lipolysis by bacteria Collins and Hammer used fats dispersed in agar media containing Nile blue sulphate as an indicator. Apart from the importance of these enzymes in nature for the destruction of fats, they are industrially important because of their action in rendering butter, milk, tallow, and allied products rancid, and are medically of interest for their action upon fats in the intestinal canal.

Enzymes of Fermentation (*The Cleavage of Carbohydrates by Bacteria.*)—The power to assimilate carbon dioxide from the atmosphere is possessed only by the green plants and some of the colored algae, and the sulphur or thiobacteria. All other living beings are thus dependent for their supply of carbon upon the synthetic activities carried on by these plants to the same degree in which they are dependent upon similar processes for their nitrogen supply. The return of this carbon to the atmosphere is, of course, brought about to a large extent by the respiratory processes of the higher animals. The carbon, which, together with nitrogen, forms a part of protein combinations, is freed, as we have seen in a previous section, by the processes of protein cleavage. That, however, which is inclosed in the carbohydrate molecule, is set free by the action of yeasts, molds, or bacteria, by an enzymatic process similar in general to that described above for the process of protein cleavage. In this process many different enzymes are involved.

The power of carbohydrate cleavage is possessed by a large number of the yeasts and bacteria. The process, as has been indicated, is of great importance in the cycle of carbon compounds for the return of carbon to its simplest forms, and is, furthermore, as will be seen in a later section, of great utility in the industries. In each case the power to split a particular carbohydrate is a more or less specific characteristic of a given species of micro-organism, and for this reason has been extensively used as a method for the biological differentiation of bacteria. In the course of much careful work upon this question it has been ascertained that the specific carbohydrate-splitting powers of any given species are constant and unchanged through many generations of artificial cultivation. Thus, differentiation of the gram-negative bacteria, the diphtheria group, and to some extent of the members of the pneumococcus-streptococcus group, can now largely be made by a study of their sugar fermentations.

In most of these cases, as far as we know, the cleavage is produced by a process of hydrolysis. A convenient nomenclature which has been adapted for the designation of these ferments is that which employs the name of the converted carbohydrate adding the suffix "ase" to indicate the enzyme. There are thus ferments known as amylase, cellulase, lactase, etc.

Amylase (Diastase or Amylolytic Ferment).—Amylases or starch-splitting enzymes are formed by many plants (malt) and by animal organs (pancreas, saliva, liver). Among micro-organisms amylase is produced by many of the streptothrix group, by the spirilla of Asiatic cholera and of Finkler-Prior, by *B. anthracis,* and many other bacteria. A large number of the bacteria found in the soil, furthermore, has been shown to produce amylases. By cultivating bacteria upon starch-agar plates, amylase can be readily demonstrated by a clearing of the medium immediately surrounding the colonies (Eijkmann).

Since, of course, there are several varieties of starches, it follows that the exact chemical action of amylase differs in individual cases. The determination of the structural disintegration of starch by these ferments is fraught with much difficulty, owing to the polymeric constitution of the starches. Primarily, however, a cleavage takes place into a disaccharide such as maltose (hexobiose), and the nonreducing sugars and dextrin. Beyond this point, however, the further cleavages are subject to much variation and are not entirely clear. The dextrins upon further reduction yield eventually maltose, and this in turn, dextrose.

Another most interesting example of amylolytic activity is the fermentation of starch by such organisms as the *B. granulobacter pectinovorum* with the production of acetone and butyl alcohol. This reaction is now used industrially for the preparation of acetone, using a corn meal mash as the substrate. Dextrose is first formed, and from this, acetone, butyl alcohol, acetic and butyric acid, together with hydrogen and carbon dioxide are produced. The chemical mechanism of the fermentation is thus seen to be highly complex (Speakman, Weinstein and Rettger).

Cellulase.—Cellulose is fermented by a limited number of bacteria, most of them anaerobes. The chemical process by which this takes place is but partially understood.

Gelase.—An agar-splitting ferment has been found by Gran and Waksman.

Invertase.—The enzymes which hydrolytically cause cleavage of saccharose into dextrose and levulose are numerous. The chemical process takes place according to the following formula:

$$C_{12}H_{22}O_{11} + H_2O = C_6H_{12}O_6 + C_6H_{12}O_6$$
saccharose   dextrose   levulose

Invertase is produced by many of the yeasts. It is one of the most common of the enzymes produced by bacteria, and has been found in cultures of *B. megatherium, B. subtilis,* pneumococcus, some streptococci, *B. coli,* and many others. Invertase is usually very susceptible to heat, being destroyed by temperatures of 70° C. and over. A slightly acid reaction of media abets the inverting action of these enzymes. Strong acids and alkalis inhibit them. Inverting enzymes may be precipitated out of solution by alcohol. Antiseptics even in weak concentrations will inhibit their action.

Lactase.—Lactose-splitting ferments are extremely common both among bacteria and among the yeasts. The process is here again a hydrolytic cleavage resulting in the formation of the monosaccharides, dextrose and galactose.

Maltase.—A maltose-splitting ferment has also been found in the cultures of many bacteria, leading to the formation of dextrose.

Lactic Acid Fermentation.—Lactic acid (oxypropionic acid, $C_3H_6O_3$) is one of the most common substances to appear among the products of bacterial activity, both in media containing carbohydrates and in those consisting entirely of albuminous substances. In most of these cases, the lactic acid is formed merely as a by-product accompanying many other more complicated chemical cleavages. In some instances, however, lactic acid is produced from carbohydrates, both disaccharides and mono-saccharides, as an almost pure product due to a specific biochemical process. The reactions taking place in this phenomenon may be briefly expressed according to the following formulae:

$$C_{12}H_{22}O_{11} + H_2O = 4C_3H_6O_3$$
$$\text{lactose} \qquad\qquad \text{lactic acid}$$

or

$$C_6H_{12}O_6 = 2C_3H_6O_3$$
$$\text{dextrose} \quad \text{lactic acid}$$

In the same way lactic acid may be produced by bacteria from levulose.

Examples of lactic acid formation are furnished by the *Streptococcus lacticus*, and *B. lactis aërogenes*. In the case of the former, the fermentation may indeed proceed by the simple chemical process indicated in the formulae, since the action of the bacillus is entirely unaccompanied by the evolution of gas.

Numerous other bacteria produce large amounts of lactic acid from lactose, possibly by chemical processes less simply formulated. Among these are bacilli of the colon group, *B. prodigiosus*, *B. proteus vulgaris*, and many others. Although lactic acid is usually the chief product in the bacterial fermentation of the simpler carbo-hydrates, acetic, formic, and butyric acids may often be found as by-products in var-iable amounts.

Oxydases (Oxidizing Enzymes).—The most common example of oxidation by means of bacterial ferments is the production of acetic acid from weak solutions of ethyl alcohol. This process, which is the basis of vinegar production, is universally carried out by bacterial ferments. While possessed to some extent by a considerable number of micro-organisms, acetic acid formation is a function preëminently of the bacterial groups described by Hansen, including *Bacterium aceti* and *Bacterium pasteurianum*. To these two original groups, a number of others have since been added.

The organisms are short, plump bacilli, with a tendency to chain-formation, and occasionally showing characteristically swollen centers and many irregular involution forms. In the production of vinegar, as generally practiced by the farmer with cider or wine, these bacteria accumulate on the surface of the fluid as a pellicle or scum which is popularly known as the "mother of vinegar." Destruction of these bacteria by disinfectants or by sterilization with heat promptly arrests the process of vinegar formation. Chemically, the conversion of the alcohol consists in a double oxidation through ethyl aldehyde into acetic as shown in the following formulae:

$$\text{I.} \quad 2C_2H_5(OH) + O_2 = 2CH_3(COH) + 2H_2O$$
$$\qquad \text{alcohol} \qquad\qquad\qquad \text{ethyl aldehyde}$$
$$\text{II.} \quad 2CH_3(COH) + O_2 = 2CH_3(COOH)$$
$$\qquad\qquad\qquad\qquad\qquad \text{acetic acid}$$

Alcoholic Fermentation (*Zymase*).—The formation of alcohol as an end-product of fermentation is of great importance in a number of industries, primarily in the production of wine and beer. While accomplished by a number of bacteria, this form of fermentation is carried out chiefly by the yeasts.

Expressed in formulae the simplest varieties of alcoholic fermentation, from nono- and di-saccharids, may be represented as follows:

$$C_6H_{12}O_6 = 2C_2H_5(OH) + 2CO_2$$
dextrose ethyl alcohol

or

$$C_{12}H_{22}O_{11} + H_2O = 4C_2H_5(OH) + 4CO_2$$
saccharose ethly alcohol

In all cases the process may not be so simple as indicated by the equations, since by-products, such as higher alcohols, glycerin, succinic and acetic acids, may often be found in small traces among the end-products of such fermentations. The conditions which favor alcoholic fermentation by the yeasts are extremely important, since, upon observance of these, depends much of the uniformity of result which is so desirable in the industries mentioned above. The optimum concentration of sugar for the production of the highest quantity of alcohol is at or about 25 per cent. The tempera- ture favoring the process ranges about 30° C. Under such conditions fermentation may continue until the alcohol forms almost a 20 per cent solution. Most of the fermentations important in the wine, beer, and spirit industries, take place under anaerobic conditions, since the carbon dioxide which is formed soon shuts out any excess of air.

In the industrial employment of yeasts for fermentative purposes, it is necessary to work with specific strains, and in scientifically conducted vineyards, breweries, and distilleries the study and pure cultivation of the yeasts form no unimportant part of the work. Certain races of yeasts are more uniform in their fermentative powers than others, and the by-products formed by some races differ sufficiently from those of other races to cause material differences in the resulting substances. In the wine industries, the yeasts differ much from one another according to climatic and other environmental conditions. In vineyards, natural inoculation of the grapes occurs by transportation of the yeast from the soil to the surface of the grapes by wasps, bees, or other insects, through whose alimentary canals the micro-organisms pass uninjured. In the autumn the yeast is returned to the soil by falling berries and remains alive in the upper layers of the ground throughout the winter months. In actual practice this natural yeast inoculation is not depended upon, but pure cultures of artificially cultivated yeasts are employed in order to assure vigorous growth of the proper organism upon which flavor and bouquet depend to a considerable degree. In some of the wine-growing countries these are supplied by special government experiment stations.

Denitrifying Bacteria.—Nitrogen is most readily absorbed by plants in the form of nitrates. These are furnished to the soil chiefly by the protein decomposition in- duced by the proteolytic bacterial enzymes. It is self-evident, therefore, that any cleavage which reduces nitrogenous matter beyond the stage of nitrates, to nitrites and ammonia, detracts from the value of the nitrogen as a foodstuff for plants, and the eventual setting free of nitrogen in the elementary state renders it entirely valueless for any but the leguminous plants.

Nevertheless, this process of nitrogen waste or denitrification is constantly going on in nature. In the course of ordinary decomposition, there is a constant reduction of nitrogenous matter to nitrites and salts of ammonia, actively taken part in by a host of bacteria, as many as 85 out of 109 investigated by Maassen being found to possess this power. This, however, is not nearly so harmful a source of nitrogen waste as the process technically spoken of as true denitrification, in which nitrates are reduced, through nitric and nitrous oxides, to elementary nitrogen.

This phenomenon, more widely spread among bacteria than at first believed, depends essentially upon simple oxygen extraction from the nitrates by the bacteria, and for this reason goes on most actively when the supply of atmospheric oxygen is low. The first bacteria described as possessing this power of denitrification were the so-called *B. denitrificans* I and II, the first an obligatory anaerobe, the other a facultative aerobe. Since then numerous other bacteria, among them *B. coli* and *B. pyocyaneus*, have been shown to exhibit similar activities. It is important agriculturally, therefore, to know that many species which are able to utilize atmospheric oxygen when supplied with it, will get their oxygen by the reduction of nitrates and nitrites when free oxygen is withheld. It is thus clear that a loss of nitrogen is much more apt to proceed rapidly in manure heaps which are piled high and poorly aerated. There are other factors, however, in regard to the physiology of these micro-organisms, which must be considered for practical purposes.

In order that these bacteria may develop their denitrifying powers to the best advantage, it is necessary to supply them with some carbon compound which is easily absorbed by them. This, in decomposing material, is furnished by the products of the carbohydrate cleavage going on side by side with the proteolytic processes. It is still more or less an open question whether the facilitation of denitrification brought about in manure heaps by the presence of hay and straw is due to the carbon furnished by these materials, or whether it is due to the fact that bacilli of this group are apt to adhere to the straw which acts in that case as a means of inoculation.

The actual danger of nitrogen depletion of the soil by denitrifying processes is probably much less threatening than was formerly supposed; for, in the first place, the conditions for complete denitrification are much more perfect in the experiment than they ever can be in nature, and the nitrifying processes going on side by side with denitrification make up for much of the loss sustained.

GENERAL ANABOLIC OR SYNTHETIC ACTIVITIES OF BACTERIA

Nitrogen Fixation by Bacteria.—The constant withdrawal of nitrogenous substances from the soil by innumerable plants would soon lead to total depletion were it not for certain forces continually at work replenishing the supply out of the large store of free nitrogen in the atmosphere. This important function of returning nitrogen to the soil in suitable form for consumption by the plants is performed largely by bacteria.

It is well known that specimens of agricultural soil when allowed to stand for any length of time without further interference will increase in nitrogenous content, but that similar specimens, if sterilized, will show no such increase (Waksman). The obvious conclusion to be drawn from this phenomenon is that some living factor in the unsterilized soil has aided in increasing the nitrogen supply. Light was thrown upon this problem when Winogradsky, 1892, discovered a micro-organism in the soil which possessed the power of assimilating large quantities of nitrogen from the air. This bacterium, which he named *Clostridium pasteurianum*, is an obligatory anaerobe which in nature always occurs in symbiosis with two other facultatively anaerobic micro-organisms. In symbiosis with these, it can be cultivated under aerobic conditions and thus grows readily in the upper well-aerated layers of the soil.

Although, until now, no other bacteria with equally well-developed nitrogen-fixing powers have been discovered, yet it is more than likely that *Clostridium pasteurianum* is not the only micro-organism endowed with this function. In fact, *Penicillium glaucum* and *Aspergillus niger*, two molds, and two other bacteria described by Winogradsky, have been shown to possess this power slightly, but in an incomparably less marked degree than *Clostridium pasteurianum*. According to some calculations unsterilized soil may, under experimental conditions, gain as much as twenty-five milligrams of nitrogen in a season, a statement which permits the calculation of a gain of twelve kilograms of nitrogen per acre annually. It is very unlikely, however, that such gains actually occur in nature, where nitrogen fixation and nitrogen loss usually occur side by side.

Agriculturally of even greater importance than the free nitrogen-fixing bacteria of the soil are the bacteria found in the root tubercles of a class of plants known as "leguminosae." It has long been known that this class of plants, including clover, peas, beans, vetch, etc., not only does not withdraw nitrogen from the soil, but rather tends to enrich it. Upon this knowledge has depended the well-known method of alternation of crops employed by farmers the world over. The actual reason for the beneficial influence of the leguminosae, however, was not known until 1887, when Hellriegel and Wilfarth succeeded in demonstrating that the nitrogen-accumulation was directly related to the root tubercles of the plants and to the bacteria contained within them.

These tubercles, which are extremely numerous—as many as a thousand sometimes occurring upon one and the same plant—are formed by the infection of the roots with bacteria which probably enter through the delicate root-hairs. They vary in size, are usually situated near the main root-stem, and, in appearance, are not unlike fungus growths. Their development is in many respects comparable to the development of inflammatory granulations in animals after infection, inasmuch as the formation of the tubercle is largely due to a reactionary hyperplasia of the plant tissues themselves. They appear upon the seedlings within the first few weeks of their growth as small pink nodules, and enlarge rapidly as the plant grows. At the same time, later in the season, when the plants bear fruit, the root tubercles begin to shrink and crack. When the crops are harvested, the tubercles with the root remain, rot in the ground, and reinfect the soil.

Histologically the tubercles are seen to consist of large root cells which are densely crowded with micro-organisms.

The micro-organism itself, *B. radicola*, was first observed within the tubercles by Woronin in 1867. The bacilli are large, slender, and actively motile during the early development of the tubercles, but in the later stages assume a number of characteristic involution forms, commonly spoken of as "bacteroids." They become swollen, T- and Y-shaped, or branching and thread-like. Their isolation from the root tubercles usually presents little difficulty, since they grow readily upon gelatin and agar under strictly aerobic conditions. On the artificial media the bacillary form is usually well retained, involution forms appearing only upon old cultures.

The classical experiments of Hellriegel and Wilfarth conclusively demonstrated the important relation of these tubercle bacteria to nitrogen assimilation by the leguminosae.

These observers cultivated various members of this group of plants upon nitrogen-free soil—sand—and prevented the formation of root tubercles in some, by sterilization of the sand, while in others they encouraged tubercle formation by inoculation. An example of their results may be given as follows: (Pfeffer)

	Nitrogen Contents of Seed and Soil, in Grams	Nitrogen Contents of Crop, in Grams	Gain or Loss
Oats	0.027 gram	0.007 gram	—.020
Peas	0.038 gram	0.459 gram	+.421

Lupinus luteus was cultivated upon sterilized sand. Some of the pots were inoculated with *B. radicicola,* others were kept sterile. Comparative analyses were made of the plants grown in the different pots with the following striking result:

Root Tubercles	Harvested Dry Weight	Nitrogen Present	Nitrogen Added in Seed, Soil, and Soil-Extract	Gain or Loss of Nitrogen
Present	{ (a) 38.919	.998	.022	+.976
	{ (b) 33.755	.981	.023	+.958
Not present....	{ (c) 0.989	.016	.020	—.004
	{ (d) 0.828	.011	.022	—.011

The great importance of this process in agriculture is demonstrated, furthermore, by a comparison made by the same observers between a legume, the pea, and one of the common nitrogen-consuming crops, oats (Hellriegel and Wilfarth). Exactly what the process is by which the bacteria supply nitrogen to the plant is as yet uncertain. Although the degenerating bacteroids in old nodules are bodily absorbed by the plant, this cannot be conceived as the only method of supply, since the total nitrogen gain many times exceeds the total weight of bacteria in the nodules. It is probable that the micro-organisms during life take up atmospheric nitrogen and secrete a nitrogenous substance which is absorbed by the plant cells.

Although formerly the relationship between plant and bacterium was regarded as one of symbiosis and of mutual benefit, the opinions as to this subject show wide divergence. While, according to some authors, the entrance of the bacteria into the plants is regarded as a true infection against which the plant offers at first a determined opposition as evidenced by tissue reactions, other observers, notably A. Fischer, regard the plant as a parasite upon the bacteria, in that it derives the sole benefit from the relationship and eventually bodily consumes its host.

Nitrifying Bacteria.—A process diametrically opposed in its chemistry to denitrification and reduction is that which brings about an oxidation of ammonia to nitrites and nitrates. The actual increase of nitrates in soil allowed to stand for any length of time and examined from time to time has been a well-established fact for many years; but it was believed until a comparatively short time ago that this increase was due to a simple chemical oxidation of ammonia by atmospheric oxygen. The dependence of nitrification upon the presence of living organisms was finally proved by Munz and Schlössing in 1887, who demonstrated that nitrification was abruptly stopped when the soil was sterilized by heat or antiseptics. It remained, however, to isolate and identify the organisms which brought about this ammonia oxidation. This last step in our knowledge of nitrification was taken in 1890, by Winogradsky. Winogradsky found that the failures experienced by others who had attempted to isolate nitrifying bacteria, were due to the fact that they had used the common culture-media largely made up of organic substances. By using culture-media containing no organic matter, Winogradsky succeeded in isolating free from the soil, bacteria which have since that time been confirmed as being the causative factors in nitrification. During his first experiments this author observed that in some of his cultures the oxidation of ammonia went only as far as the stage of nitrite formation, while in others complete oxidation to nitrates took place. Following the clues indicated by this discrepancy, he finally succeeded in demonstrating that nitrification is a double process in which two entirely different varieties of micro-organisms take part, the one capable of oxidizing ammonia to nitrites, the other continuing the process and converting the nitrites to nitrates. The nitrite-forming bacteria discovered by Winogradsky, and named nitromonas or nitrosomonas, are easily cultivated upon aqueous solutions containing ammonia, potassium sulphate, and magnesium carbonate. According to their discoverer they develop in this medium within a week as a gelatinous sediment. After further growth this sediment seems to break up and the bacteria appear as oval bodies, which swim actively about and develop flagella at one end. Upon the solid media in ordinary use they cannot be cultivated. Special solid media suitable for their cultivation and composed of silicic acid and inorganic salts have been described by Winogradsky and by Omeliansky.

Other nitrite-forming bacteria have since been described by various observers, all of them more or less limited to definite localities. Some of these are similar to nitrosomonas in that they exhibit the flagellated, actively motile stage. In others, this stage is absent.

The nitrite-forming bacteria, apart from their great agricultural importance, claim our attention because of their unique position in relation to the animal and vegetable kingdoms. Extremely sensitive to the presence of organic compounds, they are able to grow and develop only upon media containing nothing but inorganic material; and this entirely without the aid of any substances comparable to the chlorophyl of the green plants. The source of energy from which this particular class of bacteria derive the power of building up organic compounds from simple substances is to some extent a mystery. The carbon which they unquestionably require for the building up of organic material may be, as Winogradsky believed, derived to a certain extent from ammonium carbonate. But it is also quite certain that they are capable of utilizing directly atmospheric carbon dioxide. In the absence of chlorophyl or of any highly organized chemical compound, it seems likely that the energy necessary for the utilization of the carbon obtained in this simple form is derived from the oxidation of ammonia during the process of nitrification.

The conversion of nitrites into nitrates is carried on by other species of bacteria also discovered by Winogradsky. These bacteria are much more generally distributed than nitrosomonas and probably include a number of varieties. The organism described by Winogradsky is an extremely small bacillus with pointed ends. Capsules have occasionally been demonstrated. It may be cultivated upon aqueous solutions containing:

	Per Cent
Sodium nitrite	.1
Potassium phosphate	.05
Magnesium sulphate	.03
Sodium carbonate	.1
Ferrous sulphate	.04

The development of the organism is slow and sparse, and is directly inhibited by the presence of organic matter. It is strongly inhibited by the presence of ammonia.

Formation of Pigment by Bacteria (*Chromobacteria*).—A large number of bacteria, when cultivated upon suitable media, give rise to characteristic colors which are valuable as marks of differentiation. For each species, the color is usually constant, depending, to a certain extent, upon the conditions of cultivation. In only a few of the pigmented bacteria is the pigment contained within the cell body, and in only one variety, the sulphur bacteria, does the pigment appear to hold any distinct relationship to nutrition. In most cases, the coloring matter is found to be deposited in small intercellular granules or globules. The absence of any relationship of the pigment to sunlight, as is the case with the chlorophyl of the green plants, is indicated by the fact that most of the chromobacteria thrive and produce pigment equally well in the dark as they do in the presence of light. Among the most common of the pigment bacteria met with in bacteriological work are *Staphylococcus aureus, B. pyocyaneus, B. prodigiosus,* and some of the green fluorescent bacteria frequently found in feces.

The chemical nature of these pigments has been investigated quite thoroughly and it has been shown that they vary in composition. Some of the pigments, like that of *Staphylococcus aureus*, are probably nonprotein and of a fatty nature (Buchanan). They are insoluble in water but soluble in alcohol, ether, and chloroform. Because of their probable composition, they have been spoken of as "lipochromes." Other pigments, like the pyocyanine, which lends the green color to cultures of *B. pyocyaneus,* are water soluble and are probably of protein composition. Pyocyanine may be crystallized out of aqueous solution in the form of fine needles. The crystals may be redissolved in chloroform. Aqueous solutions retain their color. Solutions in chloroform, however, are changed gradually to yellow.

The power of pigment production of various bacteria depends in each case upon cultural conditions. In most cases, this simply signifies that pigment is produced only when the micro-organism, finding the most favorable environmental conditions, is enabled to develop all its functions to their fullest extent. Thus, a too high acidity or alkalinity of the culture medium may inhibit pigment formation. Oxygen is necessary for the production of color in some bacteria, since the bacteria themselves often produce the pigment only as a leuko-body which is then oxidized into the pigment proper. A notable example of this is the pigment of *B. pyocyaneus*. In other cases, temperature plays an important rôle in influencing color production. Thus, *B. prodigiosus* does not usually produce its pigment when growing in the incubator at 37° C. By persistent cultivation in an unfavorable environment, colored cultures may lose their power of pigment production.

Sulphur Bacteria.—Wherever the decomposition of organic matter gives rise to the formation of hydrogen sulphide, in cesspools, in ditches, at the bottom of the sea, and in stagnant ponds, there is found a curiously interesting group of micro-organisms, the so-called sulphur bacteria or thiobacteria. Red, purple, and colorless, these bacteria all possess the power of utilizing hydrogen sulphide and by its oxidation into free sulphur obtain the energy necessary for their metabolic processes. The color-less sulphur bacteria, the beggiatoa and thiothrices, usually appear as threads or chains which, in media containing sufficient hydrogen sulphide, are usually well-stocked with minute globules of sulphur. If found upon decomposing organic matter, they often cover this as a grayish mold-like layer. The red sulphur bacteria, of which numerous species have been described by Winogradsky, may appear as actively motile spirilla (thiospirillum) or as short, thick bacillary forms.

The physiology of all the sulphur bacteria, and especially of the colored varieties, is of the greatest interest in that these micro-organisms are among the few members of the bacterial group which behave metabolically like the green plants. The higher organic substances play little or no part in the nutrition of these micro-organisms. Strictly aerobic, the colorless thiobacteria are independent of sunlight, while the red and purple varieties exhibit their physiological dependence upon light by accumulating under natural conditions in well-lighted spots. Both varieties possess equally the power of oxidizing hydrogen sulphide as a source of energy. The sulphur is then stored as elemental sulphur within the bacterial body and when a lack of foodstuffs sets in, the store of sulphur can be further oxidized into sulphurous or sulphuric anhydrides. With this sole source of energy, these bacteria are capable of flourishing aerobically, while an absence of hydrogen sulphide, even in the presence of organic foodstuffs, leads to a rapid disappearance of their sulphur contents and an inability to develop.

In the case of the colored thiobacteria, the red pigment appears to fulfil, to some extent, a function comparable to that of the chlorophyl of the green plants.

Engelmann, who has studied this pigment spectroscopically, has found that besides absorbing the red spectral rays there is an absorption of rays on the ultra-red end of the spectrum. The absorption of the red rays between the lines B and C of the spectrum, and of violet rays at the line F, is the same as that of the absorption spectrum of chlorophyl, and it is in the zone of these rays that the physiological effects of chlorophyl are most active. In addition to these absorption bands, the bacterio-purpurin of the red sulphur bacteria shows absorption of the invisible ultra-red rays of the spectrum.

Engelmann, with a microspectroscope, projected a spectrum into a microscopic field in which green algae or, in the case under discussion, red sulphur bacteria, had been placed. Other sources of light were, of course, excluded. By adding emulsions of strictly aerobic bacteria to such preparations, an accumulation of micro-organisms was observed at those points in the spectrum at which most oxygen was liberated. In the case both of chlorophyl and of the red sulphur bacteria such areas of bacterial accumulation (in oxygen liberation) occurred in the zones of the absorption bands mentioned above.

REFERENCES

BASS-BECKING, L. G. M., and PARKS, G. S. Physiol. Rev., 1927, 7:85.
BUCHANAN, R. E., and FULMER, E. I. Physiology and Biochemistry of Bacteria, Baltimore, 1928, 1:115, 122, 373.
CLARK, W. M., et al. U. S. Public Health Service, Hygiene Laboratory Bull. No. 151, 1928.
COLLINS, M. A., and HAMMER, B. W. J. Bacteriol., 1934, 27:473, 487.
COULTER, C. B. J. Gen. Physiol., 1928, 12:139.
DAVIS, D. J. J. Infect. Dis., 1907, 4:73.
DORYLAND, J. J. Bacteriol., 1916, 1:135.
EIJKMANN, C. Centralbl. f. Bakteriol., I. Abt., 1901, 29:841; 1903, 35:1.
ENGELMANN, T. W. Botanische Zeitung, 1888, 46:661, 667, 693, 709.
FERRÁN, J. Centralbl. f. Bakteriol., I Abt., Orig., 1898, 24:28.
FILDES, P. Brit. J. Exper. Pathol., 1929, 10:151.
FUHRMANN, F. Einfuhrung in die Grundlagender teknischen Mykologie, Jena, 1926.
——— Vorlesungen uber Bakterienenzyme, Jena, 1907, p. 45.
GILLESPIE, R. W. H., and RETTGER, L. F. J. Bacteriol., 1938, 36:605, 621, 633.
GORINI, C. Hyg. Rund., 1893, 3:381.
——— Rev. d'ig. e san. pubb., 1893, 4:549.
GRAN, H. H. Bergens Museum Aarbok, 1902, hft. 1.
HAMMARSTEN. Textbook of Physiological Chemistry, translated by Mandel.
HELLRIEGEL, H., and WILFARTH, H. Ztschr. d. Ver. f.d. Rübenzücker Industrie, 1888.
HUNTOON, F. M. J. Infect. Dis., 1918, 23:169.
JORDAN, E. O. Food Poisoning, University of Chicago Press, 1931.
KLUYVER, A. J. Science, 1932, 76:527.
KNIGHT, B. C. J. G. Bacterial Nutrition. Medical Research Council, London, Spec. Report Ser. No. 210, 1938.
KOESSLER and HANKE, M. T. J. Biol. Chem., 1919, 39:539.
LLOYD, D. J. J. Path. & Bacteriol., 1916, 21:113.
MAASSEN, A. Arb. a.d.k. Gsndhtsamtě, 1901, 18:21.
MORGAN, H. J., and AVERY, O. T. J. Exper. M., 1924, 39:289, 335.
MUELLER, J. H. J. Bacteriol., 1922, 7:309, 325; 1935, 29:383, 515; 1935, 30:513, 525; 1937, 34:153, 163, 381, 429.
MUNZ, A., and SCHLÖSSING. Compt. rend. Acad. d. sc., 1877, 84:401; 1889, 109:423.
OMELIANSKY, W. L. Centralbl. f. Bakteriol., II Abt., 1899, 5:537.
OPPENHEIMER, C. Die Fermente und ihre Wirkung, Leipzig, 1903.
PFEFFER, W. Pflanzenphysiologie, Leipzig, 1897.
PLOTZ, H. and GELOSO, J. Ann. de l'Inst. Pasteur, 1930, 45:613.
PROSKAUER, B. and BECK, M. Ztschr. f. Hyg. u. Infektionskrankh., 1895, 18:128.
RAHN, O. Physiology of Bacteria, Philadelphia, 1932, pp. 22–34.
RETTGER, L. F., and NEWELL, C. R. J. Biol. Chem., 1912, 12:341.
RIVERS, T. M., and POOLE, A. K. Johns Hopkins Hosp. Bull., 1921, 32:202.
RUBNER, M. Hyg. Rund., 1903, 13:857.
——— Arch. f. Hyg., 1904, 48:260.
SMITH, T., BROWN, H. R., and WALKER, E. L. J. Med. Research, 1906, 9:193.

SPEAKMAN. J. Biol. Chem., 1920, 41:319; 1920, 43:401.

STEPHENSON, M. Bacterial Metabolism, Longmans, Green and Co., London and New York, 1930.

THJÖTTA, TH., and AVERY, O. T. J. Exper. M., 1921, 34:97, 455.

USCHINSKY. Centralbl. f. Bakteriol., 1893, 14:316.

VON ANGERER, K. Arch. f. Hyg., 1919, 88:139.

WAKSMAN, S. A. Principles of Soil Microbiology, Baltimore, 1927, p. 558.

WAKSMAN, S. A., and BAVENDAM, W. J. Bacteriol., 1931, 22:91.

WEINSTEIN, L. and RETTGER, L. F. J. Bacteriol., 1933, 25:201.

WILSON, P. W., and PETERSON, W. H. Chem. Rev., 1931, 8:427.

WINOGRADSKY, S. Arch. Sci. Biol., St. Petersb., 1892, 1:87, 127.

WORONIN, M. Ann. Sci. Nat. Bot., ser. 5, 1867, 7:73.

CHAPTER VII

THE EFFECTS OF PHYSICAL AGENTS ON BACTERIA

Physical forces acting upon bacteria determine many of the properties and characteristics of these organisms (Buchanan and Fulmer). Bacteria, like other cells, are responsive to changes in the physical components of their environment. By the action of physical forces upon them they may be stimulated, attenuated, caused to produce variants, or killed (Hampil). The physical forces which we shall consider here are: heat (temperature), desiccation, radiations (electromagnetic, light, x-rays, radium), electricity, pressure (mechanical, osmotic, gaseous), surface tension, agitation, trituration, and high-frequency sound waves. Some of these forces produce chemical changes, others bring about mechanical disorganization of the cells. In many cases these forces act in such inseparable combinations that it is impossible to isolate the effects of one force or agent from the effects of others acting simultaneously. The effects of all vary with their intensities and the time during which they act.

Temperature.—Of all these forces, heat at various temperatures has the most general action and is the physical agent applied with most important consequences for the study and cultivation of bacteria and for the destruction of bacteria through its use for the sterilization of materials.

Temperature influences the rates of chemical reactions and many physical processes. This effect is usually expressed in terms of the *temperature coefficient* of these reactions as the ratio between the velocity constants of the reactions at two different temperatures. The symbol Q_{10} is usually employed to signify the value of this ratio, quotient or coefficient for a difference of 10° C. It varies with the actual temperatures at which it is determined. For most chemical reactions its value is greater than 2, while for most physical processes its value is nearer unity. But due to complex conditions and catenary reactions in protoplasmic systems, it is not possible always to determine from the value of Q_{10} whether the process is chemical or physical. As Buchanan and Fulmer have stated: "The great significance of the increased rate of reaction with increase in temperature is evident when one recognizes that a reaction for which $Q_{10} = 3$ proceeds more than fifty-nine thousand times as rapidly at 100° as at 10°, if there is no change in the temperature quotient for each degree increase in temperature." It is important, in studying bacterial metabolism, testing disinfectants and investigating other problems in bacteriology, to bear in mind that an increase of 10°C. in the temperature range of 18° to 37° C. will usually at least double the rate of the reactions.

In order to have a more adequate expression for the complex relationship between temperature and rates of reactions at different ranges in the temperature scale, the symbol μ, taken from the van't Hoff-Arrhenius equation, is used. This has been called the symbol of the "thermal increment" as a criterion of the effect of temperature. It has been extensively used in biological studies by Crozier to test the assumption that each group of reactions having the same "temperature characteristic (μ) are processes influenced by a common catalyst.

While it is customary to speak of an optimum temperature for bacterial growth, it is necessary, in the final analysis, to define the phase or characteristic of bacterial activity to which the term is applied. Bacteria will remain in a resting state without development and may die at certain low temperatures. Increase in temperature above a certain point will inhibit their activities and finally kill them. Bacterial activity in the range between these minimum and maximum temperatures is quite varied. The optimum temperature for rapid multiplication is not always the optimum temperature for the greatest crop yield, because injurious waste products accumulate most rapidly at this temperature and the endogenous catabolism of the death-phase has an even greater temperature coefficient than that of the anabolic metabolism of growth. The optimum temperatures of fermentative, proteolytic and synthetic processes are not always the same as those of growth and differ among themselves. The optimum temperatures for constancy of form in relation to phases of the growth curve vary. The formation of spores and flagella in some cases have different temperature optima from those governing toxin formation and virulence. Antigenic constitution also is affected by temperature. Edwards and Rettger have shown that the maximum growth temperatures of bacteria bear a definite relationship to the minimum temperatures of destruction of respiratory enzymes. Classification of organisms in three large groups on the basis of the relationship of temperature to growth is as follows (Tanner):

GROUP	TEMPERATURE IN DEGREES CENTIGRADE			TYPES
	Minimum	Optimum	Maximum	
Psychrophilic	0	15–20	30	Many water bacteria Cold storage growths
Mesophilic	15–25	37	43	Most pathogens
Thermophilic	25–45	50–55	85	Bacteria from soils, water, thermal springs

It is apparent from these data that the same species may develop within a wide temperature range, and it may be possible, by persistent cultivation at special temperatures, to adapt certain bacteria to grow luxuriantly at temperatures removed by several degrees from their normal optimum. In such cases it may often occur that special characteristics of the given species may be lost. An example of this is the loss of virulence and of spore-formation which takes place when anthrax bacilli are cultivated at 42° C., or the loss of the power to produce pigment when B. prodigiosus is grown at temperatures above 30° C.

The vegetative forms of most of the pathogenic bacteria may grow at temperatures ranging between 20° and 40° C. This can, however, by no means be regarded as applicable to all of the pathogenic bacteria, as some of these, like the gonococcus, the pneumococcus, the tubercle bacillus, and others, are delicately susceptible to temperature changes and have the power of growing only within limits varying but a few degrees from their optimum. Others, on the other hand, like bacilli of the colon group, *Bacillus anthracis, Spirillum cholerae,* etc., may develop at temperatures as low as 10° C. and as high as 40° C., or over. The range of temperature at which saprophytic bacteria may develop is usually a far wider one.

Lethal and Destructive Effects of Temperature.—Bacteria can be killed by exposure to low and high temperature. Important use is made of lethal temperatures to obtain bacterial products and to rid materials of living bacteria by sterilizing them by heat.

The resistance of bacteria to extremes of temperature depends on the species of micro-organism, upon the growth stage, and upon whether or not the organisms contain endospores. Spores have an enormously greater resistance than vegetative forms to heat at high and low temperatures. The explanation of the high thermal resistance of spores probably is to be found in the concentrated, dehydrated state of the protoplasm contained in them.

The effect of temperature is further influenced by the conditions under which it is applied. The hydrogen-ion concentration of the medium in which bacteria are heated affects the results, heating in acid media producing death more readily than in alkaline media. Bacteria in a dry state withstand higher temperatures for a longer time than bacteria in a moist state. Hence, differences occur between the times and temperatures required for dry hot air, hot water or steam to produce the same effect. The time-period of exposure is inseparable from the temperature in determining the result produced. In addition, the number of organisms present in the material has a bearing upon outcome of the exposure.

Low temperatures are much less destructive than high ones. In most cases a temperature of 5 to 10° C. is useful in keeping bacteria alive for long periods, as metabolic processes are thereby largely inhibited and life is maintained without actual development in a sort of resting state. Actual destruction by low temperatures rarely takes place. The exposure of diphtheria, typhoid and other bacilli to temperatures of liquid air and liquid hydrogen (— 250° C.) has been carried out without killing the organisms. Meningococci and gonococci die out rapidly when exposed to 0° C. On the other hand, freezing bacteria in water kills the organisms more readily. This, however, is not a dependable means of destruction and does not prevent the spread of typhoid fever through the medium of contaminated ice. Park showed that most, but not all, typhoid bacilli in water were killed when the water was frozen, and Hutchins and Wheeler have presented evidence that typhoid fever has been spread by ice. Repeated freezing and thawing may kill bacteria and may cause a more or less extensive disruption of the cells. This method has been used to obtain relatively unaltered endocellular constituents of bacteria.

The older bacteriological literature contains records of many determinations of what has been called the *thermal death point* of bacteria. This term is defined as "that temperature which will kill under specified conditions."[1] The term is misleading and should be discarded. The death of bacteria under the influence of temperature is an orderly process of accelerated physical and chemical reactions resulting in coagulation (Chick). It has a high temperature coefficient ($Q_{10} = 7$ to 10) in the

1 Buchanan and Fulmer, *Physiology and Biochemistry of Bacteria,* Baltimore, 1930.

region 50° to 100° C. The time element, therefore, is too important a factor to be arbitrarily chosen in connection with a process whose rate is so greatly influenced by temperature. From these older determinations has come the practically useful knowledge that the vegetative forms of pathogenic bacteria are killed by exposure to 50° to 60° C. in water or broth in fifteen to sixty minutes. The many additional factors which we have mentioned, hydrogen-ion concentration, numbers of organisms, age of culture and species of bacterium influence the result and must be kept constant in order to give meaning to any determination of *thermal death point*. "There is no one time and temperature combination which alone may be defined as the thermal death point." [2]

A more acceptable expression is *thermal death time*, as used by Esty after its introduction by Bigelow in 1921 to designate this time-temperature relationship under specified conditions. Since then a number of studies, which we shall mention in sections on specific organisms, have been made to determine thermal death times of tubercle bacilli, spirochetes and other pathogenic bacteria. In much of the older work, temperatures much higher than those which the animal body can withstand were chosen. Since the advent of therapeutic measures based upon diathermy and artificial fever produced by high frequency electrical currents it has become increasingly important to determine thermal death times within the range 39° to 42° C., as has been done by Carpenter, Boak and associates. In the pasteurization of milk, a temperature of 142° to 145° F. is applied during thirty minutes, as this combination kills the tubercle bacilli and other vegetative forms of pathogens without deleteriously affecting the milk. In sterilizing bacterial vaccines by heat, it is advisable to kill the organisms at a temperature which produces the least change in their composition. For this purpose heating to 60° C. for 30 to 60 minutes is the usual procedure, but it is probable that the cellular material would suffer less alteration if the suspensions were heated at a lower temperature for a longer time.

Sterilization by Heating.—The most widely applicable and efficient physical agent for sterilization is heat.

Heat may be applied in the form of dry heat or as moist heat, these methods being of great practical value, but differently applicable according to the nature of the materials to be sterilized. The two methods, moreover, show a marked difference in efficiency, temperature for temperature. For the recognition of this fact we are largely indebted to the early researches of Koch and Wolffhuegel, and of Koch, Gaffky, and Löffler.

These observers were able to show that the spores of anthrax were destroyed by boiling water at 100° C. in from one to twelve minutes, whereas dry hot air was efficient only after three hours' exposure to 140° C. Extensive confirmation of these differences has been brought by many workers. An explanation of the phenomena observed is probably to be found in the changes in the coagulability of proteins brought about in them by the abstraction of water. Lewith, working with various proteins, found that these substances are coagulated by heat at lower temperatures when they contain abundant quantities of water, than when water has been abstracted from them. On the basis of actual experiment with egg-albumin he obtained the following results, which illustrate the point in question:

2 J. R. Esty, *Newer Knowledge of Bacteriology and Immunology,* Chicago, 1928, Chap. 21, pp. 285–300.

Egg-albumin in dilute aqueous solution, coagulated at 56° C.
Egg-albumin with 25 per cent water, coagulated at 74–80° C.
Egg-albumin with 18 per cent water, coagulated at 80–90° C.
Egg-albumin with 6 per cent water, coagulated at 145° C.

Absolutely anhydrous albumin, according to Haas, may be heated to 170° C. without coagulation. It is thus clear that bacteria exposed to hot air may be considerably dehydrated before the temperature rises sufficiently to cause death by coagulation, complete dehydration necessitating their destruction possibly by actual burning.

Bacteria exposed to moist air or steam, on the other hand, may absorb water and become proportionately more coagulable.

The same principle, as Lewith points out, probably explains the great resistance to heat observed in the case of the highly concentrated protoplasm of spores.

Apart from the actually great efficiency of moist heat when compared with dry heat of an equal temperature, an advantage of great practical significance possessed by moist heat lies in its greater powers of penetration. An experiment carried out by Koch and his associates illustrates this point clearly. Small packages of garden soil were surrounded by varying thicknesses of linen with thermometers so placed that the temperature under a definite number of layers could be determined. Exposures to hot air and to steam were then made for comparison, and the results were as tabulated:

| Media | Temperatures, Centigrade | Time of Application, Hours | Thicknesses of Linen Temperatures Reached within | | | Sterilization |
			Twenty Thicknesses	Forty Thicknesses	One Hundred Thicknesses	
Hot air	130–140°	4	86°	72°	below 70°	incomplete
Steam	90–105.3°	3	101°	101°	101.5°	complete

This great penetrating power of steam is due presumably to its comparatively low specific gravity which enables it to displace air from the interior of porous materials, and also to the fact that as the steam comes in contact with the objects to be disinfected a condensation takes place with the consequent liberation of heat. When a vapor passes into the liquid state it gives out a definite amount of heat, which in the case of water vapor, at 100° C., amounts to about 537 calories. This brings about a rapid heating of the object in question. Following this process the further heating takes place by conduction, and it is, of course, well known that steam is a much better heat conductor than air.

Moist heat may be applied as boiling water, in which, of course, the temperature varies little from 100° C., or as steam. Steam may be used as live, flowing steam, without pressure, the temperature of which is more or less constant at 100° C., or still higher efficiency may be attained by the use of steam under pressure, in which, of course, temperatures far exceeding 100° C. may be produced, according to the amount of pressure which is used.

The spores of certain bacteria of the soil which cannot be killed in live steam in less than several hours may be destroyed in a few minutes, or even instantaneously, in compressed steam at temperatures ranging from 120° to 140° C. (Magoon).

In all methods of steam sterilization, it is of great practical importance, as von Esmarch has pointed out, that the steam shall be saturated, that is, shall contain as much vaporized water as its temperature permits. Unsaturated, or so-called "super-heated steam" is formed when heat is applied to steam, either by passage through heated piping or over heated metal plates. In such cases the temperature of the steam is raised, but no further water-vapor being supplied, the steam exerts less pressure and contains less water in proportion to its volume than saturated steam of an equal temperature. The superheated steam, therefore, is heated considerably over its condensation temperature and becomes literally dried. In consequence, its action is more comparable to hot air than to saturated steam, and up to a certain temperature its disinfecting power is actually less than that of live steam at 100° C. Von Esmarch, who has made a thorough study of these conditions, concludes that up to 125° C., the efficiency of superheated steam is lower than that of live steam at 100° C. Above this temperature, of course, it is again active as in the case of ordinary dry heat.

PRACTICAL METHODS OF HEAT STERILIZATION.—*Burning.*—For objects to be destroyed or which can withstand incandescence, actual *burning* is a certain and easily applicable method of sterilization. Flaming, by passage through a Bunsen or an alcohol flame, is the method in use for the sterilization of platinum needles, cover slips, or other small objects which are used in handling bacteria in the laboratory.

HOT AIR.—Sterilization is carried out in the so-called "hot-air" chambers, simple devices of varied construction. The apparatus most commonly used consists of a sheet-iron, double-walled chamber, the joints of which, instead of being soldered, are closed by rivets. The inner case of this chamber is entirely closed except for an opening in the top through which a thermometer may be introduced, while the outer case has a large opening at the bottom and two smaller ones at the top. A gas-burner or electric heater is adjusted under this so as to play directly upon the bottom of the inner case or along the inner walls. A thermometer is fitted in the top in such a way that it penetrates into the inner chamber. The air in the chamber is heated directly by the flame or electric heating coil and by the hot air, which, rising from the flame, courses upward within the jacket between the two cases and escapes at the top. To insure absolute sterilization of objects in such a chamber, the temperature should be kept between 150° and 160° C. for at least an hour. In sterilizing combustible articles in such a chamber, it should be remembered that cotton is browned at a temperature of 200° C. and over. This method is used in laboratories for the sterilization of Petri dishes, flasks, test tubes, syringes and pipets, and for articles which may be injured by moisture. Both heating and subsequent cooling should be done gradually to avoid cracking of the glassware.

MOIST HEAT.—Instruments, syringes, and other suitable objects may be sterilized by *boiling* in water. Boiling for about five minutes is sufficient to destroy the vegetative forms of all bacteria. For the destruction of spores, boiling for one or two hours is usually sufficient, though the spores of certain saprophytes of the soil have been found occasionally to withstand the moist heat at a temperature of 100° C. for as long as sixteen hours. The addition of 1 per cent of sodium carbonate to boiling water hastens the destruction of spores and prevents the rusting of metal objects sterilized in this way. The addition of carbolic acid to boiling water in from 2 to 5 per cent concentration usually insures the destruction of anthrax spores, at least, within ten to fifteen minutes.

LIVE STEAM.—Exposure to live steam is probably the most practical of the methods of heat sterilization. It may be carried out by simple makeshifts of the kitchen, such as the use of potato-steamers or of wash boilers. For laboratory purposes, the original steaming device introduced by Koch has been almost completely displaced by devices constructed on the plan of the so-called "Arnold" sterilizer (Fig. 10). In such an apparatus, water is poured into the reservoir *A* and flows from there into the shallow receptacle *B*, *formed* by the double bottom. The flame underneath rapidly vaporizes the thin layer of water contained in *B*, and the steam rises rapidly, coursing through the main chamber *C*. Steam which escapes through the joints of the lid of this chamber is condensed under the hood and drops back into the reservoir. Exposure to steam in such an apparatus for fifteen to thirty minutes insures the death of the vegetative forms of bacteria.

FRACTIONAL STERILIZATION.—In the sterilization of media by such a device, the method of fractional sterilization at 100° C. is employed. The principle of this method depends upon repeated exposure of the media for fifteen minutes to one-half hour on three succeeding days. By the first exposure all vegetative forms are destroyed. The media may then be left at room temperature, or at incubator temperature (37.5° C.) until the following day, when any spores which may be present will have developed into the vegetative stage. These are then killed by the second exposure. A repetition of this procedure on a third day insures sterility. It must always be remembered, however, that this method is applicable only in cases in which the substance to be sterilized is a favorable medium for bacterial growth in which it is likely that spores will develop into vegetative forms.

Exceptionally the method may fail even in favorable media when anaerobic spore-forming bacteria are present. Thus, it has been observed that anaerobic spores, failing to develop under the aerobic conditions prevailing during the intervals of fractional sterilization, have developed after inoculation of the media with other bacteria, when symbiosis had made their growth possible. Tetanus bacilli have, in this way, occurred in cultures of diphtheria bacilli employed for toxin production. Furthermore, spores slightly injured by heat may require an unusually long time for germination.

In noting the period of an exposure in an Arnold sterilizer, it is important to time the process from the moment when the temperature has reached 100° C. and not from the time of lighting the flame.

The principle of *fractional sterilization* at low temperatures is applied also to the sterilization of substances which cannot be subjected to temperatures as high as 100° C. This is especially the case in the sterilization of media containing albuminous materials, when coagulation is to be avoided, or when both coagulation of the medium and sterilization are desired.

In such cases fractional sterilization may be practised in simply constructed sterilizers, such as a Koch inspissator or, in the case of fluids, such as blood serum, by immersion in a water bath at a temperature varying above 55° C., according to circumstances. Exposures at such low temperatures may be repeated on five or six consecutive days, usually for an hour each day.

STEAM UNDER PRESSURE.—The use of steam under pressure is the most powerful method of heat disinfection which we possess. It is applicable to the sterilization of fomites, clothing, or any objects of a size suitable to be contained in the apparatus at hand, and which are not injured by moisture. In laboratories this method is employed for the sterilization of infected apparatus, such as flasks, test-tubes, Petri plates, etc., containing cultures. The device most commonly used in laboratories is the so-called autoclave, of which a variety of models may be obtained, both stationary and portable. The principle governing the construction of all of these is the same. The apparatus usually consists of a gun-metal cylinder supplied with a lid, which can be tightly closed by screws or nuts, and supplied with a thermometer, a safety-valve, and a steam pressure gauge. In the simpler autoclaves, water may be directly filled into the lower part of the cylinder, and the objects to be sterilized supported upon a perforated diaphragm. In this case the heat is directly applied by means of a gas flame. In the more elaborate stationary devices, steam may be let in by piping it from the regular supply used for heating purposes. Exposure to steam under fifteen pounds pressure (fifteen in addition to the usual atmospheric pressure of fifteen pounds to the square inch) for fifteen to twenty minutes, is sufficient to kill all forms of bacterial life, including spores.

In applying autoclave sterilization practically, attention must be paid to certain technical details, neglect of which would result in failure of sterilization. It is necessary always to permit all air to escape from the autoclave before closing the vent. If this is not done, a poorly conducting air-packet may be left about the objects to be sterilized, and these may not be heated to the temperature indicated by the pressure. It is also necessary to allow the reduction of pressure, after sterilization, to take place slowly. Any sudden relief of pressure, such as would be produced by opening the air-vent while the pressure gauge is still above zero, will usually result in a sudden ebullition of fluid and a removal of stoppers from flasks.

The temperature attained by the application of various degrees of pressure is expressed in the following table:

Pounds Pressure	Temperature, Centigrade	Pounds Pressure	Temperature, Centigrade	Pounds Pressure	Temperature, Centigrade	Pounds Pressure	Temperature, Centigrade
1	102.3°	7	111.7°	13	119.1°	20	126.2°
2	104.2	8	113	14	120.2	22	128.1
3	105.7	9	114.3	15	121.3	24	129.3
4	107.3	10	115.6	16	122.4	26	131.5
5	108.8	11	116.8	17	123.3	28	133.1
6	110.3	12	118	18	124.3	30	134.6

Desiccation.—The abstraction of water from a bacterial cell sets up a series of chemical and physical changes which may or may not result in the death of the cell. The final outcome, as in so many other instances, depends upon the species of organism, the growth phase, the presence or absence of an endospore, the hydrogen-ion concentration of the environment, the gases in the atmosphere around the cell, the temperature and the rapidity with which the drying is accomplished. In addition, protective coatings of proteins or gelatinous capsules increase the resistance of bacteria to drying.

There are apparently several causes of the death or attenuation of organisms under the influence of desiccation. These are gradual denaturation of proteins, a destruction of enzymes, plasmolytic effects due to increased concentration of salts, and probably a germicidal action of oxygen, as suggested by Paul, Birstein and Reuss to explain the death of staphylococci dried on garnets.

Hammer, who found that bacteria frozen and dried in a vacuum retained their viability, recommended that vacuum desiccation at a low temperature be used to preserve pure cultures during long periods. This method has been successfully applied by Brown and Swift and by Flosdorf and Mudd in their "lyophile" apparatus. In this way virulence as well as other characters are preserved.

Preservation of cultures under sterile paraffin oil has been found to be effective and convenient, as shown by Lumière and Chevrotier, by Birkhaug and by Morton and Pulaski.

By the natural process of drying in air, vegetative forms of most pathogenic bacteria are killed within a few hours. Even the tubercle bacillus, which is somewhat more resistant than other bacteria, is killed by air desiccation within a few days. The danger of transmission of infection at a distance by the dried bodies of bacteria in the atmosphere exists but is not as important as it was formerly thought to be. Cleaning of walls and floors and natural desiccation have supplanted the older expensive and ineffectual processes of fumigation in the sanitation of premises previously occupied by patients with communicable disease.

Endospores, on the other hand, are extremely resistant to further desiccation. They survive for long periods in the air, soil and on dry fomites.

Light and Other Radiations.—Whether we regard radiation as waves or particles or both (and it is not for the bacteriologist to decide), the laws governing the action of radiation upon substances appear to be directly applicable to the bacteria. These laws state that only the rays absorbed are effective and that the effect produced is proportional to the intensity of the absorbed ray. Energy is transferred from the radiation to the absorbing medium. In the case of a living unicellular organism, it is not a matter of indifference what part of its substance absorbs the radiation. Absorption by an inert pigment will have little effect. Absorption by material which thereby produces a toxic substance, or absorption by nuclear particles or by material of "vital significance" to the cell will have profound effects upon the organism. The result may be a stimulation of growth, change or attenuation of certain properties, the production of variants or the death of the organism.

There is an immense literature on this subject. It has been reviewed in some detail in the eighth chapter of the book by Buchanan and Fulmer, to which we have referred. In this section we shall summarize only a part of the knowledge of the effects exerted upon bacteria by visible and ultraviolet light, x-rays and radium.

Light.—A sharp distinction must be drawn between the action of light upon the culture medium or fluid containing bacteria and the action upon the cells. It was the opinion of Downes and Blunt, who in 1877 first showed that sunlight killed bacteria, that death was caused by oxidation. Since then several investigators have found that hydrogen peroxide was formed in aqueous media exposed to *sunlight* and *ultraviolet light* and attributed the lethal action to the germicidal effect of peroxides. It has been disproved by experiment that oxygen is essential for the process and it appears to be definitely established that the action of peroxides is negligible.

On the other hand, there is abundant evidence, presented by Clark, Norton and others, that light exerts its effect by a direct photochemical action upon the bacteria exposed to it. We (Bayne-Jones and Van der Lingen) found that the temperature coefficient of the lethal action of ultraviolet light was sufficiently close to unity to suggest that the process was fundamentally a physical one. Clark regards it as a photo-electric effect, producing electronic and molecular changes leading to a coagulative denaturation of protein in the cell. Lisse and Tittsler have demonstrated that a reduction of the potential charge on *Bact. coli* accompanies death produced by ultraviolet light. This is in harmony with Clark's conception of the mechanism of the action.

After the demonstration by Downes and Blunt that sunlight killed bacteria, Koch showed that exposure to sunlight killed tubercle bacilli in two hours or less. The demonstration of the lethal action of sunlight through glass plates was made by Marshall Ward in 1892 and 1893. Long exposures of 2 to 6 hours were required to obtain the result.

Bacteria strongly absorb ultraviolet light of wave length 290 mμ and less. *Ultraviolet light* in the spectral region 280 to 254 mμ is especially effective in its lethal action on bacteria. The ultraviolet radiations in the Schumann region of the spectrum 125 to 170 mμ are also strongly germicidal.

In general, it may be said that visible light acting during a long time on bacteria exerts an inhibiting effect, and that ultraviolet light, in proportion to its absorption and energy exerts a lethal action, as shown by Gates' study of the effects of monochromatic radiations.

Every one who has investigated the effects of ultraviolet light upon bacteria has noticed an apparent increase in growth of organisms adjacent to areas on a plate in which the organisms have been killed. It is possible that this is evidence of a stimulative effect of radiations. Hollaender and Duggar found that sublethal doses of monochromatic ultraviolet radiation produced an apparent initial increase of colony-forming organisms and an extension of the lag phase.

Henri noted the appearance of "mutants" of the anthrax bacillus in cultures exposed to ultraviolet light. The possibility of the production of variants by the action of radiations will be discussed in Chapter IX.

The effect of ultraviolet rays of low intensity and of visible light can be re-enforced by *photodynamic sensitization*. Certain dyes, such as eosin and erythrosin, added to bacterial suspensions exposed to visible light cause the killing of bacteria by rays which would be otherwise relatively innocuous. This action, demonstrated by von Tappenheimer and investigated by Clark and others, is, in the opinion of Bedford, due to fluorescence and selective absorption of light and to peroxide formation.

Quartz is transparent to ultraviolet light, and glass of special composition can be made to transmit rays as short as 330 mμ. These radiations are completely absorbed by ordinary glass, by thin layers of fluids containing proteins, and by tissue cells. They do not penetrate tissue to a depth greater than 1 mm. In the practical use of ultraviolet light as a germicide, these matters must be taken into consideration.

Various types of mercury vapor arcs and carbon arc lamps emitting ultraviolet light are in use to sterilize the air in surgical operating rooms (Hart), and to sterilize drinking water, water in swimming pools and other materials containing bacteria which can be exposed directly to the radiations or brought under their influence in thin layers in quartz vessels. Heliotherapy and ultraviolet light therapy are based in part upon the known germicidal action of light of short wave length. They depend for their success, however, almost entirely upon an increase in the defensive powers of the animal built up through a complex series of reactions under the stimulus of these radiations.

Polarized light is not injurious to bacteria. It was found by Bhatnagar and Lal to stimulate the growth of *B. coli* and *Vibrio cholerae*.

In spite of a considerable amount of investigation of the effects of *x-rays* upon bacteria, the reports are still too contradictory to permit generalizations. Wyckoff and others have found that x-rays kill bacteria. On the other hand, Dozois, Tittsler, Lisse and Davey, using the total radiation from a Coolidge x-ray tube at 30 K.V.R.M.S. (without filters) did not detect any change in the electrophoretic migration velocity or viability of *B. coli* with exposures as great as 3000 milliampere-minutes at 15.2 cm. target distance. This dose was about 100 times as great as that applied by Wyckoff. It is possible that fluorescent light of wave length 231 to 390 mμ excited by x-rays acting upon the container or the materials enclosing bacteria may play a part in the lethal action which has been occasionally observed (Newcomer). According to Claus, the lethal effect of x-rays on *B. coli* is enhanced in the presence of inorganic salts.

Cathode rays were found by Wyckoff and Rivers to kill *Bact. coli, Bact. aertrycke* and *Staphylococcus aureus*. It was calculated that the absorption of a single 155 kilovolt electron killed the cell.

The evidence on the effect of *radium* upon bacteria is conflicting. Numerous investigators have failed to find that rays from radioactive substance kill bacteria. On the other hand, radium and radium-emanation have been found by Dorn, Baumann and Valentiner, Chambers and Russ and others to kill *B. coli, Staphylococcus aureus*, the tubercle bacillus and other pathogenic bacteria after long exposures of 1 to 4 hours. The lethal action was attributed to the α and β particles. The γ-rays are apparently harmless. It is possible that these radiations may stimulate growth or promote variation in bacteria (Spencer).

The possibility that bacteria may be stimulated by the *"mitogenetic rays"* of Gurwitsch has been discussed in Chapter V.

Electric Current.—An *electric current* passing through a suspension of bacteria carries the organisms to the positive pole, by virtue of the negative charge on the cells, as we have shown in Chapter V. In the same place we have reviewed the measurements of the conductance of bacteria and have found that the resistance of the organisms is usually greater than that of the fluid in which they are suspended. It is obvious, therefore, that in the passage of an electric current through a suspension of bacteria, heating and electrolytic effects will be produced upon the suspending medium and also within the cells. Bacteria and their spores can be killed by the passage of a sufficiently strong current through a suspension of them. Gelpi and Devereux and others are of the opinion that a directly lethal action is exerted by the current upon the organisms and that changes in the medium are only contributory. Beattie and Lewis in 1913 introduced this method of electrical sterilization of milk. It has been applied in the "electropure" process of "pasteurization." This method has not had any extended trial in the treatment of infections, but Grossman and Appleton have investigated the possibility of the electrosterilization of tissues.

Pressure.—In Chapter V we have considered the effects of changes of *osmotic pressure.* By sudden and large reductions of osmotic pressure bacteria can be destroyed by *plasmoptysis.* Similar extremes of increased osmotic pressure, produced by transferring bacteria from dilute to concentrated solutions, *plasmolyze* the cells, but do not always kill them. In fact, bacteria appear to be unusually resistant to changes in osmotic pressure.

Mechanical pressure applied to bacteria in suspension does not disrupt them, since it acts equally from all sides. Enormous pressures have been applied without killing the organisms. Larson, Hartzell and Diehl used pressures ranging from 3000 to 12,000 atmospheres. Pressures up to 3000 atmospheres did not kill bacilli and cocci. A pressure of 6000 atmospheres per square inch killed all the non-spore-forming organisms in fourteen hours, but the spores of *Bacillus subtilis* were not regularly killed by pressures up to 12,000 atmospheres in this time.

Sudden release of pressure, especially when gases are present, destroys bacteria. The rapid expansion of gas dissolved in the cells ruptures them. Application of this method to obtain disintegrated cells for the preparation of vaccines has been described by Crowther, following the observations of Larson, Hartzell and Diehl.

Agitation and Trituration.—Mechanical action which disrupts the organization of the cells will kill bacteria. Shaking may effect the state of protoplasm of the cell or may be violent enough to fracture the cell membrane. Trituration of bacteria, by grinding them in a mortar with sand, or in a vessel with glass beads, is a well known procedure used to reduce the cells to fragments for the purpose of extracting their contents. Bacteria, however, are resistant to mechanical action of this sort. It is usually necessary to freeze the bacteria and to continue the grinding process for a long time in order to break up the cells.

Supersonic vibrations, produced by sound waves of frequencies of the order of 290,000 per second, have a most destructive effect upon cells and unicellular organisms. These high-frequency sound waves, produced by piezo-electric oscillations, shake cells and organisms into nonviable fragments. It is probable that oxidation is produced by the hydrogen peroxide formed in water subjected to sonic energy, as shown by Flosdorf, Chambers and Malisoff. At the same time, it is probable that cavitation is produced by liberated gas, as suggested by Schmidt and Uhlmeyer. The profound physiological effects of these high-frequency, high-intensity sound waves have been studied by Wood and Loomis, Johnson and others. They have been used in practice by Chambers and Gaines to sterilize milk. Rivers, Sonadel and Chambers inactivated the elementary bodies of vaccinia by sonic vibrations with a frequency of about 8900 cycles per second. In this process the elementary bodies were not disrupted.

As we have discussed *surface tension* in Chapter V and shall consider it in several subsequent chapters, we shall not do more than mention it here. However difficult it may be to separate the chemical action of substances from the physical effects of changes in surface tension produced by them, the fact remains that surface tension is one of the important physical forces which determine the properties and behavior of bacteria.

REFERENCES

BAYNE–JONES, S., and VAN DER LINGEN, J. S. Johns Hopkins Hosp. Bull., 1923, 34:11.

BHATNAGAR, S. S., and LAL, R. B. Nature, 1926, 117:302.

BEATTIE, J. M., and LEWIS, F. C. Med. Res. Comm. Spec. Rep. Ser. No. 49, London, 1920.

BEDFORD, T. H. B. Brit. J. Exper. Pathol., 1927, 8:437.

BIRKHAUG, K. E. Science, 1932, 76:236.

BOAK, R. A., CARPENTER, C. M., and WARREN, S. L. J. Exper. M., 1932, 56:741.

BROWN, J. H. Abs. Bacteriol., 1926, 9:8.

BUCHANAN, R. E., and FULMER, E. I. Physiology and Biochemistry of Bacteria, Baltimore, 1930, 2:1–206.

CARPENTER, C. M., BISHOP, F. W., and WARREN, S. L. J. Exper. M., 1932, 56:719.

CHAMBERS, H., and RUSS, S. Proc. Roy. Soc., London, B, 1912, 84:124.

CHAMBERS, L. A., and GAINES, N. Scient. Am., 1932, 146:367.

CHICK, H. J. Hyg., 1910, 10:237.

CLARK, J. H. Physiol. Rev., 1923, 2:277.

CLAUS, W. D. J. Exper. M., 1933, 57:335.

CROWTHER, D. J. Ind. & Eng. Chem., 1932, 10:43.

CROZIER, W. J. J. Gen. Physiol., 1924, 7:189.

———— Proc. Nat. Acad. Sc., Washington, 1924, 10:461.

DORN, E., BAUMANN, E., and VALENTINER, S. Ztschr. f. Hyg. u. Infektionskrankh., 1905, 51:328.

DOWNES, A., and BLUNT, T. P. Proc. Roy. Soc., London, B, 1877, 26:488; 1878–9, 28:199.

DOZOIS, K. P., TITTSLER, R. P., LISSE, M. W., and DAVEY, W. J. Bacteriol., 1932, 24:123.

EDWARDS, O. F., and RETTGER, L. F. J. Bacteriol., 1937, 34:489.

ESTY, J. R. Newer Knowledge of Bacteriology and Immunology, Chicago, 1928, Chap. 21, pp. 285–300.

FLOSDORF, E. W., and MUDD, S. J. Immunol., 1935, 29:389.

———— CHAMBERS, L. A., and MALISOFF, W. M. J. Am. Chem. Soc., 1936, 58:1069.

GATES, F. L. J. Gen. Physiol., 1929, 13:231, 249.

GELPI, A. J., and DEVEREUX, S. D. Science, 1932, 76:391.

GROSSMAN, L. I., and APPLETON, J. L. T. Dental Cosmos, 1931, 73: 147, 250, 370, 482.

HAAS, H. Prag. med. Wchnschr., 1876, 1:639, 659, 676.

HAMMER, B. W. J. Med. Research, 1911, 24:527.

HAMPIL, B. Quart. Rev. Biol., 1932, 7:172.

HART, D. Arch. Surg., 1937, 34:874.

———— J. Thoracic Surg., 1938, 7:525.

HENRI, V. Compt. rend. Acad. d. sc., Paris, 1914, 158:1032.

HILL, C. McD., and CLARK, J. H. Am. J. Hyg., 1927, 7:448.

HOLLAENDER, A., and DUGGAR, R. M. J. Bacteriol., 1938, **36:17.**

HUTCHINS, R. H., and WHEELER, A. W. Am. J. M. Sc., 1903, 126:680.

JOHNSON, C. H. J. Physiol., 1929, 67:356.

KOCH, R. Proc. X. Internat. Med. Congress, Berlin, 1890.

KOCH, R., and WOLFFHUEGEL, G. Mitt. a.d. Kaiserlich. Gesndthsamte., 1881, 1, No. 8.

LARSON, W. P. Newer Knowledge of Bacteriology and Immunology, Chicago, 1928, Chap. 9, p. 179.

LARSON, W. P., HARTZELL, T. B., and DIEHL, H. S. J. Infect. Dis., 1918, 22:271.

LEWITH, S. Arch. f. exper. Path. u. Pharmakol., 1890, 26:341.

LISSE, M. W., and TITTSLER, R. P. Technical Bull. No. 276, 1932. Penn. State College, School of Agriculture and Experimental Station.

LUMIÈRE, A., and CHEVROTIER, J. C. r. acad. sci., 1914, 158:1820.

MAGOON, C. A. J. Bacteriol., 1926, 11:253.

MORTON, H. E., and PULASKI, E. J. J. Bacteriol., 1938, 35:163.

Newcomer, H. S.   J. Exper. M., 1917, 26:657.
Norton, J. F.   Newer Knowledge of Bacteriology and Immunology, Chicago, 1928, Chap. 29
    pp. 371–377.
Park, W. H.   J. Am. M. Ass., 1907, 49:731.
Paul, T., Birstein, G., and Reuss, A.   Biochem. Ztschr., 1910, 25:367.
Rivers, T. M., Smadel, J. E., and Chambers, L. A.   J. Exper. Med., 1937, 65:677.
Schmidt, F. O., and Uhlmeyer, B.   Proc. Soc. Exper. Biol. & Med., 1930, 27:626.
Spencer, R. R.   U. S. Public Health Reports, Washington, 1934, 49:183; 1935, 50:1642.
Stabler, S. H.   Am. J. Hyg., 1931, 14:433.
Swift, H. F.   J. Exper. M., 1921, 33:69.
Tanner, F. W.   Bacteriology, New York, 1928, pp. 186–199.
Von Esmarch, E.   Ztschr. f. Hyg., 1888, 4:197, 398.
Von Tappenheimer, H.   Ergebn., d. Physiol., 1909, 8:726.
Ward, H. M.   Proc. Roy. Soc., London, B., 1892, 52: 393; 1893, 53:23.
Wood, R. W., and Loomis, A. L.   Phil. Mag., 1927, 4:417.
Wyckoff, R. W. G.   J. Exper. M., 1930, 52:435, 769.
Wyckoff, R. W. G., and Rivers, T. M.   J. Exper. M., 1930, 51:921.

CHAPTER VIII

THE EFFECTS OF CHEMICAL AGENTS ON BACTERIA

DISINFECTION

General Effects of Chemical Environment.—The responsiveness of bacteria to their chemical environment has been illustrated by many examples cited in the preceding chapters of this book. It has been shown that their composition, physical properties, metabolism, growth, death and morphology are influenced by chemical substances in the natural or artificial media in which bacteria occur. This influence is so profound and widespread that it is, in fact, impossible to deal adequately with any property of bacteria without taking into consideration, directly or indirectly, the factors of chemical environment. Buchanan and Fulmer have summarized in a systematic treatise a large amount of the information on this subject, including the effects of both nutritional and non-nutritional substances. Since we have already dealt with some of these nutritional effects and shall consider others in subsequent chapters, our purpose here will be to describe a few of the general non-nutritional actions of chemicals upon bacteria and to consider in some detail their injurious effects, under the general topic of disinfection.

Water.—In 1898, Ficker showed that distilled water is toxic for some bacteria. Since then, experiments have confirmed the general truth of this statement. At the same time they have brought to light a complexity of conditions. Probably few tests have been made with absolutely pure neutral water. It has been found that the rate of death of bacteria in water is increased greatly by increased hydrogen-ion concentration, at pH 4, and increased also in alkaline water (Winslow and Falk) at pH 8. Traces of copper and other metals, traces of salts, and protective colloids or other substances yielded by the bacteria affect their rate of death in water. As bacteria are resistant to changes in osmotic pressure, their immersion in water does not readily destroy them by plasmoptysis. Undoubtedly, however, diffusion rates are affected by a transference of the organisms from a saline solution to water. As suspensions of bacteria in water are used at times in various tests, and as many compounds in aqueous solution are applied to bacteria, it is necessary to be aware of the possible toxic effect of water (Winslow and Brooke) and to guard against it.

The survival of bacteria in natural waters of streams and lakes is a different matter. Organisms, such as the typhoid bacillus, may survive in natural waters four or five days (Jordan). But these waters are really dilute complex solutions and may contain nutriment.

Salt Effects.—In low concentrations nearly all inorganic salts stimulate bacterial growth. As the concentration is increased these salts become toxic, injuring the cells in one way or another and finally killing them. The action we refer to here is distinct from any lethal effects of osmotic pressure, to which, as we have shown, bacteria are

98

resistant. The effects are referable to the ions of these electrolytes in their action upon the cell membrane, influence upon permeability, physical state of the protoplasm, effect upon endogenous catabolism and the activities of cellular enzymes. It has been known for a long time that sodium chloride is relatively toxic for bacterial cells. Fabian and Winslow, in a study of the influence upon viability of various anions in combination with sodium, have demonstrated that both the stimulative effects of numerous sodium salts in low concentration and their toxic action in higher concentration are due to their sodium content. In the inhibiting effect the hydrogen-ion concentration was of equal importance. Winslow and Dolloff, after extensive investigations of the effects of electrolytes upon bacterial viability, have come to the conclusion that the influence of sodium, potassium, magnesium, calcium —a wide variety of metallic cations—is qualitatively identical, varying only in degree. A great deal has been written about the physiologically antagonistic effects of ions. There is some evidence that the toxic action of an ion can be neutralized by another different ion. Winslow and his associates have questioned this doctrine of ion antagonism as applied to bacteria. They noted evidence of quantitative antagonism, but under the conditions of their experiments, found that the qualitative effects of all cations were alike. From these studies there has come a large amount of information applicable to the analysis and control of disinfection. Electrolytes alter the charge on bacteria (Winslow and Fleeson) affect permeability and diffusion (Shaughnessy and Winslow), and exert direct toxic actions. The salts we have been considering here are not usually classed as antiseptics or germicides in the concentrations used in these experiments. Nevertheless, they play a sufficiently important part in the disinfection process to require careful attention. The addition of one of these electrolytes to a germicide may increase or decrease the action of the germicide through an effect upon the dissociation of the germicide as well as through actions upon the bacterial cells. The different results obtained by various methods of testing germicides can be explained in part by these salt-actions.

Theoretical Considerations of Disinfection.—Since the time of Koch's fundamental researches upon chemical disinfection a very large literature has accumulated on this subject. For reviews of it the reader is referred to the works of Buchanan and Fulmer, Chick, Reichel and Bürgi and Laubenheimer (see references).

Koch noted that in general the injurious action of certain chemicals was an orderly process requiring time for its completion, that its rate was increased by increase in temperature and that there were differences between the concentrations of substances required to inhibit the growth of bacteria and those required to kill them. The process was further studied in detail in 1897 by Krönig and Paul, who devised methods which have been followed in principle, but with varying technical differences, in most of the subsequent investigations. This principle, stated in the words of Chick, is "the exposure of a measured number of living bacteria to some disinfectant and enumeration of the survivors by means of plate cultures from time to time until disinfection is complete." [1] We shall see that it is often desirable and sufficient to determine the end-point of a disinfection process by simple transfers to broth media or by inoculation of animals. But for certain quantitative work in the analysis of the process, enumeration of viable bacteria is essential. Many examples

[1] H. Chick, *A System of Bacteriology in Relation to Medicine*, London, 1930, Vol. 1, Chapter V, p. 178.

of the disinfection process can be illustrated graphically by the curves reproduced in Fig. 11, reproduced from Chick's article, showing the time-survivor relationships of anthrax spores in 5 per cent phenol at 33.3° C. From this it is seen that the initial rapid reduction in the number of viable organisms is followed by a gradual reduction until all are killed. It is apparent that there is a relationship between the number of bacteria surviving in unit volume and the time which had elapsed. The graph of the logarithms of the concentration of survivors plotted agianst time is a straight line. These data seem to indicate that the disinfection process is governed by the law of mass action and that it may be a monomolecular reaction. Chick has shown, however, that other cases of disinfection do not fit into this scheme. Falk and Winslow have analyzed some of the deviations from this logarithmic order and have emphasized the point of view, in which all agree, that the process is so complex that mathematical formulation, when possible, may be very suggestive but is incapable of stating the whole sequence of events.

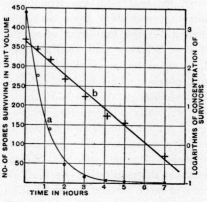

FIG. 10.—DISINFECTION OF ANTHRAX SPORES WITH 5 PER CENT PHENOL.

Curve *a*, survivor time curve. Curve *b*, logarithms of concentration of survivors (from Chick).

In our opinion, disinfection by chemicals is primarily a chemical process, subject to the individual peculiarities of the bacteria and subject to the influences exerted by physical forces upon both components of the reaction—the chemical and the bacterial. We may list, with comments, the most important factors to be considered, as follows:

A. *Factors relating to the chemical disinfectant:*
1. Chemical nature of the substance, inorganic, organic, structure.
2. Ionization constant.
3. Concentration.
4. Solubility in the menstruum and in bacterial cellular constituents.
5. Affinities for bacterial cell protoplasm or constituents.
6. Mode of action, oxidation, precipitation, etc.

B. *Factors relating to the bacteria:*
1. Species of organism.
2. Chemical composition of the organism.
3. Growth phase, especially in relation to differences in susceptibility of young cells as compared with old cells or differences between cells of same age. Young cells are often more susceptible than older ones.
4. Special structures, spores, capsules.
5. Previous history of the culture. Resistant forms can be selected or produced by gradually increased exposure to toxic agents.
6. Dissociation in relation to differences in susceptibility.
7. Number of bacteria in the test mixtures.

C. *General factors affecting both components and the process as a whole:*
1. Temperature. The temperature coefficient of disinfection is high. $Q_{10} = 2$ to 5.
2. Surface phenomena, especially adsorption and surface tension, and the relationship of

these to changes in concentration of substances in interfacial films, changes in permeability and diffusion.

3. Hydrogen-ion concentration.
4. Presence of other electrolytes, which influence both ionization of the chemical and the properties of the cells.
5. Presence of organic substances, especially proteins, which may react with the substance or form protective films in the organisms, usually reducing the action of the disinfectant.
6. Pressure. Important in some cases, especially in reference to gaseous substances.
7. Time.

These factors influence the disinfection process both in the test tube and in the animal body. In the animal, however, a large number of additional factors come into play. We shall consider these later.

It seems to us obvious that no one theory can be made sufficiently comprehensive at present to include all of these elements. The analogy between disinfection and a chemical reaction indicates the fundamental nature of the process. Our purpose in this exposition is clearly stated in the words of Chick, as follows: "Although the correct interpretation of the observed phenomena in disinfection is a matter of theoretical importance as promising an insight into the life-processes of the bacterial cell, the important matter from the practical point of view is to realize that the process is a gradual one and that in any collection of bacteria a minority will survive very much longer than the majority and on these attention must be focused in order to obtain security from infection." [2]

We have been using the term "disinfection" as if its meaning were clearly understood. Unfortunately, that is not the case. Patterson has emphasized the historical fact that the words "disinfectant" and "antiseptic" came into use before the nature and activities of bacteria were known. Changes in the knowledge of micro-organisms have clothed these words with layers of meanings. For the sake of precision, we shall state here the modern acceptable definitions, quoting from Patterson's paper and other sources.

1. *Disinfectant.*—"An agent that frees from infection." A disinfectant is usually a chemical agent which destroys bacteria or other micro-organisms. In our opinion there is no point in limiting this term to substances used to destroy only harmful or pathogenic micro-organisms, or to exclude bacterial spores from the field of activity of substances called disinfectants. It is customary to speak of disinfection by light, heat and chemicals, all these physical and chemical procedures having a common property in the killing of all forms of micro-organism, both vegetative and spore. The mechanism of lethal action is not important in the definition, since the result characterizes the substance or agent.

It is necessary again to qualify this definition by reference to the factors of time, temperature, concentration, etc., which we have listed above. A substance which in sufficient concentration and acting under favorable conditions kills bacteria, may when in low concentration either stimulate or, as is more usual, inhibit bacterial life-processes without actually killing the organisms.

It is apparent, therefore, that although we shall be able to establish categories of processes and results, we shall not be able to make hard and fast classifications of substances under these definitions.

Synonyms.—Germicide, bactericide; germicidal, bactericidal.

2. *Antiseptic.*—"A substance that opposes sepsis, putrefaction or decay" by preventing or arresting the growth or action of micro-organisms. An antiseptic may prevent growth by inhibiting reproduction or by destroying the organisms. In low concentration a substance may inhibit growth:

2 *Ibid.*

in high concentration it may kill bacteria. Attention is called to the numerous factors which influence these actions. In a statement from the U. S. Department of Agriculture, dated June 18, 1928, issued under the federal Food and Drug Act, time or duration of application was emphasized. Salves, ointments and dressings which remain in contact with the body for long periods were admitted to be antiseptics if they *inhibited* the growth of bacteria. Mouth washes, douches, gargles and preparations of like nature, which are in contact with the body for but brief periods of time, were permitted to be called antiseptics only if they *destroyed* bacteria in the dilutions recommended and in a comparably brief period. This is an example of a practical definition, with emphasis on the factor of time and, of course, concentration.

In our opinion the term antisepsis connotes inhibition rather than destruction of bacteria. Synonyms.—Bacteriostatic, bacteriostasis.

3. *Sterilization.*—The process of freeing material from micro-organisms, vegetative, spore and virus forms. Chemical and physical agents sterilize by destruction of bacteria. Filtration sterilizes by mechanical removal of micro-organisms.

4. *Asepsis.*—The prevention of access of micro-organisms to materials. Bacteriological asepsis, in seeking to prevent all kinds of micro-organisms from getting into materials is more exclusive than surgical asepsis, which guards chiefly against the entrance of pathogenic bacteria into wounds.

For the sake of completeness, we should mention *deodorant.* A deodorant is a substance or thing that destroys or masks offensive odors. Deodorants may or may not have antiseptic or disinfectant properties. Their function is to replace one smell by another and, of course, have nothing to do with killing bacteria or preventing infection. Nevertheless, in this connection popular belief still clings to old miasmatic notions and the outmoded sewer-gas school of etiological thought.

The methods of testing, standardizing and comparing disinfectants vary in different countries, in different states in this country, and in different laboratories everywhere. In addition, it is necessary to employ various methods suitable both to the substances and the vehicles in which they are incorporated. Most of these methods of standardization are based on comparing the action of the particular disinfectant or antiseptic to some commonly used substance under identical conditions. Many years ago, phenol was chosen as a substance of reference and the ratio of the action of the tested substance to that of phenol became known as the "phenol coefficient." The first "carbolic acid coefficient" method to come into general use was that devised about 1900 by Rideal and Walker. It is still used, particularly in England. A modification of this method by Anderson and McClintic became widely used in the United States under the name of the Hygienic Laboratory Method. Newer methods, with the backing of law, are replacing the Hygienic Laboratory Method in this country. Such methods are those in use in the laboratories of the Food and Drug Administration of the U. S. Department of Agriculture, under which supervision of all antiseptics and disinfectants shipped in interstate commerce has been placed by federal law. The procedures used for testing disinfectants by the "F.D.A. Methods" were developed by Shippen and Reddish and are set forth in detail in an official publication of the Department of Agriculture, from which we shall quote extensively in the section on technical procedures in this book. The F.D.A. phenol-coefficient method requires tests of antiseptic or disinfectant action against strains of *B. typhosus* and *Staphylococcus aureus* of known susceptibility to phenol. Provisions are made also for tests in the presence of organic materials and a "cup-plate" method applicable to salves, toothpastes and other commercial products composed of chemicals incorporated in more or less inert materials. These methods have aided in securing standardized procedures.

The following tabulated differences between the F.D.A., Rideal-Walker and

Hygienic Laboratory methods is quoted from Circular No. 198 of the U. S. Department of Agriculture.

DIFFERENCES IN MEDIA AND MANIPULATION OF THE THREE METHODS OF DETERMINING PHENOL COEFFICIENT

Item	F. D. A. Method	R–W Method	H. L. Method
Composition of medium.	Peptone,* 10 gm. Liebig's beef extract, 5 gm. Salt, 5 gm. Water, 1,000 c. c. Boil 20 minutes	Peptone, † 20 gm. Liebig's beef extract, 10 gm. Salt, 10 gm. Water, 1,000 c. c. Boil 20 minutes	Peptone,* 10 gm. Liebig's beef extract, 3 gm. Salt, 5 gm. Water, 1,000 c. c. Boil 15 minutes.
Acidity of medium......	pH 6.8.	+ 1.5. No definite pH	Unadjusted but pH between 6.0 and 7.0.
Amount of culture medium in tube...........	10 c. c.	5 c. c.	10 c. c.
Amount of culture added to diluted disinfectant.	0.5 c. c. to 5.0 c. c.	0.5 c.c. to 50 c.c.	0.1 c. c. to 5.0 c. c.
Resistance of test culture to phenol (dilutions killing in 10 minutes but not in 5 minutes)..	1–90.	1–90 to 1–110.	No limits stated.
Condition of tube in test.	Plugged with cotton.	Plugged with cotton.	Open tubes.
Temperature of test......	20° C.	15–18° C.	20° C.
Time intervals of the test.	5, 10, and 15 minutes.	2½, 5, 7½, and 10 minutes.	5, 7½, 10, 12½, and 15 minutes.
Amount of medication mixture transferred (size of loop)	4 mm. loop (of No. 23 B and S. gage wire).	4 mm. loop (of No. 27 Imperial gage wire).	Spiral loop (four spirals wrapped around a No. 13 B. and S. gage wire. Made of No. 23 B. and S. gage wire).
Calculation of phenol efficient	Highest dilution not killing in 5 minutes but killing in 10 minutes divided by same for phenol.	Highest dilution not killing in 5 minutes but killing in 7½ minutes divided by same for phenol.	Mathematical mean of highest dilutions showing no growth in 5, 10, and 15 minutes divided by same for phenol.

* Armour's. Special batch set aside for disinfectant testing.   † Allen and Hanbury's.

Since different substances act upon bacteria in different ways, inhibiting or killing them by oxidation, coagulation or by other means, and since these substances are affected differently by the same factors, it is misleading to compare all substances to phenol. Phenol coefficients give information useful for orientation and for the satisfaction of legal requirements. It is often advisable, however, to extend the comparison to substances of fundamentally similar constitution, as in the cases of mercurials and silver salts, or to a series of homologues, as in the alcohols and resorcinols. Furthermore, the values of phenol coefficients do not indicate the value of an antiseptic or disinfectant as a chemotherapeutic agent. The conditions in or upon an infected animal are immensely more complex than those reproducible in the test tube. Claims for the efficacy of the substance in killing or inhibiting bacteria in or upon the animal body must be substantiated by tests made *in vivo*. Such tests on animals are recognized procedures of chemotherapy.

The inhibition of gas production by yeast, observed by Dreser in 1917, was used by Pilcher and Sollmann as a means of comparing the activity of disinfectants. It was included in the U. S. Pharmacopoeia (Revision X) as a useful means of standardizing silver compounds, comparing them with silver nitrate. Later, Peterson used the method to standardize and classify mercurials, comparing their disinfectant action with that of mercuric chloride. The method was improved by Branham, who tested the inhibitory activity of a number of related and unrelated compounds. The method is simple and rapid and provides useful information.

Data on Antiseptics and Disinfectants.—Antiseptics and disinfectants have many practical uses in the preservation of decomposable organic materials, the sterilization of inanimate objects, and, in medicine and surgery, for prevention and treatment of infections. A vast array of chemical compounds and commercial preparations, many of which are exploited with exaggerated claims, might be passed in review. The space available here permits our recording brief comments on only a few of these substances. We shall not define the conditions of time, temperature and other factors influencing the action of these disinfectants, since we have repeatedly referred to them. Phenol coefficients, determined according to the methods referred to above, express values obtained at 20° C.

Acids.—The mineral acids have disinfectant powers proportional to their degree of dissociation in solution. They owe their action chiefly to the hydrogen-ion concentration which they produce. A 0.2 per cent solution of sulphuric acid kills *B. typhosus* in water in about one hour. Boric acid, less dissociated, is usually employed as an antiseptic in 1 to 2 per cent solutions. Nitric and fluoric acids exert an anti-bacterial effect through their anions as well as through the hydrogen-ion.

Organic acids, though less dissociated in solution than mineral acids, are sometimes more active as disinfectants. Thus benzoic acid is about seven times as effective as hydrochloric acid, showing that either the whole molecule or the organic radical has a disinfecting capacity (Reid).

Alkalis.—Disinfectant action of alkalis is proportional to dissociation and therefore to the resultant OH-ion concentration, as a rule. Some hydroxides, however, such as barium hydroxide, are more actively disinfectant than their degree of dissociation would indicate. In these cases the metallic cation exerts a direct toxic action on the bacteria. The OH-ion is less toxic than the H-ion. One per cent NaOH or KOH solution kills the vegetative forms of bacteria within five minutes. Spores of anthrax bacilli are killed in 10 minutes by 30 per cent NaOH. Tubercle bacilli are more resistant than other vegetative forms and many spores to the action of alkalis. Use is made of this property of tubercle bacilli to obtain them from sputum and feces freed from contamination with other bacteria by treating the material with 2 to 4 per cent NaOH for one-half hour at 37° C. Alkalis dissolve most bacteria.

Some organic bases are disinfectant, but are not used extensively.

Combinations of fatty acids with sodium, producing various *soaps*, have distinct and valuable properties. The action of soaps is due in part to free alkali contained in the preparations, to the constituents of the soap, and to the concordant effect of the reduction in surface tension produced by the soap, provided the degree of surface tension reduction is optimal for interaction of other components of the mixtures with bacterial substance. The antiseptic properties of soaps have been investigated by Walker, who found the hemolytic streptococci, and especially pneumococci, were susceptible to laurate, oleate and linoleate soaps. Larson and Nelson found that sodium ricinoleate killed the streptococci of scarlet fever and neutralized scarlatinal toxin. These actions of soaps are complex processes, depending upon both the alkali and the organic radical produced on hydrolysis. Eggert, who investigated various soap derivatives, and hydroxy soaps, found compounds which have relatively specific germicidal action upon hemolytic streptococci, staphylococci, *B. typhosus* and *B. coli.*

Hampil has shown that soaps inhibit the bactericidal action of phenolic germicides. On the other hand, the germicidal action of mercuric chloride and certain other mercurials was enhanced by the presence of soaps. This effect was most marked against *Staphylococcus aureus.* The germicidal action of mercurials against *B. typhosus* and related organisms was not increased in the mixtures with soap.

Oxidizing Agents.—We shall consider here the substances which owe their disinfectant action to oxygen. Ozone and nascent oxygen liberated by various compounds destroy bacteria. In practice the chief oxidizing disinfectants are peroxides, potassium permanganate, sodium borate, and probably the hypochlorites. *Peroxide of hygdrogen* is an active disinfectant in water. The commercial preparations vary from 3 to 30 per cent solutions of H_2O_2. The 3 per cent by weight solution of H_2O_2 of the U.S.P.X. will kill vegetative forms of bacteria within a few minutes, depending upon the amount of inert inorganic material present in the mixtures. *Potassium permanganate* is a strong disinfectant but readily combines with inert organic matter. *Sodium perborate* used as an antiseptic in the treatment of some types of gingivitis is, in our opinion, overrated.

Many bacterial toxins lose their poisonous properties when oxidized, as shown by Neill. It seems not unlikely that more use of oxidizing agents may be made in the future in the treatment of bacterial intoxications.

Halogens.—Free Cl, Br, I and F are highly toxic to bacteria in the order listed here. In practice the chief use has been made of the disinfecting properties of *chlorine* and *iodine.* As the chlorine-ion is not toxic, the disinfectant action of chlorine compounds depends almost entirely upon free *chlorine* liberated from them or, in the case of the oxyacids, partly upon oxidation. Chlorine gas is used for disinfection. On a large scale it is applied to the "sterilization" of drinking water and purification of water of swimming pools. To kill the vegetative forms of colon-typhoid organisms a concentration of at last 1 part per million of free chlorine must be maintained. As chlorine readily combines with organic matter, its action is deflected by such material in the water. Free chlorine may be added to water from cylinders of the gas or derived from hypochlorites, such as *chloride of lime* (calcium hypochlorite).

Chloride of lime is probably a single compound with the formula $CaOCl_2$. The action of acids or even of atmospheric carbon dioxide upon this substance results in the liberation of chlorine. For instance:

$$Ca(OCl)_2 + 2HCl = CaCl_2 + 2HOCl$$
$$2HOCl \quad + 2HCl = 2H_2O + 2Cl_2$$

Hypochlorous acid may also decompose with the liberation of oxygen as shown in the following equation:

$$2HClO = 2HCl + O_2$$

It is conceivable that some of the disinfecting value of chloride of lime and hypochlorites in general is really due to the vigorous oxidizing action resulting from this decomposition. On the other hand, there is much evidence to show that chlorine may attack the protein molecule directly by replacing "H" in the amino groups, thus:

$$—R—CO—NH—R— \quad\quad + Cl = R—CO—NCl—R— \quad\quad + H$$

The chloramines thus formed seem to be toxic and result in the death of the bacteria. Bleaching powder is readily soluble in about twenty parts of water. Its bactericidal action depends on the hypochlorous acid formed. After water precipitation, an efficient dosage is ten pounds to the million gallons. The high germicidal action of chloride of lime, together with its relatively low cost, suggested its use as a wound dressing. Solutions of calcium or sodium hypochlorite were found to be too irritating to be practicable, owing to the alkalinity of any available preparations. It has been possible to prepare neutral and comparatively nonirritating solutions of sodium hypochlorite by several different methods. The most famous of these is *Dakin's Solution*, which was used extensively during the World War of 1914-1918.

The chlorine antiseptics in general, and particularly the hypochlorite type, have the disadvantage of exerting their disinfectant action over an exceedingly short space of time. The reaction between the hypochlorite solution and the proteins of the bacterial body or of the serum and pus in the wound, is almost instantaneous, and having taken place, no further toxic action is shown. It is, therefore, necessary in treating wounds with these solutions to repeat the application at frequent intervals, or else to apply through some sort of a continuous feed apparatus so that a fresh supply of the antiseptic is brought in contact with the wound at short intervals.

In order to overcome this disadvantage to some extent, Dakin prepared a number of different organic chlorine compounds which were soluble in oil, and which yielded up the chlorine rather slowly to the wound secretions, so that the action continued over a comparatively long time. *Chloramine-T* (1) and *dichloramine-T* are the two most practicable compounds; these substances have the following formulae:

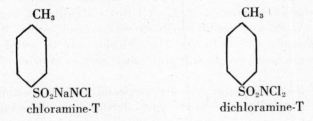

They contain chlorine-replacing hydrogen in an amino group, and this chlorine is liberated slowly, in contact with protein material. They are used in solution in oil, either chlorinated paraffin oil or oil of eucalyptol, and are applied as a spray or on gauze.

Eusol.—The simple neutralization of calcium hypochlorite with boric acid renders it comparatively nonirritating, and under the name of eusol this solution has been widely used.

For the original and some of the later papers on the use of Dakin's solution and the chloramines, the reader is directed to the sources listed in the references.

Iodine.—Compounds of iodine have been used as disinfectants during the past forty years. Terchloride of iodine (ICl_3) is a strong disinfectant. A 0.1 per cent solution kills the vegetative forms of bacteria in one minute and a 1 per cent solution destroys spores within five to ten minutes. *Iodoform* (CHI_3) is weakly antiseptic in itself, but when introduced into wounds where active reducing processes are taking place—often as a result of bacterial growth—iodine is liberated from it and active bactericidal action results. Tincture of iodine, containing 7 per cent of iodine in 90 per cent alcohol, with 5 per cent potassium iodide, is the most commonly used iodine preparation for prophylactic treatment of wounds, surgical sterilization of the skin and for the treatment of some infections.

Compounds of Heavy Metals.—The heavy metals, in extreme dilution have been found by numerous investigators to be extraordinarily toxic for micro-organisms, particularly for certain *Algae*. This effect, called the "oligodynamic action" of metals, has been attributed to the metallic ions, colloidal surface phenomena, and radiation. It continues to be a subject of investigation and must be taken into account when water used for solutions of nutriments or as a suspending fluid for bacteria is drawn from copper or silver vessels.

Copper sulphate is noted for its efficiency in preventing the growth of *Algae* in impounded waters. It will also kill typhoid bacilli in twenty-four hours in a concentration of 1 part to 400,000. This amount does not render the water unfit for drinking.

Zinc chloride is less active than copper sulphate as an antiseptic.

Gold salts have been used in the form of *sanocrysin* in the treatment of tuberculosis, but have no general application.

Arsenical compounds, such as salvarsan, so important in the treatment of syphilis, have no significant use as disinfectants against bacterial infections of animals. In the form of Paris green and other compounds arsenical preparations are used extensively in agriculture and industry to inhibit the growth of bacteria and molds.

Silver nitrate, 1:10,000, inhibits the growth of bacteria. The presence of chlorides and organic compounds greatly reduces its activity, as insoluble precipitates are formed. Silver nitrate is about one fourth as effective as mercuric chloride. It has a somewhat selective action upon gonococci. Hence it is instilled routinely in a 1 per cent solution into the eyes of newborn children as a prophylactic against gonococcal ophthalmia neonatorum.

Silver citrate, silver lactate and numerous protein-silver and colloidal silver preparations are used as antiseptics, particularly in the prophylaxis and treatment of gonorrhoea. They have uses also in the treatment of other types of infection of the mucous membranes of the eyes, nose and throat. Much information about them and about many other antiseptics may be found in the yearly editions of *New and Non-*

official Remedies, issued by the Council on Pharmacy and Chemistry of the American Medical Association. The organic and colloidal silver preparations are less antiseptic than silver nitrate, but much less irritating. Pilcher and Sollmann have arranged them according to their dissociation into silver ions and inert material, and according to their antiseptic powers in the following order: (1) silver nitrate type; (2) strong silver protein preparations (protargin, strong); (3) protargol type (silver-protein); (4) collargol type (colloidal silver stabilized with protein); (5) argyrol type (mild silver-protein). Blood, proteins and sodium chloride interfere with the antiseptic action of the silver compounds.

The most commonly used mercury compound is the bichloride ($HgCl_2$). For many years a 1 : 1000 solution of bichloride of mercury has been used as a generally practical disinfectant. A dilution of 1 : 50,000 kills some bacteria and a 1 : 100,000 solution is inhibitory. Most spores are killed in one hour by a 1 : 500 solution. Solutions of this compound have the disadvantage of causing irritation of the skin.

Since 1920 there has been great activity in the synthesizing of organic mercury compounds for use as disinfectants. Some of these compounds have extraordinarily high phenol coefficients, being several thousand times as potent as carbolic acid. We cannot review all of them here, but will mention, as representative of this group, mercurochrome, metaphen, merthiolate, and phenylmercury nitrate.

Mercurochrome, the disodium salt of 2 : 7-dibrom-4-hydroxy-mercuri-fluorescein, was introduced by Young, White and Swartz in 1919. It has been extensively used as a prophylactic antiseptic, skin disinfectant and as a chemotherapeutic agent for the treatment of many infections. Papers reporting favorable results from the use of mercurochrome, which we have not the space to review in detail here, have been numerous. In our opinion, the claims for it have not been substantiated, though it is admittedly difficult to arrive at a fair estimation of the value of such a compound. We would place it just below tincture of iodine as a surface antiseptic. The complexities of the factors entering into an evaluation of claims for mercurochrome and other antiseptics have been illustrated by the experimental investigations of von Oettingen and his associates. Mercurochrome is usually applied to wounds in a 2 per cent solution. (See series of papers by Hill.)

Metaphen, the anhydride of 4, nitro-5-hydroxy-mercuri-orthocresol, contains 56 per cent of mercury in organic combination. It has been shown by Raiziss and Severac and by Birkhaug to be a very active germicide against the vegetative and spore forms of bacteria. Its ability to sterilize the skin was demonstrated by Scott and Birkhaug, and a 0.5 per cent aqueous solution in alcohol and acetone, colored with a dye, was devised for the purpose of sterilizing the field of a surgical operation. Metaphen has been recommended for intravenous injection in the treatment of septicemias, but as it has a possible deleterious effect upon phagocytes and apparently reduces the antibacterial activities of the blood, its use for this purpose has not yet been established (Douglas and Birkhaug).

Merthiolate, sodium ethylmercuri-thiosalicylate, containing 49 per cent of mercury, is a potent germicide for spores and vegetative forms of bacteria. For sterilizing instruments it is used in a 1 : 1000 solution, and for applications to mucous surfaces it is used in 1 : 5000 or 1 : 30,000 dilutions. Powell and Jamieson have described its properties as a germicide and as a preservative for biological products, showing that when used as a preservative in vaccines and serums it maintains antiseptic action for at least three years.

Phenyl-mercuri-nitrate has marked antiseptic properties *in vivo* and *in vitro,* as shown by Weed and Ecker and Birkhaug.

Formaldehyde.—Formaldehyde (H-COH), or methyl aldehyde, is a gas which is easily produced by the incomplete combustion of methyl alcohol. In aqueous solution this substance forms a colorless liquid with a characteristic acrid odor, and in this form is largely used as a preservative for animal tissues and as a germicide. It is marketed as "formalin," which is an aqueous solution containing from 35 to 40 per cent of the gas and which exerts distinctly bactericidal action on vegetative forms in further dilutions of from 1 : 10 to 1 : 20 (formaldehyde gas 1 : 400 to 1 : 800). Anthrax spores are killed in 35 per cent formaldehyde in ten to thirty minutes. Unlike the phenols, the addition of salt to formaldehyde solutions does not increase its efficiency, but similar to them, additions of ethyl and methyl alcohol markedly reduce its germicidal powers.

Alcohol.—Ethyl and methyl alcohol are weak disinfectants. Anthrax spores have remained alive for as long as four months in 50 per cent ethyl alcohol. Nevertheless, a 50 per cent solution of ethyl alcohol kills the vegetative forms of bacteria in about fifteen minutes. This is the most effective concentration of alcohol. The addition of ethyl alcohol to aqueous solutions of mercuric chloride enhance the disinfectant action of the $HgCl_2$. Alcohol reduces the disinfecting action of phenol and formaldehyde.

Phenol.—Carbolic acid (C_6H_5OH) in a 1 : 1000 solution inhibits bacterial growth, and a 1 : 100 solution kills most of the vegetative forms of bacteria within twenty minutes. A 5 per cent solution, commonly used for disinfecting materials, instruments and excreta, kills bacterial spores in a few hours. This compound acts as a molecule and apparently is not significantly dissociated; or at least its disinfectant action is disproportionately greater than its dissociation. Its action is not greatly reduced by the presence of organic matter and the presence of sodium chloride enhances its action. Its disinfecting power is reduced by the presence of ethyl alcohol.

Cresols.—Ortho-, meta- and paracresol, isomeric compounds differing only in the position of the OH radical having the formula ($C_6H_4CH_3OH$), are stronger disinfectants than phenol. They are usually employed in a mixture known as *tricresol.* Cresols, from coal tar, emulsified with green soap, are sold under the trade names of *lysol* and *creolin.* Lysol is about four times as active as phenol and creolin about ten times as disinfectant as phenol.

Both phenol and tricresol have been used extensively in 0.5 and 0.15 per cent concentrations, respectively, to preserve biological products such as vaccines and therapeutic sera. They are not toxic for man in the doses used, according to Leake and Voegtlin, but there is some evidence that tricresol in serum injected intraspinously may increase a reaction in the spinal meninges, adding to the so-called "chemical meningitis" following intrathecal injections of serum.

Thiocresols have been synthesized by the introduction of the sulphydryl group (SH—) into the molecule. These compounds are said to promote healing through the stimulation of the mitosis of tissue cells by the sulphydryl group. At the same time they act as disinfectants through the antibacterial effect of the cresol radical.

Reimann has reported the beneficial results of the application of thiocresols to infected ulcers.

Hexylresorcinol.—In 1913 and 1921, Johnson synthesized a series of alkyl resorcinols and found a rapid increase in the disinfecting power as the homologous series was ascended. Continuation of these studies by Leonard demonstrated that the phenol coefficients of the ethyl, propyl, butyl, amyl and hexyl compounds were respectively 2, 5, 22, 54, 72. Hexylresorcinol is a strong germicide, killing vegetative forms of bacteria in less than one minute (fifteen seconds). It destroys spores also after somewhat longer contact. It has been used as an oral and wound antiseptic and as a urinary antiseptic. The substance can be obtained in crystalline form and is marketed in a 1 : 1000 solution in aqueous 30 per cent glycerine.

Leonard and Frobisher have demonstrated a parallelism between the disinfecting powers of the members of this homologous series and their ability to reduce the *surface tension* of water at the air-liquid interface. The relationship held up to the hexyl compound. With the successive additions of CH_2 groups beyond this, disinfecting power decreased while surface tension reducing capacity remained great. Inferences have been drawn from these experiments that there is a definite relationship between disinfecting capacity and ability to reduce surface tension. In our opinion, there is no causal relationship here. Some surface tension reducents are not germicidal, some solutions with surface tension value of 37 dynes per centimeter, equally as low as that of commercial hexylresorcinol solution, are only weak antiseptics, and an inert substance with strong surface tension reducing power may displace antiseptic substances from the interfacial film between the bacterial cell and the surrounding complex solution. Undoubtedly surface action is important in disinfection, but surface tension reduction is only one of many factors in this process. Reduction of surface tension is inseparable from other actions of the chemical causing this reduction. Therefore, a substance cannot be said to be a disinfectant simply because it reduces surface tension.

As mentioned above phenol coefficients of most organic disinfectants vary with the length of the alkyl chain in the molecule. Increase in the length of the chain tends to increase both the surface activity and the germicidal power, up to a certain point. The studies of Cowles throw new light on the relationship between the germicidal power of primary, secondary and tertiary alcohols and surface tension effects. He found that, for the organisms tested, there is an approximate surface tension level corresponding to the various bactericidal dilutions of these alcohols. For *B. typhosus* this is about 36 dynes /cm., for *Staphylococcus aureus* about 30 dynes /cm. In progressing from primary to secondary to tertiary alcohols there is a fairly regular decrease in surface activity. The results of measurements by Cowles suggest that the bactericidal power and the ability to lower surface tension follow parallel courses. In the opinion of Cowles this apparent relationship between surface tension and germicidal activity is understandable if both functions are linked to adsorption.

Dyes.—As Churchman has pointed out, dyes are used in bacteriology to make organisms visible, to display their structure, to reveal their chemical nature and to influence their growth. In this chapter our interest is chiefly in the last of these four purposes. The aniline or "coal tar" dyes have selective affinities for components of the bacterial cell, and through these affinities, when applied to bacteria, some of

these dyes inhibit bacterial reproduction. This inhibitory action has been called by
Churchman "selective bacteriostasis." A number of these dyes are actually bactericidal
also.

The basic triphenylmethane dyes exert selective bacteriostatic action upon all
except about 10 per cent of the species of gram-positive bacteria. Gentian violet and
related dyes (crystal and methyl violets) in dilutions as high as 1 : 200,000 inhibit
the growth of B. subtilis, but even in much higher concentration have no antiseptic
action upon gram-negative organisms, such as the bacteria of the colon typhoid group.
The tubercle bacillus, although gram-positive, is not inhibited by 1 : 10,000 gentian
violet. The dyes of the flavine series, acriflavine and proflavine, have an inhibitory
action upon gram-negative bacteria, acting also in high dilutions. Churchman has
noted a "reverse" selective bacteriostatic action in the inhibitory effect of acid
fuchsin upon B. anthracis.

The mechanism of the bacteriostatic action of dyes is not fully understood.
Churchman believed that the dyes acted chiefly by paralyzing the reproductive mechanism without otherwise injuring the bacteria. He called the process genesistasis. In
several communications from 1924 to 1930 Stearn and Stearn developed a chemical
theory of this action, based upon the amphoteric behavior of bacteria. They concluded
that, as the gram-positive bacteria have a lower isoelectric point than the gram-
negative organisms, the former combine more readily with basic, the latter with acid
dyes. They do not agree with the suggestion of Dubos that the inhibiting effect is due
to the action of the dye in poising the medium at an oxidation potential outside the
range in which the inhibited organism can grow.

The work of Browning and his associates has proved that the most potent
bacteriostatic and bactericidal dyes are members of the triphenylmethane (gentian
violet, crystal violet, fuchsin, malachite green, brilliant green), the acridine
(acriflavin) and the anil quinoline groups. The acid organic dyes are less effective
as antiseptics or disinfectants. Many azo-dyes also have significant antibacterial
actions.

Practical use is made of this knowledge in the treatment of infected wounds and
certain forms of septicemia. It has been possible to free wounds of gram-positive
bacteria by painting them with gentian violet. In our experience, the dye-therapy of
septicemias has not been successful.

In practical bacteriology, dyes are used to separate micro-organisms. Basic
triphenylmethane dyes added to media will inhibit gram-positive organisms; acridine
dyes will, in the same way, inhibit gram-negative bacteria. Media containing dyes
are helpful in the isolation of typhoid bacilli from feces, to secure cultures of tubercle
bacilli, to distinguish between members of the Brucella group, and for other purposes,
the details of which will be given elsewhere.

Bacterial Chemotherapy—Sulfanilamide.—Guided by conceptions of a therapeutic index, originating in Ehrlich's work on salvarsan, investigators for many years
have been looking for substances highly poisonous for bacteria but with low toxicity
for the animal host. The search has been for compounds with properties of specific
parasitotropism. Innumerable laborious tests have been made of antiseptics acting
upon bacteria in cultures only to find that the substances had relatively little or even
harmful effects in vivo. Nevertheless, this appeared to be the logical procedure for

developing a rational bacterial chemotherapy. Little but discouragement came of it. One reason for failure may be that too much attention has been paid to specific toxicity and too little thought given to the part played by the host through its action upon compounds and through the response of its defensive mechanism to drugs.

This rather hopeless situation was changed dramatically in 1936 and 1937 when Colebrook and his associates in England, Bliss and Long, and Mellon and his co-workers, in this country showed that the active principle of prontosil had an extraordinary protective and curative effect upon hemolytic streptococcal infections of animals and human beings. This substance, p-aminobenzenesulfonamide, $NH_2 <\!=\!> SO_2NH_2$, is now officially designated as sulfanilamide. First synthesized by Gelmo in 1908, it had been used occasionally in various azo compounds tested against streptococci, but had remained largely unnoticed for almost thirty years. Taken up at once by clinicians sulfanilamide and its numerous derivatives have been used for the treatment of infections caused by bacteria, viruses, protozoa and helminths. It is still too early for an evaluation of results. But it is now clear that its use is most successful in the treatment of infections due to hemolytic streptococci, and that it is of value in the treatment of gonococcal and meningococcal infections, and in undulant fever. Sulfapyridine is particularly effective in the treatment of certain types of pneumonia. Additional details will be given in the chapters dealing with various diseases.

The mode of action of sulfanilamide is not yet clearly understood. It is definitely bacteriostatic by direct action upon micro-organisms. But this action may be inhibited by peptones, and perhaps other degradation products of proteins, as shown by Lockwood who found it to be most beneficial in invasive infections in which necrosis of tissue was minimal. Sulfanilamide appears also to enhance phagocytosis and may stimulate other defensive mechanisms of the host.

Since 1937 hundreds of papers have been published on the use of sulfanilamide and its derivatives. Much of this literature has been reviewed critically by Mellon, Gross and Cooper in their excellent monograph *Sulfanilamide Therapy in Bacterial Infections*. Although the limitations of the range of action of this drug against bacterial infections are not known we share with Mellon and others the opinion that the successful employment of sulfanilamide in the treatment of diseases caused by diverse pathogenic microorganisms is the greatest advance in chemotherapy since the discovery of salvarsan.

REFERENCES

ANDERSON, J. F., and McCLINTIC, R. B.   J. Infect. Dis., 1911, 8:1.

———— Hygienic Lab. Bull. No. 82, 1912. See also: U. S. Public Health Rep., 1921, 36:1559.

BIRKHAUG, K. E.   J. Am. M. Ass., 1930, 95:917.

———— J. Infect. Dis., 1933, 53:250.

BLISS, E. A., and LONG, P. H.   Bull. Johns Hopkins Hosp., 1937, 60:149.

BRANHAM, S.   J. Infect. Dis., 1929, 44:142.

———— J. Bacteriol., 1929, 18:247.

BROWNING, C. H.   Applied Bacteriology, London, 1918. For a succinct review see: System of Bacteriology in Relation to Medicine, London, 1930, 1:202–206.

BUCHANAN, R. E., and FULMER, E. I.   Physiology and Biochemistry of Bacteria, Baltimore, 1928, 2:192–556.

BÜRGI, E., and LAUBENHEIMER. K. Handb. d. path. Mikroorganismen, Kraus and Uhlenhuth, Edited by Kolle, Berlin, 1931, Volume III, Chapter XIV, p. 835; Chap. XV, p. 987.

CARREL, A., DAKIN, H. D., *et al.*   Rev. d'hyg., 1915, 37:1016.
CARREL, A., and DEHELLY, G.   Treatment of Infected Wounds, New York, 1917.
CHICK, H.   A System of Bacteriology in Relation to Medicine, London, 1930, 1:Chap. V, p. 178.
CHURCHMAN, J. W.   J. Exper. M., 1912, 16:221, 822; 1913, 17:373.
———— J. Exper. M., 1923, 36:1; 37:543.
———— Newer Knowledge of Bacteriology and Immunology, Chicago, 1928, Chap. III, 19–37.
COLEBROOK, L., and KENNY, M.   Lancet, 1936, 1:1279; 2:1319.
———— BUTTLE, L. A. H., and O'MEARA, R. A. Q.   Lancet, 1936, 2:1323.
COWLES, P. B.   Yale J. Biol. and M., 1938, 11:127.
DAKIN, H. D.   Brit. M. J., 1915, 2:315.
DAKIN, H. D., and DUNHAM, E. K.   Handbook of Antiseptics, New York, 1917.
DOUGLAS, R. G., and BIRKHAUG, K. E.   J. Infect. Dis., 1933, 53:55, 71.
DRESER, H.   Ztschr. f. exper. Path. u. Therap., 1917, 19:285.
DUBOS, R.   J. Exper. M., 1929, 49:575.
EGGERT, A. H.   J. Exper. M., 1929, 49:53; 1929, 50:299; 1831, 53:27.
FABIAN, F. W., and WINSLOW, C.-E. A.   J. Bacteriol., 1929, 18:265.
FALK, I. S., and WINSLOW, C.-E. A.   J. Bacteriol., 1926, 11:1.
FEIRER, W. A., and LEONARD, V.   Surg., Gynec. & Obst., 1928, 47:488.
FICKER, M.   Ztschr. f. Hyg., 1898, 29:1.
FROBISHER, M.   J. Bacteriol., 1927, 13:163.
HAMPIL, B.   J. Bacteriol., 1928, 16:287.
———— Am.   J. Hyg., 1931, 13:623.
HILL, J. H., *et al.*   Johns Hopkins Hosp. Bull., 1923, 34:220, 372; 1929, 44:40; Arch. Int. Med., 1925, 35:503; J. Am. M. Ass., 1929, 92:111.
JOHNSON, T. B., and LANE, F. W.   Am. J. Chem., 1921, 43:348.
JORDAN, E. O., RUSSELL, H. L., and ZEIT, F. R.   J. Infect. Dis., 1904, 1:641.
KOCH, R.   Mitt. a.d. Kaiserl. Gesndhtsamte., 1881, 1.
KOLMER, J. A.   Principles and Practice of Chemotherapy, Philadelphia, 1926. See esp. Part II, pp. 48–190.
KNAYSI, G.   J. Infect. Dis., 1930, 47:303, 322, 328.
KRÖNIG, B., and PAUL, T.   Ztschr. f. Hyg., 1897, 25:1.
LARSON, W. P., and NELSON, E.   Proc. Soc. Exper. Biol. & Med., 1925, 23:357.
LEAKE, J. P., and COBBITT, H. B.   Hyg. Lab. Bull., No. 110, 1917. U. S. Pub. Health Service.
LEONARD, V.   J. Urol., 1924, 12:585.
———— J. Am. M. Ass., 1924, 83:2005.
LEONARD, V., and FEIRER, W. A.   Dental Cosmos, 1927, 69:882.
LEONARD, V., and FROBISHER, M.   Tr. Am. Ass. Genito-Urim. Surg., 1925, 18: 333.
LOCKWOOD, J. S.   Ann. of Surg., 1938, 108, 801.
MELLON, R. R., GROSS, P., and COOPER, F. B.   Sulfanilamide Therapy of Bacterial Infections. Springfield, 1938.
NEILL, J. M.   J. Exper. M., 1926, 44:199, 215, 227, 241.
PATTERSON, A. M.   Am. J. Pub. Health, 1932, 22:465.
PETERSON, J. B.   J. Am. M. Ass., 1926, 87:223.
PILCHER, J. D., and SOLLMANN, T.   J. Lab. & Clin. M., 1922–23, 8:301; 1923–24, 9:256.
POWELL, H. M., and JAMIESON, W. A.   Am. J. Hyg., 1931, 13:296; 14:218.
———— Proc. Indiana Acad. M., 1937, 46, 66.
RAIZISS, G. W., and SEVERAC, M.   J. Lab. & Clin. M., 1923, 9:71.
———— J. Infect. Dis., 1927, 40:447.
REDDISH, G. F.   Am. J. Pub. Health, 1927, 17:320.
———— J. Lab. & Clin. M., 1929, 14:649.
———— Newer Knowledge of Bacteriology and Immunology, Chicago, 1928, Chap. XXII, 301–309.
REICHEL, H.   Handb. d. path. Mikroorganismen., ed. by W. Kolle, R. Kraus, and P. Uhlenhuth. Berlin, 1931, 3:Chap. XIV, p. 835.
REID, J. D.   Am. J. Hyg., 1932, 16:540.

REIMANN, S. P. J. Am. M. Ass., 1930, 94:1369.
——— Am. J. Cancer, 1931, 15:2149.
——— Ann. Surg., 1931, 93:624.
RIDEAL, S., and WALKER, J. T. A. J. Roy. San. Inst., 903, 24:424.
——— Approved Technique of the Rideal-Walker Test, London, 1921.
SCOTT, W. W., and BIRKHAUG, K. E. Ann. Surg., 1931, 93:587.
SHAUGHNESSY, H. J., and WINSLOW, C.-E. A. J. Bacteriol., 1928, 15:69.
SHIPPEN, L. P. Am. J. Pub. Health, 1928, 18:1231.
SMITH, L., DRENNAN, A., and CAMPBELL, W. Brit. M. J., 1915, 2:129.
STEARN, A. E., and STEARN, E. W. J. Bacteriol., 1924, 9:491; 1930, 19:133.
TAYLOR, H. D., and AUSTIN, J. H. J. Exper. M., 1918, 27:155.
U. S. Dept. of Agriculture, Circular No. 198, 1931.
VOEGTLIN, C. Hyg. Lab. Bull. No. 112, 1918, U. S. Public Health Service.
VON OETTINGEN, W. F. J. Am. M. Ass., 1932, 99:127.
WALKER, J. E. J. Infect. Dis., 1923, 32:287; 1924, 35:557; 1926, 38:127.
WEED, L. A., and ECKER, E. E. J. Infect. Dis. 1931, 49:440; 51:309; 52:354.
WINSLOW, C.-E. A., and BROOKE, O. R. J. Bacteriol., 1927, 13:235.
WINSLOW, C.-E. A., and DOLLOFF, A. F. J. Bacteriol., 1928, 15:67.
WINSLOW, C.-E. A., and FALK, I. S. J. Bacteriol., 1923, 8:215.
WINSLOW, C.-E. A., and FLEESON, E. H. J. Gen. Physiol., 1926, 8:195.
YOUNG, H. H., SCOTT, W. W., and HILL, J. H. J. Urol., 1924, 2:237.
YOUNG, H. H., WHITE, E. O., and SWARTZ, E. O. J. Am. M. Ass. 1919, 73:1483.

CHAPTER IX

BACTERIAL ECOLOGY AND FLORA OF THE NORMAL BODY

BACTERIAL ECOLOGY

Ecology is the study of the mutual relation between organisms and their environment. Occasionally, it is possible to limit this study to a determination of the reactions between an organism and its physical and chemical surroundings. In most cases, however, there are both animate and inanimate elements in the environment. The environment of an organism is as much a product of the presence and activities of other living things as it is of non-living chemical substances and physical forces. This is especially so in the case of the bacteria, which in nature occur almost always in association with other bacteria, with fungi and with animals and plants. It is natural and logical, therefore, to apply the term ecology to the study of the general and special phenomena of the mutual relations between bacteria and living organisms and to the mutual relation between bacteria and their non-living environment.

Habitat.—Bacteria are ubiquitous under the conditions which permit the existence of living organisms. As these conditions are diverse and vary in one or another factor, organisms tend to be segregated in certain elemental states, in geographical regions and in animate or inanimate bodies depending upon conditions of moisture, food supply, temperature, and many other conditions. The organism becomes adapted to a certain environment or finds an environment favorable to its existence. In this broad sense, the term *habitat* may properly be applied to the places of abode of bacterial species and populations. It must be recognized, however, that the term has been very loosely used in bacteriology and that only secondary importance can be given to it in many instances. It is to be found as an item in all classifications of bacteria. In his discussion of some fallacious tendencies in bacteriologic taxonomy, Hall has objected to the importance attributed to habitat as a criterion for the identification or classification of bacteria or any other living thing.

Nevertheless, it is convenient to group bacteria according to their habitat, as a general knowledge of the flora of any region of the earth or atmosphere, or of the flora of animals and plants, is helpful in orientation.

As bacteria are found in the *air*, it is usually stated in connection with such organisms that the air is their habitat. As a matter of fact, bacteria do not propagate in the air. They exist in the atmosphere as spores or vegetative forms with some resistance to desiccation. The common organisms of the air are spore-bearing aerobes, spores of fungi, resistant cocci and rods. Chromogenic forms are common in the air. As bacteria are swept into the air along with dust, or are sprayed into the air by the forceful expirations of animals, different groups or organisms will be found in the air in different localities. The microbiology of the upper air has become a special field of study for bacteriologists who have worked in coöperation with Lindbergh and other aviators. In 1934 Proctor made collections and cultures at altitudes of 20,000 feet or more. He found that the upper air is a vehicle for transmission of many types of organisms common to water and soil. Pathogenic bacteria do not survive for any appreciable length of time in the air, probably only a few hours in most instances.

The *soil* is the habitat of many organisms. Some reach the soil in the excreta or cadavers of animals, others, such as the numerous autotrophic bacteria, actinomycetes and fungi, are indigenous. This vast and complex population has been described, as far as knowledge permits, by Waksman and others. The spore-bearing anthrax and tetanus bacilli may remain viable for years in the soil.

Water in all natural situations is the habitat of many kinds of micro-organisms from the sulphur bacteria to pathogens for man. Pathogenic bacteria, however, are usually not present except in those waters which are directly contaminated from human sources. The most important source of contamination is the urinary and fecal excretions of man. Typhoid and dysentery bacilli and cholera vibrios may remain alive for relatively long periods in streams, ponds and wells, and may even multiply in these waters if there is present a sufficient quantity of organic nutriment. Purification of sources of drinking water has eliminated many of the dangers due to pollution. But water-borne typhoid fever is still occurring in communities in this country, and water-borne cholera is prevalent in India. The common nonpathogenic *B. coli* persists in water longer and in greater numbers than the pathogenic members of the group of intestinal bacteria. Therefore, in the bacteriological examination of water, *B. coli* is searched for and is used as an index of fecal pollution. Since we shall not devote a section of this book to the bacteriology of water, the reader is referred to special textbooks on hygiene and sanitation for information on this subject.[1]

Animals are the habitat of numerous varieties of bacteria. The relations thus established are of the utmost importance for the whole subject of medical bacteriology.

Holman, in an epitome of the knowledge of *bacterial associations,* has assembled many examples of the relations between various bacteria. When different varieties of bacteria occur together in the same medium or locus, one may prevent the growth or annul the effects of the other, in a relationship known as *antagonism.* In contrast to this, two or more groups of bacteria may work together in a relation of *synergism,* producing a result which the single species alone could not have brought about. Bacterial synergism results in important chemical changes in substrates. Its importance in mixed infections is probably equally as great. But etiological research in singling out one species as the cause of a disease has neglected the investigation of the more intricate mixed infections. Bacteria may live in and upon higher organisms without doing them harm or receiving special benefits. Such relationships are examples of *commensalism.* Occasionally, the bacteria assist the activities of their hosts while deriving benefits of food and protection from them, in a true *symbiosis.* Finally, bacteria have a relationship of *parasitism* to higher organisms, injuring their hosts in various degrees. These relationships affect both organisms in the association, provoking adaptive changes, and perhaps cyclic and mutational variations. Bacteria have been active agents in the natural selection of man and animals and plants.

---

[1] For methods of bacteriological examination of water see: *Standard Methods for the Examination of Water and Sewage,* American Public Health and American Water Works Assoc., N. Y., as revised periodically.

Synergism.—In 1923, Kämmerer introduced the term synergism as a designation of the associated activities of two or more species of bacteria acting upon a single substrate. The result produced, in this case the formation of urobilin from bile pigment, was greater than that which either species alone could bring about. We agree with Holman in preferring this term to the term symbiosis as a designation of these less intimate bacterial associations. There are many examples of synergism, from the communal activities of organisms of the same species to cumulative effects of associated organisms of widely different species. Churchman and Kahn showed that although a single cell would not grow in the presence of gentian violet, thirty cells could initiate growth. These thirty cells accomplished much more than thirty times what one cell could accomplish. Aerobes by exhausting oxygen in a container of medium permit anaerobes to multiply. Castellani has described many synergistic fermentation processes, as for example the production of gas from maltose, mannite and sorbite by a mixed culture of *B. morgani* and *B. typhosus*, although neither organism alone produces grossly demonstrable amounts of CO_2 from these carbohydrates. Among the many conditions necessary for this result one of the most important "seems to be that the added bacillus though inert on those particular compounds must be capable of producing fermentation with gas in glucose." [2] Gas production by bacterial synergism was investigated further by Holman in 1926.

The knowledge of bacterial synergism in cultures and in the soil harmonizes with old and new knowledge of mixed infections. It is obvious, as Castellani has pointed out that the trend of scientific medicine since Pasteur and Koch has been toward the mono-etiology of disease. The conception of even an infectious disease as having a single etiology is in general too narrow, and there are many infections which result from the synergetic activities of several varieties of microbes. Vincent's angina is an example of the combined action of spirochetes and fusiform bacteria. In wound infections, streptococci and anaerobic organisms may proliferate much more rapidly when several kinds of organisms are growing in the same locus, as shown by Douglas and his associates. Many additional examples of mixed and secondary infections whose course indicates that synergetic action of bacteria is of importance have been described by Seitz, who has discussed the relation between streptococci and the diphtheria bacillus in the production of diphtheria. Studies of the various virus diseases, of influenza, of hog cholera, of measles and other infectious diseases have indicated, as Dochez has pointed out, that secondary invasion is of considerable importance in infectious disease. It seems probable that the simultaneous increase in streptococci, pneumococci and influenza bacilli in the nasopharynx found by Webster to occur in association with the incidence of more or less severe infection of the upper respiratory tract, is another case of bacterial synergism of significance in human pathology.

Commensalism.—By this term we refer to the mutual but almost inconsequential association between bacteria and higher organisms. The bacteria in the intestinal tract may be classed as commensals. Apparently they are not essential to the life of flies (Pearl), and probably are not essential to man. It is admitted that the conditions of a sterile existence are so rigorous that it is not possible to say at present whether the failure of an animal to survive under "aseptic" conditions is due to the lack of bacteria

2 A. Castellani, *J. Am. M. Ass.*, 1926, 87:15.

in its intestine or the severe restrictions imposed by the sterile environment and sterilized food. Numerous saprophytic bacteria on the skin of animals are to be regarded as commensals.

Symbiosis.—This word is applied properly to a mutually beneficial relation between one organism and another. It is more intimate than synergism, and when it is used in bacteriology it should be limited to the relationship in which the bacterium derives benefit from its residence in or upon a higher organism and in which the higher organism derives benefit from its bacterial partner. Such relations are rare. The relation between nitrogen-fixing bacteria in root-nodules of legumes is an example of symbiosis between plants and bacteria. The intracellular micro-organisms of some insects live in symbiosis with their hosts. Wallin and Portier have suggested that a similar relation exists between man and micro-organisms. It is true that the intracellular organisms known as *Rickettsiae* exist in symbiotic relationship with insects and crustaceans. But no such relationship has been demonstrated in man. We are not convinced by the bacteriological evidence presented by Wallin that bacteria are symbionts in the cells of vertebrates. Some of the filtrable viruses appear to exist in symbiosis with the cells of animals and plants.

Buchner has described very numerous examples of intracellular symbiosis but does not list any clear example relating to the associations between man and bacteria. Symbiosis, in fact, is nearly always somewhat injurious to one of the partners. It is in reality a type of infection.

Parasitism.—The bacteria which are capable of living and multiplying within the human body are called parasites, in contrast to the multitude of micro-organisms, called *saprophytes*, which though unable to hold their own under the environmental conditions found in the tissues of high animals, lead a hardy existence in the dead materials of soil, water, excreta, cadavers and other inanimate substances. The separation is by no means a sharp one and carries with it other implications which the use of these terms always conveys. As a rule, parasites are much more fastidious than saprophytes as to nutritional and temperature requirements under conditions of artificial cultivation.

Bacteria exhibit all stages of an evolving parasitism. Between the strict parasites and the saprophytes there is a large class of bacteria, to which the majority of pathogenic varieties belong. These bacteria, capable of developing luxuriantly upon many kinds of artificial substrates as well as upon animal tissue are often spoken of as facultative parasites.

An illuminating discussion of parasitism as a factor in disease was published by Theobald Smith in 1921. It is pointed out here that the phenomena of disease of interest to medical men are largely epiphenomena in an evolving parasitism, and that these products tend to lessen and disappear as the parasitism approaches a biological balance or equilibrium. The rapid and destructive actions of some micro-organisms are the expression of a bungling parasitism. The skilful or well adapted parasite enters its host, resides for long periods in the tissues at the expense of the host, and may produce destructive lesions only as a means of securing an exit from its host in order to take up a new berth in another host. On the basis of its relation to the animal, Theobald Smith has defined four critical phases in the life-cycle of the microbe: "(*a*) its entry into the body and through protecting tissues; (*b*) its transportation and multiplication in certain tissues; (c) its escape from those tissues and from the host as a whole; (d) its transfer to another host."

In adopting the parasitic habit, bacteria lose numerous characteristics while gaining or developing a few special qualities. Parasites have less varied metabolic processes than their facultatively parasitic or saprophytic relatives. Parasitic members of one species tend to be alike serologically and to be similar in their elective localizations in tissues. Thus typhoid bacilli are a more homogeneous group with more restricted fermentative capacities than the hardier paratyphoids, and the paratyphoid bacilli in turn are somewhat less heterogeneous in all their properties than the colon-aerogenes types to which they are related.

In Chapter XII we shall continue this discussion in connection with the fundamental factors of pathogenicity and infection. A knowledge of the general characteristics of parasitism is essential to the understanding of the causes and control of communicable disease. From the practical point of view it discloses the possibility of breaking the parasitic cycle at one or another of its critical points.

Although we have been considering chiefly the relations between parasitic bacteria and man, we do not wish to obscure the importance of the bacterial parasites of lower animals. Some of these parasites are adapted strictly to lower animal hosts, others such as the micro-organisms of tetanus, anthrax, tuberculosis, glanders, plague, undulant fever, rabies and other diseases pass readily from animals to man. Hull, Meyer and many others have clearly described the reservoir of disease in lower animals. Veterinary and human pathology have much in common. Aside from the great advances which have been made through experimentation on animals, a great deal applicable to the course of infections in man has been learned from observation upon the natural history of disease in lower animals in both its sporadic and epidemic manifestations.

The worker in medical bacteriology cannot neglect the "spontaneous" infections of his laboratory animals (Meyer). Guinea-pigs (Holman) have pseudotuberculosis, infections with paratyphoid bacilli, caseating lymphangitis due to streptococci. Rabbits contract respiratory and septicemic infections, due chiefly to *Bacterium lepisepticum*. Mice and rats are naturally susceptible to paratyphoid-like bacilli, Friedländer bacilli and other organisms. These conditions furnish abundant material for study, but also complicate many experimental procedures.

BACTERIAL FLORA OF THE NORMAL HUMAN BODY

In studying bacteria in disease, it is of considerable importance to have a clear idea of the morphological and cultural characteristics of forms which are frequently encountered in different parts of the human body under normal conditions.

The surfaces and cavities of the body which communicate with the external world always contain considerable numbers of bacteria representing a large variety of species. Some of these may be commensals associated with that particular part of the body, others may be accidental and temporary invaders, members of pathogenic groups which, either because of the reduced virulence of the strains or the increased resistance of the individual are not capable under the circumstances of causing their specific infection.

It is such conditions which may lead to many erroneous etiological conclusions and which render the investigation of the causation of diseases in the skin, the mouth, intestines and other locations extremely difficult. It is best to discuss this from the point of view of individual locations.

On the Normal Skin.—Exposed surfaces of the body collect many kinds of saprophytic cocci and bacilli. While most of these are chiefly important to the medical bacteriologist because of the troubles they cause as contaminants of cultures taken from lesions of the skin or of material, such as blood, obtained by puncture through the skin, there are several types requiring special attention to differentiate them from pathogens. *Bacillus subtilis,* the common spore-forming aerobe of dust and hay infusions, is not unlike the anthrax bacillus in certain stages of growth. Cultural characteristics, the type of endospore, motility and lack of pathogenicity distinguish it from *Bacillus anthracis.* Caution must be exercised in expressing an opinion based upon the forms of the rods seen in stained smears from superficial lesions. The white and yellow *staphylococci* are common in and on the skin. They may or may not produce lesions, leading a more or less commensal existence in the crevices, pores of sweat glands and hair follicles of the skin. When the skin is injured, they may proliferate abundantly and produce such lesions as stitch abscesses, furuncles, and sometimes severe pyogenic infections. *Diphtheroids,* some of which closely resemble the diphtheria bacillus in morphology, are constant inhabitants of the skin. Finally non-pathogenic *Mycobacteria,* acid-fast rods resembling the tubercle bacillus, occur normally in the skin, particularly in regions where sebaceous secretion accumulates, as in the axillae and about the genitalia.

In the Normal Mouth and Pharynx.—The mouth and pharynx are the habitat of numerous bacteria. Saliva itself is not a good culture medium, and, indeed, may, according to some investigators, show very slight inhibitory or even bactericidal powers. But these, at best, are not very potent, and the saliva thus is a basis for a fluid medium which furnishes water as a solvent and a reaction suitable for a great many different bacteria.

Sloughing epithelium, decayed teeth, food particles, etc., furnish suitable nutrition. Catarrhal inflammation, which is rarely entirely absent, favors the lodgment of bacteria upon the mucous membranes. Accumulated exudates and secretions beneath the margins of the gums offer favorable conditions for bacterial growth.

In view of these facts, it is surprising that the frequent accidental injury of the gums and oral and pharyngeal mucous membranes so rarely leads to serious infection, and ends so readily. This is a fact which has not as yet been adequately explained.

Staphylococci can almost always be isolated from the mouth. They are usually of the *albus* variety, but not infrequently *Staphylococcus aureus* also can be found.

Of the *streptococci* the *viridans* is almost always present. The isolation of a viridans from inflammatory processes of the mouth and throat, therefore, has very little true significance, unless it is isolated from a closed process, such as a tooth abscess, or unless other strong corroborative evidence can be adduced. The *hemolyticus* variety is less frequently found in the normal mouth, but may be present without causing disease. However, the isolation of a hemolyticus from an inflamed tonsil or pharynx is much more likely to mean that there is an etiological relationship, and it is of course well known that many of the severe inflammations in this location are of hemolyticus origin.

In examinations made many years ago by one of us, 30 per cent of people examined harbored *pneumococci* in their mouths, at one time or another, in the course of the cold months. Since then, the typing of the pneumococcus has made it possible to show that the pneumococci most frequently present in the mouth belong to Type 4 and the "higher" types. In the investigations of Dochez and Avery, which are described in another place, it was found that this type caused only about 9.8 per cent of pneumonias, but was found with considerable frequency in normal mouths. The other and more virulent types may be found in the normal mouth, as well, but are more apt to represent recent contact with pneumonia cases or a transitory carrier state. This, at least, is suggested by the writers mentioned above, though probably a definite, conclusive statement cannot be made concerning it at the present time, because of the difficulty of tracing contacts.

Of the nonpathogenic gram-positive cocci the *Micrococcus candicans* and occasional pigment forming micrococci are not infrequent.

Micrococcus tetragenus is very often an inhabitant of the mouth and, as a matter of fact, one sees it most frequently in routine work in Löffler's cultures taken for the purpose of diphtheria diagnosis.

Of gram-negative micrococci there is a considerable variety which, without being pathogenic, may be cultivated from the mouth and throat and add no little confusion to meningococcus carrier examinations. Most common among these are the *Micrococcus catarrhalis*, which is described in another section, and may be distinguished from the meningococcus by its heavier growth, its growth at room temperature and its failure to produce fermentation of dextrose and maltose. The *Micrococcus flavus*, which frequently has led to error in similar work, is a pigment forming gram-negative coccus often found in the throat, which grows at room temperature, and in most cases agglutinates spontaneously in normal horse serum. Another which forms very dry colonies, the *Micrococcus pharyngis siccus*, is often isolated, but easily recognized. In addition to this, Elser and Huntoon have described three different chromogenic groups of similar organisms often found in the mouth and throat. These probably do not exhaust all the possible gram-negative micrococci that can be isolated from this locality, but it is really only of importance to make sure in human examination whether one is dealing with a true meningococcus, with a *Micrococcus catarrhalis*, or with other saprophytes.

True *meningococci* are of course often found in normal or slightly inflamed throats during the carrier state, which is discussed at considerable length in another place. As discussed there, these organisms when they are present are usually located high up in the pharynx near its roof, and successful search for carriers depends very largely upon care in reaching the right spot with the swab.

Of bacilli, the mouth contains a large variety at different times. Few of these, however, are confusing from the bacteriologist's point of view, except some of the diphtheroids. The *pseudodiphtheria bacillus*, or *B. hofmannii*, may be present without having any relationship to disease. It is described in another section. The other larger and more irregular *diphtheroids* are not uncommon, and are easily distinguished from true diphtheria bacilli by their appearance and cultural characteristics.

Chain-forming gram-positive bacilli and large obviously saprophytic varieties may be present in very dirty mouths, but offer no bacteriological difficulties.

Of the gram-negative bacilli, *proteus, aerogenes,* and special members of the *Friedländer* group may be present. We have known one man who habitually had a *Friedländer* culture in his mouth, without ever suffering any harm from its presence.

The *fusiform bacillus* described in another section in connection with Vincent's angina, is almost always present between the gums and the teeth in mouths that are dirty, with carious teeth or where there is some inflammation of the gums themselves. It is an observation that we make almost every year with our students, that, if a platinum loop is passed between the base of the tooth and the gums, and smears taken from a number of students, the bacteria usually associated with Vincent's angina, spirochetes and fusiform bacilli, can be seen in one or another of the cases examined.

Spirilla and spirochetes are almost habitually present. True *treponemata* (Noguchi's classification) are almost always present in locations like those described for the fusiform bacilli, and even on the mucous membranes, especially when small spots of necrosis or inflammation occur. Most frequently discussed among these are the large spirochete, associated with Vincent's angina, the *Spironema vincenti*. There are, likewise, present very frequently the *Treponema macrodentium* and *microdentium*, classified thus by Noguchi. These organisms are best observed under the dark field, but can also be stained in smear if strong gentian violet or carbolfuchsin are used. It is important to note that morphologically the macrodentium is very similar to the *Treponema pallidum,* and in the dark field examination of sphilitic lesions of the mouth and throat, this similarity must be carefully taken into account. We have seen cases in which we were unwilling to make a definite diagnosis on these findings alone. It is our belief that whenever extensive necrosis of the tissues of the mouth and pharynx occur in consequence of other infection or injury, the necrotic tissues are apt to be invaded by fusiform bacilli and spirochetes, which in subsequent examination dominate the bacteriological picture. We believe, however, that in the large majority of these cases, perhaps including the clinical picture spoken of as Vincent's angina, the treponemata and fusiform bacilli are secondary to the primary etiological factors, such as those mentioned. These organisms are anaerobic. We believe that the early contention of Tunnicliff that the spirochetes and fusiform bacilli found in Vincent's angina are different stages of the same organism, is not generally accepted today.

The normal mouth is also apt to contain occasional members of the *leptothrix* and *streptothrix* groups. One of these, the *Leptothrix innominata* of Miller, is supposed to be characteristic of the mouth flora. It may appear as a large gram-positive bacillus form which is believed by some writers to be a true bacillus, rather than a leptothrix, and is spoken of as the *B. maximus buccalis* (Miller).

In the Nose and Accessory Sinuses.—That the nasal mucosa should be a favorable site for the deposit of numerous micro-organisms follows from the fact that air is constantly passing in and out during respiration. The varieties of bacteria to be found in the nose, therefore, may belong to any that happen to be present in the inhaled air.

The subject of the bacteriology of the nose deserves more attention than has been given to it, for infections of the nasal sinuses and the conditions which lead to them, are being recognized as of the utmost importance to general health. Earlier investigators claimed that the passage of bacteria in the air to the deeper respiratory organs is very largely arrested by a sort of filtering action in the nose. In animals, the tracheal mucus, as well as the mucous membrane of the posterior portions of the healthy nose, are usually sterile, although the vestibulum nasae is usually heavily contaminated. It has been determined that between three-fourths to four-fifths of the bacterial flora of the inspired air are held back in its passage through the nose.

Küster came to the conclusion that we cannot speak of a characteristic nasal flora, that practically all the organisms with which a man can come in contact through the air settle there for a longer or shorter period. In the healthy nose, however, few organisms, except diphtheroids, gain a permanent foothold.

The *cranial sinuses*, ethmoidal, frontal, maxillary and mastoid are usually sterile. They are often invaded by pathogenic bacteria, particularly streptococci producing disabling disease which we shall consider elsewhere. The bacteriology of the mastoid sinuses has been worked out in detail by Skoog (1932).

In the male and female, the normal *urethral orifices* harbor a number of gram-positive and gram-negative cocci and incompletely identified bacilli. Occasionally acid-fast rods are found in these places. These organisms have no pathogenic significance, but are apt to increase the difficulties of diagnosis in suspected cases of gonorrhea or tuberculosis. The chief organism in the normal *vagina* appears to be a member of the *Lactobacillus* group and is known as Döderlein's bacillus.

Bacteria in the Tissues.—There is definite evidence that even the tissues themselves may not always be sterile in normal human beings. This has led, we believe, to a certain amount of error in etiological conclusions when blood cultures and cultures from normal or slightly diseased lymphatic tissues have been taken, and diphtheroid and various coccus forms isolated. There is a constant entrance of bacteria into the portal circulation from the intestines. These are very largely disposed of in the liver, but it may well be that the liver does not always eliminate all the bacteria from the portal circulation, and that some of these then lodge in other tissues and become latent there.

The latency of bacteria in the healthy body can no longer be questioned. We have long known that *Treponema pallidum*, the spirochetes that infect mice, and many trypanosomes can remain present for a long time in the circulation and in the tissues of animals and man without giving rise to characteristic symptoms or even to any symptoms. We have found *Treponema pallidum* in the testes of rabbits four months after inoculation without there having been the slightest tissue reaction, and in human syphilis this latency is well recognized. Tetanus spores may remain latent in the spleen and other organs of guinea-pigs under certain experimental conditions. We have seen a very convincing example of latency of streptococci in the tissues of the hand. A very severe hemolytic streptococcus lesion subsided under surgical treatment, and four months later a purely cosmetic secondary operation was undertaken at a time when there was not the slightest trace of infection, and hemolytic streptococci were again isolated from the tissues at this operation. There was, incidentally, no sign of infection of the wound, which healed uneventfully.

The investigations of Torrey and others have shown that from lymph nodes, the seat of various nonbacterial conditions, such as sarcoma, Hodgkin's disease, etc., many varieties of diphtheroids may be isolated, and Rosenow has reported a number of blood culture results in which diphtheroids and cocci were isolated from the blood in the presence of febrile conditions which obviously were not due to the particular organisms isolated.

Not much can be said about this problem of latency at the present time because little is known about it, but the possibility should be kept in mind, and should cause great conservatism whenever isolations from the tissues are made, and the etiological question is raised.

Bacteriology of the Intestinal Tract.—The stomach receives large numbers of bacteria with the food ingested, but under normal conditions passes them on to the intestine with the gastric digest. Under normal conditions there is no indigenous flora of the stomach, although mouth bacteria swallowed with the saliva must be constantly passing through the lumen of the stomach. In conditions of stasis, due to obstruction, *Sarcinae* and a large organism known as the Opler-Boas bacillus proliferate in the stomach. The upper regions of the small intestine also are relatively free from bacteria. In the *large intestine*, however, there is an enormous proliferation of bacteria. Rettger has likened the large intestine of man and lower animals to "a veritable culture tube in which definite bacterial types appear to be struggling constantly to gain supremacy."

A large proportion of the feces is composed of bacteria, most of which are dead. The numbers present in the feces are enormous. Determinations by Strassburger's method of separation by centrifugation indicate the normal adult excretes about 8 grams (dry weight) of bacteria daily, calculated by Rettger to be about 128 trillions of organisms. MacNeal and his associates, Matill and Hawk have confirmed these estimates. A large proportion of the fecal nitrogen and fecal fat is contained in the excreted bacteria (Sperry).

The bacterial flora of the intestinal canal varies at different ages, with health and disease, and is to a considerable extent dependent upon diet. Also, many of the bacteria that cause specific diseases of the intestinal canal, such, for instance, as the typhoid bacillus, the paratyphoid bacilli, the dysentery group, and some of the doubtfully pathogenic organisms like the Morgan bacilli, are very closely related in morphology and cultural reactions to nonpathogenic and saprophytic inhabitants of the bowel. In no type of bacteriological work, therefore, is it more necessary to have an intelligent understanding of the bacterial species that are likely to be found without pathogenic significance.

Furthermore, the intestinal canal is a large test-tube from which bacterial products can be absorbed in sufficient amounts to cause illness. In it, different kinds of food supply nutritive material which may assist one or another species, and various conditions of aerobiosis and anaerobiosis may prevail. It is more than likely, therefore, that many so-called cases of intestinal poisoning, formerly loosely spoken of as ptomaine poisoning, may be caused by substances formed within the intestine by bacterial action upon the food, rather than upon the relatively smaller amount of fermentative and putrefactive products taken in with partially decomposed food.

The intestinal canal of the child at birth is sterile. The meconium of such children has been found by many investigators to be free from bacteria. But this does not last very long. Within a few hours after birth, infection takes place, and from then until death, the intestinal canal is constantly the seat of a voluminous and varied bacterial life. Kendall, who has written much on this subject, and in his book has brought together much of the information, gathered from the researches of Escherich, Herter, and his own investigations, has classified the different stages of bacterial flora in man, as follows:

1. Bowel at birth, sterile.
2. First to the third day a period of "adventitious bacterial infection."

After this time there is the period of establishment of the characteristic infantile intestinal flora which gradually changes as the diet approaches more and more that of the adult, into the characteristic flora of the adult.

In the earliest days during the stage of "adventitious infection," when the child is getting its first bacteria from the air and objects with which its mouth comes in contact, the bacterial flora is determined largely by accident.

When the child begins to take food, it is of great importance for the determination of the bacterial flora, whether it is being breast fed or being fed on artificially modified cows' milk.

In breast-fed children, the upper part of the small intestine will usually contain enterococcus, *Streptococcus lacticus,* and a general predominance of the coccoid form. Lower down toward and behind the ileocecal valves, the *B. aerogenes* and the colon bacilli appear. In the lower parts of the cecum and the rectum, the anaerobic *B. bifidus* of Tissier and similar anaerobes predominate, and many proteolytic bacteria may be present.

In contrast to this, in artificially fed infants, the bowel is relatively richer in the colon group, and the *B. aerogenes* type; *B. mesentericus* and other anaerobic spore-formers will be present in considerable numbers, and in the lower bowel the *B. bifidus* types are largely replaced by colon bacilli, *B. acidophilus* and similar organisms. Very early there may be also present in children a curious tetanus-like organism spoken of as Bienstock's *B. putrificus.*

Tissier, who has done a great deal of work on this problem, described the flora of a five-year-old child in which the gradual transition from the milk to the mixed diet was taking place as follows: "Constant fundamental flora, *B. bifidus,* enterococcus, colon bacillus, *B. acidophilus.* Variable adventitious organisms, *B. perfringens,* cocci, and a number of other gram-negative bacilli, together with some yeasts."

As adult life is attained, there is a gradual relative increase of organisms of the colon type, which eventually constitute about 75 per cent of the intestinal bacteria.

All who have studied this subject have found that diet has a definite and important bearing upon the intestinal flora and that definite changes may be brought about in the bacterial contents of the bowel by purposefully adjusting the diet. The studies of Herter, of Kendall, and of Rettger, particularly, have contributed to our knowledge of this subject. Herter laid particular stress upon the importance of the Welch bacillus and its subvarieties upon intestinal putrefaction. In this he was not entirely in agreement with Rettger and others who believe that the Welch bacillus attacks proteins but slightly, being chiefly concerned with carbohydrate fermentation. Herter produced indicanuria in dogs by feeding large amounts of meat, and found that with such feeding the colon and ileum contained considerable numbers of anaerobic bacilli. He believed that this bacillus is particularly concerned with a chronic putrefactive activity which takes place in the large intestine, in the course of which anaerobic bacilli produce butyric acid. In consequence of this, there may be a considerable intestinal irritation and carbohydrate intolerance. Other writers like Friedman believe that constipation favors the increase of these putrefactive organisms. Simonds has made an exhaustive study of the relationship of the Welch bacillus group to intestinal conditions, and has reviewed the literature extensively. He summarizes his studies on this problem as follows: "In the case of gas bacillus diarrhea, the presence of an excess of carbohydrates in the intestinal content brings about conditions in the lower ileum and first part of the colon which are particularly conducive to the growth of *B. welchii*. The absence of lactic acid producing bacteria, as pointed out by Kendall, renders conditions still more favorable to the multiplication of these organisms. They, therefore, rapidly increase in numbers, produce irritating butyric acid, and are swept on in excessive numbers into the lower bowel. The number of spores produced will be measurably proportional to the number of bacilli which reach the lower part of the bowel; hence, the excessive number of spores of *B. welchii* in the stools in cases of gas bacillus diarrhea." Simonds' results substantiate the work of Kendall and Day to the effect that children and adults with diarrhea who showed large numbers of gas bacilli in the stools are made worse by feeding sugars, and that prompt improvement results when the diet is changed to one largely composed of protein. An addition of lactic acid by the feeding of butter-milk still further aids in eliminating the Welch bacillus. Kendall has shown by prolonged experimentation on monkeys, dogs and cats that feeding with cows' milk, to which sufficient lactose has been added to simulate breast milk, produces a bacterial flora in such animals which approaches that of the normal nursing infant. The stools take on an acid reaction, and organisms like *B. bifidus* and the enterococcus begin to predominate. In order to bring this about, he states, it is necessary to continue the feeding for considerable periods. Kendall divides the pathological cases in which it can be reasonably suspected that abnormal bacterial conditions of the intestinal tract play a causative part, into those which are due to the action of the bacteria upon proteins, and those in which it is chiefly a matter of carbohydrate fermentation. In the case of the abnormal proteolytic processes, there may be a liberation of substances like histamin and other toxic amins, and there may even be the formation of specific toxins such as those which have been recently produced by Bull and others from the Welch bacillus. Abnormal carbohydrate splitting may result in hyperacidity and in stasis of the bowel. Secondary putrefaction, resulting from this stasis, may produce symptoms of intoxication.

The investigations of Rettger and Cheplin since 1921 have proved that in most instances the intestinal flora can be radically changed by diet. The simultaneous administration of lactose and milk culture of *Lactobacillus acidophilus* replaces a putrefactive flora with an aciduric flora, and in about 25 per cent of the cases suitable strains of *Lactobacillus acidophilus* become implanted in the intestine. It is not possible to secure implantation with *Lactobacillus bulgaricus*. Beneficial results have followed this type of transformation of the intestinal flora. As we cannot deal adequately with these questions here, the reader is referred to papers of Rettger, the monograph of Kopeloff and the annotated bibliography published by Frost and Hankinson.

Numerous species of *anaerobic bacteria* are inhabitants of the large intestine. Until recently attention has been directed chiefly to the large group of spore-bearing anaerobes of the genus *Clostridium,* including the putrefactive and fermentative organisms mentioned above.

In 1933 Eggert and Gagnon reopened a neglected field of intestinal bacteriology by their critique of the genus *Bacteroides,* which includes the non-sporulating obligate anaerobes. They reported a systematic study of eighteen species of gram-negative members of this genus. Two of these species had been isolated by Distaso; sixteen were new. In 1935 Eggert added to this knowledge by describing eleven species of gram-positive non-sporulating anaerobes isolated from feces. Later the investigation of the gram-negative *Bacteroides* was extended by Weiss and Rettger who reached the conclusion that these forms are the predominant organisms in the intestine of most human adults. For their classification they proposed 4 groups, based primarily upon serology and secondarily on morphology, and were inclined to regard the gram-positive varieties described by Eggert as possibly belonging to another genus.

These important new developments are going forward in Professor Rettger's laboratory. The results should clarify classification of the genus *Bacteroides* and show the relationship of these organisms to the fusiform bacteria. From these studies a better understanding of intestinal bacteriology is to be anticipated. To the medical bacteriologist, who encounters these organisms in anaerobic cultures from appendiceal abscesses and peritonitis, the newer knowledge of this group will be particularly useful.

REFERENCES

BUCHNER, P. Tier und Pflanze in Intracellularer Symbiose, Berlin, 1921.

CASTELLANI, A. J. Am. M. Ass., 1926, 87:15.

CHURCHMAN, J. W., and KAHN, M. C. J. Exper. M., 1921, 33:583.

CUNNINGHAM, J. S. J. Infect. Dis., 1929, 45:474.

DOCHEZ, A. R. Tr. Ass. Am. Physicians, 1921, 36:188.

DOUGLAS, R. S., FLEMING, A., and COLEBROOK, L. Lancet, 1917, 1:605.

EGGERT, A. H., and GAGNON, B. H. J. Bacteriol., 1933, 25:389.

———— J. Bacteriol., 1935, 30:277

ESCHERICH. Darmbakterien des Sauglings, Stuttgart, 1886, p. 9.

FRIEDMAN. Tr. Chicago Pathol. Soc., 1901. Cited from Simonds.

FROST, W. D., and HANKINSON, H. Lactobacillus Acidophilus, an Annotated Bibliography to 1931, Milton, Wis., 1931.

HALL, I. C. J. Bacteriol., 1927, 13:245.

HERTER. The common Bacterial Infections of the Intestinal Tract, New York, 1907.

HOLMAN, W. L. Newer Knowledge of Bacteriology and Immunology, Chicago, 1928, Chap. VIII, pp. 102–119.

———— J. Med. Research, 1916, 35:151.

HOLMAN, W. L., and MEEKISON, D. M. J. Infect. Dis., 1926, 39:145.

HULL, T. G. Diseases Transmitted from Animals to Man, Springfield, Ill., 1930.

KÄMMERER, H. Klin. Wchnschr., 1923, 2:1153; 1924, 3:723.

KENDALL, A. G. Bacteriology, General, Pathological and Intestinal, Philadelphia, 1928.

KENDALL, A. G., and DAY, A. A. Boston M. & S. J., 1911, 741; 1912, 753.

KOPELOFF, N. Lactobacillus Acidophilus, Baltimore, 1926.

Küster, E. Handb. d. pathog. Mikroorgan., editer by Kolle, R Kraus and P. Uhlenhuth, Jena, 1929, 3rd ed., Vol. 6, Chap. VII, p. 355.

MacNeal, W. J., Latzer, L. L., and Kerr, J. E. J. Infect. Dis., 1909, 6:123, 571.

Matill, H. A., and Hawk, P. B. J. Exper. M., 1911, 14:433.

Meyer, K. F. Newer Knowledge of Bacteriology and Immunology, Chicago, 1928, Chap. XLV, p. 607.

———Proc. Inst. Med. Chicago, 1931, 8:234.

Neumann. Ztschr. f. Hyg., 1902, 40:33.

Nissle, A. Handb. d. pathog. Mikroorgan., W. Kolle, R. Kraus and P. Uhlenhuth,, 3rd ed., Jena, 1929, Volume VI, Chapter VIII, p. 391.

Pearl, R. Scientific Monthly, 1921, 13:144.

Portier, P. Les Symbionts, Paris, 1918.

Proctor, B. E. J. Bacteriol., 1935, 30, 363.

Rettger, L. F. J. Biol. Chem., 1906, 2:71.

——— Newer Knowledge of Bacteriology and Immunology, Chicago, 1928, Chap. XLVI, p. 639.

Rettger, L. F. and Cheplin, H. A. Intestinal Flora, New Haven, 1921.

——— Arch. Int. Med., 1922, 29:357.

Seitz, A. Handb. d. pathog. Mikroorgan., ed. by W. Kolle, R. Kraus, and P. Uhlenhuth, Jena, 1929, 3rd ed., Chap. V, p. 505.

Simonds, J. P. Monogr. Rockefeller Inst., 1915, No. 5.

Skoog, T. Acta Otolaryngol, Scand., 1932, 18:41.

Smith, T. Tr. Ass. Am. Physicians, 1921, 36:172.

——— Science, 1921, 54:99.

Sperry, W. M. J. Biol. Chem., 1929, 81:299.

Strassburger, J. Ztschr. f. Klin. Med., 1902, 46:413.

Waksman, S. A. Principles of Soil Microbiology, Baltomore, 1932, 2nd ed.

Wallin, J. E. Symbiontism and the Origin of Species, Baltimore, 1927.

Webster, L. T., and Clow, A. D. J. Exper. M., 1932, 55:445.

Weiss, J. E., and Rettger, L. F. J. Bacteriol., 1937, 33:423.

Wolman, A., and Gorman, A. E. Water-borne Typhoid Fever Outbreaks, Baltimore, 1932.

——— Am. J. Pub. Health, 1931, 21:115.

CHAPTER X

VARIABILITY OF BACTERIA

Since the beginning of the study of bacteria there have been differences of opinion regarding the constancy or variability of these organisms. At different times and in different countries one or the other doctrine has been predominant, influencing not only procedures but also observations and interpretations of phenomena, since the viewpoint of the observer often determines what he sees or selects for description.

Before 1876, most bacteriologists accepted the doctrine that bacteria were extremely variable. This was a natural inference from what they found in the mixed cultures with which they were unknowingly working and from the general biological knowledge that all living organisms are in some degree variable, showing different forms and properties at different stages of their life cycles. These notions culminated in the theory of *pleomorphism* set forth by Nägeli in 1877, in which he appeared to consider all bacteria one species. In reply to criticisms, Nägeli, in 1882, reported confirmation from pure cultures of some of his observations on variability of form and reasserted his opinion that distinctions between species of bacteria had little scientific value.

Until about 1872, Cohn was in sympathy with this point of view, stating that his genera and species were not natural, that the possibility was not excluded that various species might come from one and the same "mother form" and that even various genera might be only the developmental stages of one and the same individual. By 1876, Cohn had changed his mind. He regarded his genera as natural and laid down the notions of constancy and stability of bacterial species which so profoundly influenced Robert Koch and his pupils. It is interesting to note that Cohn's groupings were faulty, in that he included in his genus of nonmotile micrococci the motile and variable *B. prodigiosus* and several other organisms now known not to be micrococci.

Koch's first statement in 1878, that he had found the bacteria constant in form and uniform in action, was repeated in many of his subsequent publications and insisted upon as a dogma of *monomorphism* by his pupils in Germany, England and in this country. Variations were noticed by these workers, but new species were created to accommodate many of the variants. A rigid set of cultural conditions were established and certain forms and functions were selected as normal under these conditions. Irregular forms were usually discarded as "involution forms" or, as they were no doubt in many cases, forms of contaminating bacteria. Koch admitted that the pathogenic tubercle bacilli probably evolved from saprophytes, and by 1890 he conceded some variability in bacteria. But, as Theobald Smith has pointed out, there is little in the publications of Koch and his associates to remind one of "the plasticity of microorganisms within certain limits."

It seems evident now that while Nägeli and his adherents erred in uniting unrelated phenomena, often the results of mixed cultures, they were sound in their general biological conceptions of bacterial variability. On the other hand, while Cohn and Koch and their followers were in error in separating the true and natural phenomena of variation in bacteria and enforced a somewhat unbiological point of view, they were right in insisting upon the precise and controllable methods through which so much progress has been made. These methods are still valid in their application to modern studies of variability.

Since the time of Pasteur, bacteriologists in France have been presenting evidence contradictory to the theory of monomorphism. Almquist in Sweden, since 1893, has published numerous accounts of bacterial variability. Lehmann and Neumann have had an important influence in furthering the theory of pleomorphism, and Theobald Smith has for years opposed radical "species making." Admirable and documented summaries of the older observations on bacterial variability, together with some of the newer knowledge, are available in the publications of Löhnis, Hadley, Gotschlich, in papers and discussions presented at the Deutsche Vereinigung für Mikrobiologie [1] in 1924, and in Arkwright's monograph. These make it unnecessary for us to review the long record of this subject here.

The modern sharp conflict between the doctrines of monomorphism and pleomorphism seems to have begun in 1912 in Germany with the publications of Baerthlein and Eisenberg on mutation forms of B. coli in which variations in colony-form (rough, smooth, intermediate, and secondary colonies) were well described and related to other characteristics. Hort, in England, published his observations on the special reproductive forms of bacteria in 1917, and in this country Mellon in 1919 began the series of publications of his observations on variability and cyclogenic changes exhibited by bacteria. The two investigations which brought the subject of bacterial variability prominently into the foreground were the studies of variations in bacteria in relation to agglutination by salts and specific serum by Arkwright in 1921 and, in the same year, the discovery by De Kruif that in a pure culture of B. lepisepticum there were individuals of differing virulence recognizable by the forms of their colonies. De Kruif called this splitting of the species "microbic dissociation." These studies introduced the modern investigation of the R and S (rough and smooth) and intermediate types of bacterial colonies and their correlation with other properties of the organisms.

The results of these investigations and of numerous other studies to which we shall refer in subsequent chapters prove that bacteria vary in form, in function and in chemical and antigenic composition. So many instances of bacterial variation, within so-called "species," have been rigorously demonstrated and readily confirmed that the fact of bacterial variability is no longer in question. These variations should now become a part of the description of the organisms. In this place we shall discuss the significance and possible mechanisms of bacterial variation.

Monomorphism and Pleomorphism.—The conflict between the doctrine of monomorphism and pleomorphism is not confined to considerations of form, structure, biochemical activity, chemical and antigenic composition and pathogenicity. If simple polymorphism and multiplicity of function alone were involved, the theory of monomorphism would still be capable of satisfactorily including the observed differences

---

[1] See *Centralblt. f. Bakt.* I Abt. 1924, 93:Beiheft p. 2, 22, 81, 94.

by establishing statistical means which would represent the species as a broad unit of grouped variations. The theory of pleomorphism, on the other hand, includes far-reaching conceptions of variability based upon phases of life cycles, special reproductive forms and sexual conjugation in the bacteria.

It is certain that strict monomorphism is no longer tenable. On the other hand, as we have stated in Chapter II, with the exception of the endospore cycle in bacilli, there is no convincing evidence proving the existence of the hypothetical life cycles and sexual phases of bacteria. At present, we can neither deny nor affirm the occurrence of cyclogenic variations and sexual conjugation in bacteria. We agree with Miss Evans and others that on the basis of broad biological analogies these things are possible. But our position is that while analogies between the bacteria and fungi, algae and other organisms may direct investigation and the formation of theories, they do not materially strengthen incomplete observations. Little is to be gained from the citation of one unconvincing piece of work in support of another equally inconclusive. As all will agree, rigid proofs are required to establish these broader concepts of pleomorphism.

Methods of Studying Variability.—Some of the methods used to study bacterial variability are simple, direct and readily controlled. Others are complex, not easily controlled and subject to the risk of contamination. Interpretation of reported results requires a knowledge of *all* the details of the methods used to obtain them.

Direct continuous observation of cells passing through various stages is one of the most certain means of proving cyclogenic changes. This can be done visually or by motion photomicrography. It has not been sufficiently employed even when applicable. Repeatable production of variations on heat-sterilized media, with strict attention to bacteriological "asepsis," as in the many verifiable instances of dissociation into smooth and rough colony types, growth of nonmotile organisms from an originally motile strain, noncapsulated from capsulated varieties and similar phenomena, are the methods which have yielded unquestionable results. When these methods are inadequate, complicated maneuvers are employed which cause the organism to be removed from direct observation, place it in media of doubtful sterility or expose it to contamination. In this group we place those methods requiring prolonged incubation periods, long series of transfers from tube to tube, the serial plate-washing transfer method of Hauduroy, which Brown and Frobisher have shown to be subject to an unusual risk of contamination, filtration through Berkefeld and Chamberland candles, which we shall discuss more fully later, cultivation in filtered media containing serum or lipoids, passage from animal to animal, and purposeful growth in mixed cultures with other organisms. The results obtained by these means should be subject to especially critical review and should be repeated with such variations in technic as will exclude or render highly improbable the possible fortuitous and unsuspected rôle of extraneous organisms. It is obvious also that a patchwork fabric of disconnected morphological observations based on organisms removed and stained from cultures at different periods of time cannot be convincing as evidence of cyclogenic changes unless confirmed by continuous observations or readily repeatable in sequence. The literature contains evidence that not all details of procedures have been described, as some maneuvers thought to be insignificant at the time have been omitted, to be disclosed later when their importance required assessment. Since errors may be made on account of the unsuspected entrance of foreign organisms into cultures, the passage of vegetative forms of bacteria through filters and the common but incompletely understood spontaneous infections of animals, it is obvious there are grounds for skepticism of the results of many studies of bacterial variation. Questions of contamination cannot be summarily dismissed. It is readily admitted, however, that objections based on this ground have been completely removed from connection with many important investigations of variability.

Factors Influencing Variation.—The variability inherent in bacteria may become manifest as the result of the influence of a number of factors. These may be grouped, for convenience, as follows:

1. External factors: physical and chemical environment in culture media and in the animal body.
2. Internal factors:

   (a) Simple growth phases, morphological and functional variations in relation to the growth curve.
   (b) Mutations.
   (c) Bacteriophage.
   (d) Cyclogenic in relation to cycles of vegetative forms, cycles of special reproductive forms such as endospores, gonidia, budding or branching, or cycles of sexual stages, with conjugation of gametocytes or fusion in symplasm.

Characteristics and Mechanisms of Variation.—The establishment of strict conditions relating to periods of incubation, temperature, composition of media, etc., by Koch and his followers was the result of their knowledge that those conditions favored the predominance of relatively uniform shapes, sizes, biochemical and pathogenic activities of bacteria. When the conditions were changed, forms and functions other than those regarded as normal appeared.

There is abundant evidence that the forms and activities of bacteria vary under different *external physical and chemical conditions*. Undoubtedly some of the forms thus produced are abnormal, incapable of reproduction and therefore rightfully classed as involution forms. They may be produced by plasmoptysis or plasmolysis, and by other ill-defined environmental conditions. On the other hand, many of these forms, as for example the bizarre forms in old cultures of the cholera vibrio and *B. megatherium* are not dead but are capable of reproducing the common vegetative forms of the respective organisms. Furthermore, some of the so-called involution forms occur in young cultures and give rise to the common forms. This is evidence neither for nor against an essential cyclogenic variation, since the significance of these forms in the life cycle has not been established.

Other responses to environmental changes are more permanent. Anthrax bacilli cultivated at 42° C. become permanently asporogenous. The cultivation of typhoid bacilli on medium containing phenol causes the appearance of a nonflagellated strain. Capsulated organisms lose their capsules on artificial media and virulence often rapidly declines. Toxin production may be made to appear and disappear by changes in the culture medium. In contrast to these losses of characteristics, organisms may apparently gain ability to ferment carbohydrates in the surrounding medium, develop a capsule, or display other properties which were absent, latent or masked in the original strain.

It is apparent from these examples of variation in response to external factors that we are dealing with two types of variability. One type results in the production of temporary variants which retain their properties only as long as a special set of conditions are maintained. These are readily reversible. The second type results in the production of relatively permanent variants which retain their properties for longer periods under a diversity of conditions. Such variants may be "stabilized," but these are also to some extent reversible. External conditions thus elicit temporary and more permanent alterations. Mechanisms of heredity are no doubt involved in each one of these types of variation. In both instances the cellular processes are complex and a sharp line of division cannot be drawn between them.

The simplest expressions of variability due to *internal factors* have already been discussed in Chapter III on the growth and death of bacteria. It was shown there that a progression of changes in the shapes and sizes of cells during the growth of a culture could be correlated with the growth curve. The series of morphological changes has been called *cytomorphosis* by Henrici, who found no convincing evidences of a life cycle in his studies of these variations. In Chapter II also we have described the variations in bacterial resistance to injurious agents, and the changes in metabolic and reproductive activity which occur at different periods during the first twenty-four to forty-eight hours of growth. These variations do not require any further analysis here. Their existence and importance are clearly recognized.

The sudden appearance of variants among organisms derived from a single colony or even a single organism has been called *mutation*. The term was introduced prominently into bacteriological language by Neisser and Massini in their descriptions of the different forms of colonies and cells found by them in cultures of *B. coli mutabile*. These forms, later confirmed by Kowalenko, were designated as examples of mutations, according to DeVries. Since then the tendency has been to apply the term "dissociation" to variations of this type in order to use a broad designation that does not commit the user of it to a belief in the existence of chromosomes and genes in bacteria, since geneticists have definitely related mutation phenomena to nuclear structure. As there is still so much uncertainty in regard to the form and organization of nuclear material in bacteria, it is not possible to express a definite opinion on this subject. The interchanges of chromomeres between coccoid cells of the avian tubercle bacillus described by Lindegren and Mellon may be the anatomical basis for both sexual and mutational phenomena, but this has not yet been established. For these reasons it seems best to reserve the term mutation until instances are known to which it may be fully applied.

Closely associated with possible mutations or at least with numerous evidences of variability based upon apparently internal factors are those alterations induced or produced by bacteriophage. D'Herelle, in discussing the extremely numerous variants of different organisms which occur under the influence of bacteriophage, has called both the temporary and irreversible types "mutations." Since he believes that the bacteriophage is an ultravirus parasite of bacteria, he likens these bacterial variants to the mutations known to occur in higher animals and plants under the influence of parasitism. Hadley has called attention to the close association between lytic phenomena and variation. Since neither the true nature of the bacteriophage nor the mechanism of variation is known with certainty, definite conclusions cannot be drawn. It is certain, however, that bacteriophage is intimately associated with some types of bacterial variation.

In the section on bacterial reproduction in Chapter II we discussed in some detail the evidence on life cycles of bacteria. Extremely varied forms within species are said to be *cyclogenic* or related to the possible asexual or sexual phases of the *life cycles* of bacteria. Small rod-like or filamentous forms have been seen attached to larger forms, apparently connected by an intercellular bridge. These, like coccoid forms seen in juxtaposition in cultures of bacilli and cocci, have been called micro- and macro-gametocytes and their apposition has been considered by some investigators to be evidence of sexual conjugation. The conglomeration of amorphous bacterial substance seen in some cultures, designated "symplasm" by Löhnis has been regarded as a form of sexual fusion. It is impossible to reject or accept these various forms as proof of a sexual phase, since the evidence at hand is incomplete and unconvincing— a defect for which we cannot criticize the investigators, as the difficulties in the way of absolute proof seem insurmountable at this time. Enderlein's cyclogeny appears to us to lack all substantiation; in fact we doubt whether his diagrams at 10,000-fold magnification are representative of actual minute structures in cells.

In Chapter II also we have dealt with the cyclogenic aspects of *endospore formation*. The discovery of Mellon and Anderson that the endospore of *B. subtilis* differs antigenically from the vegetative cell, the well known fact that certain organisms have more active metabolic processes after passage through the spore stage, and other characteristics of sporulation, are in harmony in indicating that the endospore is more than a simple resting or resistant stage. It is the best established example of a life cycle sequence in bacteria, with variation in form accompanying variation in function.

Evidence has been accumulating that an internal factor of variability may result in the production of viable fragments of bacterial cells. These particles may be the so-called gonidia, defined by Löhnis as "organs of *asexual* reproduction formed by the contraction of the plasmatic cell content, which leave the parent cell by breaking the parent cell wall or become liberated when the cell dissolves. They may be formed in cells of ordinary size or in cells that become markedly enlarged. In the latter case the cells are known as *gonidangia*. The gonidia have the ability to multiply by fission in the same minute gonidial form for many generations, but eventually they become transformed into the ordinary cell type." [2] Many bacteriologists during the past eighty years have described minute granular bodies occurring inside of bacterial cells, apparently possessing the ability to undergo further independent development when freed from the cells. Löhnis, Hadley, Mellon and others, calling these bodies gonidia, attach cyclogenic importance to them. Others who have seen them refer to them as viable fragments of cells or dwarf bacteria.

The clearest description of these minute bacterial forms has been given by Hadley and his collaborators. Organisms 0.3–0.5 μ in diameter and with a maximum length of 1.5 μ were obtained from cultures of typhoid-dysentery organisms by growth in broth containing 0.5 per cent lithium chloride, pancreatin, or by aging. When material from these cultures or from serial transfers in broth over long periods was spread on agar plates no visible growth occurred, but, with a lens, colonies,

---

[2] This quotation is from a personal communication from Philip Hadley, who informs us that he uses the term *gonidium* in this sense.

called G-colonies, could be seen having diameters from 0.004 to 0.2 millimeter. The forms in these colonies were coccoid or rod-shaped and were usually gram-positive whatever their original source. By use of the Hauduroy technic or by repeated transfers in tubes of broth, visible growth was obtained and the final culture resembled or duplicated the original organism. The G-forms were relatively inert in their metabolism and reduced in pathogenicity. The reversion process was always slow, an important criterion of cyclogenic character.

The G-forms discovered by Hadley were found to be readily filtrable through N, V and W Berkefeld candles. Others have used filters as the primary segregation apparatus to obtain these minute forms from cultures and other materials. In this country, Mellon and his associates have described minute filtrable forms of tubercle bacilli; Kendall, using a special medium, has reported the occurrence of very small filtrable forms of cocci and typhoid bacilli; and Brueckner and Sherman have found these G-type organisms in enormous numbers—a trillion (10^{12}) per gram—in feces, milk, soil and hay infusions.

The segmentation of tubercle bacilli into granules and the subsequent development of delicate rods from these granules with the final production of the usual bacillary forms have been observed by Kahn in a long series of direct microscopic observations of single cells. Opposed to these observations and conceptions is Wyckoff's failure to find any evidence of vitality or slowly reverting growth in the granules of Shiga bacilli obtained from lithium chloride cultures, although he made serial photographic records of these coccoid granules over long periods. Much additional information on this subject, together with a discussion of the Pettenkofer bodies of Kuhn, may be found in Klieneberger's review.

The important general questions arising from these observations and their interpretation may be stated as follows:

1. Are there minute, filtrable forms of bacteria?
2. Are these small, filtrable forms distinct "species"?
3. Do these minute, filtrable forms represent a stage in the life cycles of larger bacteria?
4. Are the filtrable forms related in any way to the ultraviruses?

The statement of the questions in these terms appears to place primary emphasis on filtrability. As a matter of fact, filtrability has been given undue prominence in this connection, since the passage of a particle through an unglazed porcelain filter or other porous structure is only in part related to its size and is in a large part determined by physical and chemical conditions affecting both the filter and the particle. We shall deal with the physics of filtration more fully in another place. It is sufficient to repeat here that the electric charge upon the particle as compared with that on the walls of the pores of the filter, the H-ion concentration of the medium, the surface tension properties of the medium, the presence of lipins in the fluid filtered, the pressure, the time required for filtration, and many other conditions, to say nothing of defects in the apparatus, influence the results. Particularly to the point here are the experiments of Ward and Tang, Grinnell and others, showing that bacteria and viruses suspended in broth were filtrable, although they were not filtrable from salt solution, and the demonstration by Varney and Bronfenbrenner, that the K-medium of Kendall aids the passage of the usual bacterial forms through Berkefeld filters. In view of all these factors, it is obvious that filtrability cannot be the chief criterion of size of bacterial forms. Nevertheless, it seems established that apart from the usual forms which may pass through filters, small organisms, dwarf forms of bacteria and viable granules are filtrable. Other criteria than filtrability must be considered in the interpretation of results obtained by filtration.

Some of the filter-passers are definite types or species of micro-organisms. Such are the anaerobic gas-forming cocci and *Pneumosintes*, vibrios, spirochetes and other forms.

The question as to whether certain minute forms represent a stage in the life cycles of larger bacteria is difficult to answer. The chief criterion adopted here is that of the slow reversion to the original form after many transfers and long periods of incubation. While the well known latency or dormancy of a few "normal" forms which pass through the filter might account for this slow resumption of the usual growth phases in some cases, in others these latent forms have not been demonstrated to be present and are apt to be lost, if they were present, during the long series of transfers required to produce reversion. Slow reversion has been a characteristic of Hadley's G-types. The rapid reversions described by Kendall in his experiments with the typhoid bacillus are more readily interpreted as growth from normal forms passing through the filters aided by his K-medium than as evidences of a minute form in a cyclostage of the organism. Seastone and Lawrence, working in our laboratory at Harvard, made a thorough attempt to repeat Kendall's work, following procedures outlined by him as far as possible and using, in part of the investigation, material for the K-medium supplied directly by Kendall. Rapid growths of typhoid bacilli in media inoculated with filtrate were obtained once from a filtered broth culture and once from a filtrate of the K-medium cultures. These results were entirely explicable on the basis of the experiments of Grinnell, Varney and Bronfenbrenner and others, which we have cited. Seastone and Lawrence failed to confirm Kendall's results and found in Kendall's contributions no convincing evidence of a filtrable stage as part of the life cycle of bacteria. We realize, however, that there is a valid basis for differences of opinion with respect to the nature of the bacterial fragments or dwarf forms which pass through filters. The question cannot be settled by means of the evidence available at present. While the evidence is strongly suggestive that bacteria may have gonidial stages which are filtrable, a definite conclusion cannot be reached on this point at this time.

Our fourth question raised by these studies of bacterial variability concerns the possible relationship between gonidial or minute, filtrable forms of bacteria and the ultramicroscopic viruses. We shall deal with the question broadly here, deferring the presentation of most of the details to the appropriate chapters on encephalitis, herpes, poliomyelitis and other virus diseases. In those places we shall discuss more fully the work of Rosenow, Kendall and others who maintain the thesis that the viruses are filtrable stages of ordinary bacteria. Two lines of argument are used by the supporters of this opinion. One line of argument follows from their finding the usual forms of bacteria in the lesions of these diseases or in cultures from these lesions. This is a most unsubstantial basis of support. More commonly, bacteria are not found either in stains or cultures from virus-infected tissue. When bacteria are discovered in these sites, we know from the work of Bull, Tang and Castaneda, and the experience of many others, that intercurrent infection, agonal invasion or postmortem contamination are the probable explanations of their presence. It is extraordinarily difficult to obtain consistently sterile tissue from animals that have died of an acute disease in which the general physiological defensive mechanisms, including that opposed to the entrance of bacteria from the intestine into the blood stream, are broken down before death. The frequent association of bacterial invasion, usually an invasion of the bacteria in the environment of the animal, with filtrable virus infection is well known. The experiments of Tang and Castaneda have a direct bearing upon the report by Evans and Freeman on the cultivation of cocci and bacilli from nerve tissue from cases of encephalitis and show the possibility of heterogeneous bacterial invasion as an explanation of the occurrence of bacteria in such locations. We believe that the same criticisms apply to Rosenow's isolation of streptococci from the lesions of poliomyelitis.

The second line of argument is advanced through the increasing knowledge of the filtrability of bacteria. Here the weight of evidence at present seems to us to be preponderantly against the opinion that filtrable viruses are phases in the life cycles of bacteria. These viruses have properties altogether different from any known properties of bacteria; they appear to be necessarily associated with living cells of plants and animals; none has ever been cultivated upon media free from living cells and no bacterial forms have been found in tissue cultures in which viruses are propagated. From pathological and immunological standpoints the virus diseases have distinctive characteristics, although they have also many qualities in common with infectious diseases due to bacteria. In summing up these differences and in suggesting certain postulates to be fulfilled in investigations of these problems, we (Zinsser) do not wish to be understood as throwing out of court the theory of cyclic relationship between bacteria and the virus group. Indeed, the possibility of such a relationship exists and is one of the most important problems confronting the bacteriologist to-day.

Transmutation of Bacteria.—We use this broad term to refer to several published examples of extraordinary variability, transcending the extreme limits of morphological genera. One of these was the conversion by Noguchi of a strain of *B. bifidus* into the spore-bearing *B. mesentericus*. The other is the account of the metamorphosis of streptococci into spore-bearing rods with characteristics resembling *B. subtilis*, published by Miss Evans in 1932. The photographs of Miss Evans' preparation show coccoid granulation of the bacilli, with small round bodies along the sides of the cells. Diphtheroidal rods occurred in the chains of streptococci. These morphological variations are common in these types of organisms. But the actual sequence of changes in the metamorphosis of cocci into spore-bearing rods and rods of this type into cocci has not been observed and such evidence is not supplied by this report. Our respect for the investigator makes us reluctant to raise again the old cry of "contamination" which has so often proved a false alarm in investigations of variability, but we must confess that it occurs to us as an explanation of these results.

Microbic Dissociation.—Putting aside any further discussion of these unsolved problems of bacterial life cycles and mechanisms of variability, we shall review some of the important and well established phenomena of variation, called in general phenomena of "dissociation."

Some of the most conspicuous changes of this character take place on media customarily used for the routine cultivation of the organisms. The progeny of a single cell or of a few cells taken from certain colonies when streaked on a plate may grow side by side in widely different colony forms. The three chief types of these colonies are: (1) the smooth, glistening, moist, round, convex, homogeneous, regular colonies, called the *smooth* or S-type; (2) the somewhat larger wrinkled, granular, indented, serrated, friable, flattened or nodular colonies, called the *rough* or R-type; and (3) the mucoid or M-type. Between these there are many types with mixed or intermediate characteristics. In Figure 8 we have reproduced pictures of typical S, R and secondary colonies. Hadley's G-type, a minute, barely visible, round, relatively translucent form of colony, is distinct from all other types. The S-forms frequently give rise to R-forms, but the production of S-forms from R colonies is more difficult. By repeated selection of colonies, relatively stable types can be maintained almost indefinitely.

Although there are enough exceptions to any general rule to indicate that each organism may be a law to itself, there are certain characteristics which can be correlated with these chief types of colonies. Following Hadley we may list a few of these in summary, as follows:

Smooth or S-type.—Homogeneous clouding in broth; homogeneous suspensions in 0.85 per cent solution of NaCl; soft, buttery growth on agar; flagella and active motility in motile species; capsules and production of specific carbohydrate in capsulated varieties; cells "normal" in size and shape as rods or cocci; biochemical activities marked; carry somatic and flagellar or capsular antigens; coarse flocculation with antisera; usually virulent or toxic (if a pathogen) (some streptococci are more virulent in the R-form); associated with acute infections; sensitive to bacteriophage; resistant to phagocytosis; efficient immunizing agents.

Rough or R-type.—Granular growth in broth; spontaneous agglutination in salt solution; granular, tenacious or friable growth on agar; usually lack flagella in motile species and lack capsules in nonmotile species; cells, both small and large, often filamentous, with tendency to branching and fungus-like growth; biochemical activities reduced; carry only somatic or group antigens; usually lack virulence and ability to produce toxin; more common in convalescence and in chronic infections; less sensitive to bacteriophage; susceptible to phagocytosis; usually poor immunizing agents.

Mucoid or M-type.—The colonies are mucoid in consistency; the organisms are usually encapsulated.

G-types.—These are not well known. They appear to be relatively inert, difficult to propagate, reduced in pathogenicity, usually gram-positive irrespective of original source; said to be readily filtrable; revert slowly to the original form of the bacterial organism.

The list of characteristics of bacteria associated with types of colonies, which we have given above, is subject to the further qualification that many of the biological characters of bacteria vary independently as a result of "dissociation." Mackenzie, Fitzgerald and Irons, from studies of variants of dysentery and paratyphoid bacilli, concluded that there was no uniform pattern for the altered characters of R-variants nor for those of the reversion cultures derived from them. Complete reversion of biochemical, colonial and of antigenic characters was not observed in any instance.

A few typical examples of dissociative variation are the following:

With the pneumococcus, the conversion of an S or smooth organism into a non-virulent R organism is easily accomplished. We know that such an alteration is characterized not only by changes in cultural behavior on solid and fluid media but by a loss of virulence and an antigenic change. The complete antigen of the virulent organism is constituted of a carbohydrate and a protein fraction, the carbohydrate being a partial antigen and determining type-specificity. The rough (R) organism has apparently lost its capacity to produce the carbohydrate fraction. In consequence, the antibodies produced by it are different from those produced by injecting the complete antigen into the S form. The R organisms still retain a latent capacity for the production of the carbohydrate, since by proper manipulation in the animal body or in culture, in the presence of dead S organisms or extracts containing the complete antigen, these R organisms may return to and be stabilized in the virulent S form. Still more curious is the fact that an R organism derived originally from one type of pneumococcus can, by appropriate methods, be converted into an S form of another type. It is demonstrable that such changes in both directions can take place in the animal body as well as in the test tube. With organisms like the typhoid bacillus, four separate dissociants can be obtained and reproduced in stable form. In these at least four different antigenic fractions are involved, and it appears as though we had only scratched the surface and that most bacteria were composed of what Maurice Nicolle has spoken of as "a mosaic of antigens." With toxin-forming organisms like the diphtheria bacillus dissociation changes, in which cultural alterations are associated with the loss of toxin production, can take place in the test tube and in the convalescent throat. In certain of the streptococci the significant antigenic changes which accompany cultural modifications depend upon alterations in the protein part of the antigen rather than the carbohydrate. In *B. pertussis* a gradual antigenic dissociation of the virulent organism can go on through four separate phases.

The significance of this knowledge for epidemiology and immunology is very great. It reveals possible explanations for the gradual attenuation of organisms carried for a long time in the convalescent body, as in diphtheria carriers. It suggests lines of thought concerning the genesis and decline of epidemics. It revolutionizes the procedures of immunization. Already we know that much of the older work on bacterial vaccination is probably unreliable because of failure always to use smooth cultures containing the complete antigen. This is probably true of typhoid prophylaxis, since new experimental investigations have shown that the old Rawlins strain is only partially effective because it has largely gone rough. It indicates that in whooping-cough the older vaccines produced with stock strains may have dissociated into phases 2, 3 or 4, and can therefore no longer be regarded as fully effective. We might multiply such examples to apply to almost any group of micro-organisms in which immunological studies have been only partially successful or unsatisfactory. Many irregularities in agglutination and other immunological reactions have been explained. But before this part of the field has been thoroughly explored a vast amount of investigation has yet to be made.

The results of these studies on variability obviously complicate diagnostic bacteriology and throw a mass of confusing data before both the clinician and the systematic bacteriologist. A broad survey of the general significance of these trends in medical bacteriology has been ably presented by Hadley. There remain, as Fred has shown and all know well, notably stable physiological characters of bacteria. Obviously a synthesis and harmonizing of points of view will come about when sufficient knowledge has been acquired. It is evident, however, that bacteriology has been rejuvenated through these investigations of variability in the "changing bacteria," as Winslow has expressed it. The scientific scope of bacteriology has been greatly expanded and its practical possibilities multiplied.

REFERENCES

ARKWRIGHT, J. A. Path. Bacteriol., 1921, 24:36.
────── Variation, System of Bacteriology in Relation to Medicine, London, 1930, 1:Chap. IX, 311–374.
BAERTHLEIN, K. Centralbl. f. Bakteriol., I Abt., 1912, 66:21.
BROWN, J. H., and FROBISCHER, M. Johns Hopkins Hosp. Bull., 1927, 40:318.
BRUECKNER, H. J., and SHERMAN, J. M. J. Infect. Dis., 1932, 51:1.
COHN, F. Beitr. z. Biol. d. Pflanzen, 1872, 1:Hft. 2, 127–224, esp. pp. 130, 151; 1875, 1:Hft. 3, 141–207, esp. p. 142; 1876, 2:Hft. 2, 249–276, esp. p. 274.
D'HERELLE, F. The Bacteriophage and Its Behavior, Baltimore, 1926, p. 219.
────── Yale J. Biol. & M., 1932, 4:55.
DE KRUIF, P. J. Exper. M., 1921, 33:773; 1922, 35:561, 621.
────── Proc. Soc. Exper. Biol. & Med., 1922, 19:34, 37, 38, 40.
EISENBERG, P. Centralbl. f. Bakteriol., I Abt., 1912, 66:1.
ENDERLEIN, G. Bakterien-Cyclogenie, Berlin, 1925.
EVANS, A. C. J. Bacteriol., 1929, 17:171.
────── U. S. Pub. Health Rep., 1927, 42:171; 1932, 47:1723.
EVANS, A. C., and FREEMAN, W. U. S. Public Health Rep., 1926, 41:1095.
FRED, E. B. Proc. Nat. Acad. Sc., Washington, 1932, 18:455.
GOTSCHLICH, E. Variabilität der pathogenen Bakterien, Handb. d. pathog. Mikro-organismen, ed. by W. Kolle, R. Kraus and P. Uhlenhuth, Berlin, 1929, 3rd ed., 1: Chap. 2, 206-249.
GRINNELL, F. B. J. Bacteriol., 1929, 18:175.
HADLEY, P. Microbic Dissociation, J. Infect. Dis., 1927, 40:1–312; 1937, 60:129.
────── Proc. Inst. Med. Chicago, 1932, 9:62.
HADLEY, P., DELVES, E., and KLIMEK, J. J. Infect. Dis., 1931, 48:1–159.
HAUDUROY, P. Compt. rend. Soc. de biol., 1926, 95:1523; 1927, 97:1392.
HENRICI, A. T. Morphologic Variation and the Rate of Growth of Bacteria, Springfield, Ill., 1928.
HORT, E. C. Proc. Roy. Soc. London, Ser. B., 1917, 89:468.
────── J. Hyg., 1920, 18:369.
KAHN, M. C. Am. Rev. Tuberc., 1929, 20:150.
KENDALL, A. I. Northwestern Univ. Bull., Chicago, 1931, 32: No. 5, Sept. 28; No. 8, Oct. 19.
────── Science, 1932, 75:295.
KLIENEBERGER, E. Ergebn. d. Hyg. Bakteriol., Immunitätsforsch. u. Exp. Therap., 1930, 11:499.
KOCH, R. Untersuchungen über die Wundinfektionskrankheiten, Leipzig, 1878. Translated by W. W. Cheyne in publication of New Sydenham Soc., London, 1880, p. 71.
────── Verhandl. d. X Internat. Med. Congresses, Berlin, 1890, 1:35–47. Quoted from Löhnis.
KOWALENKO, A. Ztschr. f. Hyg. u. Infectionskrankh., 1910, 66:277.
LEHMANN, K., and NEUMANN, R. O. Atlas und Grundriss der Bakteriologie, München, 1912. For English translation see the 7th edition, Bacteriology, Especially Determinative Bacteriology, by R. S. Breed, H. H. Boysen, P. A. Hansen and W. Reiner-Deutsch, New York, 1931.
LINDEGREN, C. C., and MELLON, R. R. Proc. Soc. Exper. Biol. & Med., 1932, 30:110.
LÖHNIS, F. Studies upon the Life Cycles of the Bacteria, Memoirs, Nat. Acad. Sc., Washington, 1921, 16:2nd Mem.

MACKENZIE, G. M., FITZGERALD, H., and IRONS, V. Proc. Soc. Exper. Biol. & Med., 1933, 30:536.
MASSINI, R. Arch. f. Hyg., 1907, 61:250.
MELLON, R. R.   J. Bacteriol., 1917, 2:89, 269; 1919, 4:505.
——— Am. J. M. Sc., 1920, 159:874.
——— J. Med. Research, 1920, 42:61.
MELLON, R. R., and ANDERSON, L. J. Immunol., 1919, 4:203.
MELLON, R. R., and JOST, E. L. Am. Rev. Tuberc., 1929, 19:483.
MELLON, R. R., and FISCHER, L. W. J. Infect. Dis., 1932, 51:117.
NÄGELI, C. von. Die niederen Pilze in ihren Beziehungen zu den Infectionskrankheiten und der
    Gesundheitspflege, München, 1877, pp. 20, 22.
——— Untersuchungen über niedere Pilze, München, 1882, pp. 130, 138.
NEISSER, M. Centralbl. f. Bakteriol., I Abt. Ref., Beiheft, 1906, 38:98.
NOGUCHI, H. J. Exper. M., 1910, 12:182.
RETTGER, L. F., and GILLESPIE, H. B. J. Bacteriol., 1933, 26:289.
ROSENOW, E. C., TOWNE, E. B., and WHEELER, G. W. J. Am. M. Ass., 1916, 67:1202. (And series
    of later papers to be referred to elsewhere.)
SEASTONE, C. V., and LAWRENCE, M. B. J. Infect. Dis., 1933, 52:20.
SMITH, T. Ann. M. Hist., 1932, 4:524.
TANG, F., and CASTANEDA, R. M. J. Bacteriol., 1928, 16:431.
VARNEY, P. L., and BRONFENBRENNER, J. Proc. Soc. Exper. Biol. & Med., 1932, 29:804.
WARD, H. K., and TANG, F. J. Exper. M., 1929, 44:1; 50:31.
WINSLOW, C.-E. A. Science 1932, 75:121.
WYCKOFF, R. W. G. Science, 1932, 76:240.
——— J. Exper. M., 1934, 59:381.
ZINSSER, H. Science, 1932, 75:256.

CHAPTER XI

CLASSIFICATION OF BACTERIA

Since 1773, when Mueller gave the first "definite named description of any organism now included among the bacteria," there have been some sixty or seventy published classifications of the bacteria. Buchanan has reproduced most of these in a large monograph on the history of classification, codes of nomenclature and the status of names which have been applied to groups of bacteria. A useful set of diagrammatic summaries of the more important classifications has been published by Buchanan, Breed and Rettger, and Miss Enlows has provided a list of the generic names of bacteria.

None of these classifications is satisfactory and no classification or rules of nomenclature have the force of international sanction. In this country several committees of the Society of American Bacteriologists have carefully studied the nomenclatures and classifications proposed by many systematists. They are moving with the International Botanical Congress and the International Society of Microbiologists toward the adoption of rules for naming micro-organisms and a general agreement upon arrangements of groups and the recognition of type species. The preliminary report of the American Committee was followed in 1920 by a final report (Winslow *et al.*) which contained a proposed classification. This classification has served as the basis of Bergey's *Manual of Determinative Bacteriology*, with its extensive subdivision and introduction of many new names. None of these is "official" in the sense of having been adopted formally by the national organization of bacteriologists. Bergey's classification and nomenclature have not been officially adopted by the Society of American Bacteriologists.

The American Committee adopted the International Rules of Botanical Nomenclature (Vienna, 1905, and Brussels, 1910) in so far as they could be made to apply to bacteriology. These rules were modified by the Cambridge Congress (1930) and the Amsterdam Congress (1935). The most important rules that are of interest to bacteriologists, taken from the latest edition of the Botanical Codē (1935) are reprinted in Bergey's *Manual*.

For years there has been as great confusion as at present in the classification of bacteria. There are many obvious reasons for this. A morphological system is not sufficient for the differentiation of bacteria, because many organisms with totally different properties are identical morphologically. Biochemical, antigenic and pathogenic properties have been drawn upon to provide the additional criteria needed for identification. The differentiation of bacteria is based upon a study of all the characteristics of the organisms. Hence the modern systems of classification utilize the knowledge of the morphology, physiology, metabolism, chemical composition, antigenic structure, pathogenicity and virulence of the bacteria. Morphology is still accorded primary importance in the establishment of large groups, but form, like the other criteria, fluctuates in "weight" in different categories. In some cases, as in the streptococci, fermentative reactions are of minor importance as compared with action upon blood cells. In others, as in the typhoid-dysentery group, fermentative differences with respect to one or two carbohydrates is more important than morphology for differentiation. Modern systems of bacteriological classification are making provision for this shifting emphasis on different characteristics of these multifarious micro-organisms.

The great mass of bacteriological knowledge is the product of specialized workers, each group particularly interested in some one field. These workers, busily engaged in studying chiefly what certain bacteria do rather than what they are, have had neither the time, inclination nor broad training required to give them a view of the whole subject. Therefore they have established groups of organisms for their own convenience and have named thousands of species on incomplete and uncorrelated descriptions. These habits of bacteriologists have added to the confusion and complexities of nomenclature. The medical bacteriologist has rarely been a systematist. By his carelessness in spelling, lack of regard for even unofficial but relatively rational rules and his rash new baptisms of already named species, the medical bacteriologist has contributed greatly to the difficulties of classification. Although no system has been adequate, satisfactory or official, we think that it would be advantageous for the medical bacteriologist to become more familiar with at least the trends of nomenclatural practice, and the genders of generic names (Van Eseltine).

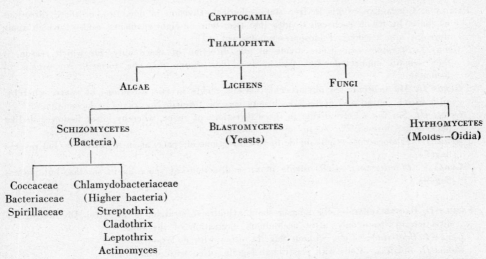

The main question, of course, is this: Are the bacteria classifiable? The answer to that will come only when these organisms are more completely known. The variability of the bacteria, of which we have described many examples, is still unestimated in its extent and significance. Older concepts of species have been greatly broadened. The species concept has passed from a restricted view of characteristics to a concept of statistical distribution of qualities about a mean, and is constantly widening. In some instances it is possible to state fairly rigid definitions, in many other cases a definition can be only vague and temporary. The relationships among the bacteria are not known with certainty. Hence taxonomy cannot be authoritative. Finally, the position of bacteria among other living things is still indefinitely known, since these organisms have characteristics which relate them to the blue-green algae, the fungi and to the protozoa. With reservations required by these uncertainties, we shall note here several classifications of a general and specific nature, the tendency of which is to indicate the relationships of groups of the bacteria and to designate the names of the most important pathogenic organisms. As will be seen, however, the nomenclature is very variable.

Since the bacteria do not contain chlorophyl and have on the whole a predominance of plant-like characteristics, they are usually placed in the plant kingdom. The relationship of the bacteria to simple plants may be graphically represented by the diagram on page 143.

One of the older classifications, based largely upon morphology, motility and situation of flagella, was that of Migula. This classification, published in 1900, is not adequate for our present needs. But as it had a fairly general acceptance in medical bacteriology and contains many of the names still used by the medical bacteriologist, we produce it here, as follows:

Bacteria (Schizomycetes).—Fission fungi (chlorophyl free), cell division in one, two, or three directions of space. Many varieties possess power of forming endospores. Whenever motility is present, it is due to flagella.

FAMILY I. COCCACEAE.—Cells in free state spherical. Division in one, two, or three directions of space, by which each cell divides into two, four or eight segments, each of which again develops into a sphere. Endospores not formed.

Genus I. Streptococcus.—Cells divide in one direction of space only, for which reason, if they remain connected after fission, bead-like chains may be formed. No organs of locomotion.

Genus II. Micrococcus (Staphylococcus).—Cells divide in two directions of space, whereby, after fission, tetrad and grape-like clusters may be formed. No organs of locomotion.

Genus III. Sarcina.—Cells divide in three directions of space, whereby, after fission, bale-like packets are formed. No organs of locomotion.

Genus IV. Planococcus.—Cells divide in two directions of space, as in micrococcus, but possess flagella.

Genus V. Planosarcina.—Cells divide in three directions of space as in sarcina, but possess flagella.

FAMILY II. BACTERIACEAE.—Cells long or short, cylindrical, straight, never spiral. Division in one direction of space only, after preliminary elongation of the rods.

Genus I. Bacterium.—Cells without flagella, often with endospores.

Genus II. Bacillus.—Cells with peritrichal flagella, often with endospores.

Genus III. Pseudomonas.—Cells with polar flagella. Endospores occur in a few species, but are rare.

FAMILY III. SPIRILLACEAE.—Cells spirally curved or representing a part of a spiral curve. Division in one direction of space only, after preceding elongation of cell.

Genus I. Spirosoma.—Cells without organs of locomotion. Rigid.

Genus II. Microspira.—Cells rigid, with one or, more rarely, two or three polar undulated flagella.

Genus III. Spirillum.—Cells rigid, with polar tufts of five to twenty flagella usually curved in semicircular or flatly undulating curves.

Genus IV. Spirochaeta.—Cells sinuously flexible. Organs of locomotion unknown, perhaps a marginal undulating membrane.

FAMILY IV. CHLAMYDOBACTERIACEAE.—Forms of varying stages of evolution, all possessing a rigid sheath (Hülle), which surrounds the cells. Cells united in branched or unbranched threads.

Genus I. Streptothrix.—Cells united in simple, unbranched threads. Division in one direction of space only. Reproduction by nonmotile conidia.

(Note: This is now unsatisfactory. *Streptothrix* has branched filaments. Filaments without branching are called *Leptothrix*.)

Genus II. Cladothrix.—Cells united or pseudodichotomously branching threads. Division in one direction of space only. Vegetative multiplication by separation of entire branches. Reproduction by swarming forms with polar flagella.

Genus III. Crenothrix.—Cells united in unbranched threads, at first with division in one direction of space only. Later the cells divide in all three directions of space. The daughter cells become rounded and develop into reproductive cells.

Genus IV. Phragmidiothrix.—Cells at first united in unbranched threads, dividing in three directions of space, thus forming a rope of cells. Later some of the cells may penetrate through sheath, and thus give rise to branches.

Genus V. Thiothrix.—Unbranched, nonmotile threads, inclosed in fine sheaths. Division of cells in one direction only. Cells contain sulphur granules.

FAMILY V. BEGGIATOACEAE.—Cells united in sheathless threads. Division in one direction of space only. Motility by undulating membrane as in Oscillaria.

Genus beggiatoa.—Cells with sulphur granules.

Bergey's *Manual of Determinative Bacteriology* is now the most complete work on classification and nomenclature. Since its first appearance in 1923 it has consistently gained in authority as a guide and reference book. The fifth edition (1939) by Breed, Murray and Hitchens, assisted by a distinguished group of specialists, is a vast work of scholarship. It contains descriptions of 1335 species of bacteria with 5600 references to the places of original publications of descriptions. With each edition groupings have been changed and new names introduced. In the latest, nine new generic names occur, and many older names are relegated to the lists of synonyms. Many of these changes are the inevitable results of increased knowledge of the characteristics and relationships of bacteria. Some, however, appear to be arbitrary, though supported by reasons. We and others may disagree with some of the decisions. Confusion is increased to no small extent by this novel and fluctuating terminology. Nevertheless, the influence of the *Manual* is definitely in the direction of system and order, and the book is indispensable for all bacteriologists.

The table on page 146 is an abstract of a portion of the 1939 *Manual's* classification, arranged for the convenience of the medical bacteriologist.

Throughout this book we have used older terms, common names and familiar designations of the bacteria, with no attempt to be consistent. In connection with each organism we have placed the name given in Bergey's *Manual* at the head of the chapter.

The useful groupings of bacteria according to fermentative capacities, biochemical reactions and immunological relationships will be given wherever appropriate in subsequent chapters.

For convenience, we place here a general classification of pathogenic organisms divided into two groups according to their reaction to Gram's stain. One group of bacteria, stained with basic triphenylmethane dyes, such as gentian violet, and then treated with iodine followed by alcohol, retains the original dye. These are called gram-positive. Organisms of the other group lose the original dye when treated with

Diagrammatic Abstract of a Portion of Bergey's *Manual*, 1939
Class: SCHIZOMYCETES

Order	Family	Tribe	Genus	Species, etc.
Eubacteriales	Rhizobiaceae		Alcaligenes	Alc. faecalis
	Pseudomonadaceae	Spirilleae	Vibrio Spirillum	Cholera group Rat bite fever
		Pseudomonadeae	Pseudomonas Phytomonas	Pyocyaneus group Plant pathogens
	Micrococcaceae		Micrococcus Staphylococcus Gaffkya Sarcina	Micrococci Pyogenic cocci M. tetragenus
	Neisseriaceae		Neisseria Veillonella	Meningococcus and Gonococcus Anaerobic cocci
	Parvobacteriaceae	Pasteurelleae	Pasteurella Malleomyces	Hemorrhagic septicemia; plague; tularemia Glanders
		Brucelleae	Brucella	Brucellosis; undulant fever
		Hemophileae	Hemophilus Noguchia Dialister	Influenza group Trachoma Pneumosintes group
	Lactobacteriaceae	Streptococceae	Diplococcus Streptococcus Lactobacillus	Pneumococcus Streptococci Acidophilus group
	Enterobacteriaceae	Eschericheae	Escherichia Aerobacter Klebsiella	Colon group Aerogenes group Friedländer group
		Erwineae	Erwinia	Plant pathogens
		Serrateae	Serratia	B. prodigiosus
		Proteae	Proteus	Proteus group
		Salmonelleae	Salmonella Eberthella Shigella	Paratyphoid group Typhoid group Dysentery group
	Bacteriaceae		Listerella Kurthia Flavobacterium Actinobacillus Bacteroides Fusobacterium Bacterium	Monocytogenes Zopfius group Actinobacillosis Necrophorus group Fusiforms Miscellaneous
	Bacillaceae		Bacillus Clostridium	Aerobic spore-bearers; anthrax Anaerobic spore-bearers
Acrinomycetales	Mycobacteriaceae		Corynebacterium Mycobacterium	Diphtheria Tubercle bacilli
	Actinomycetaceae		Leptotrichia Erysipelothrix Actinomyces	Leptothrix Actinomycosis
Chlamydobacteriales	No pathogens in this order.			
Thiobacteriales	No pathogens in this order.			
Myxobacteriales	No pathogens in this order.			
Spirochaetales	Spirochaetaceae		Spirochaeta Saprospira Cristispira Borrelia Treponema Leptospira	Saprophytes Saprophytes Molluscs Relapsing fever Syphilis Weil's disease

iodine followed by alcohol and take the color of a contrast counter stain. These are called gram-negatives. Numerous characteristics can be correlated with these gram-staining differences, as summarized by Churchman.

CLASSIFICATION OF MORE IMPORTANT PATHOGENIC BACTERIA
ACCORDING TO GRAM'S STAIN

Gram-positive (Retain the gentian violet)	Gram-negative (Take color of counterstain)
Streptococci	Meningococcus
Pneumococci	Micrococcus catarrhalis
Staphylococci	Gonococcus
Micrococci	Bacterium coli
Bacillus subtilis	Bacterium aerogenes
Bacillus anthracis	Proteus
Bacillus tetani	Bacillus typhosus
Bacillus welchii	Paratyphoid bacilli
Bacillus botulinus	Dysentery bacilli (all bacteria of colon-typhoid
Bacillus diphtheriae	dysentery group)
Bacillus tuberculosis and other acid-fast bacteria	Friedländer's bacillus
Many actinomycetes	Bacillus pyocyaneus
	Bacillus influenzae
	Koch-Weeks bacillus
	Morax-Axenfeld bacillus
	Ducrey's bacillus
	Bacillus mallei
	Bacillus pestis
	Brucella group (infectious abortion and undulant fever)
	Bacterium tularense
	Vibrio cholerae

REFERENCES

Bergey's *Manual of Determinative Bacteriology*, by D. H. Bergey, R. S. Breed, E. G. D. Murray and A. P. Hitchins. Williams and Wilkins Co., Baltimore, 1939, 5th ed.

The fifth edition of this *Manual* was issued in April, 1939, when the page proof of this *Textbook* was almost ready for the press. As many revisions as possible have been introduced to conform with the classifications and nomenclature of the new *Manual*.

BUCHANAN, R. E. General Systematic Bacteriology, Baltimore, 1925.

BUCHANAN, R. E., BREED, R. S., and RETTGER, L. F. Bacteriol., 1928, 16:387.

CHURCHMAN, J. W. Newer Knowledge of Bacteriology and Immunology, Chicago, 1928, Chap. III, 19–37, esp. p. 25.

ENLOWS, E. M. A. Generic Names of Bacteria, Bull. No. 121, 1920. Hygienic Laboratory, U. S. Pub. Health Service.

MIGULA, W. System der Bakterien, Jena, Vol. 1, 1897; Vol. 2, 1900.

VAN ESELTINE, G. P. J. Bacteriol., 1933, 26:569.

WINSLOW, C.-E. A., BROADHURST, J., BUCHANAN, R. E., KRUMWIEDE, C., ROGERS, L. A., and SMITH, G. E. J. Bacteriol., 1917, 2:552; 1920, 5:191.

SECTION II

INFECTION AND IMMUNITY *

CHAPTER XII

FUNDAMENTAL FACTORS OF PATHOGENICITY AND INFECTION

When micro-organisms gain entrance to the animal or human body and give rise to disease, the process is spoken of as infection.

Bacteria are always present in the environment of animals and human beings and some find constant lodgment on various parts of the body. The mouth, the nasal passages, the skin, the upper respiratory tract, the conjunctivae, the ducts of the genital system, and the intestines are invariably inhabited by numerous species of bacteria, which, while subject to no absolute constancy, conform to more or less definite characteristics of species distribution for each locality. Thus the colon organisms are invariably present in the normal bowel, Döderlein's bacillus in the vagina, B. xerosis in many normal conjunctivae, and staphylococcus, streptococcus, various spirilla, and pneumococcus in the mouth. In contrast, therefore, with the bodies of animals and man, there is a large flora of micro-organisms, some as constant parasites, others as transient invaders; some harmless saprophytes and others capable of becoming pathogenic. It is evident, therefore, that the production of an infection must depend upon other influences than the mere presence of the micro-organisms and their contact with the body, and that the occurrence of the reaction—for the phenomena of infection are in truth reactions between the germ and the body defenses—is governed by a number of important secondary factors.

In order to cause infection, it is necessary that the bacteria shall gain entrance to the body by a path adapted to their own respective cultural requirements, and shall be permitted to proliferate after gaining a foothold. Some of the bacteria then cause disease by rapid multiplication, progressively invading more and more extensive areas of the animal tissues, while others may remain localized at the point of invasion and exert their harmful action chiefly by local growth and the elaboration of specific poisons.

The inciting or inhibiting factors which permit or prohibit an infection are dependent in part upon the nature of the invading germ and in part upon the conditions of the defensive mechanism of the subject attacked.

Bacteria are roughly divided into two classes, saprophytes and parasites. The saprophytes are those bacteria which thrive best on dead organic matter and fulfil the important function in nature of reducing by their physiological activities the excreta and the dead bodies of more highly organized forms into those simple chemical substances which may again be utilized by the plants in their constructive

---

* This section on Infection and Immunity should be regarded as an outline of the most important facts. For detailed information the student should consult one of the larger and more specialized treatises.

processes. The saprophytes, thus, are of extreme importance in maintaining the chemical balance between the animal and plant kingdoms. Parasites, on the other hand, find the most favorable conditions for their development upon the living bodies of higher forms.

While a strict separation of the two divisions cannot be made, numerous species forming transitions between the two, it may be said that the parasites comprise most of the so-called "pathogenic" or disease-producing bacteria. Strict saprophytes may cause disease, but only in cases where other factors have brought about the death of tissues, and the bacteria invade the necrotic areas and break down the proteins into poisonous chemical substances such as ptomaines, or through their own destruction liberate toxic constituents of their bodies. In this sense diphtheria bacilli and tetanus bacilli are, strictly speaking, saprophytes, although they are highly pathogenic. They do not penetrate into the tissues and the tetanus bacillus can develop only on the dead tissues of trauma or in wounds complicated by other infections. Locally established, however, these organisms can grow and produce poisons which are absorbed and may kill the patient. Saprophytism can thus be associated with a high degree of pathogenicity when toxins of great potency are elaborated.

THE PROBLEM OF VIRULENCE

The pathogenic micro-organisms differ much among themselves in the degree of their disease-inciting power. Such power is known as *virulence*. Variations in virulence occur, not only among different species of pathogenic bacteria, but may occur within the same species. Pneumococci, for instance, which have been kept upon artificial media or in other unfavorable environment for some time, exhibit less virulence than when freshly isolated from the bodies of man or animals. It is necessary, therefore, in order to produce infection, that the particular bacterium involved shall possess sufficient virulence.

Virulence was formerly regarded as a much more stable species characteristic than it is at present. In a separate section on bacterial dissociation we have gone more fully into these matters. Dissociation phenomena as they occur in individual species are discussed in the several chapters dealing with the bacterium concerned. We have learned that a virulent organism may dissociate into nonvirulent forms under special environmental conditions either within the body or in the test tube. Highly virulent "smooth" pneumococci may be rapidly changed into nonvirulent "rough" pneumococci by a few generations' cultivation on inactivated immune serum or on unfavorable media such as those containing bile. They may spontaneously so change on ordinary culture media or even in the body, in the course of convalescence, as shown by Shibley. Under other conditions, either within the animal body or in the test tube, these nonvirulent rough organisms may return to the smooth form. With these changes in biological behavior, both in the animal body and in culture, there is associated a chemical antigenic change of immunological significance. Analogous dissociation conditions probably govern the fluctuations in virulence of all pathogenic micro-organisms.

In an effort to cast light upon this problem, Bail, following in the footsteps of Kruse, Deutsch and Feistmantel, formulated his so-called "aggressin-theory."

Bail was first led to his theory by researches which he had made in conjunction with Petersson into anthrax immunity. He had noted, as had others before him, that animals, highly susceptible to anthrax, often possessed marked bactericidal powers against this bacillus. When such animals, whose serum should surely be capable of bringing about the death of at least a few hundred anthrax bacilli, were injected with doses far less than this number they nevertheless succumbed rapidly and the bacilli multiplied enormously in their bodies. He argued from this that the injected micro-organisms must possess some weapon whereby they were enabled to counteract the protective forces of the animal organism. In an anthrax-immune animal, as a matter of fact, no proliferation of bacteria took place and the injected germs were rapidly disposed of by the protective forces.

The theory of Bail contains the following basic principles:

Pathogenic bacteria differ fundamentally from nonpathogenic bacteria in their power to overcome the protective mechanism of the animal body, and to proliferate within it. They accomplish this by virtue of definite substances given off by them, probably in the nature of a secretion, which acts primarily by protecting them against phagocytosis. These substances were named by Bail, "aggressins." The production of aggressins by pathogenic germs is probably absent in test-tube cultures, or, at any rate, is greatly depressed under such conditions, but is called forth in the animal body for the influences encountered after inoculation.

These aggressins can be found, according to Bail, in the exudates about the site of inoculation in fatal infections. He obtained them, separate from the bacteria, by the centrifugation and subsequent decanting of edema fluid, and pleural and peritoneal exudates.

The theory of Bail was attacked chiefly by Wassermann and Citron, Wolff, and Sauerbeck. The criticism which these investigators made of Bail's views has succeeded in placing the aggressin theory in doubt.

The sterile aggressin exudates could be shown to possess a considerable degree of toxicity and the aggressive action could be duplicated by aqueous extracts of bacteria. Citron was able to show by the Bordet-Gengou method of complement fixation, that the exudates of Bail contained quantities of free bacterial receptors, now known to be specific soluble carbohydrate, which, in uniting with immune body, would neutralize any destructive power on the part of the infected animal.

The earlier knowledge of the relationship of the bacterial capsule to bacterial virulence has been, in principle, upheld by later investigations. Danysz was the first to suggest this relation, in studies in which he correlated the development of capsules with an artificially induced increased resistance of anthrax bacilli to arsenic solutions. Subsequently the coincidence of capsule formation with pathogenicity was described by Shibayama with plague bacilli, by Preisz with anthrax and by numerous other observers working with Friedländer bacilli, pneumococci and streptococci. Gruber and Futaki noted the resistance of capsulated anthrax bacilli against phagocytosis in preparations in which noncapsulated organisms were readily engulfed by the leukocytes.

The beginning of modern knowledge of virulence was made by Arkwright when he discovered that from one and the same culture of dysentery bacilli two distinct races of organisms could be developed. One of these, which he designated as the rough, was granular in its colony formation on agar and, in broth, instead of evenly clouding the medium, it had a tendency to sedimentation and floccular growth. At the same time, the rough was less virulent than the original culture. This observation was confirmed by De Kruif with the bacillus of rabbit septicemia, by Jordan with paratyphoid bacilli, and by Blake and Trask, Reimann, Grinnell and others with the pneumococcus; while Pittman has obtained rough and smooth influenza strains. In the case of many of these investigations the strains used have been cultivated from single cells, thus rendering it certain that the phenomenon was one not far removed from a true mutation. In the case of the pneumococcus, the cultivation of virulent single cell strains in immune serum, in the presence of bile or on simple media, results presently in the formation of rough colonies which may entirely lose their virulence, while smooth colonies from the same plate, recognizable even with the naked eye, remain as virulent as at first. Together with loss of virulence and the changed cultural characteristics these rough varieties cease to agglutinate type-specifically and lose their capsules.

That such changes can take place *in vivo* was shown by Ho Yü in our laboratory. He found that diphtheria bacilli were changed from the fully pathogenic toxin-producing type to an atoxic variant in the throats of convalescent cases and that, with this change, there was an alteration in the appearance of colonies. The same change could be obtained in cultures to which inactivated bacterial antiserum had been added. Antitoxic serum did not have the same effect.

Reversion from rough, nonvirulent to smooth virulent has been obtained by Griffith with the pneumococcus, by animal passage, a result which has been confirmed by Reimann and others. Dawson and Sia have produced a similar reversion in the test tube by growing R pneumococci in broth containing 10 per cent anti-R serum and dead S organisms. These conditions are described at greater length in the section on bacterial dissociation.

We have given a brief account only of the rapidly accumulating facts which are being discovered about bacterial dissociation and its relationship to virulence. In the paragraphs on the bacterial antigen, the correlation between dissociation forms and antigenic changes have been set forth. It is plain that all this information has brought us much closer to an understanding of the phenomena of virulence fluctuations and must needs have a profound influence both on the theory and the practice of immunology. It is obvious, for instance, that if the virulent dissociant is the only one which contains the total antigenic structure, this is the only form which is of any value in active immunization; and it is also plain that if bacteria can gain and lose virulence as a result of environmental influences outside and within the animal body, such facts must have a determining effect upon the rise and fall of epidemic disease in communities.

Dosage.—Whether or not infection occurs depends also upon the *number of bacteria* which gain entrance to the animal tissues. A small number of bacteria, even though of proper species and of sufficient virulence, may easily be overcome by the first onslaught of the defensive forces of the body. Bacteria, therefore, must be in sufficient number to overcome local defenses and to gain a definite foothold and carry on their life processes, before they can give rise to an infection.

There are, of course, bacteria which may possess a virulence so high for a given species of animals that a single organism is capable of causing infection. This is probably true of the highly virulent races of the anthrax bacillus and we are quite sure that a single smooth Type I pneumococcus may cause a fatal infection in a rabbit. In human infections it is not unlikely that highly virulent plague bacilli, *Treponema* of syphilis or *Rickettsia* of typhus fever may cause infection with extremely small doses.

Path of Infection.—The portal by which bacteria gain entrance to the human body is of great importance in determining whether or not disease shall occur. Typhoid bacilli rubbed into the abraded skin may give rise to no reaction of importance, while the same micro-organism, if swallowed, may cause fatal infection. Conversely, virulent streptococci, when swallowed, may cause no harmful effects, while the same bacteria rubbed into the skin may give rise to a severe reaction.

Animals and man are protected against invasion by bacteria in various ways. Externally the body is guarded by its coverings of skin and mucous membranes. When these are healthy and undisturbed, micro-organisms are usually held at bay. While this is true in a general way, bacteria may in occasional cases pass through uninjured skin and mucosa. Thus the Austrian Plague Commission found that guinea-pigs could be infected when plague bacilli were rubbed into the shaven skin, and there can hardly be much doubt of the fact that tubercle bacilli may occasionally pass through the intestinal mucosa into the lymphatics without causing local lesions.

Even after bacteria of a pathogenic species, in large numbers and of adequate virulence, have passed through a locally undefended area in the skin or mucosa of an animal or a human being by the path most favorably adapted to them, it is by no means certain that an infection will take place. The bodies of animals and of man have at their disposal weapons of defense, both in the blood serum and the cellular elements of blood and tissues which, if normally active, will usually overcome a certain number of the invading bacteria. If these defenses are depressed, or the invading micro-organisms are disproportionately virulent or plentiful, infection takes place.

Bacteria, after gaining an entrance to the body, may give rise merely to local inflammation. They may, on the other hand, from the local lesion, gain entrance into the lymphatics and blood vessels and be carried freely into the circulation. The transitory occurrence of bacteria in the blood stream is called *bacteremia* or *bacteriemia*. Persistence of organisms in the blood, with multiplication of bacteria in the circulation or in a focus on a heart-valve or lesion of the wall of a vessel is designated by the term *septicemia*. Carried by the blood to other parts of the body, they may gain foothold in various organs and give rise to secondary foci of inflammation, necrosis and abscess formation. Such a condition is known as *pyemia*. The disease processes arising as the result of bacterial invasion may depend wholly or in part upon the mechanical injury produced by the process of inflammation, the disturbance of function caused by the presence of the bacteria in the capillaries and tissue spaces, and the absorption of the necrotic products resulting from the reaction between the body cells and the micro-organisms.

Bacterial Poisons.—It is more than likely, however, that a toxic factor is involved in all infections.

It was in his investigations into the nature of these poisons that Brieger was led to the discovery of the *ptomaines*. These bodies, first isolated by him from decomposing beef, fish and human cadavers, have found more extended discussion in another section. They are not true bacterial poisons in the sense in which the term is now employed. They are produced from protein material by bacterial action, and are cleavage products derived from the culture medium upon the composition of which their nature intimately depends. The bacterial poisons proper, on the other hand, are synthetic products of the bacteria themselves, dependent upon the nature of the medium only as it favors or retards the full development of the physiological functions of the micro-organisms. The poisons, produced to a greater or lesser extent by all pathogenic micro-organisms, may be of several kinds. The true *toxins*, in the specialized meaning which the term has acquired, are soluble products of the bacterial cells, passing from them into the culture medium during life. They may be obtained free from the bacteria by filtration and in a purer state from the filtrates by chemical precipitation and a variety of other methods. Examples of such poisons are those of *B. diphtheriae* and *B. tetani*. If cultures of these bacteria are grown in fluid media for several days and the medium is then filtered through porcelain candles, the filtrate will be found highly toxic, while the residue will be either inactive or comparatively weak. Moreover, if the residue possesses any toxicity at all, the symptoms evidencing this will be different from those produced by the filtrate.

There are other micro-organisms, however, such as the cholera spirillum and the typhoid bacillus, by which no such exotoxins are formed. If such bacteria are cultivated and separated from the culture fluid by filtration, as above, the fluid filtrate will be toxic to a slight degree, whereas the residue may be very poisonous. In these cases, we are dealing, evidently, with poisons not secreted into the medium by the bacteria, but attached more or less firmly to the bacterial body. Such poisons, separable from the bacteria only after death by some method of extraction, or by autolysis, were termed by Pfeiffer *endotoxins*. The greater number of the pathogenic bacteria act chiefly by means of poisons of this class.

The first observation of intracellular poisons was made by Buchner, who induced sterile abscesses and symptoms of toxemia in animals with dead cultures of staphylococci. Pfeiffer's studies on the endotoxins of many bacteria then followed and the conception was definitely established by his work on the cellular poisons of the cholera spirillum.

A number of bacteria give rise to both the true exotoxin and to an endotoxin. The Shiga dysentery bacillus, for instance, possesses an endotoxin quite similar to that of other members of this group of organisms; at the same time it secretes a true exotoxin with which an antitoxin can be obtained. The exotoxin causes specific injury to the central nervous system and is pharmacologically quite distinct from the endocellular poison.

Most true exotoxins are easily separated from the bacterial cell and are rather delicately susceptible to heat. However, this is not always the case. The Dick toxins of scarlet fever streptococci have considerable heat resistance, and this is also true of snake venoms which are, in other respects, similar to bacterial exotoxins. In regard to the ease of separation from the cell, the toxic substance of the whooping cough bacillus appears to be a true exotoxin as far as antitoxin production is concerned, but is closely associated with the cell body, as though it were in this respect an endotoxin. There is, thus, in the secondary characteristics, considerable difference between the various poisons grouped together as exotoxins. *The all-important characteristic which distinguishes them from other poisonous substances and which justifies their being considered in a separate classification is their common property of giving rise to antitoxin production in animals.* It is on the basis of this property alone that we classify bacterial poisons into exotoxins and other toxic substances. The importance of such a differentiation for clinical medicine is obvious. Only when an organism produces a true exotoxin can we hope to produce an antitoxic serum for therapeutic purposes. Immune sera produced with other organisms are antibacterial rather than antitoxic, since their effectiveness consists entirely in action upon the bacteria either by bactericidal coöperation with alexin or by opsonic acceleration of phagocytosis.

The chief organisms that produce exotoxins in the sense in which we have defined them above are the bacilli of diphtheria, tetanus and botulism; some of the anaerobes of wound infections; the hemolytic streptococci of scarlet fever and erysipelas; certain strains of *Staphylococcus aureus* and the Shiga dysentery bacillus. It is not at all impossible that true toxins may be found in other organisms by suitable methods. Some of those mentioned have been discovered within the last few years. Nonbacterial substances that belong in this class are the vegetable poisons, ricin, crotin, robin, abrin, snake venoms, spider and scorpion poisons and possibly some of the enzymes.

For a review of the results of chemical investigations of bacterial toxins the reader is referred to Eaton's monograph on this subject.

In addition to the exo- and endotoxins, some of the bacteria produce non-specific toxic substances which can be obtained by washing young agar cultures with salt solution and filtering, or by filtering young broth cultures. These poisons are not very potent, but are quite definite and seem to act chiefly as capillary poisons. They have been spoken of as bacterial X-substances.

Most of the exotoxins are delicately susceptible to heat, being destroyed or weakened by exposure to 70° C. or over. To this rule, however, there are a number of exceptions which we have mentioned. The Dick scarlet fever toxin is also heat resistant although the recent investigations of Ando suggest that possibly the heat resistant fraction is an allergic factor while the true toxic constituent is heat sensitive. Most of the exotoxins deteriorate readily on standing. The general opinion held by biochemists at the present time is that the exotoxins are proteins. Glenny and Walpole state that the purified diphtheria toxin obtained by acetic acid precipitation in the cold behaves like a proteose. Wells suggests that the toxin radical may possibly be nonprotein but may be attached to a protein.

The chemical nature of toxins has been considerably elucidated by the work of Eaton and of Pappenheimer on the diphtheria toxin. The studies of all these workers agree in revealing that the toxin is a protein which contains about 0.0005 mg. of nitrogen per flocculating unit. That the toxins isolated by these investigators are pure substances is indicated by the fact that titration reveals a complete parallelism between nitrogen contents and antitoxin neutralization.

We have no reliable information concerning the chemical change which takes place during the transformation of toxin to toxoid.

Mode of Action.—Many of the bacterial poisons possess definite selective action for special tissues and organs. Thus, soluble toxins of the tetanus bacillus and *B.*

botulinus attack specifically the nervous system. Certain poisons elaborated by staphylococci, the tetanus bacillus, streptococci, and some other bacteria attack primarily the red blood corpuscles. Other poisons act on the white blood corpuscles.

It seems probable, from the researches of Meyer, Overton, Ehrlich, and others, that such selective action of poisons depends upon the ability, chemical or physical or both, of the poisons to enter into combination with the specifically affected cells. From the nature of the combinations formed, it seems not unlikely that the physical factors, such as solubility in the cell plasma, also play an important part.

Observations of a more purely bacteriological nature have tended to bear out these conclusions. Wassermann and Takaki, for instance, have shown that tetanus toxin, which specifically attacks the nervous system, may be removed from solution by the addition of brain substance. Removal of the brain tissue by centrifugation leaves the solution free from toxin. In the same way it has been shown that hemolytic poisons can be removed from solutions by contact with red blood cells, but only when the red blood cells of susceptible species are employed.

Similar observations have been made in the case of leukocidin, a bacterial poison acting specifically upon the white blood cells.

That bacterial poisons injected into susceptible animals rapidly disappear from the circulation is a fact which bears out the view that a combination between affected tissue and toxin must take place. Doenitz has shown that within four to eight minutes after the injection of certain toxins, considerable quantities will have disappeared from the circulation. Conversely, Metchnikoff has observed that tetanus toxin injected into insusceptible animals (lizards) may be detected in the blood stream for as long as two months after administration. With the exception of the toxin of the *B. botulinus*, ingestion in the presence of a healthy mucous membrane and normal digestive juices does little injury. The botulinus toxin acts through the intestinal canal.

The properties of individual toxins are dealt with in the respective sections concerned with the bacteria which produce them.

LOCAL TISSUE REACTIVITY—SHWARTZMAN PHENOMENON

In 1927 Shwartzman observed a new phenomenon of local skin reactivity to bacterial culture filtrates. The basic experiment was as follows: A single injection of culture filtrate of *B. typhosus* was made into the skin of a rabbit. Twenty-four hours later a quantity of the same filtrate was injected intravenously. Four hours after the intravenous injection severe hemorrhagic necrosis appeared at the prepared site in the skin. The area became dark blue, swollen, with a red border, and extended from the superficial layers of the skin through the entire thickness of the abdominal wall to the peritoneum. Histologically the tissue showed disruption of venules, hemorrhage, thrombosis and necrosis of all cells in the area. For the production of this effect, now known as the Shwartzman phenomenon, it is necessary to give the second injection intravenously.

Active preparatory and reacting principles have been obtained from *B. typhosus*, *B. coli*, meningococci and other bacteria. A quantitative relation exists between the amounts injected intradermally and intravenously. These materials have antigenic properties as well as destructive action upon tissues. Use of these properties has been made in the titration of antimeningococcal serum and other immune sera developed to counteract the poisonous effects of toxic substances contained in bacterial cells and also various bacterial poisons. Not all rabbits are suitable for the demonstration of the phenomenon. Mice and rats are usually non-reactive.

The nature of this phenomenon is not clearly understood. It may be a form of allergy, if the term is used to denote simply altered reactivity of cells. Apparently it is not true anaphylaxis nor an example of the Arthus phenomenon. Shwartzman regards it as a state of reactivity due to functional disturbance in the susceptibility of the animal tissue elicited by means of certain active principles of bacteria. In his opinion these active principles are related to exotoxins. It is probable that similar reactions occur in the skin and mucosae in the course of bacterial infections.

REFERENCES

ARKWRIGHT, J. A.   J. Path. & Bacteriol., 1921, 24:36.

BAIL, O.   Arch. f. Hyg., 1905, 52:272.

———— Wien. klin. Wchnschr., 1905, 18:211, 428.

———— Centralbl. f. Bakteriol., I Abt., 1900, 27:10, 517; 1902, 33:343.

BAIL, O., and PETERSSON, A.   Centralbl. f. Bakteriol., I Abt., 1903, 33:756; 1903, 34:167, 445; 1903, 35:102, 247; 1904, 36:266, 397.

BAIL, O., and WEIL, E.   Centralbl. f. Bakteriol., I Abt., 1905, 40:371; 1906, 42:51.

———— Wien. klin. Wchnschr., 1906, 19:839.

BLAKE, F. G., and TRASK, J. D.   J. Med. Research, 1923, 44:100.

BRIEGER, L.   Ueber Ptomaine, Berlin, 1885.

DANYSZ, J.   Ann. de l'Inst. Pasteur, 1900, 14:641.

DAWSON, M. H., and SIA, R. H. P.   J. Exper. M., 1931, 54:681.

DEKRUIF, P. H.   J. Exper. M., 1921, 33:773; 1922, 35:621.

DEUTSCH, D. L., and FEISTMANTEL, C.   Die Impfstoffe und Sera, Leipzig, 1903.

DOENITZ, W.   Deutsche med. Wchnschr., 1897, 23:428.

EATON, M. D.   Recent chemical investigations of bacterial toxins. Bacteriol. Rev., 1938, 2:3.

EHRLICH, P.   Das Sauerstoff-Bedürfniss des Organismus, Berlin, 1885.

GLENNY, A. T., and WALPOLE, G. S.   Bio-Chem. J., 1915, 9:298.

GRIFFITH, F.   J. Hyg., 1928, 27:113.

GRINNELL, F. B.   J. Exper. M., 1931, 54:577; 1932, 56:907.

GRUBER, M., and FUTAKI, K.   München. med. Wchnschr., 1906, 53:249.

JORDAN, E. O.   J. Am. M. Ass., 1926, 86:177.

KRUSE, W.   Beitr. z. path. Anat. etc., 1892, 12: 333.

METCHNIKOFF, E.   L'Immunité dans les maladies infectieuses, Paris, 1901.

MEYER, H.   Arch. f. exper. Path. u. Pharmakol., 1899, 42:109; 1901, 46:338.

OVERTON, E.   Studien über die Narkose, Jena, 1901.

PAPPENHEIMER, A. M., Jr.   J. Biol. Chem., 1937, 120:543

PITTMAN, M.   J. Exper. M., 1931, 53:471.

PREISZ, H.   Centralbl. f. Bakteriol., I Abt., 1910, 55:503.

REIMANN, H. A.   J. Exper. M., 1925, 41:587; 1929, 49:237.

SACHS, H.   Beitr. z. chem. Phys. u. Path., 1902, 2:125.

SHWARTZMAN, L.   Phenomenon of Local Tissue Reactivity and Its Immunological, Pathological and Clinical Significance. Paul B. Hober, Inc., New York, 1937.

SHIBAYAMA, G.   Centralbl. f. Bakteriol., I Abt., 1905, 38:482; 1906, 42:144.

SHIBLEY, G. S., and ROGERS, E. S.   Proc. Soc. Exper. Biol. & Med., 1932, 30:6.

WASSERMANN, A., and TAKAKI, T.   Berl. klin. Wchnschr., 1898, 35:5.

WELLS, H. G.   The Chemical Aspects of Immunity, New York, 2nd ed., 1929.

YÜ, HO.   J. Bacteriol., 1930, 20:107.

CHAPTER XIII

DEFENSIVE FACTORS OF THE ANIMAL ORGANISM

RESISTANCE AND IMMUNITY

The mere entrance of a pathogenic micro-organism into the human or animal body through a breach of continuity in the mechanical defenses of skin or mucosa does not necessarily lead to the development of an infection. The opportunities for such an invasion are so numerous, and the contact of members of the animal kingdom with the germs of disease is so constant, that if this were the case, sooner or later all would succumb. The animal body possesses further physiological means of defense, by virtue of which pathogenic agents are, even after their entrance into the tissues and fluids, disposed of, or at least prevented from proliferating and elaborating their poisons. The power which enables the body to accomplish this is spoken of as "resistance." When this resistance, which in some degree is common to all members of the animal kingdom, is especially marked, it is spoken of as "immunity."

From this it follows naturally that the terms resistance and immunity, as well as their converse, susceptibility, are relative and not absolute terms. Degrees of resistance exist, which are determined to a certain extent by individual, racial, or species peculiarities; and persons or animals are spoken of as immune when they are unaffected by an exposure or an inoculation to which the normal average individual of the same species would ordinarily succumb. The word does not imply, however, that these individuals could not be infected with unusually virulent or large doses, or under particularly unfavorable circumstances. Thus, birds, while immune against the ordinary dangers of tetanus bacilli, may be killed by experimental inoculations with very large doses of tetanus toxin. Similarly, Pasteur rendered naturally immune hens susceptible to anthrax by cooling them to a subnormal temperature, and Canalis and Morpurgo did the same with doves by subjecting them to starvation.

Absolute immunity is rare. The complete insusceptibility of cold-blooded animals (frogs and turtles) under normal conditions to inoculation with even the largest doses of many of the bacteria pathogenic for warm-blooded animals, and the immunity of all the lower animals against leprosy, are among the few instances of absolute immunity known (Lubarsch). Apart from such exceptional cases, however, resistance, immunity and susceptibility must be regarded as purely relative terms.

The power of resisting any specific infection may be the natural heritage of a race or species, and is then spoken of as *natural immunity*. It may, on the other hand, be acquired either accidentally or artificially by a member of an ordinarily susceptible species, and is then called *acquired immunity*.

Natural Immunity.—*Species Immunity.*—It is well known that many of the infectious diseases which commonly affect man, do not occur spontaneously in animals. Thus, infection with *B. typhosus*, the vibrio of cholera, or the meningococcus

157

occurs in animals only after experimental inoculation. Gonorrheal and syphilitic infections not only do not occur spontaneously, but are experimentally produced in animals with the greatest difficulty—the consequent diseases being incomparably milder than those occurring in man. Other diseases, like leprosy, influenza, chickenpox, herpes zoster, etc., have never been successfully transmitted to animals.

Conversely, there are diseases among animals which do not spontaneously attack man. Human beings are immune to rinderpest, and, to a lesser degree, against chicken cholera.

Among animal species themselves great differences in susceptibility and resistance toward the various infections exist. Examples of this are the resistance to anthrax of rats and dogs, and the immunity of the common fowl against tetanus.

The factors which determine these differences of susceptibility and resistance among the various species are not clearly understood. Diet in some instances may influence these relations, inasmuch as carnivorous animals are often highly resistant to glanders, anthrax, and even tuberculous infections, to which herbivorous animals are markedly susceptible. It is likely, too, that the great difference between animals in metabolism, temperature, etc., may call for special cultural adaptation on the part of the bacteria. The fact that the bacillus of avian tuberculosis—whose natural host has a normal body temperature of 40° C. and above—will grow on culture media at 40° to 50° C., whereas *B. tuberculosis* of man cannot be cultivated at a temperature about 40° C., would seem to lend some support to this view. The difference in the resistance of warm- and cold-blooded animals has already been noted. There are few instances, however, in which such simple explanations are valid.

Racial Immunity.—Just as differences in susceptibility and immunity exist among the various animal species, so the separate races or varieties within the same species may display differences in their reactions toward pathogenic germs. Algerian sheep, for instance, show a much higher resistance to anthrax than do our own domestic sheep, and the various races of mice differ in their susceptibility to anthrax and to glanders.

Similar racial differences are common among human beings. As a general rule, it may be said that a race among whom a certain disease has been endemic for many ages is less susceptible to this disease than are other races among whom it has been more recently introduced. The ravages of tuberculosis among Negroes, American Indians, and Eskimos, bear witness to this fact.

Such racial immunity or susceptibility is hereditary only in the sense of natural selection, not as inheritance of an acquired characteristic. It is important to remember, however, that differences in customs of personal and social hygiene may confuse the issue. In some countries a disease is so prevalent that most individuals have had it and have become artificially immune during childhood. Thus in regions where yellow fever, malaria, and typhus fever prevail, acquired immunity, without available history of previous attack, has often been interpreted as racial resistance. In some instances, as in typhus fever, the disease in childhood is often so mild that it has not been recognized.

Differences in Individual Resistance.—In bacteriological experimentation with smaller test animals, a direct ratio may often exist between body weight and dosage in determining the outcome of an infection, provided the mode of inoculation has been the same and the virulence not excessive. In guinea-pigs, rabbits, mice, etc., bred from the same stock and fed and raised under similar conditions, there is often so great a similarity in susceptibility to infection or to toxin, that these animals can be used for standardization of toxins or bacterial virulence. The use of guinea-pigs for diphtheria antitoxin standardization and that of mice in determining the virulence of pneumococcus are cases in point.

In man, the existence of individual differences is a well-established fact, although we must not forget that the conditions of infection are not subject to the uniformity and control which animal experimentation permits. Of a number of persons exposed to any given infection there are always some who are unaffected, and there are great variations in the severity of the disease in those who are attacked. The most reasonable explanation for such differences seems to lie in individual variations in metabolism or body chemistry. Depressions, for instance, in the acidity of the gastric secretion would predispose to certain infections of gastro-intestinal origin. Anatomical differences, too, may possibly influence resistance. Thus, Birch-Hirschfeld believed that certain anomalous arrangements of the bronchial tubes predisposed to tuberculosis. The general physiological states vaguely expressed as being "fit" or in "good" or "bad" condition, fatigue, malnutrition, or chronic disease have unquestionable importance in determining susceptibility or resistance.

The mysterious individual differences which seem to exist in susceptibilities, confusing the epidemiological study of such diseases as poliomyelitis, meningitis and encephalitis, have led to speculations concerning constitutional differences in susceptibility. The relationship between diphtheria susceptibility and blood groupings has been the subject of studies by Hirszfeld and Friedberger; and in this country, Jungeblut has investigated the relationship of susceptibility with the development of the endocrine glands. There is too little experimental evidence to support any statement and while the subject is an extraordinarily interesting one, it is as yet largely speculative. It is confidently anticipated that in the future it will be possible to correlate states of resistance or susceptibility to infection with genetic factors, the activities of hormones and the content of certain vitamins, notably A and C, in the animal body. Knowledge concerning these factors is accumulating.

Acquired Immunity.—Many of the infectious diseases rarely occur more than once in the same individual. This is the case with typhoid fever, yellow fever, and most of the exanthemata. A single attack of any of the diseases of this class alters the resistance of the individual so that further exposure to the infective agent is usually without danger, either for a limited period after the attack, or for life. Resistance acquired in this way is spoken of as *acquired immunity*.

This protection conferred by certain diseases against a second attack was recognized many centuries ago, and there are records which show that attempts were made in ancient China and India to inoculate healthy individuals with pus from smallpox pustules in the hope of producing by this process a mild form of the disease and consequent immunity.

Influenced by these reports, but more definitely by the observation that milkmaids who had contracted cowpox were spared when smallpox epidemics swept over the neighborhood, Jenner developed our method of smallpox vaccination. No experimental progress was made after this until Pasteur's first observation, which was purely accidental, but one of those accidents which gave clues of discovery to great observers.

The failure of animals to die after inoculation with an old culture of the bacilli of chicken cholera, fully potent but a few weeks previously, pointed to the attenuation of these bacilli by their prolonged cultivation without transplantation. With this observation as a point of departure Pasteur carried out a series of investigations with the purpose of discovering a method of so weakening or attenuating various incitants of disease that they could be introduced into susceptible individuals without endangering life and yet without losing their property of conferring protection.

The experimental work which he carried out to solve this problem gave science the first examples of the application of exact laboratory methods to problems of immunity.

ACTIVE IMMUNITY

Active Artificial Immunity.—The process of conferring protection by treatment with either an attenuated form or a sublethal quantity of the infectious agent of a disease, or its products, is spoken of as active immunization.

Whatever the method employed, the immunized individuals gain their power of resistance by the unaided reactions of their own tissues. They themselves take an active physiological part in the acquisition of this new property of immunity. For this reason, Ehrlich termed these processes "active immunization."

Immunization with Attenuated Cultures.—In the course of experiments upon chicken cholera Pasteur accidentally discovered that the virulence of the bacilli of this disease was greatly reduced by prolonged cultivation upon artificial media. This was especially noticeable in broth cultures which had been stored for long periods without transplantation. By repeated injections of such cultures into fowls, he succeeded in rendering the animals immune against subsequent inoculations with lethal doses of fully virulent strains.

During the same year, 1880, in which Pasteur published his observations on chicken cholera, Toussaint succeeded in immunizing sheep against anthrax by inoculating them with blood from infected animals, defibrinated and heated to 55° C. for ten minutes. Toussaint wrongly believed that the blood which had been used in his immunizations was free from living bacteria. In repeating this work Pasteur showed that the protection in Toussaint's cases was conferred by living bacteria, the virulence of which had been reduced by heat.

Later Pasteur discovered that he could reduce the virulence of anthrax bacilli much more reliably than by Toussaint's method, by cultivating the organisms at increased temperatures (42° to 43° C.). By this process he was able to produce vaccines of roughly measurable strength, with which he succeeded in immunizing sheep and cattle.

It is well known to bacteriologists that certain of the pathogenic micro-organisms, when passed through several individuals of the same animal species, become gradually more virulent for this species. In his studies on the bacillus of hog cholera, Pasteur observed that when this micro-organism was passed through the bodies of several rabbits it gained in virulence for rabbits, but became less potent against hogs. He succeeded, subsequently, in protecting hogs against fully virulent cultures by treating them with strains which had been attenuated by passage through rabbits. The principle thus established is still in use.

A further principle of attenuation for purposes of immunization was, at about this time, contributed by Chamberland and Roux, who reduced the virulence of anthrax cultures by growing them in the presence of weak antiseptics (carbolic acid 1: 600, potassium bichromate 1: 5000, or sulphuric acid 1: 200). Cultivated under such conditions the bacilli lost their ability to form spores and became entirely avirulent for sheep within ten days.

Immunization with Virus Changed by Animal Passage.—Jennerian vaccination is an example of active immunization with a living virus which has been modified for one species by passage through another. The virus of vaccinia is the smallpox virus, altered by passage through cattle, until in man it produces only a local lesion which, nevertheless, confers a five-to-seven-year immunity and sometimes a longer one against the unaltered smallpox virus. In rabies, while Pasteur's original attenuation was considered largely to depend upon the process of drying, it is very probable that the virus fixé which is the dog street virus, passed through generations of rabbits, has been attenuated for man by rabbit passage.

Immunization with Sublethal Doses of Fully Virulent Bacteria.—The use of fully virulent micro-organisms in minute quantities for purposes of immunization was first suggested by Chauveau, and is naturally inapplicable to extremely virulent organisms like *B. anthracis.* The principle, however, is perfectly valid, and has been experimentally applied by many observers, notably by Ferran in the case of cholera. A similar method proved of practical value in the hands of Theobald Smith and Kilbourne in prophylaxis against the protozoan disease, Texas fever. This process, however, is a dangerous one and can have little future in the active immunization of man.

Immunization with Dead Bacteria.—Suggested by Chauveau, the method of active immunization with gradually increasing doses of dead micro-organisms was successfully employed by Pfeiffer in laboratory animals. The method is especially useful against that class of bacteria in which the cell bodies (endotoxins) have been found to be more poisonous than their extracellular products (toxins). From a practical point of view, the method is of the greatest importance in routine laboratory immunization against *B. typhosus, Vibrio cholerae, B. pestis,* and a number of other bacteria. This method of immunization is the basis of most methods of bacterial vaccination in human prophylaxis. It is not successful in all cases. With anthrax bacilli and the "M" dissociants of streptococci killed organisms produce little or no immunity. This problem is discussed in the chapter on streptococci and in connection with the "Vi" antigen of typhoid bacilli.

Immunization with Bacterial Products.—Many bacteria when grown in fluid media produce extracellular, soluble poisons which remain in the medium after the micro-organisms have been removed by filtration or centrifugalization. Since the diseases caused by such micro-organisms are, to a large extent, due to the soluble poisons, animals can be actively immunized against this class of bacteria by the inoculation of gradually increasing doses of the specific exotoxin. This method is naturally successful against those micro-organisms which possess the power of toxin formation to a highly developed degree. Most important among these are *B. diphtheriae* and *B. tetani.*

Local Immunization.—Besredka has been the most active advocate in recent years of the idea that individual tissues can be separately immunized by local contact with the antigen. His method of vaccination against cholera, typhoid and dysentery consists in feeding dead cultures so that the mucous membrane of the bowel, which is the portal of entrance for these infections, may be locally immunized. In the same way, he believes that immunization of the skin will protect against anthrax, basing his opinion upon the hypothesis that the anthrax bacillus produces no infection if it can be introduced into the body without injury to the skin. While the principle of local variations in the resistance of individual tissues is correct, the practicability of this principle has not been demonstrated.

PASSIVE IMMUNITY

The methods of immunization described in the preceding paragraphs have been termed active because in all of them the virus or toxin of the disease whether in subinfectious doses, or modified by attenuation, or killed, has been introduced into the body of the animal; the consequent immunity has developed as a result of specific physiological reaction of the inoculated subject to the virus or toxin. The individual has produced his own immunity by reaction to the antigen with which his tissues have been in contact.

The discovery of antitoxic antibodies and the therapeutic experiments of von Behring and his collaborators, in 1890 and 1892, on the protective powers of antitoxins established a new principle of immunization, in which protection was achieved by injecting the serum of an actively immunized animal into a normal one. The specific antibodies introduced with the serum of the *actively* immunized animal created a temporary specific immunity in the recipient. Such immunization is spoken of as *passive* because the animal receiving the serum becomes immune purely as a result of the specific antibodies introduced, without having in any way reacted physiologically to the antigen, or contributed to the antibody production.

Passive immunization is practically applicable chiefly against diseases caused by bacteria which produce powerful toxins, and the sera of animals actively immunized against such toxins are called antitoxic sera. In the treatment of diphtheria and tetanus, the respective antitoxic sera have reached broad and beneficial therapeutic application.

Passive immunization against micro-organisms not characterized by marked toxin formation was attempted by Richet and Héricourt, experimenting with cocci, and by Babés, in the case of rabies. Micro-organisms, however, which exert their harmful action rather by invasion than by secreted, soluble toxins, do not produce antitoxins in the sera of immunized animals. The substances which they call forth in the process are bactericidal and are directed against the invading organisms themselves.

In contrast to the usefulness of the antitoxic sera, passive immunization with antibacterial sera has been relatively disappointing. In certain types of pneumococcus infection, in meningitis, and in a number of other conditions, treatment with antibacterial sera is undoubtedly of great benefit if applied at a sufficiently early stage of the disease. Prophylactically, many of the sera would be of great value, but the practical occasion for their use in this way is naturally limited.

Duration of Passive Immunity.—When antitoxin has been injected in the form of horse serum, subcutaneously, we know from the studies of Henderson-Smith that it takes about seventy-two hours for the highest concentration to be attained in the blood stream. After this a rapid diminution takes place which is to some extent dependent upon the speed of development of anti-bodies against the horse serum. Glenny and Hopkins, studying the matter in rabbits, find that within the first twenty-four hours there seems to be an initial loss of 50 per cent after intravenous injection; after that a gradual decrease, approximately 25 per cent, from day to day, lasting about six days; after this, probably due to the eliminating effect of precipitins, which are now beginning to be formed, there is an acceleration of the disappearance of the antitoxin. If the rabbits have been previously sensitized to horse serum and precipitin formation thereby favored, the accelerated phase of elimination may begin on the third or fourth day, leading to a much more rapid eventual complete absence. We may say that in ordinary human cases, the antitoxin injected into man may be expected to disappear from the circulation within about three weeks. These facts have considerable practical importance when for clinical reasons the problem of reinjection with an antitoxic or antibacterial serum arises. The most frequent situation involving this problem is that of the reinjection of tetanus antitoxin in traumatic injuries. A patient badly lacerated may be given prophylactic tetanus antitoxin. Two or three weeks later it may be necessary to reopen the wound for surgical repair. This engenders a danger of the resuscitation of quiescent tetanus spores and by the time the operation is to be performed, the antitoxin previously given may have disappeared. In such cases reinjection is often advisable, but questions of serum sickness must be kept in mind and controlled.

Antibodies.—In the foregoing sections we have seen that the process of active immunization so changes the animal body that it becomes highly resistant against an infection to which it had formerly been susceptible. In the absence of visible anatomical or histological changes accompanying the acquisition of this new power, investigators, in order to account for it, were led to examine the physiological properties of the body cells and fluids of immunized subjects. While it was reasonable to suppose that all the cells and tissues might have taken part in a physiological change so profoundly influencing the individual, the blood, because of its close relation to inflammatory reactions, and because of the ease with which it could be obtained and studied, claimed the closest attention. The bactericidal properties of normal blood serum noted in 1886 by Nuttall, von Fodor, and Fluegge aided in pointing to this tissue as primarily concerned in immunity.

The study of the blood serum of immunized animals as to changes in chemical composition or physical properties had shed little light upon the subject. Beljaeff found little or no alteration from the normal in the blood sera of immunized animals as to index of refraction, specific gravity, and alkalinity. Joachim and Moll agreed in stating that immune blood serum was comparatively richer in globulin than normal serum. This has since been confirmed. The first progress toward understanding was made by the investigations of Nuttall, von Fodor, Buchner, and others, who not only demonstrated the power of normal blood serum to destroy bacteria, but also showed that this property of blood serum became diminished on preservation and was destroyed completely by heating to 56° C. The thermolabile substance of the blood serum possessing this power was called by Buchner, *alexin*.

Soon after this, von Behring, in collaboration with Kitasato and Wernicke, in 1890 and 1892, made further important advances in elucidation of the immunizing processes by showing that the blood sera of animals actively immunized against the toxins of diphtheria and tetanus would protect normal animals against these poisons. He believed, at the time of discovery, that such sera contained substances which had the power of destroying the specific toxins which had been used in the immunization. He called these bodies *antitoxins*. While von Behring's first conception of actual toxin destruction soon proved to be erroneous, his discovery of the presence in immune sera of bodies specifically antagonistic to toxins was soon confirmed and extended.

Ehrlich, soon after von Behring's announcement, showed that specific antitoxins could also be produced against the poisons of some of the higher plants (antiricin, anticrotin, antirobin), and Calmette produced similar antitoxins against snake poison (antivenin). Other observers have, since then, added to the list of poisons against which antitoxins can be produced. Kempner produced antitoxin against the poison of *B. botulinus*, and Wassermann, against that of *B. pyocyaneus*. Antitoxin was produced by Calmette against the poison of the scorpion, and by Sachs against that of the spider. Thus a large number of poisons of animal, plant, or bacterial origin have been found capable of causing the production of specific antibodies in the sera of animals into which they are injected.

The formation of antitoxins directed against soluble poisons, however, did not explain the immunity acquired by animals against bacteria like *B. anthracis*, the cholera vibrio, and others which, unlike diphtheria and tetanus, produced little or no soluble toxin. It was evident that the antitoxic property of immune blood serum was not the sole expression of its protective powers. Much light was shed upon this phase of the subject by the discoveries of Pfeiffer in 1894 along the lines suggested by Nuttall and Buchner. Pfeiffer showed that when cholera spirilla were injected into the peritoneal cavity of cholera-immune guinea-pigs, the micro-organisms rapidly swelled up, became granular, and often disintegrated by a process of lysis or dissolution. The same phenomena could be observed when the bacteria were injected into a normal animal together with a sufficient quantity of cholera-immune serum. The reaction was specific since the destructive process took place to any marked extent only in the case of the bacteria employed in the immunization.

Metchnikoff, Bordet, and others were able to show that the lytic process would take place *in vitro*, as well as in the animal body. The existence of a specific destructive process in immune serum was thus established for the vibrio of cholera and soon extended to other micro-organisms. The constituents of the blood serum which gave rise to this destructive phenomenon were spoken of as *bacteriolysins*.

Following closely upon the heels of Pfeiffer's observation came the discovery of another specific property of immune serum by Gruber and Durham. These workers noticed that certain bacteria, when brought into contact with the serum of an animal immunized against them, were clumped together, deprived of motility, and firmly agglutinated. They spoke of the phenomenon as agglutination and of the substances in the serum giving rise to it as *agglutinins*.

Knowledge of serum activity was further enlarged by Kraus, who in 1897 showed that precipitates were formed when filtrates of cultures of cholera, typhoid, and plague bacilli were mixed with their specific immune sera. He called the substances which bestowed this property upon the sera *precipitins*.

Although all early observations upon antibodies were made with bacteria or bacterial products, it was shown before long that the bacterial reactions were only special instances of a general biological law; and that there were many other *antigenic* substances in nature with which analogous antibodies could be induced.

Antitoxins may be produced with a variety of poisons of plant and animal origin. Sensitizing, agglutinating and precipitating effects may, likewise, be produced by the use of a large number of different substances. Chief among these, because of the great aid they have given to the theoretical investigation of the phenomena of immunity, are the red blood cells. Bordet and, independently of him, Belfanti and Carbone showed in 1898 that the serum of animals repeatedly injected with the defibrinated blood of another species exhibited the specific power of dissolving the red blood corpuscles of this species. This was the first demonstration of hemolysis—a phenomenon which, because of the ease with which it can be observed *in vitro*, has much facilitated investigation.

The knowledge that specific cytotoxins or cell-destroying antibodies could be produced by injection of red blood cells suggested the possibility of analogous reactions for other tissue cells. It was not long, therefore, before Metchnikoff and, independently of him, Landsteiner succeeded, by repeated injections of spermatozoa, in producing a serum which would seriously injure these specialized cells. Von Dungern obtained similar results with the ciliated epithelium of the trachea. Since then a host of cytotoxins have been produced with the cells of various organs and tissues. Neisser and Wechsberg produced leukotoxin (leukocytes); Delezenne reported neurotoxin and hepatotoxin; Surmont, pancreas cytotoxin; and Bogart and Bernard, suprarenal cytotoxin.

It was at first supposed that the discovery of the cytotoxins would exert a profound influence upon our knowledge of pathology. Unfortunately, however, it has turned out that most of the earlier work was inaccurate, the lesions produced by the supposedly cytotoxic sera often depending, not upon a specific cytotoxic action but upon hemagglutination with resulting embolism and necrosis. It would be of great importance to reopen the cytotoxin problem in the light of the present increased chemical knowledge of immunity. Organ specificity has a definite experimental basis, and specific cytotoxic elements occur in the sera of animals immunized with the materials of individual organs. Earlier work was also very much confused by ignorance of the heterophile antigens.

The many points of similarity existing between bacterial toxins and digestive ferments suggested to several observers the possibility of producing antibodies against the latter. As a result, a number of antiferments have been obtained, chief among which are antilab (Morgenroth), antipepsin (Sachs), antisteapsin (Schütze), and antilactase (Schütze). The knowledge of anti-enzymes, however, is in a very confused state at the present time.

Antigens.—This term was coined to designate any substance which gave rise to the development of specific antibodies in the circulation of animals to which it had been administered subcutaneously, intravenously, or in any manner which avoided passage through the intestinal canal and hydrolysis by the intestinal enzymes. Antigens fed by mouth may also incite antibodies, but only when they manage to get through the intestinal mucosa and into the circulation in an unchanged condition.

The definition of an antigen must be chemical as well as immunological. All natural proteins are antigenic if, as Wells puts it, "the term protein is limited to those colloidal amino-acid aggregates which contain the full quota of amino-acids found in complete proteins."

The important structural units are the aromatic amino-acids. Gelatin, which is composed chiefly of diamino-acids, is not an antigen. The protamins are not antigenic. Chemical protein structure is the necessary criterion for an antigen but, in addition to this, the physical factor of molecular magnitude is also significant. It is possible that the nondiffusibility of the proteins has some influence upon the antigenic function.

The antigenic substance of proteins is easily destroyed by cleavage, even the higher cleavage products, polypeptides and proteoses, no longer showing antigenic properties. Other influences beside cleavage can destroy the antigenic activity of proteins. The action of alkali was found by Dakin to initiate a process known as racemization in which there is a rearrangement of the CH—CO groups in the molecule, and such racemization results in the development of resistance to hydrolysis by enzymes, loss of optical activity and of antigenic function.

The most important and mysterious attribute of antigens is their specificity. By this term is meant the fact that an antigen induces the formation of antibodies which react subsequently only with the inciting antigen or other antigens that are closely related in chemical structure. Wells and Osborn, particularly, have shown that there is a definite relationship between chemical structure and specificity. Moreover, the work of Obermeyer and Pick, and, subsequently, of Landsteiner, has shown that when a protein molecule is altered by the introduction of iodine, $N = N$ groups or NO_2 groups, etc., and such altered protein is used for immunization, the resulting antibodies are specific for the alteration forms utilized in the treatment, whatever the source of the original protein before alteration. The artificial production of such compound proteins, particularly by Landsteiner and his assistants, has led to a great deal of new knowledge of immunological reactions.

Work of the last few years has shown that we must modify our original belief that only proteins can be complete antigens. It has been found that the acetyl-polysaccharide of Type I pneumococcus, first isolated by Enders and Pappenheimer and chemically studied by Heidelberger, may form protective antibodies in mice and produce immunity in human beings and horses; whereas they do not possess these antigenic properties for rabbits. This difference in the antigenic properties of certain substances in individual animals is a conception which necessitates considerable reorganization of immunological theories.

PARTIAL ANTIGENS.—Of the greatest importance for the knowledge of infectious diseases have been the discoveries concerning the so-called partial antigens or haptenes. Landsteiner demonstrated the existence of such relations in connection with his extensive studies on compound proteins. If, for example, an azoprotein was produced by the treatment of chicken serum with metanilic acid, an antibody could be obtained by the immunization of an animal with this compound, which reacted with similarly produced azoprotein in which a protein other than chicken serum had been used. A similarly produced but not antigenic azoprotein in which gelatin was treated with metanilic acid would inhibit subsequent precipitation between a true azoprotein and its antibody in an experiment such as the one below.

1. Azoprotein produced with metanilic acid introduced into chicken serum
2. Antiserum obtained by immunization with the above
3. Similarly azotized gelatin or Witte peptone

$$1 + 2 \quad = \text{precipitate}$$
$$1 + 3 \quad = \text{no precipitate}$$
$$1 + 3 + 2 = \text{no precipitate}$$

In bacteria, the antigen has been shown to consist of at least two important fractions. The antigenic structure is closely related to virulence and to all bacterial dissociations. The relations are best illustrated by reference to those demonstrated to exist in the pneumococcus group. The antigen of a smooth pneumococcus consists of loosely combined protein and carbohydrate elements. In this total antigen, the carbohydrate determines specificity and is what Ehrlich would have termed the haptene group. By itself it does not induce antibody formation, but combined with the protein in the bacterial body, it lends the specificity to the antibodies produced by the combined antigen. The rough pneumococci contain only the protein part of the antigen. This part of the antigen can produce antibodies of its own with the specificity for itself but now entirely deprived of the type specific haptophore carbohydrate. The protein and the carbohydrate are so loosely combined in this group of organisms that mere autolysis or solution separates them. The carbohydrate substance is one which we, at first, called residue antigen but which Heidelberger and Avery have named "S.S.S.," or soluble specific substance. It dissolves easily in water and is precipitable by alcohol.

These relations are true as far as concerns the carbohydrate fraction originally isolated from pneumococci. The complete carbohydrate, containing the acetyl group, is now known, from the studies of Enders and Pappenheimer and Avery and Goebel, to be a functional antigen, capable of stimulating the production of protective antibodies.

HETEROPHILE ANTIGEN.—Another type of partial antigen or haptene is the lipoid of the Forssmann heterophile antigen. The injection of emulsions of guinea-pig organs or those of a group of animals including horses, mice and pigeons into rabbits produces hemolytic antibodies for sheep corpuscles. This was a purely empirical observation made in the course of other work. The antigen, called heterophile for obvious reasons, is present in the organs of some animals and not in that of others. If one of these organs, let us say a horse kidney, is extracted with alcohol, a lipoid can be obtained which will react with the heterophile antibody but which will not produce a heterophile antibody if injected by itself. We have thus again a complex antigen consisting of a protein linked with an alcohol-soluble lipoid. Together, they induce antibody formation. The lipoid will react with the antibody so formed but will not induce antibody production if injected by itself. The lipoid represents, therefore, the haptene.

The Nature of Antibodies in General.—We have no idea in what the process of antibody formation in the body consists. Ehrlich's side-chain theory will be briefly discussed in connection with the toxins. There has been recently a revival of the earlier views of Buchner, who believed that the only possible explanation for the multiple specificities was to assume that the antibody contains some of the actual constituents of the antigen. Manwaring, who has taken this up, has formulated the theory that after the antigen has been distributed to cells there is a synthetic process in which parts of the antigenic material become incorporated in the cellular protoplasm. Quantitative studies such as those of Hooker do not uphold these views. Ehrlich's idea, after all, that the antibody represents the overproduction on the part of the cell of the specific atom group which is capable of reacting with the cell in the first place, is nothing more than a restatement of the observed facts: (a) that any protein injected into the body must be dealt with by specific enzymes that emanate from the cells; (b) that antibodies like all other circulating substances must be the results of cell metabolism; and (c) that since it is known that antigens react with the cells of injected animals, there must be a specific chemical apparatus in the cells by which this reaction is carried out. Further than this, we have no clues to the process.

Antibodies have not been purified to the same extent to which this has been possible with some antigens. However, almost all work agrees on the fact that the antibody is a serum globulin which differs from the normal globulin of the same animal largely in being of greater molecular size. According to Felton, all the protective substances present in pneumococcus horse serum can be precipitated by 15-20 per cent ethyl alcohol at 0° C. If this material is washed with water, it leaves behind a residue soluble in salt solution which contains practically all the protective antibodies.

Antibodies are distributed in different globulin fractions in different animal species. There is no rule about this, but it has been empirically shown that certain antibodies, for instance, are contained in the pseudoglobulin in horses but in the euglobulin in rabbits. Many similar examples can be cited.

Also, considerable differences are found between the antisera produced with identical antigens in different animals. Thus, for instance, ultrafiltration and ultracentrifugation have revealed that pneumococcus antibody globulin of horses is about three times larger in molecular size than the same antibodies in rabbit serum.

The union of antigens and antibody must be in the first instance a chemical one; otherwise it would be impossible to explain the delicate specificity of the reaction. After the union has taken place, it seems that the globulin, which either is the antibody or is carried along with it, coats the surfaces of the colloidal particles of the antigen. The sensitized antigen is thus covered with the antibody globulin and in its general behavior in the electric current and otherwise becomes practically a globulin particle.

Unitarian Conception of Antibodies.—Ehrlich's original idea was that every so-called "antibody reaction" was due to an independent antibody. Therefore, he spoke of antitoxins, agglutinins, precipitins, etc. A view since then particularly sponsored by Dean and by ourselves is that all these antibody effects are due to a single sensitizing antibody. This antibody unites specifically with the antigen, which is thereby altered so that, if a toxin, it is neutralized; if a colloidal particle, it is precipitated; if a bacterium, it is agglutinated; and if there are leukocytes present, it is more easily phagocyted.

The above is simply a brief outline of the relations, which cannot be discussed in detail in the available space.

Zone phenomena appear in all antibody reactions. Older explanations for these occurrences are unsatisfactory. According to the newer understanding of the nature of antibodies and the probability of their union with antigen as layers or films around the antigen particles, it seems likely that Marrack's interpretation of the zone phenomena is correct, in that he attributes them to the presence of antibody modified either by preservation or slight heat which is preferentially absorbed by the antigen but has lost its specific effect in sensitizing to electrolytes or alexin or other biological effects.

REFERENCES

ASCOLL, G., and FIGAR, F.   Berl. klin. Wchnschr., 1902, 39:634.
BABÉS and LEPP.   Ann. de l'Inst. Pasteur, 1889, 3:384.
BELFANTI, S., and CARBONE, I.   Gior. d. r. Accad. di med. di Torino, 1898, 46:321.
BELJAEFF, W.   Centralbl. f. Bakteriol., I Abt., 1903, 33:293, 369.
BESREDKA, A.   Immunisation locale, Paris, 1925.
BOGART and BERNARD, L.   Compt. rend. Soc. de biol., 1901, 53:161.
BORDET, J.   Ann. de l'Inst. Pasteur, 1898, 12:688.
BUCHNER, H.   Centralbl. f. Bakteriol., I Abt., 1889, 6:561.
CALMETTE, A.   Ann. de l'Inst. Pasteur, 1898, 12:343.
———— Compt. rend. Soc. de biol., 1894, 6:120.
CHAMBERLAND, C., and ROUX, E.   Compt. rend. Acad. d. sc., 1883, 96:1088, 1410.
CHAUVEAU.   Compt. rend. Acad. d. sc., 1881, 92:844.
DELEZENNE, C.   Ann. de l'Inst. Pasteur, 1900, 14:686.
———— Compt. rend. Acad. d. sc., 1900, 131:427.
EHRLICH, P.   Deutsche med. Wchnschr., 1891, 17:976, 1218.
FERRAN, J.   Compt. rend Acad. d. sc., 1885, 101:147.
FORSSMANN, H.   Die heterogenetische Antigene, etc., in Handb. d. path. Mikroorg., W. Kolle, R. Kraus and P. Uhlenhuth, Berlin, 1930, 3rd ed., Vol. 3, p. 469.
GLENNY, A. T., and HOPKINS, B. E.   J. Hyg., 1922, 21:142; 1923, 22:12, 37; 1924, 23:208.
GRUBER, M., and DURHAM, H. E.   München. med. Wchnschr., 1896, 43:285.
HÉRICOURT, J., and RICHET, C.   Compt. rend. Acad. d. sc., 1888, 107:690.
HISS, P. H., and ATKINSON, J. P.   J. Exper. M., 1900, 5:47.
HIRSZFELD, L.   Konstitutionsserologie und Blutgruppenforschung, Berlin, 1928.
JOACHIM, J.   Arch. f. Physiol., 1902, 93:558.
JUNGEBLUT, C. W.   J. Immunol., 1933, 24:157.
KEMPNER, W.   Ztschr. f. Hyg. u. Infectionskrankh., 1897, 26:481.
KRAUS, R.   Wien. klin. Wchnschr., 1897, 10:736.
LANDSTEINER, K.   Centralb. f. Bakteriol., I Abt., 1899, 25:546.
———— Die Spezifizität der Serologischen Reaktionen, J. Springer, Berlin, 1933.
LUBARSCH, O.   Ztschr. f. klin. Med., 1891, 19:80, 360.
MARRACK, J. R.   The Chemistry of Antigens and Antibodies, Med. Research Council, Spec. Rep. Ser. No. 230; London, 1938.
METCHNIKOFF, E.   Ann. de l'Inst. Pasteur, 1895, 9:433; 1898, 12:263.
MORGENROTH, J.   Centralbl. f. Bakteriol., I Abt., 1899, 26:349.
NEISSER, M., and WECHSBERG, F.   Ztschr. f. Hyg. u. Infectionskrankh., 1901, 36:299.
NUTTALL, L.   Ztschr. f. Hyg., 1888, 4:353.
PASTEUR, L.   Compt. rend. Acad. d. sc., 1880, 90:239, 952, 1030; 1882, 95:1250.
PASTEUR, CHAMBERLAND, and ROUX.   Compt. rend. Acad. d. sc., 1881, 92:662, 1378.
PEARCE, R. M.   J. Exper. M., 1906, 8:400.
PFEIFFER, R.   Ztschr. f. Hyg. u. Infectionskrankh., 1894, 18:1.

PFEIFFER, R., and ISSAEFF. Ztschr. f. Hyg. u. Infectionskrankh., 1894, 17:355.

SACHS, H. Fortschr. d. Med., 1902, 20:425.

———— Beitr. z. chem. Phys. u. Path., 1902, 2:125.

SALMON, D. E., and SMITH, T. Proc. Biol. Soc. Washington, 1886, 3:29.

SCHÜTZE, A. Deutsche med. Wchnschr., 1904, 30:308.

———— Ztschr. f. Hyg. u. Infectionskrankh., 1904, 48:457.

SMITH, T., KILBOURNE, F. L., and SCHROEDER, E. C. Bull. No. 3, p. 67.

SURMONT, H. Compt. rend. Soc. de Biol., 1901, 53:445.

TOPLEY, W. W. C. An Outline of Immunity, Wm. Wood & Co., Baltimore, 1933.

U. S. Dept. Agric., Bureau animal indust., 1893, Annual Report, 1881–2, p. 290.

VON BEHRING, E. Ztschr. f. Hyg. u. Infectionskrankh., 1892, 12:1, 45.

———— and KITSATO. Deutsche med. Wchnschr., 1890, 16:1113, 1145.

———— and WERNICKE. Ztschr. f. Hyg. u. Infectionskrankh., 1892, 12:10.

VON DUNGERN. München. med. Wchnschr., 1899, 46:1228.

VON FODOR, J. Deutsche med. Wchnschr., 1886, 12:617.

WASSERMANN, A. Ztschr. f. Hyg. u. Infectionskrankh., 1896, 22:263.

WELLS, H. G. The Chemical Aspects of Immunity, New York, 1929, 2nd ed. See this book for thorough discussion of the chemical antigen problems. References to and discussion of most of the work here considered will be found in this book.

ZINSSER, H., ENDERS, J. F., and FOTHERGILL, L. D. Immuunity Principles and Application in Medicine and Public Health. 5th ed. of Resistance to Infectious Diseases. New York, 1939.

CHAPTER XIV

TOXINS AND ANTITOXINS

The Toxin-Antitoxin Reaction.—The discovery of antitoxin and its specific antagonistic effect upon toxin furnished an opportunity for the accurate investigation of the relationship of a bacterial antigen and its antibody. Toxin-antitoxin reactions were the first immunological processes to which experimental precision could be applied, and the discovery of principles of great importance resulted from such studies. A great deal of the work was done with diphtheria toxin and antitoxin and it is for this reason that the analyses carried out by Ehrlich on these substances are described in considerable detail in this chapter. The facts elucidated with diphtheria toxin are in principle applicable to similar substances.

The simplest assumption to account for the manner in which an antitoxin renders a toxin innocuous would be that the antitoxin destroys the toxin. Roux and Buchner, however, advanced the opinion that the antitoxins did not act directly upon toxin, but affected it indirectly through the mediation of tissue cells. Ehrlich, on the other hand, conceived the reaction of toxin and antitoxin as a direct union, analogous to the chemical neutralization of an acid by a base.

The conception of toxin destruction was conclusively refuted by the experiments of Calmette. This observer, working with snake poison, found that the poison itself (unlike most other toxins) possessed the property of resisting heat to 100° C., while its specific antitoxin, like other antitoxins, was destroyed at or about 70° C. Nontoxic mixtures of the two substances, when subjected to heat, regained their toxic properties. The natural inference from these observations was that the toxin in the original mixture had not been destroyed, but had been merely inactivated by the presence of the antitoxin, and again set free after destruction of the antitoxin by heat.

The conclusions of Calmette were later put in question by the observations of Martin and Cherry who concluded from work done with the venom of an Australian snake that the heating acted not by destroying the antitoxin in a united toxin-antitoxin complex but merely prevented further union with antitoxin not yet in combination. Morgenroth, however, later found that Calmette's original interpretation was the correct one. He found that by acidifying a neutralized snake venom antitoxin mixture with hydrochloric acid up to a concentration of N/18 the toxin was dissociated, and a toxin-HCl combination resulted which withstood boiling for thirty minutes.

The nonparticipation of the living tissue cells in these reactions was demonstrated by Ehrlich himself. Kobert and Stillmarck had shown that ricin possessed the power of causing the red blood cells of defibrinated blood to agglutinate in solid clumps, a reaction which could easily be observed *in vitro*. Ehrlich, who had obtained antiricin in 1891 by injecting rabbits with increasing doses of ricin, found that this antibody

171

possessed the power of preventing the hemagglutinating action of ricin in the test tube. By a series of quantitatively graded mixtures of ricin and antiricin, with red blood cells as the indicator for the reaction, he succeeded in proving not only that the toxin-antitoxin neutralization was in no way dependent upon the living animal body, but that definite quantitative relations existed between the two substances entirely analogous to those which govern reactions between different substances of known chemical nature. Similar quantitative results were subsequently obtained by Stephens and Myers for cobra poison and its antitoxin, by Kossel for toxic eel blood serum, and by Ehrlich for the hemolytic tetanus poison known as tetanolysin. These quantitative relationships were of basic importance for future studies.

The introduction of the test tube experiment into the investigation of these reactions permitted much more exact observation, and by this means, as well as by careful, quantitatively graded, animal experiments, the further facts were ascertained that toxin and antitoxin combined more speedily in concentrated than in dilute solutions, and that warmth hastened, while cold retarded, the reaction—observations which in every way supported Ehrlich's conception of the chemical nature of the process.

Ehrlich's Analysis of Diphtheria Toxin.—Shortly after the discovery of diphtheria antitoxin, it became apparent that no two sera, though similarly produced, could have exactly the same protective value. It was necessary, therefore, to establish some measure or standard by which the approximate strength of a given antitoxin could be estimated. Von Behring attempted to do this for both tetanus and diphtheria antitoxins by determining the quantity of an immune serum which, in each case, was needed to protect a guinea-pig of known weight against a definite dose of a standard poison. He ascertained the quantity of standard toxin bouillon which would suffice to kill a guinea-pig of 250 grams, and called this quantity the "toxin unit" or M.L.D.[1] This unit was later more exactly limited by Ehrlich, who, considering the element of time, stated it as the quantity sufficient to kill a guinea-pig of the given weight in from four to five days.

Appropriating the terminology of chemical titration, von Behring spoke of a toxic bouillon which contained one hundred such toxin units in a cubic centimeter, as a "normal toxic solution" and designated as "normal antitoxin"[2] a serum capable of neutralizing, cubic centimeter for cubic centimeter, the normal poison. A cubic centimeter of such an antitoxic serum was sufficient, therefore, to neutralize one hundred toxin units. In the experiments of von Behring, toxin and antitoxin had been separately injected. Ehrlich improved upon this method by mixing toxin and antitoxin before injection, thereby obviating errors arising from differences which may have existed in the depth of injection or rapidity of absorption.

In order, however, that any such method of standardization of antitoxin may be practically applicable, it is necessary to produce either a stable toxin or an unchangeable antitoxin. This Ehrlich achieved for antitoxin by drying antitoxic serum *in vacuo* and preserving it in the dark, at a low temperature and in the presence of

---

1 M.L.D. = Minimum lethal dose.

2 Since those not familiar with this subject have great difficulty in deciding for themselves what a standard antitoxin unit is, we would like to warn them in this place not to assume that the present standard unit of antitoxin has any quantitative relationship whatever to the normal antitoxin set up by von Behring at this time. Further discussion of the antitoxin unit will be found in the next chapter.

anhydrous phosphoric acid. By the use of such a stable antitoxin, various toxins may be measured and other antitoxic sera estimated against these.

Given thus a constant antitoxin, the standardization of toxins would be a comparatively simple matter were the poison obtainable in a perfectly pure state. Unfortunately for the ease of measurement, however, this is not the case. The problem is rendered difficult by a number of complicating factors, many of which have been brought to light by Ehrlich in his researches into the quantitative relations.

It has been noted that toxin solutions would deteriorate with time; that is, a toxic bouillon which was found soon after production to contain, say, eighty toxic units in each cubic centimeter, would, after four or five months, be found to contain but forty units in the same gross quantity. It had lost, therefore, in this case, just one-half of its toxic power. In spite of this loss, however, Ehrlich found that such boullion had retained its full original power of neutralizing antitoxin. If the reaction was purely one of chemical neutralization, there seemed to be but one explanation of this. The toxin molecule must contain two separate atom groups. One of these must possess the power of binding antitoxin and be

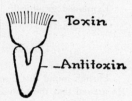

FIG. 11.—TOXIN AND ANTITOXIN.

stable; this he designates as the "haptophore" or "anchoring" group. The other, the one by which the toxin molecule exerts its deleterious action, must be more easily changed or destroyed; this he calls the "toxophore" or "poison" group. In the altered toxin bouillon in which a part of the poisonous action has been lost while the anti-toxin-neutralizing power is intact, the toxophore group of some of the toxin must have been changed or destroyed. Such altered toxin he speaks of as "toxoid."

In support of this hypothesis and for the purpose of perfecting the methods of standardization, Ehrlich was led to determine, for a large variety of specimens of diphtheria toxin, the precise quantity, in cubic centimeters, which was necessary to neutralize exactly one arbitrarily established standard unit of antitoxin. This he accomplished by making a series of toxin-antitoxin mixtures, in each of which the quantity of antitoxin was exactly one unit, while the amount of toxin was gradually increased. These mixtures were injected into guinea-pigs of 250 grams weight. It is self-evident that in such an experiment the mixtures containing the smaller quantities of toxin would have no effect upon the guinea-pigs. Soon, however, a mixture would be reached in which toxin would be sufficiently in excess of antitoxin to produce the symptoms of slight poisoning, as evidenced in local edema, rise of temperature, etc. The largest quantity of toxin which could be added without producing such symptoms was then regarded as exactly neutralizing the antitoxin unit. This quantity of toxin Ehrlich speaks of as "Limes zero" (Limes = threshold) or, briefly, "L_0."

For instance:

    1 antitoxin unit + 0.15 c.c. toxin = no reaction
    1 antitoxin unit + 0.16 c.c. toxin = slight reaction
at point of infection, scarcely visible = L_0
    1 antitoxin unit + 0.17 c.c. toxin = marked local reaction
    1 antitoxin unit + 0.19 c.c. toxin = late paralysis
    1 antitoxin unit + 0.20 c.c. toxin = death in six days
    1 antitoxin unit + 0.21 c.c. toxin = death in four days L_+

In this example L_0, in which the toxin and antitoxin apparently neutralize each other, was 0.16.

But since judgments as to what was the slightest noticeable reaction in guinea-pigs might differ, Ehrlich thought it more exact, in standardizing a poison against an antitoxin, to determine a unit of toxin which would depend upon finding the quantity which would not only neutralize one antitoxin unit but leave, in addition to this, enough toxin in excess to kill a guinea-pig of

250 grams in four to five days. This value which, in other words, would be the amount of toxin which in the presence of an antitoxin unit would give the effect of one M.L.D., he called the threshold of death and "limes death" or L+.

A priori, one would assume that the difference between L_0 and L+ should be equal to one M.L.D. This, however, Ehrlich found is never the case. Thus, let us assume, for the sake of simplicity, that we have a toxin [3] of which 0.01 c.c. represented the M.L.D. or the amount that would kill the guinea-pig of 250 grams in four to five days, and that the L_0 dose of this toxin is found to be 1 c.c. or 100 M.L.D. The L+ dose of this toxin would not unlikely be 2.01 c.c. or 201 M.L.D. The difference between L_0 and L+ in this example would then amount to 101 M.L.D. instead of 1 M.L.D. as one might expect if the reaction were simply one between a single neutralizing toxin and an antitoxin.

Expressed graphically, the conditions may be stated as follows:

> M.L.D. = 0.01 c.c. of the toxin bouillon.
> L+ (neutral. of 1 antitox. unit yet killing 1 pig) = 2.01 c.c. or 201 M.L.D.
> (complete neutral. of 1 antitox. unit)   = 1. c.c. or 100 M.L.D.
> _____
> Difference = 1.01 c.c. or 101 M.L.D.

Ehrlich found this discrepancy again and again, and tried to explain it in the following manner: He argued that the toxoids formed by deterioration of toxin might be conceived as possessing three different degrees of affinity for antitoxin. If their affinity for antitoxin were equal to, or more marked than, that of the toxin itself, they could have no influence upon the dose L+. If, however, their affinity for antitoxin were weaker than that of toxin, each fresh toxin unit added to the L_0 dose would, first uniting with antitoxin, replace a corresponding quantity of these nontoxic substances of weaker affinity, and L+ would be reached only after all of these "epitoxoids," as Ehrlich called them, had been replaced, and toxin became free in the mixture.

Thus, in analyzing our example, we have:

> 100 toxin-antitoxin + 100 epitoxoid-antitoxin = L_0;
> add 1 M.L.D., and we have 101 toxin-antitoxin + 99 epitoxoid-antitoxin + 1 epitoxoid free;
> add 101 M.L.D. and we have 200 toxin-antitoxin + 100 epitoxoid free + 1 M.L.D. free = L+

Two facts, however, led Ehrlich to abandon the opinion that epitoxoid was merely a variety of toxoid. He found, in the first place, that the stated relations between L_0 and L+ were true for perfectly fresh toxin bouillon in which little or no deterioration had taken place. He observed, furthermore, that in old, altered toxin bouillon, while M.L.D. was very much affected, the quantity needed to kill a pig constantly increasing, and the number of actual fatal doses in L_0 constantly decreasing, L+ remained practically unchanged.

Simply stated, this means that the epitoxoids or substances which have weaker affinity for antitoxin than toxin itself are already present in fresh cultures and are not increased with time. For this reason, Ehrlich has separated these substances from toxoids. He calls them "toxon" and believes them to be, like toxin, primary secretory products of the diphtheria bacilli. The toxoids themselves, Ehrlich believes, are of two kinds, those with a stronger affinity for antitoxin than toxin itself (protoxoids), and those whose affinity for antitoxin is equal to that of toxin. These latter he calls "syntoxoids."

Method of Partial Absorption of Toxin.—Ehrlich gathered data in support of his views from what he terms the "method of partial absorption" of toxin by antitoxin.

For the sake of quantitative study, Ehrlich assumed that a fully neutralized toxin-antitoxin compound had a valency of 200 for toxin. Since the original units set up by him were entirely arbitrary, such an assumption is of course not warranted as an actual chemical description of what occurs. However, for his purposes it was justifiable, since the number of M.L.D. contained in an L_0 or fully neutralized mixture was usually a factor of 100, usually exceeded 100 M.L.D. but never reached 200. It was an ingenious method of studying quantitative relations, an example of which is as follows:

Given a toxin, the unit (M.L.D.) of which is 0.024 c.c., he first determines the L+ dose which,

---

[3] We have here selected an example quite distinct from that which was used above to illustrate the L_0 and L+ doses. This is done to emphasize the fact that these values must be separately determined for every toxin.

tested against the standard antitoxin unit, in this case is 2.05 c.c. But 2.05 c.c. = 85 M.L.D. (or 2.05 ÷ .024) units. By mixing the L_+ dose of toxin and antitoxin in such a way that the quantity of antitoxin is gradually increased, while the toxin remains always L_+, and determining upon animals the amount of free toxin contained in each mixture, the following table may be constructed:

0	antitoxin unit representing	0	valencies $+ L_+ =$	85	free M.L.D.
0.1	antitoxin unit representing	20	valencies $+ L_+ =$	85	free M.L.D.
0.25	antitoxin unit representing	50	valencies $+ L_+ =$	60	free M.L.D.
0.8	antitoxin unit representing	160	valencies $+ L_+ =$	10	free M.L.D.
0.9	antitoxin unit representing	180	valencies $+ L_+ =$	3.5	free M.L.D.

It is plain that the substances with the strongest affinity for antitoxin must be bound first by the antitoxin. This does not diminish the toxic value of the mixture; and the neutralizing elements are the protoxoids. Next are bound syntoxoids and toxins, and, finally, the toxons. It is obvious that, by this method, the constitution of any given toxin may be ascertained, and Ehrlich constructed, on the basis of these observations, what he termed his toxin spectrum. Minor differences of toxicity and affinity for the antibody caused him, by the partial saturation method described, still further to divide toxin into proto-, deutrero-, and trito-toxin.

The most important fact brought out by the partial absorption method of Ehrlich is the quantitative irregularity in which successful antitoxin fractions neutralize when added to a constant amount of toxin.

The explanation he offers is not, however, the only possible one, and indeed is less likely than some others. Ehrlich's assumptions are based upon the conception that the toxin-antitoxin reaction is like that of a strong acid and a strong base in which the reaction is complete and proceeds by a straight line.

Arrhenius investigated the toxin-antitoxin reaction from a physical-chemical point of view, and has shown that the union of the two reacting substances is more like that of a weak acid and a weak base. At each point in the neutralization there are present united compound and dissociated free toxin and antitoxin. For each relative concentration an equilibrium is established, since the reaction is reversible, and follows the laws of mass action.

Thus for each particular mixture one could assume the conditions as follows:

$$K = \frac{\text{Free Toxin} \times \text{Free Antitoxin}}{\text{Toxin-Antitoxin}}$$

or

(Free Toxin) (Free Antitoxin) = K (Combined Toxin-Antitoxin)

The amount of free dissociated toxin determines the toxicity of each mixture. As a matter of fact, the curves of neutralization of tetanolysin by antitoxin followed very closely the type of curve found in the neutralization of boric acid and ammonia.

When a strong acid, in solution, acts upon a base, say hydrochloric acid upon ammonia (NH_3), strong acid having the property of complete dissociation in relatively concentrated solutions, little or no ammonia would remain unbound. A weak acid, like boric acid, however, not being as completely dissociated, would leave some ammonia uncombined even after more quantitatively sufficient boric acid had been added. Arrhenius and Madsen believe that toxin and antitoxin possess weak chemical affinity for each other, their interaction being comparable to that taking place between a weak acid and a base. Toxin-antitoxin solutions, therefore, would contain the neutral compound, but at the same time uncombined toxin and antitoxin. The qualities which Ehrlich ascribes to toxon, they believe, are due to the unbound toxin present in such mixtures. In studies in which they inhibited the hemolytic action of ammonia by gradual addition of boric acid, they were able to show complete parallelism between the conditions governing this neutralization and those concerned in their tetanus experiments. Their explanation has the advantage of great simplicity over that of Ehrlich's and also the fact that it takes into account the laws of dissociation, which always takes place in solutions in which the union of two substances occurs. Objections to the ideas of Arrhenius and Madsen have been brought forward by Nernst, Bordet and others, largely on the basis that toxin and antitoxin are probably colloidal in nature, and that the laws of dissociation in colloidal reactions are not, as yet, clear. We do know, however, that antigen-antibody complexes can dissociate, and the work of Loeb has shown that reactions of proteins are, after all, in many ways strictly analogous to ordinary chemical reactions between less complexly constituted substances.

A great many of the irregularities observed by Ehrlich in the quantitative relationship of antigen-antibody union become more clear as a result of recent work carried out on the quantitative relationships between diphtheria toxin and antitoxin and between pneumococcus carbohydrates and their antibodies. This may be illustrated from the work of Heidelberger and Kendall with the latter substances. When these investigators quantitatively studied the union between Type III pneumococcus antibody and a chemically pure Type III carbohydrate, they found—on adding increasing amounts of carbohydrate to constant amounts of antibody—that a point was first reached at which only slight traces of antibody were left in solution. Further additions accomplished a neutralization in which traces of both substances, or no trace of either could be detected in solution. Still increasing the carbohydrate until a trace of free carbohydrate appeared, they determined that instead of a neutral point, as assumed by Ehrlich, there was rather an *equivalence zone* within which the mixtures were to all intents and purposes neutral, but the ratio of the two components could vary in the ratio of antibody to carbohydrate as 40-1 to 5-1. The two reagents, therefore, are multivalent in regard to each other, and instead of a single mass-action formula, a number of different mass-action formulas must be applied, the principle however remaining the same, according to the original conception of Arrhenius and Madsen.

Bordet, Landsteiner and others have brought out another point of view which might explain the quantitative relations which exist in toxin-antitoxin mixtures as worked out by Ehrlich. They emphasize the analogy of these reactions with colloidal reactions, assuming that when antitoxin is mixed with toxin in amounts insufficient to completely neutralize, the units of antitoxin are not taken up by a corresponding fraction of the total toxin present, leaving a part of the toxin absolutely free, but that the antitoxin is equally distributed over all the toxin units present, leaving all of them partially saturated. This would not sharply neutralize a part of the toxin, leaving another part entirely free to exert its activity, but would partially neutralize all the toxin. It is more or less analogous, as Bordet brings out, to different degrees of coloration which are produced when starch absorbs varying quantities of iodine. They compare it to an adsorption phenomenon, rather than to a true chemical reaction.

More or less in harmony with this view is the Danysz effect, which is as follows: When diphtheria toxin is added to its antitoxin in two fractions, a definite period elapsing between the addition of the first and the second fraction, much more toxin remains free than when the total quantities are mixed at once.

The Danysz phenomenon was quite correctly interpreted by its discoverer as due to the ability of the toxin to unite with antitoxin in multiple proportions. This view was lost sight of during the avidity controversies started by Ehrlich, but recent work has confirmed Danysz' original idea. Both the studies of Healey and Penfield and those of Pappenheimer show that the first fractions of toxin added to a constant amount of antitoxin neutralize considerably more than their antitoxin equivalents. There is, therefore, less free antitoxin left for neutralization of subsequently added amounts of toxin, and the mixture is inevitably poisonous. That the reaction is reversible is indicated by the fact that this toxicity diminishes slowly as the mixture is allowed to stand for three or four days.

The Side-chain Theory.—We have seen that the extensive researches of Ehrlich into the nature of the toxin-antitoxin reaction led him to believe that the two bodies underwent chemical union, forming a neutral compound. The strictly specific character of such reactions, furthermore, diphtheria antitoxin binding only diphtheria toxin, tetanus antitoxin only tetanus toxin, etc., led him to assume that the chemical affinity between each antibody and its respective antigen depended upon definite atom groups contained in each.

Ehrlich had, in 1885, published a treatise in which he discussed the manner of cell nutrition and advanced the opinion that in order to nourish a cell, the nutritive substance must enter directly into chemical combination with some elements of the cell protoplasm. The great number and variety of chemical substances which act as nutriment led him to believe that the highly complex protoplasmic molecules were made up of a central atom group (Leistungs Kern) upon which depended the specialized activities of the cell, and a multiplicity of side chains (a term borrowed from the chemistry of the benzol group), by means of which the cell entered into chemical relation with food and other substances brought to it by the circulation. If we illustrate graphically by the chemical conception in salicylic acid, the benzol ring represents the "Leistungs-Kern," or radical, while COOH and OH are links by means of which a variety of other substances may be brought into relation with the radical, for instance, as in methyl salicylate.

Just as nutritious substances are brought into workable relation with the cell by means of such atom groups, so Ehrlich believes toxins exert their deleterious action only because the cells possess atom groups by means of which the toxin can be chemically bound (Fig. 12). These Ehrlich in his later work calls "receptors." The receptors or side chains present in the cells and possessing by chance specific affinity for a given toxin, are, by their union with toxin, rendered useless for their normal physiological function. By the normal repair mechanism of the body these receptors are probably cast off and regenerated. Regenerative processes of the body, however, do not, as a rule, stop at simple replacement of lost elements, but, according to the hypothesis of Weigert, usually tend to overcompensation. The receptors eliminated by toxin absorption are not, therefore, simply reproduced in the same quantity in which they are lost, but are reproduced in excess of the simple physiological needs of the cell. Continuous and increasing dosage with the poison, consequently, soon leads to such excessive production of the particular receptive atom groups that the cells involved in the process become overstocked and cast them off to circulate freely in the blood. These freely circulating receptors—atom groups with specific affinity for the toxins used in their production—represent the antitoxins. These, by uniting with the poison before it can reach the sensitive cells, prevent its deleterious action.

The theory of Ehrlich in brief, then, depends upon the assumptions that toxin and antitoxin enter into chemical union, that each toxin possesses a specific atom group by means of which it is bound to a preëxisting side chain of the affected cell, and that these side chains, in accordance with Weigert's law, under the influence of repeated toxin stimulation, are eventually overproduced and cast off by the cell into the circulation.

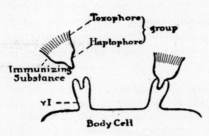

FIG. 12.—TOXIN AND BODY CELLS.

It stands to reason that this theoretical conception would be vastly strengthened were it possible to show that such receptors or toxin-binding atom groups actually preëxisted in the animal body, and such support was indeed given by the experiments of Wassermann and Takaki. These observers succeeded in showing that tetanus toxin could be rendered innocuous if, before injection into animals, it was thoroughly mixed with a sufficient quantity of the fresh brain substance of guinea-pigs. Similar observations were independently made by Asakawa, and variously confirmed. Kempner and Schepilewsky showed a similar relation to exist between brain tissue and botulismus toxin, and Myers brought proof of analogous conditions in the case of suprarenal tissue and cobra poison.

Although we have dealt almost entirely with diphtheria toxin and antitoxin, these are by no means the only substances to which the principles discussed apply. Other similar toxin-antitoxin reactions occur in the following cases:

Tetanus bacilli produce both a tetanospasmin and a tetanolysin, both of which incite neutralizing antitoxin.

Bacillus botulinus.—The anaerobic bacillus of meat poisoning produces a potent toxin of which there are at least two different types.

Bacillus welchii produces a toxin discovered by Bull and Pritchett in 1917, against which an antitoxin can be made.

Vibrion septique produces a powerful toxin peculiar in that it kills with a very short incubation period. The toxin kills regularly only when intravenously injected. An antitoxin has been prepared from horses and sheep.

Bacillus oedematiens produces a powerful poison against which an antitoxin has been prepared.

Shiga dysentery bacillus produces a soluble toxin in addition to an endotoxin. An antitoxin has been produced against this soluble toxin.

Hemolytic streptococci of scarlet fever, erysipelas, and possibly some other diseases produce a toxin against which an antitoxin can be prepared. It is not impossible that there are two substances in the filtered broth of such cultures. Studies by Japanese investigators indicate that there is a heat sensitive true toxin together with a more stable Dick toxin in such streptococci cultures.

Staphylococcus.—Certain strains of *Staphylococcus aureus* in addition to producing hemolysins and leukocidenes, may produce a true soluble exotoxin described by Parker in 1924. This substance is heat unstable and produces a neutralizing antitoxin.

Snake Venoms.—Antitoxins have been prepared against most snake venoms, of which there are a considerable variety. Cobra poison always tends to separate toxic elements and the vipers of the western hemisphere not only differ among themselves but contain in each case a number of antigenically separate toxin elements. The production of antigen, therefore, is a difficult procedure, but is being successfully carried out by using mixtures of the poisons of a number of snakes and producing in this way a polyvalent serum.

REFERENCES

ARRHENIUS, S. Immunochemistry, New York, 1907, 175.

ASAKAWA. Centralbl. f. Bakteriol., I Abt., 1898.

BEHRING, E. Deutsche med. Wchnschr., 1893, 19:543, 1253.

BORDET, J. L'Immunité. Paris, 1920.

BUCHNER, H. Schutzimpfung und andere individuelle Schutzmassregeln, in Handb. d. spec. Therap. innerer Krankh., ed. by Penzoldt and Stinzing, Berlin, 1894, 1:116.

CALMETTE, A. Ann. de l'Inst. Pasteur, 1895, 9:225.

DANYSZ. Ann. de l'Inst. Pasteur, 1902, 16.

DREYER, G., and MADSEN, T. Ztschr. f. Hyg. u. Infectionskrankh., 1901, 37:250.

EATON, M. D. Recent Chemical Investigations of Bacterial Toxins, Bacteriol. Rev., 1938, 2:3.

EHRLICH, P. Deutsche med. Wchnschr., 1891, 17:976, 1218; 1898, 24:597.

———— Klin. Jahrb., 1897, 6:299.

———— Gasammelte Arbeiten zu Immunitätsforschung, Berlin, 1904.

———— Fortschr. d. Med., 1897, 1898, 35.

———— Das Sauerstoffbedürfniss des Organismus, Berlin, 1885.

EHRLICH, P., KOSSEL, H., and WASSERMANN, A. Deutsche med. Wchnschr., 1894, 20:353.

HEALEY, M., and PENFIELD, S. Brit. J. Exper. Pathol., 1935, 16:535.

KEMPNER, W., and SCHEPILEWSKY, E. Ztschr. f. Hyg. u. Infectionskrankh., 1898, 27:213.

KNORR, A. Fortschr. d. Med. 1897, 15:657.

KOSSEL, H. Berl. klin. Wchnschr., 1898, 35:152.

MARRACK, J. R. The Chemistry of Antigens and Antibodies, Med. Res. Council, Spec. Rep. Ser. No. 230, London, 1938.

MARTIN, C. J., and CHERRY, T. Proc. Roy. Soc. London, 1898, 63:420.

MYERS. Centralbl. f. Bakteriol., I Abt., 1899, 1.

PAPPENHEIMER, A. W. JR., and ROBINSON, E. S. J. Immunol., 1937, 32:291.

STEPHENS, J. W. W., and MYERS, W. J. Path. & Bacteriol., 1898, 5:279.

STILLMARCK, R., and KOBERT, R. Arb. a.d. pharmazeut. Inst. zu Dorpat, 1889, 3:59.

WASSERMANN, A. Ztschr. f. Hyg. u. Infectionskrankh., 1896, 22:263.

WASSERMANN, A., and TAKAKI, T. Berl. klin. Wchnschr., 1898, 35:5.

WEIGERT. Verhandl. d. Gesellsch. deutsch. Naturf. u. Aerzte, Frankfurt, 1896.

ZINSSER, H., ENDERS, J. F., and FOTHERGILL, L. D. Immunity Principles and Application in Medicine and Public Health. New York, 1939.

CHAPTER XV

PRODUCTION AND TESTING OF ANTITOXINS

DIPHTHERIA ANTITOXIN

Diphtheria toxin and antitoxin are discussed in considerable detail in this chapter not only because of their importance, but also as an example of the general principles underlying all such reactions. Briefer references to toxin and antitoxin in other conditions are incorporated in the chapters dealing with the other infections.

Method of Production.—The methods for producing diphtheria antitoxin vary only in minor technical details. The first requisite for successful antitoxin production is the possession of a strong toxin. The various means of obtaining this are outlined in the section on diphtheria toxin.

The *toxin* used should be of reasonable potency. Many methods for the concentration of toxin have been devised.

Older methods of toxin production which depended to a large extent upon hit or miss empirical media are gradually being superseded by the use of synthetic media containing those factors most favorable for toxin production. The studies of Mueller have resulted in the production of a synthetic medium containing various amino acids together with pimelic acid and nicotinic acid (in the complete absence of peptone) which is now satisfactorily used in the Massachusetts Antitoxin Laboratory. This medium has been improved by Mueller with Pappenheimer and Cohen by the removal of excess iron by means of calcium phosphate precipitation. The exact formula for this medium may be found in the paper of Pappenheimer, Mueller and Cohen of 1937. Not only is a very high titer of toxin produced in this medium by suitable diphtheria strains, but the absence of protein and peptone renders it particularly valuable for eventual purification of the toxin.

For antitoxin production on a large scale, horses have been found to be the most useful animals. They should be healthy but need not be young. In fact, horses of considerable age but otherwise in good condition are sometimes remarkably good antitoxin-producers. Horses having some natural antitoxin are the most likely to yield good antitoxin on immunization. It is advisable to give them a mallein test.

The toxin injections are made subcutaneously. Because of the differences in susceptibility noted in various horses, it is advisable that the first doses of toxin should be preceded by antitoxin.

Park advises the preliminary injection of 3000 units of antitoxin, followed the next day by 10 M.L.D. of toxin diluted with 50 c.c. of salt solution. Subsequent injections are given every second day, the doses increasing by 100 per cent for the first seven injections, by 75 per cent for the next seven, and then by 50 per cent for the next series. As the volume of toxin grows larger, the increase per dose is diminished gradually to 10 per cent.

Usually a trial bleeding is taken about a month after immunization is started, and if a satisfactory level of antitoxin content has been attained, large bleedings are taken. The exact procedure varies in different laboratories; but the usual procedure is to give from two to five injections of toxin followed a week or ten days later by one or two bleedings of 7 to 10 liters. Then follows another course of injections and more bleedings.

Ramon's anatoxin, which is diphtheria toxin treated with 0.2 to 0.4 per cent formalin and incubated, may be used instead of toxin. This anatoxin or toxoid is used in larger initial doses (20 c.c. for the first dose) and need not be preceded by antitoxin.

The immunizing effect of either toxin or toxoid may be enhanced by addition of other substances. Ramon has suggested the use of tapioca, alum and calcium chloride. The addition of 0.5 to 1.0 per cent of these substances to the toxin used for injection may result in considerable increase in antitoxin production.

Horses vary in the strength of antitoxin which they will produce and in the rate at which they attain their peak content. To produce useful plasma a horse must reach a level of at least 300 to 500 units, and this point should be approached within three months. Any horse reaching 800 units may be considered satisfactory and those exceeding 1500 units are exceptional. Archipoff reports a horse which yielded 3500 units per c.c.

In order to obtain serum, a cannula is introduced into the jugular vein and the blood is allowed to flow into high glass cylinders with citrate solution. In this way, large quantities of blood may be obtained. As much as 9 liters may be taken at a time every two weeks, without injuring the animal. Ligature of the vein after bleeding is unnecessary.

The cylinders and flasks are allowed to stand for two or three days at or below 10° C. At the end of this time, plasma may be pipetted or siphoned away from sediment and stored in the refrigerator. In order to diminish the chances of contamination, 0.5 per cent of carbolic acid or 0.4 per cent of tricresol may be added.

Antitoxin is fairly stable and, if kept in a cool, dark place, may remain active, with but slight deterioration, for as long as a year. Kept in a dry state, *in vacuo*, over anhydrous phosphoric acid, by the method of Ehrlich, it retains its strength indefinitely.

Standardization.—Antitoxin units being measured in terms of toxin, uniformity of measurement necessitates the possession of a uniform toxin. Antitoxin being more stable than toxin, uniformity of toxin is obtained by means of a standard antitoxin maintained in a central laboratory. This was first done by Ehrlich in Germany, and is now done for the United States by the National Institute of Health.

Bottles of the distributed antitoxin are marked with the number of units contained in each cubic centimeter. Dilutions of this are mixed with varying quantities of the toxin to be tested, the mixtures are allowed to stand for one hour to permit union of the two elements, and injections into guinea-pigs of 250 grams weight are made. Thus the L+ dose of the toxin is determined. (The L+ dose is the quantity of poison not only sufficient to neutralize one antitoxin unit,[1] but to contain

---

[1] The unit of antitoxin is the amount of antitoxin which when mixed with an L+ dose of toxin and injected subcutaneously into a guinea-pig weighing 250 grams will preserve the life of the guinea-pig for four or five days only.

In commercial practice, where a margin of safety is advantageous, the unit of antitoxin is considered to be that amount of antitoxin which will save the life of a guinea-pig if injected together with an L+ dose of toxin.

an excess beyond this sufficient to kill a guinea-pig of 250 grams in four to five days. L+ is chosen rather than Lo, the simple neutralizing dose, because of the difference between toxins in their contents of toxoid and toxon.)

The L+ dose of the toxin having thus been determined, this quantity is mixed with varying dilutions of the unknown antitoxin. Thus, given an antitoxin in which 300 to 400 units to the c.c. are suspected, dilutions of 1:200, 1:250, 1:300, etc., are made. One c.c. of each of these is mixed with the L+ dose of the toxin, and the mixtures are injected into guinea-pigs of about 250 grams. If the guinea-pig receiving L+ plus the 1:250 dilution lives and the one receiving L+ plus the 1:300 dilution dies in the given time, we know that the unit sought must lie between these two values, and further similar experiments will easily limit it more exactly. The possibility of error in carrying out such measurement is much diminished by the use of larger quantities of dilutions higher than those given. Four c.c. is the volume usually injected.

Flocculation of Toxin-antitoxin Mixtures (Ramon Test).—Our knowledge of toxin-antitoxin reactions has been considerably increased by Ramon's observation of mutual precipitability of the two substances when mixed under suitable circumstances. Such precipitation of toxin by antitoxin had been noticed by Calmette with snake venom and antivenin, but the method had been little used either practically or theoretically.

Since there is an optimum flocculation point, this method is used for the preliminary standardization of antitoxin. The methods used are relatively simple and have been adapted for practical purposes by a number of workers, particularly Glenny and his associates. Protocols for the flocculation titration are given in the Section for Technical Methods. The brief directions given below describe the test as used for routine preliminary standardizations by Dr. Elliott Robinson at the Massachusetts Antitoxin Laboratory:

The toxin used should contain 10 to 12 Lf units per c.c. (An Lf unit is the volume of toxin flocculating with one unit of antitoxin.) Such a toxin would have originally an M.L.D. of about 0.002 c.c. or less and an L+ in the neighborhood of 0.10 to 0.15 c.c. Its Lf value is determined by testing it against a number of sera which have been accurately standardized by the Ehrlich method. The average Lf value of the toxin as indicated by the flocculation tests with these sera is taken as the flocculating value to be used in determining the antitoxin content of other sera.

In a series of small tubes of uniform diameter, quantities of serum (undiluted or diluted) varying from 0.06 to 0.15 c.c. are measured, each tube getting 0.01 c.c. more than the preceding one. In the case of serum known to be of relatively slight antitoxin content, the serum is used undiluted, but in the case of sera of higher antitoxin content, the serum is diluted to a suitable degree not exceeding usually one to eight. To the tubes containing serum or serum dilution, the standard toxin then is added in amounts of 1 c.c.

In the case of concentrated antitoxin the test is done by measuring 2 c.c. of toxin into each of a series of tubes and to this is added undiluted concentrated antitoxin by means of a Trevan-O'Brien syringe.

After the test is set up and the toxin and antitoxin mixed, the tubes are placed in a water bath at a temperature of approximately 42° C. Incubation at this temperature gives fairly speedy flocculation which usually begins in from fifteen minutes to about three hours.

The end-point is taken as the amount of serum in the tube which gives the first evident flocculation. If the standard toxin contains 12 Lf units per c.c. and if, for example, flocculation occurs first in a tube containing 0.12 c.c. of a 1:4 dilution of the serum, then 0.03 c.c. (0.12 c.c. divided by 4) of serum neutralizes 12 Lf units of toxin, so 1.0 c.c. of serum neutralizes 400 Lf units or contains 400 units of antitoxin (0.03:1.0 = 12:x; x = 400).

As to accuracy, the Ramon test has been found to be of considerable usefulness for preliminary determinations of serum values. With the sera of some horses *in vitro* and *in vivo* tests check up quite regularly. In many other cases the Ramon test shows a higher unitage than the guinea-pig method. A discrepancy between two tests with serum from the same horse usually remains constant for that horse whatever the fluctuations of antitoxin following. Since the actual ability of the serum to save life is the quality to be measured, the guinea-pig test will probably not be superseded, but time and expense are saved by Ramon's procedure.

Intracutaneous Standardization.—A number of different routine methods modified from the original Römer technic are in use for the intracutaneous antitoxin standardization. The method in general is gradually superseding others as probably the most accurate as well as the cheapest. The method published by Glenny and Allen is satisfactory and simple.

A guinea-pig with a white skin is chosen and hair removed either with a sulphide paste or by plucking. Anesthetic may be used to facilitate injection, but it is not necessary. The total amount for each injection is 0.2 c.c. Injections should be about one inch apart, intracutaneously into the thicker areas of skin on the flank, not too near the midline. About 1/500 M.L.D. still gives definite reaction. The minimum reacting dose is the M.R.D. The intracutaneous dose corresponding to the subcutaneous L+ dose is the Lr, which gives a positive skin reaction when mixed with one antitoxin unit. This is usually determined against a fraction of a unit, so that the dose employed in testing is the Lr/20 or Lr/500 depending upon whether 1/20 or 1/500 of a unit of standard antitoxin was used. For the standardization of the antitoxin the amount of serum which, when mixed with one Lr/500 toxin, just fails to give a positive reaction is said to contain 1/500 unit antitoxin.[2]

One of the most recently introduced methods for estimation of the potency of diphtheria antitoxin is the intracutaneous test on rabbits. The method has the advantage over any of the techniques in which guinea pigs are used in that a large number of reactions can be carried out on a relatively small number of animals. Details of the technique as employed at the Antitoxin Laboratory of the Massachusetts Department of Public Health are as follows:

Intradermal Potency Tests on Rabbits.—All dilutions are made with physiological salt solution, measured with a standard 100 cc. burette. Volumetric pipettes calibrated "to contain" are used in making serum and toxin dilutions, and washed out as in the method for subcutaneous tests in guinea pigs. A specially calibrated "to contain" pipette is used for measuring the standard antitoxin. Ordinary serological 1.0 c.c. pipettes are used for measuring the final dilutions into tubes for the toxin-antitoxin mixtures.

Diphtheria toxin with a known L+ dose is diluted so as to contain about 1/12 L+ per c.c. The serums are diluted so as to cover the probable potency range of the serum. One cubic centimeter of diluted toxin is distributed into small shell vials. To the toxin one cubic centimeter of the serum dilution is added. The toxin and serum dilution is mixed thoroughly by inverting the tubes three times. Then 0.1 c.c. of the mixture is injected intradermally into the rabbit skin.

A standard diphtheria antitoxin is put on to make any correction necessary for the toxin used in the test.

The reactions are read 66 to 72 hours after injection. The potency of a serum is determined by the dilutions of serum and standard antitoxin which fail to give a reaction and by the highest dilution of serum which gives a lesser reaction than one of the standard antitoxin dilutions. At least two rabbits are used in each test, and the test repeated if discordant results are obtained or if no end-point is reached on one or both rabbits.

Rabbits of the same breed are preferred. Chinchillas seem to be more reactive than the New Zealand whites.

2 A. T. Glenny and K. Allen, *J. Path. & Bacteriol.*, 1921, 24:61.

SCHEME FOR DILUTING TOXINS AND SERUMS

Toxin Dilutions

Toxin 1 c.c. + Saline 9 c.c. (Dil. A)
Dil. A 4 c.c. + Saline 76 c.c. (Dil. B)
Dil. B has + 1/12 L+ per c.c.

Standard Antitoxin Dilutions

S. A. 0.66 c.c. + Saline 19.34 c.c. (Dil. A)		
Dil. A 1.8 c.c. + " 2.2 c.c. (Dil. B)		
2.0 c.c. + " 2.0 c.c. (Dil. C)		
2.2 c.c. + " 1.8 c.c. (Dil. D)		
2.4 c.c. + " 1.6 c.c. (Dil. E)		
2.6 c.c. + " 1.4 c.c. (Dil. F)		
2.8 c.c. + " 1.2 c.c. (Dil. G)		

Typical Serum Dilution

Serum 1 c.c. + Saline 19 c.c. (Dil. A)
Dil. A 1 c.c. + " 9 c.c. (Dil. B)

Dil. B 1 c.c. + " 10 c.c. (Dil. C)
Dil. B 1 c.c. + " 11 c.c. (Dil. D)
Dil. B 1 c.c. + " 12 c.c. (Dil. E)

Mixtures for injection contain

Toxin Dilution B, and
Standard Antitoxin Dilutions, C, D, E, F, or G; or
Serum Dilutions C, D, or E.

The method has been criticized and modified in various ways. A recent discussion of the matter by Jensen of the Copenhagen Serological Institute can be found in Acta Pathalogica et Microbiologica Scandinavica, Supplement 14.

Since 1902, the production and sale of diphtheria antitoxin has been regulated by law in the United States. From time to time, antitoxin is bought in the open market and examined at the hygienic laboratories of the National Institute of Health. Antitoxic serum which contains less than three hundred and fifty units to each cubic centimeter is not permitted upon the market.

Concentration.—In a previous section we have seen that Hiss and Atkinson and others have shown an increase in the globulin contents of blood serum of immunized animals. It has been shown, furthermore, that the precipitation of such serum with ammonium sulphate carried down in the globulin precipitate all the antitoxic substances contained in the serum.

Gibson devised a method—which has undergone various modifications—of separating the antitoxin-carrying pseudoglobulin from the other serum constituents. The method in use at the Massachusetts Antitoxin and Vaccine Laboratory is, in principle, as follows:

First Precipitation.—This is to remove fibrinogen and euglobulin.

Select plasma from horses showing approximately the same antitoxic strength. The plasma is mixed and then diluted with half its volume of water, thoroughly mixed, and enough saturated ammonium sulphate solution is added to bring the saturation of the entire mixture to the point between 28 and 32 per cent saturation which will precipitate out all the euglobulin. This point is determined as follows: to 100 c.c. of plasma diluted with 50 c.c. of water, enough saturated ammonium sulphate solution is added to bring the concentration to 28 per cent. Filter. Dilute with an equal volume of physiological salt solution, then saturate with dry sodium chloride and if there is turbidity it is evident that not all the euglobulin is precipitated. There should be a very faint opalescence to the solution. If the precipitate of euglobulin is too heavy, then perform the test again, bringing the concentration of ammonium sulphate to 29 per cent saturation, and so on up to 32 per cent. The less potent plasma will require the higher concentration of ammonium sulphate.

Saturation at 28 to 32 per cent precipitates the fibrinogen and euglobulin. After adding ammonium sulphate solution, place the containers in a water bath and heat rapidly to 57° C, and hold at this temperature 1½ hours, after which heat as rapidly as possible to 63° C. Filter when cool.

Second Precipitation.—To the measured filtrate obtained from the 28 to 32 per cent saturation, add enough saturated ammonium sulphate solution to bring the concentration of the mixture to 50 per cent saturation. In this saturation all the pseudoglobulin is precipitated, while the albumins remain in solution. Filter through hardened papers. When drained, remove the papers with the precipitates and lay on coarse filter papers to absorb the fluid. Smooth off the precipitate into an even cake, and when sufficiently firm place two precipitates together. Put butter side to butter side. Place between dry, coarse filter papers and make a pile of not more than six precipitates. Change the papers frequently, then make a larger pile of twelve precipitates, and put in a veneer press. Press gently at first, changing the filter papers as soon as moist, and each time gradually increase the pressure. Combine any precipitates that are thin and then press until the absorbing filter papers take out no more water.

Dialysis.—Remove any crystallized salt from the filter papers. Break up the precipitate into small particles and place in cellophane bags. Dialyze in running water.

At the end of two days the contents of the bags are measured and tested for sulphates, which should not be in excess of the amount in the tank water. The reaction is tested and if between pH 6 and 7 do not adjust. Add a preservative such as tricresol or "3 Cresols" Mulford to a final concentration of 0.35 per cent.

Park and Thorne have found that the use of such concentrated antitoxin is, therapeutically, equally efficient as the unconcentrated, and possesses the advantage of less frequently giving rise to the secondary reactions in skin and mucous membranes occasionally noticed after the use of ordinary antitoxin, and referable, probably, to some other constituent of the horse serum.

Diphtheria antitoxin is therapeutically used in doses ranging from 10,000 to 30,000 units. For prophylactic immunization of healthy individuals, about 1000 units should be used. Such use, however, is much less common than it was formerly.

TETANUS ANTITOXIN

Production.—The production of tetanus antitoxin is, in every way, analogous to that of diphtheria antitoxin. It is necessary in the first place to produce a powerful tetanus toxin. The methods of procuring this will be discussed in the section upon tetanus toxin. Suffice it to say here that the most satisfactory method of obtaining toxins consists in cultivating the bacilli upon veal broth containing 0.5 per cent to 2 per cent sodium chloride and 1 per cent peptone. It has been advised, also, that the broth should be neutralized by means of magnesium carbonate rather than with sodium hydrate. The bacilli are cultivated for eight to ten days at incubator temperature and the broth filtered rapidly through Berkefeld filters. The toxin may be preserved in the liquid form with the addition of 0.5 per cent carbolic acid, or may be preserved in the dry state after precipitation with ammonium sulphate.

It is necessary to determine the strength of the poison.

This is done according to von Behring by determining the smallest amount of toxin which will kill a white mouse of 20 grams weight within four days. This is most easily done by making dilutions of the toxin ranging from 1 : 100 to 1 : 1000, and then injecting quantities of 0.1 c.c. of each of these dilutions subcutaneously into white mice. In this way, the minimal lethal dose is ascertained.

For the actual production of antitoxin, horses have been generally found to be the most favorable animals. They should be healthy and from five to seven years old.

The first injection of toxin administered to these animals should be attenuated in some way. Various methods for accomplishing this have been in use. In America, the first injection of about ten to twenty thousand minimal lethal doses [3] (for mice of 20 grams weight) is usually made subcutaneously together with sufficient antitoxin to neutralize this quantity. In Germany, von Behring used, for his first injection, a much larger dose of toxin to which about 0.25 per cent terchloride of iodine had been added. Immediately after an injection, the animals will usually show a reaction expressed by a rise of temperature, refusal of food, and sometimes muscular twitching. A second injection should never be given until all such symptoms have completely subsided. This being the case, after five to eight days double the original dose is given together with a neutralizing amount of antitoxin or with the addition of terchloride of iodine. Again after five to eight days, a larger dose is given and thereafter, at similar intervals, the quantity of toxin is rapidly increased. Ramon, in France, uses formalinized anatoxin (toxoid) for the first immunizing injections. In America the neutralizing antitoxin is omitted after the third or fourth injection. The increase of dosage is often controlled by the determination of the antitoxin contents of the animal's blood serum. The immunization is increased until enormous doses (500 c.c.) of a toxin in which the minimal lethal dose for mice is represented by 0.0001 c.c., or less, is borne by the horse without apparent harm.

The antitoxic serum is then obtained by bleeding from the jugular vein, as in the case of diphtheria antitoxin. It may be preserved in the liquid state by the addition of 0.5 per cent of carbolic acid or 0.4 per cent of tricresol.

Standardization.—The universal prophylactic use of tetanus antitoxin has, as in the case of diphtheria antitoxin, necessitated its standardization. A variety of methods are in use in different parts of the world. In the following description the American method only will be considered as laid down under the law of July, 1908, and based upon the work of Rosenau and Anderson at the United States Hygienic Laboratories at Washington.

In conjunction with a committee of the Society of American Bacteriologists, these authors have defined the unit of tetanus antitoxin as follows:

The unit shall be ten times the least amount of serum necessary to save the life of a 350-gram guinea-pig for ninety-six hours against the official test dose of standard toxin. The test dose consists of 100 minimal lethal doses of a precipitated toxin preserved under special conditions at the hygienic laboratory of the National Institute of Health. (The minimal lethal dose is, in this case, unlike von Behring's minimal lethal dose, measured not against 20-gram mice, but against 350-gram guinea-pigs.)

In the actual standardization of tetanus antitoxin, as in that of diphtheria antitoxin, the L+ dose of toxin is employed. The L+ dose is, however, in this case, defined as the smallest quantity of tetanus toxin that will neutralize one-tenth of an immunity unit, plus a quantity of toxin sufficient to kill a 350-gram guinea-pig in just four days. At the Hygienic Laboratory at Washington, a standard toxin and antitoxin are preserved under special conditions, and standard toxin and antitoxin, arbitrary in their first establishment, are kept constant by being measured against each other from time to time. In measuring the antitoxin thus preserved, at the National Institute of

---

[3] According to Park the "horses receive 5 c.c. as the initial dose of toxin of which 1 c.c. kills 250,000 grams of guinea-pig, and along with this a sufficient amount of antitoxin to neutralize it."

Health, a mixture of one-tenth of a unit of antitoxin and 100 M.L.D. of the standard toxin must contain just enough free poison to kill the guinea-pig in four days. Instead of distributing the L+ dose, the government now sends out standard antitoxin against which the manufacturer produces his own L+ dose.

In measuring an unknown antitoxin serum against this L+ dose of toxin, a large number of mixtures are made, each containing the L+ dose of the toxin and varying quantities of the antitoxin. Dilutions must always be made with 0.85 per cent salt solution and the total quantity injected into the animals should always be brought up to 4 c.c. with salt solution, in order to equalize the conditions of concentration and pressure. The mixtures are then kept for one hour at room temperature in diffused light. After this they are subcutaneously injected into a series of guinea-pigs weighing from 300 to 400 grams. The following example of a test is taken from the article by Rosenau and Anderson quoted above.

No. of Guinea-Pig	Weight of Guinea-Pig, Grams	Subcutaneous Injection of a Mixture of		Result
		Toxin (Test Dose), Gram	Antitoxin, C.C.	
1	360	0.0006	0.001	death in 52 hours
2	350	.0006	.0015	death in 97 hours
3	350	.0006	.002	symptoms
4	360	.0006	.0025	slight symptoms
5	350	.0006	.003	no symptoms

In this series the guinea-pig, receiving 0.0015 c.c. of the antitoxin, died in approximately four days; 0.0015 c.c. therefore represents one-tenth of an immunity unit.

In employing antitoxin for prophylactic purposes, above 1500 units should be used.

REFERENCES

Behring, E. Ztschr. f. Hyg. u. Infectionskrankh., 1892, 12:1.
———— Deutsche med. Wchnschr., 1900, 26:29, 156.
Doenitz. Die Wertbem. d. Heilsera, in Handb. d. path. Mikroorg., ed. by Kolle and Wassermann, 2nd ed.
Frazer and Williams. J. Am. M. Ass., 1924, 82:1114.
Gibson. J. Biol. Chem., 1906, 1.
Glenny, A. T., and Allen, K. J. Path. & Bacteriol., 1921, 24:61.
Glenny, A. T., and Okell, C. C. J. Path. Bacteriol., 1924, 27:187.
Hiss, P. H., and Atkinson, J. P. J. Exper. M., 1900, 5:47.
Kretz, R. Handb. d. Techn. u. Methodik., d. Immunitätsforsch., ed. by R. Kraus and C. Levaditi, Berlin, 1909, 2:1.
Madsen, T. Handb. d. Techn. u. Methodik., d. Immunitätsforsch., ed. by R. Kraus and C. Levaditi, Berlin, 1907, 1:35, 71.
Mueller, J. H. Proc. Soc. Exper. Biol. and M., 1937, 36:706.
Pappenheimer, A. M., Jr., Mueller, J. H., and Cohen, S. Proc. Soc. Exper. Biol. and M., 1937, 36:795.
Park, W. H., and Thorne. Am. J. M. Sc., 1906.

RAMON, G.   Compt. rend. Soc. de biol., 1922, 86:661, 711, 813.
———— Ann de l'Inst. Pasteur, 1923, 37:1001.
ROSENAU, M. J., and ANDERSON, J. F.   U. S. Hyg. Lab. Bull. No. 43, Treas. Dep. Pub. Health &
    Mar. Hosp. Serv., 1908.
U. S. Reg. on Biol. Products, Feb. 12, 1919, App. par. 72.
WATSON, A. F., and WALLACE, V.   J. Path. & Bacteriol., 1924, 27:289.

CHAPTER XVI

SENSITIZING ANTIBODIES (PHENOMENA OF LYSIS, AGGLUTINATION, PRECIPITATION, ETC.)

Alexin and Sensitizing Antibodies.—In the preceding chapters we have dealt solely with toxin-antitoxin reactions. There are many species of pathogenic bacteria, however, which produce no exotoxins and, therefore, stimulate the production of no antitoxin when introduced into animals. The resistance of the immunized animal cannot therefore be explained by the presence of antitoxin in the blood.

Von Fodor, Nuttall, Buchner, and others had demonstrated, in 1886 and the years following, that normal blood serum possessed the power of killing certain of the pathogenic bacteria. Nuttall made the discovery that this bactericidal power became gradually diminished and could be destroyed by exposure of the serum to a temperature of 56° C. for one-half hour. Buchner called this thermolabile substance upon which the bactericidal character of the serum seemed to depend "alexin."

Our knowledge of the bactericidal action of serum was extensively increased by the discovery, by Pfeiffer and Issaeff, that cholera spirilla injected into the peritoneal cavity of a cholera-immune guinea-pig were promptly killed and almost completely dissolved. The same phenomenon could be observed when the spirilla, mixed with fresh immune serum, were injected into the peritoneal cavity of a normal guinea-pig. This type of lysis is the "Pfeiffer phenomenon."

The processes observed by Pfeiffer as taking place intraperitoneally were shown by Metchnikoff, Bordet, and others to take place, though to a lesser extent, *in vitro*. Bordet, furthermore, observed that the bacteriolytic digestive power of such immune serum, when destroyed by heating, or after being attenuated by time, could be restored by the addition of small quantities of normal blood serum. It could, in other words, be "reactivated" by normal serum. From this observation Bordet drew the conclusion that the bactericidal or bacteriolytic action of the serum depended upon two distinct substances. The one present in normal serum and thermolabile, he conceived to be identical with Buchner's alexin. The other, more stable, produced or at least increased in the serum by the process of immunization, he called the "sensitizing substance." This substance, he believed, acting upon the bacterial cells, rendered them vulnerable to the action of the alexin. Without the previous preparatory action of the "sensitizing substance" the alexin was unable to act. Without the coöperation of alexin, the "sensitizing substance" produced no visible effects.

A few years later, Bordet was able to show that exactly analogous conditions governed the phenomenon known as "hemolysis" or disintegration of red blood cells.

It had been known for many years that in the transfusion of blood from an animal of one species into one of another species, injury was done to the red corpuscles which were introduced. Observed in the test tube, the red cells in the heterologous serum were seen to give up their hemoglobin in the fluid, the mixture taking on the red transparency characteristic of what is known as "laked" blood. Buchner had shown that the hemolyzing action of the normal serum was subject to the same laws as the bactericidal power of serum, in that it was destroyed by heating. He assumed that both the bacteriolytic and the hemolytic activities of normal serum were due to the same "alexin." Metchnikoff had pointed out the analogy between the two phenomena as early as 1889.

Bordet observed that the blood serum of guinea-pigs previously treated with the defibrinated blood of rabbits developed powers of dissolving rabbits' corpuscles, and that this hemolytic action could be destroyed by heating to 56° C., but "reactivated" by the addition of fresh normal serum. He had thus produced an immune hemolysin, just as Pfeiffer had produced immune bacteriolysin, and had demonstrated the complete parallelism which existed between the two phenomena.

A practical test tube method was thus available for the investigation of the lysins, just as a practical test tube method for antitoxin researches had been developed by Ehrlich in his ricin-antiricin experiments.

The path of investigation thus pointed out by Bordet was soon explored in greater detail by Ehrlich and Morgenroth.

Since the thermolabile substance or alexin, renamed by Ehrlich "complement," was already present in normal serum and had been shown to be little, if at all, increased during the process of immunization, this substance could have no relation to the changes taking place in the animal body as immunity was acquired. The more stable serum-component, however, the "substance sensibilisatrice" of Bordet, or, as Ehrlich now called it, the "immune body," was the one which seemed specifically called forth by the process of active immunization.

Having in their possession, at that time, the blood serum of a goat immunized against the red blood cells of a sheep, Ehrlich and Morgenroth inactivated it (destroyed the complement or alexin) by heating at 56° C. The serum then contained only the substance sensibilisatrice or immune body. To this inactivated serum they added sheep's red corpuscles, without obtaining hemolysis. Having left the inactive serum and the sheep's corpuscles in contact with each other for some time, they separated them by centrifugalization. To the supernatant fluid, they now added sheep-blood corpuscles and normal goat serum (complement) and found that *no* hemolysis took place. The immune body had apparently gone out of the serum. The red cells which had been in contact with the serum and separated by the centrifuge were then washed in salt solution and to them complement was added in the form of fresh normal serum. Hemolysis occurred. It was plain, therefore, that the immune body of the inactivated serum had gone out of solution and had become attached to the red blood cells, or, as Ehrlich expressed it, the immune body by means of its "haptophore" atom group had become united to the corpuscles. In contrast to this, if normal goat serum (containing complement only) was added to sheep corpuscles and separated again by centrifugation, the supernatant fluid was found to be still capable of reactivating inactivated serum (immune body). This he interpreted as proving that the complement was *not* bound to the corpuscles directly, but was attached to the amboceptor.

The following is the experimental plan by which these relations can be demonstrated:

A. Corpuscles and alexin. Left thirty minutes at 38° C. Centrifuged and divided into:
  1. Supernatant fluid. Add corpuscles and heated immune serum = Hemolysis
  2. Sediment of red cells. Add heated immune serum = No hemolysis

B. Corpuscles and heated immune serum. Left at 38° C. as above. Centrifuge:
  1. Supernatant fluid. Add corpuscles and alexin = No hemolysis
  2. Sediment of red cells. Add alexin = Hemolysis

If the three factors concerned—corpuscles, immune body, and complement—were mixed and the mixture kept at 0° C., no hemolysis occurred; yet, centrifugalized at this temperature, the immune body was found to have become bound to the corpuscles, the complement remaining free in the supernatant fluid. If the same mixture, however, was exposed to 37° C., hemolysis promptly occurred.

From such observations, Ehrlich concluded that complement did not directly combine with the corpuscles, but did so through the intervention of the immune body. This immune body, he reasoned, possessed two distant atom groups or haptophores; one, the cytophile haptophore group, with strong affinity for the red blood cell; the other, or complementophile haptophore group, with weaker avidity for the complement. Because of this double combining power, Ehrlich speaks of the immune body as "amboceptor." These views are graphically represented in Figure 14.

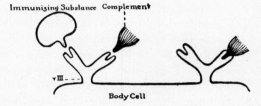

Fig. 13.—Ehrlich's Conception of Cell Receptors, Giving Rise to Immune Bodies.

Thus, according to Ehrlich and his pupils the alexin, or complements, acts upon the antigen indirectly only through the "Zwischenkoerper" or amboceptor. These views of Ehrlich have been described in more or less detail, though theoretically untenable, because they form an excellent introduction to a study of these phenomena.

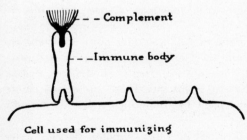

Fig. 14.—Complement, Amboceptor or Immune Body, and Antigen or Immunizing Substance.

Bordet pointed out many of the uncertainties of the amboceptor point of view. The only thing that we can say with certainty is that alexin or complement does not go into union with the unsensitized antigen, but that the action of the alexin upon the antigen is made possible only by preliminary sensitization. This complex then is amenable to alexin action. It is neither necessary, nor is it justifiable on the basis of experimental fact, to assume that the sensitizing antibody is an amboceptor or a sort of bridge between the antigen and the alexin. The difference is a fundamental one, and all the facts are on the side of the Bordet view. It is better, therefore, to refer to the substances involved as sensitizer and alexin, instead of as amboceptor and complement. As we shall see, we believe that the sensitizing antibody, whether in the process of lysis, agglutination, precipitation, etc., is in all cases the same substance.

Isolysins.—We have seen that the blood cells of one animal, injected into an animal of another species, give rise to a hemolytic substance in the serum of the second animal, which is strictly specific for the variety of cells injected. Such hemolysins, when produced in one animal against blood cells of another species, are spoken of as *heterolysins*. In studying the nature of hemolysis, Ehrlich and Morgenroth discovered that hemolysins could also be produced if an animal were injected with red blood cells of another member of its own species. Such hemolytic substances they called *isolysins*. In their experiments they injected goats with the washed red blood corpuscles of other goats and found that the serum of the recipient developed the power of causing hemolysis of the red blood cells of the particular goat whose blood had been used for injection. It did not, however, possess the power of producing hemolysis in the blood of all goats, nor did it produce hemolysis with the red corpuscles of its own blood. It is thus shown that the specificity of the hemolysins extends even within the limits of species.

The production of *autolysins*, that is, of substances in the blood serum which will produce hemolysis of the individual's own corpuscles, was unsuccessful. The only exception to this is the observation of Donath and Landsteiner, who discovered an autolysin in the blood serum of patients suffering from paroxysmal hemoglobinuria. In these cases the sensitizing substance or amboceptor appeared to be absorbed by the red blood cells only at low temperatures—probably in the capillaries during exposure to the cold, and hemolysis subsequently resulted in the blood stream by the action of complement.

Iso-agglutinins and blood typing in human beings are discussed in a subsequent section, under Agglutination.

Action of Alexin or Complement.—Alexin is an active substance present in normal blood and not increased in amount by immunization. It acts together with the immune antibodies in the sense that, when the antigen has been specifically sensitized by the antibody, the complex so formed can be acted upon by the alexin. In this process the alexin is removed from solution either by fixation to the sensitized antigen or by being used up in the discharge of its functions or, most probably, by both.

Alexin does not act upon the antigen alone except in certain nonspecific absorptions which have little immunological significance and which can easily be distinguished from the specific processes. It does not unite with free antibody, free, that is, in being unattached to the antigen for which it is specific. These circumstances are the underlying principles of alexin or complement fixation which will be separately discussed.

Alexin is destroyed by heat at 56° C. in fifteen to thirty minutes. It deteriorates on standing with a speed proportionate to the temperature. Thus it may last for several days in the ice-chest. As it deteriorates on standing it develops anticomplementary powers, an expression by which it is meant that the deteriorated blood serum which, at first, acted strongly in hemolyzing sensitized cells will now prevent such action if added together with fresh complement. Such anticomplementary properties can be eliminated by heating to 56° C. The conditions involved in these changes are not understood.

An important question has been: is there only one complement or alexin or.

are there many? Ehrlich and his coworkers at first believed that the same serum might contain a number of different alexins and that one of these might be active for hemolysis, another for the bactericidal effects. It is admitted at the present time that there is only one functionally active alexin in every serum. On the other hand, the alexins of the different species are not equally active on the same sensitized systems. The literature on this problem is reviewed in a recent paper by Dingle and others. A few examples of such differences of activity may be stated as follows: Goat complement may be lytic with rabbit, but not with goose immune serum, while pigeon complement may be active only with goose serum. In an antihuman hemolytic system guinea pig complement gives lower titers with rabbit or guinea pig antibody than does rabbit complement. In a recent work by the authors cited, it was found that with anti-influenza-bacillus horse serum, fresh human serum is an effective alexin, while guinea pig complement, normal rabbit and horse sera are not active. The bactericidal function of anti-influenza guinea pig serum can be activated by human, rabbit and guinea pig complement. Similar bactericidal functions of rabbit sera can be activated by human and rabbit complement but not by guinea pig complement. Many other examples might be given.

Nature of Alexin.—The facts that alexin is easily destroyed by heat, deteriorates readily and either activates or accelerates various immunological processes have suggested that it is very similar to the substances known as enzymes. This is probably true, though it is not possible at the present time to define the term enzyme either chemically or physiologically. Alexin has a number of further resemblances to enzymes. It acts, quantity for quantity, more strongly in concentration than when diluted. When inactivated by moderate heat, 50° to 51° C., it may regain part of its activity within twenty-four hours on standing.

Alexin can be inactivated also by a number of physical effects. If serum is diluted about 1 : 10 and vigorously shaken in a shaking machine for twenty minutes, it is materially weakened in its action. Hypertonic salt solution, even without causing precipitation, may not only inactivate but preserve the alexin from deterioration. Alexin, to which salt to the concentration of about 5 to 10 per cent has been added, may be kept in the ice-chest for weeks, and on redilution with distilled water to isotonicity will be active.

In 1938 Ecker and his associates discovered that a definite relation exists between the amount of vitamin C in the diet and the activity of complement in the serum of guinea pigs. These studies indicate that ascorbic acid is essential to the development of complement.

Quantitative Relationship between Amboceptor and Complement.—Morgenroth and Sachs demonstrated that within certain limits an inverse relationship exists between these two bodies. If for a given quantity of red blood cells a certain quantity of amboceptor and complement suffices to produce complete hemolysis, reduction of either the complement or the amboceptor necessitates an increase of the other factor. As amboceptor is increased, in other words, complement may be reduced and *vice versa*.

This being the case, titration of either of the two active agents must be carried out with reference to a standard quantity of the other.

Alexin action can be quantitatively estimated by titration with sensitized red blood cells. Thus a standard amount of red cell suspension, *i.e.*, 0.5 c.c. of a 5 per cent suspension by moist volume, is put into each of a series of tubes and to each is added a fixed amount of an inactivated immune serum containing specific sensitizer for the particular red cells (in practice usually sheep cells) employed. Decreasing amounts of fresh guinea-pig serum (alexin) ranging from 0.2 c.c. of a 1 : 10 dilution are added to the tubes and hemolysis observed in the water bath at 37.5° C. The smallest amount of alexin giving complete hemolysis is the unit.

Conversely, with a constant amount of alexin, the sensitizer contents of an immune serum can be titrated as follows:

0.01 c.c. of complement fresh guinea-pig serum	+	0.5 c.c. of 5 per cent emulsion sheep's corpuscles	+	Inactivated hemolytic serum	0.01 c.c. = complete hemolysis 0.009 c.c. = complete hemolysis 0.005 c.c. = complete hemolysis 0.003 c.c. = complete hemolysis 0.001 c.c. = complete hemolysis 0.0009 c.c. = partial hemolysis 0.0005 c.c. = no hemolysis 0.0003 c.c. = no hemolysis

In the above titration 0.001 c.c. of the inactivated immune serum represents the unit for 5 per cent cells in the presence of 0.01 c.c. of the alexin used in the experiment. Since the antiserum remains relatively stable if inactivated and kept in the ice-chest, a balanced hemolytic system can be obtained as required, for experimental or practical purposes, by setting up a series of tubes each containing 0.5 c.c. of a 5 per cent suspension of cells with 0.001 c.c. of the preserved immune serum and adding varying amounts of fresh guinea-pig serum in the range of 0.005 to 0.02 c.c.. In this way the alexin unit for the system to be used on each day can be rapidly determined.

In all experiments and titrations in which sensitizer and alexin are quantitatively balanced it is of the greatest importance that the several tubes compared shall contain equal volumes. Alexin action is more rapid and stronger in concentration. Thus 0.02 c.c. of alexin may completely hemolyze an amount of sensitized cells in a total volume of 2 c.c. which it would take 0.05 c.c. of the same alexin to hemolyze if the volume were increased to 5 c.c. In routine work the total volume for 0.5 c.c. of cells is usually taken as 2.5 c.c

Alexin-splitting.—Ferrata was the first to show that when fresh serum is dialyzed against distilled water and the serum thus divided into precipitated globulins and albumins in solution, neither fraction will exert alexin action alone but, put together again, the original activity is completely restored. This has been confirmed and it is recognized that any method by which the globulins and albumins can be separated will divide the alexin into a globulin and albumin fraction. Passing CO_2 through diluted serum is an excellent manner of accomplishing this purpose. Brand found that both fractions were easily destroyed by heat, but that the globulin fraction deteriorated rapidly on standing in salt solution. When the two fractions are allowed to act upon sensitized cells, the globulin fraction must first become attached to the sensitized antigen before the albumin fraction can act. For this reason, the globulin fraction is spoken of as midpiece, the albumin fraction as endpiece.

Since these observations were made, Whitehead, Gordon and Wormall have found that there is probably a third and possibly a fourth alexin fraction.

Fixation of the Complement.—Bordet and Gengou in 1901 devised an ingenious method of experimentation by which small quantities of any given immune body (amboceptor) can be demonstrated in serum. The term "fixation of complement," by which their method of investigation is now generally known, explains itself as the steps of experimentation are followed. They prepared the following mixtures:

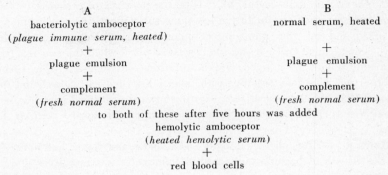

A

bacteriolytic amboceptor
(*plague immune serum, heated*)
+
plague emulsion
+
complement
(*fresh normal serum*)

B

normal serum, heated
+
plague emulsion
+
complement
(*fresh normal serum*)

to both of these after five hours was added
hemolytic amboceptor
(*heated hemolytic serum*)
+
red blood cells

Results:
A showed no hemolysis.
B showed hemolysis +.

The conclusion to be drawn from this was that in A the presence of immune body had led to absorption of all the complement. In B, there being no bacteriolytic immune body to sensitize the bacteria and enable them to absorb the complement, the latter substance was left free to activate the subsequently added hemolytic amboceptors. The Bordet-Gengou phenomenon has been extensively used by Wassermann

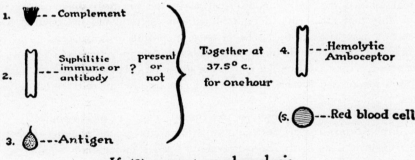

1.   - - -Complement

2.   - - -Syphilitic immune or antibody   present or not

Together at 37.5° c. for one hour

4.   - - -Hemolytic Amboceptor

3.   - - -Antigen

(5.   - - -Red blood cell

If (2) present, no hemolysis.
If (2) not present, hemolysis.

FIG. 15.—SCHEMATIC REPRESENTATION OF COMPLEMENT FIXATION IN THE BORDET-GENGOU REACTION, AS CONCEIVED BY EHRLICH.

and Bruck, Neisser and Sachs, and others to demonstrate the presence of immune bodies in various sera.

It should be noted that this method, if valid, must presuppose the identity of the hemolytic and bactericidal complement in the activating serum.

Fixation of Complement by Precipitates.—It has been found by Gengou and confirmed by Moreschi, Gay, and others, that when the serum of an animal immunized with the serum of another species or with a foreign albumin is mixed with a solution of the substance used in the immunization, the precipitate formed will remove complement from the mixture. In other words, precipitates formed by the reaction of precipitin with its antigen will fix complement. This is of great importance in complement-fixation tests; for because of insufficient washing, the blood cells used in producing the hemolytic amboceptor, may, from the presence of serum, give rise to a precipitin as well as a hemolysin. In the test done subsequently, a precipitin reaction may take place and by thus removing complement may give a false result. The absorption of complement of such precipitates takes place when the two reacting factors, the precipitin and its antigen, are in dilution—so high a visible precipitate cannot be observed. This fact, together with others, have led us to the belief that the so-called precipitins are true sensitizers, exerting toward unformed proteins the same function that the so-called sensitizer or amboceptor exerts toward cellular formed antigens.

Agglutination.—Although Metchnikoff and Charrin and Roger had noticed peculiarities in the growth of bacteria cultivated in immune sera, which were unquestionably due to agglutination, the first recognition of the agglutination reaction as a specific function of immune sera was the achievement of Grüber and Durham. While investigating the Pfeiffer reaction with *B. coli* and the cholera vibrio, Gruber and Durham noticed that if the respective immune sera were added to bouillon cultures the cultures would lose their even, cloudy appearance and flake-like clumps would sink to the bottom of the tube, the supernatant fluid becoming clear. Gruber, at the same time, called attention to the fact that immune sera would produce this effect both on the micro-organism used in their production, and to a less extent, upon other closely related bacteria.

Widal applied the agglutination reaction to the practical diagnosis of typhoid fever, finding that the serum of typhoid patients agglutinated the typhoid bacillus. The reaction was also shown to be of great importance in bacteriological species differentiation. Since animals immunized against a definite species of bacteria acquire in their sera specific agglutinating powers for these bacteria and only slight agglutinating powers for related species, immune sera can be used in differentiating between varieties.

Agglutination may be observed microscopically or macroscopically. Motile bacteria brought into contact with agglutinating serum in the hanging drop rapidly lose their motility,[1] as in the case of typhoid bacilli, and gather together in small clumps or masses. The microscopic picture is easily recognized and the reaction takes place with varying speed and completeness according to the strength of the agglutinating serum.

As the reaction approaches completeness, the clumps grow larger and individual micro-organisms become more and more scarce, finally leaving the medium between clumps entirely clear.

Macroscopically observed, in small test tubes or capillary tubes, agglutination results in the formation of flake-like masses which settle into irregular heaps at the bottom, leaving the supernatant fluid clear, in distinct contrast to the even, flat sediment and the clouded supernatant fluid of the control. Agglutination can also be

---

[1] Motility has no relation to the mechanism of agglutination.

observed when bacteria are grown in broth to which immune serum has been added. Instead of evenly clouding the broth, the micro-organisms develop in clumps or chains. This is the so-called "thread-reaction" of Pfaundler.

Agglutinins act upon dead as well as upon living bacteria. For the microscopic tests bacterial emulsions killed by formalin were introduced by Neisser. Ficker pre-

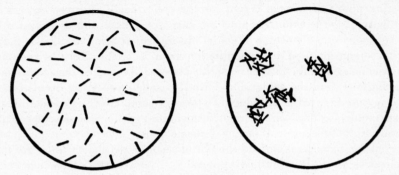

FIG. 16.—MICROSCOPIC AGGLUTINATION REACTION.

pared an emulsion of typhoid bacilli, which is permanent, and may be employed for macroscopic agglutinations. The preparation of standardized formalinized bacterial suspensions for agglutination has been advocated by Dreyer chiefly for the purpose of lending more accuracy to comparative agglutinin estimations. Like all other antigen-antibody reactions, agglutination is quantitative. The titer of a serum in any given test

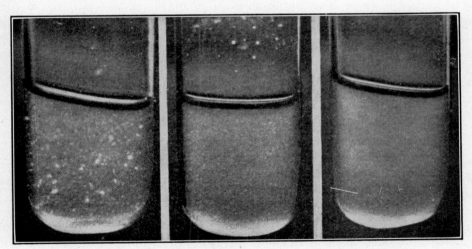

FIG. 17.—MACROSCOPIC AGGLUTINATION REACTION.
1. Coarse flocculation (H-type). 2. Fine flocculation (O-type). 3. Control homogeneous suspension of bacteria in saline.

must directly depend upon the amount of antigen exposed in a given volume of bacterial suspension.

Specificity.—From the very beginning, Gruber and Durham had claimed specificity for the agglutination reaction, and in this sense it was clinically utilized by

Widal for the diagnosis of typhoid fever. It was noticed, however, even by these earliest workers, that the serum of an animal immunized against one micro-organism would often agglutinate, to a less potent degree, other closely related species. Thus, the serum of a typhoid-immune animal may agglutinate the typhoid bacillus in dilutions of 1 : 1000, and the colon bacillus in dilutions as high as 1 : 200; while the agglutinating power of normal serum for the colon bacillus rarely exceeds 1 : 20. The specificity of the reaction for practical purposes, thus, is not destroyed if proper dilution is carried out, the degree of agglutinin formation being always far higher for the specific organism used in immunization than it is for allied organisms. The specific immune-agglutinin in such experiments is spoken of as the chief agglutinin (hauptagglutinin), and the agglutinins formed parallel with it, as the partial agglutinin (metagglutinin), terms introduced by Wassermann. Hiss has spoken of these as major and minor agglutinins. The relative quantities of the specific chief agglutinin and partial agglutinins present in any immune serum depend upon the individual cultures used for immunization, and the phenomenon is dependent upon the fact that certain elements in the complicated bacterial cell body may be common to several species and find common receptors in the animal body. Whenever an immune serum agglutinates a number of members of the group related to the specific organism used for its production, the reaction is spoken of as "group agglutination."

The partial agglutinins have been studied by Castellani and others, by a method spoken of as the "absorption method." This consists in the separate addition of bacterial emulsions (agglutinogens) of the various species concerned in a group agglutination, to the agglutinating serum. In this way, specific and partial agglutinins can be separately removed from the immune serum by absorption—each by its corresponding agglutinogen. In such experiments all agglutinins will be removed by the organisms used for immunization, a partial removal only resulting from the addition of allied strains. This method has thrown much light upon the intimate relations existing between members of various bacterial species, and has been particularly valuable in the study of the typhoid-colon-dysentery group. It is important to mention, however, that groups as determined by agglutination tests do not always correspond to classification depending upon morphological and cultural characteristics.

In carrying out agglutinin absorption, a serum of potent titer is diluted to about 1 : 50 and mixed with a thick suspension of the bacteria with which the absorption is to be done. After an hour in the incubator, the suspension is put into the ice-chest for several hours and is then centrifugalized. The supernatant fluid is then retested for agglutination.

The method is valuable in the investigation of antigenic differences between organisms closely related to each other.

Dissociation and Agglutination.—As far as agglutination is concerned, the first suggestion that bacterial alteration might influence serum reactions was made by Smith and Reagh when they showed that bacterial flagella might give rise to an agglutinin different from that incited by the bacterial bodies. Similar observations were subsequently published by others, and Eisenberg and Volk as well as Joos showed that typhoid bacilli produced two different agglutinins which could be separately studied by immunizing animals with unheated and with heated organisms.

These and other disconnected observations gained significance when Weil and

Felix, in 1916, published their studies upon the *Proteus X19* which they had isolated from a typhus patient and which has since gained diagnostic importance in this disease. They found that these organisms could be dissociated into one form that grew in spreading colonies on agar (the H form) and another nonmotile one (the O form) which made sharply outlined, compact colonies. The latter was the one especially significant by its agglutination in typhus serum. Immunization with the H organisms produced agglutinins for both, whereas immunization with the O organisms produced agglutination of the O forms only. The H agglutinations showed light, large flake-like clumps, the O agglutinations took place in smaller, dense granules. The difference, it has since been shown, is due to the separate existence of a flagellar antigen which, in the older investigations, had been destroyed by heating. (See chapter on the typhoid bacillus.)

Modern studies of dissociation have elucidated these conditions still further and have shown that, within each species, there are as many different agglutinative specificities as there are antigenic differences in the several dissociation forms. Thus, in a non-motile group like the pneumococci there is an S agglutinin due to antibody formation by the whole antigen and specific for the haptophore carbohydrate fraction of this antigen. There is a similar specific agglutinin for each type depending upon the character of the respective S.S.S. There is an R agglutinin specific for the bacterial protein fraction which is not as type specific, but more species specific than are the S.S.S. agglutinins.

In the cases of motile organisms, the flagellar antigen is added to the other two in each instance.

Bordet showed, in 1896, that the union of bacteria with the specific antibody was not alone capable of causing agglutination. This did not take place until the sensitized bacteria had been acted upon by electrolytes. He demonstrated this by allowing immune serum to act upon a bacterial suspension until it had agglutinated, then separating the agglutinated bacteria by centrifugation and resuspending the organisms in distilled water. Although these organisms were attached to antibody, *i.e.*, sensitized, they did not clump until salt solution was added. The process was thus shown to be a "two-phase" one. The first phase consisted in union with the antibody. In the second phase the sensitized bacteria flocculated under the influence of the salt.

In the subsequent understanding of the phenomenon, much useful information was gained by studies such as those of Neisser and Friedmann and others which proved that, just as electrolytes will flocculate various colloidal suspensions, they will agglutinate bacteria either with or without the presence of serum. At the same time it was shown, however, that bacteria sensitized with immune serum were agglutinated by amounts of salt far less than those necessary to agglutinate the normal organisms.

Northrop and De Kruif have subjected the physical mechanism to analysis by determining the changes that take place in bacterial suspensions, as the result of sensitization, both in regard to changes of electric charge and in regard to cohesive forces. It has been known for a long time that bacteria in suspension carry negative charges in solutions having a pH on the alkaline side of the iso-electric point of the bacterial protein, which is about pH 3 to pH 4.

Northrop and De Kruif define the mechanics of clumping in the following way:

Bacteria, like other suspensions, are prevented from precipitating by a balance between the repellent forces of the like charges carried by the particles and the cohesive force, perhaps identical with surface tension, which tends to draw them together. The presence of salt lowers both the potential and the cohesive forces, but when the bacteria have absorbed serum with the specific antibodies, the serum prevents the lowering of the cohesive force with a relative lowering of the potential. When the potential difference drops below a certain critical value of about 15 millivolts, the cohesion overcomes it and agglutination results.

Coulter, studying the agglutination of red blood cells, showed that the optimum pH for agglutination of normal cells is 4.7, but that when they are sensitized with immune serum this shifts to pH 5.3, which is the iso-electric point of the serum globulin which carries the antibody. Shibley defines the conditions as follows: In process of sensitization the bacteria are coated selectively by the globulin of the antibody. In consequence, the bacteria take on the character of particles of denatured globulin. Subsequent agglutination follows the laws of the flocculation of denatured protein particles.

The specific part of the agglutination reaction is thus the union with the antibody and it is not necessary to assume that this antibody is in any way different from any other. After the union has taken place agglutination results under the influence of the physical mechanism described above.

Prozones and Agglutinoids.—Early in the study of agglutinins it was noticed that sera which would agglutinate bacteria in high dilution would fail to agglutinate when they were mixed with the bacteria in concentration. Thus a serum might fail to agglutinate in dilutions up to 1 : 40 or 1 : 80, but would completely agglutinate the same bacterial suspension in dilutions, let us say, from 1 : 100 to 1 : 5000.

This was what Ehrlich called the proagglutinoid zone. He noticed that, while this phenomenon was occasionally present in fresh sera, it was more frequently and more markedly noticeable in old sera and in heated sera. Shibley has studied this aspect of the matter and finds that heating to 70° C. at pH 7 may extend the proagglutinoid zone up to a dilution of 1 : 640.

For a time it was assumed that this effect might be a purely nonspecific affair due to some sort of colloidal inhibition produced by changes in the serum due to the heating. For it is well known that heated serum may act as a protective colloid, preventing the flocculation of colloidal suspensions by electrolytes or by other colloids. This idea had to be abandoned, however, in view of the fact that the proagglutinoid effect is a specific one.

The specificity of the prozones is demonstrable in two ways. In the first place, bacteria that have been subjected to the action of serum showing such a prozone, without being agglutinated, will no longer agglutinate when subsequently emulsified in a potent agglutinating serum. Again, absorption of a prozone serum with the homologous bacteria will remove the prozone. This last experiment must be done with care in regard to the amount of bacteria used in the absorption, since any excess will also remove true agglutinin.

What probably happens is that the deteriorating processes mentioned modify the globulin in which the antibody is carried in the serum. When the bacteria become selectively coated with the antibody in the process of union, they now act like particles of this altered globulin which exerts a protective colloidal action, just as heated serum will protect other colloidal suspensions against flocculation. This is consistent not only with the mechanical facts of agglutination but also with the specificity known to govern the prozone phenomena. Shibley, who has studied these conditions in detail, and has demonstrated how large a prozone can be created by heating a serum, has also shown that the same process alters the physical conditions of the antibody responsible for the prozone. When heating had produced a prozone and the serum was then filtered through a Berkefeld filter, the agglutinoids, so-called, were removed.

Nonspecific Agglutination.—Some bacteria agglutinate spontaneously with such ease that the tendency is a difficult obstacle to accurate diagnostic work. With the hemolytic streptococci this is perhaps easily explained by the natural tendency to form long chains. With other organisms, such as the gram-negative cocci in the throat and pharynx, and with some other bacteria which agglutinate easily in normal serum, the phenomenon must depend upon their ability to absorb protein without the intervention of specific antibodies, thus changing their suspension equilibrium in a manner analogous to that which takes place with other bacteria in the presence of immune serum. Shibley has shown that some bacteria may be rendered agglutinable by salts by the simple addition of egg-white, an observation which has been made by Loeb in the case of colloidion particles.

Acid agglutination is the phenomenon noticed when bacteria are agglutinated on the addition of acid to the iso-electric point of the bacterial protein. It has been suggested that acid agglutination could be used for bacterial differentiation on the basis of chemical differences of the bacterial protoplasm, pitching the iso-electric points at different pH levels. Little of practical value has come of this.

Iso-agglutinins and Other Iso-antibodies.—In a preceding section, we described the experiments which Ehrlich and Morgenroth carried out with the hemolysis of goat corpuscles. They found that on occasion it was possible to produce hemolysins in one goat by injecting it with the corpuscles of another. This indicated that there must be an antigenic difference between the corpuscles of the two goats. It was never possible to produce hemolysins by injecting an animal with its own cells. Together with hemolytic antibodies, agglutinins often occurred. The phenomena of iso-antibodies thus discovered was studied in other animals, but no observation of value was made in man until 1899 when Shattock probably saw the agglutination of red corpuscles of man in the blood serum of other individuals. While there may be some doubt as to whether the phenomenon observed by Shattock was true iso-agglutination, it is quite certain that he did not correctly interpret it. Landsteiner was the first to describe the occurrence accurately and recognize it as a congenital antigenic difference between individuals of the human species. In 1901 he described three separate groups into which he could divide 22 individuals on the basis of iso-agglutinins of the red corpuscles. In 1902 a fourth group was added by Landsteiner's pupils Decastello and Stürli. The four groups had thus been adequately described when Jansky in 1907 and Moss in 1909 confirmed and extended the discovery. Unfortunately the last two writers established new classifications of the four groups, each giving them numerical arrangement, but Moss reversing Jansky's, so that Jansky's I became Moss' IV, and *vice versa.*

In tabulating the groups we have given all three of the groupings, but we recommend adherence to the now growing custom of referring to the individual groups by the letters which indicate Landsteiner's views of the antigenic structures of the individual red cells. This is easier and avoids the confusion which the numerical nomenclatures carried with them. Incidentally, it also respects priority.

SERA

				4	2	3	1
Moss				4	2	3	1
	Jansky			I	II	III	IV
				α, β	β	α	O
4	1	O		−	−	−	−
2	2	A		+	−	+	−
3	3	B		+	+	−	−
1	4	AB		+	+	+	−

(CELLS, at left margin)

The groups are thus named according to the antigen which is contained, by Landsteiner's interpretation, in the corpuscles. By the assumption of two separate antigenic units, the four groups can be explained. In group O the cells are not agglutinated by any serum, but the serum has both antibodies α and β. In group A the cells have this antigen, the serum has antibody β. In group B the serum has antibody α; and in group AB, where the cells have both antigens, the serum has no agglutinins and therefore acts on the cells of none of the other groups. Thus the nomenclature describes, at the same time, the mutual relationships.

The average percentage distribution of the groups among Europeans and Americans is approximately as follows:

Group O... 40 to 46
Group A... 32 to 43
Group B... 10 to 12
Group AB.. 3 to 6

The groupings are hereditary by Mendelian principles. This has made it possible to work out genetic formulae, for a consideration of which we refer to the articles by Ottenberg and Beres and by Hirschfeld. Bernstein, who does not accept the conception of Landsteiner in regard to the two antigens and their respective antibodies, has advanced a theory of his own which is thoroughly discussed in Hirschfeld's paper.

In medicine this subject has become of the greatest importance because of the increasing practice of transfusing blood from one individual to another. In selecting donors it is essential that there shall be no incompatibility of groups. It is always desirable to use a donor of the same group to which the recipient belongs. It is always advisable to match bloods before transfusion even though, by previous test, the groups of donor and recipient are known. Only in emergency should this be omitted. It is a simple procedure and will not only guard against error but will take care of the rare but existing exceptions to the rules which have occasionally been noticed. Thus Ottenberg has described a case in which a B donor, in addition to his α agglutinin reacted slightly with the cells of O and B. Such cases are extremely rare but should be kept in mind.

The tests may be done in a number of different ways; the most easily carried out, however, is the so-called slide agglutination which was introduced during the War.

In order to properly type an unknown blood, sera from groups A and B should be available. A drop of these sera is put upon a slide and the corpuscles of the unknown blood added either in the form of a fraction of a drop of the blood taken directly from the finger or ear of the subject, or, better, a fraction of a drop of defibrinated blood or blood taken into about twice its volume of salt solution or sodium citrate solution. The preparation of the blood to be tested is so simple that nothing further need be said. The corpuscles so obtained are mixed with the types of sera of types A and B. By referring to the table it will be easily seen that, if:
The blood agglutinates in neither of the sera, the subject belongs to Type O.
If the cells agglutinate in Type A, and not in Type B serum, the subject belongs to Type B.
If the corpuscles agglutinate in Type B and not in Type A serum, the subject belongs to Type A.
If the corpuscles agglutinate in both sera, the subject belongs to Type AB.

Though hereditary, the grouping is not present in the child at birth. According to studies by Unger, only about 25 per cent of newborn infants have cells that can be agglutinated. And only about 13 per cent of newborn children have iso-agglutinins. Incompatibility between mother and child may occur.

Blood Group Factors M, N and P.—The existence in human red blood corpuscles of several antigens different from those we have discussed in connection with the four chief blood groups has been demonstrated by Landsteiner and Levine. These antigens or factors called M, N and P were discovered by injecting rabbits with the erythrocytes containing them. The antiserum thus obtained is rendered monovalent for these antigens by absorption of the other antibodies present in it. Studies of the distribution of the M, N and P factors have shown that they occur in all four blood groups but are not related to these group factors. These three new factors are inheritable. M and N may occur together or separately, but no case is known where M and N were both lacking. These additional factors extend the scope of blood group determinations in relation to questions of paternity and almost make it possible to demonstrate individual differences in human blood.

The practical procedures and broad immunological, anthropological, medicolegal and surgical aspects of blood-group differentiation have been dealt with in special monographs. As the subject is beyond the scope of this book, the reader interested in it is referred to the books and articles listed among the references at the end of this chapter.

Precipitation.—R. Kraus, of Vienna, demonstrated that the sera of animals immunized against *B. pestis, B. typhosus,* and *Vibrio cholerae,* when mixed with the clear filtrate of bouillon cultures of the respective organisms, produce macroscopically visible precipitates. These precipitates occurred only when filtrate and immune serum were homologous, *i.e.,* when the animal from which the serum had been obtained had been immunized by the same species of micro-organism as that which was used in the test; it was for this reason Kraus spoke of them as specific precipitates. It was evident, therefore, that during the process of active immunization with these organisms, a specific antibody had been produced in the serum of the treated animal, which, because of its precipitating quality, was named precipitin. This peculiar reaction was soon found to hold good, not only for the bacteria used by Kraus, but also for other bacteria, few failing to stimulate the production of specific precipitins in the sera of immunized animals. The phenomenon of precipitation, however, is not limited to bacterial immunization, but has been found, like the phenomena of agglutination and lysis, to depend upon biological laws of broad application. Thus, Bordet found that the blood stream of rabbits treated with the serum of the chicken gave a specific precipitate when mixed with chicken serum. Tchistovitch demonstrated a similar reaction with the sera of rabbits treated with horse and eel sera. By the injection of milk, Wassermann, Schütze, and others produced an antibody which precipitated the casein of the particular variety of milk employed for immunization.

All antigenic substances will, then, produce precipitating antibodies, and the precipitation reaction is nothing more than another manifestation of the union of an antigen and its antibody which, in this case, is governed by the circumstances that result from the fine dispersion of the antigen. In agglutination reactions the antigen is present in the relatively large masses of the bacterial cells. In the precipitation reaction the antigen is dispersed in colloidal particles of infinitely smaller magnitude. In both cases the specific phase of the reaction is the union of antibody with antigen, a union in which the antigen particles are coated with the antibody globulin as in agglutination. The second phase, then, consists in the flocculation of these sensitized particles by the electrolytes, in a mechanism in every way analogous to that which brings about agglutination of bacteria. It is natural that there should be quantitative differences in the relation of antigen and antibody in the two reactions, since in the one instance the antigen is present in large particles, while in the other the particles are small with an enormously greater surface exposed for distribution of the antibody.

In agglutination reactions a reasonably potent serum can be diluted several thousand times before the agglutinating power is extinguished. In precipitation reactions the serum will lose precipitating power if diluted more than, at most, twenty times. In titrating precipitating sera we dilute the antigen solution and can detect it, with a potent precipitating serum, in dilutions of from one to many thousand times. The difference is easily undersood if we consider that equivalent masses of an antigen divided into particles as small as protein micellae would expose a surface at least ten thousand times greater than the same mass divided into particles of bacterial size. If we then consider the mechanism of the reaction in which the individual particles are coated with antibody globulin, the conditions become clear. We have discussed them in a simple calculation as follows.

Diameter of the bacterium $= 0.005$ mm.
Diameter of the antigen particle $= 0.000,000,5$ mm.

Then:

$$\text{The volume of the individual bacterium} = \frac{4}{3}\pi\left(5\frac{10^{-3}}{2}\right)^3$$

$$\text{The volume of the individual antigen particle} = \frac{4}{3}\pi\left(5\frac{10^{-7}}{2}\right)^3$$

and:

Mass of bacterium : mass of particle : : 10^{-9} : 10^{-21}

The amount of material composing a single bacterium, therefore, would be sufficient to form 10^{12} particles of the molecular magnitude. Now let us consider the surfaces exposed:

$$\text{The surface of a single bacterium of the specified size} = 4\,\pi\left(5\frac{10^{-3}}{2}\right)^{2}$$

$$\text{The surface of a protein particle of the specified size} = 4\,\pi\left(5\frac{10^{-7}}{2}\right)^{2}$$

and:

$$\text{Surface of protein particle : surface of bacterium : : } 10^{-14} : 10^{-6}$$

Thus the surface exposed by a single bacterium is 10^{8} the surface of a single protein particle.

But in equivalent masses of material divided, respectively, into bacteria or into protein particles there would be 10^{12} as many particles as bacteria. Uniting this with the preceding statement regarding the individual surfaces, it becomes clear that the total surface exposed by a given mass of antigenic material divided into particles as large as bacteria would be to the total surface of the same mass of material divided into protein particles as 1 is to 10^{4}, or as 1 is to 10,000.

The specificity of precipitins is of the greatest importance, since these reactions are used for the differentiation of animal proteins. In regard to bacterial precipitins it may be said that, just as in agglutination, there is in precipitation a certain degree of group reaction. The precipitin obtained with a colon bacillus, for instance, will cause precipitation with culture-filtrates of closely allied organisms, though in a less marked degree. According to Kraus, such confusion may easily be overcome by the proper use of dilution and quantitative adjustment, similar to that used in agglutination tests. Norris found that the precipitates given by immune sera with the filtrates of the homologous bacteria were invariably heavier than those given with allied strains and that the latter could be eliminated by sufficient dilution.

Specificity is of practical importance in the forensic use of the precipitin reaction introduced by Uhlenhuth, Wassermann and Schütze, and Stern. The precipitin reaction furnishes a means of distinguishing the blood of one species from that of another. Thus blood spots, dissolved out in normal salt solution, can be recognized by this reaction as originating from man or from an animal, even after months of drying and in dilutions as high as 1 : 50,000. Since the value of this test depends entirely upon the strict specificity of the reaction, this question has been studied with especial care, notably by Nuttall.

Precipitating antisera against protein solutions are prepared by two or three injections—best given intravenously in rabbits—at intervals of five or six days. The sera or protein solutions used should be sterile.

In carrying out forensic tests with antihuman precipitating serum, the following technic may be used:

1. 0.2 c.c. immune serum + 2 c.c. unknown protein solution
2. 0.2 c.c. immune serum + 2 c.c. known protein solution of variety suspected (similarly diluted)
3. 0.2 c.c. immune serum + 2 c.c. protein solution of different nature (similarly diluted)
4. 0.2 c.c. immune serum + 2 c.c. salt solution.
5. 0.2 c.c. unknown protein solution + 0.2 salt solution

If the test is positive, a precipitate appears in tubes 1 and 2, but not in any of the others. The precipitate should appear within fifteen to twenty minutes.

An equally serviceable method is the so-called "ring test." In this procedure, 0.2 c.c. of the undiluted immune serum is placed in each of a series of small tubes and 0.2 c.c. of each dilution of the protein antigen solution is carefully layered upon the immune serum in each tube. The precipitate forms at the line of juncture of the reagents.

In the fields of botany and zoology the precipitin reaction has added another fundamental method to those already available for the demonstration of species relationships. In some respects it is the most important of these, since it indicates a basic similarity in protein structure which is retained long after life habits, anatomical structure and physiological properties may have become considerably altered. Nuttall has studied this extensively and has shown the overlapping antigenic relationships of the blood within various groups. An example of these is the following, which shows the precipitation relationships of the blood of various species of apes in relationship to man.

The serum is an antihuman serum produced by rabbit injection.

The percentages are in comparison with the amounts of precipitate formed in the first tube, *i.e.*, antihuman *vs.* human serum, in comparable dilutions.

	Per Cent
Man	100
Chimpanzee (loose precip.)	130
Gorilla	64
Ourang	42
Cynocephalus	42
Ateles	29

The value of the precipitin reaction in determining organ specificities and in facilitating investigations of antigen structure have been described in the section on antigens.

REFERENCES

BORDET, J. Ann. de l'Inst. Pasteur, 1895, 9:462; 1898, 10:193; 1898, 12:688; 1899, 13:225.

BORDET, J., and GENGOU, O. Ann. de l'Inst. Pasteur, 1901, 15:129, 289.

BRAND, E. Berl. klin. Wchnschr., 907, 44:1075.

BUCHNER, H. Centralbl. f. Bakteriol., I Abt., 1889, 5:817; 1889, 6:1, 561.

——— Arch. f. Hyg., 1893, 17:112, 179.

CASTELLANI, A. Ztschr. f. Hyg., 1902, 40.

CHARRIN and ROGER. Compt. rend. Soc. de biol., 1889.

COULTER, C. J. Gen. Physiol., 1920, 3:307.

DAREMBERG, G. Arch. de méd. expér. et d'Anat. path., 1891, 3:20.

DINGLE, J. H., FOTHERGILL, L. D., CHANDLER, C. A. J. Immunol., 1938, 34:357.

DOAN, C. A. The Transfusion Problem, Physiol. Rev., 1927, 7:1.

DONATH, J., and LANDSTEINER, R. München. med. Wchnschr., 1904, 51:1590.

DREYER, G., WALKER, E. W. A., and GIBSON, A. G. Lancet, 1915, 1:324.

ECKER, E. E., PILLEMER, L., WERTHEIMER, D., and GRADIS, H. J. Immunol., 1938, 34:19.

EHRLICH, P. Ges. Arb. z. Immunitätsforsch., Berlin, 1904.

EHRLICH, P., and MORGENROTH, J. Berl. klin. Wchnschr., 1899, 36:6.

EISENBERG and VOLK. Ztschr. f. Hyg., 1902, 40:155.

FERRATA, A. Berl. klin. Wchnschr., 1907, 44:366.

FICKER, M. Berl. klin. Wchnschr., 1903, 40:1021.

GAY, F. P. Centralbl. f. Bakteriol., I Abt., 1905, 35:172.

GENGOU, O. Ann. de l'Inst. Pasteur, 1902, 16.

GRAMENITZKI, M. Biochem. Ztschr., 1912, 43:481.

GRINNELL, F. B. J. Exper. M., 1931, 54:577.

GRUBER, M., and DURHAM, H. E. München. med. Wchnschr., 1896, 43:285.

HEKTOEN, L., and RUEDIGER, G. F. J. Infect. Dis., 1904, 1:379.

HIRSCHFELD, L. Ergebn. d. Hyg., Bakteriol., Immunitätsforsch. u. Exper. Therap., 1926, 8:367.

HIRSZFELD, L. Konstitutions-Serologie und Blutgruppenforschung, Berlin, 1928.

JANSKY, J. For analysis and translation see KENNEDY, J. A. J. Immunol., 1931, 20:117.

KISS, J. Ztschr. f. Immunitätsforsch. u. exper. Therap., 1909, 3:558.

KRAUS, R. Wien. klin. Wchnschr., 1897.

LANDSTEINER, K. Centralbl. f. Bakteriol., I Abt., 1900, 27:357.

——— Wien. klin. Wchnschr., 1901, 14:1132.

LANDSTEINER, K., and LEVINE, P. Proc. Soc. Exper. Biol. & Med., 1926–27, 24:600, 941.

——— J. Exper. M., 1928, 47:757, 48:731.

——— J. Immunol., 1929, 16:123.

LATTES, L. Individuality of the Blood in Biology and in Clinical and Forensic Medicine, trans. by L. W. H. Bertie, London, 1932.

LI, C. P. J. Exper. M., 1929, 50:245.

MARRACK, J. R. The Chemistry of Antigens and Antibodies, Medical Res. Council, Spec. Rep. Ser. No. 230, London, 1938.

METCHNIKOFF, E. Ann. de l'Inst. Pasteur, 1889, 3:61, 265; 1891, 5:456; 1895, 9:433.

MORGENROTH, J., and SACHS, H. Collected Studies on Immunity, by Ehrlich, trans. by C. Bolduan, New York, 1906, 250.

MOSS, W. L. Tr. Ass. Am. Physicians, 1909, 24:419.

——— Bull. Johns Hopkins Hosp., 1910, 21:63.

NEISSER, M., and FRIEDMANN. München. med. Wchnschr., 1904, 51:456, 827.

NEISSER, M., and SACHS, H. Berl. klin. Wchnschr., 1905, 42:1388, 1906, 43:67.

NORRIS. J. Infect. Dis., 1904, 2:3.

NORTHROP, J. H., and DE KRUIF, P. J. Gen. Physiol., 1922, 4:639.

NUTTALL, G. Ztschr. f. Hyg., 1888, 4:353.

——— Blood Immunity and Blood Relationship, Cambridge University Press, 1904.

OTTENBERG, R., and BERES, D. The Newer Knowledge of Bacteriology and Immunology, Chicago 1928, p. 909.

PFAUNDLER, M. Centralbl. f. Bakteriol. I Abt., 1898, 23:9, 71, 131.

PFEIFFER, R., and ISSAEFF. Ztschr. f. Hyg. u. Infectionskrankh., 1894, 17:355.

SCHÜTZE. Ztschr. f. Hyg. u. Infectionskrankh., 1901.

SHATTOCK, S. G. Tr. Path. Soc., Lond., 1899, 50:279.

——— J. Path. & Bacteriol., 1900, 6:303.

SHIBLEY, G. S. J. Exper. M., 1926, 44:667; 1929, 50:825.

SMITH, T., and REAGH, A. L. J. Med. Research, 1903, 10:89.

SNYDER, L. H. Blood Grouping in Relation to Clinical Legal Medicine, Baltimore, 1929.

STEFFAN, P. Handbuch der Blutgruppenkunde, München, 1932.

STERN. Deutsche med. Wchnschr., 1901.

UHLENHUTH. Deutsche med. Wchnschr., 1900, 46; 1901, 6:17.

VON DECASTELLO, A., and STÜRLI, A. München. med. Wchnschr., 1902, 49:1090.

VON FODOR, J. Deutsche med. Wchnschr., 1886, 12:617.

WASSERMANN, A. Deutsche med. Wchnschr., 1900, 29.

WASSERMANN, A., and BRUCK, C. Med. Klin., 1905, 1:1409.

WASSERMANN, A., and SCHÜTZE. Berl. klin. Wchnschr., 1901, 6.

WEIL, E., and FELIX, A. Wien. klin. Wchnschr., 1916, 29:33.

——— Ztschr., f. Immunitätsforsch., u. exper. Therap., 1920, 29:24.

WIENER, A. S., LEDERER, M., and POLAYES, S. H. J. Immunol., 1930, 19:259.

WIENER, A. S., ROTHBERG, S., and FOX, S. A. J. Immunol., 1932, 23:63.

WHITEHEAD, H. B., GORDON, J., and WORMALL, A. Bio-Chem. J., 1925, 19:618; 1926, 20:1044.

ZINSSER, H. J. Immunol., 1930, 18:483.

CHAPTER XVII

PHAGOCYTOSIS

The studies on immunity which we have outlined in the preceding sections have dealt entirely with the phenomena occurring in the reaction between bacteria or bacterial products and the body fluids. These studies formed the basis of a theoretical conception of immunity formulated chiefly under the leadership of Ehrlich, Pfeiffer, Kruse and others. Parallel with these developments investigations on immunity were carried on which brought to light many important facts concerning the participation of the cellular elements of the body in its resistance to infectious germs.

The inspiration for this work and the greater part of the theoretical considerations based upon it emanated from Metchnikoff and his numerous pupils at the Pasteur Institute in Paris. The phenomenon which these observers studied in great detail and upon the occurrence of which they based their conceptions of immunity, is known as *phagocytosis.*

Metchnikoff built up his conception of what he called phagocytosis from a study of inflammatory reactions in the daphne or water flea. He noted that in these simple forms invading yeast cells or foreign particles were removed by ingestion within wandering ameboid cells, and correlated this observation with the ingestion of anthrax bacilli within the blood cells of higher animals. He compared the process of phagocytosis to cell nutrition.

Among the lowest unicellular animals the nutritive process consists in the ingestion of minute particles of organic matter by the cell. The rhizopods, which may be found and studied in water from stagnant pools or infusions, when observed under the microscope, may be seen to send out short protoplasmic processes, the pseudopodia, by means of which they gradually flow about any foreign particle with which they come in contact. If the ingested particle is of an inorganic nature and indigestible, it will be again extruded after a varying period. If, however, the ingested substance is of a nature which can be utilized in the nutrition of the protozoon, it is rapidly surrounded by a small vacuole within which it is gradually dissolved and becomes a part of the cellular protoplasm. This digestion within the unicellular organism is due to a proteolytic enzyme (Mouton) which acts in the presence of a weakly alkaline reaction. This has been shown by the actual extraction, from amebae, of a trypsin-like ferment.

As we proceed higher in the scale of the animal kingdom, we find that this power of intracellular digestion, while not uniformly an attribute of all the body cells, is still well developed and a necessary physiological function of certain cells which have retained primitive characters. In animals like the *Cœlenterata,* in which there are two cell layers, an entoderm and an ectoderm, the ectodermal cells have lost the power of intracellular digestion, while the entodermal cells are still able to ingest and digest suitable foreign particles. It is only as we proceed to animals of a much

higher organization that the function of cell ingestion of crude food is entirely removed from the process of general nutrition. Nevertheless, in these animals also, the
actual cell ingestion of foreign particles occurs, but it is now limited entirely to a
definite group of cells. In the higher animals and in man, this function of phagocytosis is limited to the white blood cells of the circulation, or leukocytes, to certain
large endothelial cells lining the serous cavities and blood vessels, and to cells of
mesenchymal origin which contribute to the formation of giant cells within the tissues. A convenient division of these phagocytic cells is that into wandering cells and
fixed cells. The wandering cells are the polymorphonuclear leukocytes, called microphages by Metchnikoff, and certain large mononuclear elements or macrophages.

The macrophages and fixed cell phagocytes observed by Metchnikoff are in all
likelihood derivatives of what is now spoken of as the reticulo-endothelial system.
This term was originated by Aschoff, who grouped together a special type of cells
widely distributed in the animal body but, according to him, similar in mesothelial
origin and in function. The possibility of there being such a special system of cells in
many organs of the body was first mentioned by Ranvier, who described the so-called
clasmatocytes, wandering cells in the connective tissue of the omentum. These cells are
characterized, among other things, by their capacity for taking up intravital dyes like
trypan blue. They are variously distributed, and include the lining cells of capillaries,
of lymph sinuses, of the sinuses of the spleen and of serous cavities. They include also
the clasmatocytes of reticular connective tissue, certain cells of the lymphatic tissues in
lymph nodes and in the thymus, the Kupffer cells of the liver and large mononuclear
cells in the circulating blood spoken of as histiocytes. The finer differentiation between
all these cells is a matter of considerable histological difficulty, and depends largely
upon nucleus form, staining reaction and especially the distribution of granules
when stained with neutral red, Janus green and other vital dyes.

Considerable importance is attributed to-day to the rôle played by clasmatocytes
and other cells of the reticulo-endothelial system in local immunity. The subject has
been extensively studied by Gay and his associates. According to their observations,
when broth or starch is injected into the pleural cavity, the initial polymorphonuclear
exudate is replaced in about seventy-two hours by one consisting chiefly of mononuclear cells of the general class of clasmatocytes. If, at this time, virulent streptococci are injected into the same location, the animals are found protected against
many times the fatal dose. Phagocytosis of organisms in tissues is chiefly mononuclear, and there seems to be an extraordinary mobility of clasmatocytes through
tissues into areas of invasion. In the natural immunity of animals against various
infections, such tissue-phagocytes often play a predominating rôle. Pigeons, for instance, as Kyes has shown, injected with pneumococci—to which they are resistant—
destroy the organisms in enormous quantities by phagocytosis by the Kupffer cells in
the liver and the mononuclear cells in many other organs. The same thing takes place
in the lungs, lymph nodes and spleen in many forms of natural resistance. It is more
than likely, also, that giant cell formation as it occurs in the course of removal of
insoluble organisms like tubercle bacilli, blastomycetes and foreign particles of various kinds originates in the coalescence of fixed tissue phagocytes.

In studying the cellular activities which come into play whenever foreign material
of any description gains entrance into the animal body, a definite reaction on the part

of the phagocytic cells may be observed. When we inject into the peritoneal cavity of a guinea-pig a small quantity of nutrient broth, and examine the exudate within the cavity from time to time, we can observe at first a diminution from the normal of the cells present in the peritoneal fluid. This may be due either to an injury of the leukocytes by the injected substance, or to an actual repellent influence which the injected foreign material exerts upon the wandering cells. Very soon after this, however, the exudate becomes extremely rich in leukocytes, chiefly of the polymorphonuclear variety, the maximum of the reaction being reached about eighteen to twenty-four hours after the injection. After this, there is a gradual diminution in the leukocytic elements until the fluid in the peritoneal cavity again reaches its normal condition. It is plain, therefore, that the presence of the foreign material in the peritoneal cavity has, after a primary repellent action upon the phagocytes, attracted them in large numbers to the site of the foreign substance. Such repelling or attracting influences upon the leukocytes are spoken of as negative or positive *chemotaxis*. The reasons for chemotaxis are not well understood. In the case of bacteria, chemotactic attraction or repulsion is intimately dependent upon the nature of the microorganism, and probably has a definite relationship to its virulence. Whether or not the principles of chemotaxis may serve to explain the hypo- and hyper-leukocytoses diagnostically utilized in clinical medicine is by no means positive. It is likely, however, that the two phenomena are closely associated (Iverman).

We have seen that the invasion of the animal body by foreign material, living or dead, is followed by a prompt response on the part of the phagocytic cells. In the case of bacteria, when these are deposited in the subcutaneous areolar tissues, the inflammatory reaction which follows brings with it an emigration of microphages (polynuclear leukocytes) from the blood vessels—and these are the so-called pus cells. When the injection of bacteria is intraperitoneal, after a primary diminution, there is an increase of leukocytes in the peritoneal cavity which results in the formation of a copious turbid exudate. If the pus of an abscess or the exudate from an infected peritoneum is examined microscopically, it will be seen that many of the microphages have taken bacteria into their cytoplasm. That fully virulent living bacteria can be so taken up has been variously proven. The phagocytosis is, therefore, not simply a removal of the dead bodies of bacteria previously killed by the body fluids, but represents an actual attack upon living and fully virulent micro-organisms. That the ingested bacteria are often alive after ingestion is proved by the fact that the injection of exudate containing, so far as can be determined, only intracellular bacteria, has, in several instances, been found to give rise to infection.

After the bacteria have remained for some time within the cytoplasm of the leukocyte, vacuoles may be seen to form about them, similar to those mentioned in discussing the digestive processes of amebae. If the preparations are, at this stage or later, stained with a 1 per cent solution of neutral red, it will be found that the bacteria, colorless under normal conditions, will be stained pink, an evidence of their beginning disintegration. At a later stage in the process of intracellular digestion, the bacteria will lose their form, and appear swollen, granular and vacuolated, and finally will be no longer distinguishable. If, on the other hand, the ingestion of bacteria brings about the death of a leukocyte, the neutral red will not stain the bacteria, the digestive vacuoles will not form, and the leukocyte itself will disintegrate.

It must not be forgotten, however, that not all micro-organisms are equally susceptible to phagocytosis. Virulent, capsulated organisms resist ingestion more energetically than their avirulent dissociation forms. Others again, like the tubercle bacillus and the anthrax bacillus, for instance, oppose great difficulties to intra-cellular digestion.

To a certain extent the variety of the bacteria determines the variety of phagocyte attracted to the point of invasion. In the cases of most of the bacteria of acute diseases, the microphages or polymorphonuclear leukocytes are the ones upon which the brunt of the battle devolves. Other invaders, like the *B. tuberculosis*, blastomycetes, and others, find themselves opposed chiefly by macrophages. Cells of animal origin, such as the dead or injured cells of the animal's own body or the cells of other animals artificially introduced, are ingested by macrophages. This is true also of many parasites of animal nature.

It is clear, thus, that the process of phagocytosis is a universal response on the part of the body to the invasion of foreign particles of dead material, of alien cells, and of living micro-organisms. It remains to be shown upon what basis this process may be regarded as an essential feature in protecting the body against infection and against the invasive property of bacteria.

The researches of Metchnikoff brought out the important fact that phagocytosis is regularly more active in cases in which the infected animal or human being eventually recovers. In animals, furthermore, which show a high natural resistance against any given micro-organism, phagocytosis is more energetic than it is in animals more susceptible to the same incitant. Thus, experimenting with anthrax infection in rats, Metchnikoff was able to show that, in these animals, a more rapid and extensive phagocytosis of anthrax bacilli takes place than in rabbits and guinea-pigs and other animals which are susceptible to this infection. While different interpretations have been attached to this phenomenon, its actual occurrence may be accepted as a proven fact.

In his later investigations, Metchnikoff was able to show that direct parallelism existed between the development of immunity in an artificially immunized animal and the phagocytic powers of its white cells. He showed that rabbits artificially immunized to anthrax, responded to anthrax infection by a far more active phagocytosis than did normal, fully susceptible animals of the same species.

The fundamental differences between the conclusions drawn from these phenomena by the school of Metchnikoff and by that of the German workers may be clearly stated as follows: Metchnikoff believed that phagocytosis was the factor which determined immunity, while Pfeiffer and others maintained that the determining factors upon which recovery or lethal outcome depends, were the fluids of the body and their constituent immune body and complement, while the phagocytosis which occurred coincidentally, was merely a means of removal of the bacteria after the outcome had already been decided.

In the further developments of his theory, Metchnikoff claimed that the immune body and complement—the presence of which in blood serum and exudates he by no means overlooks—are derivatives of the leukocytes.

Investigations of the mechanism of phagocytosis have harmonized the originally conflicting cellular and humoral theories of immunity.

MECHANISM OF PHAGOCYTOSIS

Opsonins and Tropins.—Although the theories of immunity were at first classified as the humoral and the cellular or phagocytic theories, the separation was never, even in the minds of the warmest partizans, an absolute one. Thus, Buchner and his successors looked for the origin, first, of alexin, then of antibody, in the leukocytes, and Metchnikoff attributed to immune serum the quality of stimulating the leukocytes (stimulins) to increased phagocytosis. The serum, according to Metchnikoff, acted, not directly upon the bacteria, in the nature of bactericidal or lytic substances, but rather upon the leukocytes, stimulating their activities. Denys and Leclef were the first to oppose this view. On the basis of experiments done upon streptococcus immunity in rabbits, they came to the conclusion that the serum aided phagocytosis rather by its action upon the bacteria than by its influence upon the leukocytes.

Wright in 1903 and 1904 undertook a systematic study of the relation of the blood serum to phagocytosis. Using his own modifications of the technic of Leishman, he first determined the direct dependence of phagocytosis upon some substance contained in the blood-serum. He proved that this serum component acts upon the bacteria directly and not upon the leukocytes, is bound by the bacteria, and renders them subject to phagocytosis.

The experiments by which this was done were simple ones, identical in principle with those carried out by Denys and Leclef. They consisted in mixing, in a series of tubes, leukocytes and serum, centrifugalizing after an hour and adding to the leukocytes a suspension of staphylococci. The phagocytic activities of the leukocytes that had been in contact with serum was slightly or not at all increased over those of leukocytes that had not been subjected to serum contacts. In another series of tubes, staphylococci were mixed with serum and centrifugalized after an hour's exposure. When such organisms were put together with leukocytes, a great enhancement of phagocytosis was observed.

It was shown, in other words, that organisms had absorbed something from the serum which rendered them more easily phagocytable.

When we have further discussed the mechanism of this process, it will become apparent that we have here merely another example of the change brought about in bacteria by sensitization with serum constituents. In preceding sections, we have described the effect of sensitization by antibodies which rendered bacteria or red blood cells subject to alexin action. In other sections, we have discussed the experiment which demonstrated that the absorption of antibodies by bacteria changed their suspension equilibrium in such a manner that they were flocculated by electrolytes, such reactions constituting agglutination and precipitation. In the present instance, we see that sensitization with serum antibodies in the presence of phagocytes renders the bacteria phagocytable. This is what we mean by the unitarian conception of antibodies.

Because of their action in preparing the bacteria for ingestion, Wright called the responsible serum constituents "opsonins" ($\dot{o}\psi\omega\nu\epsilon\iota\nu$).[1] Working with normal serum he found that the opsonic powers were almost completely removed by heating to 56°

---

[1] $\dot{o}\psi\omega\nu\epsilon\iota\nu$ = to prepare food.

C.; the same temperature which destroyed alexin. Neufeld and Rimpau, soon after this, confirmed Wright's observations, in principle, with immune serum, but found that, in this case, the tropic power resisted heating up to about 70° C.

Confusion arose from the fact that the opsonic action of normal serum seemed to be completely destroyed by degrees of heat identical with those which destroyed alexin, whereas in immune serum the tropic action was as thermostable as that of any other antibody effects. The difficulty lay probably with disregard in the earlier work of the factor of virulence. Wright worked with staphylococci, Neufeld and his associates largely with virulent pneumococci. Cowie and Chapin carried out an experiment with staphylococci and normal serum which seemed to indicate that a combination of heated normal serum and diluted normal serum not in itself sufficient to exert opsonic action might restore the activities lost in the heating. And Dean showed that although heated immune serum was capable of causing phagocytosis by itself, the activity was greatly enhanced by the addition of a little diluted fresh normal serum. The conception that grew out of these investigations was that both normal opsonins and immune tropins are heat-stable substances, but that the phagocytosis-enhancing properties in both cases involved the coöperation of alexin or complement. As in the hemolysis of sensitized cells, a low concentration of the heat-stable immune body (as in normal serum) requires the participation of a relatively large amount of alexin. On the other hand, when, as in immune serum, there is a considerable amount of antibody, very little or no alexin is necessary.

The understanding of the reaction has been increased in studies made by Ward and Enders. They have shown that the action of the alexin is largely an accelerating one, even in the case of virulent pneumococci. In diluted immune serum heated to 56° C., phagocytosis of the pneumococcus may take place without the addition of alexin, but only after contact of many hours. The degree of phagocytosis obtained in six hours in the presence of a heated serum alone may be attained in one hour in the presence of alexin.

The relations revealed by Wright will be more easily understood from the tabulation of the following simple experiment:

Mixtures	*Average Bacteria per Leukocyte*
Washed leukocytes + staphylococci	1.2
Leukocytes + serum + staphylococci	20.0
Leukocytes + serum, then washed and staphylococci added	2.4
Staphylococci + serum, then washed and leukocytes added	18.4
Leukocytes + heated serum + staphylococci	4.2

There are still a good many uncertainties in the analysis of the mechanism of phagocytosis. We may summarize the present state of our knowledge more or less as follows:

Spontaneous phagocytosis, that is, the ingestion of bacteria by leukocytes in the absence of serum, is slight or entirely absent. It is difficult to assume the complete absence of any serum in such experiments, because minute amounts may remain adsorbed to the surfaces of the cells.

Normal serum considerably stimulates phagocytic processes, but does this by sensitization of the bacteria by some serum constituent which is absorbed by the micro-organisms. The substances absorbed in this process are specific and are not identical with the alexin. Yet this opsonic action is almost completely eliminated by heating at a temperature which destroys alexin. While phagocytosis in heated normal serum may eventually take place, contact necessary for this must be prolonged beyond several hours and never attains values comparable to those seen when alexin is present. Normal opsonin is effective against organisms such as the staphylococci and others to which a considerable normal resistance exists and against the less virulent dissociation forms of highly pathogenic varieties. It is not effective against highly virulent, capsulated bacteria.

Immune opsonins or tropins are effective against virulent organisms and are not destroyed by heating to 56° C. They can be specifically absorbed out of serum. They do not depend upon the participation of an alexin-like substance but their activity is accelerated by the presence of alexin.

From all these observations it seems reasonable to assume that both normal and immune opsonic or tropic action depends upon a dual mechanism which consists in the coöperation of an immune body or sensitizer and an alexin and, in this way, is similar to other antibody reactions in which alexin participates. In normal serum there is a relatively small amount of sensitizer but a large amount of alexin. When, as in heated serum, the alexin is removed, the normal antibody is insufficient to bring about an appreciable amount of phagocytosis. In immune serum the organisms are heavily sensitized and a certain degree of phagocytosis is possible without alexin. But when, in such cases, alexin is also present, the phagocytic action is powerfully accelerated.

The diminished power of leukocytes to take up bacteria without the coöperation of serum was demonstrated, after Wright, by Hektoen and Ruediger, who worked with gradually increasing dilutions of serum. The contention of the Wright school, however, that leukocytes are entirely impotent for phagocytosis without the aid of serum, cannot be regarded as proven, in face of the work of Loehlein and others who have observed phagocytosis on the part of washed leukocytes.

The specificity of opsonins and their multiplicity in a given serum were studied mainly by Bullock and Atkins, Hektoen and Ruediger, and Bullock and Western. These authors showed that the opsonic substances in sera could be absorbed out of the sera, one by one, by treatment with various species of bacteria, a procedure analogous to the method of absorption used in the study of agglutinins.

The Technic of Wright and the Opsonic Index.—The three factors necessary for the performance of an opsonic test are (1) the blood serum to be tested; (2) an even emulsion of bacteria, and (3) leukocytes.

1. Blood serum is obtained by bleeding from the finger and receiving the blood into glass capsules. These are sealed at both ends; the blood is allowed to clot; and the separation of serum is hastened by a few revolutions of a centrifuge.

2. The bacterial emulsion is obtained by rubbing up a few loopfuls of a twenty-four-hour slant-agar culture with a little physiological salt solution (0.85 per cent) in a watch glass. A very small amount of salt solution is used at first and more is gradually added, drop by drop, as the emulsion becomes more even. The final breaking up of the smaller clumps is best accomplished by cutting off very squarely the end of a capillary pipet, placing it perpendicularly against the bottom of the watch glass, and sucking the emulsion in and out through the narrow chink thus formed.

3. The leukocytes are obtained by bleeding from the ear or finger directly into a solution

containing 0.85 per cent to 1 per cent of sodium chloride and 0.5 to 1.5 per cent of sodium citrate. Ten or fifteen drops of blood to 5 or 6 cc. of the solution will furnish sufficient leukocytes for a dozen tests. This mixture is then centrifugalized at moderate speed for five to six minutes. At the end of this time, the corpuscles at the bottom of the tube will be covered by a thin grayish pellicle, the buffy coat, consisting chiefly of leukocytes. These are pipetted off with a capillary pipette (by careful superficial scratching movements over the surface of the buffy coat).

There being, of course, no absolute scale for phagocytosis, whenever an opsonin determination is made upon an unknown serum, a parallel control test must be made upon a normal serum. This normal is best obtained by a pool or mixture of the sera of five or six supposedly normal individuals.

Serum, bacteria and leukocytes are then mixed in determined proportions and dilutions, as indicated for the particular experiment, and allowed to stand at incubator temperature, either in capillary pipettes (Wright) or, better, in small, sealed precipitation tubes slowly rotated in the incubator by a simple rotating mechanism. At the end of an hour, smears are made and stained with Wright's or Jenner's stain. The average numbers of bacteria per leukocyte and the proportion of phagocyting leukocytes are estimated and compared for the test samples and controls. The *phagocytic index* is the average number of bacteria per leukocyte. The *opsonic index* is the phagocytic index of the test sample over that of the control.

Leukocytic Substances.—We have discussed the protective action exerted by living leukocytes against bacterial infection and the relation of these cells to blood serum; furthermore, while our knowledge, as developed at present, shows that phagocytosis is aided by the serum in the ingestion of bacteria, the subsequent digestion of the germs, and possibly the neutralization or destruction of their intracellular poisons, is, as far as we know, largely accomplished by the unaided phagocytic cell. It is an obvious thought, therefore, that, in the struggle with bacterial invaders, the leukocytic defenders might be considerably reënforced if they were furnished, as directly as possible, with a further supply of the very weapons which they were using in the fight. Hiss conceived the plan of injecting into infected subjects the substances composing the chief cells or all the cells usually found in exudates, in the most diffusible form and as little changed by manipulation as possible; and he also assumed that extracts would be more efficacious than living leukocytes themselves, since if diffusible they would be distributed impartially to all parts of the body by the circulatory mechanism.

Experiments by Hiss and Hiss and Zinsser showed that leukocytic extracts injected into animals infected with various organisms exerted a distinct though not very powerful therapeutic effect. They have also had a certain degree of beneficial effect in human beings suffering from various infections. However, it is our present opinion, based chiefly upon the researches of one of us with Tsen, that the leukocytic substances act in more or less the same way as do other nonspecific proteins, in that they produce an increased leukocytosis and perhaps, as pointed out by Jobling and Petersen in another connection, may lead to an increased presence in the blood of various proteolytic and other enzymes.

That bactericidal substances can be extracted from leukocytes by various methods has been repeatedly shown by Schattenfroh, Petterson, Korschum, and others. The researches of Petterson as well as the work of Zinsser, showed that these "endolysins," as Petterson has called them, have a structure quite different from that of the serum bacteriolysins in that they are not rendered inactive by temperatures under $80°$ C., but, when once destroyed by higher temperatures, cannot be reactivated either by the addition of fresh serum or of unheated leukocyte extracts.

Active Immunization with Vaccine in Human Beings.—Wright's publication aroused a great deal of attention because of his effort to apply opsonic index measurements to the appraisal of the results of active immunization in human beings. In this regard, most of his work has proven of limited value. Measurements of opsonic indices are subject to so much experimental variation that they cannot be done with sufficient accuracy in clinical laboratories without an amount of labor that renders them useless as practical procedures. Nevertheless, it was this work of Wright which stimulated the interest in vaccine therapy as applied to man—an interest which has since then led to results of the greatest importance in the prophylaxis and therapy of infectious diseases.

Methods of prophylactic vaccination in man had been in use with cholera and plague for many years, but it was—among other investigations—that of Wright during the Boer War which led to the final development of our present methods of typhoid prophylaxis.

The detailed procedures by which vaccines are produced in connection with individual infections are dealt with in the sections devoted to respective infections.

Wright correctly recognized the importance of using what he called autogenous vaccines, namely, the use, whenever possible, of the organisms isolated from the subject to be vaccinated. Bacterial dissociation and its relationship to antigenic structure was not, however, at this time understood. In consequence, much of the work that has been done since then must be regarded as labor lost, and the future demands a complete reëxamination of the whole subject in clinical tests.

We cannot expect to induce an active immunity by the injection of organisms that have dissociated into what is called a "rough" form and which do not contain the chemically complete and unaltered antigen of the virulent organism. There has been a great deal of work done, for instance, in active immunization against pneumonia, but with this organism—as we have seen—dissociation into rough forms can easily take place in culture, and even in simple suspension of smooth forms, dissociation of the antigen may take place by autolysis. In this case, experiments have shown that formalin treatment of smooth pneumococci may preserve the complete antigen in vaccine for some time, and Goodner's experiments on rabbits have shown the effectiveness of prophylactic vaccination with this organism in its S form.

In typhoid fever, the experiments of Felix have shown that old *B. typhosus* produces little or no increase in the bactericidal power of the blood, but that such powers are considerably increased when a smooth, "Vi" strain of *B. typhosus* is used.

It is obvious, therefore, that in all vaccination experiments of the future, whether in the laboratory or in the clinic, no results can be expected unless the organism used for the preparation of the vaccines belongs not only to a group serologically homologous with that causing the infection, but in a form representing all the antigenic structures contained in the infecting micro-organism.

NONSPECIFIC PROTEIN THERAPY

A surprising development has been the observation that profound physiological reactions accompanied by occasional therapeutic benefit in infectious diseases has followed the intravenous injection of bacteria and other proteins which apparently had no specific relationship to the nature of the infectious process. The first observations were more or less accidental, incident to attempts by various writers to treat diseases like typhoid fever by the intravenous injection of typhoid bacilli. Ichiwaka, Kraus, Gay and others injected sensitized and unsensitized typhoid bacilli intravenously into patients suffering from typhoid fever, observing a sudden drop of temperature with chill, and frequent beneficial effects on the course of the disease. It was soon found that similar results could be obtained in these diseases with colon bacilli, paratyphoid bacilli, etc. Holler obtained striking results in typhoid fever by injecting deutero-albumose. Other proteins and proteose substances were subsequently used by many observers, and important studies on the theoretical effects of the injection of such substances have been made by Jobling and Petersen. It can be regarded as quite definite that these reactions are entirely nonspecific. The substances used have been typhoid vaccine, primary and secondary albumoses, gonococcus and other bacterial vaccines, normal serum, leukocyte extracts, etc. The method has been applied to a great many definite infections, such as typhoid fever, general sepsis, pneumonia, gonorrheal infections, and to arthritis and dermatological lesions, etc. Miller has used typhoid vaccines in typhoid fever and other conditions, and, in general, concludes that there can be little doubt that in a limited number of cases rapid and sometimes permanent beneficial results are obtained after a preliminary slight rise of temperature and subsequent drop, often with a chill. He also concludes that if an amount just sufficient to incite a chill is used, that is, if the dosage is carefully controlled, the treatment is without danger. He has given two thousand intravenous injections of typhoid vaccine in the Cook County Hospital, without serious consequences, except for the development of delirium tremens in some alcoholics. He, however, carefully selected his cases. As Petersen concludes, nonspecific therapy has produced definite results, though the eventual determination of its definite value cannot yet be made. It is in the experimental stage, and according to Petersen, "its usefulness and ultimate range" cannot yet be fully judged.

The effects of the injection, as analyzed by Petersen from his own studies and a study of the literature, are as follows: After injection of the more powerful and active substances, there is at first a chill, sweating, and a definite rise of temperature; there is a leukopenia followed by leukocytosis, lowering of the blood pressure, and changes in the blood, such as increase in fibrinogen, a rise of enzyme curve and an increase in blood sugar and antibodies. The less active substances produce some increase of temperature, a slight chill and other symptoms mentioned, to a lesser degree. The beneficial effects may perhaps be to some extent explained by the increase of leukocytes and of enzymes, and the febrile reaction. Petersen makes a point of the fact that if the method is to exert beneficial effects, it is probably necessary to use it early in the disease. We are not in any position at present either to recommend or further comment upon the method, but it is an important problem for laboratory experimentation and for careful clinical application in the hands of men trained in experimental studies.

REFERENCES

ASCHOFF. Lectures on Pathology, 1924.

BULLOCK and ATKINS. Proc. Roy. Soc. Lond., 1905, 74.

BULLOCK and WESTERN. Proc. Roy. Soc. Lond., 1905, 74.

CANTACUZÈNE. Ann. de l'Inst. Pasteur, 1897.

COWIE and CHAPIN. J. Med. Research, 1907, 17:57, 95, 213.

DEAN. Lancet, 1917, 1:45.

DENYS and LECLEF. Cellule, 1895, 11.

GAY, F. P. Newer Knowledge of Bacteriology and Immunology, Chicago, 1928, p. 881.

GOODNER. J. Exper. M., 1928, 48:1, 413.

GRINNELL, F. B. J. Immunol., 1930, 19, 5:457.

HEKTOEN, L., and RUEDIGER, G. F. J. Infect. Dis., 1905, 2.

HISS, P. H. J. Med. Research, n.s., 1908, 14:3.

HOLLER. Beitr. z. Krank. u. Infekt., 1917, 6; cited from Miller, J. Am. M. Ass., 1921, 76.

IVERMAN, D. S. Arch. Path., 1938, 25:40.

JOBLING and PETERSEN. J. Exper. M., 1914, 20.

KORSCHUM. Ann. de l'Inst. Pasteur, 1908, 22.

LEISHMAN. Brit. M. J., 1902, 1.

LEVADITI. Presse méd., 1900.

LOEHLEIN. Ann. de l'Inst. Pasteur, 1905, 1906.

METCHNIKOFF, E. L'immunité dans les maladies infectueuses, 1901.

MILLER. J. Am. M. Ass., 1921, 76.

MOUTON. Ann. de l'Inst. Pasteur, 1902, 16.

NEUFELD and RIMPAU. Deutsche med. Wchnschr., 1904, 40.

PETERSEN. J. Am. M. Ass., 1921, 76.

PETTERSON, A. Centralbl. f. Bakteriol., 1905, 1:39, 423, 613; 1908, 46:405.

PIERRALLINI. Ann. de l'Inst. Pasteur, 1897.

SCHATTENFROH. Arch. f. Hyg., 1897.

SIMON and LAMAR. Johns Hopkins Hosp. Bull., 1906, 17.

SIMON, LAMAR and BISPHAM. J. Exper. M., 1906, 8.

WARD, H. K., and ENDERS, J. F. J. Exper. M., 1933, 57:527.

WASSERMANN, A., and TAKAKI, T. Berl. klin. Wchnschr., 1898.

WEICHHARDT. Kolle u. Wassermann Handbuch.

WRIGHT and DOUGLAS. Proc. Roy. Soc. Lond., 1904, 72.

ZINSSER, H. J. Med. Research, 1910, 22:3.

ZINSSER, H., and TAMIYA. J. Exper. M., 1926, 44:753.

ZINSSER, H., and TSEN. J. Immunol., 1917, 2:247.

CHAPTER XVIII

HYPERSENSITIVENESS

By the word hypersensitiveness in the technical sense is meant an increased specific reaction capacity in an individual, man or animal, to a substance which, in a normal individual of the same species, produces little or no reaction.

The manifestations of hypersensitiveness are varied and include such widely separated phenomena as the protein hypersensitiveness of animals, spoken of as *anaphylaxis*, and the *allergies* or *idiosyncrasies* of man such as hay fever, asthma, food and drug idiosyncrasies. For this reason it seemed desirable, during the earlier periods of investigation, to set up classifications which might serve as tentative guides for orderly consideration. Some of the early classifications were, however, prematurely rigid. We took this position in commenting on the subdivisions established by Doerr and by Coca as early as 1923; and in commenting upon the matter in 1927 expressed views which we believe have been justified by subsequent experimental investigation and which we repeat, in substance, in the following paragraphs.

The original classification of the hypersensitive states suggested by Doerr, as well as the comparable one of Coca, both had the logical purpose of drawing a distinction between those manifestations in which, as in protein anaphylaxis, an antigen-antibody mechanism was demonstrable, and the larger group in which no evidences of such a mechanism could be detected. This distinction, like most classifications, served a useful purpose in furnishing a scaffolding for reasoning. But it should be regarded as a purely tentative guide for inquiry, since similarities between the various conditions are striking. Correct clinical analysis and progress in therapy depend to a large extent upon the correct appraisal of the degree to which all of these conditions are based upon analogous biological laws. It has already become apparent that many of the observations necessary for an understanding of these conditions cannot be made upon animals. It is a peculiarity of hypersensitiveness that identical inciting agents produce widely divergent effects in different species of animals, and many of the problems underlying the clinical manifestations of human hypersensitiveness can therefore be solved only by observation of the human being and by conservative experiment upon clinical material, so far as this may be safely done. Doerr seems now to believe with us that the similarities between these conditions are of more significance than the divergences. Moreover, work of the last few years has tended gradually to diminish the significance of differences which were formerly assumed to be of fundamental importance.

Immunologists have taken too narrow a view of the biological significance of altered reaction capacity, and have laid too much stress upon the incidental fact of whether or not specific reaction products, of which we speak as "antibodies," appear freely in the circulation as a consequence of altered cell capacity.

When the phenomena of specific hypersensitiveness were first subjected to experimental analysis, attention was largely concentrated upon sensitization with the coagulable proteins. It was found that the mechanism which was revealed as the responsible one in these reactions did not hold good for hypersensitiveness in general; and some observers went so far as to express the belief that the allergies (hay fever, food and drug idiosyncrasies, horse asthma, etc.) were based upon a mechanism in which antigen-antibody reactions were not involved. Because such a mechanism had not been demonstrated in many of these conditions, they denied its existence and based a separate group classification of these manifestations upon what they believed was a common association by the establishment of heredity as the sole determining factor. This extreme attitude, which neglects many similarities in favor of a few differences, is untenable unless these differences can be shown to be fundamental.

These matters will become more clear as we proceed. We do not believe that there is any *fundamental* difference between the various forms of specific hypersusceptibility, whether in animals or in man. There are, of course, many varieties of manifestation which depend upon dissimilarities in animal physiology; there are many superficial variations which depend upon chemical and physiological differences of the incitant substances; there are differences of localization in tissues more highly sensitized than the rest of the body, due often to the route by which the antigen enters the physiological interior. In the last analysis, however, in all forms of hypersusceptibility the basic mechanism depends upon a specific reaction within the animal body. The confusion which may still exist is owing to a too narrow and basically unjustified limitation of the definitions of antigens. In the old definition of antigen, these substances were described as being able to incite specific antibodies which could be detected in the circulation. The fundamental attributes of an antigen are its properties of inciting a change in the body which increases the capacity of the body specifically to react with the given antigen. The change incited is a cellular one, and must depend upon the production by the cell of chemical groupings specifically capable of uniting with the inciting antigenic substance. This statement implies the fundamental definition of an antibody. Whether the antibody appears in the circulation or remains attached to the cells is practically important, since in the latter case the antibody cannot be detected in the blood serum nor the hypersensitiveness passively conveyed to another animal, but from the fundamentally physiological point of view, the two mechanisms have identical biological meaning.

On the basis of our present opinions, it appears to us justifiable to subdivide all forms of hypersensitiveness into two main classes:

1. Hypersensitiveness in which an antibody mechanism has been plainly demonstrated.

2. Hypersensitiveness which, while remaining a specifically increased reaction capacity for an antigenic substance or for partial antigens, occurs without any definite evidence of the presence of circulating antibodies.

On such a basis we can arrive at the only logical and useful classification of these phenomena, founding the differentiations upon the chemical and physical properties of the inciting agents, yet retaining the entire group of phenomena of hypersusceptibility in one fundamental immunological category.

The nomenclature, as far as the use of the words "allergy," and "idiosyncrasy" is concerned, is admittedly a loose and irregular one, following custom rather than any rigid definitions. The important matter is to describe accurately the facts known in each condition. To redefine the terms would prolong the confusion which has led to lengthy and futile discussions in the past.

Classification is purely one of convenience for discussion. All phenomena of specific hypersensitiveness are essentially immunologic in nature. There is no purely inherited hypersensitiveness ("normal" of Cooke); and all specific hypersensitiveness is the result of the appearance in the sensitized body of a specific reaction product, a true antibody or its analogue, which is incited in the first place by contact of the cells with the incitant and which, in the second place—in the mechanism of manifestations—mediates between the incitant and the cells, rendering them more than normally sensitive or capable of reaction.

ANAPHYLAXIS

As early as 1893, von Behring and his pupils had noticed that animals immunized against diphtheria toxin, with high antitoxin content of the blood, would occasionally show marked susceptibility to injections of small doses of the toxin.

The phenomena observed by them was interpreted as an increased tissue susceptibility to the toxin, and Wassermann, reasoning on the basis of Ehrlich's side-chain theory, formulated the conception that the increased susceptibility was due to receptors, increased in number by immunization, but not yet separated from the cells that had produced them; the cells thereby becoming more vulnerable to the poison. In the same category belongs the observation of Kretz, who noticed that normal guinea-pigs did not show any reaction after injections of innocuous toxin-antitoxin mixtures, but that marked symptoms of illness often followed such injections when made into immunized guinea-pigs. Other phenomena which are now regarded, *a posteriori*, as probably depending upon the principles involved in anaphylaxis, are the tuberculin and mallein reactions, fully described in another place, and the adverse effects often following the injections of antitoxins in human beings, conditions spoken of under the heading of serum sickness. The last-named condition has been made the subject of an exhaustive study by von Pirquet and Schick.

That the injection of diphtheria antitoxin in human beings is often followed, after an incubation time of from three to ten days, by exanthematous eruptions, urticaria, swelling of the lymph glands, and often albuminuria and mild pulmonary inflammations, has been noticed by many clinicians, who have made extensive therapeutic use of antitoxin. It was recognized early that such symptoms were entirely independent of the antitoxic nature of the serum, but depended upon other constituents of the serum. Symptoms of this description were by no means regular in patients injected for the first time, but seemed to depend upon an individual predisposition, or idiosyncrasy. Von Pirquet and Schick, however, noticed that in those injected a second time, after intervals of weeks or months, the consequent evil effects were rapid in development, severe, and occurred with greater regularity.

The experimental observations from which our present knowledge of anaphylaxis takes its origin are those made in 1898 by Héricourt and Richet, who observed that repeated injections of eel serum into dogs gave rise to an increased susceptibility toward this substance instead of immunizing the dogs against it. Following the lines of thought suggested by this phenomenon, Portier and Richet later made an interesting observation while working with actinocongestin—a toxic substance which they extracted from the tentacles of Actinia. This substance in doses of 0.042 gram per kilogram produced vomiting, diarrhea, collapse, and death in dogs. If doses considerably smaller than this were given in quantities sufficient to cause only temporary illness, and several days allowed to elapse, a second injection of a quantity less than one-fourth or one-fifth of the ordinary lethal dose would cause rapid and severe symptoms and often death. Similar observations were made soon after this by Richet with mytilocongestin, a toxic substance isolated from mussels. In these experiments there remained little doubt as to the fact that the first injection had given rise to increased susceptibility of the dogs for the poison used.

It was Richet who first applied to this phenomenon the term "anaphylaxis" (ἀνά against, φύλαξις protection), to distinguish it from immunization or prophylaxis.

Soon after Richet's earlier experiments, and simultaneously with his later investigations, Arthus made an observation which confirmed Richet's work, though in a somewhat different field. The observation of Arthus is universally spoken of as the "phenomenon of Arthus" (Opie).

He noticed that the injection of rabbits with horse serum (a substance in itself without toxic properties for normal rabbits) rendered them susceptible to subsequent injections made after intervals of six or seven days. Repeated injections—even of small doses—regularly produced severe symptoms and often death in these animals.

An observation very similar to that of Arthus was made by Theobald Smith in 1904. Smith observed that guinea-pigs injected with diphtheria toxin-antitoxin mixtures in the course of antitoxin standardization, would be killed if after a short interval they were given a subcutaneous injection of normal horse serum.

The fundamental facts of anaphylaxis had thus been observed, and Otto, working directly upon the basis of Smith's observation, carried on an elaborate inquiry into the phenomenon. Almost simultaneously with Otto's publication there appeared a thorough study of the condition by Rosenau and Anderson.

The researches of Otto, and of Rosenau and Anderson, besides confirming the observations of previous workers, brought out a large number of new facts. They showed that the action of the horse serum had no relationship to its toxin or to its antitoxin constituents, that the sensitization of the guinea-pigs, by the first injection, became most marked after a definite incubation time of about ten days. Sensitization was accomplished by surprisingly small doses (one one-millionth in one case, usual doses 1/250 to 1 c.c.) Rosenau and Anderson excluded hemolysin or precipitin action as explanations of the phenomena, and proved that hypersusceptibility was passively transmissible from mother to offspring, and that it was specific—animals sensitized with horse serum not being sensitive to other proteins. They, as well as Vaughan and Nicolle, showed that the reaction was not limited to animal sera, but was elicited by proteins in general, egg-albumin, milk, the extract of peas, and bacterial extracts.

These observations were the fundamental ones. In the time immediately following, many theories of anaphylaxis were advanced and many faulty ideas conceived, quite logical in the light of the limited knowledge available at that time, but no longer tenable as more precise analyses have followed. The earlier ideas of Gay and Southard, and those of Besredka depended chiefly upon the mistaken premise that the substance which sensitized in the first injection was not the same as that which incited the harmful effect at the second or subsequent injections. In the same category at the present time belong the earlier views of Wolff-Eisner, and in a less definite way, the theories of Vaughan and Wheeler. The latter, however, have had an important influence upon subsequent developments which will be referred to below.

Von Pirquet and Schick, from the beginning, recognized the analogy of the anaphylactic phenomena to other immune reactions, and believed that the reaction was dependent upon an antigen-antibody union. Similar views were held by Rosenau and Anderson. In order to make the subject clear, however, without unnecessarily lengthening its discussion, we must abandon the historic method of treatment, and define the various elements that enter into the reaction more systematically.

Wells in 1921 laid down the criteria which must be met in order that a condition may be regarded as one of true anaphylaxis. They were as follows: "The observed toxicity of the injected material must depend upon sensitization of the animal, that is, the substance must not produce similar symptoms in the non-sensitized animal" (of the same species). "It should be possible to demonstrate passive sensitization with the serum of a sensitized animal." This we would modify somewhat since, of course, in the early stages of developing hypersusceptibility, an animal, though sensitive, may have but slight or even no demonstrable antibodies in his serum.

It would perhaps be more accurate to say that it must be possible to produce passive sensitization to an antigen by the administration of serum which contains antibodies to this antigen. If dealing with guinea-pigs, it should be possible by the Dale method, to demonstrate typical reactions as described below with the uterus of the sensitized guinea-pig. After recovery from anaphylactic shock, a condition of desensitization should be apparent if quantitative conditions are taken into account. These criteria are applicable, at the present time, only to those types of anaphylaxis in which circulating antibodies are present. It would be a mistake in the light of our present knowledge to base an exclusive classification upon these criteria, as other factors must be considered.

Anaphylactic Antigen.—Everything that has been said about antigens in general applies to the substances which sensitize, the sensitizing power being merely an additional property resulting from the specific incitement of an altered reaction capacity in the host, whether that results—as in protein anaphylaxis—in the formation of circulating antibodies, or whether—as in certain allergies like the tuberculin reaction—it expresses itself merely in an increased reaction capacity of the cells themselves.

Partial antigens or haptenes may induce shock but do not sensitize, as one would expect from the definition of these substances given in our section on antigens.

Compound antigens may induce hypersensitiveness, and a great deal of important fundamental knowledge has been gained by the use of such substances in anaphylactic experiment.

Methods of Sensitization.—Experimental sensitization may be active or passive, and differs to some extent according to the species of animal under observation. The early experiments were chiefly done with guinea-pigs, which can be actively sensitized by a single injection of various amounts. When dealing with animal sera such as horse serum quantities of anywhere from 0.1 to 1 c.c. are most suitable. Minute amounts, however, will suffice, and Rosenau and Anderson succeeded, in one case in sensitizing with 0.000001 c.c. of horse serum. If so sensitized, the animals become hypersusceptible at varying periods, hardly ever in less than six days, the ideal time for reinjection ranging between two and three weeks, somewhat dependent upon the amount given. Various statements have been made as to the relationship of the incubation time and the initial dose given to guinea-pigs. The ideal time for injection is that at which the maximum amount of antibody has been formed on the cells with the minimum amounts of circulating antigen and antibody in the blood. Small amounts injected into guinea-pigs require a relatively longer incubation period, but extremely large amounts (5 to 10 c.c.) may have a similar effect. The method of administration, to some extent, governs the incubation period in the same way that it governs the speed of antibody formation. However, the administration of the antigen to guinea-pigs and other animals may be carried out in any way, except by feeding, and even feeding may result in a certain amount of hypersusceptibility by passage of small amounts of undigested antigen through the intestinal wall.

Sensitization in man, we shall see, may take place through the placenta and through the intestines and respiratory tracts. Conditions in man seem to be particularly favorable for such spontaneous methods of sensitization because of feeding habits and the frequency of physiological disturbances. These are matters of the utmost importance in connection with human idiosyncrasy and will be further dealt with.

When sensitizing guinea-pigs with bacterial proteins or pollen and some other vegetable proteins, it is necessary to inject anywhere from six to ten times on consecutive days, and to test about three weeks after the last injection.

In dogs active sensitization is hard to obtain by one injection. Single doses of 2 to 3 c.c. of normal horse serum are usually followed by sensitization in three weeks, at least such results seem to have been obtained with some regularity by Simonds and others. Such sensitization, however, is not as acute and severe as that generally observed in guinea-pigs under similar conditions. Weil, however, obtained acute shock in dogs by giving two sensitizing injections within a few days, and testing with large quantities of serum after two and three weeks.

Rabbits are difficult to sensitize with a single dose under any circumstances, but may easily be sensitized by repeated injection.

The lower monkeys are difficult to sensitize, but this has been accomplished by Kopeloff who used large and repeated injections of proteins.

The peculiarities of human sensitization are discussed in the next chapter.

Passive Sensitization.—Passive sensitization was first demonstrated by Nicolle, and by Otto, who showed that the hypersusceptible state could be passively transferred to normal animals by injecting them with the serum of anaphylactic animals. In such experiments the serum of the anaphylactic animal is first injected in quantities of 0.5 c.c. or preferably more, and twenty-four hours later an injection of the specific antigen—that is, the protein used for sensitization—is given. The animals so treated show typical symptoms of specific anaphylaxis and often die.

Simultaneous inoculation of the two substances, either mixed or injected separately, does not produce the same effect except in special instances. A fact, observed by Otto, is that the serum of guinea-pigs which have been given the sensitizing or first injection will confer passive anaphylaxis on the eighth or tenth day after injection, before the animals themselves show evidences of being actively hypersensitized. It is also true that occasionally the serum of anti-anaphylactic animals will possess the power of conferring passive anaphylaxis.

Such observations were at first confusing. We know now that amounts of antibody too slight to be easily detected in test tube experiment may still sensitize, and to explain the last point—namely, the conferring of passive immunity by desensitized animals—it is of course not at all out of the question that in such animals there may still be circulating antibodies.

It is by means of the passive method of sensitization that the relations between anaphylaxis and antibodies have been most successfully studied. Doerr and Russ showed that the power of a serum to convey anaphylaxis passively depended directly upon its contents of specific antibody. It was then shown by Nicolle, Otto, and others, that a reaction can be produced by this method only when an interval, not less than four to six hours, is allowed to elapse between the injection of the antibodies and the injection of the antigen. During this time the antibody passes out of the blood-stream and becomes attached to the cell.

It was also shown by Weil that passive sensitization could be conferred by the injection of precipitates formed in the test tube between an antiserum and its antigen, a thing which we can now well understand in view of the knowledge we have of the dissociation of antibody from such precipitates.

Anaphylaxis may be transmitted passively by inheritance. Thus the young of anaphylactic guinea-pigs show hypersusceptibility, irrespective of whether the mother became hypersusceptible before or after the beginning of pregnancy. Such anaphylaxis has no reference to the condition of the father, and is not transmitted by the milk, except possibly in ruminants (scours).

The nature of the anaphylactic antibodies has aroused much discussion. By many observers they were regarded as special anaphylactic antibodies, separate from precipitins, opsonins, etc.; Friedberger identified them with precipitins. The direct quantitative relationship between precipitating antibodies and the power to convey passive sensitization, described by Doerr and Russ, would point in the same direction, as would the above-mentioned experiments of Weil. Since all antibodies developed against a single antigen are one and the same, the sensitizing antibody is the same substance which, under other methods of observation, prepares the antigen for agglutination, etc.

Site of the Anaphylactic Reaction.—When the antigen and antibody are injected simultaneously or within a very short period of one another, no anaphylactic symptoms occur. The study of this interval has gradually led to the recognition that the anaphylactic reaction, whatever it may be, takes place upon the body cells and that the interval in passive sensitization is necessitated by the time required for the anchoring of the antibodies to the cells of the tissues. Experiments by Pearce and Eisenbrey (1910) showed that a hypersusceptible dog remained sensitized even when his entire blood volume was substituted with that of a normal dog. The principle has been made especially clear by the introduction of direct methods of observation of the smooth muscle of animals by Schultz and by Dale, a method which was used to good effect by Weil. It seems fairly clear from such work that acute protein anaphylaxis as we see it in guinea-pigs and other laboratory animals is due to the direct reaction between antigen and a specific antibody, the reaction occurring upon the body cells and not in the blood stream.

Whether or not an injury may occur when antigen meets antibody in the circulation has been much discussed. There are experiments on record by Friedemann in which he obtained reactions in rabbits by the simultaneous intravenous injection of antigen and antibody, and similar occasional occurrences have been observed by Brion, Scott and ourselves. But these reactions are neither regular in occurrence, nor are they ever very severe. Weil and others have shown that a sufficient amount of antibody in the circulation may protect the cells to some extent against anaphylactic shock, but very large doses of protective antiserum are necessary to bring about this result, a circumstance which is again explained by the inhibition of union between circulating antigen and antibody, *i.e.*, a more rapid union of infected antigen with the sensitized cells than with the circulating antibody.

Although the union of antigen and antibody in the body fluids, apart from the cells, is of relatively less importance than the cellular reaction, it still has considerable significance, as for instance, in the Arthus phenomenon.

Briefly defined, the Arthus phenomenon consists in the following occurrence: When horse serum is injected subcutaneously into rabbits that have been highly immunized and in whose serum there is a considerable concentration of specific anti-bodies, the injection is followed within a few hours by local edema and infiltration which may even eventually lead to gangrene. The phenomenon is not easily produced in all animals, possibly because of the fact that for complete development a high concentration of circulating antibodies is necessary. In guinea-pigs, it is extremely difficult to produce it, and in dogs and rats a typical Arthus phenomenon has rarely been observed.

Opie's analysis of the mechanism of this phenomenon has shown that its severity is proportionate to the precipitin titre of the serum. Reactions are very severe when the titre of the blood serum ranges above 1-10,000. The phenomenon can be produced passively by injecting the antibody intravenously, following this in 24 hours with local injections of horse serum. Also, antibody can be injected locally and the anti-gens given intravenously. Moreover, the reaction can be reversed in that when horse serum is injected into the ear vein of a rabbit and followed within 24 hours by local injections of anti-horse serum, an inflammatory edema will result. When as much as 5 c.c. of horse serum is intravenously injected and followed within even a few minutes by intradermal injections of 2 c.c. of a very high titre anti-horse serum, extensive reactions can be produced.

Opie believes that this particular type of reaction results from the formation of a precipitate in the intercellular spaces, with a consequent inflammatory irritation which does its damage by the deposit of precipitate in contact with the tissue cells. Previous sensitization of the cells is not necessary.

The phenomenon has much bearing on manifestations of human sensitiveness. An illustration of how much it may operate is an experiment made by Auer, who was carrying on experiments in dogs treated with repeated heavy doses of horse serum. At the site of operation in the inguinal region of one of these dogs, a local reaction developed and he believed that this was due to the fact that a circulating protein passed into the tissues along the wound and a contact was established analogous to the Arthus phenomenon. The most common analogies to the Arthus phenomenon in man are the indurated areas that occur at the sites of injection in the later injections of rabies prophylaxis. Some of the severe local reactions in second and third injections of horse serum accompanying serum sickness are of the same order.

Symptoms of Anaphylaxis.—Anaphylaxis differs in its symptomatology and pathology according to the species of animal in which shock is produced. There are certain fundamental systematic reactions which are common to all species, but in each species there is particular localization of the immediate and severe changes which lead to acute death. As general symptoms, we may enumerate drop in blood pressure, fall of temperature, diminution of leukocytes, increased flow of chyle, and certain metabolic disturbances, the identity of which in different animal species has not been worked out.

In *guinea-pigs*, as first demonstrated by Auer and Lewis, the typical lung in-flation which leads to respiratory death is due to spasms of the muscles of the bronchioles.

In *rabbits*, acute death is not respiratory, but is a circulatory one, and has been shown by Coca to be due to spasms of the muscular coats of the arterioles of the pulmonary circulation, the rabbit's lung during shock developing remarkably increased pressure against the passage of perfusion fluid.

In *dogs,* acute anaphylactic symptoms have been localized in the liver by Manwaring and others.

Rats are not easily sensitized. A number of investigators have failed entirely, but J. T. and Frederick Parker obtained definite anaphylaxis in these animals by the administration of several injections. Anaphylaxis, even when obtained, is not acute and seems to concentrate, as it often does in dogs, in the smooth musculature of the intestine.

Mice have been actively sensitized by a number of observers.

The special manifestations of hypersensitiveness in *man* are separately dealt with.

This peculiar physiological difference in various animals in reaction to the same general mechanism of injury has been difficult to understand, but observations of Coca, Simonds, Huber and Koessler and others have been correlated by Wells into what seems a likely explanation. Wells calls attention to the fact that acute death in guinea-pigs is due to spasm of the bronchial muscles, and that anatomically the guinea-pig has a very high development of musculature in the bronchi, the smaller bronchioles being "practically nothing but muscular tubes." Similarly, Coca's findings in relation to the pulmonary circulation of rabbits coincides with the histological demonstration that the pulmonary arteries of the rabbit show a marked muscular development. Simonds has shown that the hepatic veins of dogs differ from those of all other animals in having a highly developed musculature, and it would seem, as Wells points out, as though the localization of acute changes in different organs in the various animals was dependent upon fortuitous differences in the anatomical distribution of the smooth muscle. He also points out, as further evidence, that fatal reactions in man have occurred only or most frequently in persons suffering from chronic pulmonary conditions, chiefly asthma; and Huber and Koessler have shown that asthmatic people develop a hypertrophy of the bronchial musculature which in its final histology is closely analogous to that of guinea-pigs.

Acute death may well be caused directly by the spasm of smooth muscle tissue, and the acute pathological manifestations may be dependent upon the distribution of such muscle. This does not, however, exclude the likelihood that severe anaphylactic injury may be caused in other cells in the body as well, but these, not being able to react by acute contraction, or by any other pathological alteration that can cause acute and sudden death, may still be injured severely without there being an immediately noticeable effect.

Desensitization.—When sensitized animals recover from anaphylactic shock, they do not react to a subsequent injection of the same substance made within a reasonable interval.

This desensitization, or "antianaphylaxis" as Besredka and Steinhardt have called it, appears immediately after recovery from the second injection. Antianaphylaxis may also be produced if animals which have received the first or sensitizing dose are injected with comparatively large quantities of the same substance during the preanaphylactic period—or, as it is sometimes spoken of, during the anaphylactic incubation time. This injection should not be done too soon after the first dose, but rather toward the middle or end of the preanaphylactic period.

If given within one or two days after the sensitizing injection, anaphylaxis will develop, nevertheless. The desensitized condition is a transitory state. Otto found that guinea-pigs desensitized in the above manner may become sensitive again within three weeks.

It is not necessary to actually shock an animal to desensitize it.

Another form of partial protection against anaphylaxis, by the injection of large amounts of specific antiserum, has been mentioned above. The mechanism of this is obvious, but, for quantitative reasons the method has no practical value.

The method of desensitization is in principle nothing more or less than a gradual introduction of the antigen in such a manner that the union with the sessile antibodies may be a slow one, leading to a gradual saturation and avoiding the sudden, acute changes which would follow upon more violent reactions. This can be achieved either by a very slow injection of diluted antigen or by repeated injections of small amounts. A guinea-pig that is so sensitive that 0.2 c.c. of horse serum intravenously administered would cause acute death in a few minutes, may be given many times this amount if sublethal doses of, let us say, 0.005 c.c. are injected at intervals of ten minutes, or if a much larger amount diluted with salt solution is introduced by gravity so that the first 0.2 c.c. is spread over a time interval of, let us say, five or 10 minutes. These are the principles underlying what we call desensitization and which will be discussed in the section on serum sickness in man.

Desensitization by injection into the rectum or by feeding has been accomplished but since the absorption of unchanged antigen by these routes is ordinarily slight, little hope can be expected in this direction for practical purposes.

There are certain forms of protection against anaphylactic shock produced by the injection of foreign sera, and other proteins and processes nonspecific as far as the particular anaphylactic mechanism is concerned, but there is too little positive knowledge about these to permit us to discuss them here.

Duration of Sensitiveness and of Desensitization.—One of the most mysterious things in immunology is the fact that once the cells of an animal have come in contact with an antigenic substance they are never again normal in relation to this substance. Long after active antibody production has ceased, the cells are still in a condition in which contact with this antigen will stimulate them to an antibody production more energetic than normal. Thus, if a rabbit is treated with any antigen—bacterial or animal protein—and after antibodies have been produced we allow the rabbit to rest until he has ceased to show antibodies in the circulation, and if then we reinject the same antigen and follow the curves of antibody production, they will be found to rise more rapidly and steeply than they did in the first immunization or than they do in a control animal treated in the same way at the same time. Sensitiveness, therefore, probably lasts to some degree through life. Its period of highest intensity, however, is relatively short, probably lasting only for several weeks after the incubation time of the intense contact with the antigen has elapsed. After that, the degree of sensitiveness gradually sinks in the course of months; and in the course of years it may come down to a low threshold where it has negligible practical significance. Even in this condition, however, the body is again easily stimulated to renewed sensitiveness.

Desensitization lasts only so long as the cell antibodies remain reasonably saturated. The desensitizing antigen, however, constitutes a new antigenic stimulus for a gradual return of sensitiveness.

It is obvious from this that there are two ways of preventing anaphylactic symptoms in sensitive individuals: one is a constant and repeated desensitization; the other is permanent removal from the possibilities of contact with the antigen.

Anaphylatoxin.—Vaughan and Wheeler early suggested that anaphylaxis might be a poisoning produced as follows: Antibodies are formed by the first injection, which, on subsequent reaction with the antigen administered in the second injection, lead to poisonous protein-split products. A similar idea was advanced by Wolff-Eisner. Proceeding from this general concept, Friedberger, whose extensive experimental work may be found in many articles in the *Zeitschrift für Immunitätsforschung*, elaborated a theory of anaphylaxis which may be summarized in the following way: When the antigen and antibody meet in the circulation, the union of the two renders the antigen amenable to complement action, and the action of the alexin or complement upon this complex splits off from it a poison which he calls "anaphylatoxin." He succeeded in producing poisonous substances *in vitro* by treating specific precipitates as well as sensitized and unsensitized bacteria with alexin. Injection of these substances into guinea-pigs caused acute death, analogous in symptoms to anaphylaxis. Friedberger and Hartoch showed that there was a diminution of alexin in the serum of animals suffering from acute shock in the course both of active and of passively transmitted anaphylaxis. He showed that the intravenous injection of substances which inhibited complement action *in vitro*, such as, for instance, concentrated salt solution, would diminish and sometimes prevent shock in sensitized animals, a phenomenon, however, which the writer with Lieb and Dwyer showed to be due to diminution of the irritability of smooth muscle caused by hypertonic salt. It was subsequently shown, however, that similar poisons could be produced from boiled as well as from normal bacteria, that they could be produced by the treatment of fresh guinea-pig serum with kaolin or barium sulphate. The literature of this subject is extensive. The most important contributions have been made by Bordet, Moldovan and Doerr, and by Novy and De Kruif. All of these investigations tend to show that guinea-pig serum can acquire strongly toxic properties when treated with any form of substance in fine suspension, whether this be living or dead bacteria, or protozoa, or indifferent materials such as agar, kaolin, etc. Furthermore, the direct injection of very dilute solutions of agar, etc., into guinea-pigs and rabbits may cause fatal symptoms closely resembling anaphylaxis. Moreover, it has been shown by a number of workers that blood taken from guinea-pigs and rabbits, either defibrinated or centrifuged and reinjected before the clotting was complete, could exert similar toxic action. These anaphylatoxin phenomena may be of very great importance, and possibly represent a phenomenon dependent upon delicate adjustment of the colloidal conditions prevailing in the circulating blood, and demonstrate the possible dangers accruing from the disturbance of such conditions, a matter which has been particularly emphasized by Jobling and Petersen. But we do not believe that the anaphylatoxin phenomena bear a direct relationship to the process that we may classify under true anaphylaxis. The demonstration of the cellular localization of the mechanism which causes true anaphylactic shock has amply demonstrated this.

REFERENCES

ARTHUS. Compt. rend. Soc. de biol., 1903, 55.
BESREDKA and STEINHARDT. Ann. de l'Inst. Pasteur, 1907.
COCA. J. Immunol., 1919, 4:219.
—— Tice's Practice of Medicine, New York, 1920.
DALE. J. Pharmacol. & Exper. Therap., 1913, 4.
DAWSON and GARBADE. J. Am. M. Ass., 1930, 94:704.
DOERR. Handb. d. Inn. Med., Berlin, 1926, 5:448.
—— Kolle u. Wassermann, 3rd ed., 1930, 1.
—— Ergebn. Hyg., Bakteriol. u. Immunitätsforsch., etc., 1922, 5:71.
DOERR and RUSS. Ztschr. f. Immunitätsforsch., 1909, 3.
FRIEDBERGER and HARTOCH. Ztschr. f. Immunitätsforsch., 1909, 3.
FRIEDEMANN. Ztschr. f. Immunitätsforsch., 1909, 2.
GAY and SOUTHARD. J. Med. Research, May, 1907.
HÉRICOURT and RICHET. Compt. rend. Soc. de biol., 1898, 53.
HUBER and KOESSLER. Arch. Int. Med., 1921.
KOPELOFF, N., DAVIDOFF, L. M., and KOPELOFF, L. M. J. Immunol., 1936, 30:477.
KOPELOFF, L. M., and KOPELOFF, J. J. Immunol., 1939, 36:83, 101.
JOBLING and PETERSEN. J. Exper. M., 1914, 5:19.
MANWARING, W. H., and CROWE, H. E. J. Immunol., 1917, 2:517.
MOLDOVAN and DOERR. Ztschr. f. Immunitätsforsch., 1910, 7.
NICOLLE. Ann. de l'Inst. Pasteur, 1903, 2; 1907, 5.
NOVY and DE KRUIF. J. Am. M. Ass., 1917, 68:1524.
OPIE. J. Immunol., 1924, 9:231, 255, 259.
OTTO. Leuthold Gedenkschrift, 1905, Vol. 1.
—— Munchen. med. Wchnschr., 1907.
PEARCE and EISENBREY. Cong. Am. Phys. Surg., 1910, 8.
PORTIER and RICHET. Compt. rend. Soc. de biol., 1902.
RICHET. Ann. de l'Inst. Pasteur, 1907, 1908.
ROSENAU and ANDERSON. Treas. Dep. Pub. Health & Mar.-Hosp. Serv. U. S. Hyg. Lab. Bull., 1906, 1907, 29:36.
SCHULTZ. J. Pharmacol. & Exper. Therap., 1910, 1.
SIMONDS. J. Infect. Dis., 1916, 19.
SMITH, T. J. Med. Research, 1904.
VAUGHAN. Ass. Am. Phys., May, 1907.
VAUGHAN and WHEELER. J. Infect. Dis., 1907, 4.
VON BEHRING. Deutsche med. Wchnschr., 1893.
VON BEHRING and KITASHINA. Berl. klin. Wchnschr., 1901.
VON PIRQUET and SCHICK. Die Serum Krankheit, Vienna, 1905.
WEIL, R. J. Med. Research, 1913, 27; 1914, 30.
—— Proc. Soc. Exper. Biol. & Med., 1914, 86:11.
—— J. Immunol., 1916, 1:19; 1917, 2:429.
WELLS, H. G. Physiol. Rev., Jan. 1921, 1:1.
—— The Chemical Aspects of Immunity, New York, 1929.
WOLFF-EISNER. Berl. klin. Wchnschr., 1904.
ZINSSER, H. Boston M. & S. J., 1927, 196:387.
—— Proc. Soc. Exper. Biol. & Med., 1920, 18:57.
—— Resistance to Infectious Disease, New York, 1931.
ZINSSER, LIEB and DWYER. Proc. Soc. Exper. Biol. & Med., 1915, 8:12.

CHAPTER XIX

HYPERSENSITIVENESS IN MAN

Allergy, Idiosyncrasy, Atopy.—We have mentioned in the preceding sections that the manifestations of hypersensitiveness have their individual peculiarities in every species of animal. Thus the shock in which a guinea-pig dies is physiologically of an entirely different nature from that which leads to the death of a rabbit or a dog, although in all cases the conditions can be shown to result from the union of antigen with its antibodies within the animal body. Some animals, moreover, are more easily sensitized than others. A single small injection in a guinea-pig will render it intensely sensitive in two or three weeks, whereas a rabbit or a dog will need two or three injections in order that a shock injection may lead to acute death. The smaller monkeys are very hard to sensitize at all. These differences may depend largely upon the energy of antibody production in various species, and also, possibly, upon the equilibrium that is established between the sessile, cellular antibodies and those in the circulation. We know that shock is to a large extent, and perhaps in some animals exclusively, due to a union of the antigen with the antibodies that are associated with the cells. We also know that in guinea-pigs circulating antibodies appear more slowly and never in the concentration in which they appear in rabbits. We may correlate this with the facts that in guinea-pigs with the low concentration of antibodies in the circulation there is an extreme tissue susceptibility, whereas in rabbits fatal anaphylaxis can only be obtained when the immunization has been powerfully increased, as indicated by a high concentration of antibodies in the circulation. As demonstrated by Opie's experiments, the circulating antibodies may lead to local manifestations of hypersensitiveness such as the Arthur phenomenon, where the union of antigen and antibody in the intercellular spaces may be held responsible for the reactions.

The conditions in man are peculiar in that there is a relatively slight tendency to acute generalized shock. Furthermore, there is a greater tendency than in most animals to localization of the manifestations in individual tissues, so that we may classify human hypersensitiveness clinically into respiratory, intestinal and skin manifestations. It is not unlikely that this is due to the fact that in the course of natural sensitization man becomes sensitized through the lungs, intestines or the skin, which are subjected, respectively, to higher concentrations of the antigens during sensitization than other parts of the body and may become proportionately more sensitive. On the other hand, it is also possible that even by these routes man may become generally sensitive, but that when the antigen reenters by the same routes in the course of exposure, the manifestations are there localized because the antigen is fixed at the portal of entry. When the sensitization of man is more comparable to the artificial sensitization of animals, as in antitoxin administration, the symptoms of the disease are more general and more comparable in principle to the things that take place in

231

a sensitized animal. This we will discuss in greater detail under the heading of Serum Sickness.

One of the former objections to the classification of the human idiosyncrasies with animal anaphylaxis was the fact that many of the inciting substances could not be proved to be antigenic in the sense that antibodies could be produced with them by animal injection. In many cases this has been explained by the discovery that substances like pollen do contain true antigens, and much new light has been thrown on these difficulties by the modern knowledge of haptenes. By reference to our section on the partial antigens, it will be seen that many antigenic substances are compounded of two or more fractions, and that although the whole antigen is needed for the incitement of antibodies, the partial—such as the carbohydrate fraction of bacteria— is sufficient to elicit shock. In the drug idiosyncrasies, where the question is particularly difficult to approach, the work of Obermeyer and Pick and particularly that of Landsteiner suggests that the nonantigenic drug, incorporated in the body, may form a compound antigen with the body proteins and thus fulfil all the conditions necessary to correlate these phenomena with the general mechanism of antigen-antibody reactions. Landsteiner's inhibition reactions with compound proteins are particularly suggestive in this respect.

Another important point of differentiation upon which earlier observers, especially Cooke and Coca, based their belief that human idiosyncrasy was quite separate from animal anaphylaxis was the question of *heredity*. It was claimed that animals never became hypersensitive except as the result of a preceding contact, whereas in man hypersensitiveness could appear without traceable preliminary contact and followed, in frequency and distribution, Mendelian laws. There can be no question, both from the statistics of Cooke and Vander Veer and those of Schloss, that hypersensitiveness is more frequent in some families than in others. There are, however, a number of obstacles to prevent us from assuming that this is inheritance in the genetic sense, without individual sensitization. In the first place, in a considerable percentage of the cases the sensitiveness is not present at birth but appears between the fifth and the fifteenth year. The exceptions to this rule, where it does appear at birth, can now be explained, as we shall see presently, by sensitization from the mother. In the second place, where hypersensitiveness does appear in such children after the fifth year, it is rarely identical in its specificity with the hypersensitiveness present in the parents. Thus a child may be sensitive to seafood or horse dandruff while the mother or father may have hay fever or be sensitive to veal. It is almost forced upon one to conclude that what is inherited is the capacity for being sensitized, and this is a phenomenon quite common in the animal kingdom, where the energy of antibody production is rarely the same in two animals injected with identical amounts of the same antigen.

In regard to the tracing of previous contacts with an antigen, it has become clear that it is impossible to exclude in any case that sensitization could have taken place. That *antibodies can pass through the placenta* from mother to child was shown by Rosenau and Anderson and Otto early in the study of anaphylaxis. The same observation has since then been made by many other observers. Kuttner and Ratner, in our laboratory, showed that diphtheria antitoxin could go through the placenta of man with considerable ease, the human placenta interposing only one layer of cells between the maternal and embryonic circulations. Passive sensitization, however, would not last very long, but *active sensitization can also take place through the placenta.* Ratner, particularly, has shown that protein sensitiveness can occur in children to foods in which the mother has overindulged during gestation.

Sensitization after birth without early traceable origin is also of common occurrence, since it has been shown that *proteins may pass in unchanged antigenic condition through the intestines* and that as a matter of fact they do so with great frequency. It may occur in perfectly normal people, but occurs with greater frequency and intensity in marasmatic children and in individuals with digestive disturbances.

Sensitization through the respiratory passages can take place in man and has been experimentally produced in guinea-pigs by a number of workers. A review of the literature on this subject may be found in the paper by Ratner, Jackson and Gruehl who have also experimentally reproduced the conditions governing an outbreak of respiratory sensitiveness in man to castor bean dust by subjecting guinea-pigs to inhalations of the same material.

It is thus clear that as far as heredity and preliminary sensitization is concerned there need not be any sharp dividing line between the forms of hypersensitiveness of man and those observed in animals.

Passive Transmission.—As far as passive, experimental transmission is concerned, man may be passively sensitized by intravenous injections of antibody, but of course extreme experiments, as they are possible in animals, have not been made. On the other hand, the local passive sensitization of man by the intradermal injection of the serum of sensitized individuals, as in the Prausnitz-Küstner reaction, is in all fundamental respects a passive sensitization.

There was, indeed, a difficulty formerly in identifying human hypersensitiveness with animal anaphylaxis in regard to passive transfer, a point which, we have seen, Wells set up as one of the criteria upon which was based the recognition of a true anaphylactic condition. Isolated passive sensitizations in man had been reported by Ramirez and some others, Ramirez observing the passive transfer of horse dandruff sensitiveness by the transfusion of blood from an allergic to a normal individual. Schloss had succeeded in transferring human food idiosyncrasies passively to guinea-pigs, and Longcope and his coworkers have transferred horse serum sensitiveness from patients with serum sickness to guinea-pigs. Similar observations were scattered in the literature, but it was quite apparent that the transfer could not be accomplished with regularity. The significance of this point as a means of establishing a separate classification has lost much of its force in the light of recent investigations. In the first place, it has been much weakened by the discovery by Tomscik and Kurotchkin that successful passive immunization or sensitization depends, to some extent, upon the relationship of the species of the animals representing the recipient and the donor. This was confirmed by a number of observers, among others by Avery and Tillett and by Enders. It was shown, for instance, that while it might be impossible to sensitize a guinea-pig with immune horse serum, it is possible to sensitize a guinea-pig with immune rabbit serum. This circumstance is readily understood if one considers that antibodies, so far as we know them, are carried in the globulin fraction of the serum. If the globulins containing the antibodies are chemically too far removed or heterologous from the proteins of the injected animal, it is quite likely that no association with the cells of this animal is possible. If the antibodies are from the same species or from a closely related one, such secondary relationship between the antibodies and the recipient's tissues is more easily accomplished. This kinship has an important bearing upon the results of tests.

The most important advance in this problem was made in 1921, when Prausnitz and Küstner succeeded in producing passive local hypersensitiveness in man by injecting the serum of a sensitive individual intradermally into the skin of a normal person. When again, after a period of four to twelve or more hours, the antigen was injected into the same area, a marked local reaction developed; whereas control injections into neighboring areas produced no such reaction. This so-called P.-K. reaction has been studied in detail by DeBesche, Coca and Grove, and many others. The local sensitiveness may last for several weeks. The sensitizing substance can be neutralized in the test tube. A most interesting development of this reaction is the one made by Walzer in a series of experiments which, incidentally, demonstrated the speed and regularity with which protein, in the antigenic form, may pass through the intestinal wall. He sensitized normal individuals locally by the P.-K. intradermal injection of the serum of sensitized individuals. Twelve hours later, on an empty stomach, he fed the protein to which the donor of the serum was hypersensitive. Within an hour after the ingestion, reactions appeared in the sensitized area.

There are still undoubtedly, as Coca has pointed out, a considerable number of differences between antibodies as we know them in protein-immunized animals and the antibody analogue which gives rise to the P.-K. reaction and which Coca has named *reagin*. Mixtures between the reagin and the antigen give none of the ordinary test-tube reactions, and as far as the reaction in man is concerned, it is purely local. These may or may not be quantitative differences. On the other hand, in basic principle the reagins possess the most important characteristics of antibodies, indeed are completely analogous, except in secondary manifestations. In spite of such secondary differences the analogy is compellingly close. The so-called reagins are specific circulating substances present in the hypersensitive individual with which a specific passive sensitization can be carried out. An interval between sensitization and antigen injection is necessary, indicating, as in passive anaphylaxis, the necessity of an anchoring of these antibody analogues to the cell. By preliminary attachment to the cell they mediate, as does a true antibody in animal anaphylaxis, between the cell and the antigen, rendering a cell more sensitive to contact with the antigen and to the consequences of such contact. This illustrates what we said in the beginning, that a broader definition of an antibody is necessary in the light of present knowledge to the effect that antibodies are specific substances incited by antigen injection which can mediate between the cell and the antigen in future contacts, increasing reaction capacity.

Moreover, in appraising experimental evidence of passive sensitization, one cannot expect the passively sensitized individual to have exactly the same clinical type of sensitiveness as the donor of the serum. The clinical type depends upon local distribution of antibody concentration, or upon the manner in which the antigen enters the body, and we would not expect an individual receiving into the skin serum from a food idiosyncratic to develop anything but the skin reaction, unless the amount injected is so great that all parts of the body are sensitized and unless subsequent contact with the antigen is by the gastro-intestinal canal.

Having thus discussed the points that have been made in attempts to find fundamental differences between human allergies and idiosyncrasies, it will be useful to call attention to some of the fundamental similarities.

Most striking of all is the specificity of the phenomena, which is true of idiosyncrasies whether respiratory, intestinal or otherwise localized.

Again, the similarity in the nature of reactions within certain clinical groups is independent of the chemical or physical nature of the responsible agent, and is obviously dependent upon the condition of hypersensitiveness of the cells by a mechanism which, if not identical with antibodies, forces the assumption of something fundamentally similar.

Again, as in anaphylaxis, contact of the body by a proper channel with the inciting agent is followed by symptoms with extraordinary speed and with a violence out of proportion to the amounts of the agent involved.

As in anaphylaxis, desensitization can be accomplished by a careful and systematic administration of the responsible agent, a matter that has been proved for many idiosyncrasies if not for drug sensitiveness and a few others. This again forces the analogy with antibody-like functions.

And if the clinical desensitization of man is less effective and less easily accomplished than in animals, this is easily understood if we consider that desensitization is a quantitative matter and the complete effect cannot be accomplished by a single injection or in a short time, even in an animal, unless we venture an approach to the danger line far closer than we are justified in risking in man.

Such desensitization, again, is temporary in the idiosyncrasies as in anaphylaxis, there being eventual return to sensitiveness if the subject is left alone, and as in anaphylaxis, sensitiveness once established may last through life, with perhaps a gradual fading out if new contacts are avoided over a period of many years. However, the termination of sensitivity is uncertain.

Clinical Types.—The habits of life and nutrition of man are more diversified than are those of any other animal. Man lives longer than most animals and is exposed to antigenic contacts through the skin, the intestines and the respiratory tract. Also, as we have seen, the conditions for sensitization through the placenta are peculiarly favorable in the human species. These circumstances may account for the great frequency of allergic and idiosyncratic conditions in man; and the different routes by which the several antigens get into the body, with food, by inhalation and by contact, may easily explain the different localization-types which determine the individual clinical picture. It is important to note, in this connection, moreover, that although the clinically disturbing features of any of these types center in one or the other organic system, many of them may show secondary symptoms referable to other parts of the body and practically all of them exhibit evidence of general sensitization as determinable by skin and ophthalmic reactions.

The clinical types, therefore, are not necessarily pure but may overlap, and are merely examples of relatively severe reactions in a given system determined by either disproportionately intense sensitization in the tissues through which the sensitizing antigen habitually enters, or disproportionate reaction, in a generally sensitized body, on the part of the tissues through which the antigen enters at the time of the attack.

The clinical manifestations may be considered under the following subdivisions:

1. Serum sickness following the systematic administration of foreign proteins. This condition is, in mechanism and experimental analysis, entirely analogous to anaphylaxis in animals.

2. Respiratory conditions, in which may be included rhinitis, bronchitis and asthma, which—like hay fever—are particularly associated with materials that reach the body by inhalation.

3. Intestinal idiosyncrasies which follow the ingestion of the responsible material and include not only direct disturbances of the digestive organs, but are usually complicated by skin manifestations and sometimes by respiratory attacks.

4. A group of skin manifestations which may occur either alone or associated with other symptoms.

The bacterial allergies we must treat of separately, since they form a difficult chapter in the story of hypersensitiveness which requires for its elucidation a detailed consideration of the bacterial antigen.

Serum Sickness.—The injection of foreign proteins into human beings, especially in the form of horse serum as in antitoxin treatment, causes a train of symptoms which are classified together as serum sickness. For the history of serum sickness we refer the reader to larger works on the subject, the summaries of anaphylaxis mentioned above, as well as the book of von Pirquet and Schick, *Die Serum Krankheit* (Vienna, 1905).

After first injection, the incubation period may last as long as twelve days, or longer, although it may be considerably shorter than this. Coca states that in 24 to 48 per cent of all cases the incubation period after first injection is less than eight days, while in about 14 per cent it is longer than twelve days.

The symptoms of serum sickness usually consist of an eruption at the site of injection, which ordinarily comes on quite early, some time before any general eruption is noticed. It often takes an urticarial form, and becomes general after several days. There is usually some fever, occasionally albuminuria. There may be inflammation of the joints and symptoms of neuritis. The arthritic symptoms are often of a peculiar nature, with slight tenderness, but considerable stiffness. We have seen a case in which it was difficult to tell whether or not the patient, who had received tetanus antitoxin ten days before, was developing tetanus—a case which turned out to be one of serum sickness. Serum sickness is often accompanied by leukopenia, and by drop in blood pressure and decreased coagulability of the blood. The latter manifestations, as Wells points out, bring it still closer to true anaphylaxis.

When a human being is being treated for the second time with horse serum at intervals longer than two or three weeks, the resemblance to true anaphylaxis is still greater, and the procedure is more dangerous and will vary in its manifestations, according to the length of time elapsing between the two injections. If the injections are not very much more than a month apart, there may be, according to von Pirquet and Schick, an immediate reaction, which takes the character of severe serum disease. At the point of injection there is swelling and edema within twenty-four hours, with general symptoms such as those described above but more severe, within one or two days. If the injections are months and years apart, the onset is still likely to occur more rapidly than when the antigen is given the first time.

Von Pirquet and Schick, from the beginning, believed that serum sickness was due to the reaction of antigen, which had not yet disappeared from the circulation of the patient, with antibodies which were already being actively formed.

That the presence of homologous antigens and antibody in the blood at one and the same time is possible has been experimentally shown many times in rabbits injected with large doses of horse serum. This phenomenon is entirely analogous to the observations that Longcope and Rackemann have made in human beings suffering from serum sickness. Precipitins for horse serum were shown in such patients at about the time that the symptoms developed and with the blood of such cases, horse serum sensitiveness could be passively transferred to rabbits. It has been shown, moreover, by Hooker that horse serum sensitiveness can be produced in human beings as the result of diphtheria toxin-antitoxin injections.

The development and severity of serum sickness is to some extent dependent upon the amounts of serum injected. At first injection, when not more than 10 c.c. are given, serum sickness develops in about 10 per cent of the injected individuals and is usually mild; when 50 to 100 c.c. are given, the disease develops in a much larger number, estimated by some observers as high as 90 per cent, and the severity is apt to be greater. In countries where a horse meat diet is common, many individuals may be quite sensitive to horse serum without having had antitoxin previously.

We have no hesitation in stating that serum sickness is the characteristic manifestation of true protein anaphylaxis in man.

Fortunately, dangerous or fatal cases following therapeutic horse serum injections are rare. According to Park, probably not more than 1 in 20,000 serum injections are followed by dangerous symptoms, and probably not more than one injection in 50,000 is fatal.

Administration of Horse Serum.[1]—In view of the frequency of horse-serum sensitiveness in human beings, it is well to assure oneself before every therapeutic or prophylactic administration whether or not the patient is sensitive and to what degree. Although fatal results are rare, it is always well to be cautious. The question arises most often in hospitals where infectious diseases are treated and in outpatient departments where prophylactic anti-tetanus serum must be administered. There are a considerable number of tests by which specific sensitiveness can be determined, chief among which are the skin and ophthalmic reactions. One can also find out much that is useful from a history, and this is particularly important in view of the considerable risk there is in giving foreign protein injections at any time to individuals suffering from any of the varieties of allergic asthma. While it is never possible to make a general rule to guide the physician in the management of an individual case, the following precautions are listed, since—with modifications adapted to the individual case—they will form a guide for procedure.

HISTORY.—Before injecting serum, the patient should be questioned regarding the following points:

1 The following directions for procedure are, of course, subject to the judgment of the physician who faces the problem in an individual case. They have been formulated as a general guide after consultation with clinicians accustomed to giving serum and with laboratory workers who have had experience in anaphylactic problems.

1. Has he ever had a serum injection, and when? Did the injection cause any symptoms, either immediate respiratory distress, swelling and redness at point of injection, general rash (joint pains) or other signs of acute serum sickness? Has he suffered from any form of asthma? Is he sensitive to horse dandruff or any dust or food?

2. Has he ever been immunized to diphtheria? This should make you cautious, but is much less important than the first question.

TESTS FOR HYPERSENSITIVENESS.—Patients giving a negative as well as those giving a positive history, if it is necessary to give serum, should be tested for hypersensitiveness. Two methods are available:

Ophthalmic Test.—This reaction is less sensitive than the skin test and if positive is likely to indicate the possibility of serious results of serum injections. A drop of undiluted horse serum is instilled into the conjunctiva. A positive reaction should appear within ten to twenty minutes as a diffuse reddening with a watery discharge. When the reaction has developed, it should be controlled by the instillation into the eye of a 1: 1000 epinephrine (adrenalin) solution. Individuals giving a positive eye test should not be given serum unless the circumstances seem mandatory, and then it should be given with extreme care.

Intracutaneous Test.—This can be done by injecting intracutaneously 0.1 c.c. of a 1: 10 dilution of horse serum in normal saline. The development of a large wheal with a red flare within ten to twenty minutes is an indication of sensitiveness.

Observations of the New York City Dept. of Health indicate that moderate skin reactions may occur in people who give little or no appreciable reaction to serum treatment, and moderate skin reactions are therefore not nearly so contraindicatory as the positive ophthalmic test.

If both the history and skin test are negative, it is permissible to go ahead. Even without any skin or eye reaction or history a severe reaction may occur in rare and exceptional cases.

If the skin test is moderate and there is no history as indicated above, procedure with precautions is permissible.

If the history is positive, the ophthalmic test is positive, or if the skin reaction is marked, serum administration is likely to result in severe reactions and should be carried out only if it seems mandatory for other reasons to give serum. In such cases the greatest precautions as to desensitization must be used. Serum administration in asthmatics is dangerous and should not be undertaken without consultation of a specialist.

TECHNIC.—In all administrations, slowness of injection of the serum should be practiced. This can be done by diluting the serum 50 per cent with normal salt solution and so controlling the syringe that the serum is injected not faster than 1 c.c. per minute. This is usually restricted to giving intravenous injections, where it is particularly important.

Have at hand a 1: 1000 epinephrine (adrenalin) solution, and if symptoms such as dyspnea and cyanosis, lumbar pain or cardiac symptoms appear, give immediately a subcutaneous injection of 1 c.c. of the 1: 1000 epinephrine solution. This can be repeated if indicated. Other treatment is keeping the patient warm and administering oxygen. Such reactions will be rare, and dangerous reactions are very rare and apt to occur within a short time, usually within one hour and practically always within two hours.[2]

Desensitization.—Complete desensitization in human beings is probably impossible, but in cases where it seems prophylactically or therapeutically necessary to give serum in spite of positive evidence of sensitiveness, desensitization may diminish symptoms sufficiently to remove dangerous results.

All desensitization depends upon the principle of gradual, slow and interrupted administration. A rational procedure, subject to adjustment of quantity and interval according to reactions, is as follows:

Begin with a subcutaneous injection of 0.1 c.c.—that is, 1 c.c. of a 1:10 dilution made by diluting 0.1 c.c. of serum in 0.9 c.c. of salt solution. Inject this slowly, and make sure that a swelling is formed—i.e., that you have not entered the vein. (Note 1/100 c.c. has already been given.)

If this results in no symptoms other than a moderate local one, double the dose every half hour, injecting salt solution dilutions in volumes of not less than 2 c.c. and injecting slowly. Three doses in one and a half hours will bring the total to 0.7 c.c. If symptoms result from the first, or subsequent, injections, repeat the same dose every half hour until symptoms diminish.

If no symptoms occur with the preliminary three injections, continue with a gradually increasing dosage according to indications, until the whole amount has been given.

If an intravenous injection is to be given of large amounts, continue with subcutaneous injections until 1 c.c. has been tolerated, and then slowly inject 0.1 c.c. diluted in 2 c.c. of salt solution intravenously, and double this dose every half hour until the necessary amount has been given.

These directions can only guide the physician, who must be ready to modify doses and intervals according to results.

It must not be forgotten that desensitization is laborious and time-consuming, and that complete prevention of serum sickness cannot be expected.

Hay Fever.—Hay fever is characterized by catarrhal attacks of the mucous membranes of the upper respiratory tract and of the conjunctiva which may range in severity from that of a mild cold to violent and persistent asthmatic attacks. It is due to an allergic sensitiveness to the pollen of a number of plants, about 85 per cent of all cases being susceptible to the several varieties of ragweed pollen. The disease is a common one, and it has been estimated that from 1 per cent to 2 per cent of the population of the United States suffers from some form of hay fever. Because of the nature of the allergies, the majority of cases are subject to their attacks in the late summer and autumn, when the ragweed pollinates and the light pollen is blown about. Similar conditions, however, may be caused by a considerable number of other plants, such as goldenrod. Dunbar at first regarded hay fever as due to a toxin. This view, however, was discarded when investigations of allergy reached a point where the principles could be applied to the investigation of hay fever. Except for its seasonal occurrence, due to circumstances governed by the prevalence of the incitant, hay fever is in principle entirely similar to other forms of respiratory

---

2 It should be borne in mind that the concentrated sera, such as most therapeutic diphtheria antitoxins, are apt to give relatively milder reactions than the unconcentrated ones.

idiosyncrasy. It is largely concerning this disease that most of the controversies about the relationship of anaphylaxis to human allergies were waged in the early development of the subject. The heredity theory of Cooke and Vander Veer and of Coca was maintained for this disease, and the true importance of the inherited factor has been discussed in a preceding paragraph. It is interesting to note that Blackley as early as 1873 recognized the relationship of hay fever to plant pollen and laid most of the foundations of our clinical knowledge of the disease with definite suggestions of the specific irritant factors of particular substances. For some time the allergic nature of hay fever was questioned on the claim that the ragweed pollen was not a true antigen. The work of Julia Parker, however, indicated that with appropriate methods of sensitization an antigen could be demonstrated in pollen, and any further difficulties arising in this particular problem seemed unimportant in view of our present knowledge of partial antigens.

Skin hypersensitiveness and conjunctival reactions to the pollen antigen usually run parallel with the degree of respiratory sensitiveness of the patient. The preparation of the antigens has been standardized for practical purposes by Grove and Coca.

Respiratory Idiosyncrasies Other than Hay Fever.—There is no basic difference between hay fever and the other respiratory idiosyncrasies commonly seen against horse dandruff, the hair of various animals such as cats, rabbits, guinea-pigs, etc., house dust, feathers, etc. In these conditions it has been extremely difficult to trace the origin of the hypersensitiveness, which often seemed to occur without preceding contact with the responsible substance. However, by this time a sufficient number of careful observations have determined that respiratory hypersensitiveness is acquired by previous contact so that we can regard the principle as established. Most important in this connection are Ratner's observations on the development of respiratory hypersensitiveness to rabbit hair by children sleeping on pillows stuffed with this material, and observations of similar significance with horse dandruff and orris powder by Rackemann and to castor bean dust by Ratner and Gruehl. The last-named experimenters have also been able to produce respiratory hypersensitiveness in guinea-pigs with castor bean dust and some other materials.

Passive transfer of specific hypersensitiveness with the serum of respiratory allergic sufferers has been made by the P.-K. reaction and possibly in a few cases by transfer to guinea-pigs, though this is not absolutely sure.

That the substances responsible for the respiratory idiosyncrasies are antigenic in the broad sense in which we have used this word seems quite clear.

Desensitization has been successfully practiced, thus establishing another analogy with other forms of idiosyncrasy.

Drug Idiosyncrasies.—Abnormal sensitiveness to many drugs belonging to almost all chemical classes of substances, inorganic and organic, has been noted for years by clinicians. Among them are morphine, strychnine, atropine, salicylates, halogens and their compounds, salvarsan, etc. These substances are obviously not antigenic in the ordinary sense. The hypersusceptibility is generally specific at least for the chemical group, and it seems to be a fact that the reaction elicited in the individual does not represent exaggerated symptoms of the physiological effects of the drugs, but is, in a general way, alike, whatever the drug used. The symptoms usually come on rapidly, within a few hours or days, and consist in various kinds of skin rashes and fever. In such cases, where salvarsan, iodine, etc., preparations have been used, there may be marked and rapidly developing local inflammatory effects at the point of inoculation. Drug idiosyncrasies cannot be transmitted passively, and, so far, no conclusively successful experiments on artificial hypersensitization of animals with these substances have been done.

Many instances of drug idiosyncrasies in man have been reported (Jadassohn), and in a good many of them there can be no question about the fact that the susceptibility has been acquired by prolonged contact with the drug. Such are the antipyrine case of Bruck, the quinine hypersusceptibilities reported by Dold and the potassium chloro-platinate case of Vallery-Radot. The cases reported by Dawson and Garbade, in which the idiosyncrasies extended to the levorotary quinine derivatives but not to the dextro-rotatory ones, brings the theory of the formation of a compound antigen within the body much closer to realization. Sulzberger has produced experimental hypersensitiv-ity to arsphenamines. The analogy to the work of Landsteiner and Levine with the compound proteins made with the three isomeric forms of tartaric acid is obvious.

One of the difficulties in carrying out experimental work with the drug idio-syncrasies in animals may well depend upon the length of time and the continuity of exposure which seems to have been necessary in most of the observed human cases. Dold's quinine workers varied from three to five years of exposure, and the Vallery-Radot case covered between two and three years of interrupted exposure before the idiosyncrasy developed. This is as long as the natural lives of most of the ordinary laboratory animals.

Another observation which supports the possibility that a compound antigen may be formed by contact with a drug and the body protein of an animal is the observa-tion of Jacobs that iodine added to animal sera without the presence of acid or alkali results in the formation of substances which precipitate with antisera prepared from iodinated sera.

There are a good many clinical observations which all point in the same direction and which justify us in setting up as a tentative hypothesis for the mechanism of drug idiosyncrasy the conception that when a drug is habitually brought into contact with the body proteins of an individual there is eventually formed, perhaps at first in minute quantities, a compound antigen which consists of the drug itself or a radical of the drug in combination with the serum or cell proteins. Such an antigen takes its specificity from the drug or drug radical and gains its antigenic power from the added protein. But as an antigen, it is foreign to the body and capable of arousing reaction bodies or antibodies that lead to increased reaction capacity or—in other words—allergic hypersensitiveness. It must, however, be admitted that there are still a considerable number of gaps in the train of evidence which must be closed before we can accept this view as conclusively demonstrated. As far as we know, there has been no satisfactory passive transmission, but this is not absolutely contradictory, since this is also true of tuberculin hypersensitiveness and would be unnecessary for the development of allergy in view of the wider definition of antibody formation which we have given in an earlier paragraph.

Bacterial Hypersensitiveness (Allergy).—Our knowledge of bacterial allergy begins with Koch's observation of superinfection in guinea-pigs. He found that tuberculous guinea-pigs, if reinoculated on the skin with living tubercle bacilli, reacted differently from normal animals similarly injected. In the tuberculous ones there seemed to be a preliminary violent reaction to the injected organisms not apparent in the others; but subsequently, for a short time, the local lesion in the tuberculous animals seemed to show a tendency to heal, in contrast to the steady progression of the lesions in the normal guinea-pigs. He then noted that tuberculin may be injected into normal guinea-pigs in considerable quantities without harm, but when doses of approximately 0.2 gram were injected into guinea-pigs suffering from an advanced tuberculosis, the animals were found dead in twenty-four hours.

The tuberculin reaction has remained the classical example of bacterial allergy, though it is now reasonably sure that, in any bacterial infection which becomes chronic or which with antigenically identical bacteria is frequently repeated, a state of allergy may develop. It has long been our view that in all such conditions the allergic injury must be counted as part of the general pathology of the chronic or repeated infection.

In spite of being perhaps the oldest observation of allergy, the bacterial form is still the most obscure as to mechanism. We summarized the situation some years ago in the following manner, in which we endeavor to cross-index the facts about the tuberculin reaction which are definitely established and to deduce a tentative view of the mechanism from them. Our reasoning was as follows:

1. Tuberculin sensitiveness develops only when an actual tissue reaction has been aroused by the bacteria or bacterial fragments. It cannot be induced with dissolved extractives nor with tuberculin itself. It can be induced with dead organisms which produce a tubercle. The existence of a tubercle, as was first stated by Baldwin, is necessary.

2. The specificity of the tuberculin reaction indicates that whatever induces the reaction must be a product of the tubercle bacillus. And this product cannot be a soluble toxin produced only by the living organisms, since—as we showed with Petroff—dead tubercle bacilli can produce allergy.

Keeping these facts in mind and remembering that no chemically produced products of the tubercle bacillus in a soluble form have so far induced a typical tuberculin allergy, it seems obvious that tuberculin hypersensitiveness must represent the sensitization of the body by an antigen which is produced from the tubercle bacillus by the action of the cell enzymes in the characteristic pathological lesions spoken of as tubercles. It is likely that the reason we cannot produce these bacterial antigenic substances in the test tube is that extraction implies considerable and vigorous chemical manipulation, in the course of which the antigenic nature is diminished or destroyed. This is borne out by the fact that nucleoproteins produced from tubercle bacilli are very poor antigens, since it is necessary to inject large amounts before antibody production is apparent in noticeable concentration. Moreover, our work with Grinnell indicates that a condition analogous to tuberculin allergy can be produced in guinea-pigs with autolyzed pneumococci. Here the liberation of the bacterial proteins can be easily performed by autolysis in the test tube, without chemical insult.

An extraordinary development of investigations of bacterial allergy has been the work of Dienes, who has found that when a tuberculous lesion is produced in guinea-pigs and egg white is then injected into the lesion itself, the animals become sensitive to egg white, but unlike normal guinea-pigs similarly sensitized, skin injection of egg white in the sensitized tuberculous animals now gives rise to a reaction that resembles the delayed and severe tuberculin skin reaction rather than the evanescent anaphylactic skin reaction.

As a tentative view, we have put forward the conception that bacterial allergy is a hypersensitiveness to the somatic protein antigens of the bacteria in which the cells become sensitized by the liberation of an unchanged protein bacterial substance liberated in the lesions. Such allergy can be experimentally reproduced only with organisms in which disintegration can be accomplished without the use of alkalis and other chemical substances which tend to denaturize the bacterial protein. In this form of hypersensitiveness, the antibody or its analogue can be surmised only from the fact that the increased cell susceptibility exists in a specific manner. It does not—or at least does not easily—pass into the circulation, and passive sensitization for this reason is not observed.

There is a considerable amount of discussion as to whether allergy has any relationship to immunity in bacterial diseases. From experiments with Ward and Jennings, we are inclined to believe that bacterial allergy represents a hair-trigger response of the tissues to the substances liberated from bacterial lesions, and though in its immediate manifestations it may do actual injury and give rise to clinical disease, its eventual significance is in the direction of protection. Suggestive of investigation, and not at all impossible, is the thought that a number of the peculiar and still unsolved problems in connection with streptococcus and a few other types of immunity result from a deep cellular immunity dependent upon allergic sensitization to the bacterial protein antigens as contrasted with the humoral immunity dependent upon the circulating antibodies.

To make this entirely clear, we must differentiate between the bacterial allergy just described and true bacterial anaphylaxis, which exists and can be demonstrated with all the mechanism of true protein anaphylaxis. In 1921 we showed that in guinea-pigs sensitized with living tubercle bacilli both allergy and anaphylaxis could be demonstrated, the two processes being often parallel but not necessarily so. The situation—puzzling then—has been cleared up by our understanding of the structure of the bacterial antigen described in the section on Antigens. We may summarize the situation as follows: The whole bacterial antigen gives rise to antibody formation demonstrable in the circulation. True anaphylaxis in all its manifestations, general symptoms, the uterus experiment of Dale, skin reactions and passive sensitization, can be demonstrated with the whole bacterial antigen and the sera of animals containing circulating antibodies. Indeed, reactions can be elicited in sensitized animals with the haptophore carbohydrate substance which we first called "residue antigen" and which is now known as the "soluble specific substance." This has been demonstrated by Avery and Tillett, and by Enders.

Allergy and Rheumatism.—The almost constant association of various streptococci with rheumatism without the presence of the organism in the joint lesions has led to various conceptions of an allergic pathology. The conditions are entirely too complicated to be gone into in a short discussion. The idea of such a connection is an old one, having been expressed as early as 1914 by Herry and in 1915 by Faber. We mentioned our ideas briefly in consequence of a good deal of inconclusive experimentation with Grinnell in 1925 and in a summary of bacterial allergy in 1928. The most extensive work on this problem has been done by Swift and his associates.

Bacterial allergy may also play a rôle in scarlet fever. The idea was first suggested by Bristol and was discussed by Dochez and Stevens in connection with their studies on allergic reactions with hemolytic streptococci. There is much to support such a view in the fact that the Dick skin reaction is often negative in young children and that the blood of such infants does not neutralize the Dick toxin. The heat stable element in the Dick toxin is more like the allergic substances of bacteria than it is like the true toxins, and it is not impossible that streptococcus filtrates contain two substances that are concerned with the toxemia in scarlet fever: one the heat stable allergic factor, the other the heat sensitive true toxin described by Ando and his collaborators and discussed in our section on scarlet fever.

Toxin Hypersusceptibility.—In 1895 Knorr, following an observation previously made by von Behring in horses, found that guinea-pigs systematically treated with minute doses of diphtheria toxin fail to develop immunity but become so hypersusceptible to the toxin that they may be killed with doses too small to cause death in normal animals. Similar observations were made by Kretz.

The condition has been difficult to investigate because of the high toxicity of the antigen in this case, and its mechanism has been rendered obscure by the apparent failure of attempts at passive sensitization with small doses of antitoxin. There was much doubt as to whether this phenomenon represented a true hypersensitiveness or a summation effect. The discovery of anatoxin has made possible a more systematic study of the problem. Using this substance, Neill, Fleming and Gaspari have produced in guinea-pigs what appears to represent a true specific toxic hypersusceptibility.

Skin Reactions.—Specific sensitiveness of the skin is an almost universal accompaniment of all forms of hypersensitiveness. It indicates that the cells of the skin participate in the general sensitization of the tissues and that they are probably the sites of antibodies either produced by the cells themselves or absorbed from the circulation. Skin reactivity is present both in sensitized animals and in man and is subject to differences dependent upon the differing physiologies of the species.

In guinea-pigs two definite types of skin reactions can be observed. In these animals, in protein anaphylaxis, intracutaneous injection of small amounts of the specific protein causes an immediate swelling, like an urticarial wheal, which tends to last for a short time only and is usually over within an hour. In the same animals, suffering from tuberculosis, an allergic skin reaction can be produced with tuberculin which differs from the one just described in that there is a delay of about six or more hours between intracutaneous injection and the appearance of the lesion. When the reaction appears, it shows evidence of much more than a simple edema; there is a true inflammatory reaction with tissue death, accumulation of leukocytes and, in the most severe cases, eventually central hemorrhage and sometimes necrosis. The difference between the two types can be studied in tuberculous guinea-pigs, where there may be a true immediate anaphylactic reaction that can be elicited by the bacterial carbohydrate fraction alone. This type usually occurs late, not earlier than three or four weeks after the infection. The other type is the true tuberculin reaction, which develops within eight or nine days after infection, can be elicited only with the nitrogenous fraction of the organisms, is slow in developing and severe. The two are entirely independent of each other in mechanism and may be present alone at one or another stage in the disease (Zinsser).

In rabbits all skin reactions seem to be delayed. The skin test in rabbits sensitive to horse serum was described in 1910 by Knox, Morse and Brown.

In man both types of skin reaction can be observed, the delayed reaction being generally associated with bacterial allergy, such as tuberculin sensitiveness. In almost all other cases of hypersensitiveness—that is, in serum sickness, in the various asthmas and in intestinal idiosyncrasies—reactions appear, within a few minutes after application of the antigen, in the form of small urticarial wheals which may spread in various directions with the formation of pseudopods. Such reactions reach their height in from fifteen to thirty minutes, and are usually over within one to two hours. They may be elicited by lightly scratching the skin through a drop of the antigen solution. They may also be elicited by intradermal injections of minute amounts. Such reactions have been of the greatest practical use in the diagnosis of the particular substances to which a patient is sensitive. They should not be indiscriminately carried out by those not well informed, since intradermal injections may occasionally be followed by systemic reactions, even when minute amounts or high dilutions of the antigen are used.

Ophthalmic Reaction.—The conjunctiva shares in general hypersensitiveness as well as the skin. Such reactions are elicited by instilling a small amount of the diluted antigen into the conjunctival sac. An inflammatory reaction with itching and a watery discharge develops usually within less than ten minutes. As we have seen, in the testing of patients for horse serum sensitiveness, according to Spicer, the reaction is less delicate than the skin test but, for this reason, is more definitely a measure of general susceptibility.

Gastro-intestinal Idiosyncrasy.—Food idiosyncrasy may take a great many forms. Any variety of protein food may give rise to it, the most common ones being egg and milk hypersensitiveness. Many individuals are sensitive to fish, oysters and clams, or to varieties of fruit like strawberries, etc. Any type of meat may be involved.

The severity of the hypersensitiveness may range from the occurrence of a slight urticaria lasting a short time and beginning a few hours after the food is taken to severe cases in which a small amount of the responsible food gives rise within a few minutes to violent reactions, vomiting, and edema of the tongue and pharynx. The symptoms may be entirely referable to the gastro-intestinal canal, probably secondary to edema and abnormal peristalsis. On the other hand, they may consist only of urticarial eruptions and other skin conditions such as eczema, which is common in children in which the responsible food is fed over a considerable period. Skin reactions, which can be used for diagnosis of the material to which the individual is sensitive, usually, though not always, are parallel with the hypersusceptibility.

Although in the food idiosyncrasies the question of their analogy to animal anaphylaxis has been much discussed, the experiments of Schloss and others have shown a definite parallelism with the presence of antibodies in the blood. Schloss has shown precipitins in the circulation of food idiosyncratic children and has transferred the condition passively to guinea-pigs with such serum. The subject is not entirely clear in view of the fact that passive transfer to lower animals has seemed impossible in some cases, whereas homologous passive local sensitization by the P.-K. reaction succeeded. There is still a great deal to be done in clearing up this relationship between the passive local transfer to man and the heterologous transfer to animals. It is not impossible that human serum is a peculiarly poor vehicle for the transfer of antibodies to the rodents usually available for such experiments and that success in transfer to other human beings depends largely upon the fact that the serum is homologous.

Desensitization in the food idiosyncrasies is usually very difficult, and in the severe cases prolonged treatment beginning with doses as small as 0.001 milligram is necessary. For details of these matters we must refer to the special monographs, since the subject has become extraordinarily involved.

REFERENCES

ANDERSON, SCHLOSS and MYERS. Proc. Soc. Exper. Biol. & Med., 1925, 23:180.
AVERY and TILLETT. J. Exper. M., 1929, 49:251.
BLACKLEY. Experimental Researches on the Cause and Nature of Hay Fever, London, 1873.
BRISTOL. Am. J. M. Sc., 1926, 166:853.
BRUCK. Berl. klin. Wchnschr., 1910, 47:517.
COCA. Arch. Path., 1926, 1:96.
———— Tice's Practice of Med., 1920, Vol. 2.
COCA and GROVE. J. Immunol., 1925, 10:445.
COOKE and VANDER VEER. J. Immunol., 1916, 1:201.
DAWSON and GARBADE. J. Am. M. Ass., 930, 94:704.
DEBESCHE. Am. J. M. Sc., 1923, 166:265.
DIENES. Proc. Soc. Exper. Biol. & Med., 1916, 24:32.
DOCHEZ and STEVENS. J. Exper. M., 1927, 46:487.
DUNBAR, cited from Doerr. Kolle u. Wassermann Handbuch, 2nd Ed.
ENDERS. J. Exper. M., 1929, 50:727.
FABER. J. Exper. M., 1915, 22:615.
GROVE and COCA. J. Immunol., 1925, 10:471.
HERRY. Bull. Acad. roy. de méd. Belg., Series IV, 1914, 28:76.
Hooker. J. Immunol., 1924, 8:7.
JACOBS. J. Immunol., 1932, 23:361, 375.
KNORR, quoted from Otto. Marburg Dissertation, 1895.
KNOX, MORSE and BROWN. J. Exper. M., 1910, 12:562.
KOCH. Deutsche med. Wchnschr., 1891, 43.
KRETZ. Ztschr. f. Heilk., 1902.
LONGCOPE and MACKENZIE. Proc. Soc. Exper. Biol. & Med., 1920, 17:133.
LONGCOPE and RACKEMANN. J. Exper. M., 1918, 27:341.
NEILL, FLEMING and GASPARI. J. Exper. M., 1927, 46:735; J. Immunol., 1929, 17:419.
OPIE. J. Immunol., 1924, 9:231, 255, 259.
PARK. Am. J. Pub. Health, 1928, 18:354.
PARKER. J. Immunol., 1924, 9:6.
PRAUSNITZ and KÜSTNER. Centralbl. f. Bakteriol., 1921, 86:160.
RACKEMANN. J. Exper. M., 1918, 27:341.
———— J. Am. M. Ass., 1925, 84.
RAMIREZ. J. Am. Ass., 1919, 73:984.
RATNER. Am. J. Dis. Child., 1922, 24; 1928, 36:277.
RATNER, JACKSON and GRUEHL. Am. J. Dis. Child., 1927, 34:23; 1929, 236.
SCHLOSS. Am. J. Dis. Child., 1912, 3:341.
SCHLOSS and ANDERSON. Am. J. Dis. Child., 1923, 26:451.

Spicer. J. Immunol., 1928, 15:335.

Swift. J. Am. M. Ass., 1928, 90:906; 1929, 92:2071.

Tomscik and Kurotchkin. J. Exper., M., 1928, 47:379.

Vallery-Radot. Bull. et mém. Soc. méd. d. hôp. de Par., February, 1929.

Von Behring. Deutsche med Wchnschr., 1893.

Walzer. J. Immunol., 1927, 14: 143.

Weil. J. Immunol., 1917, 2:399.

Zinsser, H. J. Exper. M., 1921, 34:495.

——— Bull. New York Acad. M., 1928, 4:351.

Zinsser and Grinnell. J. Bacteriol., 1927, 14:301.

——— J. Immunol., 1925, 10:725.

Zinsser and Petroff. J. Immunol., 1924, 9:85.

Zinsser, Ward and Jennings. J. Immunol., 1925, 10:719.

SECTION III

PATHOGENIC MICRO-ORGANISMS

CHAPTER XX

AN INTRODUCTION TO THE STUDY OF INFECTIOUS DISEASE

Infectious disease is a special case of the widely prevalent biological phenomenon of parasitism. The tendency of one form of life to establish itself within or upon the substance of another is a common occurrence in all groups of the animal and vegetable kingdoms, and furnishes material for the study of adaptation. Derived from related free-living forms, the parasites have become modified in form and chemical properties under the influence of the host environment, by steps which can often be followed. The process by which parasites develop is, as Caullery says: "in a manner of a secondary evolution superimposed upon the general evolution of the free groups from which they are derived."

Among the more complex or higher forms of life, the development of a dependent existence is the result of centuries of slow change in which extensive anatomical and functional modifications are involved; the related free representatives of the order have, as a rule, widely diverged from the parent stem, which may be available for study only in fossil forms.

In the lower forms, the protozoa and especially the bacteria, morphological simplicity, chemical elasticity and the speed with which generations succeed each other permit the study of parasitism in a more flexible state, amenable in many instances to experimental manipulation. In the study of infectious disease, we are confronted with the fundamental phenomena of parasitism in their simplest available manifestations. And in the material of bacteriology are represented all gradations from the purely saprophytic, through the facultative saprophyte and parasite, to the completely or almost completely parasitic forms.

If there has been any significant change in modern bacteriology other than the wholesome introduction of biochemical and biophysical methods, it is the growth of a broader biological point of view which is recognizing that the difficult specific problems of medicine can often be approached most effectively by study of fundamental biological principles. In this sense, the contributions of bacteriology to biology and to general physiology have already been extensive. The newer knowledge of bacterial dissociation and its accompanying chemical alterations, subject to purposeful experiment in the laboratory, is one of the most fruitful fields for the study of protoplasmic flexibility. The established knowledge of the so-called ultra-microscopic virus agents and of the bacteriophage are bringing us closer to the threshold of the origins of living matter. And the specific interactions of the antigenic materials of the parasite with the living cells of the host, expressed in antibody formation and in the development of anaphylaxis and allergy, are phenomena of a physiological signifi-

248

cance transcending their importance for purely bacteriological or medical problems.

No development of parasitism takes place without resistance on the part of the host. We may reasonably assume that there is a universal biological reluctance on the part of living protoplasm to invasion by another form of life. Water animalcules, fish eggs, frog's eggs, developing in a medium swarming with saprophytic organisms, remain uninvaded. Let a sudden frost kill them and immediately, before gross chemical changes can occur, they become culture medium for the life about them. The bodies of higher animals are incessantly in contact with innumerable species of minute living forms. Most of these remain harmless to do more than establish a frugal existence on the secretions of mucous membranes and sloughed cellular materials. But among these numerous varieties, a few develop properties of invasion or of toxin formation which permit them to overcome the resistance of the living cells. Against these, the invaded host develops special methods of defense. The struggle which ensues is infectious disease.

The properties of aggression on the part of the micro-organisms are the subject matter of bacteriology. The mechanism of defense is the material of immunology. The two disciplines deal with reciprocal reactions of parasitism, and cannot be separated. Since the processes involved represent the physiologic interplay of a living foreign protein with the tissues of a host, the manifestations of infection give clues to the understanding of the important problems of anaphylaxis and allergy. Analysis of this interaction furnishes a rational basis for the pathology of the various infectious diseases, discloses methods of diagnosis and of prognosis, and leads to the development of active and passive prophylaxis and therapy. Moreover, the investigations which thus form the logical approach to individual clinical problems are of equal importance for the study of herd or mass infection—in other words, of epidemiology and, through this, of public health and sanitation.

There are, in the evolution of infectious diseases, as in all biological phenomena, an almost infinite number of variables which modify the end result. Thus, while there are certain fundamental principles which can be generalized for all infections, each type must be studied separately, and each specific disease presents its own individual type of parasitism.

There are many bacteria habitually in contact with the skin and mucous surfaces of man and of animals which, by perfect adaptation to the conditions found in their habitual environments, fail to acquire any invasive or toxic properties. Such are the intestinal organisms of the colon and allied groups, various bacillary, spirillar and coccal varieties of the mouth and nose, the diphtheroids in these locations and in the conjunctiva, and many others of the so-called "normal flora" of these locations that might be enumerated. Such bacteria become contributors to disease only when, for some extraneous reason, tissue death permits them to penetrate beyond the surfaces.

There are other micro-organisms, like those of the typhoid and dysentery groups, the cholera spirillum, the anthrax bacillus and invaders of the anaerobic groups of bacilli, which appear to be extraordinarily resistant to the dissociative forces encountered when living outside the body and, during such saprophytic existences, retain the capacity to invade in a characteristic manner whenever they again come in contact with a susceptible host by the path to which they are adapted. There are other acute invaders, like the pneumococcus and streptococcus groups, in which the biological flexibility is such that it is not so much the species characteristics as the qualities of the individual strain which determine invasiveness or virulence. And such fluctuations in aggressiveness are determined by the immediately preceding biological history of the given strain.

The acuteness or chronicity of an infection is a direct consequence of the degree to which mutual adaptation has been evolved. In diseases like the enteric fevers, cholera, infections caused by the streptococcus, the pneumococcus, the meningococcus and many other bacteria, sharp resistance on the part of the host initiates a struggle in which invader or host is completely overcome. If the host is destroyed, the organism, not directly passed on to a new host, returns to a saprophytic environment, where the particular strain may eventually lose its invasive attributes. A similar infection occurs only when another strain of this species, in a suitably virulent form, encounters a host similar in receptiveness. If the host survives, the invader may be either completely eliminated, or so held in check by developed specific resistance that it remains dormant in the tissues, helpless against this immune individual but capable of infecting others. This leads to what we speak of as "the carrier state." But it may also happen, particularly with streptococci, pneumococci and diphtheria bacilli, that, in this prolonged contact, the retained invader—under the influence of the immune environment—gradually dissociates into a saprophytic state. That such dissociated strains may nevertheless retain the potential capacity of returning to the virulent condition is one of the great recent advances of bacterial biology which promises to shed much light on our knowledge of disease and of epidemics.

Again, the development of harmful parasitism may take place without any invasive capacity, the organisms remaining on the surface but, possibly as an evoluted mechanism of tissue destruction for nutritive purposes, producing toxins which destroy the host. In this sense, diphtheria and tetanus are instances in which the host may be killed by organisms which are essentially saprophytes.

The adaptations which underlie chronicity may take a variety of directions. In syphilis, it is not unlikely that the persistent passage of invader from host to host, through centuries, without interruptions of the parasitic mode of life, has led to an adaptation so close as to approach a high degree of mutual tolerance. The disease appears to have become less acute in the course of four centuries, and protective and immunological reactions are slow and feeble in the infected host. It is not out of question that the direction of biological development in this disease is tending toward the condition of quasi-commensalism which characterizes certain trypanosome and spirochete infections in rodents, or the sarcosporidia infection of mice, where we can speak of "infection without disease." In all these relations, a fine gradation of mutual tolerance determines the degrees of reaction, or injury and of resistance.

A form of chronicity depending upon other principles is that seen in tuberculosis, in leprosy and in some of the fungus diseases. Here, it is probably not so much the evolved tolerance, as the chemically insoluble nature of the invader which acts more in the manner of an irritating foreign body than in that of a rapidly extending or toxic aggressor. Added to this are the factors of slow growth characteristics on the part of the invaders and a relatively high resistance developed by natural selection among civilized communities. When, for instance, tuberculosis attacks very young children or natives of hitherto isolated races it may assume relatively acute characteristics. In the defensive response to each of these varieties of special parasitism, the host develops reactions of a pattern as complex as that of the invading forces. Fundamental to all of them is the antibody production aroused by the protein constituents of the parasite, and the cellular response which expresses itself in special types of inflammation. These reactions are as characteristic of the pathology of each disease as are the direct and indirect injuries to tissue exerted by the invader. For this reason, the nature of an infection can often be recognized by the development of the specific response, antibody formation, or the type of cell reaction which follows. In the more chronic invasions, the cellular reaction may often approach the mechanism observed in connection with the removal of foreign bodies.

It will be apparent from these examples that, in the parasitism which constitutes infection, a wide range of reaction is possible.

Fundamental knowledge of these variations is essential to the physician who deals with infectious diseases. Familiarity with habitual points of attack and subsequent extensions, with the pharmacological actions of specific points and with the physiological and pathological reactions by which the invaded subject is likely to react give him his clues to diagnosis, prognosis and specific therapy. Most of all, such knowledge enables him to judge how and when the special technic of the bacteriologist can aid him in any of these matters. In an increasing number of situations encountered in the clinic, such coöperation is essential to the conscientious practice of medicine. The severity of the disease, the amount of permanent damage done, and even recovery itself may often depend upon the precision and speed with which clinical sagacity is followed by cultural diagnosis, and this by appropriate specific therapy. In almost all infections, accurate bacteriological and serological analysis furnish the premises for rational treatment, specific or otherwise, for the determination of the susceptibility of contacts, for prophylaxis, for release from quarantine and for all the numerous functions in which well-trained physicians form the advance guards in the protection of public health.

MASS INFECTION

Of even greater importance for the welfare of mankind than the study of individual infections is that of the phenomena of mass infection, or epidemics. In attempting to investigate the conditions which govern the occurrence, course and control of epidemic disease, we are confronted with the additional difficulties of having to interpolate the factors of a complex environment into the already involved reactions between invader and host.

Were epidemics the simple consequences of the introduction of a source of infection into a susceptible community, the problem would be a relatively clear one. Such uncomplicated relations between cause and effect have, on occasion, governed the tempestuous outbreaks of new diseases—measles, influenza, tuberculosis, poliomyelitis, etc., among aborigines for the first time in contact with what is spoken of as the "civilized world." But practically all human communities may, to use a term used by Topley, be regarded as "infected herds" in which potential sources of all known infections are constantly present.

These potential sources of infection may be of several kinds. The least dangerous are the recognized sporadic cases. More dangerous are the atypical, unrecognized ones, which run so mild a course that their contacts with others are never restricted by control or disability. In addition to this, there are many individuals whose resistance, natural or acquired, is such that they may harbor and distribute an infectious agent without exhibiting, at any time, signs of illness. The persistence of virulent micro-organisms in the bodies of such individuals and in those of convalescents constitutes the "healthy" and "convalescent" *carrier condition*. In many carriers, the percentage varying with individual infections, gradual dissociation of the bacteria into the "rough" forms, under the influence of the host's immunity, may take place. In a considerable number, however, the organisms retain their virulence for long periods, sometimes permanently.

In nearly every community there are present carriers of typhoid, paratyphoid, diphtheria and dysentery bacilli, of meningococci and of the poliomyelitis virus; there are at all times many carriers of hemolytic streptococci and of virulent pneumococci of all types. Percentages of individual types of carriers vary according to location, season and special conditions of hygiene; but the community is never free of them. It is largely due to the carriers and unrecognized cases that sporadic disease is kept going in interepidemic periods. In infections of the intestinal type, where food and water epidemics are gradually disappearing under the influence of sanitation, such carriers form the obstacles to complete conquest of the respective diseases.

In addition to the human reservoirs which furnish sources of infection, there are instances in which the infectious agent persists in animals and in insects.

Since, therefore, it can be demonstrated that there are constantly present innumerable foci from which fully virulent micro-organisms can be distributed; and since the occurrence of a continuous series of sporadic cases indicates that given a suitable host, contact with these sources can result in disease, we can conclude that the failure of frequent epidemic outbreaks of wide distribution must be due in part to the development of some kind of community resistance.

Before proceeding to the discussion of this factor, however, it will be useful to outline the various *mechanisms of transmission* by which infections can pass from a source of virulent material to a new host.

This mechanism determines to some extent whether or not a given disease is likely or not to assume epidemic proportions. Knowing the manner of transmission, the capacity for survival of the micro-organisms away from the host, and the possible need of intermediate hosts, it is possible to deduce the environmental influences which retard or favor mass infection. From this point of view, we may consider infections under the following subdivisions:

1. Infections in which transmission ordinarily occurs only as a result of direct traumatic contact with infected material. This is the case in the surgical infections caused by the micrococci, streptococci, tetanus, the anaerobic bacillus group, and usually by anthrax and glanders. Epidemics are out of the question in such instances, except in groups habitually in occupational contact with infectious materials.

2. Contact infections not necessarily traumatic. Into this class fall the venereal diseases—syphilis, gonorrhea and Ducrey infections. It is self-evident that, however numerous such conditions may be, they are always the results of direct physical or bodily contact, and cannot become epidemic in the true sense of the word.

3. Infections acquired by the respiratory passages. Under this heading fall a large number of the true epidemic diseases. It includes the common cold, the pneumonias, influenza, meningitis, diphtheria, scarlet fever, tuberculosis, smallpox, measles, mumps, chickenpox and poliomyelitis. The manner of transmission alone indicates that this type of disease is the most difficult to control.

4. Diseases which are spoken of as intestinal infections, because the parasitic adaptation is such that the host is invaded only if the organism gains access to the digestive tract. This does not mean necessarily that the entire course of the subsequent disease is confined to the intestine. In cholera and the dysenteries, and in most of the infectious diarrheas, this is the case. But in typhoid and the paratyphoid fevers, after the initial intestinal multiplication and local injury has taken place, the bacteria enter the blood stream and the parasitic invasion is a general one. Nevertheless, the bacteria always reach the external world with the excreta—mainly the feces, sometimes the urine—of the case and the carrier. In the typhoid-paratyphoid group, carriers are numerous, often chronic, not infrequently permanent. In the dysenteries the persistent carrier rates of convalescents may amount to more than 2 per cent. In cholera, persistence of the carrier state is probably not as frequent as in other intestinal conditions. But there are features in regard to the recurrence of cholera epidemics after prolonged free intervals, without traceable importation of new sources, which indicate the capacity of the spirilla to survive in a community either in the human body or in a purely saprophytic condition. The carrier state in the intestinal infections is, for obvious reasons, not subject to seasonal fluctuations as is the case with respiratory invaders.

It is clear from this that great epidemics of intestinal infections can take place only when, from case or carrier, the infectious material reaches a common food, milk or water supply. This may occur by direct fecal or urinary contamination. But since the various bacteria of this group can survive in nature—water, food, soil, sewage—for varying periods determined by temperature, moisture, nutritive environment and saprophytic competition, the cycle of transmission may be a roundabout one. It may take the forms of (a) host to host (feces—fingers); (b) feces—food or water; (c) feces—fingers—food; (d) feces—flies—food.

The problem of prevention of the intestinal infections is a simpler one than it is in the case of the respiratory infections. Water, milk and food supplies can be and have been to a large extent protected from fecal contamination. The access of flies to fecal matter can be controlled, and food handlers can be examined for the carrier state whenever sanitary surveys of isolated cases point in this direction. It is quite impossible to establish all these expensive safeguards in isolated or poor communities and, even in the well-organized ones, the cumulative carrier problem remains as a permanent and probably, in its residual vestiges, insoluble menace. Fortunately, in most of the diseases mentioned, methods of increasing community resistance by active immunization on a large scale are available. Outbreaks of epidemics are sometimes due to failure to apply existing knowledge.

The differences in the sanitary problem depending upon the circumstances of transmission are well illustrated by the fact that in our Army cantonments in 1917, the recruit was forty-five times less likely to contract an intestinal infection than he would have been as a member of the same age group in his home community; whereas the conditions of camp life vastly increased all forms of respiratory infection, in spite of well-planned and skilful efforts to prevent them.

5. Disease in which the source of infection is an animal host from which transmission takes place without an insect vector. Many diseases of this category, such as rabies, anthrax, glanders, possess no true epidemic significance. There are several other conditions of this group, however, in which outbreaks may attain epidemic proportions, because the infectious agents appear in milk. This is particularly the case with bovine tuberculosis and, to a lesser but increasing extent, with the type of undulant fever caused by the *Brucella abortus* (*bovinus*) (Bang), an organism probably representing a bovine modification of the *Brucella melitensis*. The last named, conveyed by goat's milk, gives rise to epidemics of Malta fever. It is not improbable that many cases of Malta fever are infected by blowing dust in hot and dry countries, where goats are habitually milked in the streets.

Since rats are often infected with *Leptospira icterohaemorrhagiae*, it is likely—from circumstantial epidemiological evidence—that this disease also passes from rats (by rat urine) to man. Rats also harbor the organism of rat bite fever, and transmit it to man. But this disease does not become epidemic.

6. Diseases conveyed directly from case to case by insects. This is true of yellow fever, malaria, sand fly fever, dengue fever, African sleeping sickness, relapsing fever and some other conditions. It is the case in epidemics of typhus fever, where the rapid spread is a case to case infection by the louse. In malaria, the infection of new mosquitoes from carriers facilitates survival of the plasmodia. Mosquitoes can, of course, survive from season to season by hibernation, but it is believed, at present, that the plasmodia die out in the hibernating mosquito under the influence of low temperature. This type of transmission is separated from those considered under 7 and 8 because, for purposes of epidemiology and prevention it is of great importance whether the source of insect infection is limited to the human reservoir and whether new vectors can be produced either from animal reservoirs of infection or by insect inheritance.

The primary condition for sanitary control in the diseases of this group is obviously the isolation of cases from contact with insect vectors during the stages of the disease in which they can transmit the virus. This is feasible in most of the infections mentioned, and useful—to a high percentage—even in cases in which man can become a chronic reservoir. Other sanitary measures are prescribed by the habits, seasonal prevalence, breeding places, etc., of the particular insects involved. Conditions are more complex when several insects are concerned.

7. An animal reservoir for insect infection exists. In American typhus fever, the disease is endemic in rats. It passes from rat to rat by the rat flea and the rat louse; from rat to man by the rat flea; from man to man by the human body and head louse. The rat survives the infection and may retain the virus for a long time, not less than three weeks. How much longer is not known. The flea may harbor it for as long as three weeks, and survive. The louse becomes infectious in seven or eight days, and dies of the virus in ten or twelve. These facts determine sanitary procedure. For European typhus, this cycle has not yet been demonstrated—but louse transmission is clear, and delousing is the key to control.

In plague, there is a rat reservoir from which the disease is spread by fleas. In

African sleeping sickness, circumstantial epidemiological evidence points to an animal reservoir, and the same is true of some other conditions which we have no space to discuss here.

8. The infectious agent is hereditary in the insect vector. This is true of the Bitter Root Valley, Rocky Mountain spotted fever, possibly of its eastern and South American cousins. The Rickettsiae of this disease pass from the maternal tick into the ova and, as recent investigations have indicated, infection of the offspring by the sperm of the paternal tick is also possible.

The outline of transmission cycles which we have briefly presented sufficiently illustrates that, whether or not an infection can become epidemic is to a large extent dependent upon the type of parasitic adaptation by which transmission is governed.

Topley and others who have attempted to analyze the conception of community or mass resistance have considered it as dependent partly upon factors which are inherent in the tissues of the host and those which are dependent upon environmental conditions. Concerning the former, we possess a considerable amount of information. Concerning the latter, there is still much that is entirely vague.

Although racial increase of resistance, constantly operative by natural selection, has modified the severity of many infectious diseases, especially those which, like tuberculosis and syphilis, have thoroughly "durchseucht" the human race, this has no bearing on the present problem. Man, like any other animal species, is characterized by certain fixed degrees of susceptibility, which vary in regard to individual infectious agents. With these susceptibilities every child is born. At first, the child may be to some extent protected by passive immunization through the placenta. When this wears off, the initial susceptibility may be converted into a relative resistance, or even immunity, in the course of years through infections, immunization, physiological and structural changes due to the activities of glands of internal secretion and also by changes in items of diet, including certain vitamins.

In part, this resistance is unquestionably due to fortuitous active immunization —even without obvious disease—possibly by mild, inapparent infection and by the carrier state. In diphtheria and scarlet fever, we have direct evidence of this in the higher incidence of positive susceptibility tests in rural as compared with urban groups. In tuberculosis, mild, early infection is almost universal and protective.

In another group of diseases, such as influenza, smallpox, measles, mumps and many other conditions, the normal susceptibility of man is so extreme that infection without obvious disease is exceptional. Were it not for vaccination, smallpox would retain its former terrors. Measles and mumps, milder in childhood, are almost invariably acquired when exposure has taken place. They are children's diseases only because they are acquired early in life in crowded communities. When, as in army camps, adults from rural areas are exposed, epidemics ensue. The relative immunity of inhabitants of typhus or yellow fever areas in ordinary times is most likely due to the fact that mild attacks have been sustained in youth.

In pneumonia, the natural resistance of man is relatively high. The virulent organisms are widely prevalent throughout the winter seasons, but relatively few cases occur. The individual acquires pneumonia when the presence of the organisms coincides with influences that depress resistance. When this occurs on a large scale—

as in labor or army camps—epidemics result. In such cases, the outbreak of mass infection depends upon the unusual environmental influences which break down a naturally high resistance. Whether this high resistance is a constitutional one or whether it is acquired by the inevitably frequent contacts with pneumococci in the course of ordinary existence is questionable and not answerable until we know more about pneumococcus immunity in general.

In meningitis, epidemics occur whenever large numbers of susceptible individuals are brought together under conditions of sanitation and crowding which favor the increase of the carrier state. The conditions governing resistance in meningitis are peculiar, and not clearly understood. There are always a great many more carrier sources than cases, even in the large epidemics, and there appears to be a considerable increase of the carrier rate in the pre-epidemic phases. In the interepidemic stages, when meningitis occurs sporadically here and there, it is preponderantly a children's disease. As adult life is attained, a considerable relative resistance develops, and the distribution of cases in epidemics is such, even in crowded army camps, that we are forced to conclude that only a few of those exposed come down with the disease. Unlike the conditions in pneumonia, matters of depression by poor hygiene, exposure, overwork, etc., play little or no rôle. The healthiest and strongest are as likely to be attacked as the weak and debilitated. Whether the immunity which protects a large proportion of the exposed individuals is acquired by a preceding carrier condition, or whether it is a matter of nonspecific constitutional immunity cannot be at present decided. Moreover, we have no means of appraising the degree to which fluctuations of virulence to the meningococcus strains affects these conditions, for there is no satisfactory method of measuring experimentally the virulence of a meningococcus for man. That bacterial virulence may play a rôle is suggested by the occasional cases in which a carrier of long standing comes down with a typical attack. In this disease, as in diphtheria, the spread of epidemics appears to be chiefly favored by the accumulation of a large number of carriers and conditions of crowding, which facilitate spread of the bacteria from person to person.

In diphtheria, we can measure the virulence of strains of the organism as well as the susceptibility of exposed individuals. Studies by Dudley, analogous to those cited for meningitis, have shown that epidemic outbreaks of diphtheria are secondary to an accumulation of carriers. In diphtheria, the susceptible age for the years immediately following the second year of life is explained by the disappearance of a certain degree of passive immunity conferred from the mother with the placental blood. By the Schick reaction and direct antitoxin measurements, it can be determined that immunity increases gradually with adult life. This is certainly in part due to individual active immunization, but may—in part also—be due to nonspecific constitutional immunity. In the American army during the war, in the age group of from twenty to thirty, there were about 10 per cent in whom the Schick reaction was positive. Dangerous carriers, in ordinary times, represent about 0.01 per cent of the population. Many more than this carry non-toxin-producing strains, but it has been shown that there is a gradual dissociation in the throats of convalescents, and only a relatively small percentage of those infected with the diphtheria bacilli continue for any length of time to be "virulent" carriers. Active immunization, increasing herd resistance, offers the most natural solution to the diphtheria problem.

In poliomyelitis, where the source of infection, too, is mainly in carriers, serological studies seem to indicate that a very large proportion of adults have been in contact with the virus at some time or another. Again, only a slight percentage of the population, even in extensive epidemics, suffers from clinically noticeable infections. The immunological basis for this is uncertain. But the irregular distribution of cases during epidemics—a distribution in which relatively few new cases can be traced to contacts with preceding ones—indicates that wide differences in resistance exist, not only between children and adults, but even among children of the same age groups. In this problem, particularly, the investigation of possible constitutional immunity has been actively pursued in recent years.

An attempt has been made, chiefly by Webster, by Amoss and by Topley and Greenwood, to subject the conditions of epidemics to experimental analysis. The most promising of the methods employed has consisted in the study of communities of mice infected, by natural means, with *Bacillus enteritidis, Bacillus aertrycke, Bacterium lepisepticum* and a few other organisms. Large numbers of mice were studied in groups in which infection had been established and to which normal mice were added in varying increments and under a variety of circumstances. A great deal of useful information has been obtained by such experiments.

If infection by the natural method is carried on in a fairly numerous population of mice, without the addition of normals, and the epidemic is allowed to burn itself out, it never goes on to complete extermination, but there are always survivors. Yet a large number of such survivors are infected—a point that can be determined by the fact that they may be used to start an epidemic when new mice are added to the surviving group. If this is done, a second epidemic wave occurs, but in this wave the added animals suffer disproportionately to the survivors from the previous outbreak.

The experiments have also shown that a succession of epidemic waves can be maintained by the persistent addition, from time to time, of definite numbers of normal mice, and these waves are more prolonged and severe, the larger the numbers of the normal mouse increments added.

Another very curious observation recorded by Topley is the fact that if a large infected group is separated into a number of small groups, the total death rate is smaller than if they are left together.

A considerable number of these results of experimental epidemiology, though unexplained, can be paralleled from experience in human epidemics. We have observed, for instance, that when a unit of troops in which the ordinary military recruiting epidemics have burnt themselves out is scattered, and incorporated in new units which have also come epidemiologically to rest, new outbreaks occur. Moreover, in epidemics like influenza, even when the disease becomes almost universal, there is always a percentage of individuals who do not become infected; but when, after two or three months, a second wave appears, these individuals may come down.

Experimental epidemiology is the youngest branch of experimental bacteriology, and much may be hoped for from an extension of the method. It is of course almost impossible to reproduce with the spontaneous infection of groups of normals the many variables that must be interpolated in analyzing human conditions of living. Moreover, it is quite likely that the factors of individual habit, diet and temporary or inherited resistance fluctuate within far wider limits in man than they do in experimental animals. On the other hand, the new method offers the only controlled manner at present available for the study of phenomena, not amenable to other means of experimentation, which Topley speaks of as "herd reactions."

The part played by fluctuation of bacterial virulence in the origin of epidemics and in the rise and fall of epidemic waves is not easily appraised.[1] Bacterial strains, in nature or in the host, are composed of individuals possessing different characteristics. Amoss found in his studies of the pneumococcus that so-called "pure" cultures of pneumococcus were composite in this sense, and that even a virulent Type I pneumococcus which had been passed through one hundred and ninety mice was made up of such differing individuals. A pure culture of a single type of smoothness or roughness can probably never be obtained except by the mechanical analysis of the laboratory. Species of organisms as they are generally encountered, therefore, contain individuals of different dissociation forms and differences in virulence which depend upon the numerical proportions between highly virulent "S" organisms and the less virulent "R" forms, different environments favoring the preponderance of one or the other. In some species, especially those of the gram-negative bacilli predominantly used in experimental epidemiology, there are a series of intermediate forms.

There is practically no disagreement on the observation that the influence of specific immune serum tends to dissociate the virulent into the less virulent forms, and that a change in this direction is far more easily obtained than one in the contrary direction. Such changes may take place with great speed.

That transformation of "R" into "S" can take place both *in vivo* and *in vitro* has been shown repeatedly by many investigators. Therefore, we must assume that, in the natural relations of bacteria with their *in vivo* and *in vitro* environments, changes away from and toward pathogenicity can take place. It remains only to define the conditions under which and in which direction these changes occur.

It is thus a great temptation to include, in our efforts to explain epidemic phenomena, the alterations of bacterial virulence, together with the variables depending upon changes of host susceptibility, etc. Yet experimental epidemiologists have obtained clear-cut results to indicate that the fluctuation of virulence of bacteria has little if any influence either upon the course, the beginning, or the cessation of individual epidemics.

Webster seems to have done almost everything that is possible with a mouse population to throw light on this question. He has found that mouse typhoid organisms are equally virulent whether taken from heart's blood of acute cases or from chronic septicemia in such epidemics—that is, both early and late in the disease. There was no difference in the virulence of the mouse typhoid organism, a Friedländer bacillus, or fowl cholera organisms taken from fatal cases or from carriers, and three strains of *B. aertrycke* were equally virulent whether taken from an acute source or from the stools of healthy survivors. Moreover, strains recovered at various endemic and epidemic periods of the mouse disease showed no differences in virulence. Both Topley and Webster find that the characteristics of the individual epidemic depend largely on the virulence of the organisms, and the evidence seems to

---

[1] This discussion is largely taken from a paper published in *The Journal of Preventive Medicine*, Vol. 6, 1932, p. 497, by Zinsser and Wilson on "Bacterial Dissociation and a Theory of the Rise and Fall of Epidemic Waves."

show that virulent organisms may have a high killing power but little ability to persist in the tissues of survivors, whereas other strains that are of lower virulence and tend to become endemic have a greater tendency to persist and spread, though they do not kill.

There is one fact only in the results of experimental epidemiologists which points in the direction of the influence of virulence changes upon individual outbreaks. This is the experience of Topley and Greenwood in one of their *B. aertrycke* experiments, in which the virulence of the organism isolated between the twenty-eighth and sixtieth days of the epidemic was about five times that of the original culture.

There is another observation in these investigations which has bearing on the subject, and that is the fact that, when a mouse village has recovered and a new epidemic has been started by the addition of infected individuals and the gradual accumulation of normal mice, a considerable percentage of the survivors from the original outbreak now succumb. It is a little difficult to explain this purely on dosage, for the survivors of the first wave must have been subjected to a similarly accumulated dosage at that time, and should have developed considerable immunity at the time of the second exposure. It should be considered in this connection that the accumulating dosage assumed as the result of the presence of many infected individuals is more likely to occur under the cage conditions of the mouse experiment than in epidemics of human communities. Yet Dudley, as we have previously mentioned, has made an almost analogous observation with diphtheria and influenza in military camps, where he found that the relatively immune are "more frequently infected when mixed with the more susceptible 'junior ratings' "—from which he argues an "enhancement of virulence by passage through the less resistant material."

Nevertheless, taken as a whole, experimental epidemiology gives us little basis for assuming that enhancement of virulence is a factor of importance in the rise of an epidemic wave, or that a gradual increase of avirulent over virulent individuals in the course of the epidemic has anything to do with subsidence.

There is a general tendency in epidemiological thinking at the present time, therefore, to exclude from consideration the facts of bacterial dissociation. Nevertheless, we are inclined to agree with Stallybrass that "even if no observable variations in pathogenicity have been noted in the course of experimental epizootics, it may well be that the imposed conditions of the experiment, both in limitations or organism, impossibility of exactly reproducing community conditions, and the necessarily limited number of individuals studied are to some extent responsible for this." There is some danger that under the influence of the present tendency we might go wrong in underestimating these natural variations of the incitant organisms in their influence on epidemic disease.

There is, of course, no question of the accuracy of the observations of Webster or of Topley and Greenwood. But it is quite impossible to reproduce the extraordinary complexity of circumstances influencing human epidemics in experiments with mice, a fact fully recognized by the investigators named. And, for this reason we must consider the possible influence of the virulence factor in certain aspects of human epidemics which are not easily explained without it.

Changes in virulence cannot readily be eliminated in attempts to explain the origins of certain epidemics.

The origin of influenza epidemics is particularly mysterious in this regard; if one studies the history of the disease, it seems always to have arisen from one or, as in the last pandemic, several foci where the disease as such in its pure form had not been present before. We have a considerable amount of information to indicate that the virus causing the disease can exhibit extraordinary and sudden changes of infectivity.

Similar conditions are interesting in connection with cholera. The origin of cholera epidemics has interested us in connection with the outbreaks in southeastern Russia. Without discussing the open question of whether cholera lingers in an epidemic focus in the southeast, or is brought to European Russia from India across Persia, as some writers believe, there is considerable evidence that in the outbreak of 1921 cholera appeared in Kieff without any traceable relationship with other outbreaks. It was attributed to the importation of workmen from a place called Rhiazan where, however, no cholera cases were reported. In cholera the carrier condition does not, so far as we know, last indefinitely as in typhoid fever, and it is difficult to explain the rise and fall of epidemics except on the basis of changes on the part of the invader. In the Rostoff water supplies in 1923, as cholera was subsiding, the local bacteriologists told one of us that there was an inagglutinable vibrio that culturally was like a true cholera organism. Zlatogoroff, studying 23 strains of cholera organisms obtained from patients, with an agglutinating serum that was homologously potent up to 1 : 20,000, showed that five of them agglutinated, at the beginning, up to 1 : 5000 and eighteen did not agglutinate. Of the latter, ten acquired agglutinating powers, after animal passage, within six months, seven remained negative and one died out. It was shown also that the agglutinability of cholera organisms was lost after eighteen days of preservation in water. Agglutinability, of course, does not necessarily mean virulence but agglutinability, in a serum made with a virulent antigen taken from man, indicates that the agglutinating strain is in the same antigenic condition as the virulent one.

Pertinent also is the experience of Gautier and others with the recurrent outbreaks of cholera in Shanghai. Here the disease stops at certain seasons of the year long before the exhaustion of susceptible material. And outside of these seasons there is no cholera—which Gautier thinks is a reliable statement because the fear of the disease is such that not even a mild case would escape notice. In the absence of obvious sources for re-introduction from other foci, he leaves it an open question whether the disease is annually imported or whether the organism is constantly endemic and fluctuates in virulence. Ross also notes that cholera, however virulent, usually dies down long before it has affected more than a moderate percentage of a population, in spite of initial rapidity of spread.

In general, the origin of small outbreaks of poliomyelitis, and particularly of scarlet fever, in isolated communities in which no previous cases have appeared may be taken to necessitate investigations of a similar nature, although here we have a more definite likelihood of a preponderant influence of generalized immunity developed by subclinical infections.

Another phase of the question is that concerned with the subsidence of epidemics in general. Gill states that plague regularly dies out toward the end of the plague season, but Brooks says that such subsidence often occurs in spite of the existence of favorable climatic conditions for transmission. Dunbar and Kisler have found that the experimental infection of rats by feeding with plague bacilli becomes impossible after the fourth feeding generation, and it is suggested by a number of German authors that the gradual subsidence of plague, in parts of Europe where rat infestation is still an important factor, can be explained only on the basis of a gradual dissociation of plague bacilli in the direction of decreased virulence.

It would, of course, be less likely that fluctuating virulence would noticeably affect the phenomena of acute epidemic outbreaks; much more likely that it might have considerable influence on the changing intensity of prolonged epidemic movements in the course of periods of years. Diphtheria and scarlet fever have noticeably diminished both in Europe and the United States since 1880, and, since then, not only has incidence diminished, but case fatality as well.

The same thing is true of smallpox, though Kisskalt found that with the enormous numerical reduction of the disease in the latter part of the nineteenth and in the twentieth century there has been an obviously large number of light cases. How much this can be attributed to the persistent effects of single vaccinations, it is impossible to say.

In regard to diphtheria and scarlet fever, the prolonged period of the downward swing would preclude the assumption of a mere change due to persistent increased community resistance. The decline in Germany began noticeably in 1890 and has continued, in spite of the war years, with a diminution, according to Kisskalt, of mortality in Germany between 1900 and 1914, of 58 per cent. The same author has noticed that the relatively immune are more frequently infected if mixed with more suspectible material.

DeRudder has studied diphtheria, scarlet fever and measles from this point of view, including in his studies the influence of "Durchseuchung," or generalized community infection, which expresses itself indirectly by a relative immunity of people over fifteen years of age. He takes the age distribution of cases as a measure of the speed with which generalized infection takes place, and by elaborate statistical studies comes to the conclusion that the speed of generalized infection is to a considerable extent dependent upon the degree of virulence of the organisms; and that the gradual increase of the age period for scarlet fever and diphtheria in the years preceding 1927 was a direct expression of the slowing down of generalized community immunization in consequence of a considerable diminution of virulence of the organisms.

A matter which has interested us particularly in our contacts with typhus outbreaks is the relationship between the number of cases—that is, morbidity—and case fatality. We are aware of the fact that case-fatality statistics are hard to obtain and relatively unreliable. Nevertheless, the fact is undeniable in some of these instances because of the wide disparity of the figures available. In the Serbian epidemic, for instance, at the height of the disease the case fatality was between 60 per cent and 70 per cent, and towards the end when, in our opinion, no adequate sanitary measures could explain the drop, the case fatality had come down to approximately 10 per cent. To some extent this is probably true of the great Russian epidemic, about which, however, statistics are too unreliable to make any reliable statement.

Ross has similar things to say about cholera. In one place there was a death rate of 80 per cent in March, which dropped to 30 per cent by August and, he generalizes, that in this disease a high virulence and case fatality occur when the disease first breaks out in a new locality, the virulence diminishing as the disease disappears.

Stallybrass states that the case fatality of pneumonia is highest at the time of its greatest prevalence, and that this is true of a number of other diseases. His studies, also, of the fatality of diphtheria and scarlet fever in Liverpool from 1900 to 1915, computed by a method adapted to that used for correct death rates, show that the effect of age on fatality was eliminated and that there was a definite indication of the fluctuation of the invading organisms. His tables on the relation of density of population to case fatality in scarlet fever and enteric fever would also indicate a dependence of case fatality upon more rapid transmission.

We believe that we have observed a similar parallelism in the drop of case fatality towards the end of meningitis epidemics, but we have no actual figures to substantiate this.

It would seem to us quite impossible to apply to such facts the mere influence of increased dosage at times of highest prevalence (which can perhaps logically be used in reasoning about conditions in experiments upon artificial outbreaks in mice), unless one regards dose as increasing directly with a dissociation diminution of highly virulent organisms.

No doubt there are many outbreaks in which case fatality does not go up and down parallel with morbidity. But in approaching the problem we have outlined Professor E. B. Wilson has applied mathematical analysis to a hypothetical epidemic in which an assumption of fluctuating virulence was made as follows: In a closed population an individual introduces an infection the virulence of which, measured by case fatality rates, diminishes, in each source of infection, progressively in the course of four days. Each case, in other words, passes a strain which has a case fatality of 0.8 for two days, 0.4 for the third day and 0.2 for the fourth day. The daily contact rate is held constant at 0.0002. Calculations of the morbidity and fatality rates on this basis resulted in curves which showed a parallelism comparable to that observed in many actual epidemics.

In addition to the factors influencing epidemics which we have discussed, there are a great many other variables, some of them of considerable importance, depending upon the complexities of community life. Variations in the habits of personal hygiene, housing, public sanitation and climates naturally exert important effects upon the spread of disease, but cannot be discussed with any degree of completeness in a short chapter. To some extent, these matters are dealt with in the sections devoted to individual diseases.

A matter that has been much discussed and upon which much experimental work has been done is that of the influence of diet. That the depression of mass resistance in times of starvation plays an enormous contributory rôle to epidemic mortality is well known. The association of famine with typhus epidemics is a classical example. Many efforts have been made, especially since the knowledge of vitamins has improved our understanding of the physiology of diet, to analyze these influences in a more or less precise manner. Many experimental studies have been published in which the deficiency of one or another of the essential vitamins has been placed under suspicion of responsibility for depressed resistance to specific infections. The old observation concerning the effect of cod liver oil in tuberculosis was the point of departure for many of these investigations. Experiments on typhus fever in guinea-pigs in our laboratory have shown that animals fed on vitamin-free diets reacted much more violently to experimental Rickettsia infections than did the well-fed normal ones. Efforts on our part to explain the variations in the susceptibility of rats and monkeys to herpes virus on the basis of vitamin deficiency, in an effort to throw light on these conditions in human encephalitis, have failed to give any precise information. Analyses of the literature, moreover, proved to be contradictory and, at the present time, while it cannot be denied that dietetic deficiencies carried to the point of early starvation formidably decrease the resistance of animals to almost all infections, there is no conclusive evidence available by which one can associate any specific vitamin deficiency with a particular susceptibility.

There are in mass or herd infections, also, many more or less vague factors in which the herd reacts differently from the individual for reasons that we cannot explain. The present tendency, however, to study epidemics experimentally and to apply methods of biological analysis justify the hope that this youngest branch of bacteriological research will advance rapidly in the coming years.[2]

It is not possible, in this place, to discuss at any length the methods by which mass infection can be diminished or controlled. This has been done to some extent in the sections dealing with the individual diseases, and it is obvious that in no two conditions can the measures be the same. From the facts of transmission, the methods of interrupting the transit of a virulent organism from source to new host can be deduced. In the accomplishment of this task the coöperation of the bacteriologist, the statistician, the administrator, the engineer and the entomologist, form the solid defenses behind the skirmish line of the practising medical profession.

2 For an authoritative discussion of this entire subject see Topley and Wilson, *Principles of Bacteriology and Immunology*, 2nd Ed., Chapter 53, p. 967, Wood and Company, London, 1936.

CHAPTER XXI

THE STAPHYLOCOCCI (MICROCOCCI)

Family: *Micrococcaceae* Pribram

Genera: *Staphylococcus, Gaffkya, Micrococcus, Sarcina.*

The power to incite purulent and seropurulent inflammations and localized abscesses in man and animals is possessed by a large variety of pathogenic bacteria. Most bacterial infections in which the relative virulence of the incitant and the resistance of the infected subject are so balanced that temporary or permanent localization of the infectious process takes place are apt to be accompanied by the formation of pus. The large majority of acute and subacute purulent processes, however, are caused by the members of a well-defined group of bacteria spoken of as the pyogenic cocci. Among these, preëminent in importance, are the *staphylococci* or *micrococci.*

Many of the earlier investigators of surgical infections had seen small round bodies in the pus discharged from abscesses and sinuses and had given them a variety of names. Careful bacteriological studies, however, were not made until 1879 and the years immediately following, when Koch, Pasteur, Ogston, and others not only described morphologically, but cultivated the cocci from surgical lesions of animals and man. Of fundamental importance are the studies published by Rosenbach in 1884, in which the technical methods of modern bacteriology were brought to bear upon this subject for the first time. The group of staphylococci—so named from their growth in irregular, grape-like clusters—is made up of several members, by far the most important of which, pathologically, is the *Staphylococcus aureus.*

STAPHYLOCOCCUS AUREUS

Genus: *Staphylococcus* Rosenbach. Species: *Staphylococcus aureus*

Morphology and Staining.—This micro-organism, the most frequent cause of abscesses, boils, and many surgical suppurations, is a spherical coccus having an average diameter of about 0.8 μ, but varying within the extreme limits of 0.4 to 1.2 μ. Any considerable variation from the average size, however, is rare. The perfectly spherical character may not develop, whenever, as is usually the case, two or more are grouped together, unseparated after cell cleavage. In this case, adjacent cocci are slightly flattened along their contiguous surfaces.

In smears from cultures or pus, the staphylococci may appear as single individuals, in pairs, or, most frequently, in irregular grape-like clusters. Occasionally, short chains of three or four may be seen. In very young cultures in fluid media, the diplococcus form may predominate.

The staphylococci stain with all the usual basic aqueous anilin dyes, and, less intensely, with some of the acid dyes. Staphylococci are gram-positive, but a few

264

gram-negative forms may occur in the midst of the clusters. Gram's method of stain-ing is excellently adapted for demonstration of these cocci in tissue sections.

Although exhibiting marked brownian movements in the hanging drop, staphylo-cocci are nonmotile and possess no flagella. They are nonsporogenous and usually do not form capsules.

Cultural Characteristics.—Staphylococci grow readily upon the usual laboratory media. The simpler media, made of meat extract, are quite as efficient for their culti-vation as are the meat-infusion products. The optimum temperature for growth lies at or about 35°C., though growth readily takes place at temperatures as low as 15° C., and as high as 40° C. Slow but definite growth has been observed at a tem-perature as low as 10° C.

The most characteristic and luxuriant growth occurs under aerobic conditions, but staphylococci are also facultatively anaerobic. They grow readily in an atmos-phere of hydrogen. The optimal reaction of the medium is pH 7.4.

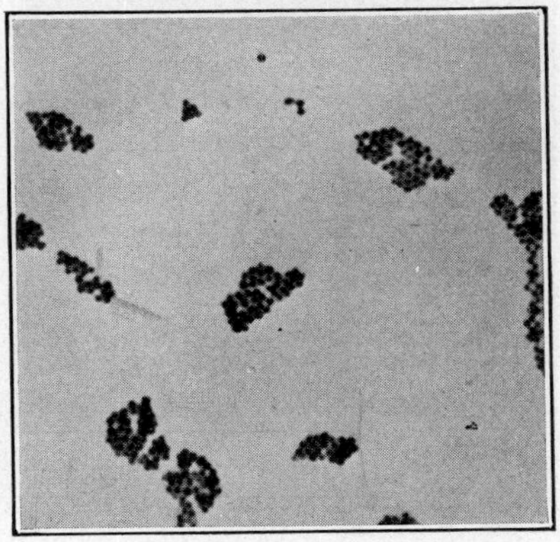

On *nutrient agar plates* the colonies are usually round 1.2 mm. in diameter, convex, opaque, glistening, with an entire edge, soft or butter-like in consistency. Typical growths have a golden yellow color, but this may vary in shade and in-tensity. Upon *agar slants* rapid growth occurs, with the production of pigment.

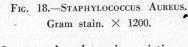

On *blood agar plates* the colonies are usually larger and in certain varieties are surrounded by zones of hemolysis. Special pathogenic prop-erties have been attributed to the hemolytic *aureus* strains.

FIG. 18.—STAPHYLOCOCCUS AUREUS.
Gram stain. × 1200.

In *gelatin stab* cultures the gelatin is liquefied in the form of a funnel-shaped depression, with final fluidification of all the medium in the tube. In general pathogenic varieties are more active liquefiers than are the saphrophytic types. The liquefaction is due to a ferment, gelatinase, which can be obtained apart from the cultures by filtration. It is an extremely thermolabile substance.

Coagulated blood-serum, as in the form of Löffler's medium, may be liquefied. This medium is excellent for growth and for the development of pigment.

In *broth,* growth is rapid, leading to a general cloudiness of the medium and, after 48 hours, to the formation of a thin surface pellicle. As growth increases, the bacteria sink to the bottom, forming a heavy mucoid sediment. The odor of old cultures is often peculiarly acrid, resembling that of weak butyric acid.

Milk is rendered acid by the fermentation of lactose.

Nitrates are reduced to *nitrites.* Litmus, methylene blue and rosaniline are de-colorized by reduction.

In *peptone water* indole is not formed, as shown by Bayne-Jones and Zinninger. In this medium the growth produces alkali.

Staphylococci *ferment* a number of carbohydrates, producing *acid, without gas,* from dextrose, lactose, maltose, mannitol and sucrose.

Many attempts have been made to devise *differential media* for the correlation of growth and biochemical activities with pathogenicity of strains of *Staphylococcus aureus*. Chapman and his associates have investigated this problem extensively, offering evidence that pathogenicity may be correlated with growth on crystal violet agar, brom-thymol-blue agar, and with the production of pigment, hemolysin, coagulase and fermentation of mannitol. In our opinion, these results are statistically indicative, but cannot supplant test on animals in individual cases.

Pigment Production.—Differences between the members of the staphylococcus group have been based largely upon the formation of pigments. The typical *Staphylococcus aureus* produces a pale yellow or golden yellow pigment. Colonies of *Staphylococcus albus* are white. Other micrococci produce bright yellow, brown or red pigments. The method of Winslow and Winslow, by which some of the growth is spread on white paper and compared with a color chart, is a useful means of determining the shade of the pigment.

FIG. 19.—COLONIES OF STAPHYLOCOCCUS AUREUS.

The pigment of *Staphylococcus aureus* is soluble in the fat solvents, alcohol, ether, chloroform and benzol and is classed as a lipochrome (Neisser). It has been suggested that this pigment may be related to the carotinoids. The pigment is not water soluble and does not diffuse into the medium.

Pigment production is not a fundamental species characteristic, as shown by Winslow, Rothberg and Parsons. For the production of pigment, *Staph. aureus* requires aerobic conditions. No pigment is produced anaerobically. On prolonged artificial cultivation pigment production is lost. Back of these changes are dissociative phenomena. The golden yellow staphylococcus may give rise to white or translucent colorless colonies associated with a variety of colony forms.

Variability.—In 1927, Biggar, Boland and O'Meara described three types of variants of *Staphylococcus aureus:* white colonies, viscid colonies, and irregular or rough colonies. Hoffstadt and Youmans, subjecting cultures to 0.5 per cent lithium chloride, ageing and animal passage, obtained from an originally smooth, yellow *Staph. aureus* eight varieties of rough colonies, differing in combinations of form and pigmentation. They obtained also the minute G-type of Hadley (Fig. 20). Organisms from the rough and G colonies fermented certain carbohydrates that were not fermentable by the original strain. The G-type organisms were said to be filterable. Reversions could be effected in sequence, in general (omitting intermediary stages), as follows: Smooth yellow → rough white → G → smooth white. There were antigenic relationships between all the types in this series. Pathogenicity, present in the original smooth yellow and certain smooth white variants, was lacking in the R and G forms. An encapsulated variant has been described by Gilbert. Capsules may be present in young broth cultures, 4 to 6 hours old, of *Staphylococcus aureus*.

Resistance.—Although staphylococci do not form spores, they are more resistant to heat than many other vegetative forms. The thermal death time of some strains is

58° C. for ten minutes, but general experience indicates that exposure to 60° C. for thirty to sixty minutes is required to kill staphylococci. They are not killed by low temperatures. When dried on threads, cloth or paper they retain vitality for six to fourteen weeks. On slant agar, at room temperature or in the ice-box, staphylococci remain alive for months.

Staphylococci undergo autolysis in suspension in broth or salt solution sealed in a tube under anaerobic conditions.

On account of the frequency and importance of staphylococci in pyogenic infections, traumatic or surgical, an immense number of studies have been made of the action of various disinfectants upon them. Many details and references are given by Neisser. A strain of *Staphylococcus aureus*, killed in ten minutes but not in five minutes, by a 1 : 90 dilution of phenol, as used in testing disinfectants by the methods of the U. S. Food and Drug Administration, may be regarded as an index of the resistance of organisms of this group to carbolic acid. Some strains are more resistant than this standard culture, others less resistant. A 1 per cent solution of phenol will kill *Staph. aureus* within fifteen minutes. The disinfectant actions of other substances are indicated approximately as follows: bichloride of mercury, 1 per cent, kills in ten minutes; hydrogen peroxide, 3 per cent, kills in two minutes; chloramine, 1 per cent, kills in two minutes; tincture of iodine kills in one minute. These are results from tests in broth. Serum and the conditions in the animal body greatly reduce the disinfectant action of these and many other

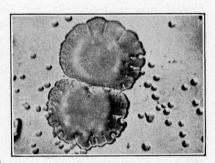

Fig. 20.—Large Rough Type Colonies Staphylococcus Aureus.

Small colonies of G forms. (From Hoffstadt and Youmans.)

substances. Growth is inhibited by boric acid 1 : 325, salicylic acid 1 : 650, bichloride of mercury 1 : 80,000, phenol 1 : 800, thymol 1 : 11,000.

Churchman showed that staphylococci were inhibited in growth and sometimes killed by basic triphenylmethane dyes. These are active bacteriostatic substances. Gentian violet 1 : 2,000,000 inhibits the growth of the staphylococcus in broth and a 1 : 125,000 dilution will inhibit growth in serum. Acriflavine, malachite green and rivanol are also strongly bacteriostatic and bactericidal for staphylococcus.

Pathogenicity.—Different strains of *Staphylococcus aureus* show wide variations in relative virulence. The most highly virulent are usually those recently isolated from human suppurative lesions, but no definite rule can be formulated in this respect. The virulence of a given strain, furthermore, may be occasionally enhanced by repeated passages through the body of a susceptible animal. Prolonged cultivation upon artificial media is likely to decrease the virulence of any given strain, though this is not regularly the case. There are, moreover, many staphylococci constantly present in the air, dust, and water, which although morphologically and culturally not unlike the pathogenically important species, may be regarded as harmless saprophytes.

The susceptibility of animals to staphylococcus infection is subject to extreme variations, depending both upon differences between species and upon fortuitous individual differences in susceptibility among animals within the same species. Animals on the whole are less susceptible to staphylococcus than is man. Among the ordinary laboratory animals, rabbits are most susceptible to this micro-organism. Mice, and especially the Japanese white mice, show considerable susceptibility. Guinea-pigs possess a relatively higher resistance.

Subcutaneous or intramuscular inoculation of a susceptible animal usually results in the formation of a localized abscess with much pus formation and eventual recovery. Intraperitoneal inoculation is more often fatal. Intravenous inoculation of doses of 0.5 c.c., or more, of fresh broth cultures of virulent staphylococci usually leads to pyemia with the production of secondary abscesses, located chiefly in the kidneys and the heart and voluntary muscles but not infrequently in other organs as well. In the kidney they occur as small foci, situated most often in the cortex, composed of a central, necrotic pus cavity, surrounded by a zone of acute inflammatory exudation. Staphylococcus lesions form histologically the typical "acute abscess." Not infrequently the pyemic condition is accompanied by suppurative lesions in the joints. Intravenous injections of virulent staphylococci preceded by injury to a bone is often followed by the development of osteomyelitis. Mechanical or chemical injury of the heart valves preceding intravascular staphylococcus inoculation may result in localization of the infection on or about the heart valves, leading to "malignant endocarditis." In rabbits all varieties of staphylococcus infection may be obtained by suitable methods of injection. If, for instance, a rabbit is given 0.5 to 1 c.c. of a young broth culture, from which the clumps have been gently centrifuged down, into the ear vein, a rapid fatal septicemia will result with organisms in the heart's blood, but no secondary localization or abscess formation. If, however, staphylococcus cultures containing clumps are gently centrifuged, the supernatant fluid taken off, and small clumps injected in not too large amounts (and the amounts must be adjusted to the virulence of the culture) the animal will pass through a protracted illness, with secondary abscess formation in kidneys, liver and other organs, in which emboli have been formed, a condition simulating accurately pyemia in human beings. The pyemic conditions following staphylococcus inoculation usually lead to chronic emaciation and death after an interval dependent upon the relative virulence of the microorganism, the amount injected, and the resistance of the infected subject.

The susceptibility of man to spontaneous staphylococcus infection is decidedly more marked than is that of animals. The form of infection most frequently observed is the common *boil* or *furuncle*. As Garré and others have demonstrated by experiments upon their own bodies, energetic rubbing of the skin with virulent staphylococcus cultures may often be followed by the development of furuncles. Subcutaneous inoculation of the human subject may give rise to an abscess, or fatal septicemia or toxemia (Burnet). The organisms are apparently present on the skin of human beings with great frequency, and it is not unlikely that in the course of daily life, they may be rubbed into hair follicles and sweat glands, and be present constantly on some part of the body, prepared for immediate invasion if an abrasion or other accident furnishes the opportunity. A simple and frequent disease, furunculosis, is, nevertheless, a condition about the pathogenesis of which we are considerably in the dark. Reductions of general resistance, especially those accompanying overwork, indoor occupations, and faulty diet, seem to be concerned in furnishing the proper conditions for invasion by the ever present staphylococci. General metabolic diseases, such as nephritis and especially diabetes, render the individual abnormally susceptible. In certain instances it has been suggested, especially by Wright, that reduction in coagulation time of the blood might influence this state of affairs.

Staphylococcus lesions of the skin are characteristic in that, after an induration, there occurs a central softening with the formation of liquid pus. It is an important observation, confirmed by much experience, that if incision is practised in the indurated and inflamed tissue before the process has come to a central head, infection is usually spread, perhaps by the opening of adjacent lymphatics. Therefore, there is much judgment required in treating even these simple lesions. Faulty surgical interference may easily convert a simple furuncle into a dangerous carbuncle.

Common among staphylococcus skin infections is *paronychia,* or infection of the nail bed of the fingers. This may often lead to troublesome extension up the fingers and into the hands. It is a cause of *conjunctivitis,* infections of the eyelids, and other ocular infections.

Especially dangerous are boils about the nose and lips, and not infrequently infections in these locations may extend rapidly, and cause fatal septicemia.

Some forms of *impetigo contagiosum,* a skin disease consisting of boil-like inflamed papules and vesicles and occurring particularly in young children, are caused by staphylococci.

In suppurative lesions of the bones, or *osteomyelitis,* staphylococci are the most frequent causative agents. This may result, after compound fracture, by infection from without, or not infrequently staphylococci will lodge in the site of mechanical injury of bone or fracture, reaching the focus through the circulation. The lesions produced in bone may consist of slow localized abscesses, or may extend along the medullary canal of the entire bone.

In addition to these most common lesions, staphylococci may cause abscesses in almost any part of the body. In cases in which resistance is low and the staphylococci particularly virulent, septicemia may follow in any of these. Unlike the rapid, acute septicemic death, however, which is likely to ensue when similar general infection with streptococci takes place, staphylococcus generalization is apt to lead to secondary foci in kidneys, liver and other organs. This leads to the condition of pyemia in which an irregular septic temperature with frequent chills is characteristic. Blood culture in such cases will give a clue to the nature of the infection. The mortality is high, 60 to 90 per cent (Parish and Clark).

Ascending infections of the genito-urinary tract, cystitis and pyelonephritis, may be caused by staphylococci.

Staphylococcus empyema and peritonitis are not particularly common, but may occur.

Puerperal sepsis, while not as commonly a staphylococcus infection as it is a streptococcic disease, may occur.

By some writers staphylococci have been held responsible for rheumatism, but there is no convincing evidence of this.

Staphylococci may also appear in meningitis. It is a curious fact that occasionally a very low-grade staphylococcus may get into the meninges, and cause a very slow and apparently mild meningitis. We have seen one such case caused by a *Staphylo-*

coccus albus recover, and another which died after a prolonged illness in which the organisms were repeatedly isolated from the spinal fluid, and, at autopsy, in which the origin was a cerebellar abscess.

Prolonged chronic infection with staphylococci may give rise to the so-called amyloid changes in liver, spleen and kidneys.

Toxic Products.—*Endotoxins.*—The dead bodies of staphylococci injected into animals may occasionally give rise to abscess formation and death. To obtain the latter result, however, large quantities are necessary, the endotoxic substances within the dead cell-bodies of these micro-organisms being neither very poisonous nor abundant (von Lingelsheim). The anaerobic autolysate of staphylococci has little or no toxicity (Burky).

Borrisow showed clearly that dead cells of *Staph. aureus* exert a strong positive chemotaxis for leukocytes.

The organisms and products derived from staphylococci in broth culture coagulate plasma. This material called *plasmacoagulase* or *staphylokinase*, studied by Gratia and Bordet, Gross and others, may be concerned in the formation of thrombi and emboli common in staphylococcus septicemia.

Broth cultures of virulent staphylococci may contain *fibrinolysin.*

Duran-Reynals discovered that invasive strains of staphylococcus and streptococcus contain a soluble substance which markedly increases tissue permeability and enhances the infections produced by these organisms, by other bacteria, and by vaccine virus. Insufficient attention has been given to the action of this *spreading factor* in the development of infectious processes.

Exotoxin.—The filtrates of cultures of certain strains of *Staphylococcus aureus* and *albus* are poisonous. As five different toxic effects have been well described, these filtrates contain either five distinct toxins or one antigenic toxin with at least five distinct actions. The evidence seems to indicate that there are several different poisons in such filtrates. They are called exotoxins because they are obtainable in broth cultures and because they lead to the production of antitoxins when injected into animals. Assuming that the effects denote separate substances, they may be listed as follows: (1) hemolysin, (2) leukocidin, (3) necrotizing toxin, (4) lethal toxin, and (5) gastro-enteric toxin concerned in food-poisoning.

Hemolysin.—In 1900, Kraus and Clairmont first noticed the hemolytic action of staphylococci on blood agar and showed that the filtrate dissolved erythrocytes. These observations were confirmed and extended by Neisser and Wechsberg. Hemolysin is produced by *Staphylococcus aureus* and, to a lesser degree, by *Staphylococcus albus*. The quantity produced varies with different strains and, contrary to the earlier opinions, is only approximately proportional to virulence and lethal toxicity. Burky's experiments showed that the lethal factor was produced in cultures independently of the hemolysin. A great many strains of staphylococci, isolated from human lesions, produce no hemolysin. But absolutely avirulent races do not, as far as we know, produce hemolysin.

The most favorable medium for hemolysin production is slightly alkaline meat infusion broth, "hormone" medium or Walbum's medium, which is a buffered phosphate peptone bouillon, containing 0.2 per cent KH_2PO_4 and 0.03 per cent $MgSO_4.7H_2O$, pH 7.4. The maximum amount of hemolysin is found in the broth from the eighth to the fourteenth day, and this may be separated from the bacteria by filtration through Berkefeld or Chamberland filters. The hemolytic action can be observed and titrated by adding 0.25 c.c. of washed red corpuscles to 1 c.c. of a series of dilutions of the filtrate. It is important to wash the red corpuscles thoroughly, to free them from serum, since Kraus showed that normal serum may contain antihemolysin. The red corpuscles of rabbits, dogs and guinea-pigs are more susceptible than those of man to the action of staphylohemolysin.

Staphylohemolysin is inactivated by heat at 60° C. in 20 minutes.

Antistaphylohemolysin formation is easily induced by subcutaneous inoculation of the staphylohemolysin into rabbits.

The work of Glenny and Stevens in 1935 cleared up confusion by showing that staphylococci produce at least two kinds of hemolysin. These are obtainable from filtrates, have different actions and are antigenically separable. The first type, called α-hemolysin, hemolyzes rabbit and sheep corpuscles at 37° C.; the second type, called β-hemolysin and also "hot-cold" hemolysin, hemolyzes sheep corpuscles only when the preliminary incubation at 37° C. was followed by cooling. This does not hemolyze rabbit corpuscles. Roy has identified the staphylococcal hemolysin which acts on human erythrocytes as β-hemolysin.

Leukocidin.—In 1894, Van de Velde discovered that the pleural exudate of rabbits following the injection of virulent staphylococci, showed marked evidences of leukocyte destruction. He was subsequently able to show that the substance causing the death and partial solution of the leukocytes was a soluble toxin formed by the staphylococcus, not only *in vivo*, but *in vitro* as well; for cultures of *Staphylococcus aureus,* grown in mixtures of bouillon and blood-serum, contained, within forty-eight hours, marked quantities of this "leukocidin." To obtain the leukocidin free from bacteria, the cultures are passed through Chamberland or Berkefeld filters, after about eight to eleven days' growth at 37° C., at which time the contents in leukocidin are usually at their highest point.

The action of leukocidin upon leukocytes may be observed *in vivo* by the simple method of Van de Velde, of injecting virulent staphylococci intrapleurally into rabbits and examining the exudate. Bail advised the production of leukocytic intrapleural exudates by the use of aleuronat and following this after twenty-four hours by an injection of leukocidin-filtrate. *In vitro* the phenomenon may be observed by direct examination of mixtures of leukocytes and leukocidin in the hanging drop on a warmed stage, or by the methylene-blue method of Neisser and Wechsberg. This method is based upon the fact that living leukocytes will reduce methylene-blue solutions and render them colorless, while dead leukocytes have lost this power. Leukocidin and leukocytes are allowed to remain in contact for a given time and to them is then added dilute solution of methylene blue. If the leukocytes have been actively attacked by leukocidin, no reduction takes place. This method is particularly adapted for quantitative tests.

All staphylococcus strains do not produce leukocidin to the same degree. Almost all true *Staphylococcus aureus* cultures produce some of this toxin, but one strain may produce fifty- and a hundred-fold the quantity produced by another. *Staphylococcus albus* gives rise to this substance but rarely, and then in small quantity.

Leukocidin seems to be similar to the soluble toxins of other bacteria. It is rapidly destroyed by heat at 58° C., and deteriorates quickly in culture fluids at incubator temperatures. It is distinct from staphylohemolysin as shown by differences in thermostability and independent production.

Soon after Van de Velde's discovery of leukocidin, Denys and Van de Velde produced an antileukocidin by treating rabbits with pleural exudate containing leukocidin. Neisser and Wechsberg later confirmed these results and showed that among staphylococci, leukocidin is not specific, the toxin of all strains of *Staphylococcus aureus* and *albus* examined being neutralizable by the same antileukocidin. Antileukocidin is often found in the normal sera of horses and man.

Leukocidin should not be confounded with "leukotoxin," a substance obtained in serum by treatment of animals with leukocytes, a true "cytotoxin," having no connection whatever with the staphylococcus.

Necrotizing Toxin.—In 1924, Parker obtained from filtrates of *Staphylococcus aureus*, grown on a modified Walbum's medium, an extremely labile exotoxin which produced necrosis when injected into the skin of rabbits. Since then numerous investigators have confirmed Parker's results. The lesion produced by the intradermally injected toxin is at first red, then becomes swollen, infiltrated with leukocytes and is not unlike an abscess. Necrosis usually occurs in two to five days. Burky has shown that not all rabbits react to this necrotizing substance in the same way, and has suggested that the failure of growth of hair of rabbits after barium sulphide depilation can be used as an indication of the rabbit's reactivity, which he finds is probably an expression of some hereditary quality. The necrotizing toxin prepared by Parker in 1924 did not kill rabbits. Parker discovered that the intradermal injection of this toxin produced immunity through the elaboration of an effective antitoxin.

Parker's investigations of skin reactivity to filtrates were prompted by the discovery of the Dick test with filtrates of scarlet fever streptococci. Skin tests with staphylococcal filtrates have been made by several workers with results only roughly analogous to those obtained by Dick and Schick tests in animals and man. The newborn animal is refractory, and with each successive year more and more animals in a group become sensitive to this staphylococcus skin-affecting or necrotizing toxin. Kobak and Pilot have shown this for man, finding that while all the mothers reacted to the toxin, none of the newborn children was susceptible. By the end of the first year 65 per cent of these children gave positive reactions. Burky showed that rabbits four months old or younger are not susceptible to the skin-necrotizing toxin, and at the same time these young rabbits were not susceptible to the lethal toxin. Evidently there is an unsolved problem of bacterial allergy disclosed here. The condition is the more complex since Bryce and Burnet, by titrations of antihemolysin in human blood, have traced a passive transfer of antitoxin from the mother to the fetus, a rapid fall in antihemolysin during the early weeks of life, and then a gradual reacquisition of humoral immunity during childhood. Burnet, who believes in the unitarian nature of staphylococcal toxin, regards this as a curve of the course of natural immunity. In contrast to this, Burky demonstrated a refractory state independent of humoral antibodies.

Lethal Toxin.—Kraus and Pribram, in 1906, discovered that the intravenous injection of the filtrates of broth cultures of certain strains of *Staphylococcus aureus* killed rabbits in five to thirty minutes. The fatal doses of their toxin was 1 to 2 c.c. per kilogram. Complete protection was secured by use of an appropriate antitoxin. Similar results were obtained by Nicolle and Césari in 1914. An antitoxin prepared by them against the filtrate of one strain neutralized the toxins of other strains of staphylococci. Russ, who studied this toxin and attempted to purify it in 1916, determined that the toxin acted upon the heart and damaged the capillary vessels in the lungs. The Bundaberg disaster in Australia in 1928, in which 12 out of 21 children died within twenty-four hours after the subcutaneous injection of a diphtheria-toxin-antitoxin preparation contaminated by *Staph. aureus*, revived interest in this subject. It was determined that these children died of acute staphylococcal intoxication. Burnet's studies, originating in the investigation of this accident, have added considerably to the knowledge of the lethal toxin produced by staphylococci. Burnet has obtained potent lethal toxin from broth cultures, and from semisolid agar cultures incubated eight to ten days in an atmosphere of 25 per cent CO_2. Burnet concluded that all the toxic effects of the filtrates could be attributable to the action of a single toxic substance. Parker, Weld and Burky, however, clearly showed that the poisons are produced independently of each other and can be absorbed separately by different antigens. They have concluded that at least the hemolytic and rapidly lethal toxins are distinct.

The strains of staphylococci found by Burky to be active producers of this lethal toxin were isolated from conjunctivae of man. The most active strain, a variety of *Staph. aureus*, produced a toxin which in doses of 0.25 to 0.5 c.c. per kilogram killed susceptible rabbits in a few minutes or within twenty-four hours. The toxin was obtained under aerobic conditions from broth cultures and from cultures in Uschinsky's synthetic medium containing asparagin and ammonium lactate as the only sources of nitrogen. After two years of artificial cultivation, this strain of staphylococcus exhibited increase in toxin production, with decreased production of hemolysin. Intradermal injection of the toxin led to the production of antitoxin. These studies open fields of new possibilities in prophylactic immunization and antitoxic serum therapy.

The *allergic phenomena* associated with the actions of staphylococci and their toxins are under investigation by Burky and others. Panton and Valentine have suggested that staphylococcal infection of the skin lowers the minimal infecting dose of the organism and that this increased sensitivity may result in further skin lesions in spite of concomitant production of antibacterial and antitoxic substances.

In 1933 Burky showed that rabbits given intravenous injections of staphylococcal toxin developed not only specific antitoxin but also a state of hypersensitiveness to the broth in which the toxin was produced. Similar effects were obtained by filtrates of cultures in media containing extract of the crystalline lens of the eye. Animals injected with lens broth toxin became allergic to lens protein and later desensitized. Staphylococcus toxin combined with low ragweed extract produced precipitins for low ragweed in the rabbit, and such injected animals had anaphylactic-like symptoms when dusted with low ragweed pollen. These newly observed phenomena have not yet been explained. But it is recognized that they have significance for both theoretical and practical immunology. In practice the information has been applied with beneficial results in the treatment of ocular infections.

Food Poisoning.—Formerly it was thought that certain varieties of paratyphoid bacilli and *Bacillus botulinus* were the only causes of the most common types of food poisoning. In 1914, however, Barber attributed the toxic symptoms of milk poisoning to a type of *Staphylococcus albus*. In 1930, Jordan, and Dack and his associates discovered that *Staphylococcus aureus* was responsible for outbreaks of food poisoning among persons who had eaten cake, milk and other products containing the staphylococcus. It was proved by tests on man and monkeys that the symptoms, vomiting, gastro-enteritis, diarrhea, fever and collapse, were due to a toxin elaborated by the staphylococcus. Immunization was produced by subcutaneous injection, but this protection was not transferable by injection of the serum of an immunized monkey. The substance appears to be an exotoxin with somewhat special properties. Jordan and McBroom, Woolpert and Dack showed that this toxin is distinct from hemolysin, dermatoxin and the lethal toxin. It is more resistant than these to heat but is unable to withstand boiling.

Immunization and Serology.—Animals, including man, can be actively immunized by repeated injections of graded doses of dead staphylococci. Some immunity together with a moderate hypersensitivity occurs after injection or infection with living organisms. A moderately successful form of vaccine therapy has been based on this knowledge. Since the work of Wright, *active immunization* of human beings suffering from chronic staphylococcus infections has been extensively practised. The material used as the vaccine has in most instances been a heat-killed (60° C. for one-half to one hour) saline suspension of autogenous culture of a staphylococcus. The procedure has been demonstrated to be of considerable therapeutic value.

Staphylococcus toxin has been used successfully in human beings by Burky for the treatment of styes, boils and chronic and acute staphylococcal infections. The therapeutic value of antitoxin remains to be determined.

Staphylococcus toxoids produced by formalin treatment of toxic filtrates have been used for active immunization. A summary of clinical results published in 1935 by Murray indicates that such toxoids may be of value in the treatment of chronic pyodermia, but have been disappointing in the more acute forms of furunculosis and in osteomyelitis. The antibacterial sera used in the past for *passive immunization* have not been successful.

Leukocytic extracts were used with success by Hiss and Zinsser in the treatment of a number of staphylococcus infections in man.

The injection of staphylococci into animals causes the production of agglutinins, precipitins and other antibodies. By means of the reactions between these antibodies and the whole organisms, or with their protein, lipoid and carbohydrate fractions, Goadby, Julianelle, Thompson and Khorazo, and others have attempted to establish antigenic and *serological groupings* of strains of *Staphylococcus aureus*. Agglutination failed to demonstrate sharply defined serological types. A soluble specific substance appears to be a more discriminatory type of antigen. By use of this carbohydrate Julianelle and his associates have defined two main types, A and B, of which Type A appears to include most of the pathogenic varieties. These groupings overlap distinctions based upon metabolism, pigment production and pathogenicity. Furthermore, the variability of the organism must be kept constantly in view in these considerations.

STAPHYLOCOCCUS ALBUS

Genus: *Staphylococcus* Rosenbach. Species: *Staphylococcus albus*

Staphylococcus albus differs from *Staphylococcus aureus* simply in the absence of the golden yellow coloration of its cultures. Morphologically, culturally, and pathogenically, it is every way similar to the staphylococcus described in the preceding section, but its toxin- and enzyme-producing powers in general are less developed than those of the aureus variety. Its close biological relationship to *Staph. aureus* is furthermore demonstrated by its agglutination in *Staphylococcus aureus* immune sera.

Staphylococcus epidermidis albus.—The *Staphylococcus epidermidis albus* described by Welch is merely one of the nonpathogenic varieties of *Staphylococcus albus* and possibly does not deserve separate classification. It may give rise to minor lesions, especially stitch abscesses.

STAPHYLOCOCCUS CITREUS

Genus: *Staphylococcus* Rosenbach. Species: *Staphylococcus citreus*

Staphylococcus citreus produces a bright yellow or lemon-colored pigment of distinctly different hue from that of *Staphylococcus aureus*. It may be pyogenic and in every way similar to *Staphylococcus aureus*, but is less often found in connection with pathological lesions than either of the preceding *staphylococci*.

A large number of staphylococci, differing from those described above in one or another detail, have been observed. They are of common occurrence and are met with chiefly as contaminations in the course of bacteriological work. Few of these have any pathological significance and none of them are toxin-producers, so far as we know. Many of them differ, furthermore, in their inability to liquefy gelatin.

Atypical pathogenic staphylococci have been described by a number of observers.

MICROCOCCUS TETRAGENUS

Genus: *Gaffkya* Trevisan

Type Species: *Gaffkya tetragena*

In 1881, Gaffky discovered a micrococcus which occurs regularly in groups of four or tetrads. He first isolated it from the pus discharged by tuberculous patients with pulmonary lesions. Observed in smear preparations from pus, the tetrads are slightly larger in size than the ordinary staphylococcus, flattened along their adjacent surfaces and surrounded by a thick halo-like capsule. Preparations from cultures often lack these capsules. The micrococcus is easily stained by the usual basic aniline dyes. Stained by Gram's method, it is not decolorized, retaining the gentian violet. It is usually metachromatic.

Cultivation.—*Micrococcus tetragenus* grows on the ordinary laboratory media, showing a rather more delicate growth than do the staphylococci.

On agar, the colonies are grayish-white. They are not more transparent than are staphylococcus colonies.

On gelatin, growth is rather slow.

The gelatin is not usually liquefied, but one of Reimann's strains produced marked liquefaction.

Broth is evenly clouded. On potato there is a white, moist growth which shows a tendency to confluence.

Milk is not coagulated. Acid is formed.

Pathogenicity.—*Micrococcus tetragenus*, according to Reimann, is not virulent for Japanese mice, as formerly reported. Guinea-pigs and rabbits show only a localized reaction at the point of inoculation. The organism has occasionally been isolated from spontaneous abscesses observed in domestic animals.

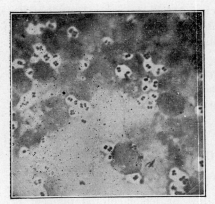

FIG. 21.—MICROCOCCUS TETRAGENUS.

In man, *Micrococcus tetragenus* is usually found without any pathological significance in sputum or saliva. The organism has been found occasionally in the blood in septicemia, in the pus of abscesses and in the spinal fluid in meningitis, indicating that some strains may be pathogenic for man.

In 1935, Reimann described a nonfatal case of *M. tetragenus* infection with septicemia, purulent arthritis and meningitis. In a review of the literature he found records of more than 170 cases of infection with this organism. From the cultures of the organism isolated from the blood, pus and spinal fluid of his patient, Reimann obtained more than fifteen from the typical white colony. One was yellow; others were pink, brown or translucent. The biological characteristics of the variants differed in a number of respects, in a manner which suggested an explanation of the contradictory criteria of a number of investigators who have studied the differentiation of *M. tetragenus* from staphylococci. The variants show so much instability and so many changes that a complete account of the behavior of this organism would require separate discussion of each type and phase of culture.

REFERENCES

BAIL, O. Arch. f. Hyg., 1897, 30:348.
BARBER, M. A. Philippine J. Sc., 1914, 9:515.
BAYNE-JONES, S., and ZINNINGER, P. Johns Hopkins Hosp. Bull., 1921, 32:299.
BIGGAR, J. W., BOLAND, C. R., and O'MEARA, R. A. J. Path. & Bacteriol., 1927, 30:261, 271.
BORRISOW, P. Beitr. z. path. Anat. u. z. allgem. Path., 1894, 16:432.
BRYCE, L. M., and BURNET, F. M. J. Path. & Bacteriol., 1932, 35:183.
BURKY, E. L. J. Immunol., 1933, 24:93, 115, 127; 1933, 25:419.
———— J. Allergy, 1934, 5:466.
———— Arch. Ophthalmol., 1934, 12:536.
———— J. Ophthalmol., 1936, 19:782, 841.
BURNET, F. M. J. Path. & Bacteriol., 1929, 32:717; 1930, 33:1; 1931, 34:471.
CHAPMAN, G. H., BERENS, C., NILSON, E. L., and CURCIO, L. G. J. Bacteriol., 1938, 35:311.
CHURCHMAN, J. W. J. Exper. M., 1912, 16:221; 1923, 37:543.
DACK, G. M., CARY, W. E., WOOLPERT, O., and WIGGERS, H. J. Prevent. M., 1930, 4:167.
DENYS, J., and VAN DE VELDE. La Cellule, 1895, 11:Fasc. 2:357.
DURAN-REYNALS, F. J. Exper. M., 1933, 58:161; 1935, 61:617.
GAFFKY, G. Mitt. a.d. Kaiserl. Gsndhtsamte, 1881, 1.

GILBERT, I. J. Bacteriol., 1931, 21:157.

GLENNY, A. T., and STEVENS, M. F. J. Pathol. and Bacteriol., 1935, 40:201.

GOADBY, K. W. J. Path. & Bacteriol., 1932, 35:657.

GRATIA, A., and BORDET, J. Compt. rend. Soc. de biol., 1920, 83:585.

GROSS, H. Ztschr. f. Immunitätsforsch. u. exper. Therap., 1932, 73:14.

HINE, T. G. M. Lancet, 1922, 2:1380.

HISS, P. H., and ZINSSER, H. J. Med. Research. 1909, 20:245.

HOFFSTADT, R., and YOUMANS, G. P. J. Infect. Dis., 1932, 51:216.

HOME, W. E. Lancet, 1909, 1:1715.

JAUMAIN, D. Compt. rend. Soc. de biol., 1922, 87:790.

JORDAN, E. O. J. Am. M. Ass., 1930, 94:1648.

JORDAN, E. O., and McBROOM, J. Proc. Soc. Exper. Biol. & Med., 1931, 29:161.

JULIANELLE, L. A., and WIEGHARD, C. W. J. Exper. M., 1935, 62:11, 23, 31.

KOBAK, A. J., and PILOT, I. Proc. Soc. Exper. Biol. & Med., 1931, 28:584.

KRAUS, R. Wien. klin. Wchnschr., 1902, 15:382.

KRAUS, R., and CLAIRMONT, P. Wien. klin. Wchnschr., 1900, 13:49; 1901, 14:1016.

KRAUS, R., and PRIBRAM, E. Wien. klin. Wchnschr., 1906, 19:493.

LANNER, E., and SCHÖNSLEBEN, G. Arch. f. Hyg., 1922, 91:349.

LOEB, A. Centralbl. Bakteriol., I Abt., 1902, 32:471.

MORGENROTH, J., SCHNITZER, R., and BERGER, E. Klin. Wchnschr., 1923, 2:1633.

MURRAY, D. S. Lancet, 1935, 1:303.

NEISSER, M. Die Staphylokokken, Handb. d. pathog. Mikroorganismen, edited by W. Kolle, R. Kraus and P. Uhlenhuth, 3rd ed., Berlin, 1928, 4: Chap. V, pp. 437-510.

NEISSER, M., and WECHSBERG, F. Ztschr. f. Hyg. u. Infektionskrankh., 1901, 36:299.

——— and Hartman, A. F. J. Exper. M., 1936, 63:149.

NICOLLE, M., and CÉSARI, E. Ann. de l'Inst. Pasteur, 1914, 28:219.

OGSTON, A. Arch. f. klin. Chir., 1880, 25:588.

——— Brit. M. J., 1881, 1:369.

PANTON, P. N., and VALENTINE, F. C. O. Brit. J. Exper. Pathol., 1929, 10:257.

PARISH, H. J., and CLARK, W. H. M. J. Path. & Bacteriol., 1932, 35:251.

PARKER, J. T. J. Exper. M., 1924, 40:761.

REIMANN, H. A., J. Clin. Investigation, 1935, 14:311, 807. J. Bacteriol., 1936, 31:385, 407; 1937, 33:499, 513.

ROSENBACH. Microorganismen bei den Wundinfektionskrankheiten des Menschen, Wiesbaden, 1884.

ROY, T. E. J. Immunol., 1937, 33:437.

RUSS, V. K. Ztschr. f. Exper. Path. u. Therap., 1916, 18:220.

THOMPSON, R., and KHORAZO, D. J. Bacteriol., 1937, 34:69.

VAN DE VELDE, H. La Cellule, 1894, 10: Fasc. 2, 401.

VON LINGELSHEIM. Atiologie u. Therapie d. Staphylokokken Infektion, Berlin-Wien, 1900.

WALBUM, L. E. Biochem. Ztschr., 1922, 129:367.

WELCH, W. H. Am. J. M. Sc., 1891, 102:439.

WELD, PARKER, and GUNTER, A. J. Exper. M., 1931, 54:315.

WINSLOW, C.-E. A., ROTHBERG, W., and PARSONS, E. I. J. Bacteriol., 1920, 5:145.

WINSLOW, C.-E. A., and WINSLOW, A. R. The Systematic Relationships of the Coccaceae, New York, 1908.

WOOLPERT, O. C., and DACK, G. M. J. Infect. Dis., 1933, 52:6.

CHAPTER XXII

THE STREPTOCOCCI

Family: *Lactobacteriaceae* Orla-Jensen. Tribe: *Streptococceae* Trevisan. Genus: *Streptococcus* Rosenbach. Type Species: *Streptococcus pyogenes* Rosenbach

Among the pyogenic cocci, there is a large and important group of organisms which multiply by division in one plane of space only, and thus give rise to appearances not unlike chains or strings of beads. The term *streptococcus* or *chain-coccus* is, therefore, a purely morphological one which includes within its limits microorganisms which may differ from each other considerably, both as to cultural and pathogenic properties. Thus, cocci which form chains may be isolated from water, milk, dust, and the feces of animals and man. These may have little but their morphological appearance in common with the pyogenic streptococci which are so important as the incitants of disease.

Within this large morphological group, distinctions of species or varieties have been made upon differences in fermentation of carbohydrates, effect upon blood cells and other substrates, pathogenicity and the antigenic differences disclosed by immunological and serological analysis. But even with information from all these sources it is not possible practically or scientifically always to recognize fixed species among the streptococci. There is much overlapping of characteristics among members of this group and a considerable degree of variability exists. The interrelationship between streptococci from different sources and the range of streptococcal variability are by no means fully understood. Those relationships were discussed thoroughly by Sherman in 1937.

In this chapter we shall discuss the pathogenic group as a whole. In the following chapter we shall consider in some detail the relation of streptococci to scarlet fever, erysipelas, suppurative and septicemic conditions and several other important diseases of man.

The same researches which led to the discovery of the staphylococci laid the basis for our knowledge of the streptococci. It is clear from Pasteur's discussion of puerperal sepsis that he recognized the streptococcus in 1878-79. At about the same time Koch saw the organism in pus from wound infections. Ogston was the first to differentiate clearly between the irregularly grouped staphylococci and chain-cocci.

Pure cultures of streptococci were obtained first by Fehleisen in 1883 and by Rosenbach in 1884. Adopting the term "streptococcus," previously introduced by Billroth, Rosenbach gave the name *Streptococcus pyogenes* to the variety of the organism isolated by him from suppurative lesions. These researches, followed by the investigations of Passet, placed the knowledge of the pathogenic properties of streptococci upon a scientific basis.

Since the time of these early studies a great many important discoveries of the actions and properties of streptococci have been made. For general reviews of historical information we refer the reader to the publications of the Thomsons, Williams, von Lingelsheim, Sherman, and McLeod and his collaborators.

Morphology and Staining.—The individual streptococcus is a spherical micro-organism measuring from 0.5 μ to 1 μ in diameter. Since the line of cleavage of cocci, when in chains, is perpendicular to the long axis of the chain, adjacent cocci often show slight flattening of the contiguous surfaces, forming, as it were, a series of diplococci arranged end to end. As a general rule the streptococci pathogenic for man, when grown upon favorable fluid and certain solid media, have a tendency to form chains made up of at least eight or more individuals, while the more sapro-phytic, less pathogenic varieties are apt to be united in shorter groups. Upon this basis a rough morphological distinction was made by von Lingelsheim, who first employed the terms *Streptococcus longus* and *brevis*. A differentiation of this kind can hardly be relied upon, however, since the length of chains is to some degree dependent upon cultural and other environmental conditions.

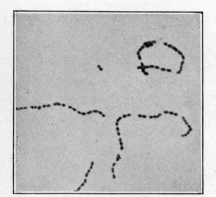

FIG. 22.—STREPTOCOCCUS HEMOLYTICUS.
Gram stain. $\times$ 1200.

True hemolytic streptococci may form cap-sules which are noticeable in smears from in-fected animals and in early cultures made upon media rich in animal fluids, but may be lost on subsequent transplantation to simpler media. The capsule here is an attribute of virulence. Seastone has found that in a serum medium streptococci may show capsules in very young cultures. As the culture ages these capsules disappear.

Streptococci do not form spores, are nonmotile, and do not possess flagella.

Change in the size and appearance of strepto-cocci may be noticed under different conditions of cultivation. Streptococci which have grown under anaerobic conditions will often show chains of the organisms of minute size. We have seen, interspersed with chains of the ordinary appearance, individual chains composed of organisms almost as small as the globoid bodies of Noguchi. It is probably these small individuals which appear under anaerobic conditions that have been responsible for Rosenow's ideas concerning the etiological rôle of streptococci in poliomyelitis. In old cultures there may be either at the ends or even in the middle of the chains, large, swollen individuals, almost as big as small yeast cells. Sometimes the cells at the ends of chains and interspersed along the chains are elongated and club-shaped, resembling diphtheroids. These swollen and bacillary forms have been interpreted as involution forms. They have also been regarded as indication of possible phylogenetic relations of the streptococci to the actinomycetes and corynebacteria. Their significance is not understood.

Streptococci are easily stained by the usual anilin dyes. They are typically gram-positive, but show variations in gram staining. The hemolytic varieties are more easily decolorized than the viridans types. In cultures a few days old most of the organisms are gram-negative. Certain varieties described as being gram-negative may be found in feces.

Cultivation.—The pyogenic streptococci are easily cultivated upon all the richer artificial media. While meat extract-peptone media may suffice for certain strains, it is usually better to employ those media which have the beef or veal infusion for a basis. For the cultivation of more delicate strains of streptococci it is well to add to the media animal protein in the form of whole blood, blood serum, or ascitic or pleural transudates. Glucose, added in proportions of 0.5 per cent, likewise renders media more favorable for streptococcus cultivation. Prolonged cultivation of all races upon artificial media renders them less fastidious as to cultural requirements. The most favorable reaction of media for streptococcus cultivation is moderate alkalinity (pH 7.4 to 7.6). Growth may be readily obtained, however, in neutral media or even in those slightly acid. The optimum temperature for growth is at or about 37.5°. Above 43° to 45° C., development ceases. At from 15° to 20° C., growth, while not energetic, still takes place. While the free access of oxygen furnishes the most suitable environment, complete anaerobiosis does not prevent development and a marked diminution of size may be seen under these conditions.

Strictly *anaerobic* streptococci have been isolated from the intestinal tract, the vagina, puerperal sepsis, granulomatous ulcers and other infections (Perrone, Schweitzer, Colebrook, McLeod). The systematists have not split the genus *Streptococcus* into two genera on the basis of oxygen requirements, as was done in the case of the aerobic and anaerobic bacilli. There are many micro-aerophilic types between the aerobes and anaerobes in both of these groups. Meleney has described several varieties of micro-aerophilic streptococci which he has found to be associated with infectious gangrene of the skin.

Anaerobic streptococci have been isolated alone from the pleural cavity of patients with chronic empyema. The micro-aerophilic form is frequently found in association with staphylococci, or, in certain types of infectious gangrene of the skin, it is found alone. In these cases, the streptococci are most easily obtained from the necrotic, subcutaneous fat. Wound abscesses following operations upon the upper gastro-intestinal tract and appendix abscesses show a high incidence of streptococcus contamination when the pus is cultured anaerobically. Cases of chronic superficial infections of the extremities have been shown to contain a form of streptococcus which could be grown at first only by aerobic cultivation at room temperature. All of these cultural variants rapidly adapt themselves to growth at 37° C. aerobically, hence these observations are of importance only for primary isolation.

In alkaline bouillon at 37.5° C., pyogenic streptococci grow rapidly, the *hemolyticus* forming long chains and having a tendency to form flakes which sink to the bottom. Diffuse clouding or homogeneous stable suspensions are associated with growth in short chains or pairs of cocci.

When sugar has been added to the broth the rapid formation of lactic acid soon interferes with extensive development. This may be obviated when mass cultures are desired by adding to the sugar broth 1 per cent of sterile powdered calcium carbonate.

In milk, *Streptococcus pyogenes* grows readily with the formation of acid, followed, in most cases, by coagulation of the medium.

On suitable agar plates at 37.5° C., growth appears within eighteen to twenty-four hours. The colonies are small, grayish, and delicately opalescent. They are round with smooth or very slightly corrugated or lace-like edges, and rise from the surface of the medium in regular arcs, like small droplets of fluid. Microscopically they appear finely granular and occasionally, under high magnification, may be seen to be composed of long intertwining loops of streptococcus chains, which form the lace-like edges. Colony form varies widely according to dissociation phase. Young colonies of M phase may be heavily slimy whereas the same strain in other phases may be finely granular or even dry.

In gelatin stab cultures growth takes place slowly, appearing after twenty-four to thirty-six hours as a very thin white line, or as disconnected little spheres along the line of the stab. The colonies on gelatin plates are similar in form to those on agar, but are usually more opaque and more distinctly white. The gelatin is not liquefied.

On Löffler's coagulated blood serum, growth is rapid and luxuriant and may show a slight tendency to confluence if the medium is very moist. Good chain formation takes place on this medium.

Classification of Streptococci.—The classification of streptococci has been an extremely difficult matter and has become of great practical importance for diagnostic and immunological study in connection with human and animal infection. We will deal therefore in the following paragraphs with the various methods of classification which have been developed in recent years, largely as a result of efforts to determine the types of these organisms associated with different varieties of infection.

Classification Based on Fermentation was one of the first methods attempted.—In another place we have indicated that the fermentation of inulin is of great value in differentiating the true streptococci from the pneumococci. Within the streptococcus group, classifications by fermentation have been set up by Gordon, by Andrewes and Horder, by Holman and others. In general writers have agreed that the streptococci pathogenic for man and domestic animals will ferment lactose and salacin; the organisms present in the human intestine may ferment mannite while this hexose is rarely fermented by streptococci from the intestines of animals. The final pH of various strains on dextrose broth has been of some aid in that this remains pH 5 to 5.2 in the "A" group of Lancefield, whereas in groups "B" and "C" from cattle and horses, from milk and from cheese the final reaction is usually lower, between pH 4.2 and 4.6. It has also been found by some observers that human strains of the "A" and "B" groups of Lancefield will ferment trehalose but not sorbite, whereas in the "C" group this reaction is reversed. For a more extensive discussion of fermentation reactions we refer the reader to the original papers, since, at the present time, differentiation by fermentation is of distinctly secondary importance as compared with those methods of classification which are based upon the study of antigenic structure.

Classification by Action on Blood Media.—An important forward step in streptococcus classification was the introduction of blood-agar plates by Schottmüller (1903) which divided the great class of streptococci into several fundamental groups according to their hemolytic action upon blood. This method was further developed by Brown and Smith whose subdivisions were as follows:

(1) α (alpha) viridans. Greenish discoloration on blood plates with partial

hemolysis about colonies. An outer clear zone may develop on preservation of the culture in the ice box.

(2) α' (alpha prime). Moderate but hazy hemolytic zone in which intact corpuscles can be found microscopically.

(3) β (beta) hemolyticus. Sharply defined clear zone. No intact corpuscles. Does not extend on preservation in ice box.

(4) γ (gamma). No hemolysis whatever. Pathogenically unimportant.

In this differentiation it is best to use horse- or rabbit-blood agar plates without dextrose which, by acid formation, inhibits hemolysis. Pour-plates are more accurate than surface streaks since a few oxygen sensitive strains may behave atypically in surface growth.

While the above classification is valuable for preliminary study it is of little immunological value since each one of the main classes fall into subgroups and β-hemolyticus strains have been found, by Grinnell and others to dissociate into viridans types.

For this reason efforts have been made to arrive at more fundamental classifications analogous to those used with the pneumococci and other bacteria, based on antigenic structure of the bacterial body.

Classification by Agglutination.—This has been a difficult task owing to the extensive occurrence of cross agglutination and to the frequent granular type of growth (spontaneous agglutination) of these micro-organisms.

Early but confusing results were reported by Moser and von Pirquet and more extensive but still incomplete results were obtained by Dochez, Bliss, Gordon and others. The most satisfactory work on this problem, to date, is that of Griffith.

The sera which Griffith uses are prepared by the injection, into rabbits, of heat killed, over-night cultures, three daily injections each week for 6 to 12 weeks—with increasing doses, until finally about 30 c.c. of culture is injected.

The agglutinations are done by the slide method. Over-night cultures are centrifugalized and a drop of the heavy sediment is mixed with a drop of serum on a slide. Coarse clumps should appear immediately under low power.

By this method Griffith examined 222 strains from scarlatina patients. One hundred and fifty-six fell into four types *viz.* 1, 2, 3, and 4. Sixty-six were heterologous. Type "2" semed to be most often associated with the most severe forms of disease and has been found in puerperal sepsis. Complications of disease were often caused by types other than the original. Use of Griffith's methods in other countries, the United States and Roumania for instance, has revealed types that do not fit in with Griffith's original ones.

Work with Griffith's methods has been extended to the study of puerperal sepsis (Colebrook), rheumatic fever (Pauli and Coburn) with results that encourage the use of this technique but indicate the large number of types which complicate the streptococcus problem and which must be cleared up before orderly immunological studies can be made.

Studies with Extracted Antigens. The problem has been approached by Lancefield on the basis of precipitin reactions with antigenic substances extracted from the organisms.

Lancefield found that hot HCl extracts of streptococci, cooled and neutralized, contained precipitable substances which were both group specific and type specific. These are as follows:

(1) Type specific "M" substance. Destroyed by trypsin digestion. Gives protein reactions. Precipitates with homologous serum. Is a "haptene" and will not induce antibodies. If immune sera are absorbed with heterologous strains they will still precipitate with this substance.

(2) Group specific "C" substance. Is a carbohydrate "haptene." Precipitates both with homologous and heterologous sera.

(3) Nucleoprotein "P" fraction. Group specific—but overlaps with organisms like pneumococcus. Is a complete antigen. Another protein "Y" has been postulated on basis of irregularities of reaction.

Lancefield's groups seem well established and correspond quite closely with differentiations obtained by fermentation reactions and with knowledge of the sources of strains.

To obtain the extracts for practical use, sedimented organisms are boiled for ten minutes in an $\frac{N}{20}$ concentration of HCl. This destroys most of the P substance. Alcohol precipitation after neutralization now brings down the "M" substance leaving "C" in the supernatant.

The following table adapted from Swift, Lancefield and Goodner illustrates the results obtained with hemolytic streptococci.

It appears from such studies that the overwhelming majority of human infections is caused by organisms of Group "A"—containing identical "C" substance, a fact of considerable importance in appraising the pathogenic importance of streptococci isolated from the female genitals before parturition or from throats in institutional infections.

The Labile Antigen of Mudd.—The studies of Mudd and his associates appear to indicate that, in the intact organisms, there is present a "labile" antigen comparable to the "Vi" substance found in virulent typhoid bacilli. The relationship of this "labile" substance to Lancefield's "C" and "M" fractions is indicated by the fact that acid hydrolysis of the labile antigen (a nucleo protein according to Sevag) yields both a type specific fraction ("M") and a group specific one ("C"), representing respectively protein and carbohydrate constituents.

The labile substance of Mudd is obtained without manipulatory deterioration by the newer physical methods—either breaking up of the bacteria by supersonic vibrations or by grinding, after desiccation, at very low temperatures. The pulverized bacteria are extracted in saline and precipitated with alcohol or by adjusting to pH 4.5. The properties of this material are the following:

It is inactivated by moderate heat and by alkalinity, but may be preserved in the dry state especially under anaerobic conditions (cysteine). Treated with sodium bisulphite it becomes hemolytic and this hemolysis is neutralized by antistreptolysin. It is not identical, however, with the oxygen-labile hemolysin of streptococcus filtrate.

Antibacterial sera absorbed with this labile antigen give *type-specific* agglutination, phagocytosis and mouse protection against whole organisms. Such results agree with those obtained by Griffith's method and the labile antigen is therefore assumed to be identical with the agglutinogen which determines Griffith's classification.

Groups established by precipitation with "C" substance	Common Habitat	Secondary Habitat	Typing

A	Human carrier
	Human infection
	  Scarlatina
	  Tonsillitis, etc.
	  Erysipelas
	  Puerperal Sepsis
	  Pneumonia
	  Surgical Infection
		Cattle Mastitis
		Laboratory infections in animals.
			Lancefield "M"
			Substance precipitation with type specific sera gave 29 types.
			Griffith slide agglutination with absorbed sera 24 types.

B	Cattle. Milk Cattle Mastitis	9 human cases puerperal sepsis, (2 with endocarditis) reported. Present without infection in throat and vagina.	4 types. In this group the carbohydrate is type specific (Lancefield) (4 types by precipitation of type specific carbohydrate.)
C	Horses. Strangles Cattle and other animals	Very rare in man, but probably can cause infection	4 types on basis of fermentation. Griffith. 2 types.
D Enterococcus	Cheese Human Intestine	Carrier in human throat innocuous	?
F	Minute organisms — Human Throat	—	4 types by slide agglutin.
G	of Long and Bliss — Human Throat Monkey. Dog Hare	—	1 Griffith type.

Other groups, H and K, are not well enough established for discussion in this place.

When the dissolved labile antigen is precipitated with immune sera within Group A (the only group examined by Mudd and collaborators) it reacts positively with sera of any of the types within the group, and since the hydrolysis of the labile antigen yields both "M" and "C" substances it is assumed that (group precipitation in solution—type specificity with whole bacteria) the labile antigen is so oriented in the bacterial cell that the type-specific portion of the molecule is reactive. It is the dominant surface antigen.

These investigations apart from their great theoretical interest have bearing on the very difficult problems involving differences between immunization with living and with killed bacteria, a question especially prominent with the streptococci, typhoid, and the anthrax bacilli. It probably involves a general principle, important for many other pathogenic species.

In order to discuss this it will be of interest to consider the matter of the dissociation forms of the streptococci.

The Dissociation of Streptococci.—Cowan was the first to describe for the hemolytic streptococcus virulent S colonies and avirulent R colonies. Todd, who studied freshly isolated strains from puerperal septicemia, found three variants. One form was a "primary" form virulent for mice which developed dull or "matt" colonies on chocolate blood agar. On serial cultivation in blood media, virulence diminished but the colonies remained unchanged. Virulence could be restored by mouse passage as long as these colonies remained "matt." When in subsequent cultures they became "glossy," virulence was irreversibly lost. Löwenthal later distinguished four dissociation variants, as did Ward and Lyons. The work of the latter writers indicated that in human infections with hemolytic streptococci two variants may be present—an organism which they called "F" because it grew flocculently in ordinary broth but remained evenly suspended in 5% horse-serum neopeptone water, and an "M" type which grew diffusely in fluid media and made flat, highly mucoid colonies on solid media, and was capsulated. This "M" variant was virulent for mice. The "F" variant had slight virulence for mice but if large amounts were injected into a mouse and the mouse died, "M" variants were recovered. In other words, the "F" was apparently the parent form. Both of these variants resisted phagocytosis in infants' blood. From these forms Ward and Lyons were able by cultivation to derive an "attenuated M" and a "C" variant which probably correspond to Löwenthal's "O" and to Todd's "glossy," avirulent type. Antibodies which led to the active phagocytosis of "M" variants could be produced only by the injection of living "M" cultures. Ward and Lyons believe that agglutination has less value in the typing of streptococci, than specific opsonin determination by which types and variants may be easily classified. They have based upon the opsonic technique a method of therapeutic transfusion which, in the hands of Lyons, seems to bring favorable results. When an organism is isolated from a patient with hemolytic streptococcus infection, the investigation of about ten donors will usually reveal one whose serum will enhance the opsonic powers of the patient's blood or the strain and variant present. Transfusion under the ordinary surgical precautions raises the patient's opsonic power and has already led to a number of cures.

The studies of Dawson, Hobbs and Olmstead are of the same general significance as the above but have contributed additional data on the antigenic structure of the dissociation phases within the "A" and "B" groups of Lancefield. They distinguish a "Mucoid" phase which includes both the "M" and "F" of Ward and Lyons; a Smooth and a Rough. The relationships of the various phases discussed in the more important investigations on this subject may be tabulated as follows:

Löwenthal; Ward and Lyons	Todd	Dawson
M F	Matt	Mucoid
Attenuated M C	Glossy	Smooth
......	......	Rough

Dawson confirmed Lancefield's observation that the type-specific substance in group "A" is a protein while in group "B" type specificity depends, as in pneumococci, on a carbohydrate. The mucoid capsular substance of the virulent dissociation phase was defined by Heidelberger and Dawson as non-specific carbohydrate. This conception will probably require modification in view of the work of Mudd and his collaborators which has been cited above, and which tends to show that this labile antigen is the chief component of the surfaces of Group A streptococci.

Immunization with Virulent Streptococci.—The most serious obstacle to the production of therapeutic antistreptococcus sera, even when proper regard is given to type-specificity and dissociation phase, has been the difficulty of producing any kind of antibody response against the most highly virulent "M" or mucoid, capsulated phases of these organisms, when killed bacteria were injected. The sera of man and animals convalescent from infection with the living bacteria contained noticeably increased opsonic and protective properties, but no amount of killed culture injections were effective. There again we are confronted with the problem of a "Vi"-like substance alluded to above. And the results of Mudd with his "labile" antigen may solve this problem. Meanwhile, however, Löwenthal has apparently overcome the difficulty by the very simple procedure of injecting very young capsulated cultures killed by heating only to 55° C. for 12 minutes. By serial injections—6 or more—of such moderately heated cultures Löwenthal claims to have produced satisfactorily protective sera—also serviceable for slide agglutination. This method deserves the most careful study since it opens a hitherto closed door toward the possible production of really effective therapeutic "type" and "phase" specific streptococcus antisera.

Resistance.—Streptococci on the ordinary culture media, without transplantation and kept at room temperature, usually die out within ten days or two weeks. They may be kept alive for much longer periods by the use of the calcium-carbonate-glucose bouillon, if the cultures are thoroughly shaken and the powdered marble thoroughly mixed with the bouillon from time to time (Hiss). Preservation at low temperatures (1° to 2° C.), in the ice chest, considerably prolongs the life of cultures. Virulence is preserved longest by frequent transplantation upon albuminous media. In sputum or animal excreta, streptococci may remain alive for several weeks. Streptococci like pneumococci may be preserved alive and with virulence unchanged by drying in the frozen condition by the method described by Flosdorf and Mudd. For ordinary purposes preservation in tubes of defibrinated rabbit's blood in the ice chest is the most practical method.

Under certain conditions some varieties of streptococci may be killed by exposure to a temperature of 55° C. for ten minutes. Usually thirty to sixty minutes heating at 60° C. is the procedure employed to kill the organisms in saline or broth suspensions. A temperature of 62° C. (143.6° F.) is maintained for thirty minutes in the practical sterilization of milk to afford a margin of safety in the killing of any streptococci which may be present. These organisms withstand low temperatures and freezing for a month or longer.

Streptococci are killed in fifteen minutes or less by: phenol 1: 200, cresol 1: 175, bichloride of mercury 1: 200 to 1: 500, hydrogen peroxide, 3 per cent solution, 1: 35; mercurochrome, 2 per cent; hexylresorcinol 1 : 1000, tincture of iodine, metaphen 1: 20,000, malachite green 1: 1800, optochin, approximately 1: 1000. These substances are all inhibitory in much higher dilution. The basic triphenlymethane dyes (gentian violet), arsenical preparations of the salvarsan type and certain acridine compounds are bacteriostatic and bactericidal for streptococci. Browning has summarized many of his own investigations and the researches of others in a discussion of the sensitiveness of streptococci to antiseptics and of the possibilities of antistreptococcal chemotherapy. Sulfanilamide is discussed in Chapters VII and XXIII.

Toxic Products.—Knowledge of the poisons produced by streptococci in culture and in the animal body is of value both as a basis for differentiation between the organisms of this group and for an understanding of their pathogenic effects. In this place we shall discuss these toxic products chiefly from the point of view of their systematic significance, and in the next chapter we shall deal with their relationship to scarlet fever and other streptococcal infections.

Exotoxins.—The grave systemic symptoms so often accompanying streptococcus infection, even when the local lesions were mild and there was no septicemia, suggested to the early investigators that these organisms produced powerful poisons which acted at a distance from the site of their formation. Toxic filtrates of cultures were obtained by a great many workers, notably by Marmorek and Savchenko. But very large doses were required to produce illness or death of animals. Clark and Felton succeeded in obtaining a filtrable toxin of streptococci in 1918. A great advance along these lines was made in 1924 when the Dicks obtained from streptococci isolated from patients with scarlet fever a toxic filtrate which produced local redness when injected into the skin of man, and a scarlatinal rash, with headache, fever and systemic symptoms when injected in doses of 0.25 to 0.5 c.c. subcutaneously into human beings. This product, called Dick toxin, is antigenic, neutralizable by convalescent serum and specifically produced antitoxin. It differs from such toxins as diphtheria and tetanus toxin by being relatively thermostable, withstanding 100° C. for a short period, and in being very stable in storage. We shall describe this toxin and record its uses in greater detail in the section on scarlet fever. It is a type of exotoxin produced by pathogenic streptococci from numerous sources as Wadsworth and his associates have shown.

Hemolysin.—Marmorek, who first noticed that certain streptococci laked red corpuscles, believed that there was a relation between virulence and hemolytic power. This is true only in a limited sense. Among hemolytic strains there is no strict correlation between virulence and production of hemolysin, but the hemolytic varieties are generally associated with severe and acutely fatal infections.

Hemolysin can be demonstrated in liquid media by incubating at 37° C. a rapidly growing culture of a hemolytic streptococcus in broth with a suspension of red corpuscles. This is often a more certain test than the blood agar plate for hemolytic activity.

The hemolysin can be obtained in the bacteria-free filtrates of young cultures of hemolytic streptococci in liquid media. Hemolysin is produced most abundantly in serum broth, reaches the maximum concentration at about the eighth to tenth hour of growth of the organism at 37° C., is thermolabile (McLeod), being destroyed at 55° C. in one hour or less, is adsorbed, in part, by filters, is inactivated by oxidation (Neill) and can be reactivated by reduction if the oxidizing process has not gone too far, is neutralized by certain normal sera and inactivated by bile salts (Gordon). In 1932, Todd produced an antigenic streptococcus hemolysin by protecting the toxin against destruction by oxidation.

There is some evidence that streptococci actually destroy hemoglobin, possibly by hemodigestion. The investigations of Rother and Seitz show that many streptococci change hemoglobin to methemoglobin and to hematin derivatives. The green-producing or viridans streptococci produce hydrogen peroxide, as shown by McLeod and Gordon, which alters the hemoglobin, forming methemoglobin and possibly other products. In addition, a hemolytic substance is liberated from the bodies of autolyzed viridans streptococci.

Hemolysin production and the elaboration of other substances acting upon blood cells are subject to so much variation on account of physical and chemical characteristics of culture media and conditions of incubation that their fundamental significance for the classification of streptococci does not seem to be as great as it was formerly thought to be.

Streptoleukocidin.—In 1905 and 1906, Ruediger and Hektoen observed that filtrates of cultures of virulent streptococci prevented the phagocytosis of nonvirulent streptococci by leukocytes. Nakayama, in 1920, using the methylene-blue reduction test of Neisser and Wechsberg as a measure of the vitality of leukocytes, made more detailed studies of streptoleukocidin. He found that nonvirulent hemolytic and non-hemolytic streptococci did not produce leukocidin, and therefore he regarded leukocidin production as a measure of virulence. Leukocidin, when produced, reached maximal concentration in 10 per cent serum broth cultures in ten to eighteen hours. It was inactivated by heating to 60° C. for thirty minutes and was unstable in storage. Leukocidin differs from streptolysin. It is inactivated by normal serum and leukocytic extracts. This inactivating substance in serum is destroyed by heat at 70° C. in thirty minutes. The studies of Channon and McLeod and Evans have corroborated these earlier observations. Gay and Oram found that clasmatocytes were resistant to the action of leukocidin.

Fibrinolytic Substance.—In 1933, Tillett and Garner reported their discovery of the capacity of hemolytic streptococci to liquefy rapidly the clotted fibrin of normal human plasma. The strains of *Streptococcus hemolyticus* used by them in the tests were derived from patients suffering from various manifestations of acute streptococcus infections. Broth cultures containing the streptococci and sterile filtrates of these cultures dissolved human fibrin in ten to forty-five minutes. Rabbit fibrin was not dissolved when the coagulum was composed entirely of rabbit constituents. When, however, rabbit fibrinogen was clotted with human thrombin, the streptococcal fibrinolytic substance dissolved the clot. The plasma of patients recovered from acute hemolytic streptococcus infections, when clotted in the presence of active cultures, was highly resistant to fibrinolysis. Serum derived from a patient convalescent from a streptococcus infection inhibited fibrinolysis by the cultures and filtrates. These studies have disclosed an apparent relation between infection and the development of resistance to the fibrinolytic activity of hemolytic streptococci. The test has been used in the study of the relationship of streptococci to rheumatic fever.

Serum Reactions.—All the ordinary immunological reactions can be carried out with streptococci. The analysis of antigenic relations upon which the specificity of such reactions depends has been discussed at length in the preceding sections of classification and dissociation.

The technique of performing such tests has been described in Section VIII

(Technical Methods). We describe here only those methods which have been particularly useful in streptococcus studies. Griffith's method for slide agglutination and the precipitation techniques of Lancefield and of Mudd involve the preparation of bacterial antigenic fractions which have been spoken of in the preceding paragraphs.

Protection tests are carried out by determining the capacity of an immune serum to protect mice against doses of virulent streptococci which are fatal to untreated mice. The requisites for accurate work are a powerful immune antibacterial serum, a highly virulent organism maintained with constant virulence, and a large group of animals of approximately the same susceptibility. The suitable degree of virulence of streptococci, such that a millionth or a hundred-millionth c.c. of a broth culture will kill animals in twenty-four to forty-eight hours, is difficult to attain and maintain. In the hands of Dochez, Avery and Lancefield protection tests indicated groupings of streptococci that coincided with groups established by agglutination tests.

Toxin Neutralization.—The blanching of the rash of scarlet fever by the intradermal injection of serum from a patient convalescent from scarlet fever indicated that immune serum could neutralize streptococcal toxin. This phenomenon is known as the *Schultz-Charlton reaction*. It is performed simply by injecting 0.1 c.c. of convalescent serum into a region of the skin where the erythema is present. If the rash is due to a toxin corresponding to antitoxin in the serum the area injected becomes pale, standing out sharply against the reddened skin around it. Scarlatinal antitoxin, produced by immunizing horses with the toxin of streptococci from scarlet fever will blanch the rash of the disease and will also prevent the occurrence of erythema when mixed with scarlatinal toxin and injected into the skin of a sensitive individual. These latter facts, demonstrated by the Dicks, are well known now. Birkhaug showed that the same series of reactions and combinations could be applied with analogous results in erysipelas, both natural and experimental. There is no doubt about the ability of various streptococcal antitoxins to neutralize the toxins of streptococci. But the work of Williams, Kirkbride and Wheeler convince us that hemolytic streptococci from different clinical diseases often produce the same kind of toxin and hence, that species differentiations on the basis of toxin-antitoxin reactions are not valid. There is evidence, which we shall summarize later, that antiscarlatinal serum is effective in the treatment of erysipelas, although we doubt whether it would be as effective as the original therapeutic sera which were both antibacterial and antitoxic. Okell and Parish, holding the opinion that streptococcal toxins differ only in potency or quantitatively, have advocated the use of a single antitoxin for the treatment of all streptococcal infections.

The Todd-Ward Technique for Reciprocal Determination of Opsonic Power of the Blood and Virulence of the Organisms.—The method employed in determining the phagocytic titre of the blood is a modification of one described by Todd,[1] and used by him for another purpose, *viz.*, the estimation of the comparative virulence of certain strains of hemolytic streptococci.

In this method, a constant amount of whole defibrinated blood is placed in a series of tubes, and to each of the tubes is added a decreasing number of organisms, so that—for example—the first tube is inoculated with 500,000 organisms, the second tube with 50,000 organisms, the third tube with 5000 organisms, and so on. The tubes are sealed and placed in a rotating box in the incubator. After some hours' incubation, the tubes are opened and the contents plated out. The plates are incubated and read next day. It is evident that whether the contents of the tubes are sterile or not—as shown by the plates—depends on three main factors, *viz.*, the number of organisms, the virulence of the organisms, and the phagocytic power of the whole blood. As the number of organisms can easily be controlled, the method can be used to determine either the virulence of the organisms, by always using the same blood, or the phagocytic power of the blood by always using the same organisms, if their virulence can be maintained at a constant level. The maximum number of organisms killed is in the one case the direct measure of the phagocytic power of the blood, and in the other case the indirect measure of the virulence of the organism. In other words, the more organisms that are killed, the more actively phagocytic is the blood in the former case, and the less virulent is the organism in the latter case.

[1] Taken from Ward, H. K., Journ. Exp. Med. 1930, 51 p. 675. The tube of pyrex 10 cm long and 7 mm inside diameter. The defibrinated blood used usually is 0.25 cc. The rotation is at 6 rpm.

Bacteriophage.—Streptococci appear to be susceptible in a semispecific manner to the transmissible lytic agent called "bacteriophage." We have studied a bacteriophage active only against strains of a streptococcus isolated from pericarditis in guinea-pigs. Shwartzman succeeded in differentiating erysipelas streptococci from other types by the selective lytic activity of a bacteriophage preparation. It is not known how far this principle may be applied.

Enterococcus.—A coccus occurring in pairs and short chains, often oval in shape, sometimes encapsulated, found frequently in the intestinal contents of infants, is in reality a streptococcus. Described first by Thiercelin, this organism has been regarded by Bergey as identical with the *Streptococcus faecalis* of Andrewes and Horder. It is a streptococcus of the viridans type and is probably the organism which Bargen has associated with ulcerative colitis.

REFERENCES

ANDREWES, F. W., and HORDER, T. J.   Lancet, 1906, 2:708, 775, 857, 1621.

ANDREWES, F. W., and CHRISTIE, E. M.   Spec. Rep. Ser. Med. Res. Counc., London, 1932, 169.

ARONSON, H.   Berl. klin. Wchnschr., 1902, 39:1006.

BARGEN, J. A.   Arch. Int. Med., 1930, 45:559; 46:1039.

BESREDKA, A.   Ann. de l'Inst. Pasteur, 1901, 15:880.

BILLROTH, T.   Untersuchungen über die Vegetationsformen von Coccobacteria Septica, Berlin, 1874.

BIRKHAUG, K. E.   Johns Hopkins Hosp. Bull., 1925, 36:248.

——— Johns Hopkins Hosp. Bull., 1925, 37:307.

——— Arch. Pathol., 1928, 6:441.

BLISS, W. P.   Johns Hopkins Hosp. Bull., 1920, 31:173.

——— J. Exper. M., 1922, 46:575.

BROADHURST, J.   J. Infect. Dis., 1915, 17:277.

BROWN, J. H.   Monographs Rockefeller Inst. Med. Res., No. 9, New York, 1919.

BROWNING, C. H.   A System of Bacteriology in Relation to Medicine, London, 1929, 2:142-149.

CHANNON, H. J., and McLEOD, J. W.   J. Path. & Bacteriol., 1929, 32:283.

CLARK, A. H., and FELTON, L. D.   J. Am. M. Ass., 1918, 71:1048.

COLEBROOK, L.   Brit. M. J., 1930, 2:134.

COLEBROOK, L., and PRÉVOT, A. R.   Ann. de l'Inst. Pasteur, 1925, 39:417.

COLEBROOK, D. C.   Spec. Rep. Ser. Med. Res. Counc., London, 1935, 205.

COWAN, M. L.   Brit. J. Exper. Path., 1922, 3:187; 1923, 4:241; 1924, 5:226.

CUNNINGHAM, J. S.   J. Infect. Dis., 1929, 45:474.

CZARNETZKY, E. J., MORGAN, I. M., and MUDD, S.   J. Exper. M., 1938, 67:643.

DAVIS, D. J.   J. Infect. Dis., 1913, 12:386.

DAWSON, M. H., HOBBY, G. L., and OLMSTEAD, M.   J. Inf. Dis., 1938, 62:138.

DE KRUIF, P. H., and IRELAND, P. M.   J. Infect. Dis., 1920, 26:285.

DICK, G. F., and DICK, G. H.   J. Am. M. Ass., 1924, 82:265, 301, 1246; 1929, 93:1784.

DOCHEZ, A. R., AVERY, O. T., and LANCEFIELD, R. C.   J. Exper. M., 1919, 30:179.

EAGLES, G. H.   Brit. J. Exp. Path., 1928, 9:330.

EVANS, A. C.   U. S. Pub. Health Rep., 1931, 46:2539; 1932, 47:1723.

FEHLEISEN.   Deutsche med. Wchnschr., 1882, 8:553.

——— Die Aetiologie des Erysipels, Berlin, 1883.

GAY, F. P., and ORAM, F.   Proc. Soc. Exper. Biol. & Med., 1931, 28:850.

GORDON, J.   Brit. J. Exper. Path., 1927, 8:38.

GORDON, M. H.   J. Path. Bacteriol., 1910, 15:323.

GRIFFITH, F.   J. Hyg., 1927, 26:363.

HEIST, G. D., SOLIS-COHEN, S., and SOLIS-COHEN, M.   J. Immunol., 1918, 3:261.

HEKTOEN, L.   J. Am. M. Ass., 1906, 46:1407.

Hiss, P. H. J. Exper. M., 1905, 6:317.

Hitchcock, C. H. J. Exper. M., 1924, 40:445.

Holman, W. L. J. Med. Research, 1916, 34:377.

Kinsella, R. A., and Swift, H. F. J. Exper. M., 1917, 25:877; 1918, 28:169, 181.

Kirkbride, M. B., and Wheeler, M. W. J. Immunol., 1926, 11:477.

Koch, R. Untersuchungen über die Aetiologie der Wundinfektionskrankheiten, Berlin, 1878.

────── Mitt. a. d. Kaiserl. Gsndthtsamte, 1881, 1.

Lancefield, R. C. J. Exper. M., 1925, 42:377, 397; 1928, 47:91, 469, 481, 843, 857; 1933, 57:571.

Lancefield, R. C., and Todd, E. W. J. Exper. M., 1928, 48:751.

Lash, A. F., and Kaplan, B. J. Am. M. Ass., 1925, 84:1991.

Loewenthal, H. Ztschr. f. Hyg., 1932, 114:379.

────── Brit. J. Exp. Path., 1938, 19:143.

Marmorek, A. Ann. de l'Inst. Pasteur, 1895, 9:593.

McLeod, J. W. J. Path. & Bacteriol., 1912, 16:321.

McLeod, J. W., and Gordon, J. J. Path. & Bacteriol., 1922, 25:139.

McLeod, J. W., et al. The Streptococci, Chap. II, pp. 28–163, in A System of Bacteriology in Relation to Medicine, London, 1929.

Meleney, F. L. Ann. Surg., 1930, 91:287; 1931, 94:961; 1935, 101:997.

────── Surg., Gyn., and Obstetrics, 1933, 56, 847.

Mudd, S., Czarnetzky, E. J., Lackman, D., and Pettit, H. J. Immunol., 1938, 34:117, 155.

Nakayama, Y. J. Infect. Dis., 1920, 27:270.

Neill, J. M., and Mallory, T. B. J. Exper. M., 1926, 44:241.

Neisser, M., and Wechsberg, F. Ztschr. f. Hyg. u. Infektionskrankh., 1901, 36:299.

Ogston, A. Brit. M. J., 1881, 1:369.

Okell, C. C., and Parish, H. J. Lancet, 1928, 1:746.

Passet. Fortschr. d. Med., 1885, 3:333.

────── Untersuchungen über die eitrigen Phlegmon, etc., Berlin, 1885.

Pasteur, L. Bull. Acad. Med., 1879, 8:260, 271.

Pauli, R. H., and Coburn, A. F. J. Exp. Med., 1937, 65, 595.

Perrone. Ann. de l'Inst. Pasteur, 1905, 19:367.

Rosenbach, A. J. F. Mikroorganismen bei den Wundinfektionskrankheiten des Menschen, Wiesbaden, 1884.

Rosenow, E. C. J. Infect. Dis., 1904, 1:280; 1920, 26:597.

Rother, W. Deutsche med. Wchnschr., 1925, 51:66, 522, 1031.

Ruediger, G. F. J. Am. M. Ass., 1905, 44:198.

Savchenko. Russki Vratch., 1905, 4:797. (Quoted by Williams.)

Schottmüller, H. München. med. Wchnschr., 1903, 50:849, 909; 1910, 57:617.

Schultz, W., and Charlton, W. Ztschr. f. Kinderh., 1918, 17:328.

Schweitzer, B. Zentralbl. f. Gynäkol., 1919, 43:641.

Seitz, A. Ztschr. f. Hyg. u. Infektionskr., 1922, 96:216.

Sherman, J. M. The Streptococci Bact. Rev., 1937, 1, 3.

Shwartzman, G. J. Exper. M., 1927, 46:497.

Simon, F. B. Centralbl. f. Bakteriol., I Abt., 1904, 35:308, 440.

Thiercelin. Compt. rend. Soc. de biol., 1902, 4:1082.

Thomson, D., and Thomson, R. Annals of the Pickett-Thomson Research Laboratory, Baltimore and London, 1924–1931, Vols. I–VII.

Tillett, W. S., and Garner, R. L. J. Exper. M., 1933, 58:485.

Todd, E. W. J. Exper. M., 1932, 55:267; Brit. J. Exper. Path., 1928, 9:91.

Tunnicliff, R. J. Inf. Dis., 1907, 48:304; J. Am. M. Ass., 1920, 74:1386.

Von Lingelsheim, W. Streptokokkeninwektionen, Handb. d. pathog. Mikroorganismen, ed. by W. Kolle, R. Kraus and P. Uhlenhuth, Berlin, 1928, 3rd ed., Vol. 4, Chap. X, pp. 789-852.

Wadsworth, A., and Coffey, J. M. J. Immunol., 1935, 29:505.

Williams, A. W. Am. J. Pub. Health, 1925, 15:129; 1929, 19:1303.

────── Streptococci in Relation to Man in Health and Disease, Baltimore, 1932.

Zinsser, H., and Parker, J. T. J. Exper. M., 1923, 37:275.

CHAPTER XXIII

STREPTOCOCCAL INFECTIONS. SCARLET FEVER

Streptococci cause many acute, chronic and fatal diseases in man and animals. They infect wounds, skin, bones, joints, heart valves and, in fact, may produce local inflammatory and purulent processes in any organ of the body. Passing from a site of infection into the blood stream, they give rise to septicemias, some of which, like puerperal sepsis, have the characteristics of distinct diseases. Mild or severe tonsillitis, scarlet fever, erysipelas, and various phlegmonous processes are the results of streptococcal infection. Allergic manifestations associated with streptococcal infections extend the range of their destructive activities. In the previous chapter we have discussed the streptococci as a group of bacteria; in this chapter we shall consider some of the most important pathological conditions caused by streptococci.

Infections of Lower Animals.—*Artificially produced infections* of lower animals have for a long time been used as a measure of the *pathogenicity and virulence* of streptococci. Different races of pyogenic streptococci show considerable variations in virulence, and there are few organisms, pathogenic for animals and man, which show comparable fluctuations in virulence.

The character or severity of the lesion in man gives little evidence as to the virulence of the organism for animals. Prolonged cultivation upon artificial media usually results in the reduction of the virulence of a streptococcus by dissociation. The passage of a streptococcus through rabbits or mice will usually, though not always, enhance its virulence for susceptible animals in general.

Among the domestic animals, those most susceptible to experimental streptococcus infection are white mice and rabbits. Guinea-pigs and rats are less easily infected, and the larger domestic animals, cattle, horses, goats, cats, and dogs, are relatively refractory to most of the strains of human origin. Almost complete immunity toward streptococcus infections prevails among birds.

The nature of the lesions following experimental animal inoculation depends upon the manner of inoculation, the size of the dose given, and most of all upon the grade of virulence of the inoculated germ. Subcutaneous inoculations may result in a simple localized abscess, or in a severe general septicemia with a hardly noticeable local lesion. Subcutaneous inoculation of mice may result in general sepsis followed by death within thirty-six to forty-eight hours. Inoculation of rabbits at the base of the ear with virulent streptococci may result in the formation of a lesion indistinguishable histologically from erysipelas in man.

This observation of Fehleisen has been repeatedly confirmed, notably by Birkhaug, who produced typical erysipelas in the skin of the sides and abdomens of rabbits by intracutaneous inoculations with cultures of hemolytic streptococci isolated from the disease in man. Marbaix showed that streptococci from other sources could produce erysipelas-like lesions in rabbits.

Strains of those organisms which have killed human beings need not necessarily have a high virulence for either rabbits or mice, though exceptions occur. It is usually necessary to pass such organisms through the animals mentioned in order to produce a virulence which will promptly kill them. Individual races will rapidly acquire such animal pathogenicity to an extreme degree, whereas other strains can be raised only to a moderate degree of virulence. These differences are not based upon anything amenable to analysis by present methods. Virulence raised through mice or rabbits is usually potent against other animals.

Although streptococcal infection is less common among lower animals than in man, *natural infections* with serious consequences occur.

Streptococcus infections are not infrequently seen in *rabbits* and many apparently normal rabbits have antistreptococcus agglutinins in their blood.

Guinea-pigs have a chronic and often fatal form of lymphadenitis, in which the cervical and abdominal lymph nodes become large sacs of caseous pus. Boxmeyer first noted the epizootic character of this disease and isolated a hemolytic streptococcus from the lesions. The colonies of this streptococcus on blood agar are at first mucilaginous and blister-like. When they are older they collapse in crinkled and concentric folds, as shown in the photographs illustrating Cunningham's paper on this disease.

Cats are sometimes the victims of fatal and communicable septicemia, with a mucopurulent discharge, due to a type of hemolytic streptococcus (Bayne-Jones).

An epizootic disease of *white mice*, due to a streptococcus, has been described by Kutschera.

Moore reported that an anaerobic streptococcus was the cause of a form of septicemia in *chickens*. This disease was communicable and usually fatal.

In *horses*, mules and donkeys, there is an acute contagious disease of the upper air passages, colloquially known as "strangles" (in German: Druse), due to the *Streptococcus equi*, a hemolytic, salicin fermenting strain. This organism was first recognized by Schütz as the etiological agent of this disease. The disease attacks chiefly young animals, and is characterized by fever, weakness, acute catarrhal inflammation of the nasal and pharyngeal mucosa, with local glandular swelling. The submaxillary lymph nodes are often involved. Pneumonia may occur. It is to be noted that this organism is quite different from the green-producing saprophytic *Streptococcus equinus* present in horse dung. We have seen streptococcus infections of the urethra in stallions which caused secondary infection of the genitalia of mares and prevented fertilization.

Streptococcal infection of the udders of *cows* is a serious disease. This form of *mastitis* renders the cows unfit for milk production and the milk drawn from infected cows is capable of producing disease in man. Several types of pyogenic streptococci, or streptococci with various pathogenic effects, may produce mastitis in cows. One of these, the so-called *Streptococcus epidemicus*, is the hemolytic streptococcus responsible for epidemic sore throat in man. Scarlet fever has been repeatedly transmitted by milk.

Streptococcus lactis (formerly spoken of as *Bacillus acidi lactici*) probably does not occur *in* the udder. Although slightly hemolytic, this streptococcus is nonpathogenic.

Hemolytic Streptococcus Infection in Man.—A variety of pathological processes may be caused by streptococci. The nature of the infection depends upon the virulence of the organism and the resistance of the subject, and probably also upon the production of toxic products.

Superficial cutaneous infections are frequently caused by streptococci and these in the milder cases may be similar to the localized abscesses caused by staphylococci. In severe cases, however, infection is followed by rapidly spreading edema, *lymphangitis,* and severe *systemic manifestations* with the development of a grave cellulitis, often threatening life.

The particular significance of streptococci in *surgically infected wounds* and the effect of their presence upon therapeutic procedures is considered in another section dealing with the bacteriology of infected wounds.

Suppurations of bone may be caused by streptococci, and constitute a severe form of osteomyelitis. Such lesions when occurring in the mastoid bone are not infrequently secondary to *otitis media* and may lead to a form of meningitis which is in most cases fatal.

Streptococcus meningitis is secondary to such lesions as *otitis* and *mastoiditis,* but occasionally primary *streptococcal meningitis* may occur in the course of bronchopneumonia. In a number of cases streptococci were associated in the spinal fluid with influenza bacilli.

In diphtheria and in smallpox, the hemolytic streptococci are frequently found as *secondary invaders.* The organisms have been found in the blood streams of fatal cases of smallpox, and in some of those that recovered.

It has long been known that the dangerous *bronchopneumonias* which occur in the course of measles and influenza may be of streptococcus origin. Both measles and influenza, as well as perhaps some other mild infections of the upper respiratory tract, render the individual susceptible to secondary infection. Under conditions such as those developed in the camps during the War, these *streptococcus bronchopneumonias* may become epidemic, probably by reason of the generalized interchange of mouth organisms among susceptible individuals crowded together under camp conditions. Under these conditions the carrier rate of hemolytic streptococci reaches high percentages. Irons and Marine, at Camp Custer, found 70 per cent of the individuals examined to be carriers of these organisms, and Levy and Alexander in certain regiments found 89 per cent to be carriers. Given, at the same time, extensive outbreaks of measles and influenza, the conditions for widespread secondary streptococcus pneumonias are established. It is not impossible that widespread ward infection may occur, in that patients who enter hospitals with measles and influenza may pick them up in the hospitals from adjacent beds, from doctors or from nurses, possibilities which indicate the great importance of prompt removal of cases developing pneumonias from measles and influenza wards, the careful hygiene of the mouths and throats of such cases, isolation of beds by screening, and the wearing of masks by doctors and nurses, not so much for their own protection as for that of the susceptible patient. MacCallum, Cole and Dochez studied the streptococcus pneumonias occurring at some of the camps. This study is reported by MacCallum in the tenth monograph of the Rockefeller Institute, issued in 1919. According to him, the streptococci seem to extend downward into the smaller bronchioles, giving rise to intensive inflammations in the air passages, then extending into the network of lymphatics surrounding the bronchioles and the pleura. There was rapid production of pleurisy and empyema, with hemorrhage about the bronchioles and infiltration of the alveolar walls themselves with leukocytes chiefly of the mononuclear variety. The appearance of these processes is quite different from that seen in the ordinary forms of bronchopneumonia.

It was formerly supposed that a number of different forms of *acute enteritis* might be due to streptococci, but this has never been positively demonstrated, and is doubtful. However, streptococcus infections of the walls of the intestines by passage into the submucosa may occasionally occur. Streptococcal appendicitis is sometimes the source of peritoneal infection.

The inflammation which is known as *Ludwig's angina* is caused by *Streptococcus hemolyticus*. The origin is usually from a focus in the teeth, tonsils or pharynx, or perhaps a *peritonsillar abscess*, and consists of acute inflammation of the areolar tissues of the submaxillary region of the neck.

Infections through the skin, through abrasions and injuries, are among the most dangerous infections caused by the hemolytic streptococcus. These are frequent among surgeons and pathologists, and their course and outcome are determined by the relationship between virulence of the strain and resistance of the individual. The local lesion may appear innocent, since, with sufficient virulence, the point of inoculation may show nothing more than a small red swelling which is soggy and edematous and looks quite different from the slower processes, with central abscess formation, caused by the less virulent streptococci and staphylococci.

Erysipelas.—This is an acute infectious disease of the skin caused by hemolytic streptococci. The streptococci occur chiefly in the lymph spaces in the corium, rarely in the subcutaneous tissue. The skin becomes red, swollen, edematous and often covered with small or large vesicles. The rash spreads peripherally with the advance of the organisms in the tissue spaces. The inflammatory exudate in the infected tissue is composed chiefly of mononuclear cells of the clasmatocyte type. Erysipelas is distinct, both clinically and pathologically, from phlegmonous inflammation, cellulitis and lymphangitis, although these conditions also are caused by hemolytic streptococci and differential diagnosis is often difficult.

Fehleisen, who in 1883 isolated a streptococcus from erysipelatous lesions and reproduced the disease in man by inoculation with organisms from cultures, was of the opinion that this streptococcus was a distinct species, which he named *Streptococcus erysipelatis*. Numerous workers, notably Petruschky, opposed this opinion, presenting evidence that streptococci from sources other than erysipelas could produce erysipelas in man.

Birkhaug, on the basis of agglutination and absorption of agglutinins claimed that the streptococci from the lesions formed a unified group. They produced a toxin which was specifically neutralizable by the antitoxic serum from animals infected with the streptococci or injected with the toxin. A toxin-streptococcal vaccine was found by Birkhaug to be useful for the immunization of patients against recurrent attacks of erysipelas.

Opposed to this are the observations of Williams, Wheeler, Okell and Parish, Wadsworth and others who have found that streptococci from erysipelas "cross-agglutinate" with streptococci from scarlet fever, that the toxins of streptococci from various lesions are not strictly correlated with pathological conditions. In general, their researches indicate that species of streptococci cannot be established on the basis of association with lesions, antigenic, fermentative or toxic properties.

An antiserum produced in horses against the toxin of streptococci from erysipelas has been used by Birkhaug, Symmers, Symmers and Lewis and others with success in the treatment of erysipelas. McCann questioned the controls of these therapeutic experiments and indicated that scarlatinal streptococcus antitoxin was as effective as the erysipelas antitoxin. The relative values of these sera are still under investigation.

In our opinion the streptococci associated with erysipelas do not constitute a distinct species.

SCARLET FEVER

For many years etiological investigations upon scarlet fever have pointed toward hemolytic streptococci, and some of the earliest investigations, such as those of Crooke carried out in 1885, called attention to the presence of streptococci in the bodies of those dead of the disease. Since that time evidence connecting the chained cocci with this disease has accumulated but was not sufficiently strong until 1923 to discourage numerous etiological claims for other micro-organisms nor to entirely defeat the supposition that the streptococci and other bacteria described represented nothing more than secondary invaders, the primary causation of the disease being attributed to a filtrable virus. Class, in 1899, described a diplococcus isolated from scarlet fever patients with which he produced skin eruptions and fever in pigs. It is more than likely that Class was actually working with a streptococcus. The supposed protozoan parasite described by Mallory in 1904 as lying between the epithelial cells of the skin in scarlet fever patients was subsequently interpreted as a probable artefact by Field and others; and later studies have not tended to support the etiological importance of the diphtheroid bacillus isolated from the upper respiratory passages by Mallory and Medlar. In 1905, as eminent an authority as Jochmann, reviewing the subject, declared himself against the probability of streptococcus causation, and similar conclusions were drawn by Landsteiner, Levaditi and Prasek on the basis of experimental transmission studies in chimpanzees. In 1921, Cristina claimed etiological significance for a gram-positive, anaerobic coccus isolated from the blood of scarlet fever patients, an observation which has been confirmed by a number of other Italian investigators, notably Catteruccia, and Caronia and Sindoni. Later publications by these authorities assert the frequent presence of the organism in scarlet fever patients as well as positive agglutination tests and other immunological reactions with the serum of human convalescents. The workers mentioned have carried out experimental infections in man and have attempted protection with killed cultures. The work is mentioned in the interests of completeness, though we are inclined to attach little importance to it at the present time.

In spite of other suggestions, interest in streptococci persisted for reasons which may be briefly reviewed as follows: Bacteriologists have known for a long time that hemolytic streptococci were invariably present in the angina of scarlet fever. Clinicians, notably Baginsky and Sommerfeld, often found hemolytic streptococci in the heart's blood of rapidly fatal cases and whenever blood cultures are positive in scarlet fever, the organism is a hemolytic streptococcus.

The accumulating evidence of the constant presence of streptococci in association with the disease gained significance when, in 1902, Moser and von Pirquet stated that serum produced with scarlet fever streptococci would agglutinate such strains. This was confirmed by Meyer in 1902 and, somewhat later, by Rossiwall and Schick. Savchenko recognized the existence of a toxic substance in streptococcus broth with which an antitoxic serum could be produced. In his article he describes scarlet fever as a severe local streptococcus infection accompanied by toxemia, and comments upon the error of concluding that because filtrates from his streptococcus cultures were nontoxic for laboratory animals, they were likewise nontoxic for man. He also asserted that the sera produced with whole cultures contained both bactericidal and antitoxic substances.

Gabrichewsky in 1907 made a vaccine consisting of streptococcus broth plus organisms from cultures in which the streptococci had grown for four days. Clinical experimentation with this material in the prophylactic vaccination of children by Gabrichewsky and by other Russian investigators resulted in the development of local rashes and general symptoms in vaccinated children. A considerable number of cases were treated with varying success with serum and prophylactic vaccinations were practiced in Russia with results that were favorably reported. Contrary opinions were nevertheless expressed by Aaronson and Neufeld and others which temporarily confused the issue.

In 1918, Dochez, Avery and Lancefield developed a method of agglutination and agglutinin absorption by means of which they classified strains of hemolytic streptococci, concluding that hemolytic streptococci from various sources could be roughly divided into four main types. With the same technic, Bliss studied twenty-five strains of scarlet fever streptococci, 80 per cent of which were agglutinated by sera made with homologous strains. None of them were agglutinated by sera made with organisms of nonscarlatinal origin. In the same year Tunnicliff, by agglutination, absorption and opsonin determination in the immue serum of sheep treated with the scarlatinal streptococci, came to similar conclusions, and Gordon, a year later, obtained evidence corroborating these results, all of them indicating that the hemolytic streptococci from scarlet fever cases represented a recognizable, specific and homologous group. Although this conception had much influence in advancing the investigation of scarlet fever and other streptococcus diseases it has had to be abandoned in the light of subsequent work.

Purely bacteriological evidence, however, would be inconclusive without the further experimental data discussed in the following paragraphs.

Animal and Human Experimentation.—Hektoen, in 1923, came to the conclusion that it was doubtful whether scarlet fever had been experimentally produced in man. He cited a number of cases, in which it *seemed likely* that such transmission had been successful. Attempts of transmission to lower monkeys were either frankly negative or questionable.

In 1923, scarlet fever was produced experimentally in man by G. F. Dick and G. H. Dick. These workers selected volunteers from rural districts and from homes where attacks of scarlet fever would not be likely to be overlooked. They inoculated these individuals by throat swabbing with cultures of a hemolytic streptococcus isolated from a secondary abscess on the finger of a nurse who had contracted scarlet fever from a patient. Three of five subjects remained well, one had a sore throat and fever but no rash, the other developed typical scarlet fever after an incubation time of forty-eight hours. Control experiments with filtered cultures of the same organisms were negative. The same controls later were inoculated with the unfiltered culture; two of them developed sore throat and fever but no rash, the third had a typical attack of scarlet fever. The streptococci associated with scarlet fever seemed to fall into two separate groups, some of them fermenting mannite, others failing to do so. The strain used in the preceding experiments was a mannite fermenter. In another experiment in which they used a non-mannite fermenter isolated from the throat of a scarlet fever patient, they again succeeded, with a pure culture, in producing experimental scarlet fever.

This observation of the Dicks was confirmed in 1926 by Nicolle, Conseil and Durand, who produced scarlet fever in man by swabbing the tonsil with scarlatinal streptococci after the fourth passage of the organisms on artificial media. Since then, there has been so much corroborative evidence from bacteriological, immunological and clinical sources that there seems little possibility of further questioning the chief, though perhaps not exclusive etiological rôle of streptococci in scarlet fever.

The conception that scarlet fever is a streptococcal infection necessitates the assumption that the rash is produced by a toxin. In addition, since one attack of scarlet fever usually confers immunity upon a person who recovers from the disease, while, on the other hand, there is little or no immunity following streptococcal infection, it is necessary to assume that the immunity is a refractory state with respect to the toxin and not necessarily to the organism. There is abundant evidence that streptococci produce a toxin which causes a scarlatiniform eruption and that the so-called scarlatina without an exanthem occurs.

Specificity of Scarlatinal Streptococci.—The Dicks and others have maintained the opinion that the streptococci causing scarlet fever are sufficiently different from other streptococci to be designated a species, *Streptococcus scarlatinae*. This opinion is based in part upon the earlier agglutination and opsonic studies of Dochez, Avery, Lancefield, Bliss and Tunnicliff. The chief basis of the opinion rests upon the supposed specificity of the toxin produced by these streptococci. The various strains of streptococci from scarlet fever differ in agglutination and antigenic properties. They differ also metabolically; some ferment mannite while others do not. It appears, furthermore, that the toxin is not specifically correlated with the source of the streptococci or pathological process produced by them. Many investigators, notably Kirkbride and Wheeler, Park and Spiegel, Williams, and Wadsworth and his associates, have demonstrated that the toxins produced by streptococci from scarlet fever are various and that streptococci from erysipelas and other streptococcal infections produce the same toxin as that derived from scarlatinal strains. Hooker has described at least two antigenically different erythrogenic toxins produced by scarlatinal streptococci. He has designated them as A and B. Definite neutralization differences could be demonstrated. Trask and Blake have found that the sera of two fatal cases of scarlet fever, pleural exudate of a third, contained toxin which was serologically different from the standard Dick toxin by cross neutralization experiments. It is apparent that the streptococci cannot be differentiated upon the basis of specific toxicity. We repeat here the conclusion reached in our last chapter, that the designation *Streptococcus scarlatinae* is not warranted at present.

Scarlatinal or Dick Toxin.—In 1924, the Dicks demonstrated that streptococci from scarlet fever elaborated a rash-producing exotoxin. They showed that this toxin, obtained from culture filtrates, could be used as a test for susceptibility to scarlet fever by applying it in intradermal injection according to the method of the Schick test. They demonstrated also that it could be used to induce immunity in animals, for the production of a therapeutic antitoxin and for the prophylactic immunization of human beings.

Preparation of Toxins.—It is obvious that the selection of one or more strains for toxin production must be considered with care. The Dick toxins have been prepared by mixing the filtrates of cultures of several strains. In New York State and elsewhere the use of the Dochez NY5 strain is increasing because this organism appears to produce a toxin of great antigenic valency.

It was thought at first that it was necessary to add blood or serum to the culture medium in order to provide suitable nutriment for toxin production by streptococci. It is now known that neither blood nor serum is required. Potent toxins are produced by these streptococci in meat infusion-peptone broths and tryptic digest broth. The streptococcus toxin broth used in the New York State Laboratory (Wadsworth) is a beef infusion to which are added 0.2 per cent dextrose and 2 per cent "Difco" proteose peptone. The reaction of this broth is pH 8.2 before autoclaving. A reaction of pH 7.4 to 7.6 is satisfactory. The streptococci are grown in this broth for seven days at 37° C. At the end of this time, 0.5 per cent phenol is added and the organisms removed by Berkefeld filtration. The filtrate is tested for potency in terms of the dilution which produces a skin reaction in a man or susceptible animal.

Such filtrate contains, in addition to the soluble exotoxin, numerous waste products of the growth of the organisms, bacterial proteins and constituents of the medium. Crude toxins are mixtures of many substances. No doubt many contradictory results obtained with these filtrates have been due to varying quantities of extraneous substances.

The *actions of the toxin* are most conspicuous in human beings. Injected into the skin of the forearm, the toxin produces within eighteen to twenty-four hours a bright red, swollen area varying in dimensions according to the amount of toxin injected and the susceptibility of the subject. This local reaction to intracutaneously injected toxin is the basis of the *Dick test,* which is used for the standardization of toxin and antitoxin and as a measure of susceptibility to scarlet fever. Injected in larger amounts subcutaneously or intramuscularly in man, the toxin may cause headache, muscular pains, vomiting, diarrhea, fever and a typical generalized scarlatiniform rash.

The lower animals are relatively insusceptible to the toxin. Guinea-pigs, mice and rats show no local or general reactions. Rats withstand large doses of the filtrate of these cultures of streptococci, although they succumb to relatively small amounts of living cultures of the same organisms, illustrating the frequent independence of toxicity from virulence.

The results of intradermal injections of the toxin into rabbits have been conflicting. Williams and her associates, and Fraser and Plummer found chinchilla and other white rabbits susceptible to the toxin. Veldee discovered that local reactions followed the injection of the toxin into the skin of the inside of the ears of white rabbits and has devised standardization procedures on the basis of this fact.

White pigs have been used by Ando and Kurauchi for skin-tests of toxin and of mixtures of toxin and antitoxin.

Kirkbride and Wheeler discovered that more than 60 per cent of white goats, preferably grade or pure-bred Saanen, one and a half to four years old, give satisfactory skin reactions after intradermal injection of streptococcus toxins. The standardization procedures of the New York State Laboratory at Albany are based on the use of these animals. At the Massachusetts Antitoxin Laboratory tests are done on the shaven backs of chinchilla or New Zealand white rabbits. Twenty-five human skin test doses give satisfactorily uniform results.

Properties of the Toxin.—The so-called streptococcus scarlatinal toxin is relatively heat stable. Most of the toxin in a filtrate is destroyed by heat at 80° C. in 30 minutes, but some remains after boiling at 100° C. for 30 minutes. On account of this relatively high resistance to heat, streptococcus toxin is somewhat different from the more thermolabile diphtheria toxin. Ando, however, who has made a special study of this question, found that some diphtheria toxin remained after boiling and that the H-ion concentration of the medium considerably affected the results of the application of heat. The difference here may not be as fundamental as was at first supposed.

The fresh filtrate may gain in toxicity when first stored. After a few weeks' storage in the refrigerator the toxicity becomes constant and then slowly diminishes. The rate of decrease is slow at 5 to 10° C., and the toxin is relatively stable in storage in the cold. The rate of deterioration at room temperature (20° C.) is much more rapid.

Alkali from glass ampules and material from certain rubber stoppers causes rapid loss of toxicity, especially of the diluted toxin.

The toxic filtrate contains at least two important components which give rise to red skin reactions when injected intradermally in man. One of these is the true *toxin*. It is precipitable from the filtrate by the addition of 2 volumes of absolute alcohol. This precipitated toxin is soluble in 0.85 per cent solution of sodium chloride and can be concentrated. The *nucleoprotein* derived from the bodies of the streptococci is precipitable from the filtrate by acidification to pH 4 to 4.2 with hydrochloric or acetic acid. The skin reactions to the toxin only are reliable as indices of susceptibility or immunity, while the reactions to the nucleoprotein are allergic in nature. The nucleoprotein component in toxic filtrates of low potency may be responsible for many of the conflicting results of studies based on Dick tests with crude filtrates.

Formaldehyde combines with the toxin and reduces its toxicity, but also diminishes the antigenic property. Ando and Veldee have reported that Dick-positive individuals can be rendered Dick-negative by injections of such *toxoid* or "*anatoxin*," but this has been shown to be true in only about 50 per cent of the cases. The usual method employed to make this toxoid is to add 0.3 to 0.4 per cent of commercial formalin to the toxic filtrate and then incubate the mixture for eight weeks at 37° C. Experience indicates that streptococcus toxoid cannot easily be reduced to a complete non-toxic condition. Immunization with such toxoids appears to be less effective than similar use of potent toxin.

Standardization of Toxin.—The scarlatinal streptococcus toxin is standardized in terms of the skin-test dose for man, according to the principles established by the Dicks. "The skin-test dose is the least quantity of toxin, which, when injected intracutaneously into persons known to be susceptible to the toxin, will induce a reaction equal to that induced on the same persons at the same time by the injection of a skin-test dose of the standard toxin supplied by the U. S. National Institute of Health (Hygienic Laboratory)." The dose is contained in 0.1 c.c. The reaction is observed twenty-four hours after the injection of the toxin. A positive skin-test is a red area measuring at least 1 centimeter in diameter.

The potency of the toxin is expressed in terms of skin-test doses. Thus if 0.1 c.c. of a 1:4000 dilution of the toxin induces a reaction equal to that induced by one skin-test dose of the standard toxin, then the tested toxin contains 40,000 skin-test doses per 1 c.c. Toxins of this potency or greater can be obtained and should be used in preference to low potency toxins.

Scarlatinal Streptococcus Antitoxin.—The serum of those who have recovered from scarlet fever possesses the capacity to blanch the rash, as demonstrated by the Schultz-Charlton phenomenon, and to neutralize the toxin *in vitro*. Animals infected with these streptococci or injected with the toxin produce antitoxin, and serum of horses thus treated is used for passive immunization in the treatment, and occasionally in prophylaxis, of scarlet fever. The antitoxin is standardized in terms of its capacity to neutralize the substance in the toxin which induces the skin-reaction. The unit of antitoxin is stated in terms of skin-test dose neutralization. The federal unit, adopted in 1929 and used since 1931 in New York State, is defined as follows: "One unit of antitoxin is the smallest amount of antitoxin which neutralizes 50 skin-test doses of scarlatinal streptococcus toxin."

In practical standardization, definite amounts of standard toxin are mixed with decreasing amounts of antitoxin and allowed to stand at least one-half hour before they are used for injection. Of each mixture 0.1 c.c. is injected intradermally into susceptible subjects and the results are noted twenty-four hours later. The unitage of the antitoxin is calculated from the amount required to neutralize one skin-test dose of toxin.

In all these procedures suitable controls with boiled toxin, and serum alone, should be made. Details of these methods, too numerous to be reproduced here, are given in the 1927 edition of *Standard Methods of the Division of Laboratories and Research of the New York State Department of Health* (pp. 366-379).

Streptococcus antitoxins and toxins have been standardized according to the principles of the flocculation method of Ramon by Dyer, Povitzky and others. Rane and Wyman have developed a flocculation test for the titration of purified scarlatina toxin, which is in usefulness comparable to the Ramon method for diphtheria toxin. Concentrated toxin is preferable to the crude product for this test. The concentration is carried out by 66 per cent saturation with ammonium sulphate, followed by dialysis and removal of the nucleoproteins with acetic acid.

The Dick Test as an Indication of Susceptibility.—The Dick test is carried out as follows: A saline dilution of the standard toxin is prepared of such strength that one skin-test dose is contained in 0.1 c.c. Exactly 0.1 c.c. of this diluted toxin is injected *into* the skin (intradermally) of the flexor surface of the forearm. Twenty-four hours later the site of injection is observed. A circular or oval red area at least 1 centimeter in both diameters is noted as a positive Dick reaction. Pale pink areas smaller than this or no visible reaction are negative Dick tests. The positive reaction is said to indicate susceptibility to scarlet fever; the negative reaction is said to indicate sufficient antitoxic immunity to be protective against scarlet fever. A control test with boiled toxin is sometimes necessary. These are the same principles as those established by the Schick test in relation to susceptibility to diphtheria.

A large number of reports on the results of Dick tests and their correlation with susceptibility have been published since the Dicks introduced this procedure in 1923. Much of the work is valueless because of errors in controls, in amounts injected, and in the use of toxins too weak or too strong. In addition, the toxic filtrate, containing a nontoxic nucleoprotein which induces allergic skin reactions, is not a sufficiently pure substance to give unequivocal results. Allergic reactions to the toxin itself may occur, but no doubt the allergic response to the injection of filtrates of cultures grown in media to which *no* serum (horse or sheep) had been added are due chiefly to the bacterial protein in these filtrates. Ando showed that the reactions induced by the nucleoprotein were allergic and were more frequent in older than in young persons, while the frequency of reactions to the toxin is less in the older subjects. Cooke has investigated and discussed the undoubted allergic element in scarlet fever and the effects of this state upon the results of Dick tests.

The Dick test is usually positive at the beginning of an attack of scarlet fever and becomes negative during the convalescence from the disease. Most persons who have recovered from attacks of scarlet fever have negative Dick tests. Others as well as ourselves have seen exceptions to these rules, but we believe that these rules are in general valid, and that usually a negative Dick test indicates a greater or less resistance to scarlet fever. We refer here to the toxic and exanthematous phenomena. We are of the opinion that the test does not indicate the same degree of resistance or suscepti-bility to infection with streptococci capable of producing scarlet fever in toxin-susceptibles. In 1929, the Dicks reported that of 20,856 persons with spontaneously negative reactions, only one contracted scarlet fever, although all passed through one epidemic and some went through several epidemics of scarlet fever. They reported that of 2157 pupil nurses and interns with naturally negative Dick tests who were exposed intimately and over long periods to patients with scarlet fever, none con-tracted the disease. This is strong evidence that a negative Dick test indicates relative insusceptibility. Our own experience has not confirmed these results entirely, though we do not regard the exceptions as disproof of this general thesis.

The number of persons from rural districts who give positive Dick reactions is greater than the number of city dwellers who show positive tests. This is correlated with the differences between the degrees of exposure of the two groups.

A general summary of the frequency of *positive* Dick tests in different age groups in an urban population is as follows:

Age	Per Cent Positive Reactions
Newborn children	10
6 months to 1 year	40 to 60
1 to 5 years	50 to 75
5 to 10 years	50 to 60
10 to 15 years	40 to 50
15 to 20 years	30 to 40
20 to 30 years	20 to 30
Over 30 years	15

In general, this indicates increasing immunity with increasing age and is correlated with the greater incidence of scarlet fever which occurs in children, especially those in the five to ten year age-group.

Active Immunization.—The Dicks have proved, and many others have confirmed their findings, that injections of the scarlatinal streptococcus toxin into human beings causes the Dick test to become negative. Upon this basis, accepting the negative Dick test as an evidence of resistance, procedures have been established for the active immunization of children and adults against scarlet fever. The toxin is injected subcutaneously in the deltoid region or intramuscularly. The dosage has been increased from year to year and differs in different places. Thus the Dicks recommended a series of five injections, with an interval of one week between each injection and with skin-test doses approximately as follows: (1) 500 S.T.D., (2) 2500 S.T.D., (3) 20,000 S.T.D., (4) 40,000 S.T.D., (5) 80,000 to 100,000 S.T.D. In 1932, the New York City Department of Health advocated a series of four injections of 500, 2000, 6000 and 12,000 S.T.D. at weekly intervals.

Severe local and general reactions, headache, vomiting and scarlatiniform rash have followed first and later injections of the toxin. We think that the reactions are more numerous and uncomfortable than is generally admitted. A less toxic preparation, such as the toxoid used by Veldee, or immunization by mouth as suggested by the Dicks, will reduce these reactions. The usefulness of formalin treated toxin or toxoid has been investigated by many observers and the present opinions may be summarized as follows: Formalin seems to deprive the toxin of some of its antigenic properties and active immunization with toxoid gives only about 50 per cent reversibility of the Dick reaction. It is still uncertain whether this effect is due to altered toxin or residual unaltered toxin.

The results of prophylactic immunization are difficult to analyze because it is obvious that in many cases immunization was not carried through to the production of a negative Dick test in persons originally susceptible. In 1931 the Dicks reported that not one of 1191 susceptible interns and nurses immunized by their method contracted scarlet fever, while during the same period there were 37 cases of scarlet fever among a smaller group of susceptible nurses and interns who had not been immunized before they went on duty in the contagious disease wards. This is substantial evidence that prophylactic immunization is a valuable method for the reduction of the incidence of scarlet fever. The wisdom of its use must be appraised by balancing the degree of danger of exposure against the severity of reaction.

Passive Immunization and Serum Therapy.—Before 1923, Moser immunized horses with living cultures of streptococci from scarlet fever and obtained encouraging results in the treatment of patients with this immune serum. In 1918, the observations of Schultz and Charlton indicated that convalescent serum contained antitoxin, and thereafter a number of investigators treated scarlet fever by injections of convalescent serum (Weaver, Debré and Paraf, and others).

Almost simultaneously, in 1924, Dochez and the Dicks published methods of serum production for the antitoxic treatment of scarlet fever. Dochez's serum was produced by permitting scarlet fever strains of hemolytic streptococci to grow in agar which had previously been injected in a mass in the subcutaneous tissues of horses. The Dicks immunized horses by injections of increasing amounts of toxic filtrates. Both types of sera are used. Those which meet the requirements of the Scarlet Fever Committee are produced according to the method of the Dicks. It is probable that the serum should possess antibacterial (so-called antiendotoxic) properties as well as antitoxic qualities to be of maximum efficiency. Unconcentrated and concentrated sera have been used.

The observations of Dochez and the Dicks were confirmed, notably by Birkhaug and by Blake and his associates. The antistreptococcus antitoxin now used in the treatment of scarlet fever is generally regarded as an efficient therapeutic agent to be recommended in severe cases.

The serum may be used for prophylactic passive immunization in emergency. But the immunity thus conferred lasts only two to three weeks.

Epidemiology and Prevention.—Scarlet fever is transmitted by materials from the nose and throat, and pus from a localized infection of ears or abscesses. It is not transmitted by means of desquamated skin. The disease is contagious throughout its course and far into the convalescent period. Convalescent and recovered patients may remain carriers, harboring the streptococci in their tonsils.

The quarantine or isolation periods for cases of scarlet fever have varied from four to six weeks. There is a tendency to base the discharge of the patient upon the plate count of the number of hemolytic streptococci obtained on a swab culture of the tonsils, accepting empirically a figure of 3 per cent of the number of all colonies of the bacteria in the plate as a safe upper limit for hemolytic streptococci. This is a crude and uncertain method and requires further investigation.

About 1.5 per cent of discharged scarlatina convalescents give rise to "return" cases, although the patients had been kept in hospital for fifty days. This indicates the existence of carriers.

Transmission of the disease by milk has not been uncommon. Rosenau and others have recorded large outbreaks of scarlet fever in Boston and elsewhere, traceable to milk.

The prevention of scarlet fever is based upon the following procedures. (1) Prophylactic: Dick tests and active immunization of the susceptibles as indicated by positive Dick reactions. (2) Prompt recognition and isolation of cases. (3) Quarantine based upon cultures to detect hemolytic streptococci in the nose and throat. (4) Passive immunization, serum therapy, for prophylaxis in emergency and to shorten the course of the disease. (5) General sanitary measures, especially those relating to the milk supply, designed to exclude from use cows with mastitis and to prevent the handling of milk by those with tonsillitis and streptococcal infections. Milk should be pasteurized.

The severity of scarlet fever fluctuates through cycles of five to six years. Much of the modern preventive and therapeutic investigation has been carried on during a period in which scarlet fever has been relatively mild.

Puerperal Sepsis.—This infection is one of the most dangerous infections caused by hemolytic streptococci. Modern methods have greatly reduced its incidence but have not yet eliminated it. Respiratory tract infection with streptococci may be one of the remaining important sources of the organisms producing this disease.

It has been claimed by Lash and Kaplan that the hemolytic streptococci from puerperal fever constitute a definite group, identifiable chiefly by the production of a specific soluble toxin. Neither the results of studies of agglutination reactions nor the tests with toxin warrant the opinion that a specific type of hemolytic streptococcus produces puerperal sepsis.

It seems apparent that the frequent isolation of anaerobic streptococci from the blood by Harris and Brown and by Colebrook indicates that the etiological agent of puerperal sepsis is not a single type of streptococcus.

Tonsillitis Caused by Hemolytic Streptococci.—Hemolytic streptococci are frequently the causative agents in pharyngitis, and are often associated with the more severe forms of *follicular tonsillitis*. Some of these tonsillar infections may be accompanied by high fever, and severe illness, and the local inflammation may be so severe that it cannot be clinically differentiated from diphtheria. Occasionally severe generalized infections may ensue.

Recurrent tonsillitis and foci of chronic streptococcal infection in the tonsils are related to allergic disorders, arthritis and rheumatic fever, as we shall describe in later paragraphs.

Epidemic Sore Throat Due to Milk Infection.—Sore throat epidemics traceable to milk have been observed in England since 1875. The onset is usually accompanied by sudden chilliness, with muscular soreness, headache and nausea. The cases are similar to the milder forms of influenza. The first observed epidemic in this country occurred in Boston in 1911, and was studied by Winslow. There were forty-eight fatal cases. Since that time a number of similar epidemics have been described, the most extensive being that which took place in Chicago in 1911, studied by Capps and Miller, and by Davis and Rosenow. There were 10,000 cases, hardly any of which came from the west side of the city. Of 622 cases investigated, 87 per cent or 537 used milk from a certain dairy, and 79 per cent of the fatal cases used the same milk. People taking milk from this dairy were fourteen times more numerous than those getting it from other sources. Of 153 nurses in a certain hospital using the milk, 80 per cent got the disease, while of 721 in other hospitals, only 4.8 per cent came down. There was a coincident epidemic of sore throats among the employees of the dairy where bovine mastitis was found in the cows. Almost 5 per cent of the cows of this dairy had mastitis, and streptococci were isolated from the milk of a cow and from the throat of a girl on the same farm. Davis and Rosenow describe the organisms isolated from these cases. In all of them they found a streptococcus which produced large colonies on blood agar, larger than the ordinary hemolytic organisms. There was moderate hemolysis, and the organism was virulent for guinea-pigs, mice and rabbits. Capsules were developed on animal passage. They believed their organism, *Streptococcus epidemicus*, to be a distinct species.

Williams and Gurley in 1932 demonstrated that some of the strains of hemolytic streptococci isolated from the udders of cows, from milk and the lesions of septic sore throat are antigenically related, according to agglutination tests, to scarlet fever streptococci. Other strains from these sources were found to be antigenically related to streptococci from erysipelas. The results of these studies together with the outcome of investigations of the toxins produced by these strains show clearly that the streptococci of epidemic sore throat do not constitute a distinct species.

Streptococcus Viridans Infections.—Most of the nonhemolytic, *viridans* or green-producing streptococci are harmless saprophytes. Some varieties, however, chiefly the organism known as *Streptococcus viridans*, are associated with subacute and chronic diseases.

These organisms cause apical abscesses of teeth, diseases of the middle ear and infections of the accessory sinuses of the nose. They play a prominent rôle in *focal infections*, and the associated metastatic infections, toxic and allergic disorders which follow the long continued local growth of bacteria in the tissues of an animal.

Streptococcus viridans is the usual cause of *subacute vegetative endocarditis*. In such cases the organisms cause firm vegetations on the mitral or aortic valves, occasionally extending along the walls of the auricles. During febrile periods, the organisms can be cultivated from the blood and they may be found in the blood during weeks or months. Some of these strains of *Streptococcus viridans* are micro-aerophilic, growing best in deep tubes of blood agar or on the bottom of a flask of blood broth. Cerebral or renal embolism may occur in this disease, and arthritic symptoms may develop. Nearly all cases of *Streptococcus viridans* endocarditis are fatal, after a longer or shorter period.

Rheumatic Fever and Arthritis.—From long continued and numerous investigations of the somewhat ill-defined pathological conditions classified clinically in one group as *rheumatic fever* and in another as *arthritis*, the facts emerging indicate that streptococci are important as etiological agents.

In the first place, there are frank streptococcal infections of the joints, produced by organisms transported to the joint from another focus of infection in the body. The forms of chronic rheumatism which concern us here have been attributed by Rosenow to *Streptococcus viridans*, which he has isolated from fluid from inflamed joints. It is probable that toxic products or states of hypersensitivity to streptococcal constituents are responsible for some of these conditions.

The disease known as *acute rheumatic fever*, in which chorea, endocarditis, and *arthritis* are prominent, has for a long time been thought to be caused by streptococci. Several possibilities have been indicated by investigations. One group of workers has presented evidence that the disease is caused by a specific coccus. In this group are Poynton and Paine, who in 1900 described a diplococcus not unlike a *Streptococcus viridans* strain, which they isolated from the blood. Rosenow also has isolated green-producing streptococci from lesions of this disease. Swift and Kinsella, however, obtained the *viridans* in only 8.3 per cent of 58 cases. In 1927 Small and Birkhaug isolated a nonhemolytic, indifferent, gamma-type, inulin fermenting streptococcus, called *Streptococcus cardio-arthritidis*, to which they attributed etiological significance in relation to rheumatic fever. There has not been any convincing proof that any single organism is the cause of this disease.

The older evidence that rheumatic fever is associated in some way with streptococcal infection is large and substantial. The newer evidence indicates that this association exists and that the disease may be an allergic manifestation of infection with streptococci of various sorts, hemolytic, green-producing or indifferent. In a previous edition of this book we have expressed our belief that the rheumatism question has been narrowed down to two etiological possibilities. One of these is the possibility that the actual injury of the joint is caused by a toxic factor something like the Dick toxin which penetrates the synovia; the other, that the body becomes allergic to the streptococcus materials and that localized allergic reactions account for the lesions in the joints, and, we now add, lesions elsewhere. Whether one or the other of these possibilities is the true explanation of rheumatic fever has not been determined. Both processes may be operative in the production of the disease.

The allergic hypothesis of rheumatic fever has received substantiation from the numerous observations of Swift and others, and from Birkhaug's studies in which he investigated the toxic properties and phenomena of hypersensitivity associated with infection with the *cardio-arthritidis* type of streptococcus.

The investigations of Coburn and Pauli, published in 1932, indicate that *Streptococcus hemolyticus* has a close relation to the rheumatic process. These investigations showed that a recrudescence of the disease was usually preceded by a pharyngeal infection with hemolytic streptococci, and that an increase in antistreptolysin is found in the blood of patients with rheumatic fever. The combined evidence, in the opinion of Coburn, "indicates that the infectious agent initiating the rheumatic process is *Streptococcus hemolyticus*."

The pathogenesis of this disease has not been completely determined, but the fact that streptococci are etiological factors appears to be established.

Finally, streptococci, chiefly organisms of the *viridans* group, have been regarded by Rosenow, Evans and others as etiological agents in poliomyelitis, encephalitis and other virus diseases. In the previous chapters on variability of bacteria and on the streptococci we have expressed our disbelief in the thesis that streptococci are phases in the life cycle of the agents of these diseases. We repeat that opinion here and will return to a discussion of the evidence on these points in the subsequent section on the ultramicroscopic viruses.

The Therapeutic Effect of Sulphanilamide.—The history of Prontosil and sulphanilamide dates back to the announcement by Domagk in 1935 that the *in vitro* antiseptic properties of the azo dyes were reduced by the addition of the sulphonamide group; but the therapeutic action *in vivo* was *not* only not reduced but when it was given to mice after intraperitoneal injections of lethal doses of hemolytic streptococci the mice did not die. After showing that Prontosil was a sulphonamide chrysoidine compound, research was stimulated to discover what part of the molecule was chiefly responsible for the striking therapeutic results. Trefouel and associates were the first to show that para-aminobenzenesulphonamide was as effective as the diaminoazobenzenesulphonamide compounds. This discovery was rapidly verified by investigators in France, England and America. The name sulphanilamide was adopted by the Council on Pharmacy of the American Medical Association and has largely supplanted a long list of proprietary and other names among which those most commonly used were "Prontosil" and "Prontylin." The original experimental work of Domagk, backed by the clinical reports on a number of serious human hemolytic streptococcus infections in which striking curative results had been obtained by the drug, was soon verified by investigators in France, England, and America.

At the Infants and Childrens Hospitals in Boston clinical results the two years (1936-1938) with sulphanilamide have substantiated the earlier reports on its remarkable therapeutic effects. The drug has completely reversed the previous unfavorable prognosis of hemolytic streptococcus infections such as meningitis, septicemia, pneumonia, erysipelas and cellulitis. In comparison to a mortality of 98 per cent from hemolytic streptococcus meningitis in the ten-year period preceding the use of sulphanilamide, there has not been a death from this type of infection in the past two years. In milder types of hemolytic streptococcus infections such as cervical adenitis, otitis media, and mastoiditis, results have not been as dramatic following the administration of sulphanilamide, but undoubtedly serious complications have been prevented and the duration of the illness shortened by the use of the drug.

Experience in other hospitals is similar to this, proving the value of sulphanilamide in the treatment of infections due to hemolytic streptococci.

REFERENCES

AARONSON. Deutsche med. Wchnschr., 29:439.

AMOSS, H. L., and BIRKHAUG, K. E. Tr. Ass. Am. Physicians, 1925, 40:5.

ANDO, K. J. Immunol., 1930, 19:223, 465.

ANDO, K., et al. J. Immunol., 1929, 17:361; 1930, 18:223, 257, 267.

ANDO, K., and KURAUCHI, K. J. Immunol., 1930, 18:341.

ANDO, K., and OZAKI, K. J. Immunol., 1930, 19:535.

BAGINSKI and SOMMERFELD. Berl. klin. Wchnschr., 1900.

BAYNE-JONES, S. J. Infect. Dis., 1922, 31:474.

BIRKHAUG, K. E. Johns Hopkins Hosp. Bull., 1925, 36:134; 37:307.

—— J. Am. M. Ass., 1926, 86:1411; 1927, 88:885.

—— J. Infect. Dis., 1927, 40:549; 1928, 43:35, 280.

—— Arch. Pathol., 1928, 6:441.

BLAKE, F. G., TRASK, J. D., and LYNCH, J. F. J. Am. M. Ass., 1924, 82:712.

—— N. York State J. Med., 1925, 25:1093.

BLISS. Johns Hopkins Hosp. Bull., 1920, 31:173.

—— J. Exper. M., 1922, 46:575.

BOXMEYER, C. H. J. Infect. Dis., 1907, 4:657.

BREED, R. S. Bacteria in Milk, The Newer Knowledge of Bacteriology and Immunology, Chicago, 1928, Chap. XXX, 380.

BURT-WHITE, H. Brit. M. J., 1928, 1:974.

CANTACUZÈNE. Compt. rend. Soc. de biol., 1911, 17:403.

CAPPS and MILLER. J. Am. M. Ass., 1912, 58:1848.

CARONIA and SINDONI. Pediatria, 1923, 31:745 (ref. J. Am. M. Ass., 1923, 81:584, 864).

CATTERUCCIA. Pediatria, 1924, 32.

CLASS. Phila. M. J., 1899, 3.

COBURN, A. F., and PAULI, R. H. J. Exper. M., 1932, 56:609, 633, 651.

COLEBROOK, L. Brit. M. J., 1930, 2:134.

COLEBROOK, L., and KENNY, M. Lancet, 1936, 1:1279.

COOKE, J. V. Am. J. Dis. Child., 1928, 35:991.

CRISTINA. Pediatria, 1921, 29:1105 (ref. J. Am. M. Ass., 1922, 78:620; 1923, 80:806).

CROOKE, G. Fortschr. d. Med., 1885, 3:651.

CUNNINGHAM, J. S. J. Infect. Dis., 1929, 45:474.

DAVIS. Am. J. Pub. Health, 1918, 8:40.

—— J. Am. M. Ass., 1929, 93:978.

DAVIS and ROSENOW. J. Am. M. Ass., 1912, 58:773.

DEBRÉ and PARAF. Paris Méd., 1922, 12:418.

DICK, G. F. Internat. Clinics, 1930, 1:150.

DICK, G. F., and DICK, G. H. J. Am. M. Ass., 1923, 81:1166; 1924, 82:265, 301, 544, 1246; 1924, 83:84; 1925, 84:803, 1477; 1929, 93:1784; 1932, 98:1436.

—— Am. J. Dis. Child., 1929, 38:905.

DOCHEZ, AVERY and LANCEFIELD. J. Exper. M., 1919, 30:179.

DOCHEZ, A. R. Proc. Soc. Exp. Biol. & Med., 1924, 24:124.

DOCHEZ, A. R., and SHERMAN. J. Am. M. Ass., 1924, 82:541.

DOMAGK, G. Deutsch. med. Wchnschr., 1935, 61:250.

DRAPER and HANFORD. J. Exper. M., 1923, 17:517.

DYER, R. E. U. S. Pub. Health Rep., 1925, 40:865.

EYRE. J. Path. & Bacteriol., 1910, 14:160.

FEHLEISEN. Die Aetiologie des Erysipels, Berlin, 1883.

FIELD. J. Exper. M., 1905, 7.

FRASER, F. H., and PLUMMER, H. Brit. J. Exper. Path., 1930, 11:291.

GAY, F. P. J. Lab. & Clin. M., 1917–18, 3:721.

GABRICHEWSKY. Centralbl. f. Bakteriol., orig., 1907, 41.

———— Berl. klin. Wchnschr., 1907, 44:556.

GORDON. Brit. M. J., 1921, 622.

HARRIS, J. W., and BROWN, J. H. Johns Hopkins Hosp. Bull., 1929, 44:1.

HEKTOEN, L. J. Am. M. Ass., 1923, 80:84.

HISS, P. H. J. Med. Research, 1908, 19.

HOLMAN, W. L. Arch. Pathol., 1928, 5:68.

HOOKER, S. B., and FOLLENSBY, E. M. J. Immunol., 1934, 27:177.

IRONS and MARINE. J. Am. M. Ass., 1918, 70:687.

JOCHMANN. Ztschr. f. klin. Med., 1905, 56:316.

KIRKBRIDE, M. B., and WHEELER, M. W. Proc. Soc. Exp. Biol. & Med., 1924, 22:85.

———— J. Immunol., 1926, 11:477; 1927, 13:19.

———— J. Am. M. Ass., 1927, 89:1394.

KUTSCHERA, F. Centralbl. f. Bakteriol., I Abt., 1908, 48:671.

LANDSTEINER, LEVADITI and PRASEK. Ann. de l'Inst. Pasteur, 1911, 25:754.

LASH, F. A., and KAPLAN, B. J. Am. M. Ass., 1925, 84:1991; 1926, 86:1197.

LEVADITI, C., and VAISMAN, A. C.r. soc. de biol., 1935, 119:946.

LEVY and ALEXANDER. J. Am. M. Ass., 1918, 70:1827.

LONG, P. H., and BLISS, E. A. J. Am. M. Assoc., 1937, 108, 32.

MacCALLUM, COLE and DOCHEZ. J. Am. M. Ass., 1918, 70:1146.

McCANN, W. S. J. Am. M. Ass., 1928, 91:78.

MALLORY. J. Med. Research, 1904, 10.

MALLORY and MEDLAR. J. Med. Research, 1916, 34.

MARBAIX. La Cellule, 1892.

MEYER. Deutsche med. Wchnschr., 1902, 28:751.

MOORE, V. A. Pathology, etc., of Infectious Diseases in Animals, New York, 1916.

MOSER and VON PIRQUET. Centralbl. f. Bakteriol., orig., 1903, 34:560, 714.

MOSER, P. Jahrb. f. Kinderh., 1903, 57:1.

———— Berl. klin. Wchnschr., 1903, 40:14.

NEUFELD. Ztschr. f. Hyg., 1903, 44:161.

New York City Dept. of Health. Weekly Bulletin, 1932, 22:273.

NICOLLE, E., CONSEIL, and DURAND, P. Compt. rend. Soc. de biol., 1926, 182:1002.

OKELL, C. C. Lancet, 1932, 1:761, 815, 867.

OKELL, C. C., and PARISH, H. J. Lancet, 1929, 1:748.

PARK. J. Am. M. Ass., 1925, 85:1180.

PARK, W. H., and SPIEGEL, R. G. J. Immunol., 1925, 10:829.

PETRUSCHKY, J. Ztschr. f. Hyg. u. Infektionskrankh., 1894, 17:59; 18:413; 1896, 23:142, 477.

POVITZKY, O. R. Proc. Soc. Exper. Biol. & Med., 1925, 22:426.

POYNTON, F. J., and PAINE, A. Lancet, 1900, 2:860, 932.

RANE, L., and WYMAN, L. J. Immunol., 1937, 32:321.

ROSENOW, E. C. J. Am. M. Ass., 1913, 60:1123; 61:1947, 2007; 1915, 65:1687.

———— Arch. Int. Med., 1921, 28:274.

ROSSIWALL and SCHICK. Wien. klin. Wchnschr., 1905, 18:3.

SAVCHENKO. Russki Vrake, 1905, 797.

SCHULTZ, W., and CHARLTON, W. Ztschr. f. Kinderh., 1918, 17:328.

SCHÜTZ. Arch. f. Tierheilk., 1888, 14:456.

SMALL, J. C. Am. J. M. Sc., 1927, 173:101.

———— J. Lab. & Clin. M., 1931, 15:1093.

STENT, L. Lancet, 1930, 1:1066.

SWIFT, H. F. Rheumatic Fever. See Textbook of Medicine, Ed. by R. Cecil, W. B. Saunders Co., Philadelphia, 1933.

SWIFT, H. F., ANDREWS, C. H., and DERICK, C. L.   J. Exper. M., 1926, 44:35.
SWIFT, H. F., DERICK, C. L., and HITCHCOCK, C. H.   J. Am. M. Ass., 1928, 90:906.
SWIFT, H. F., and KINSELLA, R. A.   Arch. Int. Med., 1917, 19:381.
SYMMERS, D.   J. Am. M. Ass., 1928, 91:535.
SYMMERS, D., and LEWIS, K. M.   J. Am. M. Ass., 1927, 89:880; 1932, 99:1082.
TRASK, J. D., and BLAKE, F. G.   J. Am. M. Assoc., 1933, 101:753.
TREFOUEL, J., NITTI, F., and BOVET, D.   C.r. soc. de biol., 1935, 120:756.
TUNNICLIFF.   J. Am. M. Ass., 1920, 74:1386.
———— J. Infect. Dis., 1921, 29:91.
VELDEE, M. V.   U. S. Pub. Health Rep., 1931, 46:693.
VELDEE, M. V.   U. S. Pub Health Rep., 1932, 47:1043.
WADSWORTH, A. B.   Standard Methods, etc.   Baltimore, 1927, pp. 88 and 328.
WADSWORTH, A. B., KIRKBRIDE, M. B., and HENDRY, J.   Am. J. Hyg., 1928, 9:371; 1929, 9:371.
WEAVER, G. H.   J. Infect. Dis., 1918, 22:211.
———— J. Am. M. Ass., 1921, 77:1420.
WHEELER, M. W.   J. Prevent. M., 1930, 4:1; 5:181.
WILLIAMS, A. W.   Am. J. Pub. Health, 1929, 19:1303.
———— J. Am. M. Ass., 1929, 93:1544.
———— Streptococci in Relation to Man in Health and Disease, Baltimore, 1932, p. 136.
WILLIAMS, A. W., and GURLEY, C. R.   J. Bacteriol., 1932, 23:241.
WILLIAMS, A. W., HUSSEY, H. D., and BANZHAF, E. J.   Proc. Soc. Exper. Biol. & Med., 1924, 21:291.
WINSLOW, C.-E. A.   J. Infect. Dis., 1912, 10:73.
ZINSSER, H.   Bull. N. Y. Acad. Med., 1928, 4:351.

CHAPTER XXIV

THE COMMON COLD, THE PNEUMOCOCCUS AND THE PNEUMONIAS

THE COMMON COLD

In dealing with infections of the respiratory tract of man, it is impossible to avoid referring briefly to the common cold which, though mild, is perhaps the most frequent of all such infections, is unquestionably transmitted from person to person, and is probably caused by a virus. The condition is of great importance because of the loss of economic efficiency which wholesale infection of a population with the common cold entails, and because the catarrhal inflammation of the nose, throat and upper bronchi, which accompanies the cold, prepares a site for the lodgment and multiplication of influenza bacilli, pneumococci, streptococci, diphtheria bacilli, perhaps meningococci, and other organisms that may lead to more serious disease. The sneezing, coughing and expectoration of individuals suffering from colds results in the promiscuous distribution of bacteria lodged in the respiratory passages of such people. Carriers of virulent organisms of various kinds, such as diphtheria bacilli, meningococci, streptococci, pneumococci in the course of their colds distribute the virulent organisms they carry to others. They not only spread the virus that has given them the "cold," but scatter a spray which contains the virulent organisms to which they themselves are immune, and, therefore, not only directly infect susceptible contacts, but transmit to them directly a condition which will make it possible for these virulent organisms to lodge in their mucous membranes, and perhaps cause the secondary more serious diseases. It has been proved that during the colder months of the year, when colds abound, the carrier rate of all bacteria and agents of respiratory diseases increases. If we consider that in any large group of people there may be 3 or more per cent of meningococcus carriers, similar percentages of pneumococcus, streptococcus carriers, a fraction of a per cent of virulent diphtheria carriers, and that in this group a number of the carriers begin to cough, spit and hawk, the percentage of all these will go up, and susceptible contacts will not only contract the cold, but will get the specific disease.

Etiology.—According to one group of investigators the common cold is caused by a filtrable virus. According to others a variety of bacteria, acting singly or in conjunction, cause this acute infection of the upper respiratory tract.

The filtrable virus theory was brought into the foreground in 1914 by Kruse, who transmitted the condition to normal human beings by instilling into their noses filtered nasal secretions from persons with colds. Foster, in 1917, confirmed Kruse's observations and claimed to have grown the virus by the anaerobic methods used by Noguchi and others for the cultivation of the treponema of syphilis. In 1929 and subsequent years Dochez, Shibley, Mills and Kneeland presented a large amount of

311

experimental evidence in support of the opinion that a filtrable virus caused the common cold. They reproduced a disease indistinguishable from the cold in man and in chimpanzees by intranasal instillations of filtrates of nasal and pharyngeal washings. The virus multiplied in chick-embryo medium. With filtrates of cultures, removed by many transfers from the original inoculation, they reproduced the disease in normal men and in chimpanzees. Similar results were obtained by Long, Doull and their associates, and by Powell and Clowes.

Walker has criticized these experiments on the basis of uncertainties in the diagnosis of a cold in man or chimpanzee, the disturbing factors introduced by preparatory instillations of broth and culture fluids and the uncontrolled possibilities of allergic reactions to bacterial products in the original filtrates. While these criticisms have force in some cases, we think that they do not invalidate the conclusions to be drawn from this work. In our opinion the evidence is convincing that some types of the infection called the common cold are caused by an ultramicroscopic virus.

On the other hand, there is much evidence that a variety of bacteria may cause colds. Experimental and accidental spraying or intranasal inoculation of human beings with influenza bacilli, *B. bronchisepticus*, *M. catarrhalis* and other bacteria have resulted in acute infections of the upper respiratory tract, and the symptoms have been those of the common cold. Variable results have been obtained with serial cultures of the nasopharyngeal flora in groups of individuals over long periods, during times when they were well and when they had colds. Of many such studies, Webster's is most convincing that there is a definite association between influenza bacilli, pneumococci and hemolytic streptococci and coryza, pharyngitis and sinusitis in man.

It seems to us that these views are not necessarily mutually exclusive or incompatible with the facts. The so-called common cold is a group of symptoms varying in intensity, and varying in combinations. Colds themselves vary in communicability. It is probable that several different causes may produce the same symptoms and related phenomena. Colds may be caused by ultramicroscopic viruses, by bacteria or by both kinds of agents acting upon the same individual.

Meanwhile, the sanitary importance of the condition must not be underestimated, and the principles of prevention are perfectly plain, although they offer almost insuperable difficulties to successful enforcement.

The striking power of the cold is probably not very great, and direct or indirect contact, relatively close in time and space, seems to be necessary for transmission. The gravity of the malady itself is so slight that it is difficult to impress upon individuals the necessity for care, and the very grave influence upon general respiratory epidemiology cannot be made clear to those not professionally interested.

General rigid attention to the prevention of colds in schools, hospitals, military units, and other closely associated groups of people should indirectly exert a very considerable effect upon the general respiratory sick rate. Prevention depends upon impressing these facts upon the public and laying stress upon the great danger of severe secondary disease.

The avoidance of close contact, sleeping in the same beds, avoidance of the kissing of children, protecting companions from contamination by coughing and sneezing, disinfection of handkerchiefs, etc., may prevent the disease from going through families as is so often the case. Children in the initial stages of severe colds should be excluded from school for a day or two.

Of especial importance is the attention to colds during the existence of epidemics of diphtheria, measles, poliomyelitis, meningitis, influenza, and the epidemic pneumonias that may take place in army camps. Under such conditions the common cold may be the main "catalyzing agent," as it were, which keeps the more serious disease active. At such times people with increased mucous secretions who cough, spit and distribute mucus with handkerchiefs and hands, are a sufficiently grave menace to call for rigid public health measures. That these cannot be successfully enforced in the general population of cities, seems plain. But they can be controlled in factories, schools, military organizations, hospitals, asylums, and perhaps, under certain conditions, in places of amusement, and innumerable opportunities for spread can thus be eliminated.

Vaccination against colds has been used extensively for prevention and with the thought that the establishment of some degree of active immunity would reduce the severity of the infection and also decrease the complications. In 1938 Dochez reported that his attempts to vaccinate by subcutaneous injections of the living cold virus had failed. Many have claimed success with so-called "cold vaccines," made up of mixtures or solutions of bacteria (streptococci, staphylococci, pneumococci, meningococci, catarrhalis-types, influenza bacilli and Friedländer bacilli). Impressions are on the whole favorable but statistical proof is lacking. If any immunity is produced by injections of these "shot-gun" prescriptions it may be specific occasionally, may be non-specific, or may be related to responses to heterophile antigens, as shown by Rockwell and Van Kirk, by Hyde and by others.

THE PNEUMOCOCCUS AND PNEUMONIA

Family: *Lactobacteriaceae* Orla-Jensen. Tribe: *Streptococceae* Trevisan. Genus: *Diplococcus* Weichselbaum. Species: *Diplococcus pneumoniae* Weichselbaum

The opinion that lobar pneumonia is an infectious disease was held by many far-sighted clinicians long before the actual bacteriological facts had been ascertained. This idea, so well founded upon the nature of the clinical course of the disease, with its violent onset and equally rapid defervescence, led many of the earlier bacteriologists to make it the subject of their investigations—a subject made doubly difficult by the abundant bacterial flora found normally in the upper respiratory passages, and by the fact that lobar and other pneumonias are caused by various organisms.

Cocci of various descriptions and cultural characteristics were isolated from pneumonia cases by Klebs, Koch, Guenther, Talamon, and many others, which, however, owing to the insufficient differential methods at the command of these investigators, cannot positively be identified with the micro-organism now known to us as *Diplococcus pneumoniae* or the pneumococcus. Although thus unsuccessful as to their initial object, these early investigations were by no means futile, in that they gave valuable information regarding the manifold bacterial factors involved in acute pulmonary disease and incidentally led to the discovery by Friedländer of *B. mucosus capsulatus.*

Communications upon lance-shaped cocci found in saliva, and capable of producing septicemia in rabbits, were published almost simultaneously by Sternberg and by Pasteur in 1881. These workers were dealing with the true pneumococcus, but did not in any way associate the micro-organisms they described with lobar pneumonia. The solution of this problem was reserved for the labors of A. Fränkel and Weichselbaum who published their results, independently of each other, in 1886, demonstrating that the *pneumococcus* is the etiological factor in a large majority of cases of lobar pneumonia.

Studies by Neufeld and Händel, and in this country by Cole and his coworkers at the Rockefeller Hospital, have shown that in the pneumococci we are dealing not with a single organism, but with a group. In this grouping three specific types, named respectively, Types I, II, and III, were segregated first. The remaining heterogeneous collection of organisms were classified for convenience as Group IV. From this group, and from Type II, twenty-nine types have been distinguished by Cooper and her associates, and therapeutic antisera have been prepared against some of them. Thirty-two types of pneumococci are now recognized. The distinctions between types, referred to here, are based entirely upon serological reactions, except occasionally in the case of organisms of Type III, whose mucoid growth is often characteristic enough to be recognized. Therapeutic antisera have been prepared against a number of these types of pneumococci.

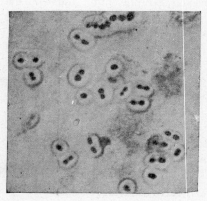

FIG. 23.—PNEUMOCOCCI, GROWN ON LÖFFLER'S SERUM.

Capsule stain by gentian-violet-potassium-carbonate method.

For a scholarly survey of the history of this field of bacteriology and for a detailed account of the characteristics and activities of the organism the reader is referred to the excellent monograph published in 1938, by White, in collaboration with Robinson and Barnes, entitled "The Biology of the Pneumococcus."

Morphology and Staining.—When typical, the pneumococcus is a rather large, lancet-shaped coccus, occurring in pairs, and surrounded by a definite and often wide capsule, which usually includes two approximated cocci without a definite indentation opposite their lines of division. The pneumococci may, however, occur singly or in short chains, and even fairly long chains are not infrequently met with under artificial cultural conditions. This may be chiefly due to the cultural conditions or may be a prominent characteristic of certain strains. Apparently the capsules of organisms making up the chains are continuous; wavy indentations are usually present, however, in the capsule of chains, and at times distinct divisions are observed.

The chief variations from the typical morphology consist either in the assumption of a more distinctly spherical coccus type, or in an elongation approximating the bacillary form. Under certain conditions of artificial cultivation a distinct flattening of the organisms, particularly of those making up chains, may be seen, and even the impression of a longitudinal line of division, characteristic of many streptococcus cultures, is not infrequently gained.

The capsules under certain conditions, especially in artificial media, may be absent or not demonstrable, and in certain strains capsules apparently may not be present under any conditions. Practically any of the described variations may dominate one and the same culture under different or even apparently the same conditions of cultivation, and all grades may occur in capsule development, from its typical formation through all variations, to its total and apparently permanent absence.

The presence or absence of capsules depends, to a large extent, upon the previous environment of the pneumococci under observation. The most favorable conditions for the development or preservation of the pneumococcus capsule are found in the body fluids of man and animals suffering from pneumococcus infection. For instance, capsules may be demonstrated with ease by the usual capsule-staining methods in the blood, serum, and inflammatory exudate of the infected rabbit and white mouse. Capsules may be equally well marked in the fresh sputum of pneumonia patients, especially in the early stages of the disease and in the exudate accompanying such pneumococcus infections as meningitis, otitis media, and empyema. In sputum and the exudates of various localized infections, the organisms are, however, frequently degenerated or under chemical conditions unfavorable for capsule staining, and satisfactory results are not then easily obtained. The same is often true of the scrapings from lungs of patients dead of pneumonia, even in the stage of red hepatization.

The swelling of the capsule under the influence of type-specific rabbit antipneumococcal serum is the basis of the diagnostic Neufeld *"quellung"* reaction.

In artificial cultivation, if the nutrient medium is not milk or does not contain serum, capsules cannot usually be demonstrated by the ordinary methods of preparing and staining. Capsules may, however, with much regularity be demonstrated on pneumococci, in agar, broth, or on almost all, if not all, artificial media, irrespective of the length of time the organisms have been under artificial cultivation if beef or rabbit serum is used as the diluent, when they are spread on the cover-glass for staining.

The pneumococcus is nonmotile and possesses no flagella. Spores are not formed. Swollen and irregular involution forms are common in cultures more than a day old.

The pneumococcus is stained readily with all the usual aqueous anilin dyes. It is gram-positive. Special methods of staining have been devised for demonstration of the capsule. The one most generally used is the copper-sulphate method of Hiss.

Huntoon's capsule stain described in the section on staining is the easiest one to apply successfully on material from cultures. It is not adapted to use on pathological material.

For simple staining of pneumococci in tissue sections, the Gram-Weigert technic is excellent. For demonstration of the capsules in tissue sections, Wadsworth has described a simple method.

Cultivation.—The pneumococcus being more strictly parasitic than many other bacteria, presents greater difficulties in its cultivation. On meat extract media growth does not take place with regularity. On those media, however, which have beef or veal infusion for their basis, growth can be obtained with considerable regularity, although such growth may be sparse and delicate.

Growth takes place most regularly at a temperature of 37.5° C. Development does not usually occur below 25° nor above 41° C. At ordinary room temperature,

18–22° C., the temperature used for gelatin cultivation, growth of most varieties of pneumococci either does not take place at all or is exceedingly slow and unenergetic.

In our laboratory, Eaton has studied strains of pneumococci, isolated from blood and exudates, which grow only at a temperature about 25° C. At 37.5° C. these organisms either fail to grow or undergo lysis rapidly, unless incubated in an atmosphere containing about 10 per cent CO_2.

Aerobic and anaerobic conditions both permit the growth of pneumococcus, there being very little difference in speed or extent of growth along the course of deep stab cultures in favorable media. The most favorable reaction of media for the cultivation of this micro-organism is a pH of 7.6 to 7.8. Slight acidity, however, does not materially hamper development.

The broth or agar base for pneumococcus media must be carefully made, both in regard to nutrient contents and reaction. Ordinary meat extract media are not usually rich enough, and even carelessly made meat infusion broth may fail to grow pneumococci. In our laboratory we have come to use the "hormone" broth and agar media almost entirely for pneumococcus and streptococcus work. Douglas' tryptic digest broth is an excellent medium for the cultivation of pneumococci.

The growth of pneumococci on all media may be considerably enhanced by the addition of animal or human serum or whole blood. Additional substances which, among others, have a favorable influence are glucose, nutrose, and glycerin. The addition of the latter substances to the media, however, probably because of acid formation, hastens the death of pneumococcus cultures. An increase of the amount of peptone used for the preparation of media is desirable for the cultivation of this micro-organism; 2 to 4 per cent of peptone may be found advantageous.

Transfer of recently isolated pneumococcus from broth culture to broth culture necessitates rather heavy inoculation, since frequent failure is experienced when only a loopful or so is transferred. Cole mentions that about 0.1 c.c. should be transferred for every 5 c.c. of broth.

In suitable nutrient *broth*, growth is rapid, and within twenty-four hours leads to slight clouding of the fluid. This clouding, as a rule, eventually disappears as the micro-organisms, sinking to the bottom of the tube or disintegrating, leave the fluid more or less clear. In broth, pneumococci have a tendency to form short chains. When glucose has been added to the broth, growth is more rapid and profuse, but considerable acid formation causes the cultures to die out rapidly. It is possible, however, to employ glucose as a growth-enhancing element in broth cultures without interfering with the viability of the cultures by adding small quantities (1 per cent) of sterile, powdered calcium carbonate. This method of cultivation in broth is especially adapted to the production of mass cultures for purposes of immunization or agglutination. The addition of ascitic fluid or blood serum to broth, in the proportion of one to three, makes an extremely favorable medium in which growth is rapid and profuse.

Upon *meat infusion agar plates*, pneumococcus growth is not unlike that of streptococcus. The colonies are small, round, and slightly more transparent than those of the streptococci. They appear more moist than streptococcus colonies and often are more flat. Microscopically, the colonies are finely granular, with dark centers and slightly corrugated lighter-colored peripheral areas. Under high magnification no such intertwining convolutions can be seen as those noticed under similar magnification in streptococcus cultures. The addition of animal protein to agar results in the more rapid development, larger size, and deeper opacity of the colonies.

Agar stab cultures show growth within twenty-four to thirty-six hours, which takes place with equal thickness along the entire course of the stab. There is nothing distinctive in these cultures to differentiate them from similar streptococcus cultures.

In gelatin plate and *stab cultures* at 22° C., growth, as a rule, does not take place. This, however, is not true of all races of pneumococci. Occasionally strains are met with which will grow fairly abundantly in gelatin at a temperature of 22° C. When the gelatin is rendered sufficiently firm to bear 25° to 26° C. without melting, growth appears slowly and sparsely as minute, grayish white, transparent colonies. The gelatin is not liquefied.

Growth upon *milk* is profuse, resulting in the production of acid and coagulation of the medium. Races are encountered in which this is suppressed and coagulation in milk is absent or long delayed.

Upon *Löffler's coagulated blood serum*, the pneumococcus develops into moist, watery, discrete colonies which tend to disappear by a drying out of the colonies after some days, differing in this from streptococcus colonies, which, though also discrete, are usually more opaque and whiter in appearance than those of the pneumococcus and remain unchanged for a longer time.

Upon mixtures of whole rabbit's blood and agar, the pneumococcus grows well, and forms, after four or five days, thick, black surface colonies, not unlike sun blisters on red paint. These colonies are easily distinguished from those of streptococci, and are of considerable differential value (Hiss).

The surface of the colony is usually slightly elevated at the center with concentric small raised rings alternating with depressions spreading to the periphery. The colony resembles the common type of "checker-man."

Pneumococcus colonies *on blood plates* may cause a slight halo of hemolysis and methemoglobin formation with a zone of greenish color about the colony after forty-eight hours or longer in the incubator.

The hemolysin formation by pneumococcus is slight, but quite definite. It occurs late, rarely sooner than forty-eight hours, but is mentioned because errors of diagnosis through ignorance of this might occur.

Wadsworth has recommended a medium composed of ascitic fluid to which agar has been added—sufficient to give a soft, jelly-like consistency. He observed prolonged viability and the preservation of the virulence on this medium.

For the purpose of differentiating pneumococci from streptococci, Hiss devised a medium of beef serum one part, and distilled water two parts, to which is added 1 per cent of inulin, and enough litmus to render the medium a clear, transparent blue. By fermentation of the inulin, the pneumococcus acidifies this mixture, causing coagulation of the serum. Streptococci, with the exception of certain nonhemolytic indifferent strains, do not ferment inulin.

Since inulin fermentation is a very important differential characteristic of the pneumococcus, it is necessary to say a few words about the irregularity with which it occurs. Occasionally, failure to ferment inulin is due to the fact that the particular strain of pneumococcus does not grow well in the inulin medium made up by the older method of Hiss. The addition of 1 per cent of peptone to this medium has been suggested by Buerger and is a distinct improvement. It may happen, however, that occasional strains will react irregularly on different preparations of inulin. These irregularities must be taken into consideration when this test is used for differential purposes.

Isolation.—For the *isolation* of pneumococci from mixed cultures or from material containing other species, such as sputum, surface smears of the material are made upon plates of neutral glucose agar, glucose serum agar, or blood agar. According to the number of bacteria present in the infected material, it may be smeared directly upon the plate, or diluted with sterile broth before planting. After incubation for twenty-four hours, the pneumococcus colonies are easily differentiated from all but those of streptococcus. With practice, however, they may be distinguished from these also, by their smoother edges and greater transparency and flatness.

The easiest way to isolate pneumococci from mixed culture and especially from material from patients like sputum, pulmonary exudate, etc., is injection into white mice. When sputum is used the sputum should be washed by gently rinsing in successive watch glasses or petri plates containing salt solution or broth. It can be injected directly into a white mouse, intraperitoneally, or, if very stringy or dry, can be rubbed in a mortar with a little broth before injection. Great care must be taken not to inject too much material. The details of this method are given in connection with clinical considerations in a subsequent paragraph. If virulent pneumococci are present, death will occur within twenty-four hours, or thereabouts. Pneumococci will be found in pure culture in the heart's blood and in large numbers in the peritoneal exudate.

Pneumococcus Types.—As stated above, Neufeld and Händel, in 1910, found that pneumococci were by no means all alike, serologically. Although all the true pneumococci have morphological and cultural characteristics which would appear to classify them as a single species, it was found that within this apparently homologous group there were sharp serological differentiations. Dochez and Gillespie not only confirmed the work of Neufeld and Händel, but made a careful study of pneumococcus types as they occurred in America, both by agglutination reactions and by protection tests on mice. They isolated a large number of pneumococcus strains, and immunized animals with them. The sera of these animals were now examined for cross-agglutination with the various strains and for their protective powers on mice. It was found that the pneumococci they studied fell into very sharp classes.

The classification of Dochez and Gillespie, which has been many times confirmed, divided the pneumococci into three main types, numbered I, II, III and included, as Group IV, a category for the pneumococci which, because of their heterogeneity, appeared to be unclassifiable by immunological methods. This classification into three fixed types and a miscellaneous group was widely accepted and has been used constantly since 1913.

The organisms classified as Type I and Type II and those relegated to Group IV are morphologically and culturally typical pneumococci. The Type III organism represents what was formerly spoken of as *Streptococcus mucosus*, but which is included among the pneumococci because it ferments inulin, is soluble in bile and has pathogenic properties which are quite similar to those of the pneumococci.

During the years between 1913 and 1928, subgroups of Type II were recognized by Avery and Clough. Lister, working in South Africa, found homogeneous types, which he called A, B and C. Lister's Types C and B corresponded to Types I and II of the American classification, respectively; his Type A was not identified with any of the three fixed types in this country. Atypical varieties of Type III were recognized by Cooper, and by Harris, Sugg and Neill. It became apparent from these studies that there were unquestionably a number of other types of pneumococci in the United States and in different parts of the world.

The chief extension of the serological differentiation of pneumococci began about 1928 when Cooper, working in the laboratory of the New York City Department of Health, found that only about 60 per cent of the cultures of pneumococci at the Harlem Hospital could be classified into types. The subsequent investigations of Cooper and her associates have established 29 additional types among the pneumococci previously classified as belonging in Group IV or as atypical members of Types II and III. By means of agglutination reactions and protection tests made with immune sera prepared by Cooper and others, 32 types of pneumococci, designated as Types I to XXXII, are now recognizable. The majority of these newly established types are quite distinct, with only slight cross-reactions occurring between some of them. The notable cross-reactions occur between Types II and V, Types III and VIII, Types VII and XVIII, Types XV and XXX. In Cooper's correlation, Type IV includes the *Pneumococcus* 10 of Griffith, and Group IVB of Robinson; Type V includes subtype IIA of Avery; Type VI includes subtype IIB of Avery; and Type VIII includes atypical III. There is some evidence that additional types will be recognized, beyond the present serological classification.

Clinical correlations can be made between the types of pneumococci and the characteristics of the disease. The recognition of the original three types formed the basis for a rational serum therapy of pneumonia and it appears from the investigations of Cooper, Park and their associates, and of Sutliff and Finland, that type-specific serum treatment can be developed for pneumonia due to most of the organisms of Types IV to XXXII. The obvious importance of these discoveries for the treatment of pneumonia and for epidemiological studies will be dealt with more fully in subsequent paragraphs.

Pneumococcus (Streptococcus) Mucosus (Type III).—First definitely described by Howard and Perkins in 1901, this variety of pneumococcus was subsequently carefully studied by Schottmüller, who isolated it from cases of parametritis, peritonitis, meningitis, and phlebitis. It has since been described by many as the incitant of lobar pneumonia and of a variety of other lesions and as often an apparently harmless inhabitant of the normal mouth. Morphologically, though showing a marked tendency to form chains, on solid media it often appears in the diplococcus form. It is enclosed in an extensive capsule, which appears with much regularity and persistence. Though very similar in appearance, therefore, to pneumococci, these bacteria do not appear in the typical lancet shape. Upon solid media they show a tendency to grow in transparent moist masses. The regularity with which this micro-organism ferments inulin medium, makes it probable that it is more accurate to place it with the group of pneumococci than with that of streptococci.

Most of the organisms of this group show the common characteristics of the pneumococci and are soluble in bile. Occasional strains, as one studied by Dochez and Gillespie, neither ferment inulin nor are bile soluble. Rarely do they cause hemolysis. From the studies carried out upon this group it must be concluded that while perfectly distinct in its formation of a heavy mucoid colony and capsulation, it is more closely related to the pneumococci than to the true streptococci. As would be expected from its capsulation, it is very virulent.

Chemistry and Serology.—The serological differentiation of types of pneumococci rests upon chemical differences in the constituents of the cells of these organisms. General information about these chemical and antigenic differences have been given in Chapter IV and in Section II. We shall summarize here the most clearly demonstrated facts with respect to the chemistry, serology and immunology of the pneumococci.

The virulent pneumococcus is composed of a cell body and a capsule. The substances in each of these parts of the cell are chemically and antigenically different. In the cell body the substances of greatest immunological importance are the bacterial *proteins* and lipoids; in the capsule the substances of greatest significance are *polysaccharides*. Common group antigens and heterophile antigens occur in the cell bodies. The type-specific substances are the polysaccharides composing the capsules.

The so-called *nucleoprotein* of pneumococci, occurring in the cell-bodies, has been shown repeatedly to be a species specific antigen (Avery and Heidelberger). It is common to all types of pneumococci and the serum of animals injected with the nucleoprotein will, under suitable conditions, react with all varieties of pneumococci, causing them to agglutinate and serving for the demonstration of other serological reactions. It is, therefore, the group antigen.

The material in the capsule is a complex polysaccharide. This is the soluble specific substance, the SSS, discovered by Dochez and Avery in 1917 in broth cultures of pneumococci and in the blood and urine of patients with pneumonia. Following the observation of similar substances in several species of bacteria and their recognition as partial antigens or "haptenes" in 1923 by Zinsser and Parker, who called them "residue antigen," the polysaccharides of the pneumococci were extensively investigated by Avery and his associates with most important results for practical and general immunology. The result of much experimental work, both chemical and immunological, has proved that these polysaccharides in the capsules are the type specific substances of pneumococci. From Heidelberger's reviews of the subject it is apparent that the chief polysaccharide of each type of pneumococcus is chemically distinct. The polysaccharide of Type I pneumococcus contains nitrogen in an amino-sugar combination, on hydrolysis yields galacturonic acid and is dextrorotatory. Type II polysaccharide is a dextrorotatory complex of weakly acidic glucose units and does not contain nitrogen. Type III polysaccharide, also nitrogen free, is levorotatory and is composed of glucose and aldobionic acid. These complex molecules of glucose and uronic acids do not contain either phosphorus or nitrogen and do not give a color reaction with iodine. They are large molecules, although the molecular weight of 118,000 assigned by Babers and Goebel to the Type III polysaccharide may not be correct.

The purified polysaccharides react readily with immune sera produced by animals injected with whole pneumococci, and sera of animals infected with pneumococci. They produce skin reactions in immunized man and animals and by combining with antibodies in the tissue fluids and blood of animals inhibit the antipneu-mococcal effects of immune serum. These substances, as originally isolated by them-selves, do not act as functional antigens. They do not stimulate the production of antibodies. They are, therefore, typical *haptenes* as defined by Landsteiner. When these polysaccharides are united to antigenic proteins, from the pneumococci or other sources, they confer their own specificity upon the complex compound and when this protein-polysaccharide compound is injected into an animal the resultant antiserum reacts sharply with the complex or isolated polysaccharide and little, if at all, with the carrier-protein. The convincing demonstration of this fact was made by Avery and Goebel, who combined the p-aminobenzyl ester of Type III polysaccharide, through diazotization, with horse serum globulin, injected this complex into rabbits and obtained an immune serum which reacted specifically with the natural Type III polysaccharide and protected mice against large doses of virulent Type III pneu-mococci. Avery has succinctly summarized the knowledge of the rôle of specific carbohydrates in pneumococcus infection and immunity.

The results of these experiments, added to those of Landsteiner on diazotized arsanilic acid proteins and other protein-haptene compounds, are confirmation of theories of the chemical basis of immunological specificity. Previously perplexing evidences of immunological reactions crossing the boundaries of biological relation-ships can be satisfactorily explained with the aid of this knowledge. Examples of this fact are the immunologically and chemically similar polysaccharides found in Type II pneumococci, in yeast and in Type B Friedländer bacilli.

The antigenic and chemical composition of the pneumococci are by no means as simply or as completely known as the above summary might seem to indicate. Other polysaccharides have been isolated in various degrees of purity from these cells. One is the "C" substance of Tillett and Francis. Another is the antigenic polysaccharide isolated by Wadsworth and Brown from Type I pneumococci. The "A" substance found by Enders in autolysates of Types I and II pneumococci has been shown to be the acetyl polysaccharide of Avery and Goebel. The acetyl polysaccharide induces immunity when injected into mice, but does not lead to the production of precipitins. It is a functional antigen. Numerous discrepancies in the results of investigations can be harmonized by correlating them with the acetylated and de-acetylated forms of this polysaccharide.

In addition, the ether soluble fraction of Type I *Pneumococcus* has been used by Wadsworth and Brown as an antigen in complement fixation tests. Other lipoids or lipoid protein compounds in pneumococci have been shown by Bailey and Shoub to have the characteristics of heterophile antigen, causing the production of hemolysin for sheep cells when injected into rabbits.

The statement that some pneumococci are capsulated while others lack capsules has been made questionable by the demonstration of Churchman and Emelianoff that all bacteria, even the R (rough) pneumococci, are actually encapsulated. It is obvious that the anatomy of bacteria requires further investigation. While there may be un-certainties in morphological terminology, the chemical and immunological discussion given above appears to be based upon well-established facts.

Enzymatic Hydrolysis of Capsular Polysaccharide.—The knowledge that the capsules of pneumococci are composed of polysaccharides and that non-capsulated pneumococci are not virulent led Avery to search for an enzyme capable of removing the capsule by hydrolysis of the carbohydrate. With Dubos he obtained from cultures of an organism isolated from a peat bog in New Jersey, a bacterial enzyme specifically hydrolytic for the Type III polysaccharide. This intracellular bacterial enzyme can be extracted from the bacilli. It removes the capsules from Type III *Pneumococcus* by decomposing the capsular polysaccharide, renders the organisms nonvirulent and readily phagocyted. Injections of the enzyme into mice protected them against virulent Type III *Pneumococcus* and exerted a curative action on an established infection. Goodner and Dubos in a study of the quantitative relation between the enzyme and course of the disease in experimental dermal pneumococcus infection in rabbits determined that the fundamental relationship is that between the quantity of enzyme and the total amount of specific polysaccharide present in the body. They point out that this "enzyme is not a therapeutic substance *per se*, but one which, by decomposing the capsular substance of the pneumococci and thus preparing the bacterial cells for phagocytosis, initiates a process which the body must be in a condition to carry on if the animal is to recover. Hence, in the use of the enzyme, this capacity of the body to complete the reaction must be reckoned with."

Bacteriolytic enzymes, active against pneumococcal polysaccharides have been found by Dubos in immune sera, in leukocytes and in animal tissues.

Variability.—*Dissociation.*—In addition to morphological and physiological variations associated with the growth curve, pneumococci exhibit striking dissociative phenomena, some of which amount to complete transformation of types. The chief phases of dissociation are the smooth, (S), rough, (R), and mucoid, (M). These expressions of variability have not only biological and systematic significance, but are important in all immunological and epidemiological investigations of pneumococci.

Although there were older observations on variations of colonies and properties of pneumococci, the modern study of these changes began in 1923 when Griffith produced avirulent strains of pneumococci by growing the organisms in type specific antisera. This loss of virulence was correlated at once with the change from the S (smooth) type to the R (rough) type. Since then there has been general confirmation of this observation, all investigators noting that the smooth colonies are made up of encapsulated organisms and that such organisms are virulent, while the rough, nodular, friable colonies are composed of noncapsulated cocci, which lack virulence. Between these types, and often present on the same blood agar plate as separate colonies or daughter colonies, there are a great variety of intermediate colony forms, and organisms of intermediate properties. The pneumococcus variants intermediate between the S and R forms have been described by Klumpen (whose paper is well illustrated), by Blake and Trask and by others whose names will be found in these communications. These observations indicate that the dissociation of S pneumococci by growth in homologous serum is not a simple S → R change but that a considerable number of intermediate variants with well-defined characteristics appear and disappear during the process. Homologous antiserum is one of the most potent influences bringing about this change from S to R in pneumococci. Its efficacy suggests that recovery from pneumonia may be in part due to a similar change in the organisms in the animal body under the influence of increasing production of anti-bacterial substances.

It has been noted by Shibley and Rogers and others that R forms are found in abundance in the lungs and exudates of persons recovering from pneumonia or in the later stages of the disease. Wadsworth and Sickles and Paul have presented evidence that this type of dissociation actually occurs *in vivo* in immunized horses and dogs.

The S → R change is associated with a diminution of agglutinability in homologous antiserum and sometimes a new agglutinability in heterologous antisera. With the loss of the capsule the organism loses its type specific substance and hence differs antigenically from the smooth form from which it was derived. R forms are group-specific only, but may regain type-specificity under special conditions. The reversion of R-forms to S-forms has been accomplished by Paul.

The first evidence that one type of pneumococcus can be converted into another type was presented by Griffith in 1928. To accomplish this Griffith injected into mice a mixture of the living R form of one type of pneumococcus and heat-killed suspension of virulent pneumococci of another type. Dawson and Dawson and Sia brought about this sort of transformation *in vitro* by growing R forms of one type of *Pneumococcus* in a medium containing homologous anti-R serum and whole heat-killed S organisms of another type. Alloway, carrying these experiments further, transformed R pneumococci of any type into S forms of different types by cultivating them in broth containing filtered solutions of alcoholic precipitates of extracts of the S forms. In this medium, R pneumococci, irrespective of their type derivation, developed and thereafter retained all the type-specific characteristics of the S pneumococci from which the extract was prepared. The R forms of pneumococci appear to be potentially capable of producing capsular polysaccharides at any time. The expression and direction of this inherent variability is governed by various stimuli, one of which is present in such an extract as that used by Alloway, but for its effective action it requires some factor present in blood and serum.

The transformation of pneumococci into streptococci may or may not occur. Topley and Wilson place these organisms in the same genus, *Streptococcus*, and use the name *Streptococcus pneumoniae* for the organism we have been calling *Pneumococcus*. This may indicate that the discussion of this question may be regarded by some as "academic." Morgenroth, Schnitzer and Berger by special methods have reported the conversion of R form pneumococci into *Streptococcus viridans* and for many years Rosenow in this country has upheld this thesis. Reimann could not confirm these observations. We are of the opinion that although R pneumococci may occasionally resemble *Streptococcus viridans* in their form, chain formation and granular growth, the common property of production of green discoloration of blood cells in agar or suspension together with these morphological similarities do not establish the fact of their transformation. Usually, under suitable conditions, the pneumococci remain soluble in bile and ferment inulin. Long-continued observation of a culture coupled with serological tests may be necessary to bring out these differences. We must admit, however, that these are borderline strains which are difficult to assign to one or the other genus and that the manipulation of the cultures may force the dissociative process to take one or the other direction. In general, we are not convinced that pneumococci can be transformed into streptococci.

Resistance.—On artificial media, the variability of the pneumococcus is not great

Cultures upon agar or bouillon should be transplanted every third or fourth day, if the cultures are kept within an incubator. In all media in which rapid acid formation takes place, such as glucose media, the death of cultures may occur more rapidly. In media containing protein and of a proper reaction, preservation for one or even two weeks is possible. The longer the particular race has been kept upon artificial media, the more profuse is its growth, and the greater its viability, both qualities going hand in hand with diminishing parasitism. The length of life may be much increased by preservation at low temperature, in the dark, and by the exclusion of air. In calcium carbonate broth and kept in the ice chest, cultures may often remain alive for months.

Neufeld has succeeded in keeping pneumococci alive and virulent, by taking out the spleens of mice dead of pneumococcus infection and preserving them in a Petri dish in a desiccator, in the dark and cold. In this way, the organisms can be cultivated from the spleen, and will be found virulent for longer periods than in culture media. The best way to get such cultures back is by injecting a suspension of the desiccated spleen, in broth, into a mouse, and recovering the pneumococcus from the heart's blood. For other methods for the preservation of cultures, the reader is referred to the Technical Section of this book.

In sputum the viability of pneumococci seems to exceed that observed in culture. The studies of Guarnieri, Bordoni-Uffreduzzi, and others have shown that pneumococci slowly dried in sputum may remain alive and virulent for one to four months, when protected from light; and as long as nineteen days when exposed to diffused light at room temperature. Experiments by Ottolenghi have confirmed these results; the virulence becomes considerably attenuated before death of the cocci. Studies by Wood, whose attention was focused chiefly upon pneumococcus viability in finely divided sputum—in a condition in which inhalation transmission would be possible—have shown that pneumococci survive for only about one and one-half hours, under ordinary conditions of light and temperature. Exposed to strong sunlight, pneumococci die within an hour.

Low temperatures slightly above zero are conducive to the prolongation of life and the preservation of virulence.

The resistance of the pneumococcus to heat is low, 52° C. destroying it in ten minutes. To germicidal agents, carbolic acid, bichloride of mercury, permanganate of potassium, etc., the pneumococcus is sensitive, being destroyed by weak solutions after short exposures.

The disinfection of sputum, difficult because of the protective coating of the secretions about the bacteria, has been studied by Wadsworth. He found that pneumococci in exudates are most rapidly destroyed by 20 per cent alcohol, other and stronger disinfectants being less efficient, probably because of slighter powers of diffusion.

As pneumococci are sensitive to many disinfectants, soaps, bile, sodium oleate, dyes and derivatives of quinine there have been many chemotherapeutic trials of all of these substances. Acriflavine has some value as an antiseptic. A large amount of work has been done with *optochin* (*ethylhydrocupreine*), introduced as a chemotherapeutic agent in 1911 by Morgenroth and Levy. This drug is at times a valuable remedy, but is limited in its usefulness by its toxicity and its tendency to injure the optic nerve. The chemotherapy of pneumococcus infections has been discussed in detail by Browning. Experimental and clinical evidence, summarized by Mellon and by others, indicates that sulfanilamide and some of its derivatives, particularly sulfa-pyridine, may be of value in the chemotherapy of pneumococcal infections (Blake).

Toxic Products.—In pneumococcus infections, as in other diseases caused by bacteria, there are evidences of toxemia, since the mechanical effects produced by the organisms cannot account for all the symptoms. Although numerous attempts have been made to demonstrate the toxins produced by pneumococci, the knowledge of these products is still very imperfect.

The capsular polysaccharides are not toxic. They interfere with the action of immune serum by combining with antibodies and they elicit allergic phenomena in immunized or hypersensitive patients and animals. But they do not injure the normal animal. The nucleoprotein of these bacteria is not essentially poisonous. It is antigenic and also gives rise to local and general disturbances when injected into a hypersensitive animal.

A poisonous crude fraction of the pneumococcus cell bodies was obtained by Macfadyen by trituration of the organisms after freezing, and extracting them with a 1:1000 caustic potash solution. Doses of 0.5 to 1 c.c. of this extract killed guinea-pigs and rabbits within a few minutes. He found a parallelism between the degree of toxicity and the virulence of the extracted culture. In 1912 Cole was inclined to believe that the poisons of the pneumococcus were of the nature of endotoxins and in 1932 he was of the opinion that autolysates of pneumococci were the only products of these organisms known to give rise to definite pathological effects.

The products of pneumococci dissolved in bile were shown by Cole to be hemolytic and toxic. The hemolytic substance was easily destroyed by heat and trypsin, was inhibited by cholesterol but was not neutralized by antipneumococcus serum. The substance causing methemoglobin was different from this hemotoxin. It is produced by the living cell and may be a peroxide.

A necrotizing toxic product of the cells was discovered by Parker.

In culture and in the animal body pneumococci liberate, probably during autolysis, a substance which causes capillary hemorrhages. This *purpura producing* material is heat stable and has some of the characteristics of a proteose. Julianelle and Reimann have investigated the derivatives of pneumococci which produce purpura and Mair discovered that susceptibility of mice to the action of this toxic material is an hereditary character.

It is not unlikely that the "virulin" obtained by Rosenow from pneumococci and pneumonic lungs was identical with or related to the polysaccharides of these organisms. Rosenow's virulin did not produce injury, but interfered with opsonins and other defensive antibodies. Pneumococcal leucocidin was described by Oram in 1934.

In 1936, Coca reported further on his studies of a fever-producing substance found in the filtrates of cultures of pneumococci. This substance was relatively toxic, elicited skin reactions in susceptible individuals and was antigenic. Further investigations are needed to determine whether or not this material is the long-sought toxin of the pneumococci.

White concluded in 1938 that the available evidence fails to bring conviction that the substances described should be regarded as true soluble toxins.

Virulence and Pathogenicity.—In the general section on virulence and in the previous paragraphs dealing with variability of pneumococci we have discussed the relation of virulence to the change from S to R forms in the process of dissociation. The R forms are nonvirulent. In this place we shall discuss other factors which influence virulence and pathogenicity.

The virulence of pneumococci is subject to much variation, depending upon the length of time during which the organisms have been cultivated. It has been mentioned above that under conditions such as those prevailing in dried sputum or blood the virulence of pneumococci may be preserved for several weeks. Ordinarily, the virulence diminishes as the cocci adapt themselves to life upon artificial media. Upon media containing animal protein, such as ascitic fluid or blood agar, this attenuation is less rapid than upon the simple meat-infusion preparations.

The maintenance of virulence is greatly aided by making transfers from broth to broth at intervals not longer than eight hours. Apparently cultures grown for as long as twenty-four hours diminish in virulence much more rapidly.

Swift has succeeded in keeping organisms of the pneumococcus and streptococcus varieties alive and virulent for a long time by centrifugating broth cultures, and drying the residue in a frozen condition *in vacuo*. This material can be kept for a very long time without death of the bacteria, and without loss of virulence.

In the blood of rabbits dead of a pneumococcus infection, sealed and kept in the dark, Foa has been able to preserve the virulence of pneumococci for forty-five days. The attenuation of virulent pneumococci on artificial media may be hastened, according to Fränkel, by cultivation of the organism at or above a temperature of 41° C.

The virulence of attenuated cultures may be rapidly enhanced by passage of the organisms through the bodies of susceptible animals.

Chesney as early as 1916 obtained evidence that there was some relationship between youth of cultures and their virulence, claiming that six- to eight-hour growths have greater infectivity than twenty-four-hour cultures. Felton made an important contribution in 1924 when, by a special method of his own of frequent transplantation at four-hour intervals, he succeeded in increasing ten millionfold the virulence of a practically avirulent strain of pneumococcus originating from a single cell.

Among the domestic animals white mice and rabbits are most susceptible. Guinea-pigs, dogs, rats, and cats are much more resistant. Guinea-pigs can be given astonishingly large doses of pneumococci without injury. Birds are practically immune. Kyes, who has studied pneumococcus infection in birds particularly, has shown that the fixed tissue cells of the liver, spleen and lungs destroy the organisms by prompt and effective phagocytosis.

The results of pneumococcus inoculation into susceptible animals vary according to the size of the dose, the virulence of the introduced bacteria, the mode of administration, and the susceptibility of the subject of the inoculation. Subcutaneous inoculation of virulent pneumococci into mice and rabbits usually results in an edematous exudation at the point of inoculation, which leads to septicemia and death within twenty-four to seventy-two hours. Intravenous inoculation is usually more rapidly fatal than the subcutaneous method. Intraperitoneal inoculation in rabbits results in the formation of a rapidly spreading peritonitis in which the exudates are accompanied by a deposit of fibrin. In almost all of these infections death is preceded by septicemia and the micro-organisms can be recovered from the heart's blood.

A definite pathological process called "dermal pneumonia" has been produced in rabbits by Goodner by the injection of virulent pneumococci into the skin of the animals. This process, which ends by crisis, lysis or fatal septicemia, is a useful experimentally produced lesion serving for the study of several pathological and immunological problems.

The production in animals of lesions comparable to the lobar pneumonia of human subjects has long been the aim of investigators. Wadsworth, recognizing that such lesions probably depended upon the partial immunity which enabled the infected subjects to localize the pneumococcus processes in the lungs after infection by way of the respiratory passages, succeeded in producing typical lobar pneumonia in rabbits by partially immunizing and inoculating them intratracheally. Lamar and Meltzer produced lobar pneumonia in dogs, in 1912, by injecting cultures in the bronchi and blowing them into the bronchioles. Similar experiments have been made by Winternitz and Hirschfelder.

Experimental pneumonia has been produced in mice by Stillman and Branch by inhalation of pneumococci by animals that have been intoxicated with alcohol before inhalation was practiced. Pneumonia occurred in 30 per cent of the alcoholized animals rendered partially immune by prolonged treatment. The same writers have shown a certain amount of localized immunization by inhalation methods which is extremely interesting in connection with Besredka's work.

The most striking parallelism between experimental infection and pneumonia in man has been obtained by Cecil and Blake. Using *Macacus* and other species of monkey, they injected small amounts, 0.1 to 0.2 c.c. of virulent pneumococcus cultures directly into the trachea, and, after an incubation time of a day or slightly longer, they obtained typical lobar pneumonias.

PNEUMOCOCCUS INFECTIONS IN MAN AND CLINICAL-BACTERIOLOGICAL CONSIDERATIONS

In man the most frequent lesion produced by the pneumococcus is acute lobar pneumonia. About 90 per cent of all cases of this disease are caused by the pneumococcus, the remainder being due to streptococci, influenza bacilli, and other organisms the relative frequency of which, in this disease, has been given in an earlier section of this chapter.

The relative frequency of the occurrence of the various types of pneumococci in man varies from year to year, in different localities and according to the ages of the patients. In order to show the incidence of the pneumococcus types in lobar pneumonia in the New York area the table on the following page is presented.

Pneumococci occur in the mouths of approximately 40 per cent of normal individuals. The relative frequency of the various types of pneumococci in the mouths of normal individuals cannot be known with certainty because of the many variables affecting the conditions. Among these variables the degree of exposure to other individuals harboring pneumococci is of the greatest importance, as shown by Smillie

INCIDENCE OF TYPES OF PNEUMOCOCCUS IN 5779 CASES OF LOBAR PNEUMONIA [1]

Types	Cases	Per Cent
I	1642	28.4
II	704	12.2
III	691	11.9
IV	275	4.8
V	409	7.1
VI	95	1.6
VII	358	6.2
VIII	397	6.9
IX–XXXII	1208	20.9

[1] Cecil, R. L. Lobar Pneumonia. From *A Textbook of Medicine*, edited by Russell L. Cecil. W. B. Saunders Co., Philadelphia, 1937.

and others. Since, however, the incidence of pneumococcus types in the mouths of normal persons has an obvious connection with the problem of auto-infection we present the following composite tabulation of the observations of Avery, Chickering, Cole, Dochez, Cecil and Park in order to give a general indication of this incidence in persons supposedly free from contacts with pneumonia patients.

INCIDENCE OF TYPES OF PNEUMOCOCCUS IN MOUTHS OF NORMAL PERSONS

TYPE OF PNEUMOCOCCUS	INCIDENCE	
	Number of Cases	Per Cent
Pneumococcus Present (all types)	328	41.52
Pneumococcus Absent	462	58.48
TOTAL	790	100.00
Type I	2	0.61
Type II	3	0.92
Type III	101	30.79
Group IV (Types IV to XXXII)	222	67.68
TOTAL	328	100.00

According to the experience of Dr. Maxwell Finland of the Boston City Hospital, the following are the commonest types of pneumococci found by him in each of a number of conditions, given in the order of their relative incidence: *Lobar Pneumonia*—Types I, III, II, VIII, VII, V, IV, XII XIV, XVIII, X, VI, IX. *Bronchial Pneumonia*—Types III, VIII, XX, V, X, XVIII, VII, IV. *Meningitis*—Types III, VIII, I, VII, X, V, also encountered II, IV, XI, XIV. *Otitis Media and Mastoiditis*—Types III, V, II, XIX.

In Dr. Finland's experience the most important organisms in regard to blood stream invasion are II, III, V, VIII, I, VII. Type III Bacteremia, according to him, being almost always fatal in adults. Type VIII, the typical III of Sugg and Harris, has the lowest mortality rate for bacteremic cases. The mortality rate of Type V (old IIa) is almost as high as that of Type II. Dr. Finland has found V and VII pneumococcus almost as favorably influenced by specific antiserum as Type I. Bullowa has reported on serum treatment of Types VIII and XIV.

There has been a great deal of discussion concerning the route by which infection of the lung comes about after the pneumococcus has entered a susceptible subject. The difficulties experienced in infecting animals by direct instillation of pneumococci into the lungs, have inclined many observers to assume that infection of the blood, or bacteremia, precedes pulmonary lodgment.

Blake and Cecil, however, succeeded in producing various types of pneumonias in the lower monkeys (*Macacus syrichtus*, etc.) by injecting small amounts of virulent organisms directly into the trachea with a fine needle. When they injected virulent pneumococcus they obtained symptoms within twenty-four hours, rapid respiration and positive blood cultures. Such monkeys often died within eight to twelve days, with typical pneumonic autopsy findings.

Winternitz, Smith and Robinson suggested another possibility. They believe that the tracheal ciliated mucous epithelium renders it difficult for bacteria to reach the lung by this open route, and call attention to the great difficulty which has been encountered in attempts to produce disease by mere inhalation without injury of the respiratory tract. They concluded that infection of the lung is generally accomplished by the entrance of the bacteria into the lymphatics surrounding the trachea through some injury to the mucosa which then affords a direct path for infection. Insufficient attention has been paid to these observations.

According to Cole, when pneumonia is secondary to septicemia it is usually of the lobular type. Experiments of Meltzer seem to indicate that infection is facilitated by closure of the small bronchioles, and cold or chilling may possibly stimulate the mucous glands so as to plug these.

In the course of the development of pneumonia the infecting organisms are located in the pulmonary alveolae and the smaller bronchioles, and appear in the sputum. In order to apply specific serum therapy all pneumonia cases should be typed whenever possible.

Pneumococcus Typing.—The determination of types of pneumococci occurring in sputum, exudates, secretions and cultures is made by serological procedures for demonstrating agglutination of the organisms, effects upon the capsules and precipitation of specific soluble substances. The chief methods are (a) inoculation of mice, (b) the Neufeld "quellung" or capsular swelling reaction and (c) precipitin tests with suitable extracts, urine, blood serum or culture filtrates. These are described in detail in the section on Technical Methods.

Blood Cultures in Pneumonia.—During the course of pneumonia, pneumococcus septicemia is common. Fränkel in 1902, stated that he believed in most, if not all, cases of pneumonia the organisms are present in the blood stream at some stage of the disease. The older literature, if carefully reviewed, shows positive blood cultures in about 25 per cent of the cases. In the Rockefeller Hospital where systematic blood cultures were made, it is stated by Cole that in 448 cases of lobar pneumonia, the pneumococci were obtained by blood culture in 30.3 per cent. When blood cultures were repeatedly made at frequent intervals the positive findings were obtained in 50 per cent.

In making blood cultures it is important that plenty of blood be taken and inoculated. The culture is taken from the basilic vein with a sterile syringe as follows:

At least 5 or 10 c.c. of blood should be added to flasks of hormone glucose broth, of a pH of 7.6 or 7.8, containing not less than 100 c.c. of broth. Hormone glucose agar plates should be made at the same time, and graded quantities of blood can be added to successive plates in order that one may obtain a numerical estimate of the number of organisms per cubic centimeter. Growth is often delayed, and no negative report should be finally turned in for at least three days.

Cole and others have attached great prognostic significance to blood cultures. Cole believes that the development of a septicemia is of very serious prognostic significance, and the typing of the organisms from the blood culture is important in this respect since the mortality of Type II cases in the blood in his experience is 73.4 per cent, and of Type III cases in the blood, 100 per cent, whereas in Group IV cases a mortality of only 52.3 per cent, and the low percentage, 26 per cent, in Type I blood culture cases, he attributes to the effect of serum treatment.

Mortality.—The death rate in pneumonia depends upon the race, sex, age and general condition of the patient, the type of infecting pneumococcus, the degree of involvement of the lung, the presence or absence of septicemia, the occurrence of complications, the promptness of specific therapy and many other factors. General experience has indicated that the average case mortality is approximately 30 per cent in untreated patients. The highest death rates occur in infections with Type I, II and III, ranging from about 35 to 50 per cent. Quoting again from Cecil [1] the following statistics are presented:

DEATH RATE FOR FIRST EIGHT TYPES OF PNEUMOCOCCAL PNEUMONIAS *

Types	Cases	Deaths	Per Cent
I	762	288	37.7
II	557	258	46.3
III	999	474	47.4
IV	166	42	25.3
V	254	73	28.8
VI	68	18	26.4
VII	227	50	22.0
VIII	295	55	18.6

* Cecil, R. L. Lobar Pneumonia. From *A Textbook of Medicine.* Edited by Russell L. Cecil. W. B. Saunders Co., Philadelphia, 1937, p. 125.

Lesions in Man Other than Pneumonia.—Aside from pneumonia, the pneumococcus may cause a number of other types of infection in human beings either subsequent to pulmonary infection, or primary.

The most common complications of pneumococcus infection of the lung are empyema, endocarditis, and pericarditis, meningitis and arthritis. Meningitis may occur as a primary disease especially in children without previous traceable pneumonia. The same may be said of arthritis.

Empyema was a very frequent and fatal complication of the war pneumonias, and pneumococci can be easily obtained by ordinary cultural methods from puncture fluid. It has recently been suggested that empyema is more apt to follow in cases which have been treated with serum, perhaps because of its effect in localizing the infection. This point has not been settled, but it would seem to us that the only manner in which such a result could occur would be by just such localizing effect, and this would mean that had not the serum localized the infection the outcome might have been fatal, a consideration which all the more persuades us of the wisdom of treating Type I cases with serum whenever possible. *Pneumococcus meningitis*, whether primary or secondary, is a very fatal disease from which recovery is rare. Direct serum treatment should always be tried if it is a Type I case, and intravenous treatment to forestall a possible septicemia should also be applied.

Pneumococcus peritonitis occurs particularly in children.

The pneumococcus also causes a very severe form of corneal ulceration which presents great difficulties to successful therapy. The bacteriologist confronted with severe ulcerative infections of the eye, in which ulcerations are especially localized on the cornea, should search particularly for pneumococci.

ANTIBODY FORMATION, IMMUNITY, AND SPECIFIC THERAPY

Recovery from a spontaneous pneumococcus infection confers immunity for only a short period. Two and three attacks of lobar pneumonia in the same individual are not unusual, and it is uncertain whether even a temporary immunity is acquired in such infections. Our recent knowledge of types has made it seem not impossible that successive attacks of pneumonia may be due to consecutive infection with different types of organisms, thus leaving open the possibility of the acquisition of prolonged immunity. But this seems doubtful in view of the fact that Chickering and others have seen individuals who have had four or five attacks within a relatively short time. By studies of recurrent attacks of experimental lobar pneumonia in dogs, Robertson has shown that while one attack results in an increased antipneumococcal immunity, it is not of sufficient degree to protect the animal against subsequent infection with the same or even smaller doses of pneumococci. The local cellular reaction appeared to be more important than generalized immunity.

Active immunization of laboratory animals may be carried out by various methods. The method usually followed is to begin by injecting attenuated or dead bacteria or bacterial extracts. Subsequent injections are then made with gradually increasing doses of living, virulent micro-organisms. Great care in increasing the dosage should be exercised since the loss of an animal after two or three weeks' treatment by a carelessly high dose of pneumococci is not unusual. Wadsworth centrifugalizes freshly grown pneumococcus cultures and to the pneumococci sediment adds a definite quantity of concentrated salt solution. At the end of twelve hours, the pneumococci are dead and considerable destruction of the cell-bodies has taken place. Dilution with water until the solution equals 0.85 per cent sodium chloride now prepares the emulsion for inoculation. The sera of animals immunized with pneumococci contain active bactericidal substances.

Specific *agglutinins* in pneumococcus immune sera were first thoroughly studied by Neufeld and since then have been made the subject of extensive studies by Wadsworth, Hiss, and many others. Pneumococci do not regularly agglutinate in diluted immune sera and agglutinations are best studied in suspensions of more concentrated immune serum. Agglutination begins at the end of about fifteen minutes, and is evidenced both by formation of clumps and by the sediment.

Specific precipitating antibodies have been demonstrated in pneumococcus immune serum by Neufeld, Wadsworth, Hiss, and others, the organism for such tests being brought into solution either with bile or with concentrated salt solution. Such sera also contain powerful opsonic substances, or, as Neufeld and Rimpau prefer to call them, "bacteriotropins." It seems most likely that such phagocytosis-aiding substances are most powerfully concerned in protection and cure. Clough has reported an increase of opsonins at the time of crisis, and Dochez has shown that protective substances may appear in the serum at or soon after the crisis. The outcome of a case according to Cole depends very largely on the virulence of the organism and on the ability of the body first to limit the local infection and to prevent the invasion of the blood with the organisms. In this process, of course, the protective and opsonic bacteriotropic substances would play a most important part.

Goodner has made a careful study of vaccination of rabbits infected with Type I pneumococci by the intradermal method. Rabbits so inoculated develop a visible local lesion, usually followed by septicemia and death. When vaccination with dead pneumococci of the homologous type is practiced, a certain amount of immunity develops five days after a single vaccination. If the rabbit is vaccinated and then infected within the period necessary for the development of the immunity, the course of the subsequent disease is shortened almost mathematically in proportion to the interval between vaccination and infection; and rabbits vaccinated five days before infection may be completely protected against the local lesion, or—at any rate— against death. Such experiments encourage the hope that eventually, with polyvalent pneumococcus vaccines, a partially successful vaccination technique may be developed under circumstances prevailing in military mobilizations, labor camps, etc., when epidemics are to be expected. Under ordinary conditions, the sporadic nature of the occurrence of pneumonia and the variety of responsible types renders practical application less likely, for obvious reasons.

The injection of pneumococci into suitable animals produces *heterophile antibodies.* After reviewing the evidence in 1936, Plummer concluded that these antibodies have little or no influence upon the course of pneumonia in man.

Passive Immunization and Serum Therapy.—The history of attempts to produce sera for passive immunization in man is extensive. For a general review the reader is referred to the monograph on "Lobar pneumonia and serum therapy," by Lord and Heffron.

The rational beginning based on the recognition of different pneumococcus types was made by Neufeld and Händel in Germany, and carried to a considerable degree of success by Cole and his associates at the Rockefeller Hospital in New York. By the immunization of horses with the various types of pneumococci mentioned above, considerable success has attended the use of sera produced with Type I. Favorable results have been obtained with antiserums for Types II, V, VII and VIII. A satisfactory therapeutic Type III serum has not been produced.

Type XIV antipneumococcus horse serum was found by Finland and Curren to have the disadvantageous property of agglutinating human erythrocytes. Serious reactions were produced in patients treated with this serum. Absorption with human red corpuscles removed these agglutinins. The sera of rabbits immunized with Type XIV pneumococci did not agglutinate human erythrocytes.

The actual method of producing serum in horses at the present time depends upon the intravenous injection of suspensions of young pneumococci which have been grown in broth. The organisms used in the earlier injections are killed either with heat or chemicals (formaldehyde). For the later injections similar killed suspensions may be employed or live organisms may be substituted. The method of Cole is to inject daily for six days the killed bacteria thrown down from 50 c.c. of a twelve-hour broth culture. Starting a week later a similar series of injections is given. Another week's rest is given and three daily injections are made, but these, by Cole's method, are of the live organisms from 2.5 c.c. of culture. The doses and times of injections will vary with individual experience in different places, but in all the principle is the old one of a series of injections followed with a bleeding a week or ten days later. If live cultures are used, the early dose must be small so as not to infect the horse. Bleeding is begun when preliminary tests show that the animal is producing serum of satisfactory potency as determined by protection tests or by other methods.

The horses are bled in the usual way, and the serum obtained. The serum is taken up, stored, and handled as in the case of other protective sera.

A great deal of very interesting work has been done upon the relative purification of pneumococcus antisera from horse protein by attempts to isolate antibodies from whole serum. Gay and Chickering precipitated dissolved pneumococcus antigen with antiserum, thus carrying down the antibodies. They then extracted these precipitates with weak sodium carbonate at 42° C., and in the supernatant fluid found protective antibodies which agglutinate pneumococci. Huntoon perfected this method of dissociation of antibody from its antigen. He treated large amounts of pneumococci with an excess of antibody, at 37.5° C. After throwing down the pneumococci with a centrifuge, he washed them with physiological salt solution, at almost the freezing point, and then treated them at a temperature of about 40° C. with weak sodium bicarbonate solution, which, as Landsteiner and others have shown, dissociates antibodies in large amounts from the antigen-antibody complex. These antibody solutions, if the volume of final solvent is about one-fourth the original serum volume, is protective in approximately the same degree as the original sera, and is almost protein free. These antibody solutions of Huntoon have been used experimentally. Their intravenous injection produces an initial chill, probably due to the nonspecific reaction caused, in our opinion, by traces of bacterial protein in the solution. Their use has been discontinued.

In 1915, Avery investigated the protective value of concentrated globulins of antipneumococcus serum prepared by fractional saturation with ammonium sulphate. At that time, the product obtained was not thought to be sufficiently potent for use in practical therapy.

An advance was made in the preparation of concentrated antipneumococcus serum by Felton in 1924. Felton precipitated practically all of the mouse-protective substance from the serum by diluting it with fifteen volumes of distilled water or weakly acid buffer solution. Combination of this method with the salting-out process and other procedures increased the degree of refinement and protective potency of the material. A solution of the precipitate in salt solution has been used extensively in the form of monovalent product or polyvalent mixtures to treat pneumonia. Good results have followed the use of Felton's serum in the treatment of Type I pneumonia, and Cecil and Plummer found that the Type II product had definite but not striking clinical value. As this material contains less than 10 per cent of the proteins present in unconcentrated serum it has the advantages of small volume for adequate dosage and is less provocative of serum sickness. Fever-producing substance in this concentrated product is a disadvantageous constituent. Whether or not its therapeutic efficiency is considerably greater than that of unconcentrated antipneumococcus serum is still a matter under debate. In 1932, Wadsworth expressed the opinion that the practical value of the refined globulins has not been demonstrated beyond question. We are impressed by the many favorable reports on the use of Felton's serum and have seen striking results from its use.

The production, processing and standardization of type specific *antipneumococcus rabbit serum* for therapeutic purposes have been described in detail by Goodner, Horsfall and Dubos, in 1937. New Zealand Red and Chinchilla rabbits are immunized by intravenous injections of suspensions of smooth strains of pneumococci, killed by heat or formalin. The immune rabbit serum in the raw state is toxic for man. To remove this toxicity the serum is heated, mixed with kaolin and filtered through a Berkefeld V candle. Standardization is carried out by the agglutination method of Heidelberger and Kabat and the results thereby are expressed in terms of the amount of antibody-protein in milligrams. With Type I antipneumococcic rabbit serum it has been determined that on the average 1 mgm. of specific agglutinin nitrogen, or 6.25 mgm. of specific agglutinin protein is equivalent to 1100 mouse-protective units. On this basis, the specific antibody content of antiserum of one type may be related to that of another.

Standardization of Pneumococcus Serum.—After a considerable amount of discussion as to which of the antibody reactions should be used for pneumococcus serum standardization, it has been generally accepted that standardization by mouse protection is the most reliable method. The pioneer work on such standardization was done largely by Neufeld. It has been developed by various pneumococcus workers, Wadsworth and Kirkbride, the workers at the Rockefeller Hospital, and a number of the manufacturers of pneumococcus serum. The standardization depends upon the amount of serum necessary to protect a white mouse of 20 grams' weight against a standard virulent culture.

One of the most important points in the standardization is to use a culture of very great and accurately known virulence. This can be produced by passage through mice. The virulence of the organism used should be so great that 0.000001 c.c. of an eighteen-hour broth culture will kill a mouse in forty-eight hours. Broth dilutions are then prepared in such a way that 0.5 c.c. of each dilution contains varying quantities of the pneumococcus culture ranging from 0.2 c.c. to 0.0000001 c.c. These dilutions should be freshly made in order that the number of organisms in the tube shall not be materially changed by growth or death before the tests are made. With each of these dilutions, then, 0.2 c.c. of the serum to be tested is mixed in a syringe and the mixture immediately injected intraperitoneally through the abdominal wall just above the groin. In some laboratories the amount of serum used for these standard tests is 0.1 instead of 0.2 c.c. The following is a typical protocol taken from a protection experiment by Dochez and Avery, which illustrates the method:

DOSE OF CULTURE C.C.*	67 (GROUP I)			A 69 (GROUP II)		
	Controls	Serum I, 0.2 C.C.	Serum II, 0.2 C.C.	Controls	Serum I, 0.2 C.C.	Serum II, 0.2 C.C.
0.1	dead	survived	dead	....	dead	dead
....	17 hours	survived	41 hours	....	18 hours	18 hours
0.01	17 hours	survived	25 hours	....	18 hours	survived
0.001	41 hours	survived	41 hours	....	18 hours	survived
0.0001	41 hours	survived	41 hours	dead	....	survived
......	....	....	....	18 hours	....	....
0.00001	96 hours	survived	41 hours	18 hours	....	survived
0.000001	48 hours	survived	72 hours	18 hours	....	survived

* The quantities in cubic centimeters representing dose of culture refer to eighteen-hour broth cultures.

The rule laid down for sera by Cole and his coworkers is that only sera should be employed which in doses of 0.2 c.c. protect against doses of 0.1 c.c. of a culture of the above description. Variations in these standards are set up in other laboratories, and constant changes are taking place in this phase of the work, but the above will sufficiently illustrate the principle applied. As this principle concerns the actual protective value of the serum it is fundamental.

A somewhat different method of standardization was introduced by Felton for the estimation of the protective and therapeutic value of antipneumococcus serum concentrated according to his method. In standardization tests, Felton has used variable amounts of serum or antibody solution and a constant number of virulent pneumococci. The unit of potency is defined as the amount of antibody (serum or concentrate) which will protect a mouse against one million fatal doses of pneumococcus culture. This is recognized as an important fundamental unit. Preparations of Felton's serum bear labels stating their content of these units and the dosage used in the treatment of pneumonia (usually 10,000 units at a single injection) is based upon Felton's unit of potency.

The significance of the mouse-protection test as a measure of therapeutic efficiency, the variables in this test and the correlation of the protection value with the titers of other antibodies in antipneumococcus serum have been the subjects of many studies. The protection test is not entirely satisfactory as a test of curative value of a serum, but is the best method available for this purpose. Precipitation and agglutination titers of the antiserum are also partial indicators of the protective value and hence of the therapeutic value.

Although the foregoing method has been much used, the introduction of concentrated serum has resulted in the desire to estimate its potency in units, since preparations of different origins should and do vary markedly in mouse-protective power. This has brought about modifications in the method described so that at present a "standard" serum is usually employed and the potency of the sample under test estimated in terms of this standard. If the standard has been assigned a value in arbitrary units, a corresponding unit value may then be estimated for a given sample. Experience with these methods has usually led to increasing the number of mice for each dose of serum to anywhere from ten to forty or fifty, depending upon the degree of accuracy desired. Even the use of such large numbers of animals does not always lead to clear-cut results.

Because of these difficulties with the mouse-protection method, various authors have attempted the substitution of quantitative precipitation tests in which more or less pure preparations of soluble specific substances are used for precipitinogen. No one of these procedures has yet received general acceptance.

The production and standardization of antipneumococci serum is described in detail in White's monograph.

Methods of Serum Treatment and Results.—Hope of success with serum treatment depends upon early diagnosis and immediate undelayed typing of the organism.

Since the serum is given intravenously it is important to be very careful in estimating whether or not the patient is sensitive to horse serum. Inquiry as to previous serum injections must be made, and intradermal and ophthalmic tests with horse serum are done by injecting, intracutaneously, with a tuberculin syringe, a small amount, anywhere from 0.5 to 0.02 c.c. of a 1:10 horse serum dilution, or by instilling a drop of a 1:10 dilution of horse serum into the conjunctival sac. If the injection is properly made, in a sensitive subject within anywhere from five to thirty minutes a large urticaria-like wheal will arise, which will remain for one-half to two hours, gradually disappearing. When either the intradermal or preferably the ophthalmic test is positive, great care should be exercised in administering the serum and attempts made at desensitization by the Besredka method, that is, gradual injection of increasing amounts. This is not absolutely reliable, but probably is of great help in most cases. It is best to begin with slow subcutaneous injection of about 0.02 c.c. of horse serum, diluted in a total quantity of 5 c.c. of salt solution. This can be repeated, gradually increasing the dose to 1 c.c. in three or four instillations if no untoward symptoms appear. Even in these preliminary injections it is best to inject very slowly, and to be sure that the needle does not enter a small venule, leaving about an hour between injections. It is difficult to lay down definite rules for quantity and manner of injection, since in each individual case an experienced worker should feel his way gradually in the case. Gradual desensitization until a large intravenous injection can be given may consume twenty-four hours or more during which time the cumulative doses may furnish a considerable fraction of the therapeutic dose.

When the time for actual injection comes, the *unconcentrated serum* is diluted with equal parts of sterile salt solution. This permits one to inject the substance more slowly. A special gravity apparatus for slow injection has been devised for this purpose by Cole and his coworkers, but with great care the injection can be done directly with a large syringe. The serum mixture should, of course, be brought to body temperature before injection. The important point is that the injection of the first 10 c.c. of the serum should occupy at least ten minutes, and this is the critical time for the development of anaphylactic symptoms during which the patient must be carefully watched. Any signs of respiratory difficulty, sudden changes in the pulse, etc., should be an indication for immediate cessation of the injection, which can be begun again when the patient has returned to normal. Felton's *concentrated serum* is injected intravenously without dilution.

The total dosage advised by Cole and his coworkers is about 90 to 100 c.c. Reinjection is a matter of judgment, and these workers advise that the treatment should be vigorously continued by reinjections every eight or ten hours, as often as it seems advisable. Cecil and Sutliff recommend the administration of 100,000 units of Felton's serum within the first twenty-four hours.

Serum disease which occasionally follows is similar to that which follows diphtheria antitoxin injections.

The *ophthalmic test* for sensitivity to horse serum is now used in preference to the intradermal test.

It is customary to withhold serum treatment until the type of pneumococcus caus- ing the pneumonia of a patient has been determined. By use of modern rapid typing methods it is possible to determine the type of pneumococcus in most cases in four or five hours.

Finland and Sutliff have carried out skin reactions with Type I SSS (soluble specific substance) in treated and untreated cases of Type I pneumonia. They obtained 7 positive tests in a series of 15 non-serum-treated patients who recovered, and of 17 Type I and Type II cases tested before the time of crisis, 3 gave positive tests. Francis has investigated skin tests with the Type I polysaccharide in 53 cases of Type I pneumonia, and in all but one of the 46 that recovered, immediate skin reactions were obtained at about the time of recovery; whereas in 7 fatal cases, re- actions were consistently negative, even when circulating antibodies were present. He believes that such a positive skin test invariably denotes that recovery has begun, and that when the test is negative, further serum treatment should be carried out. Aside from the practical interest of these observations, they appear to imply an important theoretical principle in regard to the participation of cellular hypersensitiveness in immunity, apart from the mere activity of circulating antibodies.

As we cannot deal adequately with all the practical details of serum therapy in this place, the reader is referred to textbooks of medicine, the monograph of Lord and Heffron, and, for the use of rabbit antipneumococcic serum, to the papers of Horsfall and his associates.

It has been difficult to assess the value of serum therapy in pneumonia, because of the unpredictable critical self-limitation of the disease and because of the unde- finable effects of the variables of individual resistance, age and condition of the patient, virulence of the infecting organisms, the occurrence or absence of septicemia, seasonal and yearly fluctuations in the mortality rate and a number of other factors. Before the introduction of Felton's concentrated sera, most observers agreed with Cole that only Type I serum was beneficial. A reduction of one-half to two-thirds in the case fatality rate has been reported from the use of Type I serum. Since then, Cecil and Plummer and Cecil and Sutliff have obtained good results in the specific treatment of Type II pneumonia, and Cooper and Park have reported favorably on the use of specific sera in the treatment of pneumonias due to some of the or- ganisms among the Types IV to XXXII. Little or no therapeutic benefit has been derived from Type III serum.

Promising results have been obtained by Horsfall, Goodner and MacLeod by the use of unconcentrated rabbit antipneumococcic serum in the treatment of lobar pneumonia caused by pneumococci Types I, II, V, VI, VII, VIII, XIV and XVIII.

EPIDEMIOLOGY OF PNEUMONIA

Pneumonia is endemic in most well-populated centers of the world, but seems to be particularly frequent in the temperate zones. The disease is present sporadically at almost all times of the year, but is particularly frequent during the colder months, usually reaching its annual peak in this latitude (New York-Boston) during February or March. It is not commonly an epidemic disease, but may become so under conditions of crowding, and wholesale exposure to wet and cold, incident to military life, or the life in mining camps, etc. Wherever, in other words, very close association of limited groups of people takes place under conditions of poor hygiene and crowding with coincident hardships of various kinds, pneumonia epidemics are apt to occur. The most extensive epidemics which have occurred within the last twenty years are those which took place in the South African mining districts, in Panama, and during the World War in the camps and among the armies at the front. Pneumonia of all kinds in ordinary times accounts for about 10 per cent of the death-rate, but under conditions like those occurring during the War, a much larger percentage of all deaths are due to pneumonias. The Surgeon General estimates that in the year 1918 the total number of deaths chargeable to respiratory disease (and this means, with very few exceptions, death by pneumonia of one kind or another) was 39,701, out of a strength of 2,518,499 men, which amounts to a death rate of 15.75 per thousand, and 82 per cent of all deaths occurring in the Army during this year.

In order to discuss the epidemiological and preventive problem concerned with pneumonia with intelligence, it will be necessary to discriminate between the so-called "primary" pneumonias and "secondary" pneumonias.

Inflammations of the lung may be caused by a variety of bacteria. However, for the purposes of considering the epidemiology of these diseases we need take into account only those caused by various pneumococci, the hemolytic streptococci, and influenza bacilli. The characteristics of an epidemic will vary considerably according to whether the majority of the cases are typical lobar pneumonias, coming on without previous illness, or whether most of the cases represent pulmonary infection, secondary to a preceding attack of influenza or to measles. Typical lobar pneumonia is almost regularly a pneumococcus infection and this type of the disease is by far less fatal than the other. The secondary pneumonias may be caused by many different organisms. Even in the same community, cases occurring at about one and the same time, may be caused by various pneumococci, or streptococci, the majority of the cases being due to organisms most prevalent in that particular place. Such epidemics of secondary pneumonia are the types which are most apt to develop in times of war or under other abnormal community conditions, and this type is far more fatal than is the typical lobar pneumonia.

Primary Pneumonias.—That pneumonia was a communicable disease was recognized by Johannesen and other clinicians as early as the middle of the last century. This point of view, however, was not generally accepted until quite recently. One of the difficulties that has stood in the way of a more general belief in the communicability of the disease has been the fact that many normal individuals harbor in mouth and throat pneumococci which, until recent years, were indistinguishable from the organisms found in the lungs in pneumonia. It was taken for granted, therefore, that the entrance of pneumococci into the upper respiratory passages could not, in itself, produce pneumonia, and that when the disease occurred, it was in most cases due to auto-infection, owing to unusual depression of resistance in an individual in whose mouth the pneumococcus happened to be present. Moreover, there seemed to be many instances of relationship between unusual exposure to cold and wet, and the occurrence of pneumonia, while it was rarely possible to trace definitely the origin of a case to exposure to a previous one.

Recognition that there are a number of different types of pneumococci has furnished important facts for the understanding of pneumonia epidemics. This subdivision into types has made it possible to determine, in the first place, whether or not the ordinary mouth types are identical with those found in the lungs during pneumonia, and have also permitted us to determine whether the type present in any particular case was identical with that found in a preceding case or in a closely associated contact. Following up this trail, workers at the Rockefeller Hospital have found that over 50 per cent of the mouth organisms found in normal human beings in and about New York City belong to the heterogeneous Group IV group, whereas over 80 per cent of lobar pneumonias are due to Types I, II, and III. The obvious inference from this reversed percentage is that lobar pneumonia is in most cases caused by organisms transmitted to the victim from an extraneous source, and that auto-infection with the patient's own mouth organisms cannot be regarded as a very common occurrence.

It should not be concluded from this, however, that Group IV (Types IV to XXXII) is unimportant as a causative agent in the disease, since the statistics gathered during the World War and in New York and elsewhere since 1928 show that a considerable percentage of cases may be caused by this group. However, since this group is composed of many apparently unrelated members, we are only beginning to obtain light upon the epidemiological conditions (Smillie).

It has also been shown by Stillman and others that the more virulent Types I, II, and III may disappear from the mouths of convalescents within three or four weeks, and sometimes sooner, and be supplanted at such times by the less virulent strains. Stillman has also shown that individuals associated with pneumonia patients may frequently harbor organisms of the same type as those infecting the patients, and he has found organisms corresponding to the patients' type in the dust of the sick room. It seems unquestionable, therefore, that there may be carriers of virulent pneumococci.

While auto-infection, therefore, cannot be completely excluded, it seems probable that the origin of most cases of lobar pneumonia is best explained by the acquisition of a virulent pneumococcus strain, either directly from a case or from a carrier, with a depression of resistance due to cold, exposure, etc., coincident with the presence of this virulent strain. In the light of these facts we can now understand why localized epidemics have been so often observed in institutions, war hospitals, and other crowded communities, and can justly evaluate the importance of the transmission factor in the spread of this disease. In outlining sanitary procedures for any disease it is of the utmost importance that such a thorough understanding of the relative importance of transmission and the susceptibility factor should be acquired. It is never possible to carry out all desirable measures of prevention completely, and it is, therefore, necessary to know definitely upon which factors the greatest stress must be laid in planning the sanitary campaign.

In all communicable diseases the two factors which influence spread are, in the first place, the transmission of the virulent organisms, and, in the second place, the susceptibility of the recipient. When transmission becomes general and community susceptibility is normally high, as in plague, typhoid, cholera, etc., epidemics are bound to spread rapidly. There are diseases like those mentioned above, as well as smallpox, measles, scarlet fever, and influenza, in which the susceptibility of the normal, previously unexposed individual is so great that hardly any one sufficiently exposed, will escape. It is plain that in such diseases sanitary measures must be aimed particularly at the prevention of transmission, with, wherever possible, artificial immunization of the community. There are other infections, however, chief among which we believe is pneumonia, in which the resistance of normal human beings is comparatively high. The disease will not occur in an individual simply because he has received the virulent organisms by the proper route, from a case or a carrier, but, in addition to this, there must be coincident hygienic defects which temporarily depress his resistance. A temporary coincidence of two factors, therefore, transmission of the organisms and increased susceptibility, must occur, and it is plain that in such diseases epidemic spread cannot take place to any extensive degree unless both of these factors, widespread transmission and depression of resistance, become generalized. In such cases, therefore, while proper safeguards against dissemination of the organisms must be developed, yet the efforts of the sanitarian should focus particularly upon measures by which the normal resistance of the community is maintained.

As a matter of fact, pneumonia epidemics do not occur, as a rule, in well-nourished and well-housed communities. The epidemic form of the primary disease develops only under such conditions as those prevailing in army camps during the cold weather, when men are crowded together in sleeping quarters, and are developing colds and coughs, and are, at the same time, exposed to unusual conditions of life, cold, wet, unaccustomed food and hard work. Exceptions to this are, of course, epidemics like those that have occurred in Panama and South Africa, but in these cases the community in which the disease was prevalent consisted very largely of tropical Negroes, whose greater susceptibility to pneumococcus infection is well known.

In a number of epidemics in which we have had the opportunity of studying cases, it was quite apparent that the susceptibility factor was the determinative one in individual instances. Surveys showed that, while it frequently happened that a number of cases came from the same tent, the infections were often of different bacterial types. While direct transmission from one case to another often seemed to be circumstantially proved, in only a few instances at a certain camp in which these studies were made, were such cases associated with a single type. On the other hand, a certain regiment which was ordered to the shooting range during a very wet spell, marching in the rain and camping on wet ground, developed twenty-six cases of pneumonia within sixteen days. Analysis showed that these cases were caused by all four pneumococcus types without particular relationship between contacts and types. On the other hand, a considerable number of men were found, in this same regiment, at that time, to be carriers of virulent pneumococci and streptococci without coming down with the disease.

From evidence like this, we conclude that in the sanitation of pneumonia it would be dangerous to lay too great proportionate stress upon mere transmission, but to remember that the average resistance to pneumococcus infection of the lung is fairly high among human beings, and that sanitary precautions must include a very rigid attention to the factors of warmth, ventilation in sleeping quarters, adequate food, dryness of feet, and avoidance of overwork. In communities like those of South Africa, the prevention of transmission alone cut short the epidemic, but we have already pointed out that the susceptibility factor was unusually high in these communities.

It will rarely be necessary for sanitarians working in civilized communities to be called upon to prevent epidemics of primary pneumonia. They will develop under such conditions as those prevailing in military camps and, which might well be imagined as possible, in badly managed industrial communities, schools, labor camps, etc., where laborers are forced to sleep in ill-ventilated barracks, are crowded during working hours, or in mines, and crowded institutions. Such conditions may occur among civilian populations at times of famine, and penury incident to war. Primary pneumonia epidemics will occur only when crowding, coincident with generalization of mild respiratory infections, increases the distribution of bacteria and when, at the same time, the community suffers from insufficient shelter and is perhaps undernourished and overworked. The most important factor in the prevention of such outbreaks, therefore, is attention to the ventilation of sleeping quarters, sufficient number of blankets on beds, dry feet, warm and plentiful food, and opportunities for reasonable rest. If this is combined with isolation of coughing and sneezing individuals, at least during indoor life, if spitting is stopped and careful supervision of the cleansing of eating utensils, sterilization of handkerchiefs, etc., is enforced, such epidemics should yield readily.

Cases which have been diagnosed as lobar pneumonia should be reportable, like other infectious diseases. This has already been introduced by a number of health departments. In hospitals pneumonia cases should be treated as communicable, the cases isolated, at least by maintaining proper distance between beds, screening between beds, and care in the collection and disposition of sputum and other secretions. Care of eating utensils and general cleanliness should be carried out with proper consideration of the possibilities of communication that have been spoken of above. In view of the probability of persistence of the carrier state for four weeks or longer after convalescence, great care in mouth disinfection and control of this feature before patients are returned to their homes should be practiced.

Secondary Pneumonias.—In *secondary* pneumonias we are dealing with an entirely different sanitary problem. While pneumonia may be secondary to a large number of different diseases, the only ones which are of distinct epidemiological importance in this connection are influenza and measles. There is no epidemic of measles or influenza in which there are not, at the same time, a considerable number of pneumonias, and these pneumonias are more apt to take the form of the lobular or bronchopneumonic type. In both of these diseases there is a certain amount of inflammation of the bronchial mucous membranes which seems to render the patient particularly susceptible to secondary infection with virulent pneumococci and streptococci. The peculiar susceptibility of patients with measles and influenza to pneumonia cannot be explained purely on the basis of the mild bronchial inflammation which may be considered distinctly an integral part of these diseases themselves. There is a depression of resistance to pulmonary infection which is quite out of proportion to that which accompanies many other conditions in which bronchitis and catarrhal inflammation of the upper respiratory tract are common. Measles epidemics are fortunately uncommon in urban communities, but may assume dangerous proportions in army camps, institutions, schools, etc. The mortality of uncomplicated measles is low, but the high mortality which so often accompanies epidemics of measles is almost entirely a pneumonia mortality. In one such epidemic which occurred at Camp Wheeler during the early stages of our entrance into the War, the mortality of measles pneumonias was 29 per cent. Sanitary measures under such conditions include, of course, those aimed at the prevention of the primary disease, as well as attempts at preventing the secondary pneumonias with which we are here particularly concerned. But for the saving of life, the sanitary attention to the prevention of the secondary complications is by far the more important of the two. With the prevention of the primary disease we deal in the chapter on measles, but a few words may be said in this place concerning the important measures which should be taken during measles epidemics to prevent the occurrence of secondary pneumonias. The principles of such measures are twofold, in the first place to prevent the patient who is coughing and spitting from transferring his mouth streptococci and pneumococci to others. There should be the most careful attention to the cleanliness of the mouth of measles patients, both for the reasons mentioned, as well as in order to discourage the lodgment of virulent organisms in the patient himself. Doctors and nurses should wear gauze masks when in close contact with the patient as much for the protection of the patient as for their own. A measles patient should never be allowed to remain in the same ward with pneumococcus or streptococcus cases, and as soon as a measles patient develops a severe bronchitis or pneumonia, he should be removed from the measles ward into a separate ward or room, since he has now become an active danger to other measles cases. In the measles ward itself beds should be screened one from the other, and there should be at least five feet between beds. It is of great importance that the measles patient should be put to bed and kept warm and protected from catching cold as soon as the suspicion of the disease is definite, and similar care should be taken during the course of convalescence.

In the case of influenza the conditions are similar. In the section on influenza it will be seen that this disease, in its pure form, is relatively mild and has a very low mortality. During the second and third waves of an epidemic, however, practically all influenza cases show some degree of respiratory infection, and the susceptibility to pneumonia is so great during this stage that not only is the percentage of pneumonias very high, but the mortality is appalling. During the year 1918, when the second great influenza wave struck the American Army, influenza was charged, by the Surgeon-General's Report, with 688,869 admissions among the American troops for the year, the disease and its complications causing 23,007 deaths. Eighty-two per cent of all the deaths occurring in the Army were due to acute respiratory disease.

When we consider, as we shall, in the chapter on influenza, that all the respiratory deaths chargeable to influenza are really deaths from secondary infection, and not from influenza itself, we cannot help recognizing the enormous importance of the secondary pneumonias from a sanitary point of view. The preventive measures that can be taken in guarding against secondary pulmonary infection are chiefly indirect ones, but are of great importance. Among the most important are care of the patient himself. Studies by Swift, Harlow Brooks and others during the War have shown that immediate care in bed, as soon as the first suspicion of diagnosis of influenza is made, is of the utmost value in preventing the development of secondary infection. The greatest care should be taken of the mouth of influenza patients, brushing of the teeth and cleansing of the mouth with sodium bicarbonate solution, or salt solution gargle to which 20 per cent or 30 per cent alcohol may be added. The patient should be carefully guarded from infection by the doctors and nurses who should wear gauze masks for this purpose. This is not primarily in our minds a precaution to protect the physicians and nurses, but rather the other way around. Dangers of transmission of pneumococci and streptococci from bed to bed should be guarded against as above in the case of measles. The pneumonias which occur during an influenza epidemic are very rarely due to influenza bacillus infection of the lung only. The fatal disease is caused by a large variety of organisms, including the various pneumococci, the streptococci and some others. In any one particular place the majority of cases may be due to one or another of these organisms, this depending somewhat upon the bacteria which happen to be most prevalent in this community, and are passed from mouth to mouth under conditions of generalized respiratory transmission, occurring in this place. Thus, MacCallum and Cole studied a secondary pneumonia epidemic in which hemolytic streptococci were responsible for most of the cases, but usually the pneumonias following in the train of influenza are not of a single type, but caused by any virulent member of the lung-invading group of bacteria that happened by chance to lodge on the mucous membranes of the subject rendered susceptible by his primary disease.

Thus, after an influenza epidemic has started, sanitary measures aimed at the prevention of the fatal secondary infections must focus upon the transmission factor.

Prophylactic Vaccination against Pneumococcus Infection.—The value of prophylactic vaccination against pneumonia is not yet definitely established. Wright was the pioneer in this work in 1911, but since he did not know about type differentiation, the value of his work is limited. The first hopeful experiments were made by Lister in South Africa, who typed his pneumococci by the usual agglutination method, having his own Types A, B, and C (B and C corresponding respectively to II and I of our classification), and made salt solution suspensions of the organisms, injecting at first six to seven billion, intravenously. According to White, Lister and Ordman in 1935 reported distinctly promising results from the use of mixed vaccine composed of pneumococci, streptococci and other organisms. Cecil and Austin did some experiments at Camp Upton in which they vaccinated 12,519 men against Types I, II, and III, and their results also were encouraging, but again unconvincing. Tests conducted upon a large scale, under conditions permitting the use of controls, are needed for the solution of the question of the value of prophylactic vaccination against pneumonia.

The vaccines which have been used consist of culture suspensions in salt solution killed by heating at 56° C., for one-half hour, and standardized either by counting against red blood cells or by means of the nephelometer. Three-tenths per cent tricresol may be added to preserve the suspensions which are made up so that about one thousand million pneumococci are contained in 1 c.c. The dosage advised by Cecil is three billions for the first dose, six billions for the second and nine billions for the third. In addition, fractions of the pneumococcal cells and products of cultures have been used.

Lipovaccines which consist of pneumococcus suspensions in olive oil and other vegetable oil mixtures have been used, but the method of preparing these vaccines has not been satisfactorily perfected. Felton has used antigenic polysaccharides as vaccines.

Vaccine Therapy.—The evidence derived from experiments upon animals is convincing in showing that rabbits, mice, horses and dogs can be immunized against pneumococci. Vaccines have been used not only for prophylaxis but for the treatment of pneumonia. The results of such treatment have not demonstrated the efficacy of the vaccine therapy.

REFERENCES

AVERY, O. T. J. Exper. M., 1915, 21:133; 22:804.
———— Ann. Int. M., 1932, 6:1.
AVERY, CHICKERING, COLE and DOCHEZ. Monogr. Rockefeller Inst. No. 7, Oct. 16, 1917.
AVERY, O. T., and DUBOS, R. Science, 1930, 72:151.
———— J. Exper. M., 1931, 54:51, 73.
AVERY, O. T., and GOEBEL, W. F. J. Exper. M., 1931, 54:431, 437; 1933, 58:731.
AVERY, O. T., and HEIDELBERGER, M. J. Exper. M., 1925, 42:367.
BABERS, F. H., and GOEBEL, W. F. J. Biol. Chem., 1930, 89:387.
BAILEY, G. H., and SHORB, M. S. Am. J. Hyg., 1931, 13:831.
BASSETT-SMITH, P. W. Lancet, 1918, 194:290.
BLAKE, F. G. J. Exper. M., 117, 26:67.
BLAKE, F. G., and CECIL, R. L. J. Exper. M., 1920, 31:403, 445, 499, 518, 657, 685; 1920, 32:1, 401.
BLAKE, F. G., and TRASK, J. D. J. Bacteriol., 1933, 25:289.
BORDONI-UFFREDUZZI, G. Arch. per le sc. med., 1891, 15:341.
BROWNING, C. H. System of Bacteriology in Relation to Medicine, London, 1929, 2:225.
CECIL, R. L., and AUSTIN, J. H. J. Exper. M., 1918, 28:19.
CECIL, R. L., and PLUMMER, N. J. Am. M. Ass., 1932, 98:779.
CECIL, R. L., and SUTLIFF, W. D. J. Am. M. Ass., 1928, 91:2035.
CHESNEY, A. M. J. Exper. M., 1916, 24:387.
CHICKERING. Discussion on Pneumonia, New York Academy of Medicine, April, 1920.
CHURCHMAN, J. W., and EMELIANOFF, N. V. J. Exper. M., 1933, 57:485.
CLOUGH, P. W. Johns Hopkins Hosp. Bull., 1913, 24:295.
COCA, A. F. J. Immunol., 1936, 30:1.
COLE, R. J. Exper. M., 1912, 16:644; 1914, 20:346.
———— Harvey Lecture, New York, Dec. 13, 1913.
———— J. Exper. M., 1914, 20:346, 363.
———— Proc. Inst. Med. of Chicago, 1932, 9:2, esp. pp. 14–15.
———— J. Am. M. Assoc., 1929, 93:741.
COOPER, G., EDWARDS, M., and ROSENSTEIN, C. J. Exper. M., 1929, 49:461.
COOPER, G., ROSENSTEIN, C., WALTER, A., and PEIZER, L. J. Exper. M., 1932, 55:531.
DAWSON, M. H. J. Exper. M., 1930, 51:123.
DAWSON, M. H., and SIA, H. P. J. Exper. M., 1931, 54:681.
DOCHEZ, A. R. J. Exper. M., 1913.
———— and AVERY, O. T. Proc. Soc. Exper. Biol. & Med., 1916, 14:126.
———— J. Exper. M., 1917, 26:477.

—— and GILLESPIE, L. J. J. Am. M. Ass., 1913, 61:727.

—— SHIBLEY, G. S., and MILLS, K. C. Proc. Soc. Exper. Biol. & Med., 1929, 26:562; 1930, 27:59.

—— MILLS, K. C., and KNEELAND, Y. Proc. Soc. Exper. Biol. & Med., 1931, 28:513; 1932, 29:64.

—— J. Exper. M., 1936, 63:559.

—— J. Am. Med. Assoc., 1938, 110:177.

DOCHEZ, A. R., SHIBLEY, G. S., and MILLS, K. C. J. Exper. M., 1930, 52:701.

—— J. Exper. M. Ass., 1930, 95:1553.

DUBOS, R. J. J. Exper. M., 1932, 62:259; 1937, 66:113; 1938, 67:791.

EATON, M. D. J. Bacteriol., 1934, 27, 271.

ENDERS, J. F. J. Exper. M., 1930, 52:235; 1932, 55:191.

ENDERS, J. F., and PAPPENHEIMER, A. M. Proc. Exper. Biol. & Med., 1933, 31:37.

ENDERS, J. F., and WU, C-J. J. Exper. M., 1934, 60:127.

FELTON, L. D. Boston M. & Surg. J., 1924, 190:819.

—— J. Infect. Dis., 1928, 42:256, 543; 1931, 49:337.

—— J. Am. M. Ass., 1930, 94:1893.

—— J. Immunol., 1930, 19:341, 485; 1931, 21:357; 1932, 22:453; 1932, 23:405.

—— U. S. Pub. Health Rep., 1938, 53:1855, 1938.

FELTON, L. D., and KAUFFMAN, E. J. Infect. Dis., 1931, 49:337.

FELTON, L. D., SUTLIFF, W. D., and STEELE, B. F. J. Inf. Dis., 1935, 56:101.

FERGUSON, D. U. S. Naval M. Bull., 1932, 30:409.

FINLAND, M., and SUTLIFF, W. D. J. Exper. M., 1931, 54:637, 653.

FOA, P. Ztschr. f. Hyg., 1888, 4.

FOSTER. J. Infect. Dis., 1917, 21:451.

FRANCIS, T. J. Exper. M., 1933, 57:617.

FRÄNKEL, A. Ztschr. f. klin. Med., 1886, 10:426.

FRIEDLÄNDER, C. Virchow's Arch., 1882, 87:318.

GAY and CHICKERING. J. Exper. M., 1915, 21:319.

GOODNER, K. J. Exper. M., 1928, 48:1; 1931, 54:847.

GOODNER, K., and DUBOS, R. J. Exper. M., 1932, 56:521.

GOODNER, K., HORSFALL, F. L., and DUBOS, R. J. J. Immunol., 1937, 33:279.

GRIFFITH, F. Rep. Pub. Health, Ministry of Health, London, 1923, No. 18, 1.

—— J. Hyg., 1928, 27:113.

—— System of Bacteriology in Relation to Medicine, London, 1929, 2:209.

GUENTHER, L. Deutsche med. Wchnschr., 1882.

HEIDELBERGER, M. Physiological Rev., 1927, 7:107.

—— Ann. Rev. Biochem., 1932, 1:655.

—— GOEBEL, W. F., and AVERY, O. T. J. Exper. M., 1925, 42:709.

—— KENDALL, F. E., and SCHERP, H. W. J. Exper. M., 1936, 64:559.

HISS. Centralbl. f. Bakteriol., 1902, 31.

—— J. Exper. M., 1905, 6:7, 317.

HORSFALL, F. L., GOODNER, K., MACLEOD, C. M., and HARRIS, A. H. J. Am. M. Assoc., 1937, 108:1483.

HORSFALL, F. L., GOODNER, K., and MACLEOD, C. M. New York State J. M., 1938, 38:245.

HOWARD, W. T., and PERKINS, R. G. J. Med. Research, 1901, 6:163.

HUNTOON, F. M. J. Immunol., 1921, 6:117.

JULIANELLE, L. A., and REIMANN, H. A. J. Exper. M., 1926, 43:87; 1927, 45:609.

KLEBS, E. Arch. f. exper. Path., 1875, 4:420.

KRUSE. München. med. Wchnschr., 1914, 61:1547.

KOCH, R. Mitt. a.d.k., Gsndhtsamte., 1818, 1.

KLUMPEN, W. Centralbl. of Bakteriol., I Abt. orig., 1932, 124:241.

LAMAR, R. V., and MELTZER, S. J. J. Exper. M., 1912, 15:133.

LISTER, F. S. Rep. South African Inst. Med. Res., 1913, No. 2; 1916, No. 8; 1917, No. 10.

—— Pub. South African Inst. Med. Res., 1916, No. 8.

LONG. P. H.. DOULL. J. A., BOURN, J. M., and McCOMB, E. J. Exper. M., 1931, 53:447.

Lord, F. T., and Heffron, R. Lobar pneumonia and serum therapy. The Commonwealth Fund. New York, 2nd ed., 1938.

MacFadyen, A. Brit. M. J., 1906, 2:776.

Mair, W. J. Path. & Bacteriol., 1928, 31:215.

Mellon, R., Gross, P., and Cooper, F. B. Sulfanilamide Therapy of Bacterial Infections. Springfield, Ill., 1938.

Morgenroth, J., and Levy, R. Berl. klin. Wchnschr., 1911, 48:1560, 1979.

Morgenroth, J., Schnitzer, R., and Berger, E. Ztschr. f. Immunitätsforsch., 1925, 43:169, 209.

Moss, Guthrie and Gelien. Tr. 15th Internat. Congr. Hyg., Washington, 1913.

Neufeld, F. Ztschr. f. Hyg. u. Infectionskrankh., 1902, 40:54.

——, and Händel. Arb. a.d.k. Gsndhtsamte., 1910, 34:293.

——— Berl. klin. Wchnschr., 1912, 49:680.

Neufeld and Rimpau. Deutsche med. Wchnschr., 1904.

Odell, H. R. J. Immunol., 1930, 18:73.

Olmstead, M. J. Immunol., 1917, 2:425.

——, Oram, F. J. Immunol., 1934, 26:283.

Ottolenghi. Centralbl. f. Bakteriol., 1889, 25.

Park, W. H., Bullowa, J. G. M., and Rosenblüth. J. Am. M. Ass., 1928, 91:1503.

Park, W. H. Am. J. Pub. Health, 1930, 20:403.

Parish, H. J. J. Path. & Bacteriol., 1930, 33:729.

Parker, J. T. J. Exper. M., 1928, 47:531, 695.

Pasteur, L. Bull. Acad. de méd., 1881, 10:76.

Paul, J. R. J. Exper. M., 1927, 46:807.

Plummer, N. J. Am. M. Assoc., 1936, 107:499.

Powell, H. M., and Clowes, G. H. A. Proc. Soc. Exper. Biol. & Med., 1931–32, 29:332.

Reimann, H. A. J. Exper. M., 1927, 45:1.

——— Arch. Int. M., 1936, 58:329; 1938, 62:305.

Robertson, O. H. J. Exper. M., 1937, 66:706; 1938, 67:575, 597.

Rockwell, G. E., and Van Kirk, H. C. J. Immunol., 1935, 28:475, 485.

Rosenow, E. C. J. Infect. Dis., 1907, 4:285; 1912, 11:480.

——— J. Am. M. Ass., 1913, 61:2007.

Sabin, A. B. J. Exper. M., 1931, 53:93; J. Am. M. Ass., 1933, 100:1585.

Schottmüller, H. München. med. Wchnschr., 1903, 50:849.

Sclavo. Riv. d'ig., 1894.

Shibley, G. S., and Rogers, E. S. Proc. Soc. Exper. Biol. & Med., 1932, 30:6.

Smillie, W. G. J. Am. M. Ass., 1933, 101:1281.

Sternberg. Nat. Bd. Health Bull., 1881.

——— Centralbl. f. Bakteriol., 1891, 12.

Stillman. J. Exper. M., 1917, 26:513.

Stillman, E. G., and Branch, A. J. Exper. M., 1925, 41:623, 631.

Stuppy, G. W., and Falk, I. S. J. Prevent. M., 1928, 2:175.

Sutliff, W. D., and Finland, M. J. Am. M. Ass., 1933, 101:1289.

Talamon. Progr. méd., 1883.

Tillett, W. S., and Francis, T. J. Exper. M., 1930, 52: 561.

Tillett, W. S., Goebel, W. F., and Avery, O. T. J. Exper. M., 1930, 52:892.

Trevan, J. W. J. Path. & Bacteriol., 1930, 33:739.

Wadsworth. Studies by the Pupils of W. T. Sedgwick, Chicago, 1896.

——— Proc. N. York Path. Soc., 1903.

——— Am. J. M. Sc., 1904.

——— J. Infect. Dis., 1906, 3.

——— J. Am. M. Ass., 1932, 98:779.

Wadsworth, A. B., and Brown, R. J. Immunol., 1931, 21:245, 255; 1933, 24:349.

Wadsworth, A. B., and Kirkbride, M. B. J. Exper. M., 1918, 28:805.

Wadsworth, A. B., and Sickles, G. M. J. Exper. M., 1927, 45:787.

Walker, J. E. Ann. Int. M., 1932, 5:1526.

WEICHSELBAUM. Med. Jahrb., Wien, 1886.

WELCH, W. H. Johns Hopkins Hosp. Bull., 1892, 3:125.

WHITE, B. The Biology of Pneumococcus. The Commonwealth Fund, New York, 1938.

WINTERNITZ, M. C., and HIRSCHFELDER. J. Exper. M., 1913, 17.

WINTERNITZ, SMITH and ROBINSON. Johns Hopkins Hosp. Bull., 1920, 31:63.

WOOD. J. Exper. M., 1905, 7.

WRIGHT and MORGAN. Lancet, 1914, 1:1, 87.

ZINSSER, H. New England J. Med., 1929, 200:853.

ZINSSER, H., and PARKER, J. T. J. Exper. M., 1923, 37:275.

ZINSSER, H., and TAMIYA, T. J. Exper. M., 1925, 42:311.

CHAPTER XXV

INFLUENZA—THE DISEASE AND ITS EPIDEMIOLOGY [1]

THE VIRUS AND SECONDARY BACTERIAL INVADERS

Epidemic influenza is an acute disease caused by a filtrable virus. Until recently this disease was attributed to bacterial causation. The most prominent of the suspected organisms, the Pfeiffer bacillus, known as *Hemophilus influenzae*, may now be regarded as merely one of the important secondary invaders, and will be described in another chapter. For accurate descriptions and historical considerations of both the clinical and epidemiological problems of epidemic influenza we refer the reader to Leichtenstern's book published in *Nothnagel's System*, to Thompson's *Annals of Influenza* (London, 1852) and to the more recent treatises in various medical textbooks (Zinsser, Jordan).

Uncomplicated influenza is a mild disease in which respiratory symptoms may be either entirely lacking or may be extremely mild. This is an important fact to remember in connection with etiological studies, since a large part of the bacteriological work done on this phase of influenza has had to be carried out on cases occurring late in epidemics, when secondary respiratory infection had become almost universal. The uncomplicated cases are found in considerable numbers only in the early stages of epidemic outbreaks.

The characteristics of such cases are as follows: The onset is almost regularly abrupt. Typical cases become ill suddenly, without premonition. More rarely, there are a few days of general tired feeling and malaise. The first symptoms consist of headache, feverishness, loss of appetite, pains in the back and somatic muscles, particularly in the calves of the legs; sometimes suffusion and burning of the eyeballs, and often mild sore throat. The temperature rises to anywhere from 101° to 104 ° F., and this condition continues for two or three days, when the patient gradually returns to normal, but is left quite exhausted. Occasionally, skin rashes appear in the form of erythematous patches, not at all uniform in appearance and difficult to characterize dermatologically. The spleen is usually not enlarged. The leukocytes range from 5000 to 9000.

Such cases, if they develop respiratory complications at all, suffer from nothing much more than a mild laryngitis or bronchitis, which appears toward the third or fourth day and rapidly subsides. The first two hundred or three hundred cases seen during the 1918 epidemic, among American soldiers in France, developed practically no respiratory symptoms whatever and no obvious focal lesions anywhere. The disease was so brief and mild that it was not recognized as influenza at first, and was

---

[1] As influenza is now known to be caused by a filtrable virus it would be appropriate to transfer this chapter to Section VII. However, we decided to discuss it here because of the importance of influenza among the diseases of the respiratory tract and the significance of secondary bacterial invasion.

spoken of as "three-day fever." The morbidity at such times is high, the mortality practically *nil.*

As we study the literature of past epidemics and the observations made on the 1918 epidemic in different places, we find that this experience has been universal. In the 1898 epidemic, Heyfelder speaks of Siberian fever, which was first looked upon as malaria, and noted the absence of catarrhal symptoms in the respiratory organs. Just before this, the epidemic outbreak in Constantinople was spoken of as "dengue fever," and similar, unrecognized, mild cases characterized the beginnings of the epidemic in Petrograd. During the war epidemic of 1917 and 1918, Vaughan and Palmer also noted the uncertain and mild characters of the first cases at Camp Oglethorpe (in March, 1918) and in Italy San Pietro suggested sandfly fever as a possible diagnosis.

In the later periods of the first epidemic waves, as well as in the second and third waves, the overwhelming majority of the cases, because of secondary infection, are respiratory in character, an important characteristic of the basic influenza being the susceptibility which it creates to secondary respiratory infection.

Virus Etiology.—That a filtrable virus might be the etiological agent of influenza was suggested by the characteristics of the pure uncomplicated mild cases described above, the extreme infectiousness of the disease, and the lack of uniformity of the bacteriological findings in early cases. Experimental evidence has now established the virus etiology of the disease beyond question. In 1919, Nicolle and Lebailly reported studies on the filtration of influenzal virus and its inoculation into animals and man. They filtered the blood and nasal secretions of uncomplicated grippe cases, and instilled them into conjunctival sacs and nasal cavities of several monkeys (Macacus sinicus) and into a number of human volunteers. They obtained symptoms within about six days in several monkeys, and in two men, but were unable to carry the infection into a second generation. They concluded that the "filtrates of secretions in influenza are virulent, and can infect human beings and certain monkeys by nasal and conjunctival inoculation." Soon after this, Dujarric de la Rivière filtered blood from four influenza cases and injected it into himself. He became definitely ill with influenza-like symptoms.

Claims of the filtrability of the influenzal virus on the basis of experiments carried out by filtration of influenzal secretions and inoculation into monkeys and man were also made in 1919 by Leschke, Fejes, and others. A review of most of the German etiological work is to be found in the *Centralblatt für Bakteriologie* (1919, 68: 401). Selter, failing to find influenza bacilli with any regularity in supposedly typical cases, filtered the nasopharyngeal mucus and gargle water of patients in the early stages of the disease, and sprayed it into his own throat and that of a woman assistant, both of them inhaling the spray. In both of them, after seventeen to twenty hours, mild influenza resulted. Yamanouchi, Sakami and Iwashima carried out more extensive experiments in 1919. In their first experiment they emulsified the sputum of 43 influenza patients in Ringer's solution. Part of this they filtered. The unfiltered emulsion they injected into the noses and throats of 12 healthy people. The filtrate of the same emulsion was similarly injected into the noses and throats of 12 other healthy people, 6 of whom had had influenza. All of the 24, except the ones who had had influenza recently, came down with an influenza-like malady after an incubation of two or three days. Following this, they injected the filtrate of blood of influenza patients into the noses and throats of 6 more healthy people, with similar positive results. Filtrates of sputum were inoculated into 4 healthy people, and 4 others received filtrates of blood of influenza patients, subcutaneously. All except 1, who had had influenza, came down after two or three days. Finally, pure cultures of Pfeiffer's bacilli, and mixed cultures of this organism with pneumococci, staphylococci and streptococci were injected into the noses and throats of 14 healthy people who had not had influenza. No symptoms followed these injections.

From secretions of a case of influenza, after filtration, Olitsky and Gates isolated a strictly anaerobic organism which was gram-negative and presented a bacillary appearance. They called this the *Bacterium pneumosintes*. Subsequently they isolated the same bacterium from material derived from seven further cases of influenza. Holman and Krock cultivated organisms, supposedly indistinguishable from *Bact. pneumosintes* both as to the fact that they did not produce gas and passed through tested filters as well as anaerobiosis, from the mouths of normal human beings and from two rabbits. Avery also cultivated organisms similar to *Bact. pneumosintes* from normal human throats. Olitsky and Gates can be credited with the discovery of a new group of anaerobic, filter-passing micro-organisms, probably bacteria, but etiological relationship to influenza may be excluded.

The influenza virus was finally isolated in 1933 by Wilson Smith, Andrewes and Laidlaw. They succeeded in producing fever, weakness and nasal catarrh in ferrets by the injection and nasal instillation of filtrates from throat washings of early cases. Cross immunity experiments seem to show that the virus isolated by them is closely related to but not identical with the virus of swine influenza studied by Shope. The particular interest of this similarity lies in the observations of Shope that in the diseases of swine a filtrable virus is associated with a secondary invasion of gram-negative bacilli.

These investigations have been confirmed by Francis, who obtained strains of virus from Puerto Rico, from Philadelphia and Alaska. Like the British workers, Francis used ferrets first and subsequently succeeded in transferring the virus to mice. Nasal instillation of the virus in mice is followed by the development of pulmonary lesions. The infected lung triturated in salt solution can be used after centrifugation of coarse particles for transfer. The mice are lightly anaesthetized with ether during the instillation. Death may occur on the fifth or sixth day, although this is not regular.

The experimental disease in ferrets and mice is, in its earlier stages, a pure virus infection. In such animals the pulmonary lesions are mild, but distinct. They begin at the root of the lobes, extending peripherally; are reddish, firm, and resemble certain types of bronchial pneumonia in human beings. They are not unlike the pulmonary lesions produced experimentally in rabbits by *Bacillus pertussis*.

Following infection with the influenza virus, both ferrets and mice develop active immunity to reinfection. The serum of these animals contains neutralizing bodies which can be determined both by direct neutralization of virus in vitro and by passive immunization. Repeated injection of the virus into rabbits produces specific antibodies and the serum of immunized rabbits affords passive protection against mouse-virulent virus. Neutralization tests with the serum of human patients before and after recovery from influenza indicate that infection increases neutralizing power. A considerable number of tests with convalescent human influenza serum by Francis and Magill have shown similar results. Francis has also shown specific complement fixation with immune sera and influenza virus as antigen. Magill and Francis succeeded in 1936 in cultivating the virus of human influenza on the ordinary Maitland tissue culture media, using chick embryo tissue and Tyrode solution.

Relationship of Human Influenza to Swine Influenza.—Swine influenza, or "hog flu," was recognized as a clinical entity in 1918. Koen recognized the resemblance of this disease to human influenza. It is an autumnal disease, common every year, with sudden incidence, almost 100 per cent morbidity, fever, prostration and muscular tenderness. It has a very low mortality, unless complicated, and recovery occurs in two to six days. The analogy to human influenza is obvious. It was experimentally transmitted by intranasal instillation of bronchial mucus by McBryde, Niles and Moskey in 1928, who also carried out filtration experiments which, however, were inconclusive. Shope in 1931 succeeded in transmitting an experimentally mild type of the disease with filtrates of suspensions from ground lungs and bronchial lymphnodes of affected hogs. After intranasal instillation of such material, the animals developed apathy, diminished appetite, slight cough and leukopenia. Lesions in such animals at autopsy were similar to those encountered in very mild uncomplicated swine influenza. The incubation time was about four days.

In taking cultures from the material of spontaneous swine influenza lungs for filtration, Shope invariably isolated a small gram-negative bacillus now known as *H. influenzae suis*. This organism was consistently absent from respiratory tracts of swine ill with the pure filtrate disease. The organism alone in pure culture was practically innocuous, but when the filtrable virus and the bacillus were inoculated together, the animals developed a typical swine influenza indistinguishable from the spontaneously acquired disease. The results indicate that the filtrable virus prepared the portal of entry for the bacillus and, together, they produced the typical disease. An attack of swine influenza rendered the animal immune to reinfection. Recovery from the virus disease alone seemed to immunize against both the virus and the bacillus, but instillation of the bacillus alone caused no disease and immunized against neither. This disease, like the human type, could be transferred to ferrets and, subsequently, to mice, and propagated in these animals. Cross immunity experiments have shown that the virus of swine influenza and that of human influenza are closely related, but not identical. Human influenza virus can be passed through swine in five serial passages, but is not enhanced in pathogenicity for this species, nor is it changed immunologically. The human virus cannot be transferred from swine to swine by contact alone. Recent experiments appear to show that while the gram-negative bacilli are perhaps the most common secondary invaders for which influenza virus prepares the respiratory tracts, the virus may similarly render these passages susceptible to other organisms, such as hemolytic streptococci.

Epidemiology.—As stated before, the etiological and diagnostic difficulties in connection with influenza are such that records of the disease are less apt to be reliable than would be similar records of smallpox, diphtheria, etc. However, a great deal is known about past epidemics which have been described with sufficient accuracy to permit us to recognize them definitely as true influenza epidemics. Leichtenstern, who has written a very thorough treatise on influenza, tabulates the great influenza epidemics of the world as follows:

Less extensive outbreaks seem to have prevailed in different parts of the world between 1709 and 1712.

Between 1729 and 1733 the disease, traveling from Russia westward, spread over Europe in two great waves, one in 1729 and the other in 1732.

Another epidemic started on the shores of the Baltic in 1742.

In 1757–1758, 1761–1762, and 1767 epidemics occurred of which we have but poor geographical records.

Of the epidemic of 1742, Friedrich states that all but about one-tenth of the entire population of Germany was attacked.

From 1781 to 1782 an epidemic supposed to have started in China spread through Siberia to Russia and thence to Europe.

Another traveled approximately the same route in 1788.

The same thing occurred between 1799 and 1803.

In 1827, there was an outbreak in Europe less extensive than most of the others.

Between 1830 and 1833 there were two or three pandemic waves, the first one supposedly originating in China.

Other outbreaks, again traveling from east to west, occurred in 1836 and 1847. During the latter epidemic the Prussian Army is said by Friedrich to have been attacked in its entire personnel.

These brief data, which bring us up to the pandemic of 1889, are condensed chiefly from Leichtenstern.

The characteristics of influenza epidemics are summarized by Leichtenstern in a manner which can be accepted as roughly describing the actual facts on the basis of experience with the last War epidemic. (1) The disease appears in true pandemic waves; (2) it travels with tremendous speed over the globe; (3) it is characterized by sudden mass infection; (4) it is rapidly burnt out after several weeks in one locality; (5) it is independent of season or weather; (6) it begins at first with an enormous morbidity and a relatively slight mortality; (7) it is but slightly influenced by age, sex or occupation.

The second characteristic which we have mentioned, namely, that the disease seems to originate in one particular part of the world and from there spreads out—such foci having been also described as existing in Asia (Netter), China (Pearson), etc.—is at the present time somewhat in dispute, Frost and others believing that the last two epidemics probably started in several places at once.

The pandemic of 1889 probably started in the East where it is quite likely that an outbreak of so-called "dengue fever" in Constantinople in 1888 formed one of the earliest manifestations. Late in 1888 and in early 1889, it seems to have appeared synchronously in Greenland, in Russia and in Siberia. Heyfelder saw cases in Bokhara in May, 1889, and wrote of its enormous westward speed of travel. In October it reached Petrograd, and in November entered Germany. It swept westward through France, Austria and Italy, reaching Spain in early December, New York and London by the middle of December, and by this time had also reached the United States from the other side, having traveled eastward as well as westward from its origin.

It is quite certain at the present time that influenza is spread by direct and indirect contact. It does not travel more rapidly than human communication, as shown during the 1889 epidemic by Parsons, Friedrich, and others. Communities that are out of touch with infected populations by reason of lack of communication (islands, mountain tops, etc.), usually remain uninfected. Examples of this were noted during the 1889 epidemic on the Island of Borkum, and on the Senlis mountain. In large cities the epidemics burn themselves out within a relatively short time, while in country communities where communication is slower and the population is scattered, it travels more slowly and lasts longer. According to the studies of Abbott of the epidemic in Massachusetts in January, 1890, it was shown that from the fourth of January to the tenth of February, there were about 800,000 cases, that is, about 40 per cent of the population, and the disease had practically burnt itself out in this short period. In London, the epidemic appeared in December, attained a death rate of 28.1 per thousand, during February, and began to decline in March. During the last pandemic similar facts were observed, although the state of war, necessitating the transportation of large bodies of men from one part of the world to another, rendered the correlation of influenza and travel routes extremely difficult. However, MacNeal cites a number of cases where a true connection between ship communication and the outbreak of influenza could be observed. Hospital outbreaks, such as the one described by Foster and Cookson, and prison outbreaks, such as the one described by Stanley for the San Quentin Prison, very definitely prove the importance of contact infection. Stanley shows that the disease was brought in by an infected prisoner, and that prisoners in contact with this one and with other infected inmates contracted the disease, while those who were isolated in other buildings or not in particularly close contact with others, were spared. An epidemic is rarely recognized in a large community until two weeks or longer after the first cases have appeared. Parsons calls attention to the fact that influenza is not more rapid in its spread and epidemic onset than was smallpox in the days before vaccination. He also has found evidence that shows that in localities where the outbreak seemed particularly explosive, this could often be traced to meetings of crowds at conventions or other organizations at times just preceding the beginnings of the epidemics.

Influenza epidemics are always followed by secondary and tertiary waves during which the disease, after a definite lapse of time, seems to return often in a more dangerous form. This has been noted in almost all carefully studied epidemics. Brownlee has attempted to establish a law of periodicity for the intervals between pandemics, and for the intervals between several waves of each outbreak. In general, his studies seem to show that there is an approximate period of ten years between large epidemics, and that a period of about thirty-three weeks intervenes between individual waves.

In contrast to the relatively mild onset of the primary waves, the later waves are marked by greater severity of the cases, and almost universal secondary infection. The disease takes on a much more dangerous respiratory form. The mortality becomes progressively higher during these waves than during the original outbreak.

The secondary epidemic waves do not travel with the same speed and to the same extent as do the first waves. Cases are more scattered and the period of prevalence is more prolonged. These waves never stop abruptly, but play out, in gradually diminishing ripples, into subsequent years. Also, according to Leichtenstern, these secondary and tertiary waves do not seem to take their origins from a single place, but crop up here and there from many scattered foci. As Netter says, "they have appeared in separate, synchronous or successive explosions, without connection between various reappearances in different places, as this was possible during the first appearances in 1889."

REFERENCES

DE LA RIVIÈRE, D. Compt. rend. Acad. d. sc., 1918, 167:406.

FEJES, L. Deutsche med. Wchnschr., 1919, 45:653.

FOSTER and COOKSON. Lancet, 1918, 2, 585.

FRANCIS, T., JR. Proc. Soc. Exper. Biol. & M., 1935, 32:1172.

———— Brit. J. Exper. Path., 1938, 19:273, 284

———— J. Exper. M., 1939, 69:283.

————, and MAGILL, T. P. J. Exper. M., 1936, 63:655; 1935, 62:505.

———— Penn. Med. J., 1937.

———— and STUART-HARRIS, C. H. J. Exper. M., 1938, 68:789, 803, 813.

FRIEDRICH, P. L. Arb. a.d.k. Gsndhtsamte., 1894, 9:139.

FROST. U. S. Pub. Health Serv. Rep., August 15, 1919, 550.

HEYFELDER. Wien. klin. Wchnschr., 1890, 3, 11.

JORDAN, E. O. Epidemic Influenza, Am. Med. Ass., Chicago, 1927.

———— J. Am. M. Ass., 1919, 72:1542.

————, and SHARP, W. B. J. Infect. Dis., 1920, 26:463.

LEICHTENSTERN. Influenza in the Nineteenth Century, 2nd ed., Leipzig, 1912.

LESCHKE. Berl. klin. Wchnschr., 1919, 56, 11.

MACNEAL, W. J. Arch. Int. Med., 1919, 23:657.

MAGILL, T. P., and FRANCIS, T., JR. J. Exper. M., 1936, 63:803.

MCBRYDE, C. N., NILES, W. B., MOSKEY, H. E. J. Am. Vet. Med. Assn., 1928, 73:331.

NICOLLE, C., and LEBAILLY, C. Ann. de l'Inst. Pasteur, 1919, 33:385.

OLITSKY, P. K., and GATES, F. L. J. Exper. M., 1921, 33:125, 361, 373; 1922, 36:501.

OPIE, E., et al. Surgeon General's Report, J. Am. M. Ass., 1919, 72:168.

PARSONS, H. F. Local Govt. Bd. Rep., London, 1893.

SELTER, H. Deutsche med. Wchnschr., 1918, 44:932.

SHOPE, R. E. J. Exper. M., 1931, 54:349. 373; 1935, 62, 561; 1936, 64:47:791.

————, and FRANCIS, T., JR. J. Exper. M., 1936, 64:791.

SMITH, W., ANDREWES, C. H., and LAIDLAW, P. P. Lancet, 1933, 2:66.

STANLEY, L. L. U. S. Pub. Health Serv. Rep., May 9, 1919, No. 19.

YAMANOUCHI, T., SAKAMI, K., and IWASHIMA, S. Lancet, 1919, 1:971.

CHAPTER XXVI

INFECTIONS CAUSED BY *HEMOPHILUS INFLUENZAE* AND OTHER ORGANISMS OF THE HEMOPHILIC GROUP

Family: *Parvobacteriaceae* Rahn. Tribe: *Hemophileae* Winslow *et al.* Genus: *Hemophilus* Winslow *et al.* Species: *Hemophilus influenzae* (Lehmann and Neumann) Winslow *et al.*

In the preceding chapter we have discussed influenza as a virus disease. In this chapter we shall deal with diseases caused by *Hemophilus influenzae*. These are chiefly primary and secondary infections of the respiratory tract, septicemia, endocarditis and meningitis.

Morphology and Staining.—The so-called bacillus of influenza, called also Pfeiffer's bacillus, *B. influenzae* and *Hemophilus influenzae* is a pleomorphic organism. It is usually described as an extremely small rod. 0.5 μ long by 0.2 to 0.3 μ broad. These small, regular forms occur in abundance in exudates and in the smooth types of colonies.

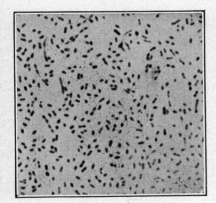

FIG. 24.—BACILLUS INFLUENZAE.

Smear from culture of organism from meningitis; growth on chocolate agar, twenty-four hours.

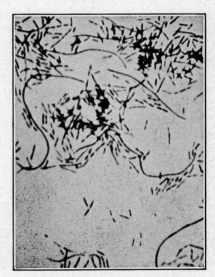

FIG. 25.—BACILLUS INFLUENZAE.
Forms from R type colony.

In other specimens of exudates, often from healing lesions, and in the rough types of colonies, the rods are considerably larger than this and the organisms may be in the form of filaments or chains of rods. Occasionally all these forms may be found in the same culture. The rods have rounded ends.

The organism is nonmotile and does not form an endospore.

Influenza bacilli stain less easily than do most other bacteria with the usual aniline dyes, and are best demonstrated with 10 per cent aqueous fuchsin (five to ten minutes), or with Löffler's methylene blue (five minutes). They are gram-negative.

355

Occasionally slight polar staining may be noticed. Grouping, especially in thin smears of bronchial secretion, is characteristic, in that the bacilli very rarely form threads or chains, usually lying together in thick, irregular clusters without definite parallelism.

Isolation and Cultivation.—*H. influenzae* is aerobic. It requires for growth both hemoglobin (or a related substance) and an accessory food factor. These essential X and V growth factors will be described below.

Before the growth requirements of the organism were understood, the isolation of the influenza bacillus was not easy. It still presents difficulties.

Pfeiffer succeeded in growing the bacillus upon serum-agar plates upon which he had smeared pus from the bronchial secretions of patients. Failure of growth in attempted subcultures made upon agar and gelatin, however, soon taught him that the success of his first cultivations depended upon the ingredients of the pus carried over from the sputum. Further experimentation then showed that it was the blood, and more particularly the hemoglobin, in the pus which had made growth possible in the first cultures. Pfeiffer made his further cultivations upon agar, the surface of which had been smeared with a few drops of blood taken sterile from the finger. Hemoglobin separated from the red blood cells was found to be quite as efficient as whole blood. Whole blood taken from the finger may be either smeared over the surface of slants or plates, or mixed with the melted meat infusion agar. In isolating from sputum, only that secretion should be used which is coughed up from the bronchi and is uncontaminated by micro-organisms from the mouth. It may be washed in sterile water or bouillon before transplantation, to remove the mouth flora adherent to the outer surface of the little clumps of pus. The blood of pigeons or of rabbits may be substituted for human blood.

For isolation we have found the best medium to be a chocolate agar made as described in the section on Media in which 5 or 10 per cent of rabbits' blood agar at a pH of 7.8 is heated to 80–90° C. and the plates prepared by shaking this brownish medium and pouring plates in tubes, cooling as rapidly as possible so that the blood may not all have settled to the bottom. Avery's sodium oleate blood medium, also described in the section on Technical Methods, may be successfully employed. This medium, favoring the influenza bacillus, seems to inhibit a great many contaminating organisms. Unheated blood plates as originally used by Pfeiffer are useful but by far the most generally convenient medium is the chocolate agar mentioned. We do not believe that partial carbon dioxide atmosphere is particularly useful with this organism.

For preservation of laboratory cultures of influenza bacilli, the best medium is fresh, defibrinated rabbit's blood, kept at room temperature in the dark. In this way, laboratory strains after several generations of cultivation outside the body can be kept alive for weeks and even months. They will not keep well either in the ice box or in the incubator.

When influenza bacilli are grown on plates in mixed culture with staphylococci and other bacteria the colonies in the neighborhood of the colony of the staphylococcus or other bacterium are often larger than those at some distance from this colony. This is known as the *satellite phenomenon*, first described by Grassberger and later studied by Rivers and Poole and others. The material produced by the staphylococcus or other foreign organism, which diffusing for a short distance through the agar stimulates the growth of influenza bacilli, is now identified with the so-called V growth-factor.

Summary of Growth Requirements.—There have been many investigations of the growth requirements of influenza bacilli and related organisms. It has been shown that *B. influenzae* requires two kinds of substances for its growth and that morphologically similar organisms can be differentiated from influenza bacilli on the basis of their need for one or the other of these substances. These substances are called the X and V growth factors.

The *X factor* is derived from hemoglobin and related compounds. Pfeiffer's early observations indicated that the iron compound in blood pigment was essential to the growth of influenza bacilli. The subsequent work of Olsen, of Fildes and of Rivers and Poole has confirmed this opinion and has shown that hematin is one of the forms of this X factor. A similar substance has been derived from vegetables and the yolk of unfertilized eggs. The substance has the properties of an organic iron peroxidase. It is heat stable, resisting autoclaving at 121° C. for fifteen minutes or longer.

The *V factor* occurs in blood also. Its nature was understood, however, only after Thjötta and Avery discovered that yeast is particularly rich in this substance. Watery extracts of yeast added to media lacking this material provide a factor permitting the growth of influenza bacilli (Rivers and Fildes). This V substance is present in many bacteria and in fresh vegetables, particularly potatoes. It has been likened to vitamin C, but this assumption has not been proved and seems to be improbable. The V factor is heat labile, being destroyed when autoclaved at 121° C. for fifteen minutes and when boiled for some time.

Procedures for the preparation of these materials and for their incorporation in culture media will be described under Technic.

Influenza bacilli and related organisms show the following differences with respect to their requirements for these growth factors. In this table the + sign indicates that the corresponding factor is essential for growth; the O sign, that the factor is not needed.

Organism	Growth Requirements: X Factor (Heat Stable)	V Factor (Heat Labile)
B. influenzae	+	+
Koch-Weeks bacillus	+	+
B. hemoglobinophilus canis	+	0
Morax-Axenfeld bacillus	0	0
Ducrey's bacillus	0	0
B. pertussis	0	0

The Morax-Axenfeld bacillus, Ducrey's bacillus and *B. pertussis* grow best on media containing fresh or heated blood, especially when first isolated. But these organisms, after cultivation on artificial media, will grow on substrates lacking both the X and V factors, or at least in media in which these factors are in concentrations too low to permit growth of influenza bacilli. There is another group sometimes spoken of as the para-influenza bacilli which require the "V" factor but do not need the "X" factor. This analysis shows further that all organisms of the influenza bacillus group are neither strictly hemophilic nor hemoglobinophilic. It suggests that the generic name *Hemophilus* is a misnomer and that the organisms grouped by Bergey and others in this genus are to be brought together for other reasons than their growth requirements.

The optimum temperature for growth of influenza bacilli is 37° C. They do not grow at room temperature. The limits of growth are reached in two or three days. To keep the cultures alive, tubes should be stored at room temperature and transplantations made at intervals not longer than four or five days.

The *colonies of B. influenzae* vary in size and characteristics with the suitability of the medium, age of the culture and dissociative phase of the organism. Upon suitable media the colonies appear in eighteen to twenty-four hours, as small, colorless transparent droplets, not unlike spots of moisture. These do not become confluent. The S form or smooth colony is round, glistening and somewhat opaque. After twenty-four to forty-eight hours a small nipple-like elevation may appear in the center of the colony. The R form or rough colony is smaller, often more translucent,

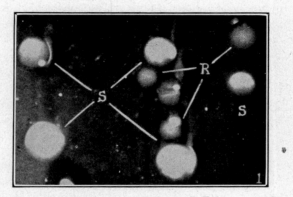

FIG. 26.—COLONIES OF B. INFLUENZAE. S AND R TYPES, AFTER PITTMAN.

and becomes crinkled with an indented edge. The diameters of all colonies are 0.5 to about 1 millimeter.

The organisms in the group of influenza bacilli do not have conspicuous *biochemical activities* (Rivers) and fermentative and other metabolic processes cannot be correlated with the sources of the cultures and their pathogenic activities. Most of the nonhemolytic strains produce acid without gas from dextrose (Stillman and Bourn) and reduce nitrates to nitrites. Others fail to show these reactions. The production of *indole*, noted by Jordan, in 1919 is a constant and fairly stable characteristic of many of the pathogenic strains, particularly those derived from influenzal meningitis (Rivers, and Rivers and Kohn). Influenza bacilli growing in blood-milk do not change the reaction of the medium. As pertussis bacilli produce an alkaline reaction in milk, this medium has some differential value.

Some varieties of influenza bacilli are *hemolytic* (Pritchett and Stillman). They produce the beta-type of hemolysis on blood agar. Apparently these hemolytic forms are a heterogeneous group, as some require only the V factor for their growth while others require both X and V factors (Rivers and Valentine). The relation of hemolytic influenza bacilli to respiratory tract infection is not clear and their incidence is not completely known, since the custom of using sodium oleate blood agar and chocolate blood agar for isolation of the organism precludes any observation on the presence of hemolytic colonies on the primary plate. Some investigators have called them pseudo-influenza bacilli or para-influenza bacilli, but we think that the most advisable allocation for them at present is in the unclassified group of hemolytic varieties of *B. influenzae*.

Dissociation and Serological Relations.—Extensive studies on variability and dissociation of *H. influenzae* have been made by a considerable number of observers. Smith studied the correlation between morphology and colony growth on various media. He described the S forms as usually cocco-bacillary and the R forms as often long and curvedly filamentous. This differentiation is certainly not exact since most marked pleomorphism and filament formation is apparent in the smooth forms seen in spinal fluid of cases with *H. influenzae meningitis*. Cultures from such spinal fluid take on the coccus-bacillary form in one generation without loss of virulence. It is thus clear that filamentous forms can occur both in the S and the R. Pittman, in addition to similar studies, described capsules on the S forms while the R forms were not capsulated. She also found that the S type produced a soluble specific substance probably, according to Dingle, a carbohydrate, which is lacking in the R forms. Pittman divided the S strains into two distinct immunological groups by precipitin reactions. S forms dissociate spontaneously into R forms in successive generations on chocolate agar and other media. The S type can be maintained best by storage in defibrinated blood or by mouse passage, especially when intraperitoneal injection of mice is carried out, together with mucin injections by Miller's technique. Pittman with great difficulty succeeded, in several instances, in reconverting the R into the S type, in some cases by cultivation in media containing R antiserum, in a single case by mouse passage. This is, however, extremely difficult and it is Fothergill's belief that such reversion can be carried out only when the original dissociation into "R" is incomplete.

It was formerly supposed that the organisms of the *H. influenzae* group were antigenically diverse. The general conclusion reached from studies of agglutination and agglutinin absorption by Wollstein, Valentine and Cooper, Rivers and Kohn was that with the exception of the bacilli isolated from *H. influenzae* meningitis, this group is serologically heterogeneous. Rivers and Kohn and others believed that the meningeal strains constituted a distinct serological type. It is now reasonably certain that the smooth or "S" *H. influenza* are serologically homogeneous, except for the possible existence of a few types as indicated by Pittman's studies. When dissociation into the rough forms takes place and the specific carbohydrate and capsule are lost, the organisms become widely heterogeneous so that serological tests have no practical significance.

Toxin Formation.—The opinion in former years has been that the poisonous substances produced by the influenza bacillus were in the nature of endotoxins and a great many observers noted toxic symptoms on the injection of whole cultures into rabbits and guinea-pigs. There is no question about the fact that such cultures in quantities of a cubic centimeter or more can exert powerful poisonous action. Parker showed that culture filtrates of young influenza bacilli would kill rabbits in doses

for this disease is so rapid in its progress and so serious that every hour counts. The diagnosis can be easily made by smear of the spinal fluid because in almost all cases of from 1.5 c.c. upward. The poisons are produced by cultivating the organisms on broth of a pH of 7.8, with 5 to 10 per cent defibrinated rabbit's blood. They were also produced actively in the chocolate broth prepared by heating the rabbit's blood

large numbers of the gram-negative filamentous forms can be seen. Such diagnosis can be confirmed in a few minutes by precipitation of the spinal fluid with serum.

Varieties of Influenza Bacillus.—Organisms morphologically like influenza bacilli and with similar growth requirements and biochemical activities have been described as varieties of the influenza bacillus or as separate species of hemophilic organisms. A number of these have been isolated from acute and chronic forms of conjunctivitis. The organisms associated with *trachoma* will be described in another place. It is improbable that influenza bacilli produce trachoma. The Morax-Axenfeld bacillus, as we have noted is not an influenza bacillus. The *pseudoinfluenza bacilli* of Pfeiffer differ only in minor ways from typical influenza bacilli and are within the range of variation of the species. The *Koch-Weeks bacillus*, isolated by Koch and Weeks from cases of Egyptian conjunctivitis, is now regarded as a true influenza bacillus.

Influenza-like bacilli have been isolated from cats (Rivers and Bayne-Jones), pleuropneumonia of rabbits and swine influenza (Shope).

It is obvious there are many problems, systematic, immunological and epidemiological, which must be solved before a completely coördinated description of the organisms in this group can be given and their pathogenic significance defined.

Hemophilic Bacillus ("Bacillus X") In Sub-acute Endocarditis:—In 1923 Miller and Branch reported a patient with sub-acute bacterial endocarditis due to a hemolytic-hemophilus bacillus. The necropsy of the patient showed vegetative endocarditis, embolic myocarditis and other lesions. The organisms were present in the heart valves in large numbers.

The organism recovered during life and from the heart valve after death and agglutinated by the patient's serum in dilutions of from 1–160 was identical with the organism described in 1919 by Pritchett and Stillman in the throats of normal persons and designated as bacillus X. A case of sub-acute endocarditis similar to the one described was observed by Fothergill and collaborators in 1932.

The organism is pleomorphic ranging from medium sized bacilli to large swollen coccus forms. Methylene blue shows polar bodies. Chain formation may be observed.

The organism is nonmotile, grows best at 37.5° C., the first generations growing most easily although slowly in broth with added blood. It grows readily on solid media only after several generations of cultivation. It does not grow on ordinary routine laboratory media although after prolonged cultivation it may be possible to grow it in broth without blood. The most outstanding characteristic is true hemolysis in all blood cultures.

It is not virulent for rabbits, guinea-pigs or mice.

For the bacteriologist engaged in pathological work it is well to have this organism in mind in connection with sub-acute endocarditis.

Colonies of Bacillus "X" may be confused with hemolytic streptococcus colonies in routine throat cultures unless this organism is thought of.

REFERENCES

FILDES, P.   Brit. J. Exper. Path., 1921, 2:16; 1923, 4:265; 1924, 5:69.

FOTHERGILL, L. D.   New Eng. J. M., 1937, 216:587.

FOTHERGILL, L. D., SWEET, M. and HUBRARD, J.   J. Pediat., 1932, 1:692.

GRASSBERGER, R.   Ztschr. f. Hyg., 1897, 25:453.

——— Centralbl. f. Bakteriol., I Abt., 1898, 23:353.

JAEHLE.   Ztschr. f. Hyg., 1901, 22:190.

KOCH, R.   Arb. a.d.k. Gsndhtsamte., 1883, 3.

——— Centralbl. f. Bakteriol., 1887, 1.

MADISON.   Am. J. M. Sc., 1910, 139:527.

MILLER, C. P. and BRANCH, A.   Arch. Int. M., 1923, 32:911.

OLSEN, O.   Zentralblt. f. Bakteriol., I Abt., 1920, 84:497; 1920, 85:12.

PARKER, J. T.   J. Am. M. Ass., 1919, 72:476.

PFEIFFER, R.   Deutsche med. Wchnschr., 1892, 18:28.

——— Ztschr. f. Hyg. u. Infectionskrankh., 1893, 13:357.

PITTMAN, M. J.   Exper. M., 1931, 53:471.

PRITCHETT, I. W., and STILLMAN, E. G.   J. Exper. M., 1919, 29:259.

RIVERS, T. M.   Am. J. Dis. Child., 1922, 24:102.

——— Bull. Johns Hopkins Hosp., 1919, 30:129; 1920, 31:50; 75:1495.

——— J. Bacteriol., 1922, 7:579.

——— J. Exper. M., 1927, 45:993.

RIVERS, T. M., and BAYNE-JONES, S.   J. Exper. M., 1923, 37:131.

RIVERS, T. M., and KOHN, L. A.   J. Exper. M., 1921, 34:477.

RIVERS, T. M., and LEUSCHNER, E. L.   Bull. Johns Hopkins Hosp., 1921, 32:130.

RIVERS, T. M., and POOLE, A. K.   Bull. Johns Hopkins Hosp., 1921, 32:202.

RIVERS, T. M., and VALENTINE, E.   J. Exper. M., 1927, 45:993.

SMITH, M. M.   J. Hyg., 1931, 31:321.

SMORODITSEFF, A. A., and collaborators.   Lancet, 1936, 2:1831.

STILLMAN, E. G., and BOURN, J. M.   J. Exper. M., 1920, 32:665.

THJÖTTA, T., and AVERY, O. T.   Proc. Soc. Exper. Biol. & Med., 1921, 18:197.

——— J. Exper. M., 1921, 34:97, 455.

VALENTINE, E., and COOPER, G. M.   J. Immunol., 1919, 4:359.

WARD, H. K., and FOTHERGILL, L. D.   Am. J. Dis. Child., 1932, 43:873.

WARD, H. K., and WRIGHT, J.   J. Exper. M., 1932, 55:223, 235.

WEEKS, I. E.   Med. Rec., N. Y., 1887, 31:571.

WOLLSTEIN, M.   J. Exper. M., 1905, 7:335; 1911, 14:73; 1915, 22:445.

WYNEKOOP.   J. Am. M. Ass., 1903, 40:574.

CHAPTER XXVII

BORDET-GENGOU BACILLUS, WHOOPING COUGH, MORAX-AXENFELD BACILLUS, ZUR NEDDEN'S BACILLUS, DUCREY BACILLUS

BORDET-GENGOU BACILLUS

Family: *Parvobacteriaceae* Rahn. Tribe: *Hemophileae* Winslow *et al.* Genus: *Hemophilus* Winslow *et al.* Species: *Hemophilus pertussis* Holland.

Whooping cough is a far more dangerous and widespread disease than is generally recognized. Morbidity statistics, here as in other conditions, are difficult to obtain with accuracy. But from figures available from Denmark and a few communities in this country, where the disease has been reportable since 1907, we may assume that, in crowded centers, at any rate, it may attain average annual rates of from 5 to 13 per thousand population. Mortality figures are of course more reliable. For the registration area of the United States between 1926 and 1934 the death rate ranged from 7 to 10 per one hundred thousand. According to Madsen the death rate from whooping cough is almost as high as the death rate from diphtheria and equal to the combined death rates from measles and scarlet fever.

The pulmonary complications that follow on the initial infection are largely responsible for the deaths, and the subacute and chronic inflammations of the lung lead to prolonged illness and pave the way for tuberculosis and other infections.

The maximum incidence of whooping cough occurs between the ages of 5 and 6. It is estimated that of children between the ages of 9 and 10 years of age, in the United States, 70 per cent have had whooping cough.

The disease seems to appear in periodic epidemics at intervals of 4 to 5 years. The periodicity is sometimes a seasonal one but Madsen did not find any regular seasonal curve in the Danish epidemics. In his opinion the great waves will occur when sufficient hitherto unattacked children have grown up. There are apparent racial differences in that the high rate in the southern part of the United States is probably due to the large colored population, and Vaughan states that the mortality among Negroes is nearly twice that among the whites. Henry's statistics for Massachusetts indicate that 33 per cent of the cases and 90 per cent of the deaths occur in children under three years of age. No age, however, is insusceptible and there are occasional cases among adults. Luttenger confirms Henry in stating that in an analysis of ten thousand cases, 80 per cent of the cases and 97 per cent of the deaths were in children under five. This, Vaughan points out, is an extremely important point in the institution of the public health measures. There seems to be a considerable excess of cases and deaths among females, and Creighton, whom we quote from Vaughan, believes that this is due to differences in the anatomy of the larynx.

Transmission of whooping cough is usually direct or by the common use of freshly contaminated utensils. The most common method of conveyance is close contact with a whooping child, but epidemiological observations, such as those of Luttenger, indicate a possibility of carrier transmission. According to Madsen carriers have not been found in any numbers. In his opinion the important factor in the spread of the disease are children with atypical or undiagnosed whooping cough.

Whooping cough may be transmitted at almost any stage of the disease and epidemiological observation seems to indicate that a child may be infectious for a considerable time before it begins to whoop. Furthermore, it is quite likely that the children may remain infectious for a long time during the stage of convalescence. The exact period, however, must await more accurate bacteriological study. As a rule isolation of the child may be discontinued safely four weeks after the beginning of the paroxysmal cough.

It would appear, therefore, that the most dangerous period begins during the late catarrhal stage just before the whoop and continues until about the end of the third week after the whoop develops. After this there is still some chance of transmission but this is relatively slight and rapidly diminishing.

Climatically there seems to be no special habitat for the disease which at the present time has extended all over the civilized world. However, because of the danger of secondary infections of the respiratory passages, the mortality is apt to be higher in cold than in hot climates. The seasonal curves are usually highest in early spring and late summer and lowest in July. The mortality curves, however, again owing to the danger of pneumonia during the cold months, are highest in February and March.

Susceptibility seems to be almost universal and children that have been definitely exposed very rarely escape.

Prevention consists in early diagnosis and isolation, exclusion from school and absolute avoidance of close contact with other children. Quarantine should continue, as stated above, for about four weeks after the beginning of the paroxysmal cough.

Etiology.—In 1900 Bordet and Gengou observed in the sputum of a child suffering from pertussis a small ovoid bacillus which, though similar to the influenza bacillus, showed a number of distinctive morphological characteristics. Undoubtedly, others saw this organism about this time and may have cultivated it on artificial media. Jochmann and Krause in 1901 named the organism *Bacillus pertussis*. At first, Bordet and Gengou were unable to cultivate the organism. They succeeded in doing this in 1906 and laid the basis for the generally accepted opinion that *B. pertussis* is the bacterial cause of whooping cough. The results of the long-continued investigations of Madsen, Kristensen and others at the State Serum Institute in Copenhagen are compatible with the hypothesis that the Bordet-Gengou bacillus is the etiologic agent of pertussis.

The theory of the bacterial etiology of whooping cough like the bacterial theory of the cause of influenza has been questioned repeatedly. A number of investigators believe that pertussis, like influenza, may be caused by a *filtrable virus* and that the bacterial organism may be a secondary, though important, factor in producing the disease. The type of interstitial pneumonia found in influenza, pertussis and experimental virus infections of the lungs of rabbits led McCordock to search for evidences of the activity of a filtrable virus in the lesions of pertussis. He found intranuclear inclusion bodies in the cells lining the alveoli of the lungs in many cases of pertussis. Such cell inclusions are generally regarded as indications of the presence of an ultramicroscopic virus. Rich was similarly impressed with the unconvincing nature of the evidence that *B. pertussis* causes whooping cough, and was led by the characteristics of the interstitial pneumonia to search for a filtrable virus as the cause of the disease. Rich also found intranuclear inclusions in alveolar cells in the lungs in pertussis and by inoculation of chimpanzees with filtrates of blood and tracheal secretions of children with pertussis he produced a catarrhal condition of the upper respiratory tract, accompanied by fever, which resembled the first stage of whooping cough. It has not been shown whether this virus is herpetic, or the same as the virus of the common cold or a specific virus of pertussis. Rich observed, furthermore, that large doses of Bordet-Gengou bacilli alone injected intratracheally in some of the chimpanzees produced a condition resembling pertussis (paroxysmal cough and lymphocytosis).

According to the observations of Toomey the pathogenesis of whooping cough is as follows: Virulent *B. pertussis*, in Phase I, indicates the disease. At the beginning the patient becomes sensitized to the soluble antigen or toxin of the organism and later becomes desensitized to this substance. By the time of the onset of the whooping cough stage the causative bacilli have become avirulent and produce a mucoid by-product, to which the patient must develop immunity.

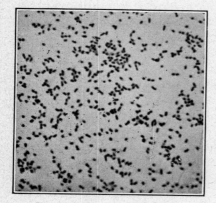

FIG. 27.—BACILLUS PERTUSSIS.

Organisms from forty-eight-hour culture on Bordet-Gengou medium.

It is obvious that the problem of the etiology of whooping cough is not solved. We shall, however, describe *B. pertussis* as the cause of the disease, concurring, for the present, in an almost universal opinion as summarized by Madsen and by Miller.

Morphology.— *B. pertussis* is very much like *B. influenzae* in shapes and sizes. In sputum and in the ciliated borders of the cells of the trachea the organisms are small ovoid rods 0.2 μ broad by 0.5 μ long. The organisms are usually separate, but may occur in masses and clumps in exudates. The forms which occur in culture are often larger than those seen in exudates and filaments are sometimes produced. *B. pertussis* is less pleomorphic than *B. influenzae*, but cannot be distinguished with certainty from the influenza bacillus on the basis of morphology alone.

B. pertussis is nonmotile and does not form an endospore. The organism is encapsulated in the S (smooth) phase.

Staining.—The Bordet-Gengou bacillus may be stained with alkaline methylene blue, dilute carbolfuchsin, or aqueous fuchsin solutions. Bordet and Gengou recommended as a staining solution carbolated toluidine blue made up as follows:

Toluidine blue	5 gms.
Alcohol	100 c.c.
Water	500 c.c.

Allow to dissolve and add 500 c.c. of 5 per cent carbolic acid in water. Let this stand one or two days and filter.

B. pertussis is gram-negative.

Cultivation.—Early attempts at cultivation made by the discoverers upon ordinary ascitic agar or blood agar were unsuccessful. They finally obtained successful cultures from sputum by the use of the following medium:

One hundred grams of sliced potato are put into 200 c.c. of 4 per cent glycerin in water. This is steamed in an autoclave and a glycerin extract of potato obtained. To 50 c.c. of this extract, 150 c.c. of 0.6 per cent salt solution and 5 grams of agar are added. The mixture is melted in the autoclave and the fluid poured into test tubes, 2 to 3 c.c. each, and sterilized. To each tube, after sterilization, is added an equal volume of sterile defibrinated rabbit blood or preferably human blood, the substances are mixed, and the tubes slanted. The pH of this medium is approximately 6. It is not necessary to adjust it.

On such a medium, inoculated with sputum, taken preferably during the paroxysms, colonies appear which are barely visible after twenty-four hours, plainly visible after forty-eight to seventy-two hours. They are small, grayish, and rather thick. After the first generation the organisms grow with markedly greater luxuriance and speed. On the potato blood medium after several generations of artificial cultivation, they form a grayish glistening layer which, after a few days, becomes heavy and thick, almost resembling the growth of typhoid bacilli. In these later generations, also, they develop readily upon plain blood agar or ascitic agar and in ascitic broth or broth to which blood has been added. In the fluid media they form a viscid sediment, but no pellicle. Characteristic slight areas of hemolysis develop about the colonies.

The *cough plate method* of Chievitz and Meyer has been shown by Madsen and his colleagues in Denmark to be a most useful means of isolating *B. pertussis*. It gives more positive results than sputum cultures and is applicable to work with children from whom it is difficult to obtain sputum. In this country a number of investigators have had similar successful results with this method. Sauer and Hambrecht isolated *B. pertussis* by the cough plate method in 98 per cent of the cases in the catarrhal stage. The method consists in holding an open Petri dish containing potato glycerin blood medium in front of a child during a paroxysm of coughing or during forced expiration. The organisms, sprayed on the plate with droplets of secretion, grow in numerous colonies after incubation of the culture at 37° C. for twenty-four or, preferably, forty-eight hours.

B. pertussis is a strict aerobe. In fluid cultures it is best grown in wide flasks with shallow layers of the medium. It grows slowly at temperatures in the region of 37° C., but does not cease to grow at 5° to 10° C. On blood agar and ascitic fluid broth it may remain alive two months.

B. pertussis does not ferment any carbohydrates, does not reduce nitrates to nitrites, and does not produce indole. It renders blood-milk alkaline.

When first isolated, the organism grows only on medium containing blood. After a variable length of time on artificial media, *B. pertussis* will grow on plain media, showing that for growth it does not absolutely require the X and V factors, described in the previous chapter. The ultimate growth on plain media, restricted biochemical activities and production of alkali in broth differentiate *B. pertussis* from *B. influenzae*.

Colonies of B. pertussis at first are small, pinpoint or about 0.5 millimeter in diameter, translucent grayish and hemispherical, resembling colonies of *B. influenzae*. After forty-eight hours' incubation, the colonies become larger, more opaque and whiter than those of the influenza bacillus. The colonial morphology may be of the smooth or rough type according to the dissociative phase of the organism.

Atypical hemolytic varieties which produced a brownish pigmentation on iron-containing media have been described by Bradford and Slavin.

Variability.—The observations by Lawson, in 1927, indicated that virulent and avirulent forms of *B. pertussis* existed and that there were three serological types of the organism. In 1931, Leslie and Gardner isolated smooth, rough and intermediate types and found that the S forms were pathogenic for animals while the R and intermediate types were avirulent. On Bordet-Gengou medium, the smooth colonies are round, glistening, hemispherical and translucent, with a small central elevation. The intermediate colonies are larger, with a roughened surface and a dense elevated center. The rough colonies are more than twice as large as the smooth forms, have indented edges, a finely nodular surface and a dense central elevation. Organisms in the smooth colonies are encapsulated. The changes in morphology from coccoid to mycelial forms under different conditions of cultivation have been described by Toomey and Takas.

These differences in colonial and cellular morphology are associated with differences in antigenicity and pathogenicity. The colony morphology is not always sufficiently characteristic to be of great value as a basis of differentiation. Chiefly by serological means, four phases of the organism have been recognized. Organisms isolated from patients are usually in phase I of Leslie and Gardner and this represents the serological phase described by Bordet and Sleeswyck. The phase II of Leslie and Gardner was not seen by Lawson. Phases III and IV appeared to correspond respectively with types B and A differentiated by Krumwiede and his associates in their serological study of *B. pertussis*.

Continued study appears to show that the original four phase dissociation may be simplified into an ordinary gradation from smooth to rough, and it is only the smooth strains which have any immunizing properties. Only smooth organisms are virulent, toxigenic and capable of providing suitable antigens for active immunization of man in the vaccine prophylaxis and treatment of whooping cough. The general opinion is that all freshly isolated strains of *B. pertussis* belong to a single serological group, as Shibley has indicated.

Pathogenicity.—The regularity and abundance with which *B. pertussis* occurs in the catarrhal secretions of patients with whooping cough, the masses of organisms, as shown by Mallory and Hornor, which lie in banks in the ciliated border of the cells of the trachea give unmistakable evidence that *B. pertussis* is pathogenic for man and is the most likely cause of whooping cough. As we have stated in the preceding paragraph the smooth, encapsulated forms are distinctly pathogenic for guinea-pigs and rabbits. Rich produced a disease like whooping cough in chimpanzees by inoculations with *B. pertussis*. Sprunt, Martin and McDearman produced lymphocytosis and interstitial mononuclear pneumonia in the monkey and rabbit by intratracheal injection of virulent organisms. The necrosis and cellular infiltration of the bronchi and bronchides, seen in children dying of pertussis, were reproduced by Gallavan and

Goodpasture in chick embryos infected with cultures of the Bordet-Gengou bacillus.

Burnet and Timmins, in 1937, showed that intranasal administration of *B. pertussis* cultures to anesthetized white mice produced interstitial pneumonia, often fatal, and typical proliferation of bacilli in the mucus lying on the ciliated surface of the bronchial epithelium. This method may be of value in determining the antigenic efficiency of vaccines.

Endotoxins have been obtained from these organisms by Bordet, Leslie and Gardner, Lawson and others by extracting the bacillary bodies in various ways. An antiendotoxic serum produced by Teissier and his associates and by the other investigators mentioned here may prove to be of value in serum therapy. Organisms in Phase I should be used as the antigens for the immunization of animals. Toomey and McClelland, by means of skin tests, demonstrated that filtrates of both cultures of *B. pertussis* contained a toxin or reactive antigen. They related this to the *exotoxin* described in 1930 by Mishulow, Mowry and Scott.

The endotoxin, prepared by extraction of the organisms in saline, has been used by Thompson for diagnostic skin tests and for tests of immunization. The test, negative in normal individuals, became positive about the tenth day of the disease and was regarded as evidence of hypersensitiveness to the infecting bacilli. Ultimately this cutaneous allergy regressed.

Serology.—As we have stated in the previous paragraph on variation, several serological types of *B. pertussis* were demonstrated by Krumwiede. Leslie and Gardner distinguished four serological phases of the organism, and this work has been confirmed by Lawson and Shibley with respect to phases I, III and IV. In 1909, Wollstein showed that specific agglutinins may be obtained in immunized animals which prove absolutely the distinctness of this organism from *B. influenzae*. Agglutinins in the serum of patients with whooping cough have not been diagnostically serviceable. To avoid confusion caused by sediments of the mucoid material occurring in suspensions of pertussis bacilli the rapid method of agglutination, described by Kendrick, is most useful. According to Madsen the results of complement fixation tests are positive after the third or fourth week of the disease. Convalescent serum has some antiendotoxic properties.

Prophylactic Vaccination.—Vaccines made of suspensions of heat-killed cultures of *B. pertussis* have been used repeatedly for the prevention and treatment of whooping cough by many investigators during many years. The method has had supporters and detractors in great numbers. In 1931, pertussis vaccine was omitted from *New and Non-Official Remedies* [1] because a review of results of its use failed to show that its efficacy had been established.

The experience of Madsen with the use of pertussis vaccine in the Faroe Islands was distinctly encouraging and Sauer reported success in the prophylactic use of the vaccine during four years. His vaccine was composed of suspension of the cells of seven or eight freshly isolated, hemolytic, smooth strains of *B. pertussis*, killed by exposure to 0.5 per cent phenol in the refrigerator for one week. Each 1 c.c. of the vaccine contained 10 billion organisms. Each child immunized was given 7 or 8 c.c. of the vaccine by injection of graded doses.

The clinical investigations of Sauer and, since then, of Kendrick and Eldering

1 J. Am. M. Ass., 1931,96:613.

have indicated that antigens prepared with so-called "Phase One" pertussis organisms are effective as active immunizing agents if employed at least a month before exposure, but that they possess no therapeutic value whatever after the disease has become manifest.

Krueger has prepared an active undenatured antigen from pertussis bacilli, in Phase I of Leslie and Gardner, by grinding and extracting the bacterial cells in Locke's solution. This extract was nontoxic.

Assessing the value of whooping cough vaccine in 1937 Madsen [2] stated: "In our experience there is no evidence that whooping cough vaccination could produce permanent immunity against the infection of the same character as that produced in the case of smallpox or diphtheria vaccination. The experience in the Faroe Islands and in Denmark indicates strongly that vaccination will produce an increased resistance to infection and induce a milder course of the disease for from one to two months after vaccination, and that its use, during the first stages of the disease, will cause it to be milder and of shorter duration; thus decreasing complications and its case fatality."

Prophylactic use of *convalescent serum* has appeared to be of some value in the protection of contacts (Debré).

Organisms Related to B. Pertussis.—The relation of *B. pertussis* to the influenza bacillus is indicated by the placing of these two organisms in the same genus, *Hemophilus*, in recognition of a number of their common characteristics. We have pointed out, however, that the supposedly fundamental characteristic of this genus is not common to these two organisms. *B. influenzae* requires the growth factors X and V; *B. pertussis* after transfer for a variable number of generations on artificial media will grow in the absence of both of these factors. An organism to which *B. pertussis* has some interesting resemblances in pathogenicity and production of alkali in milk cultures is *B. bronchisepticus*. Ferry and Noble studied the apparent close relationship between *B. bronchisepticus* and *B. pertussis* and Brown isolated *B. bronchisepticus* from a child who had the symptoms of whooping cough. Organisms resembling *B. pertussis* and *B. bronchisepticus* but not identical with either have been isolated by Eldering and Kendrick from cases of whooping cough.

B. bronchisepticus is motile, differing in this respect from nonmotile *B. pertussis*. Before the discovery of the virus agent of distemper in dogs, *B. bronchisepticus* was thought by some to be the cause of that disease. As Lawson has pointed out, there is an unsolved taxonomic problem here.

MORAX-AXENFELD BACILLUS

Family: *Parvobacteriaceae*. Tribe: *Hemophileae*. Genus: *Hemophilus*. Species: *Hemophilus duplex*

In 1896, Morax described a diplobacillus, which he associated etiologically with a type of chronic conjunctivitis to which he applied the name *conjonctivite subaigue*. Soon after this, a similar micro-organism was found in cases corresponding to those of Morax by Axenfeld. The condition which these micro-organisms characteristically produce is a catarrhal conjunctivitis which usually attacks both eyes. The inflammation is especially noticeable in the angles of the eye, most severe at or about the caruncle. There is rarely much swelling of the conjunctiva and hardly ever ulceration.

2 Madsen, T. The Abraham Flexner Lectures, Ser. 5, p. 216. Williams and Wilkins Co., Baltimore, 1937.

The condition runs a subacute or chronic course. Its diagnosis is easily made by smear preparations of the pus which is formed with especial abundance during the night.

Morphology.—In smear preparations from the pus, the micro-organisms appear as short, thick bacilli, usually in the form of two placed end to end, but not infrequently singly or in short chains. Their ends are distinctly rounded, their centers slightly bulging, giving the bacillus an ovoid form. They are usually about 2 μ in length.

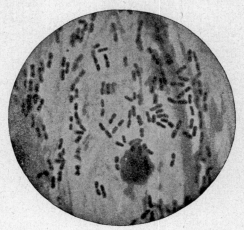

They are easily stained by the usual aniline dyes, and, stained by the method of Gram, are completely decolorized.

Cultivation.—The Morax-Axenfeld bacillus can be cultivated only upon alkaline media containing blood or blood serum.

It grows poorly, or not at all, at room temperature.

Upon *Löffler's blood serum*, colonies appear after twenty-four to thirty-six hours as small indentations which indicate a liquefaction of the medium. Axenfeld states

Fig. 28.—Morax-Axenfeld Diplobacillus.

that eventually the entire medium may become liquefied. Upon serum agar delicate grayish drop-like colonies are formed which are not unlike those of the gonococcus.

In *ascitic bouillon* general clouding occurs within twenty-four hours.

Pathogenicity.—Attempts to produce lesions in the lower animals with this bacillus have been universally unsuccessful. Subacute conjunctivitis, however, has been produced in human beings by inoculation.

ZUR NEDDEN'S BACILLUS

In ulcerative conditions of the cornea, Zur Nedden frequently found a bacillus to which he attributed etiological importance.

The bacillus which he described is small, usually less than 1 micron in length, often slightly curved, and generally found singly. It may be found in the diploform but does not form chains. It is stained by the usual dyes, often staining poorly at the ends. Stained by Gram's method it is decolorized. The bacillus is nonmotile.

Cultivation.—It is easily cultivated upon the ordinary laboratory media. Upon *agar* it forms, within twenty-four hours, transparent, slightly fluorescent colonies which are round, raised, rather coarsely granular, and show a tendency to confluence.

Gelatin is not liquefied.

Milk is coagulated.

Upon *potato*, there is a thick yellowish growth.

Upon *dextrose* media, there is acid formation, but no gas.

The bacillus forms no indole in *peptone solutions*.

Pathogenicity.—Corneal ulcers have been produced in guinea-pigs.

BACILLUS OF DUCREY

Family: *Parvobacteriaceae*. Tribe: *Hemophileae*. Genus: *Hemophilus*. Species: *Hemophilus ducreyi*

The soft chancre, or chancroid, is an acute inflammatory, destructive lesion which occurs usually upon the genitals or the skin surrounding the genitals. The infection is conveyed from one individual to another by direct contact. It may, however, under conditions of surgical manipulations, be transmitted indirectly by means of dressings, towels or instruments.

The lesion begins usually as a small pustule which rapidly ruptures, leaving an irregular ulcer with undermined edges and a necrotic floor which spreads rapidly. It differs clinically from the true or syphilitic chancre in the lack of induration and in its violent inflammatory nature. Usually it leads to lymphatic swellings in the groin which, later, give rise to abscesses, commonly spoken of as "buboes."

In the discharges from such lesions, Ducrey, in 1889, was able to demonstrate minute bacilli to which he attributed an etiological relationship to the disease, both because of the regularity of their presence in the lesions and the successful transference of the disease by means of pus containing micro-organisms. We have cultivated a typical Ducrey bacillus from a case of the chronically progressive type of phagedenic ulcer. It is our belief that some of the lesions spoken of as "granuloma inguinale" represent a secondary infection on a chancroidal basis, though, of course, this does not apply to the typical cases in which the so-called Donovan bodies are found. The chancroidal cases do not yield to antimony injections.

Morphology and Staining.—The Ducrey bacillus is an extremely small bacillus, measuring from 1 to 2 μ in length and about 0.5 μ in thickness. It has a tendency to appear in short chains and in parallel rows, but many of the micro-organisms may be seen irregularly grouped. It is not motile, possesses no flagella, and does not form spores.

Stained by the ordinary aniline dyes, it has a tendency to take the color irregularly and to appear more deeply stained at the poles. By the Gram method, it is decolorized. In tissue sections, it may be demonstrated by Löffler's methylene blue method, and in such preparations has been found within the granulation tissues forming the floor of the ulcers. In pus, the bacilli are often found within leukocytes.

Cultivation and Isolation.—Early attempts at cultivation of this bacillus were universally unsuccessful in spite of painstaking experiments with media prepared of human skin and blood serum. In 1900, Besançon, Griffon, and Le Sourd finally succeeded in obtaining growths upon a medium containing agar to which human blood had been added. They were equally successful when dog's or rabbit's blood was substituted for that of man. Since the work by these authors, the cultivation by similar methods has been carried out by a number of investigators. Coagulated blood, which has been kept for several days in sterile tubes, has been found to constitute a favorable medium. Freshly clotted blood cannot be employed, probably because of the bactericidal action of the serum. Serum agar has occasionally been used with success, but does not give results as satisfactory as those obtained by the use of the whole blood.

The best method of obtaining pure cultures upon such media consists in puncturing an unruptured bubo with a sterile hypodermic needle and transferring the pus in considerable quantity directly to the agar. If possible, the inoculation of the media should be made immediately before the pus has had a chance to cool off or to be exposed to light. When buboes are not available, the primary lesion may be thoroughly cleansed with sterile water or salt solution, and material scraped from the bottom of the ulcer or from beneath its overhanging edges with a stiff platinum loop. This material is then smeared over the surface of a number of blood-agar plates in order to obtain separate colonies.

Upon such plates, isolated colonies appear, usually after forty-eight hours. They are small, transparent and gray and have a rather firm, finely granular consistency. The colonies rarely grow larger than pinhead size, and have no tendency to coalesce. At room temperature, the cultures die out rapidly. Kept in the incubator, however, they may remain alive and virulent for a week or more.

On the simpler media, glucose agar, broth, or gelatin, cultivation is never successful. On moist blood agar and in the condensation water of such tubes, the bacilli have a tendency to grow out in long chains. Upon media which are very dry, they appear singly or in short chains.

Interest was again aroused in the chancroidal lesions because of the apparent, relative frequency of such lesions among venereally infected soldiers in Europe. We were informed by Walker that during the post-armistice periods of the existence of American troops in France, the proportion of chancroids to other venereal infections rose beyond the ordinary relative proportion of this variety of infection, apparently for the reason that prophylaxis as practiced had less effect upon chancroidal infection than it did upon the syphilitic and gonorrheal infections. Since there had apparently developed in the minds of genito-urinary specialists, a certain amount of skepticism regarding the rôle played by the Ducrey bacillus at this time, the matter was reinvestigated by Teague and Deibert. They developed a method for direct diagnostic cultivation of Ducrey bacilli from chancroidal lesions which has so much practical value that it will be well to quote it in considerable detail. The method as described by them is as follows:

A rabbit is bled from the heart with a sterile 20 c.c. syringe and the blood is distributed in amounts of 1 c.c. in small test tubes, a little larger than the ordinary Wassermann tube. The blood is allowed to clot at room temperature and is then heated for five minutes at 55° C. It can thus be preserved in the ice box or can be used immediately. Equally good results can be obtained when the tubes are kept in the ice box for three to four days before use without heating.

Pieces of stiff iron wire, gauge 18, about 5½ inches long, are bent upon themselves at one end for about ⅛ inch. Ten or twelve of these wires are placed in a 6-inch test tube and are heated in the dry sterilizer. The patient removes the dressing and a bit of the pus is picked up with the bent end of the wire, the latter having been first rubbed gently over the base of the ulcer or under its undermined edge. The pus is then transferred to a tube of clotted blood and distributed in the serum by passing the wire around the clot. A second tube is prepared in the same way. After twenty-four hours' incubation at 37° C. the serum around the clot is thoroughly stirred with a platinum loop and a smear is made. Examination with the oil-immersion lens shows characteristic chains of small gram-negative bacilli, sometimes in pure culture, sometimes in mixed culture. The organism is usually so characteristic that such an examination is sufficient basis for a positive diagnosis. Even when antiseptic powder or ointments have been applied, repeated positive cultures have been obtained by finding a bit of pus free from drug. It is not even necessary to wash the ulcer before taking cultures.[3]

3 O. Teague and O. Deibert, *J. Urol.*, 1920, 4:543.

At the time of the publication of their first paper, Teague and Deibert had cultured, by the above method, 274 sores. In most cases these were indiscriminately cultured, even in many cases when no clinically characteristic picture was apparent. Of these 274 sores, 140 yielded positive Ducrey cultures. Of the 134 negative cases, satisfactory notes were obtained of only 69, and from these notes it is apparent that 42 of these 69 negative cases at least were not chancroidal but primary syphilitic lesions. It seems to Teague fair to assume that by this method probably over 90 per cent of true chancroids can be diagnosed, and it is so simple that the physician in the clinic can take the cultures as directed and send them to the laboratory. Isolations can subsequently be made by inoculating blood-agar plates from the clotted blood tubes after twenty-four hours. The nutrient agar should have a pH of 7.2 or 7.3, and the agar must be neither too stiff nor its surface too dry. Teague's results not only furnish a simple method for the determination of mixed infection, but also reaffirm the etiological importance of the Ducrey bacillus in chancroids.

As to prophylactic treatment, recent experience seems to indicate that warm water and soap very thoroughly applied is probably more effective in the prophylaxis of this type of infection, than are the specific methods used for prophylaxis in other venereal diseases.

Pathogenicity.—Besançon, Griffon, and Le Sourd, and others, have succeeded in producing lesions in man by inoculation with pure cultures. Inoculation of the lower animals has, so far, been entirely without result.

REFERENCES

AXENFELD, T. Centralbl. f. Bakteriol., I Abt., 1897, 21:1.

BESANÇON, F., GRIFFON, V., and LE SOURD, L. Presse méd. Par., 1900, 2:385.

BORDET, J. Bull. Soc. roy. d. sc. méd. et nat. de Brux., 1907.

BORDET, J., and GENGOU, O. Ann. de l'Inst. Pasteur, 1906, 20:731; 1907, 21:720.

BORDET, J., and SLEESWYCK. Ann. de l'Inst. Pasteur. 1910, 24:476.

BRADFORD, W. L., and SLAVIN, B. Am. J. Pub. Health, 1937, 27:1277.

BROWN, J. H. Bull. Johns Hopkins Hosp., 1926, 38:147.

CHIEVITZ, I., and MEYER, A. H. Ann. de l'Inst. Pasteur, 1916, 30:503.

DEBRÉ, R. Bull. Acad. de méd., Par., 1923, 89:348.

DUCREY, A. Monatsh. f. prakt. Dermat., 1889, 9:387.

FERRY, N. S., and NOBLE, A. J. Bacteriol., 1918, 3:193.

GALLAVAN, M., and GOODPASTURE, E. W. Am. J. Pathol., 1937, 13:927.

HENRY. Am. J. Pub. Health, 1921, 11:302.

JOCHMANN, G., and KRAUSE, P. Ztschr. f. Hyg. u. Infectionskrankh., 1901, 36:193. Quoted from Hewlett, R. T., System of Bacteriology in Relation to Medicine, London, 1929, 2:395.

KENDRICK, P. Am. J. Pub. Health, 1935, 26, Suppl., 200.

———— Am. J. Pub. Health, 1933, 23:1310.

KENDRICK, P., and ELDERING, G. Am. J. Pub. Health, 1934, 24:309; 1935, 25:147.

———— J. Bacteriol., 1937, 33:71.

KRISTENSEN, B. J. Am. M. Ass., 1933, 101:204.

KRUEGER, A. P., NICHOLAS, V. C., and FRAWLEY, J. M. Proc. Soc. Exper. Biol. & Med., 1932–1933, 30:1097.

KRUMWIEDE, C., MISHULOW, L., and OLDENBUCH, C. J. Infect. Dis., 1923, 32:22.

LAWSON, G. McL. Studies on Bacillus Pertussis. Thesis, Harvard School of Public Health, July, 1932.

LAWSON, G. McL., and MUELLER, M. J. Am. M. Ass., 1927, 89:275.

LESLIE, P. H., and GARDNER, A. D.   J. Hyg., 1931, 31:423.

LUTTENGER.   Cited from Vaughan, Epidemiology.

MADSEN, T.   Boston M. & S. J., 1924, 192:50; J. Am. M. Ass., 1933, 101:187.

―――― Whooping Cough. The Abraham Flexner Lectures. Ser. 5, p. 172. Williams & Wilkins Co.,
   Baltimore, 1937.

MALLORY, F. B.   Boston M. & S. J., 1913, 169:378.

MALLORY, F. B., and HORNOR, A. A.   J. Med. Research, 1912, 27:115.

McCORDOCK, H. A.   Proc. Soc. Exper. Biol. & Med., 1932, 29:1288.

McCORDOCK, H. A., and MUCKENFUSS, R. S.   Am. J. Pathol., 1933, 9:221, 957.

MEYER.   Ann. de l'Inst. Pasteur, 1916, 30:503.

―――― Reports of Copenhagen State Serum Institute, 1921 (collected reprints).

MILLER.   J. Am. M. Ass., 1933, 100:681.

MISHULOW, L., MOWRY, I. W., and SCOTT, E. B.   J. Immunol., 1930, 19:227.

MORAX, V.   Ann. de l'Inst. Pasteur, 1896, 10: 337.

POVITSKY, O.   J. Infect. Dis., 1923, 32:8.

RICH, A. R.   Bull. Johns Hopkins Hosp., 1932, 51:346.

RICH, A. R., LONG, P. H., BROWN, J. H., BLISS, E. A., and HOLT, E. L.   Science, 1932, 76:330.

SAUER, L.   J. Am. M. Ass., 1933, 100:239; 1933, 101:1449.

SAUER, L. W., and HAMBRECHT, L.   J. Am. M. Ass., 1930, 95:263.

SHIBLEY, G. S., and HOELSCHER, H.   J. Exper. M., 1934, 60:403.

TEAGUE, O., and DEIBERT, O.   J. Urol., 1920, 4:543.

TEISSIER, P., REILLY, J., RIVALIER, E., and CHAMBESSEDES, H.   J. physiol. et de path., gén., 1929,
   27:549.

THOMPSON, A. R.   J. Hyg., 1938, 38:104.

TOOMEY, J. A.   J. Pediatrics, 1937, 10:472.

TOOMEY, J. A.   See Editorial, J. Am. M. Assoc., 1938, 110:1927.

TOOMEY, J. A., and McCLELLAND, J. E.   Proc. Soc. Exper. Biol. & M., 1933, 31:44; 1934, 32:527.

TOOMEY, J. A., and TAKACS, W. S.   J. Bacteriol., 1936, 31:44.

VAUGHAN.   Epidemiology, volume on Respiratory Diseases.

WOLLSTEIN, M.   J. Exper. M., 1909, 11:41.

YOUNG.   Cited from Lawrence W. Smith, Am. J. Dis. Child., 1924, 28:597.

ZUR NEDDEN.   Arch. f. Ophthalmol., 1902, 54:1; 1904, 59:360

CHAPTER XXVIII

MICROCOCCUS INTRACELLULARIS MENINGITIDIS (MENINGOCOCCUS) AND EPIDEMIC CEREBROSPINAL MENINGITIS

Family: *Neisseriaceae* Prévot. Genus: *Neisseria* Trevisan. Species: *Neisseria intracellularis* Holland.

MENINGITIS

Infectious processes in the meninges may be caused by many different micro-organisms.

Meningitis may be primary or secondary. Secondary meningitis may often occur during the course of pneumonia, when pneumococci, carried to the meninges by the blood stream, give rise to a usually fatal form of the disease. More rarely a similar process may occur as a secondary manifestation of typhoid fever or of infection with the influenza bacillus. Meningitis may also result secondarily by direct extension from suppurative lesions about the skull, such as those occurring in diseases of the middle ear or frontal sinuses or after compound fractures. In such cases the invading organisms are usually staphylococci, streptococci, or pneumococci.

Isolated cases of meningeal infection with *B. coli, P. paratyphosus, B. pestis,* and *B. mallei* have been reported. A frequent more chronic form of the disease is caused by *B. tuberculosis* (Gilbert and Coleman). Several viruses also cause meningitis.

Primary acute meningeal infection is due chiefly to two organisms, the *meningococcus* and the *pneumococcus.*

It is generally estimated that about 70 per cent of all acute cases of cerebrospinal meningitis are due to the meningococcus, about 20 per cent to the pneumococcus and the remaining 10 per cent to other bacteria or viruses.

The cases caused by the pneumococcus and the other less frequent incitants usually occur sporadically. When the disease occurs in epidemic form, it is almost always due to the meningococcus.

Diplococcus intracellularis meningitidis was first seen in meningeal exudates by Marchiafava and Celli in 1884. These authors not only described accurately the morphological characteristics now recognized, but also called attention to the intracellular position of the micro-organism and to its gonococcus-like appearance. They failed, however, to cultivate it.

Observations confirmatory of the Italian authors were, soon after, made by Leichtenstern. Cultivation and positive identification as a separate species was not accomplished until Weichselbaum, in 1887, reported his observations upon 6 cases of epidemic cerebrospinal meningitis. The researches of Weichselbaum were soon confirmed and extended.

Morphology and Staining.—Stained in the spinal fluid from an infected patient, the meningococcus bears a striking similarity to the gonococcus. The micro-organisms appear intra- and extra-cellularly, usually in diplococcus groups, sometimes as tetrads,

376

or even in larger agglomerations. The individual diploforms are flattened on the sides facing each other, presenting somewhat the biscuit-form of the gonococcus. The variation in size of the cocci in the same smear is a noticeable feature and of some diagnostic importance. This dissimilarity in size is noticeable also in cultures, which, especially when older than twenty-four hours, contain forms double or even triple the size of the average coccus.

The meningococcus is nonmotile and non-spore-forming. It stains easily with all the usual aqueous aniline dyes. Its behavior toward Gram's stain was long a subject of controversy, owing to the error of Jaeger, who claimed to have found it grampositive. There is no question now, however, that the cocci decolorize by Gram's method when this is carefully carried out.

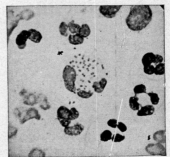

FIG. 29.—MENINGOCOCCI IN SPINAL FLUID.

In spinal fluid satisfactory preparations may be obtained by staining in Jenner's blood stain. Councilman, Mallory, and Wright were the first to notice that, when stained with Löffler's methylene blue, meningococcus stains irregularly, showing metachromatic granules in the center of the cell bodies. These granules can be demonstrated more clearly with the Neisser stain, employed for similar demonstration in the case of B. diphtheriae, and have some value in differentiating meningococcus from gonococcus.

It is important to remember that meningococci in spinal fluid undergo solution very readily, a solution which is probably an autolysis, with the result that spinal fluid, which may be full of polymorphonuclear leukocytes, contains very few recognizable organisms. This readiness of meningococci to go into solution will be spoken of below in connection with problems of cultivation.

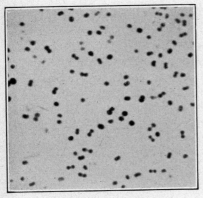

FIG. 30.—MENINGOCOCCUS.

Organisms from twenty-four-hour culture. × 2000.

Cultivation.—The meningococcus is peculiar in that there is considerable difference in the ease with which separate strains can be made to grow upon artificial media. Some meningococci grow readily upon all meat-infusion culture media. They may even grow upon some meat-extract media, but growth upon these is never profuse. It is never well to rely upon media to which no enriching substance has been added, or that have not been especially made for meningococcus cultivation when attempts are made at first isolation from human material. After the bacteriologist is familiar with the individual strains, he may at times carry his strains on the simpler media, meat-infusion agar and broth.

Growth is more luxuriant and rapid upon media to which animal protein in the form of blood serum or ascitic fluid has been added. Coagulated serum is not liquefied. For cultivation of the meningococcus directly from the human body it is wise to use the richer serum or blood media. Agar to which whole rabbit's blood has been added forms an excellent medium, both for cultivation and for keeping the organism alive. *Löffler's blood serum* is less favorable. It is advisable when cultivating directly from spinal fluid, to plant rather large quantities (1 to 2 c.c.), since many of the cocci in the exudate will fail to develop colonies, possibly because of their prolonged exposure either to the body fluids or to their own products in a closed space.

Primary isolation is sometimes made easier by incubating the cultures in an atmosphere containing 10 per cent CO_2, as carbon dioxide aids the growth of meningococci (Wherry and Erwin).

The *colonies* of meningococci are quite characteristic. After incubation for twenty-four to forty-eight hours on a transparent medium such as hemolyzed blood glucose agar, the colonies are about 1 to 2 millimeters in diameter, transparent, circular and so regularly hemispherical in shape that they are like small lenses. The cross-pieces dividing window panes can be focused by the colony when the plate is held before the eye for viewing the colony by transmitted light. By transmitted light the colonies appear to be colorless. Under oblique illumination they have a grayish, semi-opaque appearance. The characteristics of the S (smooth), R (rough) and minute discoid colonies have been well described by Rake, who has studied the dissociation of meningococci.

Upon *broth*, growth is slow and takes place chiefly upon the surface, the sediment consisting mainly of dead bacteria. Glucose added to agar or to broth renders the medium more favorable for rapid growth, but, owing to acid formation, tends to cause a more rapid death of the culture. In flasks of broth containing glucose 1 per cent, and calcium carbonate 1 per cent, however, cultures have been kept alive for as long as fourteen months (Hiss). On *milk*, growth takes place without coagulation of the casein.

While slight alkalinity or acidity does not inhibit, the most favorable reaction of media is a pH of 7.4 to 7.6.

Oxygen is necessary for development. Complete anaerobiosis, while not absolutely inhibitory, is extremely unfavorable, unless proper carbohydrates be present in the medium.

While growth may take place at temperatures ranging from 25° to 42° C., the optimum is 37.5° C. It is an important aid to the recognition of true meningococci that they never grow at ordinary room temperature. Apart from the remarkable viability displayed upon calcium-carbonate broth, the average length of time during which the meningococcus will remain alive without transplantation is rather short. Recently isolated cultures grown on agar or serum agar may die within two or three days. Accustomed to artificial cultivation through a number of generations, however, the cultures become more hardy and transplantation may safely be delayed for a week or even longer. Albrecht and Ghon have kept a culture alive on agar for 185 days. It is a strange fact that after prolonged artificial cultivation some strains of meningococcus may gradually lose their growth energy and finally be lost because of their refusal to develop in fresh transplants. Storage is best carried out at incubator temperatures. At room temperatures or in the ice chest, the diplococcus dies rapidly.

The *fermentation of carbohydrates* by organisms in this group of gram-negative cocci has differential value. Meningococci produce acid without gas from glucose and maltose. They do not ferment either lactose or sucrose. For sharply defined fermentation reactions, a luxuriant growth of meningococci is necessary. Therefore, the best media for fermentation tests are composed of serum agar or ascitic fluid agar containing the carbohydrate to be used and an indicator giving a bright color in an acid medium (Elser and Huntoon). Suitable media are described in the section on technic.

Special Meningococcus Media.—For the routine cultivation of meningococcus, there are certain media which are better than others.

As a basis for meningococcus media, we like to use hormone agar or hormone broth, or trypagar or trypsinized broth as described in the section on media. To these bases enriching substances are added. The necessity for enriching substances may have a more complex cause than the simple addition of nutrition, since, as Lloyd has suggested, the occasional first growth on simple media of meningococci directly from the human body, may depend upon the presence of a certain amount of "vitamin" furnished by the animal fluids present in the exudate. The most convenient substance to add to these media is blood in one form or another. Many varieties of blood are favorable, and human, horse, or rabbit blood can be conveniently used. The blood may be defibrinated and added directly in quantities of about 5 per cent, and if agar for plating is used, melted agar is mixed with the blood and thoroughly shaken just as the plates are poured. Laked blood is very convenient, and may be prepared by mixing whole blood with about four parts of sterile distilled water. This laked blood may be kept and mixed with the agar just before pouring the plates, after the agar has been cooled below 50° C. The blood may also be laked in ether and in this way can be kept sterile for a long time before being added to the basic medium. Blood serum and ascitic fluid can be used, but do not seem to give as good results as does laked or whole blood. The addition of ½ to 1 per cent of glucose is always favorable.

For the storage of stock cultures, Vedder's starch agar described in the section on media has been used with satisfaction.

Gordon and others also have used coagulated egg media in slants for storage of stock cultures with good results.

Egg-yolk Medium for the Storage of Meningococcus Cultures.[1]—One volume of the egg-yolk is mixed with one-half volume of physiological salt solution. The yolk and salt are thoroughly mixed, tubed and slanted. The slants are then inspissated in the usual way. This can be done in an autoclave by bringing the temperature up gradually without letting out the air, until 14 pounds pressure has been reached, and then maintaining this for twenty minutes. Great care should be taken to prevent bubbles in the medium. The tubes, after sterilization, should be plugged with paraffin, since water of condensation is necessary to make the medium useful for storage.

For fermentation reactions, solid or fluid media with various sugars and indicators, may be used. Gordon used for his fermentations a liquid medium of simple peptone water with 1 per cent blood serum and the sugar to be investigated. We prefer ascitic fluid agar slants containing the carbohydrate and an indicator.

[1] Directions of Major Foster from Gordon's laboratory.

intoxication, peritoneal exudates, and often pleural exudates. Intravenous injection of sufficient quantities of such extracts or of dead meningococci may kill rabbits, mice and guinea-pigs.

The toxic filtrates of meningococci have been used for skin tests to detect susceptible individuals and for active immunization of human beings (Ferry and Steele; Kuhns, Kisner, Williams and Moorman). An antitoxic serum for therapeutic purposes has been prepared by immunization of horses against these toxic filtrates.

The so-called *endotoxin* is resistant to boiling for thirty minutes, but is destroyed on prolonged heating. It deteriorates on standing and can be reactivated by filtrates of meningococcus cultures. Although it is possible that this material may be antigenic, an antiendotoxin has not been clearly demonstrated.

Types of Meningococci.—Until 1909 it was believed that the meningococcus group was homogeneous and that no essential difference between individual members of the group existed. In this year, Dopter found that some of the meningococci isolated from cases which occurred in Paris and environment could be distinguished by specific agglutination reactions from the ordinary or normal type. This parameningococcus, as Dopter called it, opened the way for investigations aimed at the serological classification of the group, and, as was to be expected, it was found that there were a considerable number of different meningococcus subtypes. Wollstein confirmed Dopter's work and found, among other things, that the various parameningococcus

Chemical Composition.—The protein and carbohydrate constituents of meningococci are investigated for the purposes of determining the chemical characteristics of these substances and of discovering the parts they play in immunological and serological reactions.

Boor and Miller extracted meningococci with N/100 sodium hydroxide solution, keeping the reaction at pH 7.6–7.8. To this extract, after removal of the bacteria by centrifugation, dilute acetic acid was added until a maximal precipitate had been formed. This precipitate was dissolved in sodium hydroxide solution, at pH 7.8, reprecipitated with acid, and centrifuged. After repetition of this process, the protein was dialyzed in bags of cellophane (No. 600) against distilled water for several days under a layer of toluene. The dialyzed solution was evaporated to dryness in an air current at 56° C. This acid-precipitable, alkali-soluble fraction, admittedly a mixture of proteins, was designated *nucleoprotein*. It was toxic for mice, antigenic and capable of inducing hypersensitivity in rabbits. Meningococcal and gonococcal nucleoproteins gave cross-reactions in precipitin and allergic tests. It was discovered, unexpectedly, that the meningococcus and Type III pneumococcus have nucleoprotein antigens in common. Further chemical investigations of the somatic substance of these organisms will yield information of broad significance.

The *polysaccharides* of meningococci have received attention since the discovery of "residue antigens" in these organisms and other species of bacteria by Zinsser and Parker in 1923. Rake and Scherp, in 1933, described type-specific carbohy-

strains were not wholly homologous, and suggested their possible further subdivision. Gordon examined a large number of meningococci from cases occurring among British and Canadian troops, and found that all the organisms studied by him could be divided into four definite types. He used not only the agglutination reaction, but controlled them with absorption tests. Tulloch, following up Gordon's work on a considerable material, found that, out of 356 cocci investigated, 234 gave specific results with the four type sera used by Gordon's laboratory. He found that, with remarkably few exceptions, the organisms responsible for the outbreaks among British troops were comprised in the four Gordon types. He did, however, find some organisms in the nasopharyngeal cultures of carriers which, though closely resembling meningococci, did not react with any of the type sera. There was some question, however, in his mind as to whether these represented true virulent meningococci. An important result of Gordon's investigations was to show that very many of the organisms obtained from carriers belong to one of the four types known to exist in actual cases of meningeal infection.

In America, Flexner, Rake, Branham and others have investigated the group relationships of the meningococci very carefully. Their results indicate that there are probably two main types, the normal and the parameningococcus of Dopter; and, in addition to this, a considerable number of heterogeneous intermediate types which are related to each other and to the fixed types. Therefore a diagnostic or curative serum, to be truly polyvalent, must be produced with many different representatives of organisms isolated from cases or by immunization of horses against at least four standard strains representative of the main groups of meningococci.

RELATIONS BETWEEN VARIOUS CLASSIFICATIONS OF MENINGOCOCCI

Dopter	American (R.I.)	Nicolle Debains and Jouan	Griffith and Scott	Gordon and Murray	Evans	Rake
Meningococcus	Parameningococcus	A	I	$\frac{I}{III}$	R	I–III
						V
Parameningococcus	Meningococcus	B	II	$\frac{II}{IV}$	S	II
					T ?	IIa
		C				VI ?
		D				VII ?
						VIII

Branham and others have shown that there is extensive serological diversity among meningococci. While certain types are recognizable, the antigenic patterns of the organisms in this group are complex and variable.

As far as prevalence of type is concerned, no definite rule can be established. In the extensive investigations of Gordon and his coworkers, it was found that the earliest cases were mostly his Type I, later came his Type II, especially in the London district, and after March Type IV cases began to appear, but no Type III cases were noticed until July. Branham showed that the relative proportions of meningococci which fell into the four groups of Gordon and Murray were not the same during the outbreak of meningitis in this country during 1927-30 as they were during the outbreak of the disease in 1915-1919. Since about 1927 Type II organisms have been less frequent, while Type I-III has become more important in epidemics and outbreaks of meningococcic meningitis.

The bearing of these facts upon the production and therapeutic efficacy of antimeningococcus serum will be discussed in the paragraphs on serum treatment (see page 388).

Agglutination.—Immunization of animals by repeated inoculations of meningococcus results in the formation in the blood serum of agglutinins. Kolle and Wassermann obtained from horses a serum which had an agglutinating value of 1:3000 for the homologous strain, and of as much as 1:500 for other true meningococcus strains. Similar experiments by many others have proved the unquestionable value of agglutination for species identification of this group.

Elser and Huntoon have shown that in the serum of infected human subjects agglutination of some strains takes place in dilutions as high as 1:400.

Production of Agglutinating Sera for Meningococcus Determination in Laboratories.—For this purpose, rabbits are best employed. Amoss found that young rabbits are more satisfactory than older ones for this purpose, and he used rabbits weighing between 1500 and 1800 grams. He grew meningococci on glucose-agar slants, and washed off the growth in salt solution. 0.001 c.c. of a culture is inoculated as the first dose. For the rapid production of agglutinating sera, he injected his rabbits for three succeeding days, giving a rest of five days, and then another course of three days' injection. He bled the animal two or three days after the second course of inoculation. For ordinary purposes, the slow method of three- or four-day intervals, about five or six injections, with bleeding eight or nine days after the last injection, may be used. Among English workers, Hine injected culture suspensions grown on 25 per cent hemoglobin serum agar, killed at 65° C. and brought to a standard opacity; 0.5 per cent carbolic acid was added for preservation. He standardized all his suspensions by opacity comparisons against suspensions of freshly precipitated barium sulphate. He compared by diluting his suspension in a test tube of similar dimensions as the standard tube, until the image of a small flame was just visible at the same distance from the flame as in the case of the standard tube. With such suspensions he immunized rabbits, beginning with an injection of two doses of five hundred million cocci at an interval of one hour. Six days later he gave three billion cocci, and, if the serum was satisfactory on the eighth day later, he bled the animal. This method was satisfactory in the hands of Hine, with Types I and III. With the other types he had to give larger and more frequently repeated doses. In all such immunization, experience and judgment, with frequent titration of samples of the rabbit serum taken from the ear, are necessary.

Nicolle at the Pasteur Institute used for immunization powdered meningococcus antigen prepared from growth on agar slants by suspension in salt solution, centrifugation and drying. Hine also recommended the use of rabbits ranging from 800 to 1500 grams.

that the experimental disease in these animals would be of use in the evaluation of therapeutic serum, but, thus far, the results have been disappointing.

THE DISEASE IN MAN

The disease produced in man consists anatomically in a suppurative lesion of the meninges, involving the base and cortex of the brain and the surface of the spinal

Agglutination Technic with Meningococci.—Agglutination of meningococci presents considerable difficulties because of the relative inagglutinability of many meningococcus cultures. This is a peculiarity of these organisms which has necessitated much investigation and many technical modifications. Hine found that allowing the diluted carbolic saline suspension to stand for twenty-four hours, increased agglutinability, and recommended this technic if time permits. Tulloch has called atten-

cord. The nature of the exudate may vary from a slightly turbid serous fluid to that of a thick fibrinous exudate. In chronic cases encephalitis and dilatation of the ventricles may take place. Apart from their presence in the meninges and in the nasopharynx, meningococci have not often been demonstrated in any of the complicating lesions of the disease. Reports of their presence in the conjunctivae, in the secretions from bronchial or lobar pneumonia, and in otitis media, have been reported but are not very common.

The occurrence of this micro-organism in the circulating blood of meningitis cases was first demonstrated by Elser, who found it in 10 cases.

In the discussions on epidemiology, below, we will see that Herrick and others claim that the meningococcus is probably, in the majority of cases, in the blood before it reaches the meninges, making its way to the central nervous system by way of the blood stream rather than directly along the lymphatics at the base of the skull. It seems fair to assume from blood-culture evidence that this certainly happens in many cases even though it may not be the rule. During epidemics, also, there are occasional cases in which a general septicemia due to meningococci occurs, without ever giving rise to symptoms pointing to meningeal involvement. These cases are always violent in course, usually fatal and accompanied by a profuse petechial rash.

In the interepidemic periods as well as during epidemics cases of meningococcus septicemia without meningeal symptoms, though rare, are sufficiently frequent to be thought of whenever an individual is seen who is subject to intermittent type of fever with moderate increase of leukocytes and no focal symptoms in any way discoverable to account for his condition. Blood cultures in such cases, taken in the ordinary way, may be negative, which confuses the picture. The rash characteristic of many cases of meningococcus infection may be severe and prominent in the acute cases, while it may be either completely absent or hardly noticeable in the prolonged cases. In these individuals it may be represented only by a few pink spots not unlike a mild insect bite on the extremities and sometimes on the trunk, coming and going often with the fever and hardly ever petechial. Such cases are diagnostically confusing and it is of the utmost importance that they should be recognized because they often end, sooner or later, with a general meningitis with subsequent death unless properly treated. They can be diagnosed in practically every case with persistence and care in the taking of blood cultures. If taken on suitable ascitic-infusion broth flasks, organisms so obtained may on occasion be difficult to agglutinate, perhaps because of their prolonged residence in the human body. Because of a recent mistake made by us, we advise a serious consideration of the diagnosis of meningitis septicemia whenever a prolonged case of fever with leukocytosis and a slight variable rash comes under observation. The case referred to lasted seven months and diagnosis was made by blood culture too late to avert a fatal outcome. The fever was of a tertian type. Blood for culture should be taken at a time when the temperature is beginning to rise. There is a record of a case of chronic meningococcemia lasting five months (Graves, Dulaney and Michelson).

Bacteriological Management of the Meningitis Case and Serum Treatment

In the light of our present knowledge of the bacteriology and serum treatment of epidemic meningitis, a considerable responsibility rests with the bacteriologist.

The difference between recovery and death may depend directly upon the speed with which a bacteriological diagnosis is made and a proper management of the serum treatment. When a case of suspicious fever in which slight stiffness of the neck and a developing Kernig sign are associated with the other indications of an acute infection, the first step must consist of lumbar puncture.

A sterile lumbar puncture needle is thrust into the spinal canal, a little to one side of the third or fourth lumbar space, and the fluid which is always under some pressure, is taken directly into a centrifuge tube. This fluid must then be examined as above indicated in the technical section on spinal fluid, and the diagnosis made. If possible, a smear should be made at the bedside, and an immediate Gram strain done with the first drop of fluid that flows. In this way, it may be possible to inject the first dose of serum immediately after the withdrawal of the diagnostic fluid, thus gaining valuable time.

Examination of Spinal Fluid.—The spinal fluid of meningococcus cases is slightly turbid in the very early periods, becoming increasingly purulent, with large numbers of polymorphonuclear leukocytes. In some cases the fluid which has been very purulent may clear up considerably, and then become purulent again, a matter probably dependent upon sacculation in parts of the subarachnoid space. The fluctuations in the nature of the spinal fluid under intraspinous serum treatment will be spoken of in another place. A certain amount of prognostic information can be obtained from the spinal fluid in that in severe cases that are not doing well, there will be a considerable number of organisms, extracellular. Ordinarily, the majority of the meningococci are intracellular. Such spinal fluid should be taken into sterile centrifuge tubes, brought to the laboratory without delay, slides smeared from the sediment, and stained by Jenner and by Gram. It is important to remember that because of the extensive autolysis of meningococci in the fluid, it may under some conditions be very difficult to find meningococci. In such cases, if prolonged search has failed to reveal organisms, our experience has taught us to assume that purulent fluid from a case of an acute meningitis in which there are a preponderance of polymorphonuclear leukocytes without organisms is probably "meningococcus" in origin. Streptococcus and pneumococcus fluids invariably show gram-positive cocci.

The cultivation of spinal fluid is a matter of great importance for obvious reasons. It is essential, therefore, that it should be done correctly. The method which, in our opinion, is by far the most successful, is a fairly heavy inoculation of the fluid on chocolate agar plates or slants in an atmosphere of approximately 10 per cent of CO_2. We make a point of this as one of the most important steps in the bacteriological management of meningitis cases.

It is a question whether the organisms travel along the lymphatics to the base of the skull directly, or whether bacteriemia precedes meningeal infection. It is well, always, in cases of early meningitis, to take blood cultures. In taking blood cultures it is best to inoculate hormone glucose broth flasks containing not less than 100 c.c. of culture fluid and to make a number of glucose hormone agar plates with varying amounts of blood. The presence of meningococci in the blood is, of course, an indication for intravenous as well as intraspinous injection of serum, a procedure which is in our opinion advisable in all cases, since it is quite likely that meningococcus septicemia and toxemia, constant or intermittent, are regular features of the disease.

Serum Therapy.—Although Wassermann and Jochmann prepared and successfully used antimeningococcus serum for the treatment of meningitis in 1906, the establishment of this beneficial therapeutic procedure came from the work of Flexner and Jobling. The analysis of the cases treated intraspinously with Flexner's serum in all parts of the world during the period 1908 to 1915 showed that the expected mortality of about 70 per cent in untreated cases was reduced by serum treatment to about 30 per cent. Administration of the serum early in the disease was especially beneficial, the mortality among those treated before the fourth day being only about 18 per cent.

When used to treat cases of meningitis during the early part of the World War, this original type of serum was not as effective as expected. Investigation soon revealed that previously unrecognized types of meningococci were causing the infections and that it would be necessary to produce serum of wider polyvalency in order to combat the effects of these various types of organisms. To accomplish this horses were immunized with suspensions of cultures of many serological varieties of meningococci. In some instances 20 to 60 strains were used as antigens. The production of antimeningococcus serum is still based upon this recognition of types, but is being guided more and more by an increasing knowledge of the common antigenic patterns or components of organisms in this group. By the selection of strains within the four types but yet possessing wide antigenic valencies, the number of strains required for injection into a horse to produce polyvalent serum can be reduced. Acting upon this principle, Wadsworth has used only 4 to 6 strains for the production of the therapeutically valuable antimeningococcus serum of the New York State Health Department Laboratories.

The National Institute of Health supplies to biologic products laboratories in the United States the desirable strains for use in the immunization of horses.

For use in the agglutination tests by which serums are chosen for therapeutic use, strains 331, 173, 302, and 158 are employed as antigens. A serum is satisfactory, from the laboratory standpoint, if it shows an agglutinin titer against these antigens as high as does a control serum supplied by the National Institute of Health. The exact titer shown by the control serum is not of moment, since it may vary at different times with different batches of antigen.

Preparation of Antimeningococcus Serum.—The cultures to be used as antigens are grown on dextrose serum agar slants, suspended in salt solution, pooled and injected intravenously into horses. Series of three daily injections are given with a seven-day interval between each series. Live organisms are used and the amounts injected are increased gradually. Sufficiently potent serum is produced by a horse thus treated after about three months. For the numerous technical details relating to the production and standardization of this serum, the reader is referred to the book on *Standard Methods of the Division of Laboratories and Research of the New York State Department of Health.*

Standardization of Serum.—Since it is not possible to produce typical cerebrospinal meningitis by infection of the ordinary laboratory animals with meningococci, and since there is no satisfactory measure of the antitoxic or antiendotoxic properties of antimeningococcus serum, indirect measures are used to gauge the potency of the serum. The chief of these is the agglutination test. Serum from an immunized horse which has an agglutination titer of from 1:5000 to 1:1500, respectively, against the strains of meningococci injected into the animal is regarded as being acceptably potent. This test, however, is not a fundamental measure of the curative power of the serum.

Other standardization procedures have been tried. The chief of these are the application of the Shwartzman phenomenon to the standardization of antimeningococcus serum (Powell and Jamieson, and Sickles) and the tests of antitoxic capacity devised by Ferry.

Meningococcus antitoxin, in doses of 50,000 to 100,000 units has been used with promising results by Hoyne, who administered the serum intravenously.

Concentrated serum, in the opinion of Wadsworth, has not been found to be better than the unconcentrated serum for the treatment of meningitis.

Administration of Serum.—The most important single consideration in serum treatment of meningitis is the early recognition of the case and avoidance of delay in starting the specific treatment. Failure of serum treatment can probably in most cases be referred to delay. Lumbar puncture, therefore, should be done as early as the first suspicion is aroused, and, if meningococci are found, the injection of serum should follow as rapidly as possible.

It is probably best, in the long run, to inject serum immediately upon obtaining a turbid fluid in a case in which the clinical suspicion points strongly to epidemic cerebrospinal meningitis.

The technic of serum injection consists in first withdrawing spinal fluid by tapping the canal with a sterile needle and allowing the fluid to flow out, of course without suction, holding a centrifuge tube directly over the butt of the needle. The flow is allowed to continue until the drops begin to come quite slowly, that is, a drop every ten or twenty seconds, and then the serum is injected, either by gravity or with a syringe through the same needle. It is important that the serum at body temperature shall enter the canal very slowly, and, for this reason, the gravity method is advised. A gravity arrangement can easily be constructed by attaching about eighteen inches of catheter tubing, sterilized, to the end of the needle with a small sterile funnel at the other end. The withdrawal of large amounts of fluid suddenly sometimes causes trouble, the patient breathing rapidly, and showing symptoms of threatened collapse, but this is rare, and a little judgment in withdrawing fluid which has been under considerable pressure too rapidly will usually guard against acident. During the injection of the serum, the patient should be carefully watched, since occasionally alarming symptoms may arise from too rapid increase of internal pressure. The physician must be on the alert for such symptoms and immediately discontinue the injection for the time being. Ten minutes or more should be allowed for the injection of the entire amount of serum used.

The dosage of serum should, to some extent, depend upon the amount of fluid withdrawn, and the amount injected should usually be less by several centimeters than the amount withdrawn. The average dose for an adult should be about 30 c.c. though more may be given when large quantities of fluid have been withdrawn, and when the case is very carefully watched by an experienced man. Sophian has recommended controlling the withdrawal of spinal fluid and the injection of the serum by blood-pressure measurements. Sudden drops of blood pressure, in either case, should lead to caution, and perhaps interruption of the procedure. Repetition of the injections is as important as the initial injection, as far as cure is concerned.

The action of the serum may be compared somewhat to the action of antiserum in a Pfeiffer reaction in a guinea-pig's peritoneum. Thus, probably some bacteriolysis and considerable stimulation to phagocytosis by opsonic action may result. The spinal fluid shows changes in that the numbers of organisms are diminished and the extracellular ones disappear. Purulent spinal fluid may become clearer and may even become entirely free from organisms or leukocytes. There is probably a certain amount of poison neutralization by the serum. Repetitions of the doses, therefore, must be governed to some extent by the progress of the case, clinical conditions pointing to changes in the meningeal inflammation, and observation of the spinal fluid. One injection a day for three to six days usually controls a case that is treated with sufficient promptness.

In addition to the intraspinous administration, it is wise to inject from 30 to 50 c.c. intravenously, preceding this by withdrawal of blood for blood cultures, and being governed as to repetition by subsequent blood culture control.

Every one dealing with meningitis during an epidemic must remember that occasionally meningococcus septicemia cases occur which never show meningeal infection. We have mentioned these in another place, but believe that more attention should be given them, since they are very apt to be fatal, either without meningitis, or subsequently followed by a violent meningeal involvement. Such cases displayed the clinical picture of a general severe septic infection with usually a profuse eruption in which petechial spots not unlike those of typhus fever may cover the entire body. There is an irregular septic temperature with a high leukocytosis and sometimes delirium. Blood culture will diagnose these cases and vigorous intravenous serum treatment would be indicated.

Effects of Serum Treatment.—The mortality of meningitis in the days before serum was used varied between 60 and 80 per cent. Higher mortalities have been noted in individual epidemics. The average for many different parts of the world fluctuates about 70 per cent. Since serum treatment was begun just before the year 1906, a great many statistical studies have been made which are of course subject to great error, owing to the fact that the treated cases must have included a great many treated too late to permit any kind of treatment to be effective. Flexner's statistics of cases under serum treatment show that, of 1211 cases, analyzed, those treated between the first and third day (199) showed a mortality of 18.1 per cent, those

COMPARATIVE MORTALITY REPORTED BY VARIOUS OBSERVERS *

Treatment Begun	Flexner, Per Cent	Netter, Per Cent	Dopter, Per Cent	Christomanos, Per Cent	Levy, Per Cent	Flack, Per Cent
Before third day	18.1	7.1	8.2	13.0	13.2	9.09
From fourth to seventh day	27.2	11.1	14.4	25.9	20.4	....
After seventh day	36.5	23.5	24.1	47.0	28.6	50.00

* S. Flexner, *Bull. Rockefeller Inst. M. Research*, 1917.

treated between the fourth and seventh day (346) showed a mortality of 27.2 per cent, and those treated later than the seventh day (666) showed a mortality of 36.5 per cent. The table on page 390 taken from a paper by Flexner, published by the Rockefeller Institute as a bulletin in 1917, gives similar comparative mortality statistics reported by different observers.

Altogether, then, it seems quite clear that serum treatment has made a tremendous reduction in the mortality from this otherwise so fatal disease.

Chemotherapy.—In 1937 Schwenkter, Gelman and Long reported that *sulfanilamide,* injected intraspinally and subcutaneously, gave excellent results in the treatment of meningococcus meningitis and septicemia. These results have been confirmed by Willien. Sulfanilamide has been used also in combination with antimeningococcus serum (Branham, Carbonell and Campbell).

Epidemiological Problems

Although this disease may be regarded as endemic in all crowded cities, it is chiefly important for its epidemic occurrence. Epidemics have been frequent, especially at times of war, when they appeared in barracks and mobilization camps. During the many continental campaigns in the time of Napoleon, outbreaks occurred in the various armies, and secondary epidemics among the civilian population in many cities followed in the train of these. In America, a number of limited epidemics occurred along the eastern seaboard during the early half of the nineteenth century, and in these civilian epidemics the disease particularly selected children and young adults. Extensive civilian epidemics occurred in different parts of the world in the early years of the twentieth century. In 1903, the disease appeared in East Prussia and other parts of Germany. In 1904 and 1905, it appeared in New York City and the adjacent country, on an extensive scale causing the death of three thousand people and altogether about seven thousand cases in New York City alone. In the summer following it extended to Canada, and in the years since then, small outbreaks and sporadic cases have appeared all through the more thickly populated parts of North America.

Although during epidemics many adults may come down with meningitis, the disease during interepidemic periods is very largely one attacking children under five.

During the World War, there was little meningitis among the European armies until an extensive outbreak occurred among the Canadian troops on Salisbury Plains. The increase of cases among these troops took place in February, 1915, and after this time the disease began to appear in the overseas expeditionary troops, although among these no extensive epidemic occurred at any time. Among American troops the disease was most prevalent in 1917 and 1918 among the troops gathered in the cantonments in the United States. According to the epidemiological studies of Vaughan and Palmer in the camps in 1918, meningitis showed "of all diseases, the greatest excess over the disease in civilian communities." Vaughan estimates that meningitis was forty times as frequent in the army as in civilian life. The highest morbidity occurred at Camp Jackson where it reached a rate of 25.1 per thousand, and a death rate of 7.05. Next to pneumonia, it was the most serious disease occurring in the camps. In the Surgeon General's report for 1918, the disease stood fifth as a cause of death for enlisted men in the United States and Europe, with a case mortality of 34.8 per cent.

During the army epidemics there was a definite racial difference in that, according to Surgeon General Ireland's report, the admission rate for colored troops in the United States was 2.44, whereas, it was only 1.2 for whites, and the death rate for colored troops was 0.98 against 0.41 for whites.

As to seasonal prevalence, meningitis usually develops in the late autumn and winter months, the largest case rates being coincident with the cold and wet weather, when a basic catarrhal inflammation of the upper respiratory tract creates favorable conditions for the lodgment of organisms and for the general distribution of saliva by coughing, sneezing, and spitting. During the War, the highest admission rates in the United States usually fell into the months of November, December, and January, which is the time of the highest case rate for most respiratory epidemics. Yet cases will usually trail along through the hot weather.

Meningitis epidemics, therefore, will occur chiefly in the temperate zones during the winter months at times when, during the prevalence of generalized respiratory disease, large numbers of people are crowded in close quarters, under conditions which render attention to hygiene and sanitation difficult. The reasons for this will become apparent as we study the manner of transmission.

The meningococcus does not survive easily outside the body, and rapidly dies out in dust, or even in sputum, under conditions of low temperature, deficient moisture and competition with other micro-organisms. As far as we know, it is not carried by any of the domestic animals and, therefore, the origin of infection lies in the secretions of cases and of carriers. The micro-organisms are found in the noses and throats of the sick, sometimes in the secretions of the eye where a meningococcus conjunctivitis may exist. With the secretions of these mucous membranes it reaches the outer world. The meningococci may be present in cases for a long time after convalescence, and, as we know, they are present in a considerable percentage of people who have never had meningitis, with whose secretions the organisms may be constantly transferred to contacts. Transmission probably occurs by close contact between carrier or case and new host, through the nasopharynx, where the organisms lodge and multiply. From this lodgment they pass into the meninges, either directly along the lymphatic channels to the base of the skull, or perhaps by way of the general circulation. The former route is the one favored by most observers. However, during the early periods of the World War, a few cases were reported by British clinicians, in which blood culture was positive before symptoms of meningitis had developed, and during these army epidemics, we, as well as others, saw occasional cases of general meningococcus septicemia which died without ever developing meningitis. Incidentally, it may be stated that these cases develop a generalized rash which, in some of its stages, not unlike that of typhus fever. The writer recalls a case in which he made a probable diagnosis of typhus fever which in the light of subsequent experience seems to him to have possibly been a case of meningococcus septicemia. Positive blood culture in such cases will differentiate between the two diseases. Herrick studied this phase of the problem at Camp Jackson in 1918 with great care, and came to the conclusion that in 50 per cent of the cases early blood culture will reveal general infection before clinical evidences of meningeal invasion are apparent. This observation is of the greatest importance, indicating the desirability of early blood culture in a case of doubtful diagnosis, and also for throwing light upon the wisdom of intravenous serum therapy combined with the intraspinous injections.

Infection of a healthy individual from a case is of very rare occurrence, and since there is in every epidemic a very much larger number of carriers than of cases, the carrier is the chief epidemiological problem. As far as infection of new individuals from patients is concerned, experience during the New York epidemic showed only two or three cases of infection of doctors and nurses, although the hospitals in the city were constantly handling considerable numbers of the sick. In our epidemiological experience with the army, the actual tracing of one case to a preceding one was also relatively very rare. This does not mean that the greatest precautions should not be taken to prevent such transmission in hospitals and sick room. But the epidemiological emphasis lies with the carrier.

This rareness of transmission from cases to the healthy is in our opinion due to the peculiar conditions of susceptibility that prevail in relation to meningitis, and the fact that the number of people with whom the sick come in contact is relatively small.

The susceptibility of man to meningitis is a curious one, different in some aspects from susceptibility relations to almost all other infections, except perhaps poliomyelitis. In the general population there seems to be a great variability in individual susceptibility to infection with the meningococcus, a variation which can be traced to no determinable cause. Unlike pneumonia, temporary fluctuations in well-being, produced by respiratory disease, malnutrition, exposure to cold, etc., do not seem to play a determining rôle. The disease indiscriminately picks out individuals here and there, some of them in the most robust health, strong and hardy, while sparing associates who may be feeble and run down. It is obvious that some individuals are normally resistant and will not come down, in spite of considerable exposure, while others are delicately susceptible. The difference may possibly have been produced fortuitously by the fact that some individuals may have been carriers at one time or another, and have become, thereby, spontaneously immunized. It is difficult to get at this question experimentally, and there are no serum or other reactions which we can apply at the present time, by which we can discriminate between the susceptible and the nonsusceptible of a community. There is no available method, moreover, by which we can distinguish between virulent and nonvirulent strains of meningococci.

The Carrier Problem.—The meningococcus carrier probably is the source of infection in most of the cases that develop during an epidemic. Earlier carrier work has lost value to a considerable extent, owing to the fact that the criteria of meningococcus identification of which we are now more thoroughly informed were neglected in these early studies. The flora of the nose and throat contains many gram-negative diplococci, some of which were mistaken in this earlier work for true meningococci. *Micrococcus catarrhalis, Micrococcus flavus,* and a number of other similar microorganisms probably represent a definite percentage of the earlier statistics. Three types of carriers are now recognized—chronic, intermittent and transient.

The studies of Bassett-Smith, Gordon, Mathers and Herrold, show that in the American camps under conditions of ordinary life and weather, there may be anywhere from 2 to 5 per cent of meningococcus carriers. Mathers and Herrold at the

Great Lakes Naval Training Station examined over fifteen thousand men, finding over 4 per cent to be carriers and between 1 and 2 per cent to be chronic carriers. Their work also showed that the carrier rate is higher among those taking care of cases, and that over 38 per cent of those recovering from the disease may remain carriers during convalescence for variable periods. Contacts showed a carrier rate of 36.7 per cent during a period in which the general carrier rate in the camps (15,000 men examined) was slightly over 4 per cent. The hospital corps showed a carrier rate of 13.5 per cent.

It is natural that there have been many endeavors to establish relationship between new cases and contact with carriers. This line of investigation has not been conclusive, owing to the great difficulties incident to such investigation. The transmission of respiratory organisms may take place during a very brief contact, in conversation, close association in barracks, moving-picture shows, public conveyances, sleeping quarters, etc., and the innumerable associations of this kind established by each man in the course of a day, make it almost impossible to trace them with accuracy. Among the most interesting studies made in this connection are those of Glover, who swabbed the throats of a considerable number of men in overcrowded barrack rooms, in the course of sanitary supervision during which the spacing between beds was among the many precautionary measures taken. Sanitary measures, including the spacing out in sleeping quarters, brought about a very considerable drop in the carrier rate, with coincident diminution of cases of meningitis. Meleney and Ray traced 14 out of 24 cases which occurred in an American camp to contact with carriers, and found parallelism between the incidence of cases and the rise of the carrier rate. These examples, however, are exceptional and it is relatively rare that a definite relationship of this kind can be established. It is a fact that carrier rates are high in such camps during the cold months, and in connection with the general spread of respiratory disease, and that, at such times, the incidence of the disease increases, and it is absolutely logical to assume that the new cases arise by contact with the carriers. It is of importance, however, to recognize that the tracing of the case to the individual from whom he has been infected, at times when high carrier rates exist, is not often possible, and comprehension of this must considerably influence the measures instituted for the control of the epidemic.

It is our belief that the extensive carrier examinations made during epidemics and the wholesale isolation of carriers, were relatively ineffective during the World War, and that it is far better to bend all one's energies upon a general improvement of the respiratory sick rate with the reduction of carriers, focusing the carrier examinations upon the small epidemiologically determined intimate group from which the case has come, rather than making wholesale carrier examinations of carriers of meningococcus through whole regiments and divisions.

Carrier Determination.—The bacteriological analysis of a carrier is not a simple procedure, and implies the proper control of a great many conditions which necessitate special description.

To obtain the material properly the swab must be taken from high up in the pharynx, behind the soft palate. A general swabbing of the pharynx and throat is not sufficient. The best swabs for this purpose are made by the West tube method, as follows:

A cotton swab is fixed on the end of a copper wire, about 18 centimeters long, and this is inserted in a glass tube, bent upward at the swab end, in such a way as to permit passage upward behind the soft palate. The swab is placed in the tube, both ends plugged with cotton, and is so sterilized. For large-scale work it is sufficient to take copper-wire swabs, sterilize them in a box, and bend them up carefully with the finger, being careful not to touch the cotton, just before use. Swabbing through the nose has also been practiced, but we do not believe that it is as efficient as the method described above. The swab must be taken with the patient facing the light. A tongue depressor is used, and the swab inserted so as to pass behind the soft palate. The copper wire is then thrust forward so that the swab emerges from the tube and touches the posterior and upper pharyngeal wall. Slow motion to and fro brings the cotton in contact with the sides of the upper pharynx. The swab is then immediately passed over the surface of the plate medium. It is best not to carry the inoculated swab back to the laboratory, but to plate it directly upon removing the material from the patient.

The media employed are various, but for ordinary use a glucose hormone agar, pH of 7.4 with addition of 10 per cent defibrinated or hemolyzed human or rabbit's blood, is best. The plates thus inoculated should be kept warm and immediately taken to the laboratory where they are incubated. The British prefer trypagar to the hormone agar as the basic medium for such work.

After eighteen to twenty-four hours incubation, the plates are examined and the colonies suspected of being meningococci are fished. This is not a matter which can be taught by book. The colonies are of small, rounded appearance, the recognition of which is a matter of judgment. Every bacteriologist confronted with the problem should immediately plant plates of the medium which he is going to use, with spinal fluid or with cultures recently isolated, and familiarize himself with the colonies on this medium, at various stages of growth. In spite of our not inconsiderable experience, we would do this ourselves. Plates that are too thickly covered with colonies are of no use.

On blood medium, the true meningococcus colonies do not produce any change in the blood. They are slightly translucent and look somewhat stringy. They are homogeneous and slightly glistening. They are practically indistinguishable from young colonies of *M. flavus* which is also a gram-negative diplococcus, but which is easily distinguished subsequently by the fact that it will grow at below 25° C., produces a yellow pigment on further cultivation, and has a tendency to agglutinate spontaneously in normal horse serum.

Having ringed the suspicious colonies, some of them are now picked and stained by Gram's method. Our habit is to take up part of a colony which we strongly suspect of being meningococcus, plant part of it immediately upon a plate or slant of medium, and from the rest make the Gram stain, since plating after taking material for Gram stain may increase the chances for contamination. The colonies are usually large enough to provide material for both procedures.

The suspicious colonies are now planted upon blood-agar slants, the medium being made up as for the plates. These slants should not be used directly from the ice box, but should be warmed. Dried media must not be used.

If two tubes can be inoculated, one should be kept at room temperature. Growth in the incubator for about twelve hours gives sufficient growth for further identification.

Gram stains are now made from the tubes.

If the morphological and staining properties are proper, agglutination is carried out.

Diagnostic Agglutination.—The organisms are emulsified in isotonic salt solution. Agglutination may be done against type sera, or against polyvalent serum. When large numbers of cases are examined, as in times of epidemic, it is best first to agglutinate in polyvalent serum, preferably one in which the agglutinin titer for a great many different meningococcus strains has been controlled. As a general rule, the polyvalent sera used in this country will show specific agglutinations for practically all meningococcus strains in dilutions of 1:100. For this reason 1:100 was the dilution adopted for such work in the American Army laboratories.

One-half c.c. of the bacterial emulsion is mixed with 0.5 c.c. of the polyvalent serum. A control of a similar amount of the culture suspension in 1:50 normal horse serum must always be made to guard against spontaneous agglutination. It is always well, also, to run a tube with a known meningococcus.

Since meningococci show a certain amount of resistance to agglutination, Gordon has recommended the method in general use during the World War, that is, placing the tubes in a water bath at 50° C. for twelve to eighteen hours. Evaporation must be guarded against.

Olitsky has recommended saving time by growing the organisms in normal horse serum broth directly from the colonies on the plate, discarding all those that grow in a granular form.

Carriers occasionally will develop meningitis some time after they have been recognized as carriers. Gordon mentions a number of cases in which "meningismus" developed among carriers, namely, carriers complain of severe headache, pains in the back of the neck, slight fever up to 102° F., and slight Kernig. One case he mentions had been in contact for a few hours with a case of cerebrospinal meningitis, which died within twenty-four hours. It was swabbed and found to be negative. A month later, he went to a military hospital with the symptoms above enumerated, and the swab from his nasopharynx revealed meningococcus, but curiously not of the same type as that of the case with which he had been in contact. He mentions other similar cases.

Fluegge in the early days of meningococcus carrier investigation believed that the carrier state was usually associated with local inflammations. Gordon, however, finds that, in general, there was no nasopharyngeal catarrh associated with the carrier state. But he also finds that cases with tonsillar or pharyngeal inflammations were much more difficult to free from meningococcus than others. The same he says is true of convalescents, a point which indicates the importance of bringing the mucous membranes to normal in connection with the cure of carriers. Rake inclined to regard the carrier state as of the nature of an infection.

The question of how we are to deal with meningococcus carriers in times of epidemic is a difficult one. Local treatment of the nose and throat has been tried with antimeningococcus serum, with astringent solutions, and various disinfectants, without encouraging results. Sprays of dichloramine-T and other chlorine preparations have been tried, also, in our opinion, without marked success. During the World War the British constructed rooms of about one thousand cubic feet capacity, along the sides of which steam pipes were placed at about the height of a man's waist, and jets were fitted to them in such a way that a spray of steam could be ejected. These sprays were connected with bottles containing 1 to 2 per cent chloramine, or 0.5 per cent zinc sulphate. The carriers were put into these inhaling rooms for from fifteen to twenty minutes a day, during which they inhaled the medicated spray through their nostrils. By this method, they claimed to clear up all but the most resistant cases of so-called pure meningococcus carriers. In general, it may be said that cases in which only a few meningococcus colonies form on the plates, clear up rather readily, and that the others in which the cultures are almost pure are extremely resistant to any kind of treatment. Our own impression from some experience with the various methods would lead us to conclude that the best treatment for a carrier would be careful attention to the nasopharynx, with an attempt to bring it back to normal as far as the condition of the mucous membrane is concerned, correction of tonsillar, adenoid, or septum defects, cessation from smoking or other habits that irritate the mucous membrane, and outdoor life, especially in the sunlight, with sea baths if available. Specific antiseptic treatment in general seems to us to have been a failure as far as the handling of large numbers of men is concerned. It is not possible to apply antiseptics to all foci of organisms in the nasopharynx.

The virulence of meningococci is a matter that is very difficult to determine because of our inability to produce invasive infections with regularity in any known laboratory animal. So far, extensive attempts to determine the virulence of standardized injections into mice have not succeeded. Death in most laboratory animals is due to the toxic effects and not by invasion. This is a very unfortunate circumstance, inasmuch as our failure to be able to distinguish between virulent and nonvirulent strains makes it impossible for us to tell a dangerous carrier from one who is relatively harmless, as we can in the case of diphtheria carriers. All we can do at the present time is to regard as dangerous any carrier whose meningococcus agglutinates in a polyvalent serum. Those with strains which neither agglutinate nor absorb with the polyvalent serum at our disposal, if culturally they seem to be true meningococci, must be regarded as suspicious. It seems probable that some of these problems may be solved by the application of Miller's method of inoculating mice with meningococci suspended in mucin.

OTHER GRAM-NEGATIVE MICROCOCCI

Micrococcus Catarrhalis (*Neisseria catarrhalis*).—*Micrococcus catarrhalis* is a diplococcus described first by R. Pfeiffer, who found it in the sputum of patients suffering from catarrhal inflammations of the upper respiratory tract. It was subsequently carefully studied by Ghon and H. Pfeiffer. According to these authors the pathogenic significance of the micrococcus is slight, though occasionally it may be regarded as the causative factor in catarrhal inflammations. Its chief claim to attention, however, lies in its similarity to the meningococcus and the gonococcus, from neither of which it can be morphologically distinguished. It is decolorized by Gram's stain, appears often in the diplococcus form, and has a tendency, in exudates, to be located intracellularly. Not unlike the two micro-organisms mentioned, too, it shows but slight pathogenicity for animals.

Differentiation from gonococcus is extremely simple in that *M. catarrhalis* grows easily on simple culture media and shows none of the fastidious cultural requirements of the gonococcus.

From meningococcus the differentiation is less simple, and, because of the presence of both micro-organisms in the nose, is of great importance.

Distinction between the two is made entirely upon cultural characteristics and agglutination reactions. Culturally; *M. catarrhalis* grows more heavily then meningococcus upon the ordinary culture media. The colonies of *M. catarrhalis* are coarsely granular and distinctly white in contradistinction to the finely granular, grayish meningococcus colonies. *M. catarrhalis* will develop at temperatures below 20° C., while meningococcus will not grow at temperatures below 25° C. It is not difficult to distinguish between these organisms.

Micrococcus Flavus (*Neisseria flava*).—A common inhabitant of the normal throat which grows easily on simple media and may be grown at room temperature at or below 25° C., temperatures at which the meningococcus ceases to grow. It is always important to expose suspected cultures at room temperature in the dark. A yellowish pigment is formed by the cultures, but often does not come out for several days. The very young colonies may closely resemble meningococcus colonies, but are easily distinguished in subcultures, especially when the growth is forty-eight or more hours old. There are a considerable number of chromogenic organisms closely related to the *flavus*. Elser and Huntoon describe three chief chromogenic groups, one of which has a greenish gray or greenish yellow appearance by reflected light, with an opacity that approximates the meningococcus colony. The second group is the one most closely resembling Lingelsheim's *M. flavus*.

Their third chromogenic group also makes a greenish yellow pigment, and, except for this, is very similar to the *M. catarrhalis*. A curious fact has been noted by Elser and Huntoon, namely, that some of their chromogenic organisms were easily distinguishable from meningococcus colonies at first isolation, but in the course of artificial cultivation they lost some of their original characters and their power to produce pigment, and gradually approximated the appearance of meningococcus, at least in strains long isolated.

The flavus group gives perhaps most difficulty in meningococcus carrier examinations, since the young colonies of these organisms may look very much like the young meningococcus cultures. The chief points of differentiation, apart from sugar fermentation, which confirm them, are: The fact that flavus colonies will grow out at room temperature on slants of simple media; that they begin to form pigment after forty-eight hours or so, and that they will agglutinate in normal horse serum in dilutions often as high as 1: 50, and in the meningococcus sera, indiscriminately, often as high as 1: 100. Meningococci do not agglutinate in salt solution spontaneously, unless under the conditions mentioned above as noted by Hine, and under the influence of abnormal acid or alkaline reactions. In all series in which the specific agglutination test is used for the determinations of a meningococcus, therefore, normal horse serum tubes should be set up in dilutions ranging up to 1: 50 at least, in order to exclude organisms of the flavus type.

Micrococcus Pharyngis Siccus (*Neisseria sicca*).—This organism described by von Lingelsheim is a gram-negative diplococcus often found in the normal pharynx, and is recognized by its dry, crenated colonies on simple media. According to Elser and Huntoon, it sediments spontaneously in salt solution and this, together with the fact that the colonies are formed in a way almost impossible to break up, makes it easy to distinguish it from the meningococcus. It is more difficult to distinguish from *M. catarrhalis*, but can be easily separated from this organism by the fermentation test.

Diplococcus Crassus.—This is the organism that Kutscher described as probably identical with the so-called "Jaeger" variety of meningococcus. According to Kutscher and von Lingelsheim, this organism has a tendency to wander from the normal pharynx into the central nervous system in cases of meningitis of other origin. Lingelsheim claims to have found it in the fluids of traumatic meningitis and tuberculous meningitis. It has the peculiarity that the cultures are said to be composed of gram-negative and gram-positive organisms, some of the cocci retaining the Gram stain. According to von Lingelsheim, the colonies are smaller and more compact than meningococcus colonies, and it will grow at room temperature.

Diplococcus Mucosus.—The description of this form of gram-negative diplococcus is taken from Elser and Huntoon. Its colonies may resemble meningococcus colonies on ascitic agar. They are said to differ from the meningococcus colonies by being more mucoid, resembling the colonies of the Friedländer's bacillus. The colonies have a tendency to confluence and the luxuriance of growth helps to distinguish it from the meningococcus. It grows at room temperature, and shows capsules.

FERMENTATION REACTIONS OF GRAM-NEGATIVE DIPLOCOCCI *

Strains Tested	Strains	Dex-trose	Mal-tose	Levu-lose	Sac-charose	Lac-tose	Gal-actose
Meningococcus	200	+	+	0	0	0	0
Pseudomeningococcus	6	+	+	0	0	0	0
Gonococcus	15	+	0	0	0	0	0
Micrococcus catarrhalis	64	0	0	0	0	0	0
Micrococcus pharyngis siccus	2	+	+	+	+	0	0
Chromogenic group I	28	+	+	+	+	0	0
Chromogenic group II	11	+	+	+	0	0	0
Chromogenic group III	9	+	+	0	0	0	0
Jaeger meningococcus, Kral	1	+	+	+	+	+	+
Diplococcus crassus, Kral	1	+	+	+	+	+	+

* From Elser and Huntoon, *J. Med. Research*, 1909, 20:369.

REFERENCES

ALBRECHT and GHON. Wien. klin. Wchnschr., 1901, 14:984.
BASSETT-SMITH. Lancet, 1918, 194:290.
BINGER. J. Infect. Dis., 1919, 25:277.
BOOR, A. K., and MILLER, C. P. J. Exper. M., 1934, 59:63.
BRANHAM, S. E. J. Immunol., 1932, 23:49.
———— U. S. Public Health Rep., 1930. 45:1131.

————, and LILLIE, R. D.　J. Bacteriol., 1933, 25:90.

CARBONELL, A., and CAMPBELL, E. P.　Arch. Int. M., 1938, 61:646.

COUNCILMAN, MALLORY and WRIGHT.　Special Rep. Bd. Health Mass., 1898.

DOPTER.　Compt. rend. Soc. de biol., 1909, 67:74.

ELSER.　J. Med. Research, 1906, 14:89.

ELSER, W. J., and HUNTOON, F. M.　J. Med. Research, 1909, 20:369.

FERRY, N. S.　J. Immunol., 1932, 23:315, 325; 1934, 26:133, 143.

FERRY, N. S., NORTON, J. F., and STEELE, A. H.　J. Immunol., 1931, 21:293.

FERRY, N. S., and SCHORNACK, P. J.　J. Immunol., 1934, 26:143.

FERRY, N. S., and STEELE, A. H.　J. Am. M. Ass., 1935, 104:983.

FLEXNER, S.　Centralbl. f. Bakteriol., I Abt., 1907, 43.

———— J. Exper. M., 1907, 9:105, 142, 168; 1913, 17:553.

FLEXNER and JOBLING.　J. Exper. M., 1908, 10:141, 690.

FLEXNER.　Bull. Rockefeller Inst. M. Research, 1917.

FLUEGGE.　Die Mikroorganismen, 3rd ed., 1896.

———— J. Am. M. Ass., 1937, 108:692.

————, and CARLIN, S. A.　J. Bacteriol., 1937, 34:275.

————, LILLIE, R. D., and PABST, A. M.　U. S. Public Health Rep., 1937, 52:1135.

————, and ROSENTHAL, S. M.　U. S. Pub. Health Rep., 1937, 52:685.

KUHNS, D. M.　J. Am. M. Ass., 1936, 107:5.

————, KISNER, P., WILLIAMS, M. P., and MOORMAN, P.　J. Am. M. Ass., 1938, 110:484.

GATES.　J. Exper. M., 1919, 29:321.

GHON and PFEIFFER, H.　Ztschr. f. klin. Med., 1902, 44:262.

GILBERT, R., and COLEMAN, M. B.　J. Lab. & Clin. M., 1928, 8:547.

GLOVER.　J. Hyg., Cambridge, 1918, 17:367.

GORDON.　Med. Research Com. Rep., London, 1915, 1917.

GORDON, FLACK and HINES.　Med. Research Com., Spec. Rep. Series, No. 3, London, 1917.

GORDON, M. H., and MURRAY, E. G. D.　J. Roy. Army Med Corps, 1915, 25:411.

GRAVES, W. R., DULANEY, A. D., and MICHELSON, I. D.　J. Am. M. Ass., 1929, 92:1923.

HERRICK.　Arch. Int. Med., 1918, 21:541.

HINE, T. G. M.　Med. Research Council, Spec. Rep., Series 3, No. 3, 99.

HOYNE, A. L.　J. Am. M. Ass., 1936, 107:478.

JAEGER, H.　Ztschr. f. Hyg., 1895, 19:351.

KOLLE and WASSERMANN.　Deutsche med. Wchnschr., 1906, 15.

KRAUS, V. R., and DOERR.　Wien. klin. Wchnschr., 1908, 21:12.

LEICHTENSTERN.　Deutsche med. Wchnschr., 1885.

LEPIERRE.　J. de physiol. et de path. gén., 5, No. 3.

MARCHIAFAVA and CELLI.　Gazz. d. osp., Milano, 1884, 8.

MATHERS and HERROLD.　J. Infect. Dis., 1918, 22:523.

MELENEY and RAY.　J. Infect. Dis., 1918, 23:317.

MILLER, C. P.　Science, 1933, 78:340.

———— Proc. Soc. Exper. Biol. & M., 1935, 32:1138.

MILLER, C. P., and BOOR, A. K.　J. Exper. M., 1934, 59:75.

MURRAY, E. G. D.　Med. Research Council, Spec. Rep. Ser., No. 124, London, 1929.

NUNGESTER, W. J., WOLF, A. A., and JOURDONAIS, L. F.　Proc. Soc. Exper. Biol. Med., 1932, 30:120.

POWELL, H. M., and JAMIESON, W. A.　Am. J. Hyg., 1931, 14:470.

RAKE, G.　J. Exper. M., 1933, 57:549, 561; 1933, 58:375.

———— Canadian Pub. Health J., 1936, 27, 105.

RAKE, G., and SCHERP, H. W.　J. Exper. M., 1933, 58:341, 361.

SHWARTZMAN, G.　J. Am. M. Ass., 1929, 93:1965.

SCHWENKTER, F. F., GELMAN, S., and LONG, P. H.　J. Am. M. Ass., 1937, 108:1407.

SICKLES, G. M.　Am. J. Hyg., 1933, 17:412.

SOPHIAN.　Epidemic Cerebrospinal Meningitis, St. Louis, 1913, 54.

TULLOCH, W. J.　J. Roy. Med. Coll., February, 1918, 9.

TULLOCH, W. J.   J. Roy. Army Med. Corps, 1918, 30:115.
VAUGHAN and PALMER.   J. Lab. & Clin. M., 1919, 4:647.
VON LINGELSHEIM.   Klin. Jahrb., 1906, 15:373.
WADSWORTH, A. B.   Tr. Ass. Am. Physicians, 1932, 47:161.
———— Am. J. Hyg., 1931, 14:630.
WEICHSELBAUM, A.   Fortschr. d. Med., 1887, 5:573, 620.
WILLIEN, L. J.   J. Am. M. Ass., 1938, 110:630
WHERRY and ERWIN.   J. Infect. Dis., 1918, 22:194.
WOLLSTEIN.   J. Exper. M., 1914, 20:201.
ZINSSER, H., KUTTNER, A., and PARKER, J. T.   Proc. Soc. Exper. Biol. & Med., 1920, 18:49.

CHAPTER XXIX

DIPLOCOCCUS GONORRHŒAE (GONOCOCCUS)

GONOCOCCUS

Family: *Neisseriaceae* Prévot. Genus: *Neisseria* Trevisan. Species: *Neisseria gonorrhœae* Trevisan.

Neisser, in 1879, described diplococci which he had found regularly in the purulent secretions of acute cases of urethritis and vaginitis and in the acute conjunctivitis of the newborn. His researches were purely morphological, as were the numerous confirmatory investigations which rapidly followed his announcement.

Cultivation of this diplococcus now usually spoken of as gonococcus, was not definitely successful until 1885, when Bumm obtained growth upon tubes of coagulated human blood serum. Bumm was not only able to keep the organisms alive by transplantation in pure culture, but produced the disease by inoculation of his cultures upon the healthy urethra.

Fig. 31.—Gonorrheal Pus from Urethra, Showing the Cocci within a Leukocyte.

Morphology and Staining.—The gonococcus is usually seen in the diplococcus form, the pairs being characteristically flattened along the surfaces facing each other. This gives the cocci a peculiar coffee-bean or biscuit shape. The size of the diploforms is about 1.6 μ in the long diameter, about 0.8 μ in width. Stained directly in gonorrheal pus from acute cases the micro-organisms are found both intra- and extra-cellularly, a large number of them crowded characteristically within the leukocytes. They are never found within the nucleus. The phagocytosis which produces this picture has been shown by Scholtz and others to take place in the free secretions, not in the depth, of the tissues. The intracellular position which is of considerable diagnostic importance, is lost to a great extent in secretions from chronic cases. In smears made from pure cultures the arrangement in groups of two may often be less marked than in pus, clusters of eight or more being common.

The gonococcus is nonmotile, does not form spores, and usually does not produce a capsule. An encapsulated mucoid variant has been described by Almaden. The gonococcus is easily stained with aqueous aniline dyes. Methylene blue alone, or eosin followed by methylene blue, gives good results. An excellent picture is obtained with the *Pappenheim-Saathof* stain consisting of

Methyl green	0.15
Pyronine	0.05
96 per cent alcohol	5.00
Glycerin	20.00
2 per cent carbolic acid water ad	100.00
Fix; stain 1–2 min.	

Gram's method of staining, however, is the only one of differential value, gonococcus being gram-negative. The Gram stain applied to pus from the male urethra, while not absolutely reliable because of the occurrence of other gram-negative cocci and gram-negative forms of staphylococci and streptococci, is, for practical purposes, sufficiently so to make a diagnosis. In exudates from the vagina or from the eye the morphological picture is not so reliable, owing to the frequent presence in these regions of other gram-negative cocci. The great scarcity of gonococci in very chronic discharges necessitates thorough cultural investigation; negative morphological examination in such cases cannot be regarded as conclusive.

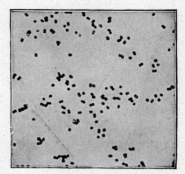

FIG. 32.—GONOCOCCUS SMEAR FROM PURE CULTURE.

Cultivation.—The gonococcus is delicate and difficult to cultivate. Bumm obtained his first growths upon human blood serum which had been heated to partial coagulation.

A medium commonly used at the present day was introduced by Wertheim, and consists of a mixture of two or three parts of meat infusion agar with one part of uncoagulated human ascitic fluid, hydrocele fluid, or blood serum. The agar is melted and cooled to 45° C. before the serum is added. The mixture may then be slanted in the test tube or poured into a Petri plate. One per cent of glucose may be added. Cultures in fluid media may be obtained by similar additions of serum to meat-infusion-peptone broth. Defibrinated rabbit's blood added to agar makes a useful medium. (See section on technic.)

Inoculations from gonorrheal material are best made by surface smearing upon plates, since the gonococcus grows best in the presence of free oxygen in a mixture with CO_2. Growth becomes more luxuriant after prolonged cultivation upon artificial media. The most favorable reaction of media is pH 7.0 to 7.4.

When the gonococcus has been cultivated from pus upon media without serum additions, the success has probably been due to the substances carried over in the pus. The ease of cultivation differs considerably with different strains of gonococci. Some grow very heavily after first isolation, but the majority show a very delicate growth even on rich ascitic glucose agar. After several generations of growth on artificial media, however, the organism develops with increasing ease and on simpler media. It may eventually be cultivated on plain agar, especially when this is made of veal infusion.

The gonococcus will develop sparsely under anaerobic conditions but has marked preference for aerobiosis. The optimum temperature is about 36° C. Growth ceases about 38.5° and below 30° C.

Upon suitable media colonies appear as extremely delicate, grayish, opalescent spots, at the end of twenty-four hours. The separate colonies do not tend to confluence and have slightly undulated margins. Touched with a platinum loop their consistency is found to be slimy. In fluid media, growth takes place chiefly at the surface.

Numerous *special and differential media* have been devised for the isolation and identification of gonococci. The best of these are (1) Levinthal's cooked blood agar, with which a clear medium is produced and (2) the heated whole blood "chocolate" agar medium of McLeod and his associates. Cultures on McLeod's medium are incubated in an atmosphere of 8 to 10 per cent CO_2. When the plates are examined the growth is covered by a solution of tetramethyl-p-phenylenediamine hydrochloride for the demonstration of the oxydase reaction. Colonies of gonococci turn a bright purple when in contact with this solution. Directions for the preparation of these media are given in the section for Technical Methods.

Carpenter concluded that his modification of McLeod's medium is the most reliable available procedure for diagnosing gonococcic infection.

Types.—As in the case of so many other organisms, it has been found that the gram-negative diplococci which cause gonorrheal infections are not a single type, but must be regarded as representing a group, including many closely related but antigenically differentiable subgroups. Such subgrouping of species formerly regarded as homogeneous has been a very natural development of the more intensive study of serum reactions, incident to diagnostic agglutination and complement fixation, and to the control of specific therapy. Torrey, and Teague and Torrey in 1907 showed that the gonococcus group is not homologous, but that agglutination and agglutinin absorption divided this group into at least three separate subtypes. Agglutinin absorption seemed to show more types than complement fixation, a matter which we would rather expect at the present day because of the almost universal experience that complement fixation reactions are not as strictly specific as agglutination. In 1910 Watabiki made a similar study of the gonococcus group, and studying a limited number of strains, confirmed the heterogeneous nature of the group by referring to them as "comparative but not distinctive differences between individual strains." In 1915 Louise Pearce made a comparison between gonococci isolated from adult males and from the vulvovaginitis of children. She came to the conclusion that strains from these two sources constituted fairly definite serologically distinct groups, that at least there was a relative distinction between the two types, but this could not be confirmed by Torrey. Hermanies studied eighty-five gonococcus strains from various sources, using for cultivation the partial tension method of Wade W. Oliver. He concluded that gonococci fall into distinct types, with little relationship to each other. Agglutinins produced by one type cannot be absorbed by strains of other types, and his eighty-five strains fell into six distinct groups.

The work of Torrey and Buckell and others on the serological relationships of the gonococci has been summed up by Tulloch as follows: "The absorption of agglutinin reaction serves to show that there is a predominant type of gonococcus comprising regular and intermediate subgroups which constitutes about 70 per cent of all strains responsible for the causation of gonorrhoea."

Occasionally, it is difficult to differentiate a gonococcus from a meningococcus. In view of the demonstration, by Miller and Boor, of common protein and polysaccharide antigens and haptenes among gonococci and meningococci it is doubtful whether strictly specific serological distinctions can be made in all cases. Furthermore, these investigators showed that gonococci have antigenic components in common with Type III pneumococci.

Recognition.—The gonococcus ferments only glucose, producing acid without gas. Failure to ferment maltose differentiates it from the meningococcus. Exceptions to this rule may exist, but they are questionable and rare.

A gonococcus, therefore, may be recognized bacteriologically by the gram-negative diplococcus form, the typical colony formation on ascitic fluid agar or blood agar, its failure to grow on simple media or at room temperature, its ability to ferment dextrose and failure to split maltose.

Precipitin reactions were used by Robinson and Meader as an aid in the diagnosis of chronic gonococcal cervicitis and vaginitis.

The source of the culture is often an aid in diagnosis. But since there are other types of infection than those of the lower genital tract, this "lead" is not dependable. Gonococcal ophthalmia, arthritis, endocarditis, septicemia, dermatitis and other types of infection occur. In addition, various kinds of gram-negative diplococci are found in exudates from the genital tract associated with inflammations not due to the gonococcus.

Resistance.—Recent cultures of gonococcus, if not transplanted, usually die out within five or six days at incubator temperature. At room temperature they die more rapidly.

The resistance of the gonococcus to light and heat is slight. A temperature of 41° to 42° C. kills it in two hours (Finger, Ghon and Schlagenhaufer). Complete drying destroys it in a short time. Incompletely dried, however, and protected from light (gonorrheal pus) it may live, on sheets and clothing, for as long as eighteen to twenty-four hours (Heiman).

It is easily killed by most disinfectant solutions in high dilution and seems to be almost specifically sensitive to the various silver salts, a fact of therapeutic importance.

Taking advantage of the low thermal death time of the gonococcus (41.5° to 42° C. for two to seven hours), Carpenter and his associates have investigated the treatment of gonococcal infections by fever artificially induced and maintained in patients by means of high frequency electrical diathermy apparatus. Remarkable improvement and cures have been reported.

Pathogenicity.—Gonorrheal infection occurs spontaneously only in man. In human beings, apart from the infection in the male and female genital tracts, and in the conjunctivae, the gonococcus may produce cystitis, proctitis, and stomatitis. It may enter the circulation, giving rise to septicemia, to endocarditis and arthritis. Isolated cases of gonorrheal periostitis and osteomyelitis have been reported. Gonococcic meningitis has been described from the clinical and bacteriological points of view by Steiner and by Branham. Branham is of the opinion that gonococcic meningitis is much more common than it is usually supposed to be.

The acute infections of the genito-urinary passages are often followed by prolonged chronic infection, which, though quiescent, may for many years be a source of social danger. In children, especially females, the infection is not rare, and may assume epidemic character, traveling from bed to bed in institutions. Such hospital epidemics can be stopped only by the most rigid isolation. This is more specifically dealt with in the paragraphs on sanitary considerations.

True gonorrheal urethritis has never been experimentally produced in animals.

While inoculation of animals has never resulted in active proliferation of the gonococcus upon the new host, local necrosis, suppuration, and temporary systemic reactions have been produced by subcutaneous and intraperitoneal inoculation. A toxin has been isolated by Nikolaysen by extraction from the bacterial bodies with distilled water or sodium hydrate solutions. It was found to be resistant to a temperature of 120° C. and to remain potent after complete drying. The same author found that the isolated toxin and dead cultures were fully as toxic for animals as living cultures, 0.01 gram killing a white mouse.

Specific injury to the nervous system by injections of gonococcus toxin has been reported by Moltchanoff.

While it is true that culture filtrates and extracts or autolysates of'the gonococcus have considerable toxicity, the question as to whether or not the organism secretes a *soluble exotoxin* is still debatable. The claim that the gonococcus does secrete a soluble toxin, advanced by de Christmas in 1897 was not confirmed. In 1931, however, Ferry and his coworkers, who grew gonococci in a pellicle on the surface of large flasks of broth, obtained a filtrate which appeared to have the properties of a soluble toxin. Further confirmation of this work is required before its significance can be determined.

Antibodies and Serological Diagnosis.—Patients infected with gonococci produce antibodies against the organisms. Although in the ordinary gonorrheal urethritis, or vaginitis, it is relatively simple to make the diagnosis by finding gonococci in the discharges, diagnosis may be difficult in cases of chronic gonococcal infection, gonorrheal rheumatism, or endocarditis, when isolation of the bacteria fails or when the connection between the local venereal disease and the general condition is obscure. Various serological diagnostic methods have been attempted, and the complement-fixation test has been found to be very useful. Many varieties of antigen have been used for this test. With the technics now employed the reaction is not as accurate as the Wassermann test in syphilis, but in the hands of experienced workers it is very serviceable (Cohn). The methods are being improved through coöperative investigations and the results are promising.

Vaccine therapy in systemic gonorrheal infection has been tried and is not effective. Immunization with filtrates of cultures has not been beneficial in therapy of acute or chronic infections.

Passive immunization with the serum of gonococcus-immune animals has also been attempted, but records on it at present are not sufficiently complete to permit definite judgment.

Chemotherapy.—In 1937 Dees and Colston successfully used *sulfanilamide* in the treatment of gonorrhea. Since then there has been an enormous outcrop of papers recording experimental and clinical observations on the value of this substance and some of its derivatives as chemotherapeutic agents in gonococcal infections. On the whole the results have been highly favorable.

Sanitary Considerations.—Of the three prevalent venereal infections, that caused by the gonococcus is probably the most common. In fact, gonorrhea is more prevalent than any other serious communicable disease. For more exhaustive statistical studies of the prevalence of these diseases the reader is referred to such books as those of Pusey, Morrow, and the larger textbooks of hygiene, such as that of Rosenau.

Although it has been well known that gonorrhea was extremely common, the astonishing prevalence among young men of draft age was revealed during the World War when the figures of the Surgeon General showed that about 5.6 per cent of the men who came into the military service were infected with a venereal disease. Considering that these diseases, in their early detectable acute stages, do not last very long, that many cases still apparent to a slight degree must surely be missed in physical examinations of large numbers of men, it seems to indicate that the estimate by many authorities of a prevalence of venereal disease in civilian life as high as 10 per cent may be very near the truth.

The data acquired from various surveys show, according to Vonderlehr and Usilton, that annually in the United States at least a million persons acquire gonorrhea. The incidence is highest. in cities of from 50,000 to 500,000 population, and lowest in metropolitan and rural areas. The mean age of acquiring the infection is 29 years for white males, 24 years for Negro males and 24 years for white females. Approximately 230,000 potential mothers in the United States acquire gonorrhea annually. There has been a slight decline in the incidence of gonorrhea in some European countries, but there is no evidence that it is on the decline in the United States according to the results of surveys of Usilton.

One of the great dangers in connection with gonorrheal infection has been the relative indifference of the public to this disease. In the past, there has been a remarkable lack of appreciation of the seriousness of the infection, which actually, in its economic and sociological importance, is equal to, if not more serious than, syphilis. The gonococcus is primarily infectious for the genital organs, but may also infect the eye, and its secondary manifestations cause disease of the prostate, epididymis and bladder of the male, of the fallopian tubes and ovaries of the female. In both it may and often does cause sterility. Invading the blood stream, it may cause endocarditis, and not infrequently an acute and subacute arthritis which is characterized by its frequent localization in single joints or the bursae about joints, and cause periarticular inflammation. It may, but rarely does, attack other organs.

A most important consideration is the difficulty of complete cure. A male who has contracted gonorrhea may seem to be completely cured, but if a posterior urethritis has occurred, the organisms may remain viable and capable of infecting others for a great many years. Individuals who, therefore, seem to have been cured for years, may still cause infection upon marriage, a fact which is the most frequent cause of gynecological lesions in women. It goes without saying that even the most careful bacteriological examination of such individuals may often fail to reveal the gonococci, even though they may be present.

Infection with gonococcus is almost invariably by sexual contact, though the organism may remain viable on wearing apparel, bed clothing, towels, hands, etc., for brief periods, especially if protected from light and drying, and others may be infected in this way. The danger of self-infection of eyes by people who are suffering from an acute discharge exists, and physicians and nurses, especially, are liable to such infection.

Gonorrheal infection of the eye is one of the most serious infections that can occur in this organ. Ophthalmia of the newborn may be due to other organisms, but is almost invariably caused by the gonococcus. It is acquired by the child in the course of delivery, from the secretions of the mother, and, if not attended to, may lead to blindness. The importance of this infection may be estimated from the following figures quoted by Rosenau from Kerr, who states that in the United States and Canada in 23.9 per cent of 351 admissions to schools for the blind in 1910 the blindness was the result of gonococcal infection.

Fortunately, the method introduced by Credé has, to a very large extent, done away with this accident. Credé, many years ago, introduced the method of instilling a 2 per cent silver nitrate solution into the conjunctival sacs of every child at birth. Since his time other silver salts have been in use, the most popular ones at the present time being protargol, 5 per cent solution, and argyrol, 20 per cent solution, which are dropped into the eye at birth. It is extremely important that this should be done properly and the entire conjunctival sac bathed in the fluid. The method is so important that it is regarded as a matter of very serious and inexcusable omission, if, under any circumstances, in dealing with any class of the population, the physician managing a childbirth fails to carry out this measure as soon as feasible after birth.

Another very important gonorrheal problem is the *vulvovaginitis* which occurs in children. In our own experience, this infection has occurred most often in connection with the children's wards in hospitals. The condition has, however, been observed in schools and in small family groups where children were infected by sleeping in the same beds with adults. In hospitals the disease may spread in epidemics, and from bed to bed, with an ease that is astonishing when one considers the delicate life of the gonococcus outside the body. It has often been extremely difficult to stop such bed to bed infection, in spite of the most rigid precautions. Epidemics are so difficult to arrest, and the consequences for the child so grave from many points of view, that it has become the custom in all well-managed hospitals to delay the admission of female children to the general children's ward until vaginal smears have been made and examined for gonococci. It is in our opinion extremely important that when such smears are made, they should be taken not only from the visible secretion, but should be taken from high up in the vagina through a small Kelly speculum, with good illumination. When there is danger of spread and a case has been inadvertently admitted, only the greatest care in avoiding indirect contact from bed to bed can stop it. As a matter of routine in children's wards, there should be separate thermometers, unless all thermometers are very carefully sterilized. Thermometers should be kept in weak carbolic solutions and washed with alcohol before use. The sterilization of diapers and towels should be attended to. Nurses handling cases with discharge should wear gloves, and there should be no common use of towels and washing utensils. Great attention should be given to the scouring of bath tubs; bed linen, night clothes, etc., should be sterilized by boiling. An interesting investigation by Lewis indicates that it may be possible to decrease or cure gonococcal vaginitis of children by injections of the ovarian hormone, theelin. This causes the vaginal mucosa to change from the delicate epithelium of the infantile state to the thicker, less vascular epithelium of the adult type.

Public Health Management of Venereal Diseases.—During the past ten years there has been a wholesome increase of interest in venereal disease prevention. There are certain general fundamental principles which apply to all venereal diseases equally. It has been unfortunate that sanitary and moral issues have been so closely interwoven in these diseases, that it has been impossible to create the free discussion and spread the information necessary to obtain the coöperation, of the public in these matters. Without public education and coöperation, large-scale public health results cannot be achieved. One of the most important factors that has prevented earlier progress in the prevention of venereal disease has been public ignorance. Women of the marriageable age have been kept in ignorance about facts concerning these infections, and often left at the mercy of chance. Accurate and clear information, free of sensationalism, will do more to reduce the venereal rate than any other single factor.

It is not the function of a book of this kind to go into the complex problems of sex education, and moral issues. We will restrict ourselves entirely to the sanitary phases of the problem. Chief among these are:

Diagnosis.—Education and knowledge of the seriousness of these infections should lead to a gradual attraction of patients to reliable clinics and physicians, thus saving them from quacks. The development of diagnostic clinics by departments of health, the improvement of clinical facilities in large cities, and the better understanding by physicians, as a whole, of the sanitary importance of these relatively simple infections, must lead to more accurate diagnosis and proper instruction of the patient.

Reporting of Venereal Diseases.—In a great many communities gonorrheal infections, as well as other venereal diseases are regarded, with other communicable diseases, subject to report. There are many reasons why such reporting systems will meet with objections, and will for many years be unsatisfactory. This, too, is a matter of education, and the fact that it will fail for the present is no reason why the principle should not be upheld. Eventually it will be accepted as a sensible and necessary step. The chief objection that has been raised against the reporting of these diseases is the permanent record, apparent disgrace and perhaps opportunity for blackmail which is opened by such public registration. When, on the other hand, we balance these dangers against those of the uncontrolled circulation of individuals capable of infecting others, there seems very little choice between the two evils. Moreover, it would be possible to develop a system of reporting whereby the reported individual could have the record destroyed when he can bring a certificate of cure from a responsible clinic or physician. This would add a further inducement to proper care and cure. At any rate, the prompt report of cases, follow-up from municipal health bureaus, and prompt destruction of the record when the individual has been cured, will greatly aid in this matter.

Hospitalization.—It will probably be impossible to hospitalize all infectious cases of venereal diseases because, unfortunately from the public health point of view, these patients are not incapacitated during their most infectious stages. We are able to confine a case of smallpox with or without consent, but persons with diseases that in their remote possibilities are responsible for far greater injury and unhappiness, are permitted to walk about and follow their own devices, through the course of their illnesses. The eventual ideal would consist in making physicians responsible for the isolation of cases which come under their care and to hospitalize those who cannot be taken care of in their own quarters. Hospitalization in separate hospitals would confer so great a stigma that it would probably be impossible. It might also be impossible to admit these cases into general hospitals in spite of special arrangements. We do not ourselves believe that compulsory hospitalization could be enforced at the present time. It should be looked upon, however, as an attempt worth making, as soon as education and general public coöperation have reached a point at which success would seem reasonably promising. The sooner the attitude toward these diseases is made one simply of sanitary principles, and the moral factors are allowed to take care of themselves under the influence of increased civilization and sense of community responsibility, the sooner these ends may be accomplished.

While it is, of course, quite impossible to do justice to as fundamentally important a problem as the sanitary control of venereal diseases in a section of this kind, it has seemed to us of great importance to point out to physicians and bacteriologists who may read this book, the enormous responsibility that falls upon them whenever they are in a position to deal with cases of this kind.

Prophylaxis.—As practiced in the United States Army stations during the World War prophylaxis consisted in injecting about 10 c.c. of a 2 per cent protargol solution into the urethra—enough to thoroughly distend it, with a glass hand syringe, holding it there with the syringe in place, for one-half minute. The procedure is twice repeated. Its success depends very largely upon early application after intercourse.

REFERENCES

ALMADEN, P. J.   J. Infect. Dis., 1938, 62, 36.

BRANHAM, S. E., MITCHELL, R. H., and BRAININ, W.   J. Am. M. Ass., 1938, 110:1804.

BOOR, A. K., and MILLER, C. P.   J. Exper. M., 1934, 59:63.

BUMM.   Beiträge zur Kenntniss des Gonococcus, Wiesbaden, 1885.

———— Deutsche med. Wchnschr., 1885, 11:508, 910.

CARPENTER, C. M.   J. Am. M. Ass., 1937, 109:1428.

CARPENTER, C. M., and LEAHY, A. D.   Am. J. Syph., Gonor., & Ven. Dis., 1936, 20:347.

CARPENTER, C. M., BOAK, R., MUCCI, L. A., and WARREN, S. L.   J. Lab. & Clin. M., 1933, 18, 981.

DE CHRISTMAS.   Ann. de l'Inst. Pasteur, 1897, 11:609.

COHN, A.   J. Lab. & Clin. M., 1936–7, 22:627

———— Am. J. Syph., Gonor., & Ven. Dis., 1938, 22, 1.

DEES, J. E., and COLSTON, J. A. C.   J. Am. Med. Ass., 1937, 108:1855.

FERRY, N. S., NORTON, J. F., and STEELE, A. H.   J. Immunol., 1931, 21:233, 293.

FINGER, E., GHON, A., and SCHLAGENHAUFER, F.   Arch. f. Dermat. u. Syph., 1894, 28:279.

HEIMAN, H.   Med. Rec., 1896, 50:887.

HERMANIES, J.   J. Infect. Dis., 1921, 28:133.

———— Laboratory Diagnosis of Gonococcal Infections, Med. Res. Comm., Nat. Health Insurance, Spec. Rep. No. 19, London, 1918.

LEWIS, R. M.   Yale J. Biol. & Med., 1932–33, 5:495.

LEWIS, R. M., and ADLER, E. L.   J. Am. M. Ass., 1936, 106:2054.

MCLEOD, J. W., COATES, J. C., HAPPOLD, F. C., PRIESTLEY, D., and WHEATLEY, B.   J. Path. and Bacteriol., 1934, 39:221.

MILLER, C. P., and BOOR, A. K.   J. Exper. M., 1934, 59:75.

MOLTCHANOFF.   München. med. Wchnschr., 1899.

NEISSER.   Deutsche med. Wchnschr., 1882, 8:279.

———— Centralbl. f. d. med. Wissensch., 1879, 17:497.

NIKOLAYSEN, L.   Fortschr. d. Med., 1897, 27.

PEARCE, L.   J. Med. Research, 1915, 21:289.

———— Rep. Surg.-Gen. Army, Wash., 1919, 1:956.

ROBINSON, G. H., and MEADER, P. D.   J. Urol., 1920, 4:551.

SCHOLTZ.   Arch. f. Dermat. u. Syph., 1899, 49:3.

STEINER, W. R.   Tr. Am. Clin. Climat. Ass., 1937, 1.

TEAGUE and TORREY.   J. Med. Research, 1907, 17:223.

THOMAS, R. B., and BAYNE-JONES, S.   Report of Committee for Survey of Research on the Gonococcus and Gonococcal Infections. Am. J. Syph., Gonorrhea and Ven. Dis., 1936, 20, Supplement.

TORREY.   J. Med. Research, 1907, 16:329.

Torrey, J. C., and Buckell, G. T.   J. Infect. Dis., 1922, 31:125.
—— J. Immunol., 1922, 7:305.
Tulloch, W. J.   A System of Bacteriology in Relation to Medicine, London, 1929, 2:237.
Vonderlehr, R. A., and Usilton, L. J.   J. Am. M. Ass., 1937, 109:1425.
Watabiki, T.   J. Infect. Dis., 1910, 7:159.
Wertheim.   Arch. f. Gynaek., Berl., 1892, 41:1.

CHAPTER XXX

BACILLUS DIPHTHERIAE, BACILLUS HOFMANNII AND BACILLUS XEROSIS

BACILLUS DIPHTHERIAE

Order: *Actinomycetales* Buchanan. Family: *Mycobacteriaceae* Chester. Genus: *Corynebacterium* Lehmann and Neumann. Species: *Cornyebacterium diphtheriae*

Since 1826, when Bretonneau of Tours published his observations, diphtheria has been an accurately recognized clinical entity. Our knowledge of the disease in the sense of modern bacteriology, however, begins with the first description of *B. diphtheriae* by Klebs in 1883. Klebs had observed in the pseudomembranes from diphtheritic throats, bacilli which in the light of more recent knowledge we can hardly fail to recognize as the true diphtheria organism. His work, however, was purely morphological and, therefore, inconclusive. One year after this announcement, Löffler isolated and cultivated an organism which corresponded in its morphological characters to the one described by Klebs. He obtained it from 13 clinically unquestioned cases of diphtheria, and, by inoculating it upon the injured mucous surfaces of animals, succeeded in producing lesions which resembled closely the false membranes of the human disease. His failure to find the bacillus in all the cases he examined, his finding it, in one instance, in a normal throat, and his inability to explain to his own satisfaction some of the systemic manifestations of the infection which we now know to be due to the toxin, caused him to frame his conclusions in a tone of the utmost conservatism. The second and third publications of Löffler, however, and the inquiry into the nature of the toxins produced by the bacillus, published in 1888 by Roux and Yersin, eliminated all remaining doubt as to the etiological relationship existing between this organism and the disease.

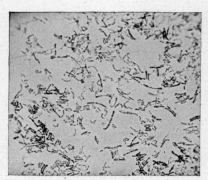

Fig. 33.—Bacillus Diphtheriae.

Innumerable observations, both clinical and bacteriological, by other workers, have, since that time, confirmed the early investigations, and it is today a scientific necessity to find the bacillus of Klebs and Löffler in the lesion before a diagnosis of diphtheria can properly be made.

Morphology and Staining.—While *B. diphtheriae* presents certain characteristic appearances which facilitate its recognition, it is, at the same time, subject to a number of morphological variations with all of which it is important to be familiar. These variations are, to a limited extent, dependent upon the age of the culture and

upon the constitution of the medium on which it has been grown. These factors, however, do not control the appearance of the organism with any degree of regularity, and
any or all of its various forms may occur in one and the same culture. It is likely that
these different appearances represent stages in the growth and degeneration of the
individual bacilli, but there does not seem to be any just reason for believing that,
as several observers (Wesbrook, Wilson and McDaniel) have stated, there is definite
correlation between its microscopic form and its biological characteristics, such as
virulence and toxicity.

The bacilli are slender, straight, or slightly curved rods. In length they vary from
1.2 μ to 6.4 μ, in breadth from 0.3 to 1.1 μ. As seen most frequently when taken from
the throat they are about 4 to 5 μ in length. They are rarely of uniform thickness
throughout their length, showing club-shaped thickening at one or both ends. Occasionally they may be thickest at the center and taper toward the extremities. When
thickened at one end only, a slender wedge shape results. Such forms are usually
straight, of smaller size than their neighbors, and
are more often stained with great uniformity.

In addition to these clubbed, granular,
barred, wedge-shaped and solid staining forms
of *B. diphtheriae*, the organism may produce
streptococcal chains, round forms or branching
forms. The branching forms are rare. They occur
both in old and young cultures, though more
commonly in older cultures. By some observers,
these branched forms have been regarded as evidences of involution or degeneration. Other investigators see in them an indication of the relationship of this organism to the actinomycetes.

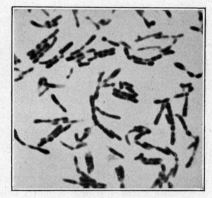

FIG. 34.—BACILLUS DIPHTHERIAE.
Gram stain. $\times$ 2000.

Although it is admitted that morphology is
not a positive index of virulence, the practised
observer can make a correct estimate in most cases from examination of the stained
organisms. A stained smear, such as that shown in Figure 33, contains many different
forms but gives an impression of a sort of uniformity, which has diagnostic value.
In Figure 34, the organisms shown in higher magnification, exhibit the clubbed
shapes, in recognition of which Lehmann and Neumann introduced the generic name
Corynebacterium.

Staining Reactions.—B. diphtheriae can be stained with the ordinary aniline dyes.
It is gram-positive.

A characteristic irregularity of staining of the organisms is of great aid in diagnosis. Stained with Löffler's alkaline methylene blue solution or with toluidine blue,
many of the rods appear traversed by unstained transverse bands between heavily
stained areas, giving them a banded or beaded appearance. The longer individuals
often have a strong resemblance to short chains of streptococci. Others may appear
unevenly granular. Granular staining is seen in the organisms obtained directly from
throat swabs as well as in those from cultures.

In direct smears from diphtheria membranes and in cultures which are eighteen
to twenty-four hours old, many of the bacilli show oval bodies situated near the ends

of the cells. These bodies, discovered by Babes and Ernst, and called Babes-Ernst or polar granules, were thought at first to be spores. All subsequent observers have agreed with Escherich that these are not spores, but probably reserve material or volutin granules. These granules stain deeply, taking on a reddish purple hue when stained with methylene blue. They are called, therefore, metachromatic granules. Special stains have been devised to demonstrate these granules very clearly. The best of these stains, in our opinion, are Neisser's and Ljubinsky's.

Details for the preparation and application of all these stains will be found in the section on technic.

Virulent organisms usually contain these granules and when stained differentially are very characteristic. But there is no evidence that the granules are secretion granules related to the production of toxin. Similar granules are disclosed by these special stains in some races of *Staphylococcus* and *B. pyocyaneus*.

In stained smears from the throat or from cultures the bacilli often have a characteristic grouping. They lie usually in small clusters, four or five together, parallel to each other or at sharp angles. Two organisms may often be seen attached to each other by their corresponding ends while their bodies diverge to form a V or Y.

Biological Characteristics.—The diphtheria bacillus is a nonmotile, nonflagellated, non-spore-forming aerobe. Its preference for oxygen is marked, but it will grow in anaerobic environment in the presence of suitable carbohydrates. It does not liquefy gelatin. The bacillus grows at temperatures varying between 19° C. and 42° C., the most favorable temperature for its development being 37.5° C. Temperatures above 37.5° C., while not entirely stopping its growth, impede the development of its toxin. The optimum temperature of incubation for the production of toxin is 34°–35° C.

Resistance.—The thermal death point of this organism is 58° C. for ten minutes, according to Welch and Abbott. Boiling kills it in about one minute. Low temperatures, and even freezing, are well borne. Desiccation and exposure to light are not so fatal to this organism as to most of the other non-spore-forming pathogenic bacteria. It has been found alive in dried bits of the pseudomembrane after fourteen weeks. It is easily killed by chemical disinfectants in the strengths customarily employed. Gentian violet inhibits its growth.

Cultivation.—The diphtheria bacillus grows readily on most of the richer laboratory media. It will grow upon media made of meat extract, but develops more luxuriantly on all those which have a meat infusion as their basis. While it will grow upon both acid and alkaline media, it is sensitive to the extremes of both, the most favorable reaction for its development being pH 7.2. Animal proteins added to the media, in the form of blood serum, ascitic fluid, or even whole blood, increase greatly the rapidity and richness of its growth. Horse serum is supposed by some to be especially favorable.

Mueller has shown that among the accessory growth requirements of *B. diphtheriae* are amino acids, nicotinic acid, beta alanine and pimelic acid.

Löffler's Medium.—The most widely used medium for the cultivation of this bacillus is the one devised by Löffler. This consists of:

Beef blood serum... 3 parts
One per cent glucose meat-infusion bouillon .... 1 part

The mixture is coagulated at 70° C. in slanted tubes and sterilized at low tem-peratures by the fractional method or in the autoclave. Upon this medium the diph-theria bacillus in twelve to twenty-four hours develops minute, grayish white, glisten-ing colonies. These enlarge rapidly, soon outstripping the usually accompanying streptococci. The medium seems to possess almost selective powers for the bacillus and, for this reason, it is especially valuable for diagnostic purposes.

Meat Infusion Agar.—Upon slightly alkaline meat infusion agar the bacillus develops readily, though less so than on Löffler's serum. Organisms which have been on artificial media for one or more generations may grow with speed and luxuriance upon this medium. When planted directly from the human or animal body upon agar, however, growth may occasionally be slow and extremely delicate. Colonies on agar appear within twenty-four to thirty-six hours as small, rather translucent, grayish specks. The appearance of these colonies is quite characteristic and easily recognized by the practiced observer. Surface colonies are irregularly round or oval, showing a dark, heaped-up, nucleus-like center, fringed about by a loose, coarsely granular disk. The edges have a peculiarly irregular, torn appearance which distinguishes them readily from the sharply defined streptococcus colonies. For these reasons agar is the medium most commonly used for purposes of isolation.

The addition of dextrose 1 per cent, nutrose 2 per cent, or glycerin 6 per cent, renders agar more favorable for rapid growth, but unfits it for the preservation of cultures, the organism drying out more rapidly, probably because of the inhibitory effect of acids produced by fermentation.

Meat Infusion Broth.—Upon beef or veal broth the diphtheria bacillus grows rapidly, almost invariably forming a pellicle upon the surface—another expression of its desire for oxygen. The broth remains clear. Broth tubes with such growth, therefore, have a characteristic appearance.

Meat Infusion Gelatin.—Meat infusion gelatin is a favorable medium for the Klebs-Löffler bacillus, but growth takes place slowly because of the low temperature at which this medium must be kept. Gelatin is not fluidified.

Milk is an excellent medium, and for this reason may even occasionally be a vehicle of transmission. There is no coagulation of the milk.

Peptone Solutions.—Upon the various peptone solutions the bacillus of diphtheria produces no indole.

Fermentation of Carbohydrates.—Serum water containing 1 per cent peptone is the most satisfactory basic medium to which to add carbohydrates for fermentation tests. *B. diphtheriae* ferments glucose, galactose, maltose, glycerin and dextrin, pro-ducing acid without gas. It does not ferment lactose, saccharose or mannite (Zinsser). It is generally agreed that fermentation reactions do not differentiate between virulent and nonvirulent forms nor between diphtheria bacilli and some of the diphtheroids.

Special Media.—Many special media have been devised for the isolation of *B. diphtheriae*. None of these has been able to supplant Löffler's serum. Blood agar, however, is a useful medium on which to spread a mixture of bacteria in order to obtain separate colonies of the diphtheria bacillus. The colonies after twenty-four to forty-eight hours are surrounded by a narrow zone of hemolysis, especially on 5 per cent rabbit's blood agar. In 1912, Conradi and Troch introduced the use of a tel-lurium salt as a differential ingredient in media for the isolation of *B. diphtheriae*.

The organism reduces the salt and the colony becomes black. Since then many variations of this medium have been tried with the result that a *potassium tellurite* medium containing blood and tryptic digest, such as the modification of Clauberg, has been found to have distinct advantages. Formulae for these media will be found in the section on technic.

Variability and Types.—It has been known for a long time that diphtheria bacilli varied in form in exudates and cultures and Roux and Yersin, as long ago as 1890, noted that there were virulent and avirulent cultures of diphtheria bacilli having approximately the same morphology. In fact, from "pure line" or single cell cultures variants have been obtained showing all of Wesbrook's morphological types and all degrees of virulence. Many studies of the *serological relationships* with respect to agglutination reactions have shown that the organisms in this group were antigenically heterogeneous, with perhaps two or three chief serological groups. The one property common to all these varieties of virulent organisms has been the production of a toxin neutralizable by antitoxin. The time-honored belief has been that all specimens of diphtheria toxin give rise to and are neutralized by one and the same antitoxin.

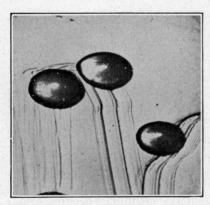

FIG. 35.—COLONIES OF *B. Diphtheriae* ON BLOOD AGAR.

Since the renewal of attention to variability that came with the discoveries of dissociative phenomena, some of the older work and the results of new studies have been brought together. It has been shown by Yü that smooth, rough and intermediate types of colonies of diphtheria bacillus cultures occur on blood agar plates. The S to R transformation took place readily, the reverse dissociation of R to S was not accomplished. R forms were avirulent, but some of the S forms also lacked toxigenicity. S forms were always isolated from the acute disease, and R forms appeared in the throats of convalescents. The smooth colonies were round and hemispherical. The rough colonies, larger than the smooth, were granular, finely wrinkled and had serrated edges. The S organisms were thinner and longer than the more plump R forms.

With lithium chloride, pancreatin, Kendall's medium and by other agents Jones dissociated *B. diphtheriae* into what he called a V type, which was nonvirulent.

Pope and Pinfield found that when diphtheria bacilli were grown on an unheated Berkefeld-filtered tryptic digest medium containing copper sulphate added to give concentrations of 20 to 50 milligrams Cu-ion per liter, the diphtheria bacillus grew in a coccoid form and produced little or no toxin. This transformation, however, was not permanent. The organism reverted to the usual form of the rod on the first transfer to mediums free from copper.

These dissociative changes have important, though incompletely understood, correlations with the phenomena of the disease in man and obviously are significant for systematic and practical immunology. It is possible that the types of diphtheria bacilli decribed by Anderson and his associates as *B. diphtheriae gravis* and *B. diphtheriae mitis* may be dissociative variants of the diphtheria bacillus. On a tellurite blood medium the colonies of the *gravis* type were irregular in outline and radially striated, resembling colonies of *B. xerosis*. The *mitis* type produced small, round, smooth hemispherical colonies. The *gravis* type was associated with severe diphtheria, in which paralysis was common. The *mitis* form was obtained from the lesions of milder diphtheria. The bacterial cells of the *gravis* type were short diphtheroids, without granules, and these cultures were nonhemolytic and fermented starch and glycogen. The *mitis* type had the usual morphology of *B. diphtheriae*, was hemolytic, but did not ferment glycogen or starch. These findings were the outcome of a search for the cause of the severe and intractable diphtheria which was first noticed in Europe about 1924. Reference to the colored plate in the article by Anderson should be made by those attempting to confirm these results, as the characteristics of the colonies are vividly represented there.

From broth cultures of *B. diphtheriae* which had evaporated on standing at room temperature six to eight months, Smith and Jordan obtained filtrates through Chamberland L_5 filters which upon serial transfers yielded visible growths. From the filtrable forms, called by these authors "protobacterial forms," the organisms passed through a series of morphologic changes: a granular stage, followed by giant cocci, then micro- and diplococci and ultimately pleomorphic bacillary forms, typical of bacilli of the diphtheroid group.

Isolation.—Cultures are taken from throats upon Löffler's blood serum. These are permitted to grow at 37.5° C. for from eighteen to twenty-four hours. At the end of this time about 5 c.c. of bouillon are poured into the tubes and the growth is gently emulsified in the broth with a platinum loop. Two or three loopfuls of this emulsion are then streaked over the surface of glucose agar, serum agar, or nutrose agar. After twenty-four hours' incubation these plates show characteristic colonies which can be easily fished and again transferred to Löffler's tubes or any other suitable medium.

Diagnosis.—Cultures from suspected throats are taken on Löffler's blood serum medium and incubated at 37.5° C. for twelve to eighteen hours. At the end of this time morphological examination by staining with Löffler's alkaline methylene blue and by some polar body stain like that of Neisser is carried out. Occasionally direct smears from the throat may show the bacilli, but it is rarely possible to make a satisfactory diagnosis in this way.

Williams has pointed out that in throat cultures in which the diphtheria bacilli are few in number it is of advantage to inoculate a tube of ascitic broth with the mixed culture. The diphtheria bacilli will appear in eighteen to twenty-four hours as a pellicle on the surface. A portion of this pellicle may then be plated on ascitic agar and isolated in pure culture from the colonies. This, however, is not necessary for routine examinations. The important point is to take cultures as early as possible on fresh and moist Löffler's medium, avoiding the dried tubes so often passed out from old stock at drug store stations. It is important to smear from the actually involved areas, examining the throat with good illumination, and to have the tubes incubated without delay, instead of carrying them about for hours after inoculation. Such cultures examined by an experienced man should give positive diagnoses in almost all of the actual cases. In the diagnosis of children and in carrier work it is important to take nasal as well as throat cultures.

Pathogenicity.—*B. diphtheriae* causes a more or less specific local reaction in mucous membranes, which results in the formation of the so-called "pseudomembranes." When these are characteristically present, infection with this bacillus should always be suspected. It should be remembered, however, that membranous inflammation is not necessarily present in all cases. We have seen positive cultures in a considerable number of people, especially in relatively insusceptible individuals, in whom the throat showed nothing more than severe congestion and catarrhal inflammation. The consequent disease depends, in part, upon the mechanical disturbance caused by the local inflammation and, in part, upon the systemic poisoning with the toxin which the bacilli produce. Although diphtheria bacilli have been found after death in the spleen and liver, we have no data which show that a true diphtheria septicemia may occur during life. The most frequent sites of diphtheritic inflammations are the mucous membranes of the throat, larynx and nose. They have also been found in the ear, upon the mucous membrane of the stomach and the vulva. Diphtheritic conjunctivitis is one of the most severe and dangerous varieties of eye infection—second only to that caused by the gonococcus. Diphtheritic wound infections, though rare, occur with sufficient frequency to be borne in mind. Diphtheric bronchopneumonia also has been observed.

The localized injuries due to the violent inflammatory reaction elicited by the diphtheria bacilli at their point of lodgment which, in the large majority of cases, are in the upper respiratory tract, constitute the immediately visible changes in the disease in human beings. In attempting to make a diagnosis of these by inspection, the clinician should remember that the pseudomembranous inflammation characterized by its adherence to the submucosa and the bleeding points it leaves, is not pathognomonic of the diphtheria bacilli, but means simply a very violent inflammatory reaction and that, while this condition is most commonly caused by the diphtheria bacillus, many other severe inflammations may give rise to similar appearances. Thus, a severe streptococcus infection of the throat may simulate a diphtheritic membrane and escharotics or other chemical or mechanical injuries may give rise to similar lesions. Another point of considerable clinical importance is the fact that diphtheritic inflammation of the throat may often be associated with other infectious processes. Streptococcus infections superimposed upon a local diphtheria infection change the appearance both of the local lesion and of the general clinical picture and are apt to lead to greater severity of the illness. Another common experience is to find, at the site of the inflammation, an ulcerative process, smears from which on staining with Gram's gentian violet or carbolfuchsin will show a typical picture of Vincent's angina with fusiform bacilli and spirilla. Owing to a number of mistakes we have made, it has become our rule whenever we see a case of Vincent's angina to take cultures on Löffler's medium as for diphtheria diagnosis, since we have on two or three occasions found almost pure cultures of diphtheria bacilli taken from the depths of such anginal ulcers. The systemic symptoms in diphtheria are not always severe since, as we shall see, adults are apt to be partially protected by the presence of diphtheria antitoxin in their blood and in consequence their disease may be both locally and systematically so mild that diphtheria might not be seriously considered on purely clinical evidence.

The mechanical injury may actually lead to death. This is particularly true in the case of children in whom extension downward with membrane formation in the larynx leads to laryngeal obstruction, necessitating tracheotomy or intubation. Death from these causes, as well as from secondary bronchopneumonia, was formerly not infrequent. This has fortunately been rendered much less frequent by antitoxin treatment, by the greater vigilance of doctors and their ability to make an early diagnosis.

The general symptoms of diphtheria are due to the action of the toxin absorbed from the lesion, and it is the toxin which determines the systemic characteristics of the disease and constitutes the most frequent cause of death. According to experiments done by MacCallum in the perfusion of the heart with diphtheria toxin, the toxin does not seem to act directly upon the heart, in spite of the fact that there seems to be definite evidence that the heart is involved in diphtheria. According to the same investigator, there do not seem to be sufficient gross or microscopic changes in the hearts of people dead of diphtheria to explain death. It is MacCallum's opinion that Passler and Romberg were probably right in stating that the effect of the poison is "chiefly upon the vasomotor control of the blood vessels." However this may be, the peril from cardiac failure after the ninth or tenth day remains a clinical fact of great importance. Injuries to other organs are apparent in albuminuria due to acute interstitial nephritis, and cloudy swelling of parenchyma cells in other organs. In view of the marked changes in the suprarenal bodies in guinea-pigs treated with diphtheria toxin, these organs have been especially investigated in diphtheria, and though usually little or no change has been found, MacCallum states that "the changes in the adrenals are likely to be more intense than in most of the other organs," showing hemorrhages and cellular degeneration. This may have direct bearing on the abnormal fall in blood pressure.

Some of our most valuable information concerning the action of diphtheria toxin in man has been obtained from rare accidents during active immunization. According to this it appears that the susceptibility of man is per gram weight considerably higher, perhaps ten times higher, than is that of guinea-pigs. The local action of the toxin results in a very severe swelling, an inflammatory area surrounded by considerable edema extending both up and down the limb from the point of injection, and even to the trunk. In the center of the inflammatory area sooner or later a large blister filled with sterile serum develops. Finally a considerable slough results. Severe intoxication gives rise to characteristic symptoms consisting of constipation, diminution of urine which may amount to anuria, rapid pulse rate and often considerable mental excitability bordering on hysteria. The temperature is moderately raised. Disturbances of the nerves and muscular system come on early. Diminished power of accommodation of the eye, exaggerated reflexes, followed by diminished knee jerks, and tenderness over the nerve trunks in the neighborhood of the injection can be noted. Action upon the heart is not apparent before the ninth day, but from then on is an important factor: it is of the utmost importance for physicians, therefore, to be prepared for late effects upon the heart in diphtheria patients at the time when acute local and general symptoms are subsiding. Paralysis of the various muscle groups affecting the ciliary muscles, the palate, respiratory muscles and, later, those of the extremities may be looked for sometime after the third week and as late as the ninth or tenth. Observations of this kind are of the utmost importance in guiding clinical procedure, especially in impressing upon physicians that a mild sore throat not recogognized as diphtheria and therefore not treated with antitoxin may be mild as a diphtheria but carry serious sequelae in its train. In slightly suspicious cases, therefore, he should not fail to have cultures taken and to give antitoxin promptly if they are positive.

For the usual laboratory animals the diphtheria bacillus is highly pathogenic. Dogs, cats, fowl, rabbits and guinea-pigs are susceptible. Rats and mice are resistant. False membranes, analogous to those found in human beings, have been produced in many animals, but only when inoculation had been preceded by mechanical injury of the mucosa. Small quantities (0.5 to 1 c.c.) of a virulent broth culture, given subcutaneously to a guinea-pig, may produce the greatest symptoms and within six to eight hours the animal may show signs of great discomfort. Death occurs usually within thirty-six to seventy-two hours. Upon autopsy the point of inoculation is soggy and serosanguineous exudate; neighboring lymph nodes are edematous. Lungs, liver, spleen, and kidneys are congested. There may be pleuritic and peritoneal exudates. Pathognomonic is a severe congestion of both suprarenal bodies. The gastric ulcerations described by Rosenau and Anderson may occur, but is by no means regularly found (2 out of 50 in our series).

Determination of Virulence.—When diphtheria or diphtheria-like bacilli are isolated from the throats of patients not showing typical clinical diphtheria, or from healthy individuals suspected of being carriers, it is important to determine whether these organisms are toxin producers. The usual criterion is their virulence for guinea-pigs. Two c.c. of a forty-eight-hour broth or ascitic broth culture are injected subcutaneously into a normal guinea-pig. This dose will kill the pig in three to five days if the culture is virulent. A control injection should always be made into another pig of the same weight, which has received an injection of antitoxin (at least 250 units) twelve to twenty-four hours previously. Neisser suggested that the intracutaneous injection of the suspected bacilli may be used for the determination of virulence. This has the advantage of economy, as several tests can be carried out on the same pig. The method as applied by Zingher and Soletsky has been to use the following modification of Neisser's method: Two guinea-pigs of about 250 grams are used for the test. The abdominal wall is prepared by shaving or plucking out the hair. A twenty-four-hour pure culture on Löffler's medium is emulsified in 20 c.c. of normal salt solution and 0.15 c.c. of this suspension is injected intracutaneously at a corresponding site into each of the two guinea-pigs. One of these animals is given at the same time an intracardial or intraperitoneal injection of about 250 units of antitoxin, or preferably is prepared by an intraperitoneal injection of antitoxin twenty-four hours before the tests are made. Six cultures may be tested in this way on two animals. Virulent strains produce a definitely circumscribed local infiltrated lesion, which shows superficial necrosis in two to three days. In the control pig the skin remains normal. This method gives results parallel to those obtained with the subcutaneous tests.

Virulence tests may be made with mixed cultures according to the principles and procedures outlined in the preceding paragraph. This method, introduced by Force and Beattie, in 1922, has been used with satisfaction by Kelly and Porter and others, including ourselves. To carry out this *field culture method* for determining virulence, the total growth on an eighteen- to twenty-four-hour Löffler's medium slant culture is emulsified in 5 c.c. of saline and 0.1 c.c. of this emulsion is injected intracutaneously into a normal guinea-pig and 0.1 c.c. intracutaneously into a guinea-pig previously protected by an intraperitoneal injection of 250 units of antitoxin. If the diphtheria bacillus is virulent swelling and necrosis will occur in twenty-four to forty-eight hours in the unprotected guinea-pigs and not in the protected animal. If staphylococci or streptococci or other organisms in the mixed growth of the throat culture are sufficiently virulent, local lesions will occur in both animals. This result is not to be regarded as a negative but as an inconclusive test, obscured by the action of the pyogenic cocci. It should be repeated using a pure culture of the suspected diphtheria bacillus.

Falk observed that electrophoretic potential differences were correlated with the virulence and toxigenicity of diphtheria bacilli and devised a method to determine virulence by measurement of the rate of migration of the organisms in an electrical field. Useful results were reported following the introduction of this *cataphoretic method* in 1928, but it has not been widely adopted. Stone and Weigel found the method to be impractical and Jones failed to find any correlation between migration velocity and virulence.

Diphtheria Toxin.—Animals and man infected with *B. diphtheriae* show evidences of severe systemic disturbances and organic degenerations, while the microorganism itself can be found in the local lesion only. This fact led even the earliest observers to suspect that, in part at least, the harmful results of such an infection were attributable to a soluble and diffusible poison elaborated by the bacillus (Löffler). The actual existence of such a poison or toxin was definitely proved by Roux and Yersin in 1889. They demonstrated that broth cultures in which *B. diphtheriae* had been grown for varying periods would remain toxic for guinea-pigs after the organisms themselves had been removed from the culture fluid by filtration through a Chamberland filter.

Since diphtheria toxin is the one from which the greater part of our knowledge concerning bacterial exotoxins has been derived, it is necessary to consider it somewhat at length. Such filtrates are toxic not only for man, but for rabbits, guinea-pigs, dogs, cats, and horses. Rats and mice are relatively insusceptible. The toxin is effective when administered by any route except the intestinal. While it probably has a severe action upon the tissues generally, it selects certain nerve centers, especially those of the vagus and the phrenic nerves. It acts also on cranial and peripheral nerves. It acts upon both the cortical and medullary cells of the suprarenals, causes hemorrhage in the adrenal medulla and leads to late degeneration of the heart muscle, which is the cause of postdiphtheritic death.

Lyman and King, Torrance and others have shown that sublethal doses of diphtheria toxin injected into guinea pigs deplete the stores of vitamin C in the suprarenal glands, the pancreas and the kidneys. Previously, in 1935, Greenwald and Harde, and Jungeblut and Zwemer observed that feeding vitamin C to guinea pigs increased their resistance to the toxin. Ascorbic acid (vitamin C) inactivates diphtheria toxin *in vitro* by oxidation and acidity, but this seems unlikely to be the mechanism of resistance operating through the function of vitamin C in the animal body.

The production of a potent toxin is of the greatest importance in antitoxin manufacture. Success depends upon a great many different factors, the first requisite being a potent strain of diphtheria bacilli, one of the best being the Park and Williams No. 8, isolated in 1895. Sudden loss of powers to form toxin has been observed. Wilcox believes that certain makes of the peptone will, after a time, diminish toxin formation, which cannot be restored by any known means. This may be due as Crowell's work suggests to transformation of the culture into a "rough" variety.

The composition of the medium is of primary importance. Madsen stated from the beginning that no good diphtheria toxin could be produced without peptone. While this is true, it is not known which type of peptone is best for the purpose. Hartley's attempts to determine this by analysis failed, but it is suspected that deutero-albumose is the important constituent. Theobald Smith showed the importance of relatively little sugar in the media, owing to the inhibiting effect of acid reactions. According to the earlier work of Davis and Ferry and others, some constituent of meat infusion was regarded as an essential accessory factor for toxin production by *B. diphtheriae*. We now know, from experience with the infusion-free medium of Wadsworth, Wheeler and Kirkbride that meat infusion is not necessary for toxin production (if it can be asserted that the peptone used is free from the infusion factor). Two per cent proteose peptone, in a solution containing, among other ingredients, 0.5 per cent sodium lactate, and 0.2 per cent dextrose is an excellent medium for the production of toxin. This medium is sterilized in the autoclave. (See section on Technic.) The alkalinity of the broth must be fairly high, since acid inhibits toxin. Formerly, the method was to make a 2 per cent peptone broth, neutralize this to litmus and to add normal soda solution to pH 8—8.2. Hartley adjusts to 7.8. The buffering action of the peptone may, according to Bunker, in part account for its importance. The best toxin is now produced in media which have undergone little heating. The substitution of sterilization by filtration for sterilization in the autoclave of media used for large scale toxin production has resulted in the routine production of toxins with L_+ values under 0.1 c.c. and containing from fifteen to thirty or more LF units. Mueller's medium is described in the section on Technic.

Hartley believes that care of the strain is important, subculturing every two days on what he calls "starter bottles" of 100 c.c. quantities on broth, and on Löffler's slants every fourteen days.

The manner of inoculation is important. The organism must be grown in flat-bottomed bottles in order to give a shallow layer of medium, and Bunker, as well as Hartley and Hartley, have recently shown how very important this point is. According to them, the shallower the layer—in other words, the better the aeration—the more rapidly the maximum toxin formation occurs. The ratio of surface area exposed to the air to the volume of medium is important. The optimum surface area volume ratio is 0.58. Plugs should be loosely inserted to permit diffusion of air. The organisms are inoculated from forty-eight-hour "starter bottles" by floating a bit of pellicle carefully on the surface of the medium. The surface of the medium is usually completely covered in about forty-eight hours. The maximum toxin formation may occur any time between four and eight days, usually on or about the seventh day. At this time it is filtered. The most favorable temperature of incubation for toxin-production is 34° C.

It seems probable that small amounts of iron and copper are important, if not essential for the production of toxin by the diphtheria bacillus. This conclusion is drawn from the work of Locke and Main who found that small amounts of iron and copper favored the production of toxin, that highly purified diphtheria toxin contained these elements and had an absorption spectrum resembling that of oxyhemoglobin. The discovery by Coulter and Stone that porphyrin compounds in toxic filtrates could be correlated with the amount of toxin further links these elements with the metabolism of the organism in which a respiratory pigment of the nature of cytochrome plays an important part. Eaton's studies indicate that the porphyrins found in crude and purified toxin are not combined with protein but are precipitated near the isoelectric point of toxin and are easily adsorbed on protein precipitates in the process of purification of the toxin.

Diphtheria toxin is not stable, being destroyed or modified rapidly on heating to about 60° C. When concentrated and dried, it may withstand 70° C. Light and oxidation destroy it rapidly. Kept in the dark in a cold place it gradually changes, in the process of what is spoken of as "ripening." After such ripening, and properly preserved, the toxicity may remain stable for months and even years, the ripening itself taking a month or two.

Concentration.—Toxin must be measured as a potency which, as will be seen in another section, is done by tests upon guinea-pigs. The stronger the toxin the better for use, average strong poisons varying in M.L.D. from 0.002 to 0.001 c.c. Toxins of lower values, such as 0.0005 c.c., can be obtained.

Diphtheria toxin can be freed from many extraneous materials and concentrated by the following methods: by salting-out with ammonium sulphate, precipitation with acetic acid (Watson and Wallace) in the cold (0° to 5° C.) at pH 4.8 (Koulikoff and Smirnoff), absorption on aluminum hydroxide and elution with a phosphate solution (Gross) and precipitation by salts of heavy metals (Smith).

Titration and Standardization.—In Section II of this book we have described the titration and standardization of diphtheria toxin in terms of the fundamental unit of toxicity, namely the M.L.D., or minimal lethal dose which after subcutaneous injection kills a 250-gram guinea-pig on the fourth day. Other "units," L_0 and L_+ doses, are derived from this and apply to results obtained with mixtures of toxin and antitoxin. The minimal skin-reacting dose (M.R.D.) of Roemer is another useful fundamental unit.

Mixtures of diphtheria toxin and antitoxin in certain proportions give rise to a precipitate. This precipitate is not due to bacterial protein, but is a toxin-antitoxin complex together with some of the components of the serum. The precipitate forms first in a tube containing a balanced neutral mixture of toxin and antitoxin. On the basis of this precipitin reaction Ramon devised his flocculation method for the titration of diphtheria toxin and antitoxin. Results are expressed in terms of LF units, referring to the amount of toxin required to cause the *indicator flocculation* with one unit of antitoxin. The method is useful in following the course of immunization of horses, to obtain an estimate of the antigenic value of toxin and toxoid and to disclose a number of the properties of these substances. One of us reported successful use of this method in 1924 (Bayne-Jones). While the method has not replaced the Ehrlich procedures, it is a valuable method for these titrations. The details of these methods will be found in the section on technic.

Toxoid or Anatoxin.—Largely as a result of the investigations of Ramon there has been a revival of the attempts to utilize altered toxin (toxoid, or, as the French prefer to call it, anatoxin) for the purposes of immunization. Anatoxin or toxoid has replaced the toxin-antitoxin mixtures in active immunization of man. The preparations now in general use are toxoid precipitated with alum.

Anatoxin or toxoid is produced by adding 0.2 to 0.4 per cent formalin to filtered toxin to which no preservative has been added. The toxin plus formaldehyde is then incubated at 37° to 40° C. until it becomes atoxic. Toxicity decreases rapidly at first but it may take several months for its complete disappearance. When no toxic action follows the injection of 5 c.c. subcutaneously into guinea-pigs, the preparation is considered atoxic and safe to use for the immunization of horses or human beings. For horses the initial dose may be from 5.0 to 20 c.c. With such toxoids considerable antitoxin values have been obtained within a relatively short time by Ramon and the method is now in use in England and is being introduced in the United States.

Glenny, Hopkins and Pope have studied this matter in considerable detail and found that diphtheria toxin, modified by formaldehyde so that it has become non-toxic, still possesses powerful immunizing properties and can be concentrated so that the antigenic power may be increased about 40 fold for the same nitrogen content. In immunizing rabbits with such antigens they find that the speed of antitoxin production is enhanced to a degree which permits the detection of antitoxin in the blood of a normal rabbit nine days after injection and guinea-pigs become Schick negative in eleven days.

Chemical Nature of Diphtheria Toxin.—The chemical composition of diphtheria toxin is not known, but a great advance in knowledge has been made by the contributions of Eaton and Pappenheimer. Omitting reference to the older work, accounts of which can be found in previous editions of this *Textbook*, we will briefly summarize the most recent findings.

For a comprehensive summary the reader is referred to Eaton's review of "Recent Chemical Investigations of Bacterial Toxins," published in 1938.

Eaton and Pappenheimer purified diphtheria toxin by various methods of precipitation and adsorption. Finally Eaton obtained preparations in which the protein nitrogen per Lf unit approached a limit of 0.004 to 0.0005 mgm. In the most active preparation the M.L.D. for a 250-gram guinea-pig contained 0.000016 mgm. of nitrogen. This preparation contained about 16 per cent of nitrogen in the dried organic residue, making this M.L.D. in terms of dry substance about 0.0001 gm. The toxin was destroyed by digestion with proteolytic enzymes.

Eaton concluded that diphtheria toxin is a protein or protein-like substance which is not easily precipitated by acid at any pH and contains no cysteine sulphur and little or no tryptophane.

Wadsworth and his associates have purified diphtheria toxin by ultrafiltration, which involves no chemical treatment. The nitrogen content of the product was between 0.001 and 0.002 mgm. of nitrogen per Lf unit.

The proteins in the filtrates of broth cultures of virulent diphtheria bacilli are derived from the bacterial cell substance and the toxic material. While it can be neither affirmed nor denied that diphtheria toxin is a protein, all indications seem to point to its protein nature. These proteins produce sensitization of animals and elicit allergic reactions in hypersensitive animals and human beings. Neill and his coworkers have demonstrated allergic reactions to diphtheria toxin in addition to the previously known allergic reactions to the bacterial proteins. The significance of these effects will be discussed in connection with the Schick test.

Epidemiology.—There is no disease in which sanitary control can accomplish so much as in diphtheria because we are furnished in this instance not only with accurate and simple methods of bacteriological diagnosis, of cases and carriers, but we have available a specific susceptibility test by means of which we can pick out the susceptible in any group, as well as methods of prophylactic protection which allow a choice between a speedy and a slow procedure, both of them of proven value. In this disease, sanitary measures have made tremendous strides and greatly reduced both morbidity and death rate since the introduction of bacteriological methods. Newsholm has studied death rates in diphtheria, and found that in earlier years, great epidemics of diphtheria used to spread through the great cities. There was such an epidemic in London in 1874. In 1872 he states that the death rate from diphtheria and croup in Boston was 35 per 100,000, but in 1881, it was close to 218 per 100,000. Epidemic waves seem to have recurred at five- and ten-year intervals, but even in the interepidemic years in cities generally, the death rate seems to have ranged anywhere from 20 to 60 per 100,000. It was and is endemic all over the world, is somewhat more prevalent in colder climates where upper respiratory inflammations are more common, and, for some unknown reason, has been relatively more common in rural than in urban communities.

Quite naturally, the disease has always been particularly a school disease among children. From studies by Schick, Hahn, and others, it appears that the newborn child is endowed with a certain amount of diphtheria antitoxin by the mother, probably through the placenta, to some degree perhaps transmitted through the colostrum. This relative immunity fades at the end of the first year of life and is gradually reacquired so that the most susceptible years are between one and perhaps nine to ten years of age. In the army, with an age group ranging from twenty to thirty years, it was found, during the World War, that about 10 per cent of the personnel was Schick positive or, therefore, susceptible.

The striking distance of diphtheria is not very large, but the organism is relatively resistant to the ordinary influences of exterior corporal circumstances, and may live for considerable lengths of time in mucus or saliva deposited on eating utensils, playthings, pencils, handkerchiefs, etc. In dried bits of membrane the bacilli may live for many weeks as Löffler has shown.

Diphtheria is transmitted from one individual to another directly or indirectly by contact or droplet infection—as in coughing, etc. It has been found that individuals may retain virulent diphtheria bacilli in nose and throat for long periods after recovery from the disease.

With the general improvement in municipal sanitation, the increasing use of active immunization of children with toxin-antitoxin or toxoid, there has been a prolonged continued decrease in the incidence of diphtheria. A part of this decreased mortality was attributed to a change in the character of the disease or increased resistance of the population, but was chiefly credited to the use of antitoxin. In 1927, however, a severe form of diphtheria appeared in Berlin (Deicher and Agulnik).

Since then this severe and paralyzing type of diphtheria, which appears to be almost completely refractory to the usual antitoxic serum, has been observed in other countries in Europe and in England. From lesions of the disease Anderson and his co-workers isolated the type of the organism called by them *B. diphtheriae gravis*. Diphtheria gravis is an indication that the monovalent antitoxin used all over the world may have to be improved by increasing its neutralizing range.

Carriers.—The problem of diphtheria carriers is one of considerable importance. Anderson, Goldberger and Hachtel studied 4039 healthy people in the city of Detroit, and found that 0.928 per cent harbored bacilli identical morphologically with the Klebs-Löffler bacillus. This figure is rather lower than those of some other investigators, but would indicate, as the writers stated, that there were from five thousand to six thousand diphtheria carriers in the city of Detroit.

Of 19 cultures isolated from 19 of the carriers, only 2 were virulent, which would indicate that only 0.97 per cent of the people examined carried organisms capable of producing disease. An interesting further point is that the *B. hofmannii* was present in at least 41.9 per cent of over two thousand individuals examined, and that 47 cultures, morphologically identified as *B. hofmannii*, were avirulent. This would confirm the impression gained, we believe, by most experienced laboratory workers that a true *hofmannii* can be distinguished with considerable certainty from a Klebs-Löffler bacillus by morphological examination alone, and that its significance is probably that of a frequently present saprophyte of the throat and pharynx. The studies of Goldberger, Williams and Hachtel also indicate that in examining for diphtheria carriers it is best not to restrict the cultures to the nose or throat, but that cultures should be taken from both places in every case.

Carriers naturally increase in crowded communities in the course of cold weather, when nasopharyngeal catarrhs are common, and we have seen as high as 17 per cent carriers in a military unit in which diphtheria and other respiratory diseases were prevalent soon after the soldiers had to be crowded together during transatlantic transportation. The carrier state in kitchen personnel is particularly important, and attention should be paid to these groups in a community whenever the source of infection is being traced. Indirect and direct contact with carriers is probably the most common method by which the disease is kept going in modern communities. Less important, though still of some significance, is that food transmission and milk epidemics have not been uncommon. Also, these will mean infection of the milk by a milk handler who is a carrier or suffering from a mild diphtheria. However, in one instance, diphtheria bacilli were isolated from the inflamed udders of a cow.

The carrier problem thus becomes the most important epidemiological feature. The carriers may either be temporary or chronic. Convalescent diphtheria cases usually get rid of their bacilli spontaneously within two, three or four weeks. Healthy individuals exposed to cases or carriers as a rule do not keep their organisms more than either a few days or a few weeks, depending perhaps to some extent upon the condition of the mucous membranes. A small percentage remain chronic carriers and, in isolated instances, it has seemed almost impossible to free these individuals of their diphtheria bacilli. They are, however, such definite menaces that prolonged isolation and vigorous attempts at cure must be made for the protection of the community. In all such cases, virulence tests should be made, since prolonged isolation implies so much interference with the life of the affected individual that it would be quite improper to confine a person unless we were sure that the organisms carried by him were capable of transmitting the disease.

Many different methods have been employed for the freeing of carriers. Not a single one of them, however, has been permanently successful. Practically all the ordinary throat antiseptics, peroxide of hydrogen, permanganate of potassium, iodine and glycerin, weak formaldehyde, various hypochlorite solutions have been used, some of them with occasional success, but without regularity in any of them. Acriflavine and other dyes have been applied and implantation of staphylococci or some of the acidophilic bacteria upon the throat in the hope of driving out the diphtheria bacilli by bacterial competition have been tried and have usually failed. The spraying of the throat with pyocyanases was in vogue a few years ago, but cannot be said to have brought encouraging results. It is probable that quite the most important thing is to correct pathological conditions of the nose and throat by the correction of a deviated septum or the removal of tonsils and adenoids, whenever necessary. Added to this, sunshine, cleanliness and the cure of chronic catarrhal inflammation are probably more important than any kind of antiseptic treatment.

The detection of carriers can easily be carried out on a large scale by a relatively small force of bacteriologists. It requires a large supply of sterile swabs and Löffler's medium, and wholesale cultures can be taken on a group as large as entire infantry regiments at war strength without too great an expenditure of energy.

Prevention.—The prevention of diphtheria for all these reasons falls into a very logical system of procedure. Whenever diphtheria breaks out in a school, institution, military unit, factory unit, etc., the first thing to do is to make a thorough inspection and immediately institute precautions against the transmission of mucus from one individual to another. This will imply supervision of the kitchen, food preparation, dish washing, prohibition of spitting, isolation of individuals who are coughing and hawking or suffering from severe catarrhal inflammations; cleanliness of sleeping quarters and mess halls, inspection of the entire group, and the taking of throat cultures; segregation of those that show positive cultures; especially attention in this regard, and repeated culturing of kitchen personnel and food handlers; Schick reactions upon the entire group, with prophylactic immunization (preferably by the active method), of those with positive Schick reactions; subsequent attention to chronic carriers. These precautions are simple and applicable with minor modifications to any kind of group in which diphtheria appears.

Schick Reaction.—The studies of Roemer and others have shown that the blood of the majority of normal adults contains a small amount of diphtheria antitoxin. This normal antitoxin probably accounts for resistance of many individuals to diphtheria. Its presence may be very easily detected by means of the Schick reaction. A standardized diphtheria toxin is diluted in normal saline so that 0.1 c.c. of the solution contains $\frac{1}{50}$ M.L.D. for a guinea-pig. This amount is injected intracutaneously. If the blood of the subject has less than some value between $\frac{1}{500}$ and $\frac{1}{250}$ of a unit of antitoxin per cubic centimeter, a positive reaction appears in twenty-four to thirty-six hours and persists four or five days or more. It consists in a slight infiltration of skin surrounded by a red areola, 1 to 2 centimeters in diameter. A negative reaction indicates that sufficient natural antitoxin is present to protect the individual against diphtheria, although he may nevertheless harbor the bacilli as a carrier. It has been found unnecessary to give prophylactic injections of antitoxin to individuals with a negative Schick reaction. Park and Zingher have found that negative reactions were obtained in 93 per cent of the newborn, and became less frequent up to the second or fifth year, when 37 per cent were negative. In older children negative reactions were more frequently met with, and about 90 per cent of adults were negative. A pseudoreaction which appears earlier than the true reaction and which usually disappears in forty-eight hours is occasionally seen in individuals who have natural antitoxin. This is due to sensitiveness to some of the proteins used in the injection, and may be reproduced in the same individual by the injection of autolysate of diphtheria bacilli or sometimes by the injection of broth media. The most satisfactory method for detection of the pseudoreaction is to make a control injection of $\frac{1}{50}$ M.L.D. of a toxin which has been heated at 80° C. for five minutes. This heating destroys the toxin, but leaves uninjured the substances which produce the pseudoreaction.

The Schick reaction has been extensively used, especially on large bodies of troops and on school children, and has been found eminently satisfactory, though, of course, as with all other biological reactions, exceptions are noted and difficulties encountered.

Antitoxin—Specific Therapy.[1]—Specific therapy in diphtheria is, of course, the main thing in clinical control. It must be remembered here as in all other forms of specific therapy that success depends as much upon the time at which the diagnosis is made as it does upon the manner of treatment. Therefore, in speaking of specific therapy, it is important to emphasize the necessity for early diagnosis. It is in this particular that the responsibility of the physician is greatest, and every severe sore throat in a child should be immediately cultured and, though not as imperative in adults, it is not a bad rule to culture all throats by the Löffler method. We have discovered a number of cases in that way, especially in military sanitation, which would not have been suspected clinically. The procedure is easy, consumes no time and requires little skill. In outlying districts the physician can easily carry out the steps himself with a simple equipment.

In order to understand the practical principles of diphtheria antitoxin treatment, it is necessary for the physician to remember chiefly two basic facts. One is the observation by Schick and others that even though diphtheria toxin does not enter so rapidly into combination with the tissues of the nervous system as does tetanus toxin, it, nevertheless, is bound to some extent and that the antitoxin probably does not reach poison that is already combined with tissue elements. It is probable that the injury once done is irretrievable, at least to a great extent, and that the antitoxin is chiefly effective against the circulating poison before such cellular attachment has been established. Experiments of Park and his coworkers have shown that if rabbits are given ten lethal doses of diphtheria toxin, they can be saved by relatively small doses of antitoxin if this is given just before or with the poison. As the time between injection of the poison and the injection of the antitoxin grows longer, rapidly increasing doses of antitoxin are necessary and if an hour or more has elapsed no amount of antitoxin will save. The second basic point is the one brought out by the measurements of Henderson Smith and others which show that antitoxin sub-

---

[1] For matters concerning production and standardization see Section II.

cutaneously injected, is but slowly absorbed and reaches its maximum concentration in the blood not much before seventy-three hours after injection. Therefore antitoxin should be given intramuscularly in all cases and in the more severe ones an additional amount may well be given intravenously.

The deductions to be made from these considerations are, first, that early diagnosis must be made, that it is essential to get the antitoxin in as early as possible, and that when the injection is made, it is better to give a sufficient amount at the first dose than to dribble it along in insufficient amounts with intervals of many hours between doses. These observations impose upon the physician great responsibilities of judgment, since in cases seen late in the disease, with very severe symptoms of intoxication, it may be necessary to resort to intravenous injections of the antitoxin in order to neutralize the toxin as rapidly as possible.

The dosage of antitoxin must vary according to severity of the case, the stage at which it is seen, and the age of the patient. In severe cases, ten thousand to thirty thousand units or more should be injected.

If intravenous injection is resorted to, precautions against the occurrence of anaphylaxis must of course be taken, but in view of the relatively slight danger of death from horse-serum injections in man, the risk of anaphylaxis in cases in which intravenous use is actually indicated, is probably much less than the risk of delaying the introduction of antitoxin into the blood. If skin tests can be done beforehand, they should be done. They take very little time and give the physician a signal of possible danger. When such intravenous injections are actually made in sensitive subjects, it seems advisable to dilute the serum 50 per cent with sterile salt solution, in order to render slow injection easier so that the injection of each cubic centimeter may occupy at least one minute.

Prophylactic Immunization.—There are two chief methods of prophylaxis in diphtheria. The first and older consists in injecting five hundred to one thousand units of antitoxin subcutaneously. This is carried out on contacts with positive Schick reactions whenever speed of immunization is desired. It is simple and the principles underlying it are obvious, but the immunization is short-lived and produces a sensitization of the subject with horse serum which naturally is undesirable under modern conditions.

Prophylactic *active immunization* of human beings against diphtheria has been carried out extensively in this country and in Europe. It is unquestionably responsible for a large portion of the reduction of the incidence and mortality of diphtheria which has taken place since 1915.

Basing the procedure upon older experimental work of Behring and on suggestions made by Theobald Smith, Park in 1915, in New York City, introduced active immunization of Schick-positive children by intramuscular or subcutaneous injections of mixtures of diphtheria toxin and antitoxin. The strength and balance of the components of this mixture were changed from time to time from one based on a content of 4 L+ doses of toxin to one containing 0.1 L+ dose of toxin per c.c. Individuals injected with these mixtures became Schick-negative and developed diphtheria antitoxin. The preparation of the toxin-antitoxin mixtures was somewhat difficult, there were a few fatal accidents from its use, and it had the disadvantage of making some recipients sensitive to horse serum.

About 1923 Ramon's work revived the older knowledge that *diphtheria toxoid,* while not poisonous, was antigenic, capable of causing an animal to produce antitoxin. Ramon found that the most effective antigen was made by treating the toxin with formaldehyde. By a reaction, not well understood, but which is not a simple combination of the aldehyde with free amino groups, formaldehyde deprives diphtheria toxin of its toxicity but leaves its antigenicity almost intact. The material thus obtained was called anatoxin by Ramon, and toxoid by American, English and German workers. It was used for active immunization of human beings and to start the immunization of horses used to produce antitoxin.

In 1931 Glenny and his collaborators showed that toxoid could be precipitated by alum and that this somewhat purified and concentrated precipitate was a better antigen than the crude formalin-toxoid. Taken up in this country at once by Havens and his associates, Glenny's results were confirmed by experimental tests and the material proven to be safe and serviceable for the immunization of children. It was found that a single injection of alum precipitated toxoid resulted in immunity in as high a percentage of children as did two or three injections of the best unprecipitated diphtheria toxoid. Since 1933 *alum precipitated diphtheria toxoid* has replaced all the older materials for use in active prophylactic immunization. Standardized preparations are readily available at health departments and drug stores throughout this country.

BACILLUS HOFMANNII (PSEUDODIPHTHERIA BACILLUS) [2]

Hoffmann-Wellenhoff, in 1888, and, at almost the same time, Löffler described bacilli which they had cultivated from the throats of normal persons and in several instances from those of diphtheritic persons, which were in many respects similar to true *B. diphtheriae,* but differed from this chiefly in being nonpathogenic for guinea-pigs. These organisms were at first regarded by some observers as merely attenuated diphtheria bacilli. More recent investigations, however, prove them to be unquestionably a separate species, easily differentiable by proper methods. They differ from *B. diphtheriae* in so many important features, moreover, that the term "pseudo-diphtheria bacillus" is hardly an appropriate one for them.

Morphology.—*B. hofmannii* is shorter and thicker than *B. diphtheriae.* It is usually straight and slightly clubbed at one end, rarely at both. Stained with Löffler's blue it occasionally shows unstained transverse bands; unlike *B. diphtheria,* however, these bands hardly ever exceed one or two in number at most. In many cultures the single transverse band gives the bacillus a diplococcoid appearance.

Staining.—Stained by Neisser's or Roux's method, no polar bodies can be demonstrated. It is gram-positive. It forms no spores, is nonmotile, and has no flagella.

Cultivation.—On the usual culture media *B. hofmannii* grows more luxuriantly than *B. diphtheriae,* developing even in first isolations from the human body upon the simple meat-extract media. On agar plates its colonies are larger, less transparent, and whiter than are those of true diphtheria bacilli. In fluid media there is even clouding and less tendency to the formation of a pellicle than with *B. diphtheriae.* A positive means of distinction between the two is given by the inability of *B. hofmannii*

2 Order, family and genus like diphtheria bacillus. Species: *Corynebacterium pseudodiphthericum.*

to form acid upon various sugar media. The differentiation on a basis of acid forma-tion was first attempted by Cobbett and has been recently worked out systematically by Knapp, and confirmed by various observers (Smith, Zinsser). The results of this work, carried out with the serum-water media of Hiss, to which various sugars were added, show that *B. Hofmannii* forms acid upon none of the sugars used, while *B. diphtheriae* acidifies and coagulates media containing monosaccharides and several

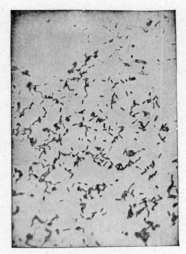

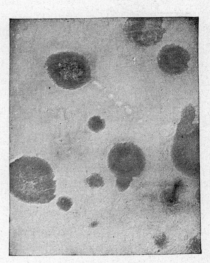

Fig. 36.—Bacillus Hofmannii   Fig. 37.—Colonies of B. Hofmannii cn Agar.

of the more complex sugars, as given in the diagram in the section following dealing with *B. xerosis*.

Differentiation can finally be made on the basis of animal pathogenicity; *B. hofmannii* being entirely innocuous to the ordinary laboratory animals. *B. hofmannii* forms no toxins, and animals immunized with it do not possess increased resistance to *B. diphtheriae*.

BACILLUS XEROSIS [3]

In 1884, Kuschbert and Neisser described a bacillus, isolated from the eyes of patients suffering from a form of chronic conjunctivitis known as xerosis. This bacillus, which, morphologically, is almost identical with *B. diphtheriae*, they be-lieved to be the etiological factor of the disease. The frequency with which it has been isolated from normal eyes, precludes this etiological relationship, and it may be safely regarded as a harmless saprophyte which may indeed be more abundant in the slightly inflamed than in the normal conjunctiva but which has no causative relation to xerophthalmia.

Morphology.—*B. xerosis* resembles *B. diphtheriae* closely. It is occasionally shorter than *B. diphtheriae*, but on the whole no absolute morphological differentia-

3 Order, family and genus like diphtheria bacillus. Species: *Corynebacterium xerose.*

tion between the two is possible. It forms no spores and is nonmotile. Polar bodies may occasionally be seen.

Cultivation.—On *Löffler's blood serum,* on *agar, glycerin agar,* and in *broth,* its growth is very similar to that of *B. diphtheriae,* but more delicate throughout. It cannot easily be cultivated upon the simple meat-extract media, nor will it grow on gelatin at room temperature. Its colonies on glycerin or glucose agar are microscopically identical with those of *B. diphtheriae.*

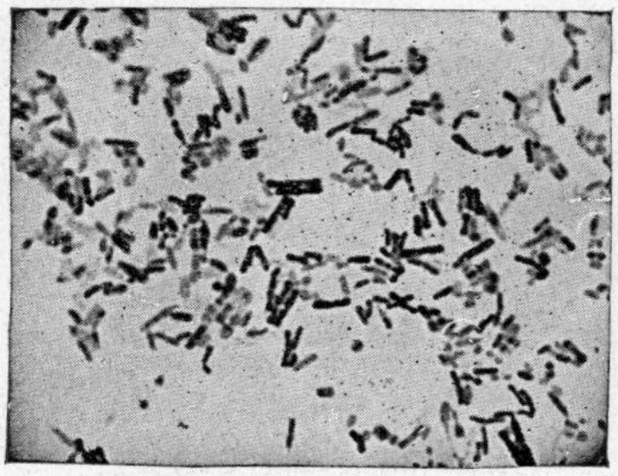

Fig. 38.—Bacillus Xerosis.

Differentiation.—It differs from *B. diphtheriae* distinctly in its acidifying action on sugar media. These relations were first worked out by Knapp for various sugars and the alcohol mannite, and have been extensively confirmed by others. A reference to the table shows that differentiation may be made by the use of two sugars—saccharose and dextrose. *B. diphtheriae* forms acid from dextrose, not from saccharose; *B. xerosis* from saccharose, and dextrose, but not from dextrin; *B. hofmannii* does not form acid from either.

B. xerosis is nonpathogenic to animals and forms no toxin.

Hiss Serum-water Media Plus 1 Per Cent	B. diphtheriae	B. xerosis	B. hofmannii
Dextrose	+	+	—
Saccharose	—	+	—
Dextrin	+	—	—

THE DIPHTHEROID BACILLI [4]

In addition to the bacteria mentioned above, there is a large group of micro-organisms spoken of as the *diphtheroid bacilli,* largely because of their morphological resemblance to the diphtheria bacillus. For this group, Lehmann and Neumann have suggested the term *Corynebacterium.* The characteristics of this group are a morphological similarity to the diphtheria bacillus, that they are gram-positive, nonmotile, often show metachromatic granules and have no spores. It is not, at the present writing, possible to formulate a classification of these organisms. They are apparently very numerous and have been isolated from a great many different sources, both in connection with the human body and in nature. Bunting and Yates have claimed that an organism of this group has etiological connection with Hodgkin's disease. Studies by many other workers, notably by Bloomfield and Fox, and studies in our own laboratory show that organisms very similar to these strains can be isolated from the skin, from the lymph nodes of healthy and diseased people, from ascitic fluid in varying conditions, and from supposedly sterile tissues. They are frequently present in the nasal mucus and in the throat, and are so ubiquitous that any association of them with specific disease must be very conservatively approached. According to the investigations of many men who have studied the flora of the nasopharynx, it seems that

[4] These organisms are grouped in the new classification as separate species of the genus *Corynebacterium.*

organisms belonging to the general group of diphtheroid bacilli are the most common saprophytes habitually present in this part of the normal human body. Some streptococci appear in diphtheroidal forms.

Very similar to this group are the bacilli of *pseudotuberculosis ovis*, isolated from necrotic lesions in the kidneys of sheep by Preisz and Nocard.

It is impossible at present to do more than indicate that the "diphtheroid bacilli" are a large heterogeneous group, held together by morphological and superficial cultural similarity and largely consisting of saprophytes and probably harmless parasites on the human and animal body.

REFERENCES

ANDERSON, J. S., HAPPOLD, F. C., McLEOD, J. W., and THOMSON, J. G. J. Path. & Bacteriol., 1931, 34:667.

ANDREWES, *et al.* Diphtheria, Its Bacteriology, Pathology and Immunology, Medical Research Council, London, 1923.

BABES, V. Ztschr. f. Hyg., 1889, 5:173.

BAYNE-JONES, S. Newer Knowledge of Bacteriology and Immunology, Chicago, 1928, Chap. 56, p. 759.

BEHRING. Deutsche med. Wchnschr.. 1913, 39.

BRIEGER and BOER. Deutsche med. Wchnschr., 1896, 783.

BRIEGER and FRÄNKEL. Berl. klin. Wchnschr., 1889, 11:12.

BUNKER, J. W. M. J. Bacteriol., 1919, 4:379.

CLAUBERG, K. W. Zentralbl. f. Bakteriol., I Abt., 1929, 124:539; 1931, 130: 324.

COBBETT. Centralbl. f. Bakteriol., 1898.

CONRADI, H., and TROCH, P. München. med. Wchnschr., 1912, 59;1652.

COULTER, C. B., and STONE, F. M. Proc. Soc. Exper. Biol. & Med., 1930, 27:715.

——— J. Gen. Physiol., 1932, 15:629.

DAVIS, L., and FERRY, N. S. J. Bacteriol., 1919, 4:217.

DEICHER, H., and AGULNIK, P. Deutsche med. Wchnschr., 1927, 53:825.

EATON, M. D. J. Bacteriol., 1936, 31, 347, 367; 1937, 33:52; 1937, 34:139.

——— J. Immunol., 1936, 30:361; 1937, 33:419.

——— Recent Chemical Investigations of Bacterial Toxins. Bacteriol. Rev., 1938, 2, 3.

ERNST, P. Ztschr. f. Hyg., 1888, 4:25.

ESCHERICH, T. Aetiologie und Pathogenese der epidemischen Diphtherie, Wien, 1894.

FALK, I. S., and JENSEN, L. B. J. Bacteriol., 1928, 15:413, 421.

FORCE, J. N., and BEATTIE, M. I. Am. J. Hyg., 1922, 2:490.

GLENNY, A. T., and BARR, M. J. Path. & Bacteriol., 1931, 34:118.

GLENNY, A. T., BUTTLE, G. A. H., and STEVENS, M. F. J. Path. & Bacteriol., 1931, 34:267.

GLENNY, A. T., HOPKINS, and POPE. J. Path. & Bacteriol., 1924, 27:261.

GLENNY, A. T., POPE, C. C., WADDINGTON, H., and WALLACE, U. J. Path. & Bacteriol., 1926, 29:38.

GOLDBERGER. Treas. Dep. Pub. Health & Mar.-Hosp. Serv. U. S. Hyg. Lab. Bull., Wash., No. 101.

GRAHAM, A. H., MURPHREE, L. R., and GILL, D. G. J. Am. M. Ass., 1933, 100:1096.

GROSS, P. Proc. Soc. Biol. & Exper. Med., 1928–29, 26:696.

HAHN. Deutsche med. Wchnschr., 1912, 38:1366.

HARRISON. Am. J. Pub. Health, 1932, 22:7.

HARTLEY, P. Brit. J. Exper. Pathol., 1925, 6:112.

HARTLEY, P., and HARTLEY, O. J. Pathol. & Bacteriol., 1922, 25:458.

HAVENS, L. C., WELLS, D. M., and GRAHAM, A. H. Am. J. Pub. Health, 1932, 22:648.

HOFMANN-WELLENHOFF. Wien. med. Wchnschr., 1888, 38:66, 107.

J. Am. M. Ass., 1932, 98:1644; 99:227.

JONES, L. Proc. Soc. Exper. Biol. & Med., 1931, 28:883; 1932, 29:1133.

JUNGBLUT, C. W., and ZWEMER, R. L. Proc. Soc. Exper. Biol. & M., 1935, 32, 1229.

KELLY, J. L., and PORTER, A. J. Am. Ass., 1923, 81:734.

KING, C. G., and MENTON, M. L. J. Nutrition, 1935, 129:141.

KIRKBRIDE, M. B., BETHELSEN, K. C., and CLARK, R. F. J. Immunol., 1931, 21:1.

KLEBS, E. Verhandl. d. Kong. f. innere Med., II Abt., Wiesbaden, 1883, 139.

KNAPP. J. Med. Research, 1904, 7.

KOULIKOFF, V., and SMIRNOFF, P. Ann. de l'Inst. Pasteur, 1927, 41:1166.

KUSCHBERT and NEISSER. Deutsche med. Wchnschr., 1884, 10:321, 341.

LOCKE, A., and MAIN, E. R. J. Infect. Dis., 1930, 46:393; 1931, 48:419.

LÖFFLER, F. Centralbl. f. Bakteriol., I Abt., 1887, 2:105; 1890.

—— Mitt. a. d. Kaiserl. Gsndhtsamte., 1884, 2:421.

LYMAN, C. M., and KING, C. G. J. Pharmacol., 1936, 56:209.

MacCALLUM. Textbook of Pathology, Philadelphia, 1916.

MADSEN, T. Handb. d. Techn. u. Methodik d. Immunitätsforsch., 1909, 2:91.

MUELLER, J. H. J. Bacteriol., 1937, 34:153, 163, 381, 429; 1938, 36:499.

NEILL, J. M., et al. J. Exper. M., 1929, 49:33.

—— J. Infect. Dis., 1929, 44:150, 224, 308.

—— J. Immunol., 1930, 18:437, 455; 19:109; 1931, 20:25.

NEWSHOLM. Epidemic Diphtheria, London, 1898.

PAPPENHEIMER, A. M. JR. J. Biol. Chem., 1937, 120, 543.

—— and JOHNSON, S. J. Brit. J. Exper. Pathol., 1936, 17:335, 342; 1937, 18:239.

—— and ROBINSON, E. S. J. Immunol., 1937, 32:291.

PARK, W. H. Am. J. Dis. Child., 1931, 42:1439.

PARK, W. H., and SCHRODER, M. C. Am. J. Pub. Health, 1932, 22:7.

PARK, W. H., and WILLIAMS, A. J. Exper. M., 1896, 1:164.

PARK and ZINGHER. J. Am. M. Ass., 1915, 5:2216;1916, 6:431.

POPE, C. G., and PINFIELD, S. Brit. J. Exper. Pathol., 1932, 13:60.

RAMON, G. Compt. rend. Soc. de biol., 1922, 86:661, 813.

—— Ann. de l'Inst. Pasteur, 1923, 37:1001; 1939, 62:5.

RAMON and DEBRÉ. Presse méd., April, 1932.

ROSENAU and ANDERSON. J. Infect. Dis., 1907, 4.

ROUX, E., and YERSIN, A. Ann. de l'Inst. Pasteur, 1888, 2:629; 1889, 3:273; 1890, 4:385.

SCHICK. Über Diphtherimmunität., Wiesbaden, 1910.

SCHREIBER. Cited from Behring, Deutsche med. Wchnschr., 1913, 39.

SMITH. J. Hyg., Cambridge, 1906, 6.

SMITH, M. L. J. Pathol. & Bacteriol., 1932, 35:663.

SMITH, T. J. Exper. M., 1899, 4:373.

SMITH, G. H., and JORDAN, E. F. J. Bacteriol., 1930, 20:25.

STONE, R. V., and WEIGEL, C. Am. J. Pub. Health, 1929, 19:1133.

TORRANCE, C. C. J. Biol. Chem., 1937, 121:31.

—— Proc. Soc. Exper. Biol. & M., 1937, 35:654.

USCHINSKY. Centralbl. f. Bakteriol., 1897, 21.

WADSWORTH, A. B., and WHEELER. J. Infect. Dis., 1928, 42:179.

WADSWORTH, A., QUIGLEY, J. J., and SICKLES, G. R. J. Infect. Dis., 1937, 61:237.

WADSWORTH, A., WHEELER, M. W., MENDEZ, L. J. Infect. Dis., 1938, 62:129.

WASSERMANN and PROSKAUER. Deutsche med. Wchnschr., 1891, 585.

WATSON, R. F., and WALLACE, U. J. Pathol. & Bacteriol., 1927, 27:289.

WELLS, D. M., GRAHAM, A. H., and HAVENS, L. C. Am. J. Pub. Health, 1932, 22:648.

WESBROOK, F. F., WILSON, F. B., and McDANIEL, O. Tr. Ass. Am. Physicians, 1900, 15:198.

WILCOX, H. L. J. Infect. Dis., 1922, 30:536.

YÜ, H. J. Bacteriol., 1930, 20:107.

ZINGHER and SOLETSKY. J. Infect. Dis., 1916, 17:54.

ZINSSER. Nelson's Loose-Leaf Medicine, Vol. IX, 205.

—— J. Med. Research, 1907, 17:277.

CHAPTER XXXI

THE TUBERCLE BACILLUS

Order: *Actinomycetales* Buchanan. Family: *Mycobacteriaceae* Chester. Genus: *Mycobacterium* Lehmann and Neumann. Species: *Mycobacterium tuberculosis* Lehmann and Neumann.

In view of the clinical manifestations of tuberculosis, it is not surprising that the infectious nature of the disease had been suspected for centuries before the bacterial cause was discovered. Fracastorius (1484–1553) had remarkably modern ideas concerning its transmission. Reproduction of tuberculosis by inoculation of tuberculous material was accomplished by Klencke in 1843. The numerous careful experiments of Villemin in 1865 demonstrated convincingly that the disease could be transmitted by inoculation of animals with tuberculous tissue and exudates. The first view of the "virus" postulated by Villemin seems to have been gained by Baumgarten who saw the bacillus in tissue sections. Robert Koch isolated the tubercle bacillus in 1882. In addition to demonstrating the bacillus in tuberculous tissues from various sources, Koch obtained pure cultures of the organism, reproduced the disease by the injection of these organisms into animals and recovered the organisms from the experimentally produced lesion. Koch's masterly work established beyond doubt the etiological relationship of the bacillus to the disease.

The tubercle bacillus is one member of a large group of organisms which have in common certain morphological features and, when stained, an ability to withstand decolorization by acid alcohol. On account of this property the organisms are called "acid-fast." In their manner of growth, occasional branching, and in the broad features of the lesions they produce in animals there are many indications of a relationship of these acid-fast bacteria to the actinomycetes. For these reasons they are correctly placed in the order: *Actinomycetales*. The generic name, *Mycobacterium*, is not synonymous with acid-fastness, as there are acid-fast forms in other species than this and some of the mycobacteria are not always acid-fast. The term was introduced by Lehmann and Neumann in 1896 in recognition of the fungus-like characteristics of these organisms. It is gaining currency as the generic name for tubercle bacilli and related bacteria.

The organisms in this group are numerous and varied. Some are strictly parasitic and pathogenic for man and animals. Many species are saprophytic in and upon man and animals and in the soil. The acid-fast bacteria parasitic upon animals have special characteristics sufficiently distinctive to serve for differentiation. These are usually referred to as *types of tubercle bacilli*, although some authorities set them apart as species. Two main groups of parasitic forms exist: the tubercle bacilli of warm-blooded animals and the tubercle bacilli of cold-blooded animals. These may be further subdivided into types according to the animal serving as the most usual host. For example, the organisms from tuberculosis in man, cattle and birds are sufficiently different to be recognizable as human, bovine and avian types. Those of fish and reptiles have other distinctive characteristics. Intermediate forms exist, showing that the relationships of these organisms are complex. We shall discuss here particularly the human and bovine types of tubercle bacilli, and comment briefly on the most important related organisms, chiefly a few of the nonpathogenic varieties. In the following chapter the acid-fast bacteria associated with leprosy and Johne's disease will be described.

For a discussion of the variability of diseases caused by mycobacteria the reader is referred to the general review published by Long in 1938. In these diseases the basic tissue responses to the presence of the acid-fast organisms are basically similar, characterized by proliferation and accumulations of monocytes, which become "epithelioid cells," by focal lesions which become necrotic and "caseated," and, as a rule, by long-continued chronic processes.

Morphology.—Tubercle bacilli appear as slender rods, 2 to 4 μ in length, 0.2 to 0.5 μ in width. Their ends are usually rounded. The rods may be straight or slightly curved; their diameters may be uniform throughout; more often however, they appear beaded and irregularly stained. The beaded appearance is due to different causes. Unstained spaces may occur along the body of the bacillus, especially in old cultures. These are generally regarded as vacuoles. The bodies of the bacilli, on the other hand, may bulge slightly here and there, often in three or four places, showing oval or rounded knobs which stain with great depth and are very resistant to decolorization. These thickenings were formerly regarded as spores, but in view of the fact that the bacilli are not more resistant against heat and disinfectants than other vegetative forms, this interpretation is probably incorrect. The bacilli are said to possess a cell membrane which confers upon them their resistance against drying and entrance of stains. This membrane contains most of the waxy substance which can be extracted from the cultures.

Various observers, following Metchnikoff, Mafucci and Klein, have demonstrated branched forms of the tubercle bacillus. These observations, variously extended and confirmed (Lehmann and Neumann), make it probable that *B. tuberculosis* is closely related to the actinomycetes.

Staining.—Tubercle bacilli do not stain easily with the ordinary aniline dyes; to these they are made permeable only by long exposure or by heating of the staining solution. Once stained, however, the dye is tenaciously retained in spite of treatment with alcohol and strong acids. For this reason, this bacillus, together with some other bacteria to be mentioned later, is spoken of as acid-fast. The acid-fast nature of the bacillus seems to depend upon the waxy substances contained in it, and has furnished the basis for differential staining methods. All the staining methods devised for the recognition of the tubercle bacillus thus depend upon the use of an intensely penetrating staining solution, followed by vigorous decolorization which deprives all but the acid-fast group of their color. Counterstains of any of the weaker dyes may then be used to stain the decolorized elements. One of the first of the staining solutions to be of practical use was the aniline water gentian violet solution of Ehrlich (11 c.c saturated alcoholic gentian violet to 89 c.c. 5 per cent aniline water). This dye, although of sufficient penetrating power, has the disadvantage of deteriorating rapidly and has in practice been almost entirely displaced by Ziehl's carbolfuchsin solution.

(Fuchsin 1 gram in 10 c.c. alcohol absolute, added to 90 c.c 5 per cent carbolic.) This staining solution, known as the Ziehl-Neelsen stain, is the one now in general use.

The formulae and procedures for the preparation and use of tne stains and media referred to in this chapter will be found in the section on technic.

Tubercle bacilli in very young culture are often not acid-fast and it is not always possible to demonstrate acid-fast bacilli in pus from cold abscesses in sputum, in serous exudates, and in granulomatous lesions of the lymph nodes which can be shown by animal inoculation to be tuberculous. Much demonstrated in such material gram-positive granules which lay singly, in short chains or in irregular clumps, and which he believed to be non-acid-fast tubercle bacilli. He found similar granules in cultures of tubercle bacilli which showed on further incubation numerous acid-fast bacillary forms. His work has been repeatedly confirmed. Their demonstration is not, however, of diagnostic value, as other bacilli form granules of the same appearance. Small rods and splinters are also found which stain by Gram's method, but not by carbolfuchsin (Liebermeister). A great deal of interest attaches to these granules because of the possibility that they may represent a minute coccoidal or filtrable stage in the life cycle of the tubercle bacillus.

To find Much's granules, smears or sections are steamed in a solution of methyl violet B.N. (10 c.c. of saturated alcoholic solution of the dye in 100 c.c. of distilled water containing 2 per cent phenol). They are then treated with Gram's iodine solution one to five minutes; 5 per cent nitric acid one minute; 3 per cent hydrochloric acid ten seconds; absolute alcohol and acetone equal parts, until decolorized. The granules may be stained by other modifications of Gram's method. Weiss has devised a combination stain. One part of Much's methyl violet is mixed with three parts of Ziehl's carbolfuchsin and filtered; slides are stained for twenty-four to forty-eight hours in the mixture. They are then decolorized as in Much's method and counterstained with Bismarck brown or safranin 1 per cent. Both acid-fast and gram-positive forms are stained by this method and in the red may be seen blue-black granules.

While the acid-fast group of bacteria is composed of a number of organisms to be mentioned later, a few only of these offer difficulties of differentiation from the tubercle bacillus. Those to be considered practically are the bacillus of leprosy and that of smegma. The latter bacillus, because of its distribution, is not infrequently found to contaminate feces, urine, or even sputum, and it is sometimes desirable to apply to suspected specimens one or the other of the stains devised for the differentiation of the smegma bacillus from *B. tuberculosis*. The one most frequently employed is that of Pappenheim. The preparations are stained in hot carbolfuchsin as before; the carbolfuchsin is then poured off without washing and the preparation immersed in solution made by saturating a 1 per cent alcoholic solution of rosolic acid with methylene blue and adding 20 per cent of glycerin. In such preparations tubercle bacilli remain red, smegma bacilli usually appear blue.

Tubercle bacilli are gram-positive.

Isolation.—Details of procedures useful for the detection and isolation of tubercle bacilli will be found in the section on technic. These methods are based upon the following principles.

1. *Detection in Stained Smears.*—The acid-fast technic should be applied. By this procedure the tubercle bacilli stained a certain color, usually red, are differentiated

by treatment of the smear with a solution of acid-alcohol and subsequent application of dye of another color. The acid-fast organisms retain the original dye. Sometimes it is impossible to find tubercle bacilli by this means in material known to contain them. Apparently there must be present about 100,000 organisms per c.c. before the probability of finding them in smears becomes significantly large. *Concentration* of the material by centrifuging the specimen after digestion of mucus and cells with acid, sodium hydroxide or antiformin increases the chances of finding the bacilli in the stained sediment. This type of concentration and digestion method is applicable to sputum, exudates, urine and feces. It can be so conducted that the tubercle bacilli are not killed while other bacteria are destroyed. Hence material containing tubercle bacilli and other bacteria can be largely purified by treating it with acid or alkali, as in Petroff's, Corper's and Hohn's methods.

2. *Detection by Isolation in Culture.*—The untreated tuberculous material if not contaminated with other bacteria can be used for direct isolation of the organism by cultivation on suitable media. Usually, however, the material contains a variety of bacteria. The sediment obtained after treatment with acid or alkali can be planted on medium and colonies of tubercle bacilli can be obtained from such cultures on gentian violet egg medium or gentian violet potato, as in Corper's or Hohn's method or the well known method of Petroff. Cultures are sometimes positive when both smears and guinea-pig inoculations fail to disclose the presence of tubercle bacilli in tuberculous material (Cunningham and Cummings).

3. *Detection by Inoculation of Animals.*—This is a time-honored method. The guinea-pig, susceptible to both human and bovine types, is used routinely for this purpose. Varying amounts of material may be injected into the animal. It is usually best to inject the sputum, exudate, urine or spinal fluid into the subcutaneous tissue of the groin. Intraperitoneal injections may cause the rapid death of the animal from intoxication or pyrogenic infection. If the material does not contain too numerous or too virulent pyrogenic organisms, staphylococci or streptococci, it can be injected without purification. If these bacteria are very numerous, as in sputum, feces and some specimens of urine, it is best to treat the material with 4 per cent solution of NaOH for thirty minutes at 37° C., neutralize with N/1 HCL, obtain the sediment by centrifugation and inject this sediment.

Guinea-pigs thus inoculated may be killed when ulcers, swollen regional lymph nodes or other indications suggesting tuberculosis have developed clearly. The usual procedure is to kill the animals for examination about six weeks after inoculation. It is better to be guided by the results of tuberculin tests in determining the proper time to kill an animal in which the superficial lesions are not conspicuous.

The organism can be isolated in cultures taken from these animals.

Cultivation.—Tubercle bacilli are not easily cultivated. The first isolations by Koch were made upon coagulated blood serum from tuberculous tissue.

Once isolated, the bacilli are best grown on *glycerin egg medium* which is described in the section on media. On this medium colonies of the human bacilli begin to appear after six or eight days as yellowish white moist crust-like flakes.

On *blood serum* at 37.5° C., colonies become visible at the end of eight to fourteen days. They appear as small, dry, scaly spots with corrugated surfaces. After three or four weeks, these join, covering the surface as a dry, whitish, wrinkled membrane.

Coagulated dog serum is regarded by Theobald Smith as a favorable medium for the growth of tubercle bacilli.

Slants of *agar*, to which the *whole rabbit's blood* has been added in quantities of from 1 to 2 c.c. to each tube, make an excellent medium.

Cultivation methods were simplified by the discovery by Roux and Nocard that glycerin facilitates cultivation. Upon *glycerin agar* (glycerin 3 to 6 per cent), at 37.5° C., colonies become visible at the end of from ten days to two weeks.

Glycerin bouillon (made of beef or veal with peptone 1 per cent, glycerin 6 per cent, slightly alkaline) is a favorable medium. It should be filled, in shallow layers, into wide-mouthed flasks, since oxygen is essential. Transplants to this medium should be made by carefully floating flakes of the culture upon the surface. In this medium, the bacilli will spread out upon the surface, at first as a thin, opaque, floating membrane. This rapidly thickens into a white, wrinkled, or granular layer, spreading over the entire surface of the fluid in from four to six weeks. Later, portions of the membrane sink. In old cultures, the membranes become yellowish. These cultures emit a peculiar aromatic odor. Cultures when first grown on solid media are a little difficult to start on glycerin broth. It is best to grow them for a few weeks on egg or glycerin egg slants containing condensation water. When growth has begun over the surface of the condensation water, this pellicle can be picked up with a bent loop without allowing it to immerse in the fluid and this floated on the surface of glycerin broth. *Glycerin potato* forms a favorable culture medium for the bacillus.

FIG. 39.—CULTURE OF BACILLUS TUBERCULOSIS IN FLASK OF GLYCERIN BOUILLON.

In cultures, tubercle bacilli are *aerobic*. Best growth is obtained under conditions allowing free access of oxygen of the air. It has been determined (Novy and Soule) that the oxygen from 500 c.c. of air is required for complete "heavy" growth of one slant culture of tubercle bacilli. Wax plugs placed in tubes, therefore, inhibit or reduce growth by restricting the oxygen supply. These plugs should be pierced. Rubber stoppers admitting a small amount of air are better than paraffin plugs.

The optimum temperature for growth of the human or bovine type is 37.5° C. Temperatures below 30° C. and above 42° C. inhibit growth. Growth of an acid-fast organism at room temperature is regarded as excluding it from the group of pathogenic tubercle bacilli of man and warm-blooded animals.

There have been many studies of the *fermentation of carbohydrates* by *Mycobacteria* (Merrill) with particular reference to tubercle bacilli (Weinzirl). The newer studies have added little to the early fundamental observation of Theobald Smith that the reaction curves of human and bovine tubercle bacilli growing in *glycerin broth* are often distinct. The human type produces a slight degree of acidity while the reaction in the culture of bovine bacillus becomes slightly alkaline. Probably all tubercle bacilli produce at first slight acidity in glycerin broth. Bovine cultures cause a reversion to alkalinity, while in the human type cultures the reaction may remain acid.

Variability and Types.—The tubercle bacilli pathogenic for man and cattle are closely related. The types producing tuberculosis in birds, fish, frogs and turtles have sufficiently distinctive properties to set them apart. The question of the existence of intermediate strains and the possibility of the transformation of one form into another is large and vexed. For a broad discussion of these and other relationships the reader is referred to Griffith's extensive treatment of the subject. We shall discuss some of the bacteriological phases of the situation here and consider questions of pathogenicity later.

Koch expressed the opinion that bovine tubercle bacilli were different from the human type, especially as regards their ability to produce infection in man. Theobald Smith, who had pointed out differences in the cultures on glycerin and differences in rapidity of growth (the bovine type growing more slowly than the human), was one of the first of many who have shown that both types are pathogenic for both kinds of animals. Differences exist, however, as we shall show (Aronson). Virulence of all tubercle bacilli diminishes on prolonged cultivation on artificial media. One of the strains which has undergone this change, the bovine strain known as B.C.G. (Bacille Calmette-Guérin) is used for prophylactic active immunization in man.

The modern studies of *dissociation* have thrown a great deal of light upon variation phenomena among tubercle bacilli and other mycobacteria. The strains split readily into S or smooth types, R or rough types, and many intermediate forms. The S colonies may be smooth, regular, and hemispherical like staphylococcus colonies, or heaped up, cerebriform, umbilicated colonies with glistening surfaces. The R colonies, larger and flatter, are crinkled, granular or nodular, with fringed and serrated edges. Some of these colony forms are shown in Figure 8. Others are well depicted in the illustrated paper by Petroff and Steenken on the instability of the tubercle bacillus. By the use of proper media transformations from S to R and the reverse can be brought about. The S forms are considerably more virulent than the R forms, and, in fact, some of the R type cultures derived from pathogenic strains are avirulent. Petroff and his associates and others have described dissociation of the B.C.G. culture, finding the S forms virulent. This has been confirmed by some and denied by others. Its significance will be more apparent in our discussion of vaccination. Kahn and Schwarzkopf have obtained R and S forms of avian tubercle bacilli from cultures derived from a single cell. Important studies of variation and dissociation of tubercle bacilli have been published by Reed, who found that the S (smooth) forms contained antigens not present in the R (rough) forms.

Life cycles of tubercle bacilli have been worked out by various investigators who have attempted to arrange in sequence by continuous or interrupted observation the pleomorphic stages of this organism. In our chapters on variability and bacterial morphology and reproduction we have discussed these findings. The studies of Kahn provide evidence that the rods break up into granules (gonidia?) and that from these granules develop first delicate rods and finally the usual forms of the organism. Mellon, in a series of reports, has described a life cycle of tubercle bacilli in which there are stages represented by non-acid-fast diphtheroids, coccoids and granules. The granular stage may constitute the filter passing phase of the organism which Mellon and Calmette are certain exist. Many of these observations require extended confirmation, although there is considerable evidence supporting the belief in pleomorphism and filtrability of tubercle bacilli. The life cycle sequences are not convincing, and, as a matter of fact, this subject is in too controversial a stage to permit anyone to hold a fixed opinion on the merits of the various reports and points of view. Confirmation of these findings are lacking.

Vera and Rettger studied the cellular variation of tubercle bacilli in microculture by means of hanging block preparations which permitted observation of single cells or microcolonies over considerable periods of time. Morphological variants were induced readily and in great diversity by alteration of food supply and oxygen tension. These variants included club forms, granules, coccoid, diphtheroid and branching cells, and spore-like bodies. Branching cells grew and segmented into bacilli of the usual form. The usual method of reproduction was fission. These investigators did not find any evidence of reproduction by granules or by filtrable forms.

Chemistry.—An immense amount of work has been done in attempts to determine the chemical composition of tubercle bacilli. In 1926, Long published a review of what was known at that time about the nature of the proteins, carbohydrates, lipoids, waxes and other substances of which tubercle bacilli are composed. Wells and Long again reviewed the chemistry of tuberculosis in 1932. A great advance was made by Anderson and his associates particularly in the isolation and study of the lipoids, fatty acids and waxes of these organisms. The fractions studied were phosphatide, acetone-soluble fat and wax. The bacillary lipoids differed from the usual plant and animal lipins. A solid saturated hexacosanic acid called phthioic acid was isolated. This had special effects upon animals. A stable amorphous unsaponifiable wax was obtained which was acid-fast and was apparently the substance in the bacilli which gave them their special staining property. Sterols were not found.

Biological tests of these fractions, chiefly by Sabin, showed that the phosphatide produced tubercle and that this property was due to phthioic acid. The unsaponifiable wax stimulated the production of undifferentiated connective tissue cells, while the phthioic acid was responsible for the proliferation of epithelioid cells. Plasma cells appeared as a characteristic response to tuberculoprotein. Sabin found that the tuberculopolysaccharides were chemotactic and toxic to neutrophil leukocytes. These studies are the foundation of what Long has called the chemical pathogenesis of tuberculosis.

Products of Growth—Tuberculins.—Tubercle bacilli do not liberate a soluble toxin. The products liberated in autolysis have the effects of producing tubercles and inflammation as we have noted in the preceding paragraph on the chemistry of these organisms. Small amounts of the filtrates of glycerin broth cultures and of various preparations of tubercle bacilli have no effect or relatively slight effect upon normal animals. When injected into tuberculous animals, these materials have powerful and characteristic actions. Phenomena of allergy are conspicuous in tuberculosis and are elicited readily by a large variety of culture products called *tuberculins*. The properties and uses of these substances are so important and extensive that a special section of this chapter will be given to a description of them.

Resistance.—The life of cultures, kept in favorable environment, is from two to eight months, varying to some extent with the nature of the culture medium. The viability of the bacilli in sputum is of great hygienic importance. In moist sputum they may remain alive and virulent for as long as six weeks, in dried sputum for more than two months.

Five per cent carbolic acid kills the bacilli in a few minutes. Used for sputum disinfection, where the bacilli are protected, complete disinfection requires five to six hours. Bichloride of mercury is not very efficient for sputum because of the formation of albuminate of mercury. Direct sunlight kills in a few hours. In general, acid-fast bacteria have the same susceptibility to heat as other non-spore forming bacteria but because of their waxy components are more resistant to chemicals.

TUBERCULOSIS

Pathogenicity.—The tubercle bacillus gives rise in men and susceptible animals to specific inflammations which are so characteristic that a diagnosis of tuberculosis may be made by histological examination, even though tubercle bacilli themselves are not found. These foci, known as tubercles, were first studied in detail by Baumgarten, and, since then, have been the object of many pathological investigations. The lesions are fundamentally alike wherever they occur, though in their detailed histological structure they may vary somewhat according to the tissue in which they appear. They begin as microscopic agglomerations of concentrically arranged monocytes, which become "epithelioid" cells. These microscopic tubercles may gradually enlarge individually, or they may grow by coalescence with neighboring tubercles. Characteristic giant cells, with peripherally arranged nuclei, appear near the centers of the tubercles and in these giant cells the tubercle bacilli are usually found. As the tubercles grow in size, the central mass becomes necrotic. Fluid pus does not form, and the centers assume a grumose and friable condition which is generally described as caseous or cheesy. Such tubercles may result from the injection of dead bacilli, as well as living ones. The cheesy degeneration may be in part due to the toxic action of the substances of the tubercle bacilli and in part to pressure and lack of vascularization. It is astonishing how difficult it is to find tubercle bacilli histologically in such lesions. This may be due perhaps to the fact that, owing to degeneration, most of the tubercle bacilli have lost their acid-fastness. If tubercles heal, as they often do, they undergo a fibrinous change, are surrounded by connective tissue and, if central necrosis has begun at the time that healing sets in, calcification results. For more detailed descriptions we refer the reader to the textbooks of pathology.

There has been a great deal of discussion concerning the manner in which tubercle bacilli enter the human and animal body in the course of spontaneous infection. A thorough discussion of this will be found in Calmette's book, *L'Infection bacillaire et la tuberculose.* Calmette believed that when a tubercle bacillus "is deposited on the surface of the skin or a mucous membrane or is introduced into the healthy body by another route" it becomes the prey of leukocytes which carry it into the lymphatic circulation and into the blood. The leukocytic enzymes are not capable of digesting the organism and eventually the organism is deposited in the lymphatics when the leukocyte degenerates.

Tubercle bacilli may remain latent in the body, in lymph nodes, especially, for long periods. It appears that the point of entrance of the tubercle bacilli into the body may be through the tonsils, and secondarily thence through the lymphatics, then to other organs. Pulmonary infection may be either by direct inhalation or indirectly through the lymphatics. Calmette believed that actual direct infection of the lung by inhaled bacilli is relatively rare. This, however, is not in agreement with the bulk of evidence, and direct inhalation is probably the most common manner of invasion.

According to the researches of Bartel and many others, it appears that direct infection through the apparently uninjured mucous membrane of the intestinal tract may take place, and after such entrance the bacilli may be carried by the lymphatics and blood to the lungs and other parts of the body. According to Calmette, in all susceptible animals, man included, and in all its varieties of localization, tuberculosis in the large majority of cases originates in a primary infection of the lymphatics which takes its origin by entrance of the tubercle bacilli through the mucous membranes of the digestive tract, chiefly the mucous membranes of the mouth, pharynx and intestine. This is the extreme view, but one that is favored in addition to Calmette by von Behring, Ravenel and others.

Opie states that first infection with tuberculosis may occur either by way of the lungs or the gastro-intestinal tract, and the occurrence of one lesion tends to prevent the other.

In man, tuberculosis is most common in the lungs where it usually starts in the apices. The apical situation of early tubercles is not entirely explained. A number of theories have been advanced, most of them based on anatomical reasoning. In the lungs there may be a miliary distribution of tubercles or, by coalescence of these, large areas of consolidation may occur, which are then spoken of as phthisis. Extension to the pleura is common.

Although pulmonary infections constitute the very large majority of cases of tuberculosis in adult life, this is not strictly true of childhood. In statistics quoted by Calmette for Europe, it was found by Hamburger and Sulka that of 160 cases in children there were only 50 per cent pulmonary lesions. According to Holt's statistics for New York, however, of 119 autopsies of tuberculous children, pulmonary lesions were found in 99 per cent. In 1515 autopsies studied by Comby during fifteen years, involvement of the tracheo-bronchial lymph nodes was found in all. Aside from the pulmonary and lymphatic infections, tuberculosis may occur in practically all other parts of the body.

Tuberculosis of the skin or lupus is a common disease. Involvement of the bones and joints may occur, and according to Fraser may in many cases occur without any previous tuberculosis. Tuberculous meningitis is not infrequent in children, and is always fatal.

The liver may be the site of tubercles, and tuberculosis of the spleen has been observed though it is not particularly common. The kidneys and the genito-urinary system are frequently involved, and the suprarenal gland may be tuberculous, and in this case may lead to a condition spoken of as Addison's disease.

In the intestines themselves, various forms of tuberculosis have been described. It appears that the only parts of the body in which tuberculosis is not common are the muscle tissues themselves, and the wall of the stomach.

Rosenberger has reported finding tubercle bacilli in the circulating blood of all cases of human tuberculosis which he examined. This announcement aroused much interest and has led to many investigations by other workers. Rosenberger's results were obtained by morphological examinations of smears of citrated blood taken from the patients, dried upon slides and laked with distilled water. Many other observers have failed to confirm Rosenberger's results. Anderson examined 47 cases in which tubercle bacilli were found in the sputum and 1 case of joint tuberculosis. In none of these 48 cases was he able to obtain tubercle bacilli, either by morphological examination or by guinea-pig inoculation. Brem subsequently found that laboratory distilled water may frequently contain acid-fast saprophytes—a fact which may account in many cases for errors when morphological examination alone is relied upon and blood examined by the technic of Rosenberger. This, too, is suggested by the finding of acid-fast bacilli in the blood of perfectly healthy individuals. Therefore, although the bacilli may be present in the blood in a certain number of cases it does not seem likely that they are so distributed in anything like the high percentages found by Rosenberger, Löwenstein has reported frequent isolations of tubercle bacilli from the blood. His results have not been confirmed.

Although, therefore, in patients suffering from tuberculosis, the presence of the tubercle bacilli in the blood is generally slight or intermittent, there may be times when large numbers of tubercle bacilli are thrown into the blood stream, and, according to the manner and quantity thus distributed, secondary foci or general miliary tuberculosis may occur.

B. tuberculosis (typus humanus) is pathogenic for guinea-pigs, less markedly for rabbits, and still less so for dogs. It is slightly pathogenic for cattle, a question discussed more extensively below.

Secondary Infection.—An important consideration in the symptomatology and prognosis of pulmonary tuberculosis is the fact that on the basis of the chronic inflammatory condition of bronchi and alveoli in the neighborhood of tuberculous processes in the bronchiectatic cavities and perhaps in cavities communicating with bronchioles, masses of bacteria of various species may accumulate and habitually lodge. Staphylococci, streptococci, gram-negative cocci, and frequently influenza bacilli may be present in such cases and materially contribute to the illness of the patient by superimposing acute and subacute inflammatory processes upon the tuberculous one.

Incidence, Mortality and Transmission.—Until the turn of the century tuberculosis was probably the most common infectious disease and led the list of causes of death. Statistics gathered from autopsy records indicated that upwards of 90 per cent of all persons had been infected with tubercle bacilli. This impression was confirmed by the great frequency of positive tuberculin reactions in adults. With a death rate of 195 per 100,000 in the Original Death Registration States and a rate above 220 in the general population tuberculosis in 1900 was still the chief cause of death. Since then its mortality has steadily declined and the disease is now at the bottom of this list. The estimated death rate in the Original Death Registration States for the year 1938 is estimated by the Metropolitan Life Insurance Company at about 43 per 100,000. The decline has been almost linear, giving a projected death rate of 37 per 100,000 for the year 1940.

The incidence or morbidity can be estimated only approximately. Kraus believes that about one-third of the population is infected.

Although there has been much discussion concerning the different methods of infection, there seems to be very little doubt at the present time that inhalation is the most common means of human infection. In coughing, expectoration and sneezing, small droplets of fluid in which all kinds of micro-organisms are found, are sprayed into the air, and these may be deposited upon the mucous membranes of people in close contact with the disease. The striking distance of such droplet infection is about three feet, but is, as Kober points out, particularly dangerous because the bacilli thus enter the respiratory passages directly from body to body. In addition to this, the tubercle bacilli may remain alive in dust sufficiently dry to be blown about by drafts and winds. Although the bacilli are not spore-bearers, their acid-fast nature renders them somewhat more resistant to desiccation and sunlight than are most other germs.

Next to direct inhalation, the most frequent method of transmission is probably through the digestive tract. Such infection may take place by direct contamination of food from the expectoration and saliva of consumptives or by indirect infection of food, and milk, through the agency of fingers, flies, etc.

Milk Infection.—After Theobald Smith had called attention to the differences between tubercle bacilli of bovine and human origins, the same question was taken up by Ravenel, who confirmed this and presented evidence as early as 1901 that the bovine bacillus has a high degree of pathogenicity for man, especially in the early years of life. The general public has probably very little idea of the frequency of tuberculosis in cattle. The Public Health Service bacteriologists in Washington revealed 6.72 per cent of samples of market milk infected with tubercle bacilli. This percentage is probably lower than that naturally found in districts with less dairy supervision, and in some of the poorer farm districts the cattle tuberculosis situation was appalling. Through control measures based on tuberculin test and slaughter of positive reactors in herds of cattle, the incidence of tuberculosis among dairy cattle have been greatly reduced.

Von Behring believed that a large percentage of all cases of tuberculosis originated in childhood from infection through the intestinal tract. He determined that tubercle bacilli may penetrate the intestinal mucosa without causing lesions. Behring's contention raised a question which is intimately bound up with the problem of the virulence of bovine tubercle bacilli for human beings. His claims are now known to have been too sweeping.

The only reliable method of approaching this problem has been to isolate the tubercle bacilli from diseased human beings and determine for each case whether the organism obtained belonged to the human or bovine type. These types can be differentiated definitely by cultural characteristics and pathogenicity, and it is not likely that the type changes during the sojourn in the human body. Granted this permanence of type, it is naturally of much value in revealing the source of an infection, to determine whether or not a human being is harboring a bacillus of the human type or one of the bovine type.

The following conclusions may be drawn from available evidence: Human adults are relatively insusceptible to bovine infection. Such infection can take place, but is unusual. Below sixteen years of age the human race is relatively more susceptible and up to this age the danger of milk infection is unquestionably great, this source accounting for about one-third of the cases. Below five years the danger is greatest. There is no doubt as to the dangers of milk infection. To avoid them requires the most rigid sanitary control of milk supplies.

Contact Infection.—Kober also calls attention to the fact that one must not be deceived into believing that childhood is the only really dangerous age for infection, and quotes the results of a French committee which, in a small group carefully investigated, found 64 cases in which the disease was transmitted from husband to wife, 43 cases in which it was transmitted from wife to husband, 38 cases transmitted from brother to sister, 19 from mother to child, 16 from other relatives, and in 33 cases it was traced to people who were not relations, but with whom the patient had been in communication. He also quotes Zasetsky who reports the case of a tuberculous woman who, in the course of eleven years married three husbands who had been previously healthy. The first one died of tuberculosis seven years after marriage, the second three years later, and the third at the time of the report had the disease, the wife in the meantime having died of tuberculosis. Contact infection and reinfection occurs occasionally among students and nurses exposed to tuberculous patients.

Infection in the Dusty Trades.—That tubercle bacilli may be conveyed in dust has been indicated, but there are other means by which inhalation of dust may favor tuberculosis by virtue of the irritant properties of inhaled dust in predisposing the lung to infection. Attention to the dangers of trades in which dust is an habitual environmental factor has been particularly emphasized by Winslow and Greenberg and by Gardner. Sommerfeld, whom we quote from Kober, made a statistical study in which he showed that in the population of Berlin, the average tuberculosis death rate was 4.93 per one thousand. The rate in the nondusty trades was 2.39, and the dusty trades 5.2. He also states that the analysis of tuberculosis in the towns in Vermont where granite and marble cutting is carried on showed a tuberculosis rate of 2.2 per one thousand against a rate of 1.3 for the whole state, and Röpke is stated by the same writer to have shown that the mortality from tuberculosis of the population in the large cutlery center, Solingen, in Germany, was reduced from 5.4 per one thousand in 1885, to 1.8 in 1910, by measures aimed at the control of the dust in workrooms. A study by Drury shows that polishers and grinders in ax factories are subject to a death rate from pulmonary tuberculosis considerably above that of others in the same mill. In the two decades from 1900 to 1919, the polishers and grinders showed a death rate of 19 per one thousand as against 6.5 of the entire mill population, and between 1 and 2.4 of the general population of the district. Gardner has shown that silicosis specifically predisposes to infection with the tubercle bacillus.

In regard to the predisposing factors to tuberculous infection, many phases enter into the problem in this disease which exert a much less direct or perhaps negligible influence in connection with other infections. There can be no question about the fact that poverty, with its coincident crowding in living quarters, close personal contact at night, insufficient warmth, and particularly undernutrition and low fat diet, play a rôle of immense importance in tuberculosis. In no disease is prevention so intimately influenced by general sociological and economic improvement as in tuberculosis.

Wernicke in a study of the relationships of diseases to social conditions shows an almost direct relationship between the provision of air space and parks in cities to tuberculosis. The statistics of the influence of the World War upon tuberculosis have not yet become available for study, but it is important to note that at the present writing we are informed by sanitarians who have returned from Europe that the sanitary problem in the European states is very largely one of tuberculosis, and that the effects of prolonged undernutrition, especially upon children, during the World War years has resulted in an increased tuberculosis rate.

The question of the inheritance of tuberculosis has frequently been raised, and a large literature on this subject has accumulated, but an analysis of this literature seems to show that inheritance must be regarded as predisposition rather than as a method of direct infection. Children of tuberculous parents are likely to be more susceptible to tuberculosis and, of course, are exposed to tuberculosis more intimately during the early years of life than are children of normal parents. There is no direct proof that tuberculosis is transmitted from mother to the fetus.

Prevention.—As to preventive measures, we must refer the reader to special books on the subject since the problem is too large to be dealt with briefly with anything like completeness.

We may assume, as premises for prevention, that tuberculosis can be transmitted at all periods of life and that foci acquired in youth may be arrested but light up under conditions of general undernutrition, malnutrition, etc., etc., in later years. Infection may be direct from person to person, indirect through contaminated food, fomites, flies; through dust, and in childhood through milk from infected cattle. The most common manner of acquiring tuberculosis is by inhalation and, next to that, probably through the digestive tract.

The most important factor in the prevention of tuberculosis is education. This must elucidate the method of infection and the importance of the economic and sociological factors as they affect habits of food, sleep and fresh air.

Direct infection must be prevented by compulsory notification, care and disinfection of expectorations, isolation, at least as far as the possibilities of sputum infection are concerned, in the home, in hospitals, etc., with introduction of pocket sputum flasks and the other simple measures by which a well-controlled tuberculosis patient can avoid infecting others. The actual prevention of expectoration in public places, the protection of public drinking places, introduction of individual cups and public cleanliness in general; especial supervision of these conditions in places of public lodgment and public amusement in schools and public conveyances; introduction of vacuum cleaning, etc.

The public must be educated in knowing that tuberculosis is a curable disease, provided that the diagnosis is made early, and clinical facilities must be arranged in cities so that accurate diagnosis in the early stages may be made and proper fresh air and nutritional care instituted if necessary, at public expense. In our cities, roofs, playgrounds, parks, etc., should be provided for school children. Summer care of children living in the crowded districts must be developed on a more generous and more important scale. The nutrition of school children in the public schools must be supervised and subsidized so that no child in a civilized community should suffer at any time from undernutrition.

An idea of the far-reaching organization which has become necessary in the campaign for the reduction of tuberculosis may be obtained from a tabulation of the various activities included in the state program of the Massachusetts Department of Public Health as published in the Commonwealth by the Health Commissioner Eugene Kelley in 1922:

> State sanatoria for the care of early and of late cases
> Open-air schools for tuberculous children in the early stages
> Dispensaries in towns of over 10,000 for the discovery and supervision of pulmonary tuberculosis
> Consultation clinics offering the services of specialists for early diagnosis
> Examination clinics for the examination of school children who are underweight and anemic
> Public health nursing for follow-up work connected with the above-mentioned institutions
> Home visiting and instruction of individuals and families in home care

Add to this the efforts to improve housing conditions, supervise public nutrition, playgrounds and parks, investigation of economic factors in homes, factories, shops, etc., education in hygiene, and an adequate supply of well-trained practitioners of medicine who may possess skill in early diagnosis and an appreciation of their public health responsibilities, and we are confronted with a task which infiltrates every byway of community activities. It is a gratifying and no less astonishing fact that so much has been accomplished.

The management of dairies is a difficult matter. Tuberculosis is very common in cattle. Burke estimates that from 6 to 15 per cent of the samples of raw market milk showed infection, and he believes that from 5 to 30 per cent of cattle are infected. The chief methods of protection consist in the establishment of accredited herds by tuberculin test and suitable economic compensation, and by pasteurization. The milk is held at 140° F. for thirty minutes, which Burke states means that the milk should leave the holder at an average of at least 142.5° F. Efficient methods should be combined with a periodical veterinary inspection.

THE TUBERCULINS

In the paragraphs on the chemistry and products of growth of tubercle bacilli we have given a brief outline of the modern investigations which are tending to show that specific cellular reactions follow the injection of various fractions and products of these organisms into normal animals. The products are toxic and the protein fractions and haptene polysaccharide combinations are moderately antigenic. They are not, however, soluble toxins in the sense of the word used in reference to diphtheria or tetanus toxin. Abscesses and tubercles are produced by injection of intact dead organisms.

When the products or whole bacteria are injected into tuberculous animals, local inflammation which may lead to necrosis occurs at the site of injection, fever may be produced and the man or animal may suffer from a mild, severe or even fatal exacerbation of the disease. This type of reaction known as the phenomenon of Koch, is due to a state of hypersensitivity to tubercle bacilli and some of its products. The various preparations capable of eliciting this reaction in the hypersensitive animal or of bringing about other effects in the nontuberculous are called *tuberculins*.

More than fifty kinds of preparations of tubercle bacilli or products of their growth in culture media have been used at one time or another as tuberculins (Baldwin, Petroff and Gardner). We shall mention only a few of these.

Ordinary tuberculins contain two definite substances—one the carbohydrate "residue" material which reacts with antibodies *in vitro*, the other a nitrogenous possibly protein material which is responsible for the tuberculin effects. These have been chemically separated by Mueller, Laidlaw and Dudley, work which invalidates the suggestion of Dreyer that tuberculin be standardized by precipitin reactions.

Old Tuberculin (Koch, TAK) (OT).—The first tuberculin made by Koch is produced in the following manner:

Tubercle bacilli are grown in slightly alkaline 5 per cent glycerin-peptone bouillon for six to eight weeks. At the end of this time, growth ceases and the corrugated pellicle of tubercle bacilli, which during growth has floated on the surface, begins, here and there, to sink to the bottom. The entire culture is then heated in a water bath at about 80° C., until reduced to one-tenth of its original volume. It is then filtered either through sterile filter paper or through porcelain filters. The resulting filtrate is a rich brown, syrupy fluid, containing the elements of the original culture medium and a 50 per cent glycerin extract of the tubercle bacilli. While the glycerin is of sufficient concentration to preserve it indefinitely, 0.5 per cent phenol may be added as an additional precaution. Dilutions of this fluid are used for diagnostic and therapeutic purposes.

New Tuberculins.—The so-called "new tuberculins" of Koch (T.A., T.O., T.R.), including the bacillary emulsion referred to as "Bazillenemulsion," are rarely used at present.

Bouillon Filtré (Denys).—This preparation consists of the filtrate (through Chamberland filters) of 5 per cent glycerin-peptone-bouillon cultures of *B. tuberculosis*. Phenol 0.25 per cent is added to insure sterility. The filtered bouillon corresponds to the unconcentrated old tuberculin of Koch, but, not having been heated, is supposed by Denys to contain important soluble and possibly thermolabile secretory products of the bacillus.

Tuberculoplasmin (Buchner and Hahn).—Buchner and Hahn, by crushing tubercle bacilli by subjecting them to a pressure of 400 atmospheres, obtained a cell juice in the form of an amber fluid, to which they attributed qualities closely analagous to those of TR.

Other tuberculins are those of Beraneck highly recommended clinically by Sahli, that of Klebs, and the tuberculin produced from bovine tubercle bacilli by Spengler.

Tuberculo-protein.—In this country improvement in the quality and constancy of tuberculin is increasing through the biochemical investigations of Seibert. She has obtained a crystalline protein from filtrates of tubercle bacilli in Long's synthetic medium and has found that this material is the active or essential component of tuberculin. A protein fraction obtained by Masucci and McAlpine by iso-electric precipitation of the filtrate of cultures of human tubercle bacilli on Long's medium is being tested extensively as a tuberculin under the name of MA–100.

Standardization.—Among the several methods which have been proposed for the determination of the potency of tuberculin preparations, two biological tests have been used. The first and oldest of these is the determination of the minimal lethal dose of tuberculin injected subcutaneously into a tuberculous guinea-pig. The second is the spermatocyte inhibition test of Long. In this method a "spermatocyte unit" is determined by finding the minimal amount of tuberculin which when injected into the testis of a tuberculous guinea-pig will cause complete inhibition of spermatogenesis. Both of these tests are subject to variability due to differences in hypersensitivity of animals and differences in the composition of the usual tuberculins of the O.T. type. The polysaccharides, which do not elicit significant skin reactions, are capable of causing the death of tuberculous guinea-pigs into which they are injected. The present methods of standardizing tuberculins are unsatisfactory. It seems to us that the direction of investigations which will lead to the most reliable standardization of tuberculin lies in the determination of a minimal skin reacting dose of a polysaccharide-free tuberculoprotein in subjects of known hypersensitivity.

Tuberculin Reaction.—*Mechanism and Significance.*—The hypersensitivity of the tuberculous animal to tubercle bacilli and products of tubercle bacilli is the best known, most typical and most extensively investigated of all the instances of allergy to bacteria and bacterial products. Nevertheless, neither the mechanism of the reaction nor its significance with respect to the resistance or susceptibility of an animal to tuberculosis has been definitely determined. Zinsser has reviewed the investigations of himself and others on this problem and has discussed some of the theories proposed to account for the tuberculin reaction. We can give only a brief résumé of the subject here.

Skin reactions, characterized by redness, swelling and edema eighteen to twenty-four hours after intradermal injection, followed in forty-eight hours, or after a longer period, by necrosis and ulceration, are generally studied as indices of this state of allergy.

The most effective ways of sensitizing an animal so that the tuberculin type of skin reaction may be elicited are by injecting into the animal living or dead tubercle bacilli. Infection with live organisms leads to the most typical and extreme degrees of hypersensitivity. Injections of dead organisms, broth culture filtrates and protein fractions of the tubercle bacilli establish hypersensitivity, but more injections of these materials are required as the materials become more remote from the live bacilli. Sabin and Joyner have shown that guinea-pigs can be rendered hypersensitive by intradermal injections of tuberculo-protein, and that the addition of tuberculo-phosphatide to the protein enhances the sensitization, so that the reactions become indurated and necrotic. The degree of sensitization artificially obtainable by the synergistic action of tuberculo-protein and tuberculo-phosphatide is comparable to that occurring naturally in tuberculous animals.

Following the injection of live or dead organisms, or chemical fractions of the bacilli, tubercles or tuberculous tissue, containing monocytes and epithelioid cells are formed. The exact nature of the effective tissue reaction is not known, but the fact, derived from experiments along this line, is that either the actual tubercle or a special type of tissue cellular reaction is essential for the establishment of the state of hypersusceptibility. The dependence of the fully developed allergic response upon tissue reactions is so clear and invariable that it must be interpreted as a fundamental premise.

The action of the tissue cells in the establishing of this type of bacterial allergy may be in part upon the antigen, producing by a biological process of lysis or autolysis an antigenic substance with special functional activities. The investigations of Dienes and Schoenheit have demonstrated that this tissue reaction is extraordinarily rapid and effective and that the tissue reaction to tubercle bacilli can serve to render an animal capable of giving the tuberculin type of reaction to soluble proteins injected into the same site. These investigators have shown that the injection of protein antigens, such as egg white and horse serum, into twenty-four-hour-old tuberculous lesions in the testes of guinea-pigs sensitized the animals in such a way that the subsequent intracutaneous injection of the specific antigen (egg white or serum) elicited a skin reaction of the tuberculin type.

This observation, which has been confirmed by Hanks, suggests that inasmuch as tubercle bacilli alter the sensitization capacity of animals toward antigenic substances from other than bacterial sources, it is not necessary any longer to regard bacterial allergy as a response peculiar to the introduction of bacterial antigens into the tissues. At the same time it becomes apparent that this allergic type of skin reaction, aside from its specificity, does not depend upon distinctive properties of the antigen used in skin testing, but that with one and the same antigen both this type of bacterial allergy and the typical anaphylactic hypersensitiveness may be revealed. The rôle of the anatomical tubercle appears to have been eliminated as an essential feature, but the function of the cellular reactions, which we have mentioned, has not been fully determined.

The hypersensitive animal is resistant to superinfection with tubercle bacilli, as first noted by Koch. It has been natural, therefore, to link *allergy with immunity*. Krause and Willis, and Krause, who studied the rapid healing of newly induced tuberculous lesions in tuberculin-hypersensitive guinea-pigs, supposed that the protection or resistance exhibited by the animals was due to a mechanical walling-off of the freshly introduced tubercle bacilli. Rich and McCordock have attacked this hypothesis, opposing, on the basis of experimental evidence and the evidence from natural tuberculous infection, the theory that the allergic reaction mechanically limits the spread of bacilli from the site of inoculation. In the opinion of Rich, allergy and immunity in tuberculosis are independent processes, do not invariably coexist, and allergy is actually harmful. Rich proposes desensitization to tubercle bacilli and their products as a means of gaining resistance against the progress of infection. The facts do not permit us to reach a decision in this controversy at this time, but we have regarded allergy as a phase of the process of immunity and continue to look upon it as a defensive mechanism, although in extreme cases its expression in the severe reactions may be harmful to the animal.

Specificity.—In most clinics the human type of old tuberculin (O.T.) is the only preparation used routinely for tuberculin tests. This practice reflects the generally accepted opinion that tuberculin reactions do not differentiate specifically between infections with the human and bovine organisms. The bacterial protein responsible for eliciting the allergic reaction is a group antigen as far as concerns human and bovine types of bacilli and the soluble polysaccharide appears to be the same, whether derived from the human or bovine bacillus. Nevertheless, quantitative differences in hypersensitivity to various tuberculins seem to exist. Therefore, in many pediatrics clinics, where it is important for diagnosis, therapy and prognosis to find out whether a child has the human or bovine type of tuberculosis, bovine O.T. is used routinely along with human O.T. for tuberculin tests.

Tuberculin reactions are sufficiently specific to distinguish between infections due to avian bacilli and those due to mammalian tubercle bacilli. These differences are chiefly quantitative, as the group antigens cause overlapping in this case also.

Diagnostic Use.—*Subcutaneous Use.*—Calmette conveniently prepares the solution for subcutaneous use by placing 2 drops of O.T. into a flask containing 100 c.c. of 0.5 per cent carbolic in salt solution. One c.c. of this solution contains approximately 1 milligram, and the injection of 0.1 c.c. of this corresponds to 0.1 milligram. This is considerably lower than the original dosage of Koch and Beck. Löwenstein has recommended 0.2 milligram for the first injection, which may be repeated without increase of dosage after twelve days. He does not believe that increase of the dose is necessary, and states that the smaller the dose the more diagnostically significant.

In cases that react negatively on first injection, repetition of the same dose may be practiced at four- to eight-day intervals; a method which seems to be preferred to increase of dosage by many writers.

The reaction itself is recognized chiefly by the changes in temperature. In a positive reaction the patient's temperature will begin to increase within six to eight hours after injection, rising sharply within a few hours to 0.5° or 1.5° higher than the temperature before injection. It then sinks more gradually than it rose, the reaction usually being complete within thirty to thirty-six hours. With the temperature there may be nausea, a chill, rapid pulse, and general malaise. Locally visible tuberculous processes, such as lupus, lymph nodes, etc., may become tender or swollen, and if the tuberculosis is pulmonary, there may be coughing and increased expectoration. The temperatures of persons subjected to the test should be taken regularly for three or four days before tuberculin is used.

Ophthalmotuberculin Reaction.—Wolff-Eisner and, soon after him, Calmette, proposed a method of using tuberculin for diagnostic purposes by instillation into the conjunctival sac. In tuberculous patients this process is followed by a sharp conjunctival congestion lasting from one to several days.

The preparation used for this purpose is produced in the following way:

Old tuberculin is treated with double its volume of 95 per cent alcohol, the precipitate allowed to settle and the alcohol then filtered off through paper. The sediment is washed with 70 per cent alcohol until the filtrate runs clear, then pressed between layers of filter paper, dried *in vacuo*. Solutions of the powder, 1 per cent by weight, are made in sterile 0.85 per cent salt solution, boiled and filtered. The solutions are used in strengths of 0.5 to 1 per cent.[1]

This reaction has been practically abandoned since many clinicians consider it dangerous to the eye, particularly in possibly lighting up local tuberculous foci.

Cutaneous Tuberculin Reaction.—Von Pirquet suggested the cutaneous use of tuberculin for diagnostic purposes. A 25 per cent solution of old tuberculin was first used. At present the undiluted substance is employed.

After sterilization of the patient's forearm, 2 drops of this solution are placed

[1] Calmette, *Compt. rend. Acad. d. sc.*, June 17, 1907.

upon the skin about 6 centimeters apart. Within each of these drops scarification is done, and the skin between them scarified as a control. Within twenty-four to forty-eight hours, in tuberculous patients, erythema, small papules, and herpetiform vesicles will appear. According to recent investigations, about 70 per cent of adults show a positive reaction. This diminishes its diagnostic value for adults.

Moro has modified this by making a 50 per cent ointment of tuberculin in lanolin and rubbing it into the skin without scarification.

Intracutaneous tests were introduced by Mantoux. The substance used is 1: 5000 solution of O.T. of which 0.1 to 0.05 c.c. is injected. The test doses usually used are 0.01 mgm. and 1 mgm. of O.T.

The value of tuberculin tests in man, with special reference to the intracutaneous test has been surveyed by Hart, who has drawn the conclusion that the Mantoux test is "the most satisfactory tuberculin test in man and should take the place of the subcutaneous and cutaneous (von Pirquet) methods for all purposes." [2] This test is widely used.

Tuberculin Test Applied to Cattle.—In cattle, the symptoms of tuberculosis are not easily detected by methods of physical diagnosis until the disease has reached an advanced stage. In consequence, cows may be elements of danger without appearing in any way diseased. Routine examination of herds by the tuberculin test has become one of the necessary measures of sanitation. According to Mohler, an accurate diagnosis may be established in at least 97 per cent of the cases. It is natural that a good deal of objection to the test is encountered on the part of dairy farmers and cattle raisers, and it has been claimed that the cattle are injured by the test. There is, however, no scientific basis for this belief, if the test is carried out carefully and intelligently. As a matter of fact, the systematic use of the test would eventually be distinctly advantageous to the owners of the cattle themselves, since it has been shown that cows, even in the early stages of the disease, may expel tubercle bacilli, either during respiration or with the feces.

The possibility that cattle may become hypersensitive to tuberculin on account of relatively minor infection with acid-fast micro-organisms which are not tubercle bacilli is receiving increasing attention. The incidence of such infections is not known and their occurrence does not appear to invalidate the general advantages gained from a knowledge of the tuberculin reaction of cattle and an intelligently directed campaign against bovine tuberculosis based upon the facts elicited by the tuberculin tests (Kiernan).

In the work of the Bureau of Animal Industry of the U. S. Department of Agriculture, *old tuberculin* (O.T.) is used in making one or more of the following officially recognized tests: (1) the subcutaneous or "thermal" test; (2) the intradermic or "skin" test; and (3) the ophthalmic or "eye" test In performing the intradermic test, most operators prefer to inject the tuberculin into the skin of the caudal fold on either side of the tail at a point two-thirds the distance from the base. The details of the dosage, methods of injection, and observation and a discussion of the advantages and disadvantages are fully presented by Ernest and Lash in their pamphlet on *Tuberculin Testing of Livestock.*

2 Hart, *Medical Research Council, Spec. Rep. Serv. No. 164*, London, 1932.

Kelser advises the intradermal injection of 0.1 c.c. of O.T. either into the caudal fold or into the lower palpebrum.

Tuberculin Test Applied to Primates.—The ordinary intracutaneous and sub-cutaneous tuberculin tests are not satisfactory for the diagnosis of tuberculosis in monkeys and primates. Schroeder and others have shown that the most satisfactory test is carried out by injecting O.T. or P.P.D. (Purified Protein Derivative) into the subcutaneous tissue at the margin of the upper eyelid of the animal. Reactions show swelling and redness of the eyelid in 16 hours and this lasts for 72 hours. Positive reactions are easily determined.

Specific Therapy.—Tuberculin was first used therapeutically, by Koch, shortly after its discovery. Hailed with the most optimistic enthusiasm, its possibilities were overestimated and hopeless cases were treated unskilfully, with unsuitable dosage. The consequence was that harm was done, the method was attacked by Virchow and others and the new therapy fell into almost complete neglect. At present, the use of tuberculin has again been revived, but with greater caution and with a thorough understanding of its limitations. The tendency has been toward smaller dosage and the limitation of the agent to early cases. No two institutions use tuberculin in exactly the same manner. It is obvious that only cases in which the process is not a very acute one, are at all suitable for treatment. The general principle of modern tuberculin therapy seems to lie in choosing doses so small that no marked general reaction shall follow.

Active Immunization—B.C.G.—Calmette worked for a number of years upon a plan of immunization based on the belief that an attenuation of living tubercle bacillus to a point where it will no longer cause a progressive tuberculous lesion will furnish material with which active immunity can be attained. This had been unsuc-cessfully tried by many previous investigators. It is, however, the most logical basis of procedure in our opinion, since, as we have stated elsewhere, resistance to tubercu-losis is dependent upon some sort of definite reaction between the tissues and the tubercle bacilli. Calmette succeeded in depriving the tubercle bacillus of its patho-genic properties by many generations of growth upon a medium of 5 per cent glycerin potato saturated with beef bile. After 230 successive generations, in the course of thirteen years he carried the organism back to the ordinary glycerin media, the bacillus though still being acid-fast now having absolutely no virulence for any laboratory animals and being incapable of forming true tubercles. Nevertheless, it is still an active producer of tuberculin. Calmette used this organism for the vaccination of young animals and young children. He regarded it as still a true tubercle bacillus because of its tuberculin production, its inability to grow at temperatures much below $37.5°$ C. and its stimulation of the production of specific antibodies. The possibility of immunization must be thoroughly sifted in clinical study, the only possible objec-tion that one can raise to such experiments resting upon the purely theoretical basis that a true tubercle bacillus attenuated on artificial media may regain its virulence gradually after injection into the body of susceptible animals.

Calmette's B.C.G. (Bacille Calmette-Guérin), as it is called, is now being admin-istered by mouth to many thousands of children. This is being done on a much larger scale than in any previous methods of active immunization, and the future should bring clearness concerning its value.

A very large number of reports has accumulated on the use of B.C.G. in man and animals. Useful summaries, with additional experimental confirmation on the protective value of this vaccine in animals have been published by Griffith and Birkhaug. The results of the use of the vaccine in man are influenced by so many factors that it is extremely difficult to obtain accurate statistics of the value of the vaccine. Whether or not the vaccine may be harmful is still somewhat uncertain. Granted that the Lübeck disaster (Calmette) was due to an error through which virulent tubercle bacilli were injected in place of the B.C.G. emulsion, there remains the possibility that this strain may regain a certain degree of virulence. Petroff claims to have obtained a virulent variant by dissociation of the culture. A few have confirmed his results while others have failed to detect virulence in the original or dissociated B.C.G. cultures. It is obvious that caution and a suspension of judgment are appropriate in dealing with these questions. On the other hand, the fact that, in spite of the administration of hundreds of thousands of doses of B.C.G., there have been no reports of serious consequences in more than isolated instances, justifies some confidence in its essential harmlessness. Opie and Freund, reviewing reports in 1937, were of the opinion that widespread use of B.C.G. has shown that it sensitizes to products of the tubercle bacillus and confers a considerable measure of protection when administered by intracutaneous or subcutaneous injection.

Having observed with Petroff that dead tubercle bacilli will produce tuberculin allergy as well as living, and believing that allergy is an indicator of resistance, we have with Ward and Jennings attempted with some success the protection of guinea-pigs with suspensions of dead tubercle bacilli, producing localized tubercles in the animals before injecting them with living organisms. Whether or not this method will have any practical application depends upon further investigation.

In the continuation of his experiments, Petroff has succeded in conferring an unusual degree of protection upon guinea-pigs by immunizing them with heat-killed tubercle bacilli. Petroff is strongly of the opinion that as protection can be gained by the use of dead organisms as vaccines human beings should not be subject to the risk attendant upon vaccination with a living tubercle bacillus, however avirulent at the time of injection.

Opie and Freund found that injections of heat-killed tubercle bacilli in rabbits caused increased resistance to infection with virulent tubercle bacilli only slightly less than that produced by B.C.G. The addition of horse serum improved the efficiency of this vaccine. Their observations indicated that this type of vaccine is useful for increasing the resistance of human beings against tuberculous infection.

Passive Immunization.—For the sake of the historical record we may mention that Maragliano's serum and Marmorek's serum, obtained from horses immunized by injections of extracts of tubercle bacilli and "toxic" products of broth, have had a transient vogue. We may say with considerable confidence at the present time that no method of passive immunization in tuberculosis has had any degree of success.

Serology.—Specific, *in vitro*, serological reactions of tubercle bacilli probably depend upon antigen-antibody reactions in which the polysaccharide haptene determines union with the antibody.

As *agglutination tests* do not distinguish between the bovine and human types of tubercle bacilli, and as the suspensions of these organisms are so apt to agglutinate spontaneously little or no use has been made of agglutination reactions for diagnosis and classification.

It does seem likely that *precipitin* reactions between the polysaccharides (Mueller) or soluble specific substances of these organisms and the serum or exudates of tuberculous animals will yield useful knowledge for diagnosis and for systematic bacteriology (Doan).

A measure of success has attended the application of *complement fixation* procedures to the diagnosis of tuberculosis. Several kinds of antigens have been used the chief of which are the various bacillary emulsions and the egg broth culture filtrate employed by Besredka, the triturated bacterial antigen which one of us prepared in work with Miller, and a host of lipoidal extracts (Pinner). In this country, a careful study of the test has been made by Wadsworth and his coworkers in the development of this diagnostic procedure at the New York State Laboratory using aqueous extracts of tubercle bacilli. Our impression is that the test is positive in about 70 to 80 per cent of cases, that it fails to give significant reactions with serum from patients with early or resting tuberculosis and that syphilitic serum may occasionally cause a false positive reaction. The test is not as useful as desired in those cases of obscure tuberculosis in which serological or laboratory aids to clinical diagnosis are most needed.

Bacilli Closely Related to the Tubercle Bacillus.—*Bacillus of Bovine Tuberculosis.*[3]—Tuberculosis of cattle (Perlsucht) was studied by Koch in connection with his early work on human tuberculosis. Koch did not fail to recognize differences between the reactions to infection in the bovine type of the disease and that of man. He attributed these, however, to the nature of the infected subject rather than to any differences in the infecting agents. This point of view met with little authoritative contradiction, until Theobald Smith, in 1898, made a systematic comparative study of bacilli isolated from man and from cattle and pointed out differences between the two types. The opinion of Smith was fully accepted by Koch in 1901. The differentiation between the human and bovine types is difficult and may take several months to complete.

Morphologically, Smith found that the bovine bacilli were usually shorter than those of the human type and grew less luxuriantly than these upon artificial media. He determined, furthermore, that, grown upon slightly acid glycerin bouillon, the bovine bacillus gradually reduces the acidity of the culture medium until the reaction reaches neutrality or even slight alkalinity. Fluctuations after this do not exceed 0.1 to 0.2 per cent on either side of neutrality. In the case of the human bacillus, on the other hand, there is but slight reduction of the acidity during the first weeks of growth; after this acidity increases and, though subject to fluctuations, never reaches neutrality. This behavior is probably due to action exerted upon the glycerin, since on ordinary bouillon no such differences between the two varieties can be noticed. These observations of Smith were confirmed by Ravenel, Vagedes, and others.

The cultural differences between the two types have been studied with especial care by Wolbach and Ernst, and Kossel, Weber, and Heuss. All of these observers bear out Smith's contention that luxuriance and speed of growth are much more marked in the human than in the bovine variety. Marked differences, furthermore,

---

3 Species: *Mycobacterium tuberculosis* var. *bovis*.

have been shown to exist in the pathogenic properties of these bacilli toward various animal species.

Guinea-pigs inoculated with the bovine type die more quickly and show more extensive lesions than those infected with human bacilli. The difference in the pathogenicity of the two organisms for rabbits is sufficiently striking to be of diagnostic value. The bovine bacilli usually kill a rabbit within two to five weeks; the human bacilli produce a mild and slow disease, lasting often for six months, and occasionally fail to kill the rabbits at all.

The practical importance of distinguishing between the two types, of course, attaches to the question as to whether the bovine and the human disease are mutually intercommunicable. This has been discussed in the preceding section dealing with the human type.

Summary.—Morphologically the bovine bacillus is a little plumper and thicker than the human type, but this cannot be regarded as sufficiently constant to be reliable differentiation. On glycerin broth, the final reaction in the case of human bacilli is considerably acid, the final reaction with the bovine is very slightly above the neutral point. The bovine bacillus does not grow as readily as the human and is not aided by the addition of glycerin to the media to the same extent as the human. The growth of the human bacillus is apt to be more luxuriant than that of the bovine, especially in earlier generations.

As to virulence, the bovine is much more virulent for all the ordinary laboratory animals than is the human. The difference is particularly marked in rabbits. Small doses of human bacilli inoculated into rabbits will kill them very late, and if quantities of less than 0.1 of a milligram are used intravenously, the rabbits may live for longer than two months, or may survive. Similar injection of the bovine type into rabbits kills with greater regularity and more extensive lesions, usually within two months.

Chemically the two organisms, human and bovine, are closely related. This is clear from the experiments of Enders who has demonstrated the immunological identity of the polysaccharides of these two organisms.

Bacillus of Avian Tuberculosis.—A disease resembling in many features the tuberculosis of man is not uncommon among chickens, pigeons, and some other birds. Koch was the first to discover in the lesions of diseased fowl, bacilli much resembling *B. tuberculosis.* It was soon shown, however, by the studies of Nocard and Roux, Mafucci, and others, that the bacillus of the avian disease represented a definitely differentiable species.

Morphologically, and in staining characteristics, the bacillus is almost identical with that of the human disease. In culture, however, growth is more rapid and takes place at a temperature of 41° to 45° C. (the normal temperature of birds), while the human type is unable to thrive at a temperature above 40° C.

The organisms grow more easily than do either the human or bovine bacilli. Colonies appear on glycerin agar within a week and cultivation may also be successful on media without glycerin. It is characteristic of the avian type that cultures on liquid media (glycerin broth) grow as readily within the liquid as on the surface. Furthermore, it is demonstrable that they may even become homogenous.

Guinea-pigs, very susceptible to human tuberculosis, are very refractory to infection with the avian type; while, on the other hand, rabbits which are resistant to the human type, succumb rapidly to infection with avian tuberculosis. Prolonged cultivation and passage through the mammalian body is said to cause these bacilli to approach more or less closely to the mammalian type. Conversely, Nocard claims to have succeeded in rendering mammalian tubercle bacilli pathogenic for fowl by keeping them in the peritoneal cavities of hens in celloidin sacs for six months.

Koch and Rabinowitsch have isolated from the spleen of a young man dead of tuberculosis, a micro-organism which, culturally, morphologically, and in its pathogenic action upon birds, seemed to belong to the avian type. Löwenstein describes a similar organism cultivated from a human case which seems to be a transitional type. Observations of this order are, however, too few at the present time to be used as the basis of a definite opinion as to the relationship between the two varieties.

L'Esperance has suggested that avian tubercle bacilli may be the cause of *Hodgkin's disease* in man. She has isolated the avian type of organism from the lesions and in guinea-pigs rendered hypersensitive to tuberculin she has reproduced lesions resembling the granuloma of Hodgkin's disease by inoculating these animals with avian tubercle bacilli.

Atypical Acid-fast Bacteria.—Occasionally, organisms resembling tubercle bacilli and possessing slight pathogenicity have been isolated from both open and closed lesions of patients with ulcers, abscesses, pneumonia and pleural effusion. One of us with Beaven found an organism with these indefinite properties in the pleural exudate of a child who had signs and symptoms of severe pulmonary disease. These organisms differ in one way or another from the true tubercle bacilli, but their place in the scheme of relationships among acid-fast bacteria cannot be assigned until this whole group has received coördinated scrutiny.

Tuberculosis in Cold-blooded Animals.—The bacillus isolated by Dubarre and Terre resembles *B. tuberculosis* in morphology and in a certain degree of acid-fastness. It grows at low temperatures, 15° to 30° C. It is nonpathogenic for warm-blooded animals, but kills frogs within a month. Except for the acid-fastness it has little in common with *B. tuberculosis.*

Similar acid-fast bacilli have been isolated from other cold-blooded animals (carp, frogs, turtles, snakes) by many observers.

There have been many attempts to show a close relationship between the tubercle bacilli of cold-blooded and those of warm-blooded animals. Moeller, Hansemann, Friedmann, Weber, Küster, and others have given this subject particular attention and it gained especial interest because of the notorious claims of Friedmann that he had succeeded in obtaining, from turtles, a strain of acid-fast bacilli which could be successfully used in actively immunizing human beings. In 1903 Friedmann described two cases of spontaneous infection of a salt-water turtle (Chelone corticata) with acid-fast bacilli, presenting lesions in the lungs which simulated pulmonary tuberculosis in the human being (cavity formation and miliary nodules). The organisms cultivated from these lesions presented much similarity to those of the human type and, according to Friedmann unlike other acid-fast bacilli of cold-blooded animals, could be grown at 37.5° C. As a possible human origin for the turtle infections Friedmann mentions that the attendant who fed these turtles suffered from a double pulmonary tuberculosis.

Upon inoculation into guinea-pigs localized lesions only were produced, and dogs, rats, and birds were immune. The implication of Friedmann's work is that his culture represented a human strain attenuated for man by passage through the turtle, although, as far as we are aware, no definite statement as to this was made.

Summarizing the work of many investigators (Weber, Taute, Küster, Allegri, Bertarelli, and others) Küster makes a statement which is, in essence, as follows: In the carp, in snakes, turtles and frogs spontaneous "tuberculosis" may occur. The organisms which cause these diseases are specific for cold-blooded animals, similar in many respects to the tubercle bacillus of warm-blooded animals, but in the latter do not produce progressive disease. Human, bovine and avian tubercle bacilli inoculated into cold-blooded animals can produce lesions which histologically simulate tuberculosis. These micro-organisms can remain a year in cold-blooded animals without losing their pathogenicity for guinea-pigs. Mutation of the tubercle bacillus of warm-blooded animals into cold-blooded ones has not been proven.

For these reasons it is quite impossible to exclude, in the apparently positive work of Friedmann and others, the isolation of a true "cold-blooded" type organism, rather than a mutation form originally of the warm-blooded type. What Friedmann's present claims in this respect are for his culture has not been stated as far as we know. The possibility of a positive immunizing value of organisms isolated from cold-blooded animals in human beings, though remote, is not out of question. The problem is so serious and important, and the experience of many workers is, so far, so inconclusive that the time has not come for commercial exploitation and the cruel deceptions of false hopes. The subject, however, deserves carefully controlled further investigations.

CHEMOTHERAPY

Chemotherapy of tuberculosis has been actively investigated by Möllgaard. Möllgaard, after much preliminary investigation based upon the early observations of Koch and others upon the effects of gold salts in tuberculosis, has developed a gold preparation which fulfills his requirements that it shall be soluble in water, rapidly diffusible, nonprecipitable by serum and decomposable without forming gold ions or other poisonous products. The preparation he used is a sodium-thio compound of gold with a formula of $Au(S_2O_3)_2Na_3$. It is a snow-white crystalline powder to which he has given the name of sanocrysin. He claims that the *sanocrysin* in dilutions as high as 1:1,000,000 has an inhibitory action upon tubercle-bacillus cultures. It can be injected in nontuberculous animals intravenously in aqueous solutions containing 1 gram in 2 c.c. Similar amounts cause a very violent reaction in the tuberculous animals. Extensive experiments are being carried on in calves and in human beings by Möllgaard in collaboration with Danish clinicians, results of which, though reported as more than encouraging, have not yet been sufficiently extensive to permit judgment. A curious and experimentally unclear phase of the work is the fact that while moderate doses of sanocrysin cause little or no reaction in normal animals or human beings, they incite violent reactions not unlike those caused by tuberculin in tuberculous subjects. These reactions, according to Madsen and his staff, can be partially neutralized with a serum of horses hyperimmunized with tubercle bacilli. That this is not an ordinary antibody effect upon tuberculin-like materials is clear from our own studies and those of Mueller, which show that the materials in tuberculin which unite with antibodies are not the same as those which cause tuberculin reactions. It seems quite likely, therefore, that the violent reactions caused by sanocrysin are not truly tuberculin effects.

There has been an immense amount of study devoted to the chemotherapy of tuberculosis. For this information the reader is referred to the volumes of Kolmer and of Long and Wells. At present there is no specific drug-therapy for tuberculosis. In 1939, however, Crossley, Northey, Hultquist and Climenko announced that certain derivatives of sulfanilamide, particularly a dodecanoyl-sulfanilamide compound, arrested the spread of tuberculosis in animals. This substance has a special property of being soluble in fats and waxes.

NONPATHOGENIC MYCOBACTERIA

The saprophytic acid-fast bacteria in the soil (Thomson) and in and upon animals are a biologically important and large group of organisms. We cannot deal with their cultural characteristics and systematic relationships here, but will mention a few of the more common varieties which are medically important because the organisms look like tubercle bacilli and are found in material suspected of being tuberculous. They present, therefore, diagnostic problems in the direct examination of nuts, butter, urine, urethral and vaginal secretions, skin lesions and certain exudates from pathological processes in man and animals. From the medical point of view, smegma bacillus is the most important of these organisms. Many of the acid-fast bacteria in this group are pigmented: yellow, orange or red. The chief example of this type is the bacillus of timothy hay, known as Moeller's bacillus or *Bacillus phlei*. This organism is not entirely devoid of pathogenicity. Aside from observations on pigment production, the growth of these organisms at room temperature (25° to 30° C.) sharply distinguishes them from mammalian tubercle bacilli.

BACILLUS SMEGMATIS

Order, Family and Genus as for Tubercle Bacillus. Species: *Mycobacterium smegmatis*

In 1884, Lustgarten announced that he had succeeded in demonstrating, in a number of syphilitic lesions, a characteristic bacillus, which he declared to be the etiological factor in the disease. The great importance of the subject of Lustgarten's communication caused numerous investigators to take up the study of the microorganisms found upon the genitals of normal and diseased individuals. As a result of these researches the presence of the Lustgarten bacilli upon the genitals of many syphilitics was confirmed; but at the same time bacilli, which in all essential particulars were identical with them, were found in the secretions about the genital organs and anus of many normal persons. The first to throw doubt upon the etiological significance of Lustgarten's bacillus, and to describe in detail the microorganism now recognized as *Bacillus smegmatis*, were Alvarez and Tavel. Similar studies were made soon afterward by Klemperer, Bitter and others.

The smegma bacilli are now known to occur as harmless saprophytes in the preputial secretions of the male, about the external genital organs of the female, and within the folds of thighs and buttocks. They are usually found, in these situations, in clumps upon the mucous membrane, and occasionally in the superficial layers of the epithelium, intra- and extra-cellularly.

Morphology.—The smegma bacilli are very similar to tubercle bacilli, but show greater variations in size and appearance than do the latter. In length the individuals may vary from 2 to 7 μ. They are usually straight or slightly curved, but according to Alvarez and Tavel may show great polymorphism, including short comma-like forms, and occasional S-shaped spiral forms.

They are not easily stained, and though less resistant in this respect than the tubercle bacillus, they yet belong distinctly to the group of acid-fast bacilli. Once stained by the stronger dyes, such as carbolfuchsin or aniline water gentian violet, they are tenacious of the dye, though less so than tubercle bacilli.

The identification of the smegma bacillus by staining methods has become of practical importance since Fränkel, Mueller, and others have demonstrated the occasional presence of acid-fast bacilli, probably of the smegma group, in sputum, and in secretions from the tonsillar crypts and throat. The methods of differentiation which have been found most practical are those which depend upon differences in the retention of stain shown by these bacilli. While it may be stated as a general rule that the smegma bacilli are more easily decolorized than tubercle bacilli, it is nevertheless important that a control, as suggested by Wood, be made with known tubercle bacilli whenever a slide of suspected smegma bacilli is examined. For the actual differentiation an excellent method is that of Pappenheim, described in detail in the section on staining. This method depends upon the fact that prolonged treatment with alcohol and rosolic acid decolorizes the smegma bacilli but not the tubercle bacilli. Coles has stated that smegma bacilli will resist Pappenheim's decolorizing agent for four hours at the most, while tubercle bacilli will retain the stain, in spite of such treatment, for as long as twenty-four hours.

The smegma bacilli have no pathogenic significance. They are found upon human beings as harmless saprophytes, and all attempts to infect animals have so far been unsuccessful. They are cultivated with great difficulty, first cultivations from man being successful only upon the richer media containing human serum or hydrocele fluid. After prolonged cultivation upon artificial media they may be kept alive upon glucose agar or ascitis agar. Their growth is slow; and the colonies, appearing within five or six days after inoculation, are yellowish white, corrugated, and not unlike tubercle-bacillus colonies.

REFERENCES

Alvarez and Tavel. Arch. d. physiol. norm. et path., Par., Oct. 1885.

Am. Rev. Tuberc., 1932, 25:285.

Anderson. Treas. Dep. Pub. Health & Mar.-Hosp. Serv. U. S. Hyg. Lab. Bull., Wash., 1909, 57.

Anderson, R. J. Phys. Rev., 1932, 12:166.

Aronson, J. D. Tr. Nat. Tuberc. Ass., 1931.

Baldwin, E. R., Petroff, S. A., and Gardner, L. S. Tuberculosis, Philadelphia, 1927.

Baumgarten, P. Centralbl. f. d. med. Wissenschr., 1878, 16:227; 1882, 20:257, 337.

—— Berl. klin. Wchnschr., 1901.

Beaven, P. W., and Bayne-Jones, S. J. Infect. Dis., 1931, 49:399.

Beck. Deutsche med. Wchnschr., 1899.

Beraneck. Compt. rend. Acad. d. sc., 1903.

Besredka, A. Ann. de l'Inst. Pasteur, 1921, 35:291.

Birkhaug, K. E. Am. Rev. Tuberc., 1933, 27:6.

Bitter. Virchow's Arch., 103.

Brem. J. Am. M. Ass., 1909, 53.

Buchner and Hahn. München. med. Wchnschr., 1897.

Burke. Am. Rev. Tuberc., 1927, 15:399.

Calmette, A. Bull. de l'Inst. Pasteur, 1924, 22:593; 1928, 26:889.

—— J. Am. M. Ass., 1931, 96:58.

—— Compt. rend. Acad. d. sc., June 17, 1907.

—— L'Infection bacillaire et la tuberculose, 1920, 110:457.

Coles. J. State Med., 1904.

Corper, H. J. J. Am. M. Ass., 1928, 91:371.

Courmont and Dor. Arch. de méd. expér. et d'anat. path., 1891.

Cunningham, J. S., and Cummings, P. L. J. Lab. & Clin. Med., 1930, 15:572. See also: Current Comment, J. Am. M. Ass., 1930, 95:1839.

Denys. Le bouillon filtré, Louvain, 1905.

Dienes, L., and Schoenheit, E. W. Am. Rev. Tuberc., 1929, 92–105; and a series of papers by Dienes in J. Immunol., 1927 to 1933.

Doan, C. A. Med. Clin. North Am., 1930, 14:279.

—— N. Eng. J. M., 1930, 203:862.

Drury. Pub. Health Rep., Wash., 1921, 5:36.

Dubarre and Terre. Compt. rend. Soc. de biol., 1897.

Ehrlich, P. Deutsche med. Wchnschr., 1882.

Fränkel. Berl. klin. Wchnschr., 1898.

Fraser. J. Exper. M., 1912, 4:16.

Frey, and Hagan, W. A. J. Infect. Dis., 1931, 49:497.

Fried, B. M. Am. Rev. Tuberc., 1924, 9:112.

Friedmann. Centralbl. f. Bakteriol., 1903, 1:34.

—— Deutsche med. Wchnschr., 1903, 2:25; 26:464.

—— Ztschr. f. Tuberk., 1903, 4:5.

Funk, E. H., and Huntoon, F. M. J. Immunol., 1930, 19:237.

Gardner, L. U. J. Indust. Hyg., 1932, 14:18.

—— Am. J. Pub. Health, 1933, 23:1240.

—— Am. Rev. Tuberc., 1929, 20, 833.

—— J. Am. M. Ass., 1934, 103:745.

Griffith, S. A. Medical Research Council, Spec. Rep. Ser. No. 152, London, 1931.

—— Bacillus Tuberculosis, in A System of Bacteriology in Relation to Medicine, London, 1930, 5:150–344.

Hamburger and Sluka. Cited from Calmette, L'Infection bacillaire de la tuberculose.

Hart, P. D. Medical Research Council, Spec. Rep. Ser. No. 164, London, 1932.

Hohn, J. Centralbl. f. Bakteriol., I Abt., 1927; 102:342.

Kahn, M. C. Am. Rev. Tuberc., 1929, 20:150.

—— Proc. Soc. Exper. Biol. & Med., 1933, 30:577.

Kahn, M. C., and Schwarzkopf, H. J. Bacteriol., 1933, 25:157.

Kelser, R. A. Manual of Veterinary Bacteriology, Williams and Wilkins Co., Baltimore, 1933, p. 308.

Kiernan, J. A., and Wight, A. E. U. S. Dep. Agric., Farmer's Bulletin No. 1069, Rev. 1930.

Klebs. Centralbl. f. Bakteriol., I Abt., 1896.

—— Deutsche med. Wchnschr., 1907.

Klein, E. Centralbl. f. Bakteriol., I Abt., 1890, 7:785.

Klemperer. Deutsche med. Wchnschr., 1885, 11.

Kober. Pub. Health Rep., Wash., Oct. 1915, 309.

Koch, R. Deutsche med. Wchnschr., 1891, 1901.

—— Centralbl. f. Bakteriol., I Abt., 1890.

—— Arb. a. d. k. Gsndhtsamte., 1882, 11.

—— Berl. klin. Wchnschr., 1882, 19:221.

—— Mitt. a. d. Kaiserl. Gsndhtsamte., 1884, 2.

KOCH, R., and RABINOWITSCH. Virchow's Arch., 1907, Beiheft, 190.

KOSSEL, WEBER, and HEUSS. Arb. a. d. k. Gsndhtsamte., 1904, 1905.

KRAUSE, A. Am. Rev. Tuberc., 1925, 11:349.

KRAUSE, A., and WILLIS, H. S. Am. Rev. Tuberc., 1920, 4:563.

KÜSTER. Handb. d. path. Mikroorg., ed. by Kolle and Wassermann, 2nd ed., 1913, 5:767.

LEHMANN, K. B., and NEUMANN, R. O. Atlas und Gundriss der Bakteriologie, München., 5th ed., 1912.

L'ESPERANCE, E. S. J. Immunol., 1929, 16:27, 37.

LIEBERMEISTER. Deutsche med. Wchnschr., 1909, 35:1324.

LINDEGREN and MELLON. Proc. Soc. Exper. Biol. & Med., 1932, 30:110.

LONG, E. R. Am. Rev. Tuberc., 1925, 9:215; 1926, 13:393; 1930, 22:467.

—— J. Infect. Dis., 1925, 37:368.

—— The Newer Knowledge of Bacteriology and Immunology, Chicago, 1928, Chap. 76, p. 1020.

—— Science, 1938, 87:23.

LÖWENSTEIN, E. München. med. Wchnschr., 1930, 77:1662; 1931, 78:261.

LUSTGARTEN. Wien. med. Wchnschr., 1884, 47.

MAFUCCI, A. Ztschr. f. Hyg. u. Infectionskrankh., 1892, 11:445.

MANTOUX, C. Compt. rend. Acad. d. Sc., 1908, 147: 355.

—— Compt. rend. Soc. de Biol., 1909, 67:356.

MARAGLIANO. Berl. klin. Wchnschr., 1899.

—— Compt. rend. Soc. de Biol., 1897.

MARIETTE, E. S., and FENGER, E. P. K. Am. Rev. Tuberc., 1932, 25:357.

MARMOREK. Berl. klin. Wchnschr., 1903, 1108.

—— Med. Klin.. 1906.

MASUCCI, P., and McALPINE, K. L. Proc. Soc. Exper. Biol. & Med., 1930, 27:661.

MELLON and FISHER. J. Infect. Dis., 1932, 51:117.

—— Proc. Soc. Exper. Biol. & Med., 1933, 30:663.

MELLON and JOST. Am. Rev. Tuberc., 1929, 19:483.

MELLON, RICHARDSON and FISHER. Proc. Soc. Exper. Biol. & Med., 1932, 30:80.

MERRILL. J. Bacteriol., 1930, 20:235.

METCHNIKOFF, E. Virchow's Arch. f. path. Anat., 1888, 113:63.

MILLER, H. J. Am. M. Ass., 1916, 67:1519.

—— J. Lab. & Clin. M., 1916, 1:2.

MILLER, H. R., and ZINSSER, H. Proc. Soc. Exper. Biol. & Med., 1916, 13:134.

MILLER, J. A. J. Am. M. Ass., 1938, 111:111.

MOHLER, J. R. U. S. Pub. Health Rep., 1908, 41.

MÖLLGAARD. Chemotherapy of Tuberculosis, Copenhagen, 1924.

MORO, E. München. med. Wchnschr., 1908, 55:216.

MUCH. Berl. klin. Wchnschr., 1908, 45:700.

MUELLER. Deutsche med. Wchnschr., 1898.

MUELLER, J. H. J. Exper. M., 1926, 43:1.

NEELSEN, F. C. A. Grundriss d. pathol. anat. Technik, etc., Stuttgart, 1892.

NOCARD. Ann. de l'Inst. Pasteur, 1898.

NOCARD and ROUX. Ann. de l'Inst. Pasteur, 1887.

NOVY, F. G., and SOULE, M. H. J. Infect. Dis., 1925, 36:168.

OPIE. Am. Rev. Tuberc., 1920, 4:629.

OPIE, E. L., and FREUND, J. J. Exper. M., 1937, 66:761.

PAPPENHEIM. Berl. klin. Wchnschr., 1898.

PETROFF, S. A. Bull. Johns Hopkins Hosp., 1915, 26:276.

—— Am. Rev. Tuberc., 1929, 20:275.

—— N. Eng. J. M., 1932, 206, 438.

PETROFF, S. A., BRANCH, A., and STEENKEN, W.   Am. Rev. Tuberc., 1929, 19:9.
PETROFF, S. A., and STEENKEN, W.   J. Exper. M., 1930, 51:831.
PETROFF, S. A., and STEWART, F. W.   J. Immunol., 1926, 12:97.
PINNER, M.   Am. Rev. Tuberc., 1925, 11; 1925, 12.
RAVENEL.   Lancet, 1901.
—— Tr. Brit. Cong. Tuberc., 1901, 3:552.
—— Univ. Penn. M. Bull., 192.
REED, G. B., et al.   Can. J. Research, 1931, 4:389; 1931, 5:111; 1932, 6:622.
—— J. Immunol., 1932, 23:385.
RICH, A. R.   Bull. Johns Hopkins Hosp., 1930, 47:189.
RICH, A. R., and McCORDOCK, H. A.   Bull. Johns Hopkins Hosp., 1929, 44:273.
ROSENBERGER.   Am. J. M. Sc., 1909, 137.
SABIN, F. R.   Phys. Rev., 1932, 12:141.
—— J. Exper. M., 1938, 68:837.
—— and JOYNER, A. L.   J. Exper. M., 1938, 68:659.
SAHLI.   Cor.-Bl. f. schweiz. Aerzte, 1906.
SCHROEDER, C. R.   Am. J. Pub. Health, 1938, 28:469.
—— Zoologica, 1938, 23:397.
SEIBERT, F. B.   Science, 1926, 63:619.
—— Am. Rev. Tuberc., 1928, 12:402; 1934, 30:713; 1938, 38:399, 523.
—— J. Exper., M., 1938, 68:413.
SMITH, THEOBALD.   J. Exper. M., 1898, 3:470; 1905.
—— Tr. Ass. Am. Physicians, 1896, 11:75.
—— Med. News, 1902.
—— J. Med. Research, 1905, 13:253, 405.
SPENGLER.   Deutsche med. Wchnschr., 1904, 1905.
STEENKEN, W., OATWAY, W. H., and PETROFF, S. A.   J. Exper. M., 1934, 60:515.
STRAUS and GAMALEIA.   Arch. de méd. expér. et d'anat. path., 1891.
SUZUKI and TAKAKI.   Centralbl. f. Bakteriol., 1911, 61.
THOMSON, H. M.   Am. Rev. Tuberc., 1932, 26:162.
VAGEDES.   Ztschr. f. Hyg., 1898.
VILLEMIN, J. A.   Compt. rend. Acad. d. Sc., 1865, 61:1012.
VERA, D., and RETTGER, L. F.   J. Bacteriol., 1938, 35:21.
VON PIRQUET, C.   Wien. klin. Wchnschr., 1907, 20:1123.
—— Med. Klin., 1907, 3:1197.
WADSWORTH, A. B., MALTANER, E. J., and STEVENS, B. S.   Am. Rev. Tuberc., 1930, 22:539.
WEIZERT.   Deutsche med. Wchnschr., 1885.
WEINZIRL, J., and DINGLE, J. H.   J. Bacteriol., 1932, 23:281.
WEINZIRL, J., and KNAPTON, F.   Am. Rev. Tuberc., 1927, 15:380.
WEISS.   Berl. klin. Wchnschr., 1909, 46:1797.
WELLS, H. G., and LONG, E. R.   The Chemistry of Tuberculosis. 2nd ed. Williams and Wilkins Co., Baltimore, 1932.
WOLBACH and ERNST.   Stud. Rockefeller Inst. M. Research, 1904, 11.
WOLFF-EISNER.   Berl. med. Gesellsch., May 15, 1907.
ZIEHL, F.   Deutsche med. Wchnschr., 1882, 8:451; 1883, 9:247.
ZINSSER, H.   Bull. N. York Acad. Med., 1928, 4:351.
ZINSSER, H., and PETROFF, S. A.   J. Immunol., 1924, 9:85.
ZINSSER, H., WARD, H., and JENNINGS.   J. Immunol., 1925, 10:719.

CHAPTER XXXII

LEPROSY

Leprosy is a chronic granulomatous disease characterized by a variety of specific lesions of the skin and other parts of the body, with deforming and destructive processes often the result of trophic disturbances due to pathological alterations in the peripheral nerve trunks. In 1874, Hansen found bacilli in material from lepromata and in 1879, Neisser confirmed this discovery in an extensive study of leprous material collected in Norway. These early observers had difficulty in staining the bacillus. It was not until after Koch's work on the tubercle bacillus and the introduction of the special staining procedures of Ehrlich and Ziehl that it was recognized that the bacterium in these lesions was acid-fast. Stains showed that Hansen's bacillus, called also *Bacillus leprae* was morphologically very much like the tubercle bacillus. It has, therefore, been placed among the mycobacteria and given the name *Mycobacterium leprae*. Neither Hansen nor Neisser succeeded in cultivating the organism.

The name *Mycobacterium leprae* is given to an organism known with certainty only in tissue lesions and the emulsions made of lepra cells. As no investigator has proved beyond doubt that any one of the various cultures claimed to be this organism is actually capable of causing leprosy, it is misleading to give a description of its cultural characteristics. The best that can be done at present is to describe the organism as it occurs in the tissues and to review a few of the most significant investigations on the etiology of the disease. In Bergey's *Manual* the organism of McKinley and Soule is accepted tentatively as the true leprosy bacillus.

Epidemiology.—Leprosy has been a widely spread disease of man since the beginning of history. In spite of confusion due to the practice of grouping many ulcerative skin diseases under the term of "leprosy," the records of the Old Testament and those in other ancient writings present a fairly clear story of the antiquity of the disease, the dread with which it was regarded and the popular belief in its communicability. The disease has occurred, and probably still exists in all countries of the world. Improvement in sanitation, in diet and in the general standard of living together with segregation and isolation of lepers has resulted in a great decrease in the number of cases developing in Europe and America. The disease, however, continues to claim many victims. It was estimated that in 1933 there were approximately four million lepers in the world.

In Europe the disease occurs chiefly in Norway, Russia and Iceland. It is more common in China, India, the Philippine Islands, Hawaii and Central Africa. In the United States the chief endemic foci appear to be California, the Gulf States: Texas, Louisiana, Mississippi, and Florida, the region of Minnesota and Wisconsin, and New York. But sporadic cases have been found in every state of the Union (Hopkins and Denny).

It is now universally agreed that leprosy is a contagious disease transmitted through prolonged and intimate contact. But the exact mode of transmission is unknown (McCoy). All the factors of transmission are not known. Many physicians working among lepers for years have escaped infection. A few others, notably Father Damien, who have devoted their lives to the care of lepers have contracted the disease. Instances of familial transmission have been clearly traced. Sometimes the child developed leprosy before its parents. In other instances one or both parents developed the disease before it appeared in their offspring. The disease is obviously not highly contagious. The *incubation period* is not known. It has been estimated by various observers to be three to six years.

Other factors in the transmission of leprosy are obscure. It is possible that the organisms may be carried from an infected person to a normal one by flies, bedbugs, mosquitoes and other blood-sucking insects. This mode of transference is thought to be mechanical, as there is no evidence that the parasite has a stage of its life cycle in an insect.

Experimental transmission of the disease to *man* appears to have been accomplished by Arning who inoculated a condemned Hawaiian criminal. He inserted a piece of a leprous nodule in the subcutaneous tissue of the arm of this man. Four and a half months later a typical leprosy nodule formed at the site of inoculation and four years after this the patient was a typical leper. This experiment, like others conducted in an area where leprosy is prevalent, is open to question because natural infection cannot be excluded. Soule and McKinley have expressed the opinion that out of 145 human inoculations reported by various observers the experiment of Arning is the only one which appears to have been successful.

Attempts to produce the disease in rats, mice, rabbits and guinea-pigs have failed. Of the various inoculation experiments in which *monkeys* were used, Reenstierna's is most suggestive. He injected ground-up leprosy nodules into the supra-orbital tissue of monkeys (*Macacus sinicus* and *Macacus rhesus*). After several weeks, a nodule appeared at the site of inoculation. This enlarged, ulcerated and healed. It was impossible to transmit the disease from these to other animals. Vacuolated cells containing lepra bacilli were found in these lesions. At the International Congress of Leprosy in Cairo, in 1938, Adler reported that he had produced a disease similar to leprosy by inoculating splenectomized Syrian hamsters with material from human leprous lesions.

The *portals of entry* of the organism into the human body are thought to be the mucous membranes of the nose and pharynx, the respiratory and gastro-intestinal tract and the skin. Early localization of lepra bacilli in the nose, along the septum, makes the nasal portal of entry seem probable.

Clinical and Pathological Features.—Although leprosy is a generalized disease, certain local lesions are conspicuous and serve to establish types of the disease. These are chiefly:

Cutaneous Lesions.—These are characteristic macular eruptions with thickened and sometimes scaly areas of the skin of the trunk, face, legs and arms. Later the skin becomes thickened and folded, especially on the face, producing the "leonine facies."

Neural Lesions.—Lepra bacilli occur in abundance in the peripheral nerve trunks, associated with thickenings of the sheaths of the nerves. Subcutaneous nerve trunks related to localized cutaneous lesions or parts of these trunks subjected to trauma are most commonly affected. The ulnar and peroneal trunks are most commonly thickened. These lesions of the nerves are accompanied by anesthesia and finally trophic deformities and destruction of the extremities and of bones and joints.

It has not been our intention to describe the lesions of leprosy with sufficient completeness to serve as a basis for differential clinical diagnosis but to indicate sites from which material may be obtained for examination for the acid-fast lepra bacilli.

There have been numerous classifications of the types and stages of leprosy. These have led to confusion. To avoid this, and to provide for a uniform basis for comparison of clinical, bacteriological and epidemiological data, Wade, in 1937, proposed a modification of the Leonard Wood Memorial Conference classification.

Bacteriological Diagnosis.—Bacteriological aid in the diagnosis is supplied through the finding of characteristic acid-fast bacteria in sections of tissue or smears from leprous lesions. *Smears* may be made from swabs of the nasal septum, material from the blade of a scalpel with which a cutaneous lesion has been deeply scraped or, preferably, incised, pulp from an aspiration of a punctured lymph node and material expressed from an excised nodule or other lesion. The organisms occur in the sputum in cases of pulmonary leprosy. If acid-fast bacteria are found in smears stained by the Ziehl-Neelsen method, and if these rods are arranged in packets and clumps, they provide strong presumptive evidence of leprosy. It must be remembered, however, that this procedure alone is not always capable of differentiating between tubercle bacilli and some of the nonpathogenic acid-fast bacteria which may occur in the nose and in folds of the skin.

Morphology.—As we are not certain that *Mycobacterium leprae* has been cultivated, we shall describe here the morphology of Hansen's bacillus only as it occurs in the lesions. The organisms are small rods, varying in length, thickness and form. The rods are from 1 to 7 μ long and 0.3 to 0.5 μ broad. They may be slightly curved and, when stained, show a beaded or granular appearance. The ends of the rods are bluntly tapered. In the lepra cells and in the tissues the organisms often lie side by side in clumps or packets having the so-called "cigar packet" formation. *B. leprae* is acid-fast, gram-positive, nonmotile and does not form endospores.

Cultivation.—Since the discovery that a bacterium occurred regularly and often in enormous numbers in the lesions of leprosy there have been numerous attempts to isolate it in cultures. Many types of media, and many conditions of cultivations have been used. The organisms obtained by culture from leprous lesions have been very numerous and varied. None has been accepted as the cause of leprosy because it has been impossible to fulfill all of Koch's postulates in the case of any of these organisms. As we have shown, the impossibility thus far of producing typical progressive and transmissible leprosy in lower animals by inoculation with material taken directly from active lesions in man has made it all the more unlikely that success in this direction would be obtained by inoculation with cultures. Many transient granulomatous lesions produced by inoculation with leprous material can be duplicated by injection of dead or nonpathogenic acid-fast bacteria. It seems to us that the granuloma produced in monkeys by McKinley and Soule by injections of their culture of *B. leprae* is the nearest approach to the establishment in an animal of a lesion with histopathological features of a leprosy nodule. It is obvious that contaminations with bacteria from the skin have occurred often in cultures from leprosy lesions.

In a review of the attempts that have been made to cultivate *Bacillus leprae*, McKinley and Soule have provided a useful summary of the sources of materials, methods used and experimental results of 34 investigators who have published accounts of organisms isolated from leprosy lesions. We have, at one time or another, seen many of these cultures and noted their great differences. The organisms isolated may be placed in the following groups:

1. *Diphtheroids* have been isolated by 17 investigators. Some of these were thought to be a nonacid-fast stage of the lepra bacillus. The organism isolated by Kedrowsky in 1901 became acid-fast during cultivation.

2. *Actinomycetes* have been isolated by Kedrowsky and Walker.

3. *Acid-fast bacteria.* Since the bacteria in the lesions are acid-fast, these are obviously of the greatest interest among the organisms isolated. The cultures of acid-fast bacteria have been of two main types (*a*) chromogenic and (*b*) nonchromogenic.

Types of the chromogenic acid-fast bacteria isolated from leprosy are the organisms grown by Rost on a salt-free bouillon medium, and the chromogens of Clegg and Duval.

In 1909 Clegg succeeded in growing an acid-fast bacillus from leprous tissue, obtaining his results by inoculating leprous material upon agar plates upon which *Amoeba coli* has been grown in symbiosis with other bacteria. On such plates the acid-fast bacilli multiplied, and subsequently, pure cultures were obtained by heating the cultures to 60° C., which destroyed the *Amoeba coli* and other bacteria. These results were confirmed by other workers and soon after that, Duval not only succeeded in repeating Clegg's experiments, but obtained cultures of an acid-fast bacillus directly from leprous lesions without the aid of ameba. He first observed that the leprosy organism would multiply around a transplanted piece of leprous tissue upon ordinary blood-agar tubes upon which influenza bacilli and meningococci were grown. He concluded that such growth depended upon chemical changes in the media and believed the formation of amino-acids essential for the initial growth. The method he subsequently described depended upon supplying these substances either by adding tryptophan to nutrient agar or by pouring egg albumin and human blood serum in Petri dishes, inspissating, at 70° C., for three hours and, after inoculating with leprous tissue, adding a 1 per cent solution of trypsin. Indirectly the same result was obtained by employing culture media containing albuminous substances and inoculating with bacteria capable of producing amino-acids from the medium. Duval has produced lesions histologically resembling leprosy by inoculating animals with his cultures.

After leprosy bacilli had been grown for several generations, they could easily be cultivated on agar slants without special additions or preliminary treatment. The cultures after prolonged preservation upon artificial media grow heavily, often lose their acid-fast characteristics, develop into streptothrix-like or diphtheroid forms and some strains become markedly chromogenic, all these characteristics suggesting saprophytism. In our opinion, it is unlikely that *B. leprae* will be found in this group of chromogenic acid-fast bacteria. Some of the *nonchromogenic acid-fast organisms* isolated from lesions of leprosy have resembled the various types of tubercle bacilli in gross appearance, others have been quite distinctive. The culture labelled "Kedrowsky strain" which one of us examined produced a whitish gray or cream colored growth, at times flaky along the edges, at other times doughy in consistency resembling the growth of avian tubercle bacilli. Nonchromogenic strains, with differing characteristics have been isolated by Duval and Wellman, Wherry and Wherry and Erwin.

Wherry incubated his cultures in an atmosphere of 10 to 20 per cent carbon dioxide, as indicated by previous experiments with tubercule bacilli (McKinley and Soule). A number of observers have regarded CO_2 as essential for such cultures.

A nonchromogenic acid-fast bacterium with unique properties was isolated in 1931 and described in 1932 by McKinley and Soule. The material used was obtained from leprosy nodules excised aseptically by dissection from underlying tissue and removal without skin. Intracutaneous injection of emulsions of these nodules into the supra-orbital regions of young monkeys (*Macacus rhesus* and *Cebus olivaceus*) produced the transient nodular lesion with pathological-histological features resembling the lepra granuloma which we have described.

Cultures were made by inoculating the various solid liquid media used in previous attempts to isolate *B. leprae* (glycerol potato, Petroff and Dorsett's egg media, hormone glycerol agar, rabbit blood agar, dextrose brain broth, etc.). The tubes were incubated at 37.5° C. in Novy jars under atmospheres containing various proportions of carbon dioxide and oxygen, prepared according to the method of Novy, Roehm and Soule. No growth occurred in tubes incubated with exposure to air or when oxygen was removed and excluded. The most favorable gaseous environment was found to be a mixture of 40 per cent oxygen and 10 per cent carbon dioxide. Growth occurred slowly. After six weeks' incubation, the colonies averaged 1 millimeter in diameter, were heaped up, had a mucoid consistency and a filamentous border. Pigment was not produced. The organisms in these colonies were acid-fast, pleomorphic, and resembled lepra bacilli. Inoculation of monkeys with large doses of the growth produced in the supra-orbital skin the nodular granuloma resembling a leprosy nodule, which we have described. The cultures did not produce tuberculosis nor a progressive leprosy.

An improvement in the method of cultivation was made by using a medium composed of minced chick embryo in Tyrode's solution (McKinley and Verder). Growth was obtained in five days in this medium and could be perpetuated with certainty by serial transfers. In this medium the organism grows as well under ordinary atmospheric conditions as under the special gaseous mixture of carbon dioxide and oxygen.

Other investigators have failed to isolate this unusual slow-growing organism from leprosy. The study of the organism is being continued by Soule.

Chemistry.—Since 1931 Anderson and a number of collaborators have been investigating the chemistry of a so-called leprosy bacillus, using for analysis cultures of the Hygienic Laboratory Strain No. 370 (Apa case). This organism was isolated from a case of human leprosy in Honolulu in 1909. It has been carried in the Mulford Biological Laboratories as Strain No. 1629. It grows luxuriantly on a synthetic medium and is highly chromogenic. From masses of this culture Anderson and his associates have isolated a polysaccharide, a phosphatide, a neutral wax-like substance (leprosin), two new alcohols of high molecular weight, with phenolic properties (χ and β leprosol), neutral fats and a series of saturated and unsaturated fatty acids. This work is highly significant for bacteriological chemistry. But in view of the fact that it is improbable that the organism studied is related etiologically to leprosy, the results cannot be expected to contribute to the understanding of the chemistry of the disease in the way in which Anderson's work on tubercle bacilli has increased the knowledge of the chemistry of tuberculosis.

Immunology and Serology.—The patient with leprosy becomes hypersensitive to substances and products derived from the acid-fast lepra bacilli growing in the tissues. Lepers are therefore allergic to a number of artificially prepared products, extracts of leprous lesions, and tuberculin-like products of the cultures of various *Mycobacteria*. There is, however, no specific skin-test material available for allergic tests in leprosy. When tuberculin is injected into a leper a febrile reaction occurs, coming on later and persisting longer than the analogous reaction in tuberculous patients. Extracts of leprosy nodules produce the same effect. In the natural course of the disease somewhat similar febrile exacerbations occur. These may arise from specific or nonspecific causes. They are sometimes followed by an improvement in the condition of the patient.

The status of diagnostic *skin tests* in leprosy was reviewed by McKinley in 1938 in a report of a survey made by him in the Philippine Islands. Preparations from the organism isolated by himself and Soule were not included among the materials tested. Over 5000 intradermal tests were made with antigens prepared from various acid-fast bacteria, some of which had been isolated from cases of leprosy. The antigens included the TPT (tuberculin-protein-trichlor-acetic acid-precipitated) of many of these organisms; the protein, polysaccharide, phosphatide, leprosin (wax), and leprosinic acid from one strain; and a protein prepared from the fibrin of the blood of cases of leprosy. None of the antigens studied proved to have any diagnostic value in skin tests. The work suggested further that the supposed strains of *B. leprae* from which the antigens were made were not related etiologically to the disease.

It has been noted frequently that the blood serum of lepers give a positive *Wassermann reaction* and many investigations of the problem thus presented have been made. This reaction may be a "false positive" reaction or may indicate that serological changes occur in leprosy like those in syphilis. The two diseases are caused by entirely different organisms and the results obtained with such a fundamentally nonspecific test as the Wassermann reaction have no etiological significance. The explanation of the positive reactions appears to us to lie in the simultaneous occurrence of syphilis or yaws with leprosy and in mistakes in clinical diagnosis (Lloyd, Muir and Mitra). Kahn tests are usually negative in leprosy (Badger).

Complement fixation tests based upon the use of a variety of culture preparations as antigens have been extensively investigated, particularly by Lewis and Aronson. These workers showed that the blood serum of patients with leprosy was able to fix complement with a variety of antigens including those derived from cultures of all representative members of the whole group of acid-fast bacteria. This property of multiple fixation of complement was thought to have diagnostic significance. The antigen prepared from Clegg's chromogenic acid-fast strain of *B. leprae* gave the most constant results. In our opinion this test in its present form is too nonspecific to be of practical value.

Treatment.—The most promising treatment of leprosy is a chemotherapeutic one based upon an ancient popular belief that chaulmoogra oil was beneficial. This oil is derived from the seeds of *Hydnocarpus wightiana* or *Taraktogenos kurzii*, trees growing in Burma and adjacent countries. The earlier reports on controlled use of this drug by Heiser in 1914 and by Rogers were favorable and since then it has been used extensively. The oil has been largely supplanted by the ethyl ester preparations

(Report of Leonard Wood Memorial Conference), which are administered by intra-muscular injection. As the injections of the oil or esters are painful, benzocaine has been added to the preparation by Johansen. The drug has apparently curative value in some cases but there is a good deal of skepticism as to its value. Diet and personal hygiene are also important factors in therapy. There is no specific vaccine or serum for the treatment of leprosy. Artificially induced fever, now under trial, may prove to be beneficial. Tests with derivatives of sulfanilamide are in progress.

Prevention and Control.—Isolation and segregation of lepers are still the chief measures of prevention and control of the disease. To these are added the incalculable effects of improvement in diet and general living conditions of people in many parts of the world. Treatment of lepers has reduced the mortality and, in some cases, has rendered the patients noninfectious and permitted them to return on parole to their homes.

The effectiveness of an isolation policy such as that practiced by the American government in Culion Island in the Philippine archipelago and at Molokai has been frequently questioned because of the large number of lepers who accumulate from year to year in the general population. Investigation of this problem by the United States Public Health Service has shown that with each year an increasing number of early cases come in with the new arrivals where formerly only advanced cases were admitted, showing that gradually the policy is having effect. Of still greater importance in connection with such a policy are the results from the improved method of treatment which, with the hope they engender, encourage early cases to seek investigation.

DISEASES OF LOWER ANIMALS

There are two diseases of lower animals which have interesting analogies to leprosy. One of these is a disease of rats called *rat leprosy;* the other is a gastro-intestinal disease of cattle known as *Johne's disease.* We shall discuss these briefly.

Rat Leprosy.—Stefansky first observed this disease among rats in Odessa, and since then it has been observed in Berlin (Rabinowitsch), in London (Dean), in New South Wales (Tidswell), and in San Francisco (Wherry in 1908 and McCoy). The disease occurs spontaneously among house rats and is characterized by subcutaneous induration, swelling of lymph nodes, with, later, falling out of the hair, emaciation, and sometimes ulceration. Its course is protracted and rats may live with it for six months or a year. When a rat suffering from this disease is dissected there is usually found, under the skin of the abdomen or flank, a thickened area which has the appearance of adipose tissue except that it is more nodular and gray and less shiny than fat. It is so like fat, however, that it is often overlooked by those unfamiliar with the condition. In this area acid-fast bacilli looking like the *B. leprae* are found in large numbers. These bacilli are also found in the lymph nodes and sometimes in small nodules in the liver and lung.

The disease can be transmitted experimentally from rat to rat and probably is transmitted naturally from rat to rat by the agency of fleas (Wherry, McCoy). Although clinically not exactly like human leprosy the condition is sufficiently like it to arouse much hygienic interest. The distribution of the disease in various parts of the world does not correspond with the distribution of leprosy. A peculiar feature of its distribution is the fact that in San Francisco, as the writer was told by McCoy, almost all the rats that suffered from this disease came from the district in which the retail meat business is located, known as "Butchertown." The organisms were made to multiply *in vitro* by Zinsser and Carey in plasma preparations of growing rat spleen. Chapin has succeeded in cultivating them by a method analogous to the trypsin-egg-albumin method employed by Duval. In the experiments of Zinsser and Carey it was found that although the organisms may retain their acid-fast characteristics for many weeks within leukocytes they degenerate rapidly within the spleen cells, a fact which seems to have some bearing on the mechanism of resistance possessed by the body against acid-fast organisms. The dissociation forms of Chapin's strain of this organism have been studied by Kahn and Schwarzkopf. This organism is probably not identical with the acid-fast organism in the tissues of leprous rats.

The organism, to which the name *Mycobacterium leprae murium* has been given has not been cultivated on media free from living tissue cells (Lowe).

Johne's Disease.—In cattle a specific granulomatous disease of the intestine has been recognized for more than a hundred years. It has been called paratuberculous enteritis, but is most commonly known as Johne's disease in honor of the investigator who discovered that the lesions contained characteristic acid-fast bacteria. The disease is characterized by emaciation, diarrhea, loss of appetite, anemia and weakness. The incubation period is long, the progress of the disease is slow and the ending is invariably fatal. The lesions of the intestinal wall are proliferative, never degenerative, resulting in profuse thickening of the mucosa, submucosa and wall of the ileum, cecum and upper portions of the colon. Epithelioid cells, plasma cells and occasional giant cells are found in the granulomatous tissue, which, lacking caseation, has only a superficial resemblance to tuberculosis. Some of the acid-fast bacilli are within cells, but many are in clumps outside of cells.

The disease was transmitted to calves by inoculation with ground-up lesions by Bang in 1906 and this has been repeated by others. The disease produced by injection or ingestion of cultures is less characteristic.

Sheep affected with Johne's disease show the same symptoms and lesions as are seen in cattle (Hagan).

Many attempts to cultivate this organism failed until Twort showed that a factor produced by the growth of other acid-fast bacteria was essential for the growth of Johne's bacillus on artificial media, at least at the beginning. Twort enriched egg glycerin media by the addition of killed tubercle bacilli and later by emulsions of killed cultures of the timothy hay organism *B. phlei*. After a variable number of transfers on artificial media containing this acid-fast factor, Johne's bacillus will grow without it. As a rule, however, cultures are maintained on Twort's medium. Alcoholic extracts of plants also contain this essential growth promoting substance (Twort and Ingram).

The organism, *Mycobacterium paratuberculosis* (Bergey) is a small acid-fast rod, 1 to 2 μ long and 0.5 μ broad. It is nonmotile and non-spore-forming. It grows best at 37.5° C. under aerobic conditions, but develops even more slowly than the bovine tubercle bacillus.

Filtrates of liquid cultures of the organism contain a substance which elicits allergic reactions in infected cattle. These filtrates, called *johnin*, have been used for diagnostic purposes, but have not been entirely satisfactory. Following an observation made by Bang that animals with Johne's disease frequently reacted when injected with avian tuberculin, Hagan and Zeissig have used intravenous injections of avian tuberculin as a diagnostic test. It has been suggested that Johne's bacillus may be a variant of the avian tubercle bacillus, but this seems unlikely.

No cases of infection of man with Johne's bacillus have been observed. For a more detailed review the reader is referred to the monographs of Twort, Stableforth and the summary published by Hagan and Thomson in 1931.

REFERENCES

ANDERSON, R. J., *et al.* J. Biol. Chem., 1932, 94:653; 1932, 97:617; 1936, 113:637; 1936, 114: 431; 1937, 121:669.

———— Ztschr. f. Physiol. Chem., 1933, 220:1.

ARNING. Verhandl. d. Versamml. deutsch. Naturf. u. Aerzte, 1886.

BADGER, L. F. U. S. Pub. Health Rep., 1931, 46:957.

BANG, B. Berl. tierärztl. Wchnschr., 1906, 759.

BANG, O. Centralbl. f. Bakteriol., I Abt., 1909, 51:450.

CHAPIN. U. S. Treas. Dept. Pub. Health Rep., 1912, 27:161.

CLEGG, T. Philippine J. Sc., 1909, 4:403.

DEAN, G. Centralbl. f. Bakteriol., 1903, 34:222.

———— J. Hyg., 1905, 5:99.

DUVAL, C. W. J. Exper. M., 1910, 12:645; 1911, 13:374.

DUVAL, C. W., and WELLMAN, C. J. Infect. Dis., 1912, 11:116.

HAGAN, W. A. Symposium Series, Am. Ass. Adv. Sci., 1938, 1:69.

———— Cornell Vet., 1938, 28:34.

———— and THOMSON, H. M. Tr. Nat. Tuberc. Ass., 1931.

———— and ZEISSIG. J. Am. Vet. M. Ass., 1929, 74:985.

HANSEN, G. A. Norsk Mag. f. Lægevidensk., 3R., 1874, 4:1.

———— Virchow's Arch., 1880, 79:32. References quoted from the article on Leprosy by E. Muir in A System of Bacteriology in Relation to Medicine, London, 1930, 5:345–382.

HOPKINS, R., and DENNY, O. E. U. S. Pub. Health Rep., 1929, 49:695.

Internat. Congress of Leprosy, Reports. Internat. J. Leprosy, 1938, 21:149.

JOHANSEN, F. A. U. S. Pub. Health Rep., 1928, 42: 3005.

JOHNE and FROTHINGHAM. Deutsche Ztschr. f. Thiermed., 1895, 21:438.

KAHN, M. C., and SCHWARZKOPF, H. Proc. Soc. Exper. Biol. & Med., 1931, 29:571.

KEDROWSKY, W. J. Ztschr. f. Hyg. u. Infectionskrankh., 1901, 37:52.

———— Trop. Dis. Bull., 1914, 4:514.

———— J. Trop. M. & Hyg., 1918, 31:17.

LEWIS, P. A., and ARONSON, J. D. J. Exper. M., 1923, 38:219.

LLOYD, R. B., MUIR, E., and MITRA, G. C. Indian J. M. Research, 1927, 14:667 (quoted from Muir).

LONG, E. R. Science, 1938, 87:23.

LOWE, J. Internat. J. Leprosy, 1937, 5:463.

McCOY, G. W. U. S. Pub. Health Rep., 1912, 23:981.

———— Arch. Dermatol. & Syhp., 1938, 37:169.

McKINLEY, E. B., and SOULE, M. H. J. Am. M. Ass., 1932, 98:361.

———— Am. J. Trop. M., 1932, 12:1, 141.

———— Medicine, 1934, 13:377.

———— Internat. J. Leprosy, 1938, 6:33.

McKINLEY, E. B., and VERDER, E. Proc. Soc. Exper. Biol. & Med., 1933, 30:659.

McKINLEY, E. B., and DE LEON, W. Internat. J. Leprosy, 1937, 5:259.

NEISSER, A. Breslauer ärztl. Ztschr., 1879, 20.

Nelsser, A. Virchow's Arch., 1881, 54:514.

Novy, F. G., Roehm, H. R., and Soule, M. H. J. Infect. Dis., 1925, 36:109.

Rabinowitsch, L. Centralbl. f. Bakteriol., 1903, 33:577.

Reenstierna, J. Ann. de l'Inst. Pasteur, 1926, 40:78.

Report of Leonard Wood Memorial Conference on Leprosy, Philippine J. Sc., 1931, 44:449.

Rogers, L., and Muir, E. Leprosy, Bristol, 1925.

Rost. Brit. M. J., 1905, 1.

Soule, M. H. The Newer Knowledge of Bacteriology and Immunology, Chicago, 1928, 250.

Soule, M. H., and McKinley, E. B. J. Trop. M., 1932, 12:1.

—— Am. Ass. Adv. Sci., Symposium Series, 1937, 1:87.

Stableforth, A. W. A System of Bacteriology in Relation to Medicine, London, 1930, 5:333.

Stefansky, W. K. Centralbl. f. Bakteriol., I Abt., 1903, 33:481.

Tidswell. Cited by Brinkerhoff in The Rat and Its Relation to Public Health, U. S. Treas. Dept., Washington, 1910.

Twort, F. W. Proc. Roy. Soc. London, Ser. B., 1910–11, 83:158.

Twort, F. W., and Ingram, G. L. Y. Proc. Roy. Soc. London, Ser. B., 1912, 84:517.

—— Johne's Disease, London, 1914.

U. S. Pub. Health Rep., 1925, 39 (Nos. 19, 40).

Wade, H. W. Am. J. Trop. M., 1937, 17:6.

—— Leprosy Rev., 1935, 6:2.

Walker, E. L. J. Prevent. M., 1929, 3:167.

Wherry, W. B. J. Infect. Dis., 1908, 5:507; 1930, 46:263.

—— J. Am. M. Ass., 1908, June 6.

Wherry, W. B., and Erwin, D. M. J. Infect. Dis., 1918, 22:194.

Zinsser, H., and Carey, E. G. J. Am. M. Ass., 1912, 58:692.

CHAPTER XXXIII

BACILLUS MALLEI AND GLANDERS

Family: *Parvobacteriaceae* Rahn. Tribe: *Pasteurelleae* Castellani and Chalmers. Genus: *Malleomyces* Hallier. Species: *Malleomyces mallei* Pribram.

Glanders is an infectious disease prevalent chiefly among horses, but transmitted occasionally to other domestic animals and to man. The micro-organism causing the disease, though seen and described by several earlier authors, was first obtained in pure culture and accurately studied by Löffler and Schütz in 1882.

Morphology and Staining.—The glanders bacillus or *B. mallei* is a rather small rod with rounded ends (Löffler). Its length varies from 3 to 4 μ, its breadth from 0.5 to 0.75 μ. Variation in size between separate individuals in the same culture is char-

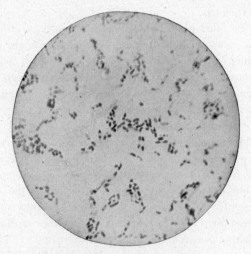

Fig. 40.—Glanders Bacillus.
From potato culture. (After Zettnow.)

acteristic. The rods are usually straight, but may show a slight curvature. The bacillus is nonmotile. There are no flagella and no spores are formed. The grouping of the bacilli in smears shows nothing very characteristic. Usually they appear as simple bacilli lying irregularly parallel, often in chains of two or more. In old cultures involution forms appear which are short, vacuolated and almost coccoid.

While the glanders bacillus stains rather easily with the usual aniline dyes, it is so easily decolorized that especial care in preparing specimens must be observed. Stained in the usual manner with methylene blue, it shows marked irregularity in its staining qualities; granular, deeply staining areas alternating with very faintly stained or entirely unstained portions. This diagnostically helpful characteristic has been variously interpreted as a mark of degeneration or a preparatory stage for sporulation. It is probably neither of the two, but an inherent irregularity in the normal protoplasmic composition of the bacillus, not unlike that of *B. diphtheriae.* The bacillus is gram-negative. It is not acid-fast.

Cultivation.—The glanders bacillus is easily grown on all of the usual meat-infusion media. It is practically indifferent to moderate variations in reaction, growing equally well upon neutral, slightly acid, or slightly alkaline culture media. Glycerin or small quantities of glucose added to media seem to render them more favorable for the cultivation of this bacillus.

Upon *agar* the colonies show little that is characteristic. They appear after twenty-four hours at 37.5° C. as yellowish white spots, at first transparent, later more opaque. They are round, with an even border, and microscopically appear finely granular. The older the cultures are, the more yellow do they appear.

On *gelatin* at room temperature, growth is slow, grayish white, and no liquefaction of the gelatin occurs. Growth upon this medium is never abundant.

In *broth*, there is, at first, diffuse clouding, later a heavy, tough, slimy sediment is formed. At the same time the surface is covered with a similarly slimy pellicle. The broth gradually assumes a dark brown color.

Sugars are not fermented.

In *milk*, coagulation takes place slowly. In litmus milk, acidification appears.

The growth upon *potato* presents certain features which are diagnostically valuable. On potatoes which are not too acid growth is abundant and within forty-eight hours covers the surface as a yellowish, transparent, slimy layer. It gradually grows darker until it has assumed a deep reddish brown hue. In using this feature of the growth diagnostically, it must not be forgotten that a very similar appearance upon potato occurs in the case of *B. pyocyaneus.*

Biological Considerations.—*Bacillus mallei* is aerobic. Growth under anaerobic conditions may take place, but it is slow and impoverished. The most favorable temperature for its cultivation is 37.5° C. It fails to develop at temperatures below 22° C. or above 43° C. On artificial media, if kept cool and in the dark, and in sealed tubes, the glanders bacillus will retain its viability for months and years. On gelatin and in bouillon, it lives for a longer time than on the other media. Exposed to strong sunlight it is killed within twenty-four hours. Heating to 60° C. kills it in two hours, to 75° C. within one hour. Thorough drying kills the glanders bacillus in a short time. In water, under the protected conditions that are apt to prevail in watering troughs, the bacillus may remain alive for over seventy days. The resistance to chemical disinfectants is not very high. Carbolic acid, 1 per cent, kills it in thirty minutes, bichloride of mercury, 0.1 per cent, in fifteen minutes.

Pathogenicity.—Spontaneous infection with the glanders bacillus occurs most frequently in horses. It occurs also in asses, in cats, and, more rarely, in dogs. In man the disease is not infrequent and is usually contracted by those in habitual contact with horses. Experimental inoculation is successful in guinea-pigs and rabbits. Cattle, hogs, rats, and birds are immune to experimental and spontaneous infections alike.

Spontaneous infection takes place by entrance through the broken skin, through the mucosa of the mouth or nasal passages. Infection in horses not infrequently takes place through the digestive tract (Nocard). In all cases, so far as we know, previous injury to either the skin or to the mucosa is necessary for penetration of the bacilli and the development of the disease.

Glanders in horses may occur in an acute or chronic form, depending upon the relative virulence of the infecting culture and the susceptibility of the subject. The more acute form of the disease is usually limited to the nasal mucosa and upper respiratory tract. The more chronic type of the disease is often accompanied by multiple swellings of the skin and general lymphatic enlargement. This form is often spoken of as "farcy."

Acute glanders in the horse begins violently with fever and prostration. After two or three days there is a nasal discharge, at first serous, later sero-purulent. At the

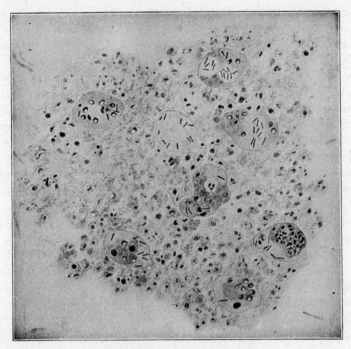

FIG. 41.—GLANDERS BACILLI IN TISSUE.
From a drawing furnished by Dr. James Ewing.

same time there is ulceration of the nasal mucosa and acute swelling of the neighboring lymph nodes. These may break down and form deep pus-discharging sinuses and ulcers. Finally, there is involvement of the lungs and death within four to six weeks.

When the disease takes the chronic form the onset is more gradual. Concomitant with the nasal inflammation there is a formation of subcutaneous swellings all over the body, some of which show a tendency to break down and ulcerate. Together with this the lymphatics all over the body become enlarged. The disease may last for several years, and occasionally may end in complete cure. In horses the chronic form of the disease is by far the more frequent. In man the disease is similar to that of the horse except that the point of origin is more frequently in some part of the skin rather than in the nasal mucosa, and the clinical symptoms differ accordingly. The onset is usually violent, with fever and systemic symptoms. At the point of infection a nodule appears, surrounded by lymphangitis and swelling. A general papular eruption may occur. The papules may become pustular, and the clinical features may thus simulate variola. This type of the disease usually ends fatally in eight to ten days. The chronic form of the disease in man is much like that in the horse, but is more frequently fatal.

The histological appearance of the glanders nodules is usually one of diffuse leukocytic infiltration and the formation of young connective tissue which preponderates more and more as the disease becomes chronic. Virchow has classed these lesions with the granulomata. From the center of such nodules B. mallei may often be obtained in pure culture. The nodules may be generally distributed throughout the internal organs. The bacilli themselves are found, apart from the nodules, in the nasal secretions, and occasionally in the circulating blood (Wassilieff).

The bacteriological diagnosis of glanders may be made by isolating and identifying the bacilli from any of the above-mentioned sources. When superficial nodules can be opened for the purpose of diagnosis this may prove an easy task. The most diagnostically helpful medium in such cases is potato. In a majority of cases, however, isolation is extremely difficult and resort must be had to animal inoculation. The most suitable animal for this purpose is the male guinea-pig. Intraperitoneal inoculation of such animals with material containing glanders bacilli leads within two or three days to tumefaction and purulent inflammation of the testicles. Such an experiment, spoken of as the "Strauss test," should always be reinforced by cultural examination of the testicular pus, the spleen, and the peritoneal exudate of the animals employed.

Toxins of Bacillus Mallei.—The toxin of B. mallei, or mallein, belongs to the class of endotoxins. The toxic products have been invariably obtained by extraction of dead bacilli (Kresling). Mallein differs from many other bacterial poisons in being extremely resistant. It withstands temperatures of 120° C. and prolonged storage without noticeable loss of strength (Wladimiroff).

In its physiological action upon healthy animals, mallein is not a powerful poison. It can be given in considerable doses without causing death. Mallein may be obtained by a variety of methods. Helman and Kalning, the discoverers of this toxin, used filtered aqueous and glycerin extracts of potato cultures. Roux (Roux and Nocard) cultivated virulent glanders bacilli in flasks containing 250 c.c. each of 5 per cent glycerin bouillon. Growth was allowed to continue at 35° C. for one month. At the end of this time, the cultures are sterilized at 100° C. for thirty minutes, and evaporated on a water bath to one-tenth their original volume. They are then filtered through paper. This concentrated poison is diluted ten times with 0.5 per cent carbolic acid before use. Concentration is done merely for purposes of conservation. The diagnostic dose of such mallein for a horse is 0.25 c.c. of the undiluted fluid, injected subcutaneously.

At the Washington Bureau of Animal Industry, mallein is prepared by growing the bacilli for five months at 37.5° C. in glycerin bouillon. This is then boiled for one hour and allowed to stand in a cool place for one week. The supernatant fluid is then decanted and filtered through clay filters by means of a vacuum pump. The filtrate is evaporated to one-third its original volume on a water bath, and the evaporated volume resupplied by a 1 per cent carbolic acid solution containing about 10 per cent of glycerin.

Diagnostic Use of Mallein.—The injection of a proper dose of mallein into a horse suffering from glanders is followed within six to eight hours by a sharp rise of temperature, often reaching 104° to 106° F. (40° C. +). The high temperature continues for several hours and then begins gradually to fall. The normal is not usually regained for several days. Locally, at the point of injection, there appears within a few hours a firm, hot, diffuse swelling, which gradually extends until it may cover areas of 20 to 30 centimeters in diameter. The swelling is intensely tender during the first twenty-four hours, and lasts for three to nine days. Together with this there are marked symptoms of general intoxication. In normal animals the rise of temperature following an injection is trifling, and the local reaction is much smaller and more transient. Injections are best made into the breast or the side of the neck.

The directions given by the United States government for using mallein for the diagnosis of glanders in horses are as follows:

Make the test, if possible, with a healthy horse, as well as with one or more affected or supposed to be affected with glanders. Take the temperature of all these animals at least three times a day for one or more days before making the injections.

The injection is most conveniently made at 6 or 7 o'clock in the morning, and the maximum temperature will then usually be reached by or before 10 P.M. of the same day.

Use for each horse one cubic centimeter of the mallein solution as sent out, and make the injection beneath the skin of the middle of one side of the neck, where the local swelling can be readily detected.

Carefully sterilize the syringe after injecting each horse by flaming the needle over an alcohol lamp or, better, use separate syringes for healthy and suspected animals. If the same syringe is used, inject the healthy animals first, and flame the needle of the syringe after each injection.

Take the temperature every two hours for at least eighteen hours after the injection. Sterilize the thermometer in a 5 per cent solution of carbolic acid, or a 0.2 per cent solution of corrosive sublimate, after taking the temperature of each animal.

The temperature, as a rule, will begin to rise from four to eight hours after the injection, and reach its maximum from ten to sixteen hours after injection. On the day succeeding the injection take the temperature at least three times.

In addition to the febrile reaction, note the size, appearance, and duration of any local swelling at the point of injection. Note the general condition and symptoms of the animal, both before, during, and after the test.

Keep the solution in the sealed bottle and in a cool place, and do not use it when it is clouded or if it is more than six weeks old; when it leaves the laboratory of the Bureau it is sterile.

If the result of the first injection is doubtful, the horse should be isolated and retested in from one to three months, when the slight immunity conferred by the first injection will have disappeared. The second injection into healthy horses usually shows no reaction whatever.

Mallein may cause reactions in the presence of other diseases than glanders, such as bronchitis, periostitis, and other inflammatory lesions and is not so specifically valuable as tuberculin for diagnosis.

Complement Fixation in Glanders.—Diagnostic complement fixation for the diagnosis of glanders has been developed by McNeil and Olmstead at the New York City Department of Health. The antigen is made by growing the glanders bacilli on a 1.6 per cent glycerin potato agar. From this stock culture transplants are made upon a neutral meat-free-veal-peptone agar. Twenty-four hour growths are washed off with distilled water sterilized at 80° C. for four hours and filtered through a Berkfeld. After filtration the antigen must again be sterilized at 80° C. for one hour.

Immunity.—Recovery from a glanders infection does not confer immunity against a second inoculation (Finger). Artificial active immunization has been variously attempted by treatment with attenuated cultures, with dead bacilli, and with mallein, but without convincing results.

The serum of subjects suffering from glanders contains specific agglutinins (Galtier). These are of great importance diagnostically if the tests are made with dilutions of, at least 1:500, since normal horse serum may agglutinate B. mallei in dilutions lower than this.

MELIOIDOSIS

A disease resembling glanders in man was first described by Whitmore and Krishnaswami in Rangoon in 1912. The chief features of the disease are septicemia, pyemia and the formation of characteristic granulomatous nodules in nearly all parts of the body. The infection has occurred not only in man but also in epizootic form among guinea-pigs and rabbits in certain laboratories. As the disease occurs also in wild rats, it is supposed that these animals are the natural reservoir of the infection. Cases of the disease have been reported chiefly from the Malay States, Indo China, and Ceylon. In 1921, Standton and Fletcher named the disease *Melioidosis* because the ancient Greeks applied the term "Melis" to a variety of conditions resembling glanders.

When Whitmore studied the organism isolated by him from lesions of this disease, he recognized that it was related to the glanders bacillus and, therefore, named the organism *Bacillus pseudo-mallei*. Other names given to the organism are *Bacillus whitmorei, Pfeifferella whitmorei*, and finally in the fifth edition of Bergey's *Manual of Determinative Bacteriology* it is listed as *Malleomyces pseudomallei*.

The organism as described by Whitmore, and Stanton and Fletcher is said to be 1 to 2 μ long, and 0.5 μ broad. Longer and broader forms are found in broth cultures. The organism is *motile*, does not form spores and is not acid-fast. It is gram-negative.

This bacterium is aerobic and grows well on the usual culture media. The colonies which are at first whitish and opaque become yellow or brown and wrinkled. The optimum temperature for growth is 37° C. Mucoid and rough variants have been described. The cultures are said to have an earthy, moldy odor. The organism liquefies gelatin. It does not produce indole. It produces acid without gas in glucose and acid with coagulation in milk.

B. whitmorei differs from *B. mallei* chiefly in being motile and in its ability to liquefy gelatin.

There is a close antigenic relationship between *B. whitmorei* and one of the serological groups of the glanders bacillus (Stanton). There is no evidence that the organism is related to *Bacterium tularense*, and melioidosis seems to be distinct from tularemia.

REFERENCES

GALTIER. J. de méd. vét., Lyon, 1901.
KRESLING. Arch. d. sc. biol., 1892.
LÖFFLER, F. Arb. a. d. k. Gsndhtsamte., 1886.
LÖFFLER, F., and SCHÜTZ. Deutsche med. Wchnschr., 1882, 8:707.

Nocard. Bull. Soc. centr. de méd. vét., 1894.

Preuser. Berl. tierärztl. Wchnschr., 1894.

Roux and Nocard. Bull. Soc. centr. de méd. vét., 1892.

Stanton, A. T., and Fletcher, W. Tr. 4th Cong. Far East. Ass. Trop. M., 1921, 2:196.

—— J. Hyg., 1925, 23:347.

—— Lancet, 1925, 1:10.

Strauss, I. Arch. de méd. expér., 1889, 1:460.

Wassilieff. Deutsche med. Wchnschr., 1883.

Whitmore, A. J. Hyg., 1913, 13:1.

Whitmore, A., and Krishnaswami, C. S. Indian M. Gaz., 1912, 47:262.

Wladimiroff. In Kraus and Levaditi, Handbuch, etc., 1908.

CHAPTER XXXIV

FRIEDLÄNDER BACILLI, PNEUMONIA, RHINOSCLEROMA AND OZENA

There is a large group of encapsulated gram-negative bacteria whose habitat and disease-producing capacities relate them to pathogens of the respiratory tract while their occurrence in the intestinal tract and their metabolic activities demonstrate that they have affinities with bacteria of the colon group. An arrangement of organisms based upon the pathogenic activity of the chief bacterium of this group would require placing them among the incitants of pneumonia and other diseases of the respiratory tract. If the emphasis were to be placed upon morphological and cultural properties, these organisms would be considered with other intestinal bacteria, particularly members of the colon-aerogenes group. Although some forms are apparently connecting links with the colon bacilli, the type species and its close relatives are sufficiently distinctive to justify setting them apart. In recognition of these facts, these bacteria have been accorded generic distinction under a variety of names. Castellani named the genus *Encapsulatus*. Bergey has called the genus *Klebsiella*, adopting the name proposed in 1887 by Trevisan. Since *Klebsiella* has not come into general use, we shall, in this case as in others, list it for reference and refer to this group by names with which medical bacteriologists are more familiar, *viz.*: the *Bacillus mucosus capsulatus* group or the group of Friedländer bacilli.

The organisms in this group are plump rods, usually short, encapsulated, nonmotile, nonsporing, gram-negative, aerobic and capable of fermenting a variety of carbohydrates with the production of acid and usually gas. The type species is Friedländer's bacillus.

BACILLUS MUCOSUS CAPSULATUS

Family: *Enterobacteriaceae* Rahn. Tribe: *Eschericheae* Castellani and Chalmers. Genus: *Klebsiella* Trevisan. Species: *Klebsiella pneumoniae* Trevisan

In 1882, Friedländer announced the discovery of a micro-organism which he believed to be the incitant of lobar pneumonia and which, in his original communications, he described as a "micrococcus."

A superficial morphological resemblance between Friedländer's micro-organism and *Diplococcus lanceolatus*, now recognized as the most frequent cause of lobar pneumonia, led, at first, to much confusion, and it was not until several years later, owing to the careful researches of Fränkel and of Weichselbaum, that the "micrococcus" of Friedländer was recognized as a short, encapsulated bacillus which occurred only rarely in lobar pneumonia. Similar bacilli were subsequently found by others observers, bacilli which, upon morphological grounds, are classified together as the "Friedländer group," or the "group of *Bacillus mucosus capsulatus*."

482

Morphology and Staining.—The Friedländer bacillus is a short, plump bacillus with rounded ends, subject to great individual variations as to size. Its average measurements are from 0.5 to 1.5 μ in width and 0.6 to 5 μ in length. Forms approaching both extremes may be met with in one and the same culture. The short, thick forms, frequently found in animal and human lesions, are almost coccoid and account for Friedländer's error in first describing the bacillus as a micrococcus. The bacilli may be single, in diploform, or in short chains. They are nonmotile and possess no flagella. Spores are not formed.

The bacillus is characteristically surrounded by a well-developed capsule which is most perfectly demonstrated in preparations taken directly from some animal fluid, such as the secretion or exudate from infected areas. It is also seen in smears made from agar or gelatin cultures. The capsule is usually large, twice or three times the size of the bacillus itself. When seen in chains or in groups, several bacilli may appear to be inclosed in one capsule. Prolonged cultivation on agar or gelatin may result in disappearance of the capsule. The bacillus is easily stained with the ordinary dyes. It is gram-negative. Capsules may often be seen when the

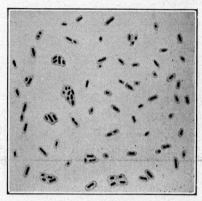

FIG. 42.—BACILLUS MUCOSUS CAPSULATUS.

From W. W. Ford, *Textbook of Bacteriology.*

more intense aniline dyes are employed. They are brought out with much regularity by any of the usual capsule stains.

Cultivation.—*B. mucosus capsulatus* is easily cultivated. It grows readily on all the usual culture media, both on those having a meat-infusion basis and on those made with meat extract. Growth takes place at room temperature (18° to 20° C.) and more readily at 35° C. A temperature of 60° C. and over kills the bacilli in a short time. The thermal death point according to Sternberg is 56° C. Growth ceases below 10° to 12° C. Kept at room temperature and protected from drying, the bacillus may remain alive, in cultures, for several months.

The bacillus is not very fastidious as to reaction of media, growing equally well on moderately alkaline or acid media. It is aerobic and facultatively anaerobic; growth under anaerobic conditions, however, is not luxuriant.

On *agar*, growth appears in the form of grayish white mucus-like colonies, having a characteristically slimy and semifluid appearance. Colonies have a tendency to confluence, so that on plates, after three or four days, a large part of the surface appears as if covered with a film of glistening, sticky exudate, which, if fished, comes off in a tenacious, stringy manner. It is often possible to make a tentative diagnosis of the bacillus from the appearance of this growth.

In *broth*, there is rapid and abundant growth, with the formation of a pellicle, general clouding, and later the development of a profuse, stringy sediment.

Stab cultures in *gelatin* show, at first, a white, thin line of growth along the course of the puncture. Soon, however, rapid growth at the top results in the formation of a grayish mucoid droplet on the surface, which, enlarging, gives the growth a nail-

like appearance. This nail shape was originally described by Friedländer and regarded as diagnostic for the bacillus. The gelatin is not liquefied. As the culture
grows older the entire surface of the gelatin tube may be covered with growth, flowing out from the edges of the nail head. The gelatin acquires a darker color and
there may be a few gas bubbles below the surface. Microscopically, colonies on gelatin plates have a smooth outline and a finely granular or even homogeneous consistency.

On *blood serum*, a confluent mucus-like growth appears.

On *potato*, abundant growth appears, slightly more brownish in color than on
other media.

In *peptone solutions*, there is no indole formation.

Nitrates are reduced to nitrites.

In *milk*, there is abundant growth and marked capsule development. Coagulation
occurs irregularly.

Fermentation of Carbohydrates.—The Friedländer bacilli ferment many carbohydrates with the production of acid and usually gas. As it was thought that subdivisions of the group could be made on the basis of differences in fermentative ability,
there have been numerous tests of the actions of these bacteria upon as many as
eighteen "sugars"—the monosaccharides, disaccharides, alcohols, pentoses, and gluco-
sides commonly used in investigations of this sort. Perkins divided the group into
three classes.

When Fitzgerald reinvestigated the fermentation reactions of bacteria in the *mucosus-capsulatus* group, he could not find any regular correlations between source of
an organism, pathogenicity and fermentative capacity. The same general conclusion
was reached in 1923 by Small and Julianelle, who after elaborate tests divided these
organisms into four ill-defined groups on the basis of their actions upon glucose, lactose and sucrose, but expressed the opinion that the fermentation reactions were too
variable and irregular to be of differential significance. The classification of Perkins
has not been substantiated and in our experience only general significance is to be
attached to the fermentation reactions of members of this group. We mean by this
that we do not depend upon the results of these tests for making distinction between
species.

Variability and Dissociation.—Some order is being introduced in the knowledge
of the relationships among organisms of the Friedländer group through studies of
their variability. A number of observers in the past have noted the extreme variations
in size and shape of Friedländer bacilli, have seen differences in the forms of their
colonies and have studied capsulated and noncapsulated races. We shall review here
only the work of Julianelle and others who have analyzed these variations by applying methods developed during the study of variability of pneumococci and other
organisms. Julianelle succeeded, by growing the organisms in homologous antiserum
(anti-R serum), in dissociating cultures of Friedländer's bacillus into S (smooth)
and R (rough) types. The S forms were mucoid, encapsulated and virulent. The R
forms gave rise to colonies that were not mucoid, but were rather friable and irregular and contained nonencapsulated organisms lacking virulence. The antigenic
changes associated with these physiological and morphological variations will be discussed in the next paragraph.

Serological Types.—The older work on the serological differentiation of organisms of this group led to no useful conclusion. The more recent work bringing together cultural studies of dissociation and chemical and immunological investigation of the antigenic components of the cells has shown, according to Julianelle (1926) that the S forms of Friedländer bacilli contain a group-specific protein antigen in their cell bodies and type-specific polysaccharide haptenes in their capsules. The noncapsulated R forms contain only the group antigen in the cell protein. Anti-R serum is not type specific and will agglutinate any member of the group. Anti-S serum is type specific. By agglutination and precipitin reactions with anti-S serum, Julianelle divided the organisms of the Friedländer group into 3 types, called A, B and C, and a group X in which he placed a number of apparently unrelated strains.

As a result of a similar study of cultures of these encapsulated organisms derived from metritis in mares, from soil and from human sources, Edwards (1928) has, in all essential points, confirmed the findings of Julianelle. Edwards found by precipitin tests that his strains of Friedländer bacilli fell in two groups. His Type I corresponds to Julianelle's Type B and included most of the cultures from mares. Edwards' Type II is identical with Julianelle's Type A.

Neither Edwards (1929) nor Julianelle (1930) has found any correlation between fermentation reactions, serological types and sources of cultures.

Julianelle has confirmed Blake's observation that soluble specific substance occurs in the urine of patients with Friedländer bacillus pneumonia and can be demonstrated by a precipitin reaction with appropriate anti-serum.

In 1925, Heidelberger, Goebel and Avery applied their methods of serological and chemical analysis to the polysaccharide of the Friedländer bacillus which previously had been noticed by Toenniessen in his studies of the "gummy substances" of bacterial capsules. They found that the polysaccharide or soluble specific substance of Julianelle's Type B Friedländer bacillus yielded glucose on hydrolysis, did not contain nitrogen, was dextrorotatory and resembled chemically the polysaccharide of Type II pneumococcus. Specific anti-Type II pneumococcus serum precipitated this Friedländer polysaccharide and the antibody to the Friedländer organism reacted with the pneumococcus polysaccharide. Cross-protection was given by these sera when injected into mice together with doses of virulent organisms of either species.

As the whole Friedländer group has not yet been analyzed according to these serological methods, it is not yet known how the *mucosus-capsulatus* organisms which cause pneumonia, rhinoscleroma, otitis media, and inguinal granuloma are distributed among these types. There is some evidence, presented by Quast, that the rhinoscleroma bacillus may be distinct from other Friedländer bacilli. Quast used complement fixation reactions to make this differentiation. On the other hand, Edwards (1929) has found strains from mares and soil to be indistinguishable culturally and serologically from organisms derived from pathological processes in man. Five of the cultures labeled *Bacterium aerogenes* isolated from soil by various investigators were identical culturally and serologically with Julianelle's Type B Friedländer bacillus, and two cultures of *Bact. aerogenes* from soil were identical with the granuloma inguinale strains. The work of Weed, Wegeforth, Ayer and Felton showed that a stock culture labeled *Bacillus lactis aerogenes* was extremely pathogenic for cats, producing a fatal meningitis when injected intraspinously into these animals. It is evident that older distinctions made largely upon habitat or source of cultures and upon fermentation reactions whose variability was not appreciated must give way before this newer knowledge. The relationships among all the organisms in the Friedländer-aerogenes group remain to be determined.

Pathogenicity.—When Friedländer first described this micro-organism, he assumed it to be the incitant of lobar pneumonia. Subsequent researches by Weichselbaum and others have shown it to be etiologically associated with pneumonia in about 7 or 8 per cent of all cases. The percentage in this country is probably lower. Such cases can often be diagnosed by the presence of the bacilli in the sputum, which is peculiarly sticky and stringy. Cases of Friedländer pneumonia are extremely severe and usually fatal. The bacillus has been found in cases of ulcerative stomatitis and nasal catarrh; in cases of severe tonsillitis in children; in the pus from suppurations in the antrum of Highmore and the nasal sinuses, and in cases of fetid coryza (ozena), of which disease it was supposed by Abel and others to be the specific cause. Whether the ozena bacillus represents a separate species or not, cannot at present be decided. The bacillus of Friedländer has been found in empyema fluid, in pericardial exudate (after pneumonia), and in spinal fluid (Edwards, 1929). Isolated cases of Friedländer bacillus septicemia have been described (Julianelle, 1930). Being occasionally a saprophytic inhabitant of the normal intestine, it has been believed to be etiologically associated with some forms of diarrheal enteritis.

A Friedländer-like organism is suspected by Walker to be etiologically related to granuloma inguinale and to represent the inclusion bodies found in smears and known as the "Donovan bodies."

B. mucosus capsulatus is pathogenic for mice and guinea-pigs, less so for rabbits. Inoculation of susceptible animals is followed by local inflammation and death by septicemia. If inoculation is intraperitoneal, there is formed a characteristically mucoid, stringy exudate.

OTHER BACILLI OF THE FRIEDLÄNDER GROUP

Bacillus of Rhinoscleroma.—This bacillus, described by von Frisch in 1882, is a plump, short rod, with rounded ends, morphologically almost identical with Friedländer's bacillus; it is nonmotile and possesses a distinct capsule. Although at first described as gram-positive, it has been shown to be decolorized with this method of staining. It forms slimy colonies, has a nail-like appearance in gelatin stab cultures, and in peptone solutions produces no indole. It differs from *B. mucosus capsulatus* (Wilde) in forming no gas in dextrose bouillon, in producing no acid in lactose bouillon, and in never coagulating milk.

Pathogenicity.—The bacillus of rhinoscleroma is but moderately pathogenic for animals delicately susceptible to the bacillus of Friedländer. Rhinoscleroma, the disease produced by this bacillus in man, consists of a slowly growing granulomatous inflammation, located usually at the external nares or upon the mucosa of the nose, mouth, pharynx or larynx. It is composed of a number of chronic, hard, nodular swellings, which, on histological examination, show granulation tissue and productive inflammation. In the meshes of the abundant connective tissue lie many large swollen cells, the so-called "Mikulicz cells." The rhinoscleroma bacilli lie within these cells and in the intercellular spaces. They can be demonstrated in histological sections and can be cultivated from the lesions, usually in pure culture. Rhinoscleroma is rare in America. It is most prevalent in southeastern Europe. The disease is slowly progressive and comparatively intractable to surgical treatment, but hardly ever affects the general health unless by mechanical obstruction of the air passages.

On the basis of older knowledge, the variety of Friedländer bacillus associated with this condition was called *Bacillus rhinoscleromatis*, and is listed by Bergey as *Klebsiella rhinoscleromatis*. There is some doubt as to whether it deserves species rank and further doubt as to its etiological relationship to the disease.

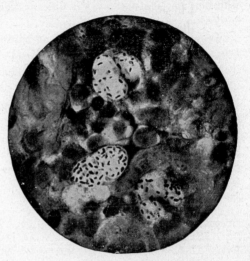

FIG. 43.—BACILLUS OF RHINOSCLEROMA.

Section of tissue showing the micro-organisms within Mikulicz cells. (After Fränkel and Pfeiffer.)

Ozena.—A somewhat definite type of atrophic rhinitis characterized by the formation of crusts in the nose and associated with an unusually foul, sickening, pervasive odor has been known for a long time as ozena. The disease has never been reproduced experimentally and we are of the opinion that the actual cause is unknown. It may be the result of some general disease, of a dietary deficiency, trophic or circulatory disorder. Certainly the evidence that any particular bacterium isolated from the lesions is anything but a secondary invader is unconvincing. Nevertheless it has been customary to regard a so-called species of Friedländer bacillus as one of the probable bacterial causes. This organism, isolated by Abel in 1896 has been handed down under the name *Bacillus ozaenae*, and is listed by Bergey as *Klebsiella ozaenae*. We doubt its specificity and etiological relationship to the disease.

In 1935 Julianelle reported on the cultural characteristics and serological properties of 19 strains of *Klebsiella ozaenae*. All reduced nitrates to nitrites, but did not form indole or liquefy gelatin. The fermentation reactions were too variable to be of value for classification. Acid and gas were produced in glucose, lactose and sucrose by most of the strains. By agglutination reactions two main types were recognized, and in addition a heterogeneous group. The organisms were antigenically distinct from Friedländer bacilli.

Another bacterium traditionally supposed to have an etiological relationship to fetid ozena is the Perez bacillus. It was isolated from crusts in the nose by Perez in 1899 at a time when, as Topley and Wilson point out, "most of the early workers entirely underestimated the difficulty of establishing the aetiological rôle of any organism isolated from such a situation as the nose." The Perez bacillus is gram-negative, nonmotile, and noncapsulated. It grows readily on ordinary media, does not liquefy gelatin and produces indole. Its cultures have a characteristic fetid odor. It is said to produce a localized lesion on the turbinate bones in the nasal cavity of rabbits after intravenous injection, but this seems doubtful in view of the proneness of rabbits to develop "snuffles." Michailoff has expressed the opinion that the Perez bacillus is an organism of the *Proteus* group. This seems highly probable. We agree with him also that the *Bacillus ozaenae liquefaciens*, described by Shiga, is the same as *Proteus vulgaris*.

Topley and Wilson, in the second edition of their *Principles of Bacteriology and Immunity* include the *Cocco-bacillus foetidus-ozaenae* (Perez's bacillus) in the group including the glanders bacillus and the bacillus of Whitmore.

REFERENCES

ABEL, R. Centralbl. f. Bakteriol., I Abt., 1893, 13:161.
———— Ztschr. f. Hyg. u. Infectionskrankh., 1896, 21:89, 189.
BLAKE, F. G. Arch. Int. Med., 1918, 21:779.
EDWARDS, P. R. J. Bacteriol., 1928, 15:247; 1929, 17:339.
FRÄNKEL. Ztschr. f. klin. Med., 1886, 10.
FRIEDLÄNDER. Virchow's Arch., 1882, 87.
———— Fortschr. d. Med., 1883, 1; 1884, 2.
FITZGERALD, J. G. J. Infect. Dis., 1914, 15:268.
HEIDELBERGER, M., GOEBEL, W. F., and AVERY, O. T. J. Exper. M., 1925, 42:709.
JULIANELLE, L. A. J. Exper. M., 1926, 44:113, 683, 735; 1930, 52:539.
———— J. Bacteriol., 1935, 30, 535.
MICHAILOFF, A. Bull. Johns Hopkins Hosp., 1926, 39:158.
MIKULICZ. Arch. f. Chir., 1876, 20.
MORRIS, M. C., and JULIANELLE, L. A. J. Infect. Dis., 1934, 55:150.
PEREZ, F. Ann. de l'Inst. Pasteur, 1899, 13:937.
PERKINS, R. G. J. Infect. Dis., 1904, 1:241.
QUAST, G. Centralbl. f. Bakteriol., I Abt., 1926, 97:174.
SHIGA, M. Centralbl. f. Bakteriol., I Abt., 1922, 88:521; 1923, 90:78.
SMALL, J. C., and JULIANELLE, L. A. J. Infect. Dis., 1923, 32:456.
TOENNIESSEN, E. Centralbl. f. Bakteriol., I Abt., 1921, 85:225.
VON FRISCH. Wien. med. Wchnschr., 1882.
WEED, L. H., WEGEFORTH, P., AYER, J. B., and FELTON, L. D. J. Am. M. Ass., 1919, 72:190.
———— A Study of Experimental Meningitis, Monographs of the Rockefeller Inst. for Med. Research, No. 12, 1920.
WEICHSELBAUM. Med. Jahrb., Wien, 1886.
WILDE, M. Centralbl. f. Bakteriol., I Abt., 1896, 20:681.

CHAPTER XXXV

THE COLON-AEROGENES-PROTEUS GROUPS

It was the custom until about 1920 to place in one genus all the aerobic gram-negative nonsporing rods found in the intestines under normal and diseased conditions. This group of "enteric organisms" contained many bacteria with differing metabolic and pathogenic capacities. It was recognized that these organisms had in common morphological features and certain cultural characteristics. Differentiation of one member of the group from another has been extremely difficult. It has been through the study of this group, particularly, that many of the modern differential methods of bacteriology have been developed. As the characteristics of the group became better known, it seemed advisable to a Committee of the Society of American Bacteriologists to set this group apart under the generic name *Bacterium*. Since then, the subdivision has been carried still farther in Bergey's *Manual*, where these intestinal organisms are listed under the tribe *Eschericheae* in the family *Enterobacteriaceae*, under the tribe *Bacterieae*, and have been given new generic names. We think that some of the new names are ill-chosen and unsatisfactory for various reasons, but that the generic name *Bacterium* has much to recommend it.

The group of intestinal organisms with which we shall deal in this and several following chapters contains both saprophytes and parasites. Many of the saprophytes are important economically and from the point of view of sanitation. Others are the causes of disease of man and animals. The subdivisions of the group may be indicated as follows:

I. The colon-aerogenes group. This includes *Bacterium coli, Bacterium aerogenes* and related organisms. It has affinities with the Friedländer bacilli which we have discussed in the preceding chapter.

II. The paratyphoid group. Most of the organisms in this group are pathogenic for man and animals. Organisms responsible for paratyphoid fevers and for some types of food poisoning are in this division.

III. The typhoid group. This is a homogeneous group of organisms, probably only one species with its variants, responsible for typhoid fever.

IV. The dysentery bacilli. A variety of organisms which cause enteritis and particularly colitis are included in this division.

Morphological characteristics, although exhibiting slight differences, are insufficient to permit diagnosis. None of the group is a spore-bearer. Stained by Gram's method they are decolorized. Cultivated upon artificial media, they grow readily both at room and at incubator temperatures.

In order to distinguish between the individual members of this group, therefore, we are forced to a careful observation of the cultural characteristics upon special media and by the study of serum reactions in specific immune sera. The most important differential characteristics are fermentative actions upon carbohydrate media, action on gelatin, and agglutinating reactions in immune sera. These points will be taken up in the description of the individual micro-organisms, and will again be summarized in the differential tables.

BACTERIUM COLI COMMUNIS AND MEMBERS OF THE COLON GROUP

Under the name of "colon bacilli" are grouped a number of varieties differing from one another in minor characteristics, but corresponding in certain cardinal points which stamp them as close relatives. While usually growing as harmless parasites upon the animal and human body, and capable of leading a purely saprophytic existence, they may, nevertheless, under certain circumstances become pathogenic and thus form a link between pure saprophytes like *B. lactis aerogenes*, on the one hand, and the more strictly pathogenic gram-negative bacilli of the paratyphoid, typhoid, and dysentery groups, on the other. As a type of the group we may consider its most prominent member, *B. coli communis*.

BACTERIUM COLI COMMUNIS

Species: *Escherichia coli*

This micro-organism was seen and described by Buchner in 1885. It was thoroughly studied by Escherich, in connection with the intestinal contents of infants.

Morphology.—*B. coli communis* is a short, plump rod about 1 to 3 μ long and varying in thickness from one-third to one-fifth of its length. Under varying conditions of cultivation, it may appear to be more slender than this or shorter and even coccoid in form. It usually appears singly, but occasionally may be seen in short chains. It stains readily and is gram-negative. Spores are not formed. It is motile, and flagella staining reveals eight or more flagella peripherally arranged. Its motility is subject to wide variations. Young cultures, in the first generations after isolation, may be extremely motile, while old laboratory strains may show almost no motility. Independent of these modifying conditions, however, separate races may show individual characteristics as to motility, varying in range between a motility hardly distinguishable from brownian movement and one which is so active as to be but little less than that of the typhoid bacillus.

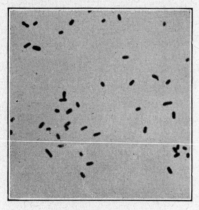

Fig. 44.—Bact. Coli.
From a smooth culture. × 1200.

Cultivation.—The bacillus is an aerobe capable of anaerobic growth under suitable cultural conditions. It grows well on the simplest media at temperatures ranging from 20° to 40° C., but finds its optimum at about 37.5° C. Upon *broth* it grows rapidly, giving rise to general clouding; later to a pellicle and a light, slimy sediment.

Upon *agar*, it forms grayish colonies which become visible within twelve to eighteen hours, gradually becoming more and more opaque as they grow older. The deep colonies are dense, even granular, oval, or round. Surface colonies often show a characteristic grape-leaf structure, or may be round and flat, and show a raised, glistening surface. Upon agar slants, growth occurs in a uniform layer.

On *gelatin* the colon bacillus causes *no liquefaction*. In gelatin stabs growth takes place along the entire line of inoculation, spreading in a thin layer over the surface of the medium.

On *potato* growth is abundant and visible, within eighteen to twenty-four hours, as a grayish white, glistening layer which later turns to a yellowish brown, and in old cultures to a dirty greenish brown color.

In *peptone solution* indole is formed. In *milk* there is acidity and coagulation. In *lactose litmus agar* acid is formed, the medium becoming red, and gas bubbles appear along the line of the stab inoculation.

In *carbohydrate broth,* gas is formed in dextrose, lactose and mannite, but not in saccharose. Levulose, galactose, and maltose are also fermented with the formation of acid and gas.

Cultures of the colon bacillus are characterized by a fetid odor which is not unlike that of diluted feces. The acids formed from sugars are chiefly lactic, acetic, and formic. The gas it produces consists chiefly of carbon dioxide and hydrogen. The bacillus grows well on media containing urine and on those containing bile. Since bile inhibits many other bacteria, this fact is useful in the isolation of the colon bacillus from water and feces.

Isolation from mixed cultures is most easily accomplished by plating upon lactose eosin methylene blue medium, or upon Endo's medium.

Distribution.—The colon bacillus is a constant inhabitant of the intestinal canal of human beings and animals. It is also found occasionally in soil, in air, in water, and in milk and is practically ubiquitous in all neighborhoods which are thickly inhabited. When found in nature its presence is generally taken to be an indication of contamination from human or animal sources. Thus, when found in water or milk, much hygienic importance is attached to it. Papasotiriu and independently of him, Prescott, reported finding bacilli apparently identical with *B. coli* upon rye, barley, and other grains. They believe that *B. coli* is widely distributed and that its presence, unless it appears in large numbers, does not necessarily indicate recent fecal contamination. These varieties of nonfecal colon bacillus are in the *aerogenes* group.

In man, *B. coli* appears in the intestine normally soon after birth, at about the time of taking the first nourishment. From this time on, throughout life, the bacillus is a constant intestinal inhabitant without dependence upon the diet. Its distribution within the intestine, according to Cushing and Livingood, is not uniform, it being found in the greatest numbers at or about the ileocecal valve, diminishing from this point upward to the duodenum and downward as far as the rectum. Adami and others claim that, under normal conditions, the bacillus may invade the portal circulation, possibly by the intermediation of leukocytic emigration during digestion. After death, at autopsy, *B. coli* is often found in the tissues and the blood without there being visible lesions of the intestinal mucous membrane (Birch-Hirschfeld). It is probable, also, that it may enter and live in the circulation a few hours before death.

The distribution of the colon bacilli in the human intestine at different periods of life, and under varying dietetic conditions has been considered in the section on the normal flora of the intestinal canal.

Extensive investigations have been carried out to determine whether the presence of this micro-organism in the intestinal tract is an indication of its possessing a definite physiological function. It has been argued that it may aid in the fermentation of carbohydrates. The question has been approached experimentally by a number of investigators. Nuttall and Thierfelder delivered guinea-pigs from the mother by cesarean section and succeeded in preserving them from infection of the intestinal canal for thirteen days. Although no micro-organisms of any kind were found in the feces of these animals, no harm seemed to accrue to them. Schottelius obtained contradictory results with chicks. Allowing eggs to hatch in an especially constructed glass compartment, he succeeded in keeping the chicks and their entire environment sterile for seventeen days. During this time they lost weight, did not thrive, and some of them were moribund at the end of the second week. Although no definite statement can be made, it is more than likely that the function of B. coli in the intestine is not inconsiderable if only because of its possible antagonism to certain putrefactive bacteria, a fact which has been demonstrated in studies by Bienstock and Tisser and Martelly.

Pathogenicity.—The pathogenicity of the colon bacillus for animals is slight and varies greatly with different strains. Intraperitoneal injections of 1 c.c. or more of a broth culture will often cause death in guinea-pigs. Intravenously administered to rabbits it may cause a rapid sinking of the temperature and death with symptoms of violent intoxication. Subcutaneous inoculation of moderate doses usually results in nothing more than a localized abscess.

In man, a large variety of lesions produced by B. coli have been described. It is a surprising fact that disease should be caused at all, in man, by a micro-organism which is so constantly present in the intestine. A number of explanations for this state of affairs have been advanced, none of them entirely satisfactory. It is probable that none of the poisonous products of the colon bacillus is absorbed unchanged by the healthy unbroken mucosa. Under these circumstances, no considerable process of immunization would be anticipated. It is also possible that, whenever an infection with B. coli does occur, the infecting organism is one which has been recently acquired from another host. Considering the subject from another point of view, colon-bacillus infection may possibly take place simply because of unusual temporary reduction of the resistance of the host.

Septicemia, due to the colon bacillus, has been described but it is doubtful whether many of these cases represent an actual primary invasion of the circulation by the bacilli, or whether their entrance was not simply a secondary phenomenon occurring during the agonal stages of another condition. Unquestionable cases, however, have been reported, and there can be no doubt about the occurrence of the condition, although it is probably less frequent than formerly supposed. An interesting group of such cases are those occurring in newborn infants, in which generalized colon-bacillus infection may lead to a fatal condition known as Winckel's disease or hemorrhagic septicemia. While it is not unlikely that under conditions of an excessive carbohydrate diet, colon bacilli may aggravate morbid processes by a voluminous formation of gas, they do not, of themselves, take part in actual putrefactive processes. It is likely, therefore, that in most of the intestinal diseases, these micro-organisms play a secondary part.

It is equally difficult to decide whether or not these bacilli may be regarded as the primary cause of peritonitis following perforation of the gut. Although regularly found in such conditions, they are hardly ever found in pure culture, being accompanied usually by staphylococci, streptococci, or other micro-organisms, whose relationship to disease is far more definitely established. Isolated cases have been reported, one of them by Welch, in which *B. coli* was present in the peritoneum in pure culture without there having been any intestinal perforation. Granting that the bacillus is able to proliferate within the peritoneum, there is no reason for doubting its ability to produce a mild suppurative process.

Inflammatory conditions in the liver and gallbladder have been attributed to the colon bacillus. It has been isolated from liver abscesses, from the bile, and from the centers of gallstones. Welch has reported a case of acute hemorrhagic pancreatitis in which the bacillus was isolated from the gallbladder and from the pancreas.

In the bladder, *B. coli* frequently gives rise to cystitis and occasionally to ascending pyonephrosis. No other micro-organism, in fact, is found so frequently in the urine as this one. The condition is observed during the convalescence from typhoid fever. The colon bacillus is by far the organism most frequently responsible for acute and chronic pyelitis and cystitis.

Localized suppurations due to this bacillus may take place in all parts of the body. They are most commonly localized about the anus and the genitals, and the region of the appendix.

Poisonous Products of the Colon Bacillus.—The colon bacillus belongs essentially to that group of bacteria whose toxic action is supposed to be due to the substances contained within the bacillary body. Culture filtrates show very little toxicity when injected into animals; whereas the injection of dead bacilli produces symptoms almost equal in severity to these induced by injection of the live micro-organisms. No antitoxic bodies have been demonstrated in serum as resulting from immunization.

Dead colon bacilli have a high toxicity for rabbits and somewhat less for guinea-pigs.

Immunization with the Colon Bacillus.—The injection into animals of gradually increasing doses of living or dead colon bacilli gives rise to specific bacteriolytic, agglutinating, and precipitating substances.

The bacteriolytic substances may be easily demonstrated by the technic of the Pfeiffer reaction. *In vitro* bacteriolysis is less marked than in the case of some other micro-organisms such as the cholera spirillum or the typhoid bacillus. Owing probably to the habitual presence of colon bacilli in the intestinal tracts of animals and man, considerable bacteriolysis may occasionally be demonstrated in the serum of normal individuals.

It is a noticeable fact that the injection of any specific race of colon bacilli produces, in the immunized animal, high agglutination values only for the individual culture used for immunization, while other strains of colon bacilli require much higher concentration than does the original strain. The subject has been extensively studied by a number of observers and illustrates the extreme individual specificity of the agglutination reaction. Thus a serum which will agglutinate its homologous strains in dilutions of 1 : 1000 will often fail to agglutinate other races of *B. coli* in dilutions of 1 : 500 or 1 : 600.

The normal serum of adult animals and man will often agglutinate this bacillus in dilutions as high as 1 : 10 or 1 : 20—a phenomenon possibly referable to its habitual presence within the body. The serum of newborn animals possesses no such agglutinating powers. The fact that agglutinins for the colon bacillus are increased in the serum of patients convalescing from typhoid fever or dysentery is probably explained, partly by the increase of the group agglutinins produced by the specific infecting agent, and partly by the invasion of colon bacilli.

Normal individuals usually give positive skin reactions in response to intradermal injections of filtrates of cultures of *B. coli* while patients who have had a chronic infection due to colon bacilli usually do not react in this manner. Steinberg and Wiltsie have interpreted the positive reactions as indicative of susceptibility to colon-bacillus toxin; the negative results as indicative of immunity.

Among the few conditions affecting man in which an artificially produced active immunity against colon bacillus would be most desirable is peritonitis following rupture of the appendix or intestine, or surgical operation. In experiments on dogs, Steinberg has shown that a considerable degree of protection against "fecal peritonitis" can be secured by intraperitoneal injection of killed colon bacilli. The state of protection was produced rapidly.

Varieties of Colon Bacilli.—A large number of distinct varieties of colon bacilli have been described. Since the observations made by Neisser and Massini in 1906 and 1907 on the variability of *B. coli mutabile,* and especially since the revival of interest in bacterial dissociation which began about 1921 bacteriologists have realized that theories of temporary depression of function cannot account for all the changes observed (Lange). In dealing with the colon bacilli, therefore, the bacteriologist is confronted with variations which may be due to several causes. There are obviously certain relatively fixed types or species within which minor variations may occur. There are next the variations of temporary character due to immediate environmental influences such as temperature, concentration of substances in the medium and other factors. Finally there are the variations of more permanence due to dissociation called inherent variability. The organisms gain and lose fermentative capacity in ways that are at times unpredictable, they do not show always a strict correlation between source and cultural characteristics, and they exhibit dissociative variability into smooth, rough, mucoid, motile and nonmotile, aerogenic and nonaerogenic, and antigenically different forms. There have been numerous confirmations of Bergstrand's observations on the variation of *Bact. coli.*

It seems best, as we have indicated in our discussion of the encapsulated bacteria of the Friedländer group, to list the main types which have been described and to postpone decision as to all the relationships until the pattern has been pieced together.

Aside from systematic and taxonomic points of view, it is of practical importance to attempt to draw a distinction between the types of *B. coli* which come from human feces and those which come from grains and uncontaminated soils, or the intestinal contents of animals. The reason for this is that the presence of *B. coli* in water supplies is used as an index of fecal pollution. The pathogens of this group, the typhoid and dysentery bacilli, are rarely searched for or found in supplies of drinking water. The search is made for the hardier and more numerous *B. coli*. The general characteristics of the group of colon bacilli are defined by the American Public Health Association Committee on Standard Methods of Water Analysis as: "Gram-negative rods, aerobic, facultatively anaerobic, growth on gelatin without liquefaction, fermentation of dextrose and *lactose* with gas formation." This definition is somewhat broad, though safely so. We know, however, that the so-called *aerogenes* types of nonfecal origin and some of the variants of the Friedländer bacillus would meet these specifications.

Other differential tests, therefore, have been devised.

1. *The Methyl Red Test.*—This test is based upon the final hydrogen-ion concentration reached by a culture in 0.5 per cent glucose broth after four days incubation at 37° C. (Clark). When methyl red is added to the culture, the indicator will be orange-red (positive) if the pH is 4.5 or less; yellow (negative) if the reaction is less acid than this. *Bact. aerogenes*, by definition, is methyl red negative; *Bact. coli* is methyl red positive.

2. *Voges-Proskauer Reaction.*—This depends upon the production of acetylmethyl carbinol from dextrose. The usual test has been carried out by adding 5 c.c. of 10 per cent sodium hydroxide to 10 c.c. of glucose broth culture after four days incubation at 37° C. A pink color indicates a positive result. *Bact. aerogenes* gives a positive Voges-Proskauer reaction; *Bact. coli* is Voges-Proskauer negative. O'Meara's modification of the medium by the addition of creatine has been found by Tittsler to be advantageous, in providing more certain and more rapidly obtained results.

3. *Growth in Sodium Citrate Medium.*—Koser discovered that *Bact. coli* was unable to utilize sodium citrate as a source of carbon, while *Bact. aerogenes* could utilize this salt. Hence, ability to grow in a synthetic medium containing nitrogen in the form of sodium ammonium phosphate and carbon as sodium citrate distinguishes *Bact. aerogenes* from *Bact. coli*.

4. Other *special tests* of differential value are the fermentation of cellobiose (Jones, 1924), the Eijkman test (growth and fermentation of glucose by *Bact. coli* at 46° C.), the decomposition of uric acid (Koser, 1918), in a synthetic medium, and the reactions in the medium of Dominick and Lauter as described by Leahy. By the use of other fermentation tests with a series of carbohydrates, subdivisions have been recognized in great numbers.

Most of these media and details of procedure are given in the seventh edition of *Standard Methods for the Examination of Water and Sewage* issued in 1933 by the American Public Health Association. The multiplicity of tests is indicative of a multiplicity of uncertainties and difficulties. Nevertheless, in most cases a practical and useful decision can be reached when all the results are in hand.

Without describing in detail the other members of the colon-aerogenes group, we may sum up the information in the tables on pages 496 and 547.

Bact. cloacae, discovered by Jordan (1890) in sewage is a motile organism, resembling *Bact. aerogenes*. It differs from all the numbers of this group in being able to liquefy gelatin. This organism is almost as closely related to the *Proteus* group as it is to the colon-aerogenes group.

Organism	Dextrose	Lactose	Saccharose	Voges-Proskauer	Methyl Red	Citrate	Gelatin
Bact. coli type	⊕	⊕	⊕	—	+	—	—
B. coli communis	⊕	⊕	—	—	+	—	—
B. coli communior	⊕	⊕	⊕	—	+	—	—
Bact. aerogenes type...	⊕	⊕	⊕	+	—	+	—
Bact. aerogenes †	⊕	⊕	⊕	+	—	+	—
B. cloacæ	⊕	⊕	⊕	+	—	+	+

⊕ indicates acid and gas formed.
† B. lactis aerogenes, Aerobacter aerogenes.

THE PROTEUS GROUP

A number of bacteria found in feces, water and sewage and decomposing materials resemble the colon bacilli in morphology and metabolic processes, but differ from them in being able to *liquefy gelatin*. They were first described and set apart in a special genus called *Proteus* by Hauser in 1885. In this genus he included three species, *Proteus vulgaris, Proteus mirabilis,* and *Proteus zenkeri. Proteus zenkeri* was incorrectly placed in this genus, since it is gram-positive, does not ferment carbohydrates and does not liquefy gelatin. In recognition of this, *Proteus zenkeri* has been placed by Bergey in the new genus *Kurthia,* along with *B. zopfius,* with which it may be identical (Wenner and Rettger). As we have stated, *Bacterium cloacae* is closely related to the *Proteus* organisms. It is likely that the Perez and Shiga ozena bacilli are in fact members of the *Proteus* group. The cultural characteristics of so-called *Proteus* have been thoroughly studied by Bengston.

The bacteria of the *Proteus* group are gram-negative pleomorphic (Dunlap and Maitland) motile rods with numerous peritrichic flagella. They are aerobic, ferment dextrose and saccharose with the production of acid and gas. They do not ferment lactose and do not usually produce acetyl-methyl carbinol. They liquefy gelatin, but, according to Rettger and Newell, they do not produce putrefactive decomposition products of protein. This is contrary to the older belief that *Proteus* bacilli were putrefactive organisms. On moist agar medium, organisms in this group rapidly spread across the surface of the plate. This type of swarming growth is characteristic of the motile forms. Nonmotile variants grow in denser round, hemispherical non-swarming colonies. It was upon the basis of this difference that Weil and Felix (1917) introduced the terms H (Hauch = film) and O (ohne Hauch = without film) to designate the motile and nonmotile forms. Since then, these letters have been applied to antigen and antibody differences and to types of agglutination clumps, the H referring to coarse clumps, the O to fine clumps. Weil and Felix OX strains have attained great importance in the diagnosis of Rickettsia diseases.

The type species of this genus is *Proteus vulgaris,* the characteristics of which are briefly as follows:

Proteus vulgaris grows best at temperatures at or about 25° C. and develops upon the simplest media. It is a facultative anaerobe and forms no spores. In *broth*, it produces rapid clouding with a pellicle and the formation of a mucoid sediment. In *gelatin*, the colonies are characteristically irregular, wherefrom the name.

Gelatin is rapidly liquefied. Liquefaction, however, is diminished or even inhibited under anaerobic conditions.

On *agar* and other solid media, as well as upon gelatin before liquefaction has taken place, characteristic colonies are produced. From the central flat, grayish white colony nucleus, numerous irregular streamers grow out over the surrounding media, giving the colony a stellate appearance. On *potato*, it forms a dirty, yellowish growth. In *milk*, there is coagulation and an acid reaction at first; later the casein is redissolved by proteolysis. *Blood serum* is often liquefied, but not by all races.

The primary pathogenicity of *Proteus vulgaris* is slight, but as a secondary invader of infected wounds, mucous membranes and cavities of the body it plays a rôle of considerable importance. In cystitis and pyelitis associated with urinary calculi or following obstruction of the urinary tract, *Proteus vulgaris* is often present and appears to be in part responsible for the pathological effects.

Outbreaks of "ptomaine poisoning" or food poisoning have been attributed to *Proteus vulgaris*. Jordan (1931), after a review of the evidence, agrees with Bengston that it has not been definitely proved that this is so.

The serum of patients with typhus fever and similar diseases agglutinates certain strains of *Proteus vulgaris*. This reaction, discovered by Weil and Felix in 1916, will be discussed in the section on Rickettsia diseases, particularly in reference to the serological diagnosis of typhus fever. The underlying cause of the production of agglutinins against Proteins X_{19}, X_2 and other strains as a result of infection with the typhus fever organism is not known. It has been definitely established, however, that *Proteus* bacilli do not cause typhus fever. Typhus fever serum reacts in a somewhat similar manner with other bacteria.

REFERENCES

ADAMI. J. Am. M. Ass., Dec., 1899.

BENGSTON, I. A. J. Infect. Dis., 1919, 24:428.

BERGSTRAND, H. J. Bacteriol., 1923, 8:173.

BIENSTOCK. Arch. f. Hyg., München and Berl., 1901, 29.

BIRCH-HIRSCHFELD. Ziegler's Beitr., 1898, 24.

BROWN, J. W., and SKINNER, C. E. J. Bacteriol., 1930, 20:139.

BUCHNER. Arch. f. Hyg., 1885, 3.

CLARK, W. M. J. Biol. Chem., 1915, 22:87.

CUSHING and LIVINGOOD. Contrib. sc. med.... pupils W. H. Welch, Balt., 1900.

DUNLAP, E. M., and MAITLAND, H. E. J. Hyg., 1932, 32:282.

EIJKMAN, C. Centralbl. f. Bakteriol., I Abt., 1904, 37:742.

ESCHERICH. Die Darmbakteriologie des Säuglings, Stuttgart, 1886.

———— Centralbl. f. Bakteriol., 1887, 1.

HAUSER, G. Über Faulnissbakterien, Leipzig, 1885.

HERTER. Bacterial Infections of the Digestive Tract, New York, 1907.

JONES, H. N. Science, 1924, 60:455; J. Bacteriol., 1926, 11:359.

JORDAN, E. O. Spec. Rep. Mass. State Board of Health, 1890.

———— Food Poisoning and Food-Borne Infection, Chicago, 1931, p. 140.

KAMEN. Ziegler's Beitr., 1896, 14.

KOSER, S. A. J. Bacteriol., 1924, 9:59.

———— J. Infect. Dis., 1918, 23:377; 1926, 38:506.

LANGE, W. F. J. Bacteriol., 1933, 25:123.

LEAHY, H. W. J. Am. Water Works Ass., 1930, 22:1490.

LEAHY, H. W., FREEMAN, J. W., and KARSAMPES, C. P. Am. J. Pub. Health, 1931, 21:11.

LEITER, L. W. Am. J. Hyg., 1929, 9:705.

LEMBKE. Arch. f. Hyg., Müunchen and Berl., 1896, 24.

MASSINI, R. Arch. f. Hyg., 1907, 61:250.

NEISSER, M. Centralbl. f. Bakteriol., I Abt. Ref., Beiheft, 1906, 38:98.

NUTTALL and THIERFELDER. Ztschr. f. Physiol. Chem. Strassb., 21, 22.

O'MEARA, R. A. Q. J. Pathol. & Bacteriol., 1931, 34:401.

———— Brit. J. Exper. Pathol., 1931, 12:346.

PAPASOTIRIU. Arch. f. Hyg., München and Berl., 41.

PRESCOTT. Centralbl. f. Bakteriol., Ref., 1903, 33.

RETTGER, L. F., and NEWELL, C. R. J. Biol. Chem., 1912, 13:341.

SCHILD. Ztschr. f. Hyg., 1895, 19.

SCHOTTELIUS. Arch. f. Hyg., München and Berl., 1889, 24.

STEINBERG, B. Am. J. Clin. Pathol., 1932, 2:187.

———— Proc. Soc. Exper. Biol. & Med., 1932, 29:1018.

STEINBERG, B., and WILTSIE, C. O. J. Immunol., 1932, 22:109.

TISSER and MARTELLY. Ann. de l'Inst. Pasteur, 1902.

TITTSLER, R. P. J. Bacteriol., 1933, 25:41.

WEIL, E., and FELIX, A. Wien. klin. Wchnschr., 1916, 29:33; 1917, 30:1509.

WELCH. Med. News, 1891, 59.

WENNER, J. J., and RETTGER, L. F. J. Bacteriol., 1919, 4:331.

CHAPTER XXXVI

THE PARATYPHOID (SALMONELLA) GROUP

Family: *Enterobacteriaceae.* Tribe: *Salmonelleae.* Genus: *Salmonella.* Species: *Salmonella schottmuelleri* = *B. paratyphosus B; Salmonella paratyphi* = *B. paratyphosus A.*

PARATYPHOID FEVERS AND FOOD POISONING

The organisms comprising the "paratyphoid" or *Salmonella* group are gram-negative nonsporing rods, aerobic, capable of fermenting a number of carbohydrates (except lactose, saccharose and salicin), with the formation of acid and gas, unable to liquefy gelatin, are usually motile and only rarely produce indole. It is seen from this definition that these organisms resemble the colon bacilli. In fact, their usual habitat is the intestinal tracts of man and animals. In pathogenicity and metabolic activity they occupy a position between the colon bacilli and the typhoid bacillus. The group further resembles the colon bacilli in its heterogeneity. The varieties of para-typhoid bacilli are very numerous and their relationships almost too complex to be reduced to schematic classification.

It is obvious that in unraveling the complexities of the relations in this group of morphologically identical bacteria all phases of the biochemical activities of the organisms should be investigated. This has been done and it has been discovered that their fermentation reactions in various carbohydrates are differential up to a certain point. The most definite knowledge of fermentation reactions which has with-stood the test of many years may be summed up as follows:

I. The inability of these organisms to ferment lactose and saccharose may usu-ally be depended upon to aid in differentiating them from typical *colon aerogenes* forms. The difficulty that arises in this connection comes not from the ability of a species of *Salmonella* to ferment these sugars but from the temporary or permanent inability of a colon bacillus to do so.

It may be stated in general that the *nonpathogenic members* of the colon group *ferment lactose* and that the *pathogens (paratyphoid, typhoid and dysentery bacilli) do not ferment lactose.* Therefore, lactose is used as the differential carbohydrate in all the common plating media employed for the separation of colon types from typhoid, paratyphoid or dysentery bacilli. These media, of which Endo's medium is a typical example, contain lactose and an indicator which gives a bright color in the presence of acid. (See section on technical methods.)

II. The production of gas from dextrose and mannite by paratyphoid bacilli differentiate them from typhoid bacilli. In Russell's double sugar medium, para-typhoid bacilli produce acid and gas in the butt, and no change on the surface of the slant.

III. The fermentation of xylose and eventual production of alkali in milk dif-ferentiates *paratyphoid B* organisms from *paratyphoid A.*

These and additional differential points are shown in the following table:

ORGANISM	MOTIL-ITY	DEX-TROSE	LAC-TOSE	MAN-NITE	XYLOSE	LEAD ACE-TATE AGAR (H_2S)	INDOLE	MILK	RUSSELL'S MEDIUM	
									Slant	Butt
B. typhosus	+	+	−	+	±	−	−	acid	−	+
B. paratyphosus A	+	⊕	−	⊕	−	−	−	acid	−	⊕
B. paratyphosus B	+	⊕	−	⊕	⊕	+	−	alka-line	−	⊕
B. coli	+	⊕	⊕	⊕	⊕	±	+	acid	+	⊕

⊕ acid and gas.   + (under carbohydrates) = acid, no gas.   − = negative.

After these distinctions are made, there remain a great number of morphologically similar organisms in a large group known as the *paratyphoid B-enteritidis* group. These organisms differ in origin, in pathogenicity and in some of their biochemical activities. These differences, however, are subtle, variable, and offer slight foundations for systematic classifications.

Modern attempts to determine the relations within the whole typhoid-paratyphoid group and particularly in the *paratyphoid B-enteritidis* group have proceeded along the lines of observation of dissociative variability and antigenic and serological analysis. We shall presently take up the discussion of the results obtained by these means. In this place we should like to introduce a word of caution.

It is obvious that the use of group and type specific serological reactions places classifications upon a chemical foundation. This is the ultimate goal of modern serology as the evidence clearly indicates that chemical constitution and chemical composition are the bases of immunological specificity. This, however, is not the same as the older notion of biological relationships as a basis of immunological specificity. Chemical constitution cuts across biological divisions of living organisms. Several well-established examples of this are the following: yeast, Type B. Friedländer bacilli and Type II pneumococci contain an apparently identical polysaccharide haptene, which attached to a protein serves as an antigen to stimulate the production of an antibody capable of reacting with any one of these three organisms. The Gärtner bacillus, several other bacteria, guinea-pig kidney and organs of certain other animals contain a common heterophile antigen. It is logical to group these organisms on the basis of their common antigenic constituents, but it is of little systematic assistance to attempt to establish their biological relationships through these facts. The common possession of a somatic antigenic substance by the typhoid and enteritidis organisms is an important chemical fact and has important diagnostic serological consequences. But it seems to us to be insufficient as a basis for insisting upon a strict confinement of the typhoid bacillus within the paratyphoid group. Antigenic similarities, resting upon a broad chemical basis, are not necessarily the final criteria of natural biological relationships. They cannot serve, in the end, as the only or even as the predominant characteristics for the establishment of genera and species.

In this chapter we shall discuss the paratyphoid bacilli first in relation to the diseases they produce in man and second in relation to their pathogenicity for animals. We shall consider the paratyphoid fevers, food poisoning, infections of animals and finally attempt to summarize the relationships of the members of the group as disclosed by observations on them by the results of antigenic analysis.

Pathogenicity for Man.—Organisms of this class may be the causative agents of a number of clinically varying conditions of man. In general, it may be said that two main types of disease can be caused by this group, (1) that in which the disease simulates a mild or severe typhoid fever recognizable as different from true typhoid fever only by isolation and identification of the paratyphoid organisms; and (2) those which fall into the category of "food poisoning" in which, after a very short incubation time, usually only a few hours, there are symptoms of gastro-enteritis which may be mild, but more frequently are explosive and severe.

Paratyphoid Fever.—Paratyphoid fever, or a typhoid-like fever, may be caused by members of the paratyphoid A or B group.

B. paratyphosus A, now called *Salmonella paratyphi*, is distinguishable from the other members of the group by its inability to ferment xylose, the persistent slight acidity it produces in milk, its failure to blacken lead acetate by the production of H_2S and its serological specificity. It is a serologically homogeneous type since nearly all strains of *B. paratyphosus A* are agglutinated by antiserum produced by injection of an animal with one strain. This organism has slight but definite antigenic affinity with what White has called the "main body of the Salmonella group," particularly through a culture known as the Sendai type.

B. paratyphosus B, or *Salmonella schottmuelleri*, differs from *B. paratyphosus A* in its ability to produce acid and gas from xylose, in blackening lead acetate by the production of H_2S, and by making milk strongly alkaline after an initial formation of acid. The first differentiation between the A and B types was made by Schottmüller in 1900, largely on the basis of the reaction in milk. Organisms in the paratyphoid B group are serologically heterogeneous, and exhibit marked variability. It is difficult always to be certain that a strain is the true *B. paratyphosus B*, and not *B. aertrycke* or some closely related variety.

Both of these organisms are excreted in the feces and conveyed from man to man by contaminated water, milk or other food, by direct and indirect contact, by carriers and the agency of flies. The modes of transmission are the same as those for typhoid fever.

The disease itself may take the form either of a very mild and short-lived enteric disturbance with slight fever, or it may take the form of a moderately severe typhoid fever with rose spots, enlargement of the spleen and positive blood culture. Paratyphoid A cases are not a very large percentage of the ordinary sick rate of communities, but occasionally small group epidemics have been studied; and, during recent years in the United States, military epidemics have occurred. Upon the return of some American militia regiments from the Mexican border, there appeared among them an epidemic of paratyphoid which consisted largely of the A type (Krumwiede). These cases presented a most varied clinical picture. The severe cases were practically indistinguishable from typhoid fever, but there were at the same time cases of very mild fever with nothing but a little diarrhea, in which diagnosis was made by stool culture and by blood culture. A large number of these became paratyphoid A carriers.

Paratyphoid B is a more common disease than paratyphoid A, and is more apt to be typhoid-like and severe. From the distinct differences between the clinical manifestations of this disease and the ordinary cases of food poisoning, it would appear that there must be a definite human paratyphoid B organism which is conveyed by the same agencies and subject to the same epidemiological laws as typhoid fever. It is difficult to base this on bacteriological evidence since it is often impossible to find any cultural or agglutinative distinctions between organisms isolated from the human blood or bowel, and other bacilli which, from their sources and general reactions, would fall into the groups of hog cholera, enteritidis, etc.

In contradistinction to true typhoid fever, the temperature due to infection with a paratyphoid organism (especially *B. paratyphosus B*) may rise more abruptly and remain more irregular throughout the disease. Gastric symptoms, vomiting, and nausea are often more prominent than in typhoid fever and enlargement of the spleen is less regularly present. Owing to the low mortality of paratyphoid fever (in 120 cases observed by Lentz less than 4 per cent, and in many other smaller epidemics no deaths have occurred), we have remained relatively ignorant concerning the pathologic anatomy of the disease. Longcope observed a case, fatal after two weeks of illness, in which there was no enlargement of Peyer's patches and no sign of even beginning ulceration. Most other observers have found less involvement of the lymphatics of the bowel than is found in typhoid fever. During the disease the bacteria can often be cultivated from the blood, and the serum of the patient may agglutinate specific paratyphoid strains. Libman has isolated the organism from the fluid aspirated from the gallbladder in a case operated on for cholecystitis. Localized pyogenic infections due to this organism occur.

During the World War there were thousands of cases of paratyphoid fever, due to one or the other of these organisms.

The organism called *B. paratyphosus C* which was responsible for many cases of paratyphoid fever during the War has been identified by Andrewes and Neave as one of the types of *B. suipestifer*.

LABORATORY DIAGNOSIS.—An etiological diagnosis is made by isolation of the paratyphoid organisms from the blood or feces of the patient.

Agglutination tests with the serum of the patient and antigens composed of separate suspensions of *B. paratyphosus* A and B are used routinely as serological aids to diagnosis. This is the application of the principle of the Widal reaction to the diagnosis of paratyphoid fever. The previous history of the patient, particularly with respect to prophylactic immunization must be taken into consideration in interpreting the results of the tests.

These bacteriological and serological diagnostic methods are in principle the same as those used in the laboratory diagnosis of typhoid fever. The detailed discussion of them will be found in the next chapter.

PREVENTIVE MEASURES.—Measures for the prevention of paratyphoid fever are identical with those advised for the prevention of typhoid. The carrier problem is practically the same and it seems logical to assume that the percentage of carriers compared with that of typhoid carriers is approximately similar to the ratio of incidence between the two diseases. Prophylactic vaccination is an important preventive measure.

Food Poisoning.—The history of the paratyphoid bacilli as incitants of disease in man began with the isolation of an organism, subsequently called *Bacillus enteritidis*, by Gaertner in 1888 from a fatal case of acute gastro-enteritis which followed the eating of contaminated meat. Gaertner obtained the same organism from the meat. This bacterium resembles *B. paratyphosus B* in many of its characteristics, but can be differentiated from *Salmonella schottmuelleri* by its ability to produce acid in Jordan's tartrate medium and by its serological reactions. A closely related paratyphoid bacillus, *Salmonella aertrycke* has been found by Jordan and Savage to be the most common cause of this type of food poisoning in this country and in England. Other varieties of paratyphoid B bacilli of animal origin also have been responsible for outbreaks of food poisoning (Damon). It is probable that rats are important as a reservoir of this type of infection.

The *clinical picture* of this variety of paratyphoid infection is fundamentally different from the one just described. Typical bacillary food poisoning comes on within less than twenty-four hours after the ingestion of the contaminated food. Its onset is acute with a rapid rise in temperature and the accompanying systemic symptoms which this implies. There is great prostration, rapidity of the pulse and nausea, vomiting and painful diarrhea. Some of these cases have been compared with cholera in the severity of their courses. The fatality has not usually been very high, although in one epidemic it was as high as 7 per cent. The organisms may in these cases also be found in the blood stream by culture, but not as regularly as in the typical typhoid feverlike form. At death they may be found in the spleen and intestines.

The symptoms of food poisoning of this type are attributed to infection with paratyphoid B organisms, and are no longer thought to be due to preformed poisons such as ptomaines. The killed cultures of these paratyphoid bacilli are toxic for rabbits and filtrates of these cultures contain a thermostable substance which on intravenous injection is very poisonous for rabbits. But when these filtrates are placed in the stomachs of the animals no symptoms of poisoning appear.

Food poisoning is a term of wide significance. In using it in this chapter we have limited the application of it to gastro-enteritis due to paratyphoid bacilli. In the chapter on staphylococci we described a type of food poisoning due to toxic products of those organisms. A third type of food poisoning, with fatal consequences due to paralysis of the important centers in the midbrain and brain stem, will be described in the section on the anaerobes, in connection with the lethal action of the toxin of *Clostridium botulinum*.

Pathogenicity for Animals.—A number of paratyphoid bacilli resembling *B. paratyphosus B* are important pathogens for animals. They may occasionally produce gastro-enteritis, food poisoning, or even more serious diseases in man. Some of the most important of these organisms are:

Bacillus of Hog Cholera (B. Suipestifer, Salmonella Choleraesuis).—The generic name *Salmonella* was proposed by Lignières in recognition of the early investigations of Salmon on hog cholera.

It was formerly believed that hog cholera was due to the bacillus which bears this name, and first described in this connection by Salmon and Smith. Since then it has been found that this disease is due to a filtrable virus. The presence of the organism in animals suffering from this disease, is, therefore, something of a mystery, but is probably due, as Dorset suggested, to the fact that the organism is a constant inhabitant of the intestine in hogs, and manages to get into the circulation as a consequence of the pathological conditions incident to hog cholera. A similar association of organisms in blood cultures, etc., with diseases of which they are obviously not the primary etiological factor has been observed in other conditions.

B. Typhi Murium (Salmonella Typhimurium).—In rodents diseases caused by the members of the paratyphoid group are common. We have spoken of Löffler's discovery of the *B. typhi murium* as the cause of an epidemic disease of mice, a condition of the greatest annoyance to breeders of mice for laboratory purposes. This organism cannot easily be distinguished from the hog-cholera bacillus and some other members of the paratyphoid B group. This opens the question as to whether human beings can be infected by organisms derived from the disease in mice. In connection with attempts at the destruction of mice by infecting bait with cultures, human infections have been reported by Troomsdorf. Meyer reported an accidental laboratory infection from which he concluded that in man the disease could produce an acute and rather severe, but short-lived disease. Shibajama reported a number of cases in all of which there was circumstantial evidence of exposure to infection. In one of them food had been taken from a wooden dish in which mouse typhoid bacilli for the infection of bait had been kept. In another, a peasant woman accidentally mixed the mouse typhoid cultures with flour. In another, again, a number of people had eaten meat of a horse which had been fatally infected by accidental mixture with its food of mouse typhoid virus. In the last instance 34 people were infected, 1 of whom died. The symptoms were violent gastro-enteritis, coming on within twenty-four hours after eating of the meat, and in many respects similar to the typical disease described by Gaertner. Rats are an important source of the paratyphoid bacilli which cause food poisoning.

B. Pestis Caviae.—The guinea-pig disease caused by the *B. pestis caviae* usually takes the form of what is commonly known as pseudotuberculosis. It may occur epidemically in laboratory guinea-pigs and kill large numbers.

Danysz Type.—A group of the organisms, the so-called Ratin or Danysz group, produces epidemic diseases among rats. This group is regarded as very close to the true Gaertner bacillus. It is pathogenic for guinea-pigs and mice, and can be transmitted to rats by feeding. There is a much enlarged spleen, with inflammatory changes in the intestinal mucous membrane and necrotic foci.

B. Abortus Equi (Salmonella Abortivo-equina).—Smith and Kilbourne attributed infectious abortion of mares to a paratyphoid B organism isolated by them from uterine discharges. This has been confirmed repeatedly, notably by Meyer and Boerner.

Salmonella Infections of Other Animals.—Paratyphoid B organisms infect sheep, swine, cattle and birds. The list is too long to be discussed in detail. *B. psittacosis*, isolated by Nocard from parrots and human beings with psittacosis is now known to be a secondary invader in this disease. Psittacosis is caused by a filtrable virus. *Salmonella pullorum*, formerly called *B. pullorum*, is the cause of white diarrhea of fowls (Rettger) and *Salmonella gallinarum* (*B. sanguinarium*) causes fowl typhoid. This organism is nonmotile and does not produce gas in dextrose (Smith and TenBroeck, and Krumwiede and Kohn). White places both of these organisms in a group designated *Meta-salmonella*.

Variability.—Paratyphoid bacilli pass through dissociative changes spontaneously and under experimentally established conditions. The transformations are most commonly from the S to R type. Reversion to the S form from the R has been produced by rapid transfer in liquid media and by animal passage (Jordan). Mucoid motile and nonmotile variants, some of which may be encapsulated, have been described by numerous students of these bacteria (Sonnenschein). Kendrick has observed that mucoid variants of *Salmonella suipestifer* may be derived from smooth and rough forms by the action of bacteriophage. These variations in colony form are associated with variations in morphology and biochemical activities. The changes in biochemical activities throw into confusion classifications based on fermentation tests. The changes in morphology may through serological analysis lead to a more orderly arrangement of the knowledge of these bacteria.

The morphological variations of chief interest here are those which affect the external layers of the organisms. In some S to R transformations flagella are lost. In other S or R to mucoid transformations a capsular material may be gained. Furthermore there are intermediate and combined types of structural variations.

It is probable that these patterns of dissociation are analogous to those described below in connection with *B. typhosus*.

Serology.—The flagellar antigen, or H antigen, of the paratyphoid bacilli has been shown by Andrewes to be both *diphasic* and *monophasic*. When the antigen is monophasic, it is type specific. The H to O transformation in a monophasic strain of organism is associated with loss of specificity and predominance of the O, somatic or group antigen. In the diphasic organisms, however, the H antigen may occur in one of two forms. Variation in such diphasic organisms is often a change from one type of H antigen to another, while the O, or somatic antigen remains unaltered, as Dible has expressed it, "the mantle of one, in some instances, appearing practically intact upon the body of another."

The antigenic pattern or "mosaic" of this complex group has been shown to be intricate and to some extent shifting. It is difficult, without distortion, to summarize White's tabulated results of his antigenic analysis of the *Salmonella* organisms. From his table we extract the following, omitting some of the types:

1. Monophasic types: *paratyphosus A*, (*typhosus*), *enteritidis*, *abortus equi* and European *suipestifer*
2. Diphasic types: *paratyphosus B*, *aertrycke*, Stanley, American *suipestifer*, Hirschfeld, *Sendai*
3. Meta-salmonella types: *pullorum* and *sanguinarium*

Several antigenically different O factors were recognized. The distribution of the stable O somatic antigenic factors among the types of Salmonella was as follows:

Stable O
Somatic Factors   *Found in These Types*
  I ...... *paratyphosus B, aertrycke*, Stanley
  II ...... *paratyphosus B, aertrycke*, Stanley, *abortus equi*

III	......	*enteritidis, typhosus, pullorum, sanguinarium*
IV	......	Newport, *morbificans bovis*
V	......	European *suipestifer*, American *suipestifer*, Hirschfeld
VI	......	*paratyphosus A*
VII	......	L
VIII	......	Bombay
IX	......	Sendai

From this it is seen that *B. paratyphosus B* and *B. aertrycke* are related through their somatic antigen, and that *B. enteritidis, B. typhosus, B. pullorum* and *B. sanguinarium* have an antigenic factor in common. The sharing of this common O antigen between *B. typhosus* and *B. enteritidis* must be taken into consideration when tests are made for the O or fine-flocculating agglutinins in the modern Widal reaction for the diagnosis of typhoid fever.

The characteristics of the labile H or flagellar antigen varies with the phase of the diphasic organisms. These organisms have as we have noted a specific phase and a nonspecific phase. An abstract of White's analysis shows the following especially significant points.

1. In its specific phase the Sendai strain has the same H-antigen as *B. paratyphosus A.*

2. The specific phase of the Stanley strain of *Salmonella* provides an H antigen like the H antigen of *B. typhosus.* For this reason, and on account of the common O antigen in *B. enteritidis* and *B. typhosus,* White would include the typhoid bacillus in the *Salmonella* group.

3. In their nonspecific phases the following types have common H factors:

A. *Paratyphosus B*, Stanley, *aertrycke*, and Newport
B. *Aertrycke* and Newport
C. *Aertrycke* and Newport
D. The *suipestifer* types, Hirschfeld and Sendai
G. Common H factor to all the diphasic types

These methods of antigenic analysis have an important bearing not only upon general immunology but upon practical procedures of prophylactic vaccination.

In addition to the more or less well-defined types to which we have referred there are numerous *"atypical paratyphoid"* bacilli groups. The biochemical properties of a number of these, chiefly organisms with retarded fermentation of lactose have been studied by Kennedy, Cummings and Morrow. These organisms produce colonies on Endo plates superficially like those of the pathogens which are unable to ferment lactose. Their latent capacity to ferment lactose does not appear until after several days (one week to ten days) in incubation at 37° C.

Morgan's bacillus No. 1 has been placed in the paratyphoid group by a number of investigators and Bergey has listed it under the name *Salmonella morgani.* This organism ferments only dextrose, producing acid and gas. It also forms indole from peptone. As this bacterium has a slight, but definite, capacity to cause enteritis and colitis in man, we have followed custom and have placed the description of it in the chapter dealing with the dysentery bacilli. In our opinion, the organism belongs in the colon group.

REFERENCES

ANDREWES, F. W.   J. Path. & Bacteriol., 1922, 25:505; 1925, 28:345.

ANDREWES, F. W., and NEAVE, S.   Brit. J. Exper. Pathol., 1921, 2:157.

DAMON, S. R.   Food Infections and Food Intoxications, Baltimore, 1928.

DIBLE, J. H.   Recent Advances in Bacteriology, Philadelphia, 1932, pp. 75, 81.

JORDAN, E. O.   J. Infect. Dis., 1923, 33:567.

———— Food Poisoning and Food-borne Infections, Chicago, 1931, pp. 142 et seq.

———— J. Prevent. M., 1929, 3:279.

KENDRICK, P.   Am. J. Hyg., 1933, 17:297.

KENNEDY, J. A., CUMMINGS, P. L., and MORROW, N. M.   J. Infect. Dis., 1932, 50:333.

KRUMWIEDE, C., and KOHN.   J. Infect. Dis., 1917, 21:141; 36:509.

LENTZ.   Klin. Jahrb., 1914, 14.

LIBMAN.   J. Med. Research, 1902, 8.

LONGCOPE, W. T.   Am. J. M. Sc., 1902, 124.

MEYER.   München. med. Wchnschr., 1905, 47.

MEYER, K. F., and BOERNER.   J. Med. Research. 1913, 29:325.

NOCARD, E.   Compt. rend. Cons. d'hyg. pub. de la Seine, Paris, 1893.

RETTGER, L. F.   J. Med. Research, 1908, 18, 277.

SALMON, D. E.   Science, 1884, 3:155.

———— Am. Vet. Rev., 1883–4, 7:546.

SALMON, D. E., and SMITH, T.   Rep. Com. Agric., Washington, 1885, 1886.

SAVAGE, W. G.   J. Prevent. M., 1932, 6:425.

SAVAGE, W. G., and WHITE, P. B.   Medical Research Council, Spec. Rep. Ser., No. 91 and No. 92, London, 1925.

SCHOTTMÜLLER, H.   Deutsche med. Wchnschr., 1900, 511.

———— Ztschr. f. Hyg. u. Infectionskrankh., 1901, 36: 368.

SCHÜTZE, H.   Lancet, 1920, 1:93.

———— J. Hyg., 1921, 20:330.

SHIBAJAMA.   München. med. Wchnschr., 1907, 54:979.

SMITH, T., and KILBOURNE.   U. S. Dep. Agric. Bureau animal indust., 3.

SMITH, T., and TENBROECK.   J. Med. Research, 1916, 35:443.

SONNENSCHEIN, C.   Centralbl. f. Bakteriol., I Abt., 1926, 100:11.

TROOMSDORF.   München. med. Wchnschr., 1903, 48.

WHITE, P. B.   Med. Research Council Spec. Rep. Ser., No. 103, London, 1926.

———— A System of Bacteriology in Relation to Medicine, London, 1929, 4:86.

CHAPTER XXXVII

BACILLUS OF TYPHOID FEVER

Family: *Enterobacteriaceae.* Tribe: *Salmonelleae.* Genus: *Eberthella.* Species: *Eberthella typhosa*

(Bacillus typhosus, Bacillus typhi abdominalis)

Typhoid fever, because of its wide distribution and almost constant presence in most communities, has from the earliest days been the subject of much etiological inquiry. A definite conception of the infectiousness of typhoid fever and its transmission from case to case was formed as early as 1856 by Budd. However, it was not until 1880 that Eberth discovered in the spleen and mesenteric glands of typhoid-fever patients who had come to autopsy, a bacillus which we now know to be the cause of the disease. Conclusive proof of such an etiological connection was then brought by Gaffky, who not only saw the bacteria referred to by Eberth, but succeeded in obtaining them in pure culture and studying their characteristics. Further proof has been supplied by accidental infections of laboratory workers.

Morphology and Staining.—The typhoid bacillus is a short rod from to 3.5 μ in length with a varying width of from 0.5 to 0.8 μ. In appearance it has nothing absolutely distinctive which could serve to differentiate it from other bacilli of the typhoid-colon group, except that it has a general tendency to greater slenderness. Its ends are rounded without ever being club-shaped. Typhoid bacilli do not form spores. They are actively motile and have twelve or more flagella peripherally arranged.

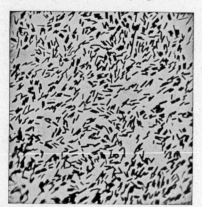

Fig. 45.—Bacillus Typhosus.

From twenty-four-hour culture on agar, showing regularity of forms.

The bacilli stain readily with the usual aniline dyes. Stained by Gram's method, they are decolorized.

Cultivation.—*B. typhosus* is easily cultivated. It will grow well upon media moderately alkaline or acid. It is an aerobic and facultative anaerobic organism. Upon *agar* plates growth appears within eighteen to twenty-four hours as small grayish colonies at first transparent, later opaque. Upon agar slants growth takes place in a uniform layer. There is nothing characteristic about this growth to aid in differentiation.

In *broth*, the typhoid bacillus grows rapidly, giving rise to an even clouding, rarely to a pellicle.

Upon *gelatin*, the typhoid bacillus grows readily and does not liquefy the medium. In stabs, growth takes place along the entire extent of the stab and over

508

the surface of the gelatin in a thin layer. In gelatin plates the growth may show some differences from that of other members of this group, and this medium was formerly much used for isolation of the bacillus from mixed cultures. Growth appears within twenty-four hours as small transparent, oval, round, or occasionally leaf-shaped colonies which are smaller, more delicate, and more transparent than contemporary colonies of the colon bacillus. They do not, however, show any reliable differential features from bacilli of the dysentery group. As the colonies grow older they grow heavier, more opaque, and lose much of their early differential value.

On *potato* the growth of typhoid bacilli is distinctive. On it typhoid bacilli, after twenty-four to forty-eight hours, produce a hardly visible growth, evident to the naked eye only by a slight moist glistening, an appearance which is in marked contrast to the grayish yellow or brown and abundant growth of colon bacilli. If the potato medium is rendered neutral or alkaline, this distinction disappears, and the typhoid bacillus grows more abundantly.

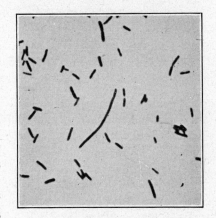

FIG. 46.—BACILLUS TYPHOSUS.

Motile, smooth type from twelve-hour culture on infusion agar, showing variation in form. × 1200.

In *milk*, typhoid bacilli do not produce coagulation. In litmus milk, during the first twenty-four hours, the color is changed to a reddish or violet tinge by the formation of acid from the small quantities of monosaccharide present. Later the color becomes deep blue, owing to the formation of alkali.

In *Dunham's peptone solution* no indole is produced.

Fermentation of Carbohydrates.—B. typhosus produces *acid without gas* from dextrose, maltose, mannite, dextrin, sorbite, dulcite and trehalose. Its action upon xylose is variable. Some strains ferment xylose rapidly, others slowly (Krumwiede, Morishima). Secondary colonies of *B. typhosus* on xylose agar plates appearing as marginal papillae, sometimes contain organisms capable of fermenting xylose.

B. typhosus does not ferment either lactose or saccharose.

Inoculated by stab and streak upon Russell's double sugar medium composed of 0.1 per cent glucose and 1 per cent lactose, the organism forms acid in the butt of the tube and no change in the reaction on the surface of the slant. This is a useful differential medium.

Typhoid bacilli, like other bacteria, produce CO_2 in their respiratory processes. This may have some bearing on the reaction observed in Russell's medium, but it does not result in the liberation of enough gas to be noticeable in the ordinary fermentation tubes.

Numerous special media have been devised for the isolation and differentiation of typhoid bacilli. These are described in the section on technical methods.

The differentiation of the typhoid bacillus from similar organisms of the typhoid, dysentery, colon group, is based chiefly on growth upon differential media in which

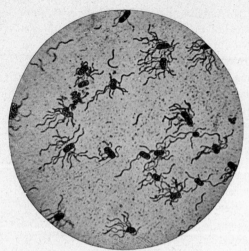

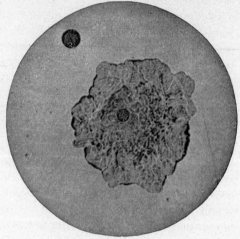

FIG. 47.—BACILLUS TYPHOSUS.
Showing flagella. (After Fränkel and Pfeiffer.)

FIG. 48.—SURFACE COLONY OF BACILLUS TYPHOSUS ON GELATIN, SHOWING CLASSICAL "MAPLE LEAF APPEARANCE."
(After Heim.)

the inability of the typhoid bacillus to form acid or gas from lactose has been the most commonly used basis for differentiation. Various indicators to show whether acid has been formed, added to such media will sharply separate this organism from the colon bacilli and their close relatives. Failure to produce gas with dextrose differentiates it from the paratyphoid group. The reader is referred to the differential tables given at the end of the chapter on the dysentery bacilli for the basic reactions upon which cultural differentiation is made. The media most convenient for this purpose are, in plates, the Endo medium, the brilliant green medium, or the eosin-methylene-blue medium, all of which are described in the section on media; and, in tubes, the most convenient medium is the Russell double sugar agar. The Russell double sugar agar is particularly useful to give a quick index of differentiation, since it contains both lactose and glucose, and, whereas the colon group give redness throughout, and a few gas bubbles, the typhoid gives no gas, a red butt due to its action in the depths of the stab on the glucose and an uncolored surface growth. The colors produced depend upon the indicator contained in the medium.

Final differentiation is best based upon specific agglutination.

Winslow, Kligler and Rothberg summarize the characteristics of the typhoid bacillus as follows: The typhoid bacillus is a gram-negative, aerobic, non-spore-forming, actively motile rod which forms translucent irregular colonies on gelatin, and a colorless growth on potato. It produces strong and prompt acid, but no gas, on media containing the hexoses, maltose, mannite, sorbite, xylose (rapid or slow), and dextrin; it does not attack arabinose, rhamnose, or lactose; produces a slight initial reddening of litmus milk, which, after two weeks, reverts to neutrality or slight alkalinity. It does not form indole, nor liquefy gelatin, does not grow in asparagin-mannitol medium, does not reduce neutral red, and causes browning of lead acetate medium (irregular). It has low tolerance for acid, but high tolerance for malachite and brilliant green dyes. It has characteristic serum agglutination.

It grows most luxuriantly at temperatures about 37.5° C., but continues to grow within a range of temperature lying between 15° and 41° C. Its thermal death point, according to Sternberg, is 56° C. in ten minutes. It remains alive in artificial cultures for several months or even years if moisture is supplied. In carefully sealed agar tubes Hiss found the organisms alive after thirteen years. In natural waters it may remain alive as long as thirty-six days, according to Klein. In ice, according to Prudden, it may remain alive for three months or over. Against the ordinary disinfectants, the typhoid bacillus is comparatively more resistant than some other vegetative forms. It is killed, however, by 1 : 500 bichloride or 5 per cent carbolic acid within five minutes.

Variability.—Morphological variations of typhoid bacilli have been frequently observed. In Figure 46 we have shown the "normal" rods occurring together with filamentous and coccoidal forms in the same young culture after twelve hours incubation at 37° C. The significance of these forms is not clear. There is no more evidence that they are involution forms than that they are phases in a life cycle. Neither opinion has been proved. We have already referred to the branching forms described by Walker and Murray and Hort. These variations, changes in colony form and variability in biochemical activity, have been reviewed by Hadley.

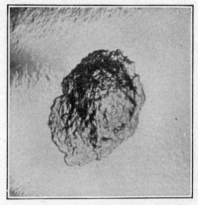

FIG. 49.—ROUGH COLONY OF BACILLUS TYPHOSUS ON AGAR.

The type of variability of greatest immediate importance is the dissociative changes from smooth to rough. The classical colony of *B. typhosus,* shown in Figure 48, is undoubtedly a rough colony, as may be seen by comparing this picture with Figure 49, a photograph of a known rough colony of the Rawlings strain isolated by Grinnell. The smooth colony is smaller, round, usually with a uniform surface and a flattened hemispherical shape. Baerthlein described these and many intermediate types in 1912, but their significance has become appreciated chiefly on account of the work of Arkwright. It was shown by Arkwright that the following chief variants of *B. typhosus* occurred: (1) smooth, motile; (2) smooth, nonmotile; (3) rough, motile; (4) rough, nonmotile. Antigenic changes, changes in pathogenicity and changes in biochemical activities are linked with these dissociations.

Antigenic Analysis and Serology.—Both the motile and nonmotile forms contain a common somatic heat stable O antigen, as shown by Grinnell. White in 1925 and 1927 had shown that the O antigen of *B. typhosus* had much in common with the O antigen of *B. enteritidis.* This has an important bearing on diagnostic agglutination tests. Fine flocculation is dependent upon O agglutinins and agglutinogens.

The smooth motile and smooth nonmotile forms contain special antigenic factors in the flagella or soluble specific substance. We shall, for convenience, continue to refer to these as H factors, although Grinnell proposed other designations. An antigenic pattern has been worked out for these four varieties of *B. typhosus* and their relationships have been established in part.

Motile smooth (MS)	$= P + S + F$
Nonmotile smooth (NS)	$\doteq P + S$
Motile rough (MR)	$= P + F \; (+R)$
Nonmotile rough (NR)	$= P \; (+R)$

Recent immunological analyses by Felix and Pitt promise to throw considerable light upon the antigenic structure of the typhoid bacillus and upon the criteria of successful immunization. According to these writers, the typhoid bacillus as we have seen contains an "O" antigen which is somatic, contains considerable amounts of carbohydrate substance and is heat stable. There is also a flagellar "H" antigen which is thermolabile. Immunization with the pure "O" produces "O" antibodies, and immunization with the motile "OH" organisms produces both "H" and "O" antibodies. The "H" antigen and antibody apparently have no relationship to protection.

In studying a considerable number of typhoid strains, Felix found that there were smooth "O" strains which were inagglutinable and others which were agglutinable in anti-"O" serum. Utilizing the mouse protection test devised by Grinnell, he finds that only the inagglutinable, smooth "O" organisms are highly virulent, whereas the virulence of the agglutinable ones is relatively low. Moreover, immunization of mice with the agglutinable strains confers little protection, whereas the inagglutinable, virulent ones serve as a potent immunizing antigen. When he immunized rabbits with agglutinable, intermediate and inagglutinable strains, he found that immunization only with living, inagglutinable virulent strains produced sera which would agglutinate these strains, and the titer of such sera was never very high. The obvious inference is that in these virulent organisms there is a third antigen which determines virulence, and which he calls his "Vi." When the sera of rabbits immunized with virulent strains are absorbed with agglutinable and inagglutinable cultures, the agglutinable strains take out all the "H" and "O" antibody but do not absorb any of the "Vi" antibody, whereas absorption with the "Vi" strains takes out all of the "Vi" antibody, together with a large part of the "H" and about half of the "O" antibodies.

The "Vi" antigen is apparently present only in living, unheated cultures. It withstands 56° C. for a very short time, but is destroyed at 60° C. Strains cultivated at temperatures below 25° and above 40° C. rapidly lose the "Vi" factor. It is obvious from Felix's studies that the only completely effective immunizing agent is an inagglutinable typhoid culture killed in such a manner that the "Vi" antigen is preserved. He suggests formolinization as the most useful method at present available, although even formol weakens the "Vi" factor. We believe that the "Vi" labile antigen described by Felix for typhoid bacilli represents a general antigenic principle applicable probably to streptococci and to anthrax bacilli—possibly to other bacteria as well.

White has confirmed the earlier observation of Smith and TenBroeck that *B. typhosus* is antigenically related to certain of the paratyphoids. Those known to be so related to *B. typhosus* through H and O factors are *B. gallinarum* (*sanguinarium*). *B. pullorum, B. enteritidis* and the Stanley strain of the paratyphoid B group.

Pathogenicity.—In animals typhoid infection does not occur spontaneously. Artificial inoculation with the typhoid bacillus does not produce a disease analogous to typhoid fever in the human being. It is probable that typhoid bacilli injected into animals do not multiply extensively and that the symptoms produced are due to the poisons liberated from the dead bacteria. Inoculation with dead cultures is followed by essentially the same train of symptoms as inoculation with live cultures. The injection of large doses into rabbits or guinea-pigs intravenously or intra-peritoneally is usually followed by a rapid drop in temperature, often by respiratory embarrassment and diarrhea. Occasionally blood may be present in the stools. According to the size of the dose or the weight of the animal, death may ensue within a few hours, or, with progressive emaciation, after a number of days, or the animal may gradually recover.

An advance of great practical significance was the discovery of Grinnell that the comparative virulence of typhoid strains could be determined by intraperitoneal injections into mice. This method has been further refined by the use of gastric mucin of swine stomachs, as first employed with meningococcus. 1 c.c. of a 5% suspension is injected with varying doses of the organisms.

Welch and Blachstein have shown that typhoid bacilli injected into the ear vein of a rabbit appear in the bile and may persist in the gallbladder for weeks. Doerr, Koch, Johnston and Meyer and his associates have all confirmed this, the last named showing that the typhoid bacillus could not only remain latent for a long time in the gallbladder of rabbits, but would appear in the blood stream after the seventh or ninth day, and persist in the gallbladder for as long as 125 days. Gay and Clay-pole have been able to produce the carrier state in rabbits with regularity by growing the typhoid cultures used for inoculation upon agar containing 10 per cent de-fibrinated rabbit's blood. Such cultures are not as readily agglutinated by immune serum as are those grown on plain agar, and it may well be that they preserved the "Vi" factor in these cultures.

Typical typhoid fever simulating the disease in man has been produced in chimpanzees, by Metchnikoff and Besredka, who produced it in connection with their experiments on protective vaccination. Rake showed that mucin mixed with the organisms injected enhanced the pathogenicity of typhoid bacilli.

Typhoid Fever in Man.—The disease is one in which a wide range of variation may occur, and in which complications are various and manifold. The organisms enter by mouth, with food, water or contact with fingers, direct or indirect, as described in the epidemiological section. Subsequently, the organisms, which pass through the stomach uninjured, multiply in the intestine, but cause no symptoms for anywhere from seven to fourteen days. During this time they probably begin to proliferate partly within the mucous membrane of the bowel, although there is little definite knowledge concerning this. The symptoms of the disease begin insidiously by gradual malaise, headache, loss of appetite and sleeplessness. During the first week of the actual signs of infection, the organisms have probably penetrated or are penetrating into the lymphatics. At this time there is a swelling of the lymphoid nodules of the intestine and Peyer's patches, and there is a moderate catarrhal inflammation of the mucous membrane. At this time too the bacilli enter the blood stream and can be found in blood culture.

Though formerly regarded as primarily an intestinal disease, the disease is in truth at this time a bacteremia, and it is not impossible that the intestinal lesions are as much due to the action of toxic products which are excreted in part through the intestinal wall, as they are due to the direct reaction caused in the intestine by local growth of the bacilli. Secondarily, the bacilli appear and can be cultivated from the spleen and the liver, and can be demonstrated in the sinuses and tissues of the lymphatic and retroperitoneal lymph nodes.

Typhoid Bacilli in the Blood during the Disease.—The investigations of many workers have shown that typhoid bacilli are present in the circulating blood of practically all patients during the early weeks of the disease. Series of cases have been studied by Castellani, Schottmueller and many others. Coleman and Buxton reported their researches upon 123 cases, and at the same time analyzed all cases previously reported. Their analysis of blood cultures taken at different stages in the disease is as follows:

> Of 224 cases during first week, 89 per cent were positive.
> Of 484 cases during second week, 73 per cent were positive.
> Of 268 cases during third week, 60 per cent were positive.
> Of 103 cases during fourth week, 38 per cent were positive.
> Of 58 cases after fourth week, 26 per cent were positive.

In making blood cultures it is advisable to place from 5 to 10 c.c. of blood in 100 c.c. of medium, either infusion broth, or infusion agar if plates are to be poured. This tends to render inhibitory factors ineffective by dilution. We have, however, isolated typhoid bacilli from blood clots in sterile tubes containing samples of blood intended for the provision of serum for Widal tests.

Typhoid Bacilli in the Stools.—The examination of the stools for typhoid bacillus is performed for diagnostic purposes in acute cases and in examinations for the purpose of detecting carriers. The examination itself is fraught with difficulties, owing to the preponderating numbers of colon bacilli found in all feces and the difficulty of isolating the typhoid bacilli from such mixtures.

Reviewing the data collected by a number of investigators, it seems probable that the bacilli do not appear in the stools, at least in numbers sufficient for recognition, much before the middle of the *second week,* or, in other words, as pointed out by Hiss, about the time that the intestinal lesions are well advanced and ulceration is occurring. Hiss, in an investigation of the subject, obtained the following results:

First to tenth day, inclusive, 28 cases examined; typhoid bacilli isolated from 3; percentage of positive cases 10.7 per cent.

Eleventh to twentieth day, inclusive, 44 cases examined; typhoid bacilli from 22; percentage of positive cases 50 per cent.

Twenty-first day to convalescence, 16 cases examined; typhoid bacilli isolated from 13; percentage of positive cases 81.2 per cent.

Stool Examination and Method of Typhoid Carrier Detection.—Fecal carriers of typhoid bacilli may be detected by cultural methods applied either to specimens of feces or to duodenal contents, obtained by a tube passed through the stomach into the duodenum. The simplest method is direct examination of the feces. The duodenal tube, however, may be positive when stool cultures are negative. As a matter of fact, in the hands of Garbat and Nichols, the duodenal method seems to have given more regular results than the stool method.

Stool Examinations.—Stool material for typhoid examination should be fresh. Preserving stools for as long as twelve hours will diminish positive findings by 50 per cent. If large numbers are

to be examined, it is a good plan to give mild, saline cathartics in the morning, so that all specimens can be collected at about the same time. It is best to collect specimens by cotton swabs, on
swab sticks thrust into tubes in which there are a few drops of salt solution to prevent drying.
We have found that rectal swabbing, if properly carried out, may be a valuable method of collecting material. If it is absolutely necessary to ship stools some distance, the addition of 20 per
cent glycerin is of advantage.

A suspension of about one part of feces to twenty-five parts of salt solution is made, thoroughly
emulsified, and allowed to stand to allow the large particles to settle. With this material, surface
smears are made with a glass rod upon plates of either Robinson and Rettger's modification of
Endo's medium, or Krumwiede's brilliant green medium, or eosin methylene blue agar, as described
in the section on media. It is of advantage to use the large plates. A bent glass rod is dipped into
the emulsion and rubbed over the surface of a plate, beginning in the center, by passing in concentric circles so that the entire plate is gently smeared. A second plate is inoculated in the
same way, without redipping. It is sometimes well to make similar plates with a 1:5 dilution of
the original suspension.

Plates for this purpose should be poured and allowed to dry on a laboratory desk for a few
hours before use, and should be kept in the dark if Endo's medium is used. Great care in the
accurate production and testing out of the media, should be taken as indicated in the section
describing these media. The plates should either be inverted in the incubator, or else earthen-ware
covers should be used. Large pieces of blotting paper inserted under the lid serve the same purpose.

After eighteen hours' growth, the plates should be examined for typical colonies. Suspicious
colonies should be immediately inoculated upon tubes of Russell double sugar medium. Slide
agglutinations against 1:100 dilution of a high titer stock typhoid antiserum should be made for
preliminary identification from suspicious colonies, of course together with morphological determination by smear and stain.

Much information can be obtained after twelve more hours, by observations of the growth in
the Russell double sugar medium. From this tube, then, the growth can be emulsified in salt
solution, and macroscopic agglutinations set up. This usually is sufficient to identify the organism,
but it is always well to set up a few sugar fermentation tubes.

Duodenal examinations are made by means of the Einhorn duodenal tube, which
is sterilized by boiling, and given to the patient the evening before the examination
is to be made, about three hours after the last meal. The patient, properly instructed,
swallows the tube and retains it throughout the night. On the following morning it has
usually passed into the duodenum, and bile can be aspirated with a sterile 20 c.c.
Luer syringe. Suction must usually be exerted, and Garbat recommends a well-fitting
syringe because such suction must often be strong. In about 5 per cent of Garbat's
cases the tube remained in the stomach and more difficulty was experienced with the
test. When there is difficulty in obtaining sufficient bile, the patient is made to sit up
in bed with his head bent forward, pressing upward on the abdomen with the palms of
his hands. Sometimes the flow of bile can be stimulated by a cold drink. Cultures of
the bile are made on plates of Endo's medium.

Typhoid Bacilli in the Urine.—Investigation has revealed typhoid bacilli in the
urine in about 25 per cent of all patients. Neumann discovered the bacilli in 11 out
of 46 and Karlinsky in 21 out of 44 cases. Investigations by Petruschky, Richardson,
Horton-Smith, Hiss, and others have confirmed these results. In general the bacilli
have not been found before the fifteenth day of the disease, and examination of the
urine, therefore, can be of little early diagnostic value. A series of 75 cases examined
by Hiss before the fourteenth day of the disease did not once reveal typhoid bacilli
in the urine. On the other hand, they have been found for weeks, months, and, in
isolated cases, for years after convalescence. They are probably present in about

12 per cent of cases during the early days of convalescence. In most of these, albumin is present in the urine in considerable quantities. The bacilli usually appear and disappear with the albuminuria.

An obstinate cystitis caused by typhoid bacilli may follow typhoid fever. Such cases have been reported by Blumer, Richardson, and others. Suppurative processes in the kidneys are less frequent. It is noteworthy, also, that in the course of, and following, typhoid fever B. coli is often present in the urine. This may obstinately persist for considerable periods.

For examination of the urine for typhoid bacilli, catheter specimens should be taken and planted directly into equal volumes of broth. Direct plates on Endo should be made at the same time. It is relatively easy under such circumstances to obtain the organism if present.

Typhoid Bacilli in the Rose Spots.—Neufeld obtained positive results in thirteen out of fourteen cases. According to his researches and those of Fränkel, the bacilli are localized not in the blood, which is taken when the rose spots are incised, but are crowded in large numbers within the lymph spaces.

Typhoid Bacilli in the Sputum.—In rare cases typhoid bacilli have been found in the sputum of cases complicated by bronchitis, bronchopneumonia, and pleurisy. Such cases have been reported by Chantemesse and Widal, Fränkel, and a number of others. Empyema, when it occurs in connection with such cases, is usually accompanied by a mixed infection. The spread of typhoid fever by means of the sputum is negligible.

Suppurative Lesions Due to Typhoid Bacillus.—During the latter weeks of the disease, suppurative lesions may occur in various parts of the body. The most frequent localization of these is in the periosteum, especially on the long bones, and in the joints. A considerable number of such lesions have been described by Welch, Richardson, and others. They usually take the form of periosteal abscesses, often located upon the tibia, occurring either late in the disease or months after convalescence, and are characterized by severe pain. Osteomyelitis may also occur, but is comparatively rare. Subcutaneous abscesses and deep abscesses in the muscles, due to this bacillus, have been described by Pratt. Synovitis may also occur.

Meningitis, due to the typhoid bacillus, occurs rarely, usually during convalescence from typhoid fever.

Peritoneal abscesses, due to the typhoid bacillus, have been reported. One of us has reported a case in which typhoid bacilli were found free in the peritoneal cavity during typhoid fever without perforation of the gut.

Isolated instances of typhoid bacilli in abscesses of the thyroid and parotid glands and in brain abscesses have been observed.

Typhoid Fever without Intestinal Lesions.—A number of cases have been reported in which typhoid bacilli have been isolated from the organs after death or from the secretions during life of patients in whom the characteristic lesions of typhoid fever have been lacking. Most of these cases must be regarded as true typhoid septicemias. In some cases the bacilli were isolated from the spleen, liver, or kidneys; in others, from the urine or the gallbladder. In one case the bacilli were isolated from an infarct of the kidney removed by operation. In this case the clinical course of the disease had pointed only toward the existence of an indefinite fever accompanied by symptoms referable to the kidneys. The Widal test, however, was positive. A summary of such cases, together with several personally observed, has been given by Flexner.

Poisons of the Typhoid Bacillus.—The first to do experimental work upon this subject was Brieger soon after the discovery and cultivation of the bacillus. That toxic substances can be obtained from typhoid cultures is beyond question. There is, however, a difference of opinion as to whether these poisons are so-called endotoxins only, or whether they are in part composed of soluble toxins comparable to those of diphtheria and tetanus.

The evidence so far seems to bear out the original contention of Pfeiffer, that the poisonous substances are products of the bacterial body set free by destruction of the bacteria by the lytic substances of the invaded animal or human being. These poisons, when injected into animals for purposes of immunization, in Pfeiffer's experiments, did not incite the production of neutralizing or antitoxic bodies, but of bactericidal and lytic substances. That these endotoxins constitute by far the greater part of the toxic products of the typhoid bacillus can be easily demonstrated in the laboratory, by the simple experiment of filtering a young typhoid culture (eight or nine days old) and injecting into separate animals the residue of bacilli and the clear filtrate respectively. In such an experiment there will be little question as to the overwhelmingly greater toxicity of the bacillary bodies as compared with that of the culture filtrate. On the other hand, if such cultures, especially in alkaline media, are allowed to stand for several months and the bacilli thus thoroughly extracted by the broth, the toxicity of the filtrate is found to be greatly increased.

Nevertheless, experiments by Besredka, Macfadyen, Kraus and Steinitzer and others have suggested that, together with such endotoxic substances, typhoid bacilli may produce a true toxin which fulfills the necessary requirement of this class of poisons by producing in treated animals a true antitoxic neutralizing body.

The typhoid endotoxins may be obtained by a variety of methods. Hahn has obtained what he calls "typhoplasmin" by subjecting them to a pressure of about four hundred atmospheres in a Buchner press. The cell juices so obtained are cleared by filtration. Macfadyen has obtained typhoid endotoxins by triturating the bacilli after freezing them with liquid air and extracting in 1 : 1000 potassium hydrate. Besredka obtained toxic substances by emulsifying agar cultures of bacilli in salt solution, sterilizing them by heating to 60° C. for about one hour, and drying *in vacuo*. The dried bacillary mass was then ground in a mortar and washed in sterile salt solution which was again heated to 60° C. for two hours. The remnants of the bacterial bodies settle out and the slightly turbid supernatant fluid contains the toxic substances.

Vaughan has obtained poisons from typhoid bacilli by extracting at 78° C. with a 2 per cent solution of sodium hydrate in absolute alcohol. In this way he claims to separate by hydrolysis a poisonous and nonpoisonous fraction. He claims, moreover, that this poisonous fraction is similar to the poisons obtained in the same way from *Bacillus coli* and the tubercle bacillus, and other protein substances, believing that the specific nature of such proteins depends upon the nontoxic fraction.

A simple method of obtaining toxins from typhoid bacilli is carried out by cultivating the micro-organisms in meat infusion broth, rendered alkaline with sodium hydrate to the extent of about 1 per cent. The cultures are allowed to grow for two or three weeks and then sterilized by heating at 60° C. for one hour, and allowed to stand for three or four weeks at room temperature. At the end of this time the cultures may be filtered through a Berkefeld or Pasteur-Chamberland filter and the filtrate be found to contain strong toxic substances.

The accounts concerning the thermostability of the various toxins obtained are considerably at variance. In general observers agree in considering them moderately resistant to heat, rarely being destroyed at temperatures below 70° C.

Intravenous inoculation of rabbits with typhoid endotoxins, if in sufficient quantity, produces, usually within a few hours, a marked drop in temperature, diarrhea, respiratory embarrassment, and death. If given in smaller doses or by other methods of inoculation—subcutaneous or intraperitoneal—rabbits are rendered extremely ill, with a primary drop in temperature, but may live for a week or ten days and die with progressive emaciation, or may survive. Guinea-pigs and mice are susceptible to the endotoxins, though somewhat less so than rabbits.

In unpublished experiments we have perfused the isolated guinea-pig heart with typhoid extracts for prolonged periods without killing it, showing that the poison does not act upon the normal heart muscle directly.

In broth cultures of the typhoid bacillus as young as five to six hours, a mildly toxic substance is formed which can be recovered in filtrates, and which, injected into rabbits intravenously, gives rise to definite symptoms, after an incubation time of an hour or more. This substance is not specific in that it is formed by many other different bacteria similarly grown, and is not antigenic in all probability. It can also be obtained by washing young agar growth repeatedly in salt solution, and filtering. This is the substance involved in the Schwartzman reaction.

IMMUNITY AND ANTIBODIES

Animals may be actively immunized by the injection of typhoid bacilli in gradually increasing doses. In practice, this is best accomplished by beginning with an injection of about 1 c.c. of broth culture heated for ten minutes at 60° C. in order to kill the bacilli. After five or six days, a second injection of a larger dose of dead bacilli is administered; at similar intervals, gradually increasing doses of dead bacilli are given and finally considerable quantities of a living and fully virulent culture may be injected without serious consequences to the animal. While this method is convenient and usually successful, it is also possible to obtain satisfactory immunization by beginning with very small doses of living micro-organisms.

There are present in the blood serum of typhoid-immune animals and human beings, bacteriolytic, bactericidal, and agglutinating substances, and to a lesser extent, precipitating and opsonic bodies but no true antitoxins.

One attack of typhoid fever protects against subsequent infection. Accurate statistics upon the matter have been difficult to obtain, however, because histories of the disease are apt to be indefinite, and until recently, no proper differentiation was made between true typhoid fever and the paratyphoid group. However, taking into consideration these possibilities of error, the estimations indicate that a second attack of typhoid fever occurs in not more than from 0.7 to 4 per cent of all cases. Two to three per cent represents a fair average of all estimates made. When typhoid fever *does* occur for the second time, it is usually of a milder type than the first attack, though this is not always the case.

Circulating antibodies disappear from the typhoid convalescent usually within the first seven months after recovery. Permanent immunity cannot, therefore, be explained upon the basis of serum antibodies. The ultimate cause for permanent immunity, in all diseases in which it occurs, must be regarded as depending upon the tissue cell. It is likely that individuals who have passed through an infection of this nature, thereafter retain a capacity to react more rapidly and effectively to small quantities of introduced antigen. A case in point is the well-known experiment of Wassermann, who immunized a number of rabbits to typhoid bacilli until a high agglutinin titer was produced. He kept these rabbits until their blood had returned to normal and no agglutinins could be found. Subsequently he reinoculated them with typhoid bacilli, at the same time giving a number of normal control rabbits similar injections. The previously treated rabbits responded with a rapid and powerful antibody production in contrast to the slower antibody curve of those that had received the typhoid antigen for the first time. Recent observations by Moon on revaccination of previously vaccinated people have given analogous results.

Bactericidal and Bacteriolytic Substances.—The bacteriolytic substances in typhoid-immune serum may be demonstrated either by the intraperitoneal technic of Pfeiffer or *in vitro*. In the former experiment a small quantity of a fresh culture of typhoid bacilli is mixed with the diluted immune serum and the emulsion injected into the peritoneal cavity of a guinea-pig. Removal of peritoneal exudate with a capillary pipet and examination in the hanging drop will reveal, within a short time, a swelling and granulation of the bacteria—the so-called Pfeiffer phenomenon. The test *in vitro*, as recommended by Stern and Korte, may be carried out by adding definite quantities of a fresh agar culture of typhoid bacilli to progressively increasing dilutions of inactivated immune serum together with definite quantities of complement in the form of fresh normal rabbit or guinea-pig serum. At the end of several hours' incubation at 37.5° C. definite quantities of the fluid from the various tubes are inoculated into melted agar and plates are poured to determine the bactericidal action. Careful colony counting in these plates and comparison with proper controls will not only definitely demonstrate the presence of bactericidal substances in the immune serum, but will furnish a reasonably accurate quantitative estimation.

Although normal human serum contains in small quantity substances bactericidal to typhoid bacilli, moderate dilution, 1: 10 or 1: 20, of such serum will usually suffice to eliminate any appreciable bactericidal action. The bactericidal powers of immune serum, on the other hand, are often active, according to Stern and Korte, in dilutions of over 1: 4000. The specificity of such reactions gives them considerable practical value, both in the biological identification of a suspected typhoid bacillus in known serum and in the diagnosis of typhoid fever in the human patient by the action of the patient's serum on known typhoid bacilli. While scientifically accurate the practical application of bactericidal determinations for diagnosis presents considerable technical difficulties and gives way to the no less accurate and much simpler method of agglutination.

Precipitins.—The investigations of Kraus, by which the precipitins were discovered, revealed specific precipitating substances, among others, also in typhoid immune sera. Since Kraus' original investigation, these substances have been studied by Norris and others.

Opsonins.—A number of observers have shown that opsonins specific for the typhoid bacillus are formed in animals immunized with these organisms. Opsonins are formed also in patients suffering from typhoid fever, but exact opsonic estimations in all these cases are extremely difficult because of the rapid lysis which these bacteria may undergo both in the serum, and intracellularly, after ingestion by the leukocytes. Klein has attempted to overcome this difficulty by working with dilutions of serum, at the same time using comparatively thick bacterial emulsions and exposures to the phagocytic action not exceeding ten minutes. Chantemesse has claimed that the opsonic index of typhoid patients was increased after treatment with a serum obtained by him from immunized horses, and Harrison has reported similar results in patients treated by a modification of Wright's method of active immunization. Klein claims to have demonstrated that in typhoid-immune rabbits, after five injections, the opsonic contents of the blood were increased to an equal extent as the bactericidal substances. Theoretically the importance of serum antibodies is rendered uncertain in this disease by the fact that the bacteria usually disappear from the blood within twenty-one days—long before the patient is cured.

Agglutination and Serological Diagnosis.—In 1896, Gruber and Durham showed that agglutination was a relatively specific immunological phenomenon. In the same year Grünbaum and Widal applied the reaction to the diagnosis of typhoid fever in man. They used as the test antigen a suspension of heat-killed typhoid bacilli and determined by dilution the smallest amount of the patient's serum which was capable of agglutinating the organisms. The test has become familiarly known as the Widal reaction. When used properly and with judgment it has been of great aid in the diagnosis of typhoid fever. The principles upon which it was based have not changed, but there have been many modifications of procedure, numerous changes in the antigens, or bacterial suspensions, and consequently in the interpretation of the results of the test.

In the early days of the study of agglutination reactions little or no attention was paid to the nature of the antigen used to produce agglutinins experimentally or to detect antibodies in the serum of an artificially immunized or naturally infected man or animal. For use in the test, typhoid bacilli were usually washed off agar slant cultures with saline, killed by heat at 60° C. for 30 to 60 minutes, and the suspension diluted to an approximately determined turbidity found to be satisfactory for observations of clumping. From the results of thousands of such tests, physicians accepted as a sort of dictum, that the agglutination of typhoid bacilli by patients' serum in a dilution of 1 : 40 or 1 : 80 was diagnostic. It was learned that this reaction usually became positive during the third week of typhoid fever.

The widespread practice of prophylactic vaccination against typhoid fever, especially among soldiers, introduced a new difficulty in the interpretation of the results of the test. It became difficult to decide whether agglutinins in the blood of a previously vaccinated febrile patient were due to infection with typhoid or paratyphoid bacilli or to the effect of the vaccine. The situation was further complicated by the occurrence of what is known as the "anamnestic reaction." This type of reaction is due to the "recall," or new formation of antibodies to a previously injected antigen under the stimulus of a newly introduced antigen of the same or different nature. Thus persons vaccinated against typhoid and paratyphoid fevers might show a reappearance or increase of antityphoid agglutinins in their blood as a consequence of infection with pyogenic cocci or other organisms. It became necessary, therefore, to introduce quantitative methods into the practical agglutination tests and to establish standards for comparison.

The reagent especially requiring standardization was the antigen. Dreyer succeeded in preparing "standard agglutinable cultures" and he and his associates at Oxford devised procedures for quantitative Widal reactions which were used extensively during the World War and still serve as guides in work of this sort. The antigens adopted by Dreyer were twenty-four-hour peptone veal broth cultures of motile typhoid and paratyphoid bacilli to which 0.2 per cent formalin was added. After suitable dilution to match a density standard and after tests for agglutinability by a serum of known potency, these suspensions were given standard factor numbers and used for quantitative determinations of the rise and fall of agglutinins in the blood of animals and patients. This was a great improvement in the method and the principle was sound. It was not known at that time, however, that antigens prepared in this way, being very sensitive to agglutinin and giving large loose flocculi, were H antigens. They contained the flagellar or H factor in abundance, while the O, or somatic antigen, obscured by the large flocculating H substance, was further rendered ineffective by the formaldehyde "preservative."

The discovery of Weil and Felix that *Proteus* and other motile bacteria including typhoid and paratyphoid bacilli have "double receptors" introduced a new problem. These antigens were designated the H, flagellar antigen, responsible for large flaky agglutination clumps and the O, somatic antigen, responsible for fine, granular, slow-forming clumps. The studies of dissociation in the typhoid-paratyphoid groups by Andrewes and Arkwright, about 1922, laid the foundations for the next advance in the generally scientific and practically useful application of the agglutination reaction. Since then, the studies of bacterial antigens and their corresponding antibodies along these lines have been very numerous. We have reviewed some of these investigations in paragraphs dealing with the antigenic analysis of typhoid and paratyphoid bacilli in their smooth and rough forms, and in the reference to monophasic and diphasic types. It is obvious that the antigenic analysis is disclosing both complexities and correlations. The knowledge on these subjects is by no means complete. For our purposes here we shall recall, in addition to what we have said about the H and O factors, that H antigens are usually more specific than O antigens, that the O, somatic antigen in any group is shared by many organisms in that group and occasionally by organisms not usually placed in that group. A typhoid patient should, moreover, agglutinate virulent organisms containing the "Vi" factor. A fact which has particular significance here is that *B. typhosus* and *B. enteritidis* have a common O antigen.

Agglutinins found in normal serums are often of the O type. The essential facts of dissociation which have a bearing on this problem have been discussed on page 512.

The outcome of these investigations is the development of the so-called *modern Widal reaction* or modern agglutination test for the diagnosis of typhoid fever. In the section on technical procedures, details are described. The special features of the test to be noted here are the following:

1. Use of the *macroscopic method,* in test tubes and with reagents in quantities of 0.3 to 0.5 c.c., or in greater amounts.

2. Serum, from blood clots in serological tubes, available in adequate amount.

3. *Standardized Antigens.* The bacillary suspensions should be of known density as measured against a standard suspension and should be tested for their agglutinability by serums of known potency. For the preparation of the H and O antigens of the typhoid bacillus, certain cultures are available in various laboratories. These are known, in the case of *B. typhosus,* as the motile strain (Felix) H 901 and the non-motile strain O 901. If these are not at hand, satisfactory H antigen can be made by adding 0.1 to 0.2 per cent formaldehyde to a broth culture of a motile strain of *B. typhosus.* The O antigen can be made from the same strain by adding an equal volume of absolute alcohol to a thick suspension of the motile organism, and incubating the mixture 24 to 36 hours at 37° C., according to the method of Bien and Gardner. The labile flagellar H antigen is destroyed by alcohol.

Similar antigens may be prepared from cultures of *B. paratyphosus* A and *B. paratyphosus* B, but the practical necessity and the results obtained give these less importance than similar procedures with respect to *B. typhosus.*

4. *Incubation.*—It is best to incubate the tubes in a water bath at 50° to 55° C. For demonstration of H, large flocculating agglutination clumps, 2 hours is sufficient at 50° to 55° C. At 37° C., 8 to 10 hours, and at room temperature 24 hours are required to determine end points. For O, fine, granular agglutination, it is necessary to incubate the tubes 24 hours at 50° to 55° C., or 10 to 12 hours at 50° to 55° and over night in the refrigerator.

These methods have been applied extensively in diagnostic laboratories in England and in this country.

The results of positive agglutination tests, obtained by these methods, seem to us to be interpretable as follows:

1. For O agglutinins: the significant titers are those above 1 to 50, since a few normal individuals have titers as high as 1 to 50, and rarely 1 to 200 or above.

2. For H agglutinins: titers of 1 to 80 or above appear to have some diagnostic significance.

3. If the "Vi" antigen could be detected it would be of great significance.

It is obvious that a carefully performed Widal reaction using the customary H-type antigens of *B. typhosus, B. paratyphosus* A and *B. paratyphosus* B is still capable of providing a certain amount of useful information. The methods in which advantage is taken of the knowledge of the antigenic components will provide additional information. It should be emphasized that the results of these agglutination tests are to be interpreted by the physician only with a full knowledge of the history of the patient, especially with reference to previous vaccination against typhoid fever, that the repetition of the tests with standardized reagents should be made in order to secure an index of the rise or fall of the agglutinin titer, and that only when the titers are high (O, 1:500, or H, 1:1000) can they be said to approach diagnostic certainty.

SANITARY CONSIDERATIONS

Typhoid fever has been constantly diminishing in civilized countries during the last one hundred years, but is still a formidable cause of death rate and disability. The morbidity rates and death rates for typhoid fever vary considerably in different communities according to the extent to which sanitary supervision of water supplies, garbage and sewage disposal, etc., have been developed. In general, the United States has been considerably behind some European communities. In a table given by Gay, in 1918, a comparison of mortality averages per 100,000 population, comparing a group of over 31,000,000 people compiled from the statistics of the 33 largest European cities, with 21,000,000 people representing the populations of 57 of the largest American cities, the European mortality average was 6.5, and the American 19.59. In similar compilations taken by Gay largely from the report of the New York State Department of Health for 1914, it is shown that there has been a progressive decrease since 1910, running parallel to increased attention to water supplies and general sanitation. For more extensive figures on the prevalence of typhoid fever the reader is referred to the above-mentioned compilation of Gay. He states that in 1900 there were about 350,000 cases of typhoid fever in the United States as estimated by Whipple, who at the same time calculates that the cost to the community of these cases must have been approximately $212,000,000.

Since 1918 the mortality from typhoid fever in the United States has decreased. In most sections, the death rate in 1937 was less than 2 per 100,000.

TOTAL TYPHOID DEATH RATE PER HUNDRED THOUSAND OF POPULATION FOR NINETY-THREE CITIES ACCORDING TO GEOGRAPHIC DIVISIONS *

	Popula-tion	Typhoid Deaths		Typhoid Death Rates					
		1937	1936	1937	1936	1935	1931-1935	1926-1930	1925
New England	2,640,933	12	11	0.45	0.42	0.49	0.70	1.31	2.48
Middle Atlantic	13,426,805	68	74	0.51	0.56	0.55	0.80	1.40	2.97
South Atlantic	2,609,531	51	40	1.96	1.55	2.58	2.70	4.50	7.01
East North Central	9,870,249	61	70	0.62	0.72	0.60	0.75	1.29	2.32
East South Central	1,330,969	28	43	2.10	3.35	3.94	4.81	8.31	13.00
West North Central	2,778,245	21	22	0.76	0.79	0.85	1.24	1.83	3.43
West South Central	2,084,616	49	79	2.34	3.99	3.82	5.36	7.32	13.08
Mountain and Pacific	4,144,087	28	32	0.68	0.80	0.88	0.88	1.80	2.33

* J. Am. M. Ass., 1938, 111:418.

As typhoid fever is largely preventable, much of the distress and expense caused by the disease is unnecessary waste.

Infection with typhoid fever always means that intestinal contents of a case or a carrier have come into direct or indirect contact with something ingested by the patient.

In the patient the typhoid bacillus begins to accumulate in the intestines during the later stages of the incubation time, and at this time will begin to appear in the feces. The organisms increase in the intestines from this time on, being distributed in very considerable numbers after the second week, and decreasing only towards the end of the disease, remaining present, however, throughout convalescence and sometimes, as we shall see, for months or years thereafter. During the second and third or later weeks, the organisms appear in the urine. It is generally stated that about 30 per cent of typhoid cases will show the organisms in the urine, but it seems likely that this is too low an estimate. Raubitschek, by precipitating considerable quantities of urine with ferric chloride succeeded in finding the bacilli in 100 per cent of his cases in the earlier stages of the disease, and in slight numbers, and perhaps intermittently, they may appear in the urine of all typhoid cases. Other unusual routes of distribution from the patient are pus from suppurations and sputum.

Since the recognized typhoid case is usually well guarded from a sanitary point of view, the greater danger of typhoid infection lies in the mild, atypical, unrecognized case and in the carrier. Atypical, mild cases will probably become more and more frequent as typhoid vaccination becomes a more generalized habit. Such a case may show nothing more than a very slight febrile movement, with intestinal disturbances and diarrhea. Unless typhoid fever is particularly looked for and suspected, many of these cases may never be put upon typhoid precautions.

Typhoid Carriers.—The great importance of the typhoid carrier in the spread of the disease has led to extensive studies of the problem in many countries. We may mention particularly the studies of Conradi and Drigalski, the paper of Sacquepée, the summary given by Kutscher in the second edition of the Kolle and Wassermann *Handbuch*, the summary of Gay and the article by Garbat, one of the monographs of the Rockefeller Institute. The first suggestion of the danger of typhoid infection emanating from convalescents long after the disease itself had been cured, came from Koch. He based this opinion at first upon purely epidemiological evidence, but in 1904 Drigalski began to isolate bacilli from individuals who were apparently in complete health. Sacquepée classifies typhoid carriers into convalescent carriers who become free of the bacilli within three months after the termination of their disease, and chronic carriers who continue to harbor the bacilli for many years, and perhaps permanently. In addition to this, there are a certain number of so-called healthy carriers in whom no history of their ever having had the disease can be adduced, the original infection having produced only a mild disorder.

The distinction between a temporary carrier and a chronic carrier is to a certain degree arbitrary. In general it may be said that in most typhoid cases the organisms disappear from the urine and feces within from six weeks to three months after recovery. Sacquepée classifies as *chronic carriers* only those in whom the organisms are still present three months after complete recovery. After this period, the length of time to which the carrier may persist is variable, depending upon whether or not chronic lesions are established. These will be discussed below. The frequency with which chronic carriers following typhoid fever occur may be gathered from the table compiled by Gay.

If we consider that the figures presented in this table must necessarily represent underestimates because of the technical difficulties attending the discovery of small numbers of typhoid bacilli, it becomes apparent that the number of potential foci for infection in a community where typhoid is prevalent is large. It is estimated that from approximately 2 to 4 per cent of all persons affected with typhoid fever continue to discharge typhoid bacilli indefinitely. (Havens.)

According to the foci upon which the carrier state depends, typhoid carriers have been subdivided by a number of writers into intestinal carriers, gallbladder carriers, and liver or bile-duct carriers. Newer methods of duodenal tube examination have made these distinctions between carriers possible.

PERCENTAGES OF CHRONIC TYPHOID CARRIERS FOUND BY VARIOUS INVESTIGATORS IN A STUDY OF CONVALESCENT CASES *

Author	Date	Number of Cases	Percentage Carriers for 3 Months and More
Lentz	1905	400	3.0
Conradi	1907	400	0.5
Klinger	1907	482	1.7
Kayser	1907	101	3.5
Semple and Greig	1908	86	11.6
Park	1908	68	5.9
Tsuzuki	1910	51	5.8
Bruckner	1910	316	3.8
Stokes and Clarke	1916	810	1.85

* Table taken from F. P. Gay, *Typhoid Fever*, The Macmillan Co., New York, 1918.

By far the most common localization of typhoid bacilli in the body of the carrier is the gallbladder. In speaking of the sequelae of typhoid fever we have seen that cholecystitis is often related to a preceding attack of typhoid fever. As a matter of fact in the course of typhoid fever the organisms are always present in the gallbladder. This was noted by Chiari as early as 1894, by Pratt, and others. Longcope took bile cultures as a routine in suspected typhoid deaths at the Pennsylvania Hospital, and found typhoid bacilli in all positive cases. In the gallbladder apparently the organisms find a protected nidus where they can persist for years. If gallstones are formed later, typhoid bacilli can often be isolated from them.

That liver-duct carriers, however, may exist independently of gallbladder infection has been shown by Garbat. He speaks of two patients who, during typhoid convalescence, manifested gallbladder symptoms. Direct culture of the bile by means of the duodenal tube method showed typhoid bacilli in "A," but not in "B." In both, the gallbladder was removed and a pure culture of typhoid bacilli obtained from both. At the time of operation, the negative culture in "B" was explained by the fact that a large stone was fixed in the cystic duct which completely occluded the passage. The bile from "B" before operation had come directly from the liver, and had not entered the gallbladder which was in this case the only site of infection. After operation, however, typhoid bacilli completely disappeared from "B," where the bile that had come from the liver had been found sterile by the original duodenal culture, but in "A," in spite of the complete removal of the gallbladder and cystic duct, repeated duodenal cultures remained positive. Similar cases have been reported in the literature, but none which seem quite as convincing as these instances reported by Garbat.

The manner in which typhoid bacilli get into the gallbladder has occupied the attention of a number of investigators. According to Küster and a more recent report by Garbat ascending infection of the gallbladder from the duodenum is a possibility, though it is probably not the most common method of infection. The fact that, according to Blumenthal, Laubenheimer and others, colon bacilli are very commonly found in the gallbladder, gives support to the possibility of ascending infection. The opinion, however, that the bile is hematogeneously infected by way of the hepatic circulation in most cases is generally accepted.

The existence of pure intestinal carriers has been suggested by Kraus and others, and in addition to the cases cited by Kraus, there is one by Garbat in which duodenal cultures were repeatedly negative, whereas the feces remained positive. Cholecystectomy on this case did not relieve the carrier condition. The intestinal carrier type, according to Kraus, may be associated with chronic intestinal ulcerations, chronic appendicitis, etc., but is unquestionably extremely rare.

Chronic urinary carriers are less common than chronic feces carriers. Yet, when they occur, they are of much greater danger to others because of the more indiscriminate distribution of urine. According to Garbat about 6.8 per cent of all typhoid cases show typhoid bacilluria for one or two months after the fever has disappeared. In such cases often the organisms are discharged intermittently, and for this reason repeated examination is necessary. Chronic urinary carriers have been reported by Prigge, Houston, and others, and are usually associated with some pathological lesion of the genito-urinary tract. In a case reported by Mayer and Ahreiner there was a pyonephrosis, and in other cases, cystitis, or other inflammations of the bladder, ureter, and kidney have been found.

By so-called healthy carriers are meant individuals who harbor typhoid bacilli in the stools and in whom no history of typhoid infection at any time in their lives can be obtained. A negative history of this kind, especially if obtained from people who have lived vigorous, active, physical lives, is unreliable. Extremely mild cases of typhoid fever, while not common, do occur, and it is not impossible that an individual with an unusual resistance may have been ill for a few weeks without going to a doctor. Scheller in examining a group of people, in connection with the investigations made of a mild epidemic, found a considerable number of temporary carriers who did not develop the disease. These people had taken milk infected from a carrier, 18 of a total of 44 acquiring the organisms without getting sick, while 32 of the same group actually got sick. It is not impossible, therefore, that individuals associated with typhoid cases and during epidemics may become temporary carriers.

Carriers may increase enormously in the course of epidemics, especially if these epidemics take place among the large groups of vaccinated people. Such conditions prevailed among the Allied and probably among the German Armies during the World War, when the opportunities for fecal transmission incident to active warfare, with open latrines, unprotected kitchens, unlimited fly breeding, and defective scattered small water supplies, made sanitary control impossible. Hundreds of thousands of men suffered from diarrheas and mild intestinal disease, without or with very slight febrile manifestations, and investigations showed that a considerable percentage of these people were actually infected with organisms of the typhoid, paratyphoid, and dysentery groups.

As to the relative importance of the typhoid carrier in the morbidity of typhoid fever, it is very difficult to adduce accurate data. It is pretty safe to say that the carrier is growing relatively more important, will in the future probably be the chief source of typhoid morbidity in well-protected communities, and is the only stumbling block which will prevent the complete eradication of the disease. Of recent years, as water, milk, and food supplies are coming more and more directly under the eyes of health authorities, the estimates of the percentage of cases due to carriers, as contrasted with other sources of infection, is growing larger. The dangerous potentialities of a carrier were clearly shown by the famous "Typhoid Mary." She transmitted the infection to at least two hundred victims.

Pathological Consequences of the Carrier State.—The most common sequela of the chronic carrier state is cholelithiasis. According to Exner and Heyworski typhoid bacilli have a particular property of decomposing the bile salts, giving rise to a precipitation of cholesterin, and Doerr produced small concretions in the gallbladder of infected animals. Typhoid bacilli have often been found in gallstones. Obstruction of the bile and stagnation due to inflammatory processes may be indirectly responsible for stone formation.

It is probable that typhoid carriers possess high resistance to second attacks, higher even than that of the ordinary individual who recovers without developing the carrier state. Küster reports that of eight hundred chronic carriers observed in the military hospital at Cologne during two and one-half years, not a single clinical disturbance attributable to the typhoid bacillus could be determined. The occurrence of cystitis, pyelitis and renal stones in typhoid carriers is not particularly common.

Occasionally, typhoid carriers may possess agglutinins and other antibodies in the blood higher than normal. Lentz examined a number of chronic carriers and found positive Widals in ten out of eleven; however, only in dilutions of $1 : 20$. Gaethgens found both agglutinins and opsonins higher in chronic carriers than in normal people, but Schone found no increase in complement fixation. In general, we would not hope for very much light from serological investigations upon the question of whether or not an individual was a carrier.

Treatment and Cure.—The importance of the typhoid carrier from the epidemiological point of view has led to innumerable attempts at cure. That there can be no doubt about the possibility of cure in most cases, by surgical gallbladder extirpation, appears certain. It will be necessary in the future, however, especially on the basis of the work of Nichols, Garbat and some German observers, to precede such operations by fecal and duodenal examinations, and it must be remembered that there may always be a certain percentage of cases which are liver-duct carriers, in contrast to gallbladder foci. Also, the operation is not without danger, with a certain amount of mortality, and cannot be applied generally upon the enormous numbers of carriers that exist.

According to Garbat and others, attempts to cure by other means necessarily depend to a very large extent upon early diagnosis of the carriers before the condition has become stubbornly chronic. But in all cases, cure by other than surgical means has been discouraging. Many different methods have been attempted. Vaccination with the ordinary typhoid vaccines has given discouraging results in the hands of Park. Irwin and Houston claimed to have cured a urinary carrier by vaccination, but Houston and Thomas failed in other cases. Petruschky in 1902 claimed that vaccination during the course of the disease might prevent the development of the carrier state. But, on the whole, vaccination has not brought the results that have been hoped from it.

Medicinal treatment has been tried but without much success. Discouraging results have been obtained with urotropin, methylene blue, salicylates, iodine and arsenic preparations. Conradi in 1910 tried chloroform with apparently successful results in rabbits experimentally converted into typhoid carriers. Bully tried this treatment upon human carriers, giving 0.5 c.c. of chloroform in capsules four times a day for twenty days, without results. Neosalvarsan has been tried without effect. The most favorable reports are those of Kahlberlah who administered tincture of iodine together with animal charcoal, and those of Geronne who combined charcoal with thymol. None of these methods have, however, been sufficiently confirmed.

Typhoid Bacillus in Transit from Source to Victim.—The typhoid bacillus which reaches the outer world in the feces and urine of carriers and cases is fortunately not very resistant. It requires moisture and a favorable temperature approaching 37.5° C. for multiplication, and suitable nutritive material. These conditions being unfavorable, it is subjected to a rapid diminution in concentration by dilution, and dies out. In sewage and feces it is subject to rapid destruction in competition with the more hardy plebeians with which it comes in contact. In feces the organisms will live for variable periods according to temperature and conditions governing decomposition. They may be destroyed within a day or two, and in cesspools, etc., where they are immediately mixed with large amounts of decomposing feces, they live for not longer than a few days. If feces are frozen, that is, deposited in the open in the winter, the organisms may live throughout the winter and enter watersheds with the thaw. In water, as a rule, they do not live more than a few days or perhaps a week, and according to Rosenau they live longer in clean than in contaminated water. In sewage their life is short. Freezing does not kill them. According to the investigations of Gaertner typhoid bacilli could be found in the flowing water of the Paris water supply. In all statements of this kind it must be remembered that no absolute rules can be set up, since we know that the viability of all micro-organisms like the typhoid bacillus depend very delicately upon temperature, nutrition, the presence of other bacteria, moisture, heat, light, reaction, etc. We have found typhoid bacilli viable after many years in sealed agar cultures preserved in the dark and in a cool place, and, while in nature the organisms disappear with relative speed, no rule can be set up. Klein claimed to have found typhoid bacilli alive in natural waters for as long as thirty-six days.

Since the organisms can remain in the soil for limited periods of time, unwashed vegetables, salads, etc., are dangerous, and oysters grown near sewage outlets may also be sources of infection.

Channels of Transmission.—Suspicion of typhoid infection by means of *water supplies* dates back to the early writing of the English physician, Budd, in 1856, who not only believed that sewage-contaminated water conveyed the disease, but suggested that the origin of this pollution lay in human feces. Since that time bacteriological investigation and sanitary water purification on a large scale has indisputably proven the danger of water supplies. In a few cases, direct proof of typhoid bacilli in the water supply has been brought, but, as a rule, indirect proof has had to be adduced, since the rapid dilution, the usual lateness of water investigation after the occurrence of cases, and the many agencies which lead to the destruction of typhoid bacilli in water supplies, have made it difficult to find the organisms in the water. Indirect evidence, however, has been sufficiently convincing in that colon bacillus tests have revealed massive fecal contamination of water to which typhoid infection could be epidemiologically traced. Also, in many localities the direct diminution of typhoid fever in a community after purification of the water supply has left little room for doubt. Thus, in Schueder's investigations of 640 epidemics, 72 per cent were directly traceable to water. *Water* was unquestionably in former years the most important means of the conveyance of typhoid fever. It must also always be taken into consideration when typhoid fever occurs in country districts where small well supplies are the chief sources of drinking water. In Schueder's statistics, 110 of his 640 epidemics could be indirectly traced to *milk*. In the rural communities typhoid fever has remained more or less stationary while, in the cities, owing probably to water-supply supervision, it has been diminishing progressively. In the examination of water, emphasis is placed upon the fact that bacteriological water examinations of this kind must always be associated with sanitary survey of the watershed and engineering examination of the purification plant. While water epidemics are constantly diminishing as large-scale water purification becomes more and more universal, there are still occasional epidemics in which accidents have occurred to ordinarily properly functioning purification plants. Such an epidemic was reported from Salem, Ohio, where investigation of the water supply revealed pollution probably due to the contamination of one of the gravity lines connecting a group of wells with the reservoir. In another epidemic which occurred in a California town, a small explosive outbreak of typhoid fever occurred owing to accident to the water supply followed by direct pumping from the river, for one day, necessitated by repairs. The diminution of typhoid fever in all cities where water supply purification plants have been installed, may be found tabulated in such books as Rosenau's *Hygiene*, Mason's book on water supply, and others.

Milk may act as a distributor of typhoid fever either by direct infection of the milk from milk handlers who are carriers, or from bottles that are returned from houses where typhoid fever or typhoid carriers exist. A considerable number of milk epidemics have been traced beyond doubt, and have usually been characterized by an explosive onset and by the fact that the majority of the patients were women and children. Milk is an excellent culture-medium for the typhoid bacillus, and an enormous increase of the organisms in the milk between contamination and consumption may occur without visible changes in the milk. *Uncooked vegetables, salad, radishes*, etc., may be responsible for typhoid infection, and it has also been shown that *oysters* may be a source of danger. Conn was the first to suggest this. Experiments by Foote showed that typhoid bacilli may be found alive in oysters, within three weeks after they had disappeared from the surrounding water. While there is very little question as to the possibility of this form of infection, it probably does not occur very often. In the investigations of Rosenau, Lumsden and Kastle it was found to be a negligible factor in the cases of typhoid fever occurring in the District of Columbia.

That *flies* play a very important rôle in the carrying of typhoid bacilli from feces to food, was suggested by Vaughan and by Veeder in 1898. Vaughan showed that in the army camps in 1898, flies flew directly from the latrines to the kitchen; in fact, he found hypochlorite of lime on the food, picked up by the flies in the latrines. During the World War, the enormous morbidity of intestinal diseases which occurred in the Allied Armies at various times, and especially during the July offensive at Château-Thierry, was caused by open latrines and flies, typhoid epidemics being avoided only by the universal vaccination of the armies.

As water supplies, milk supplies, etc., are being supervised and, therefore, excluded as sources of typhoid infection, contact infection is becoming more and more important. Recent studies of typhoid morbidity seem to indicate that contact infection is growing to be the chief problem in the prevention of typhoid fever. Frosch, who analyzed 978 cases, concluded that 65.6 per cent were contact infections, and Drigalski makes similar estimates. Such infections may be from individual to individual by close contact. They may be from cook and kitchen personnel, to raw food to consumer. Instances of such infection are frequent, the most famous one being that of "Typhoid Mary" who was made the subject of a special publication by Soper. This woman, a cook, worked for eight families in the course of ten years, during which time seven outbreaks directly traceable to her occurred. After that time her movements from place to place were usually followed by circumscribed epidemics. Again, contact infection may take place from fomites—fingers—food to mouth, that is, towels, bed clothing, underclothing, etc., and emphasizes the importance of sanitary paper towels, etc., in toilets.

The typhoid case is of relatively little danger, largely because of the fact that danger from a case is so well recognized and precautions against transmission from such a source have become matters of routine in well-regulated sick rooms and hospitals.

Prevention.—The measures which are necessary for the prevention of typhoid fever can be easily deduced from the material in the foregoing paragraphs.

Of great importance is recognition of cases, hospitalization and isolation. During such hospitalization there should be attention to disinfection of discharges, sterilization of bedding, bed pans, eating utensils, etc. Patients should never be discharged from hospitals until the urine and feces have been found free from typhoid bacilli, and several examinations at intervals of two or three days should be negative before this is considered to be the case.

Attention to sewage disposal, water supplies, filtration and chlorination of water with constant supervision of such plants from both a bacteriological, chemical and engineering point of view.

Similar supervision of milk supply, pasteurization, attention to the carrier state of the personnel of dairies and milk handlers.

Immediate epidemiological study of cases which occur and laboratory facilities for the tracing of carriers indicated by such epidemiological studies.

Examination for the carrier state of food handlers, professional cooks, and exclusion from such professions of people found to be carriers.

Community measures for the suppression of fly-breeding places and flies, screening of kitchens, and the elimination of open latrines of any kind.

The prevention of oyster culture near sewage outlets.

Finally, more and more attention must be given to generalized vaccination.

An object lesson of what can be accomplished by proper sanitation in regard to typhoid fever in spite of the considerable post-War rate of carriers which must prevail is furnished by statistics from England. Fifteen cities in Great Britain with a total population of 2,256,700 did not have a single typhoid death in 1924. All but three cities had a rate of less than two per hundred thousand, and London, the largest city in the world, had a typhoid death rate of only 1.1.

Active Prophylactic Immunization.—Work by Pfeiffer and Kolle and later by many others has shown that it is comparatively easy to immunize animals actively against typhoid infection by the systematic injection of graded doses, at first of dead bacilli, later of fully virulent live cultures. Attempts to apply these principles prophylactically were made on a large scale by Wright and his associates upon English soldiers in South Africa, and by German observers in East Africa.

The first recorded experiment of this sort upon human beings was that of Pfeiffer and Kolle, who in 1896 treated two individuals with subcutaneous injections of an agar culture of typhoid bacilli which had been sterilized at 56° C. The first injection was made with 2 cubic millimeters of this culture. Three or four hours after the injection the patient suffered from a chill, his temperature gradually rose to 105° F., and there was great prostration and headache, but within twenty-four hours the temperature had returned to normal.

This experiment showed that such injections could be practised upon human beings without great danger.

Simultaneously with the work of Pfeiffer and Kolle, Wright conducted similar experiments on officers and privates in the English army.

The actual number of persons treated directly or indirectly under Wright's supervision in an investigation covering a period of over four years comprised almost one hundred thousand cases. The methods employed by Wright have been modified several times in minor details; the principles, however, have remained the same. In the first experiments Wright employed an agar culture three weeks old, grown at 37° C., then sterilized at a temperature below 60° C., and protected from contamination by the addition of 0.5 per cent of carbolic acid. Later, Wright employed bacilli grown in a neutral 1 per cent peptone bouillon in shallow layers of flasks.

Wright's own estimation, in a careful attempt to present the subject fairly, gives a reduction of the morbidity from typhoid fever in the British Army of 50 per cent, and a reduction of the mortality of those who became infected in spite of inoculations of 50 per cent also.

Vaccinations in the United States Army, observed by Russell, removed any doubt which may have existed as to the efficacy of prophylactic typhoid vaccination. Russell's statistics showed a steady decline of typhoid in the United States Army beginning with the introduction of compulsory vaccination in 1910. In 1913 there was but one case among over eighty thousand men.

The method originally used, and later modified as will be explained, follows:

The "Rawlings" strain of *B. typhosus*, obtained from Wright, is used. Eighteen-hour agar cultures in Kolle flasks are washed off with sterile saline to an approximate concentration of one billion to the cubic centimeter. The suspension is killed at 53° C. for one hour and 0.25 per cent tricresol is added. Aerobic and anaerobic culture controls are made and a rabbit and a mouse inoculated to insure sterility. For immunization three to four doses are given ranging in quantity from five hundred million to one billion at seven- to ten-day intervals. The protection probably lasts about two years, though this is not certain.

In order to protect against the paratyphoid infections, similarly made suspensions of *B. paratyphosus* A and B. *paratyphosus* B are mixed with this suspension of *B. typhosus*, in amounts to provide 300 million to 400 million of each of the A and B types and 500 million typhoid bacilli per c.c. This is called T.A.B. or "triple vaccine."

During the World War, typhoid vaccination thoroughly justified itself. The Surgeon General's report for the United States Army, published in 1919, shows the excellent results obtained by vaccination in American troops. During the prevaccination days in the Civil War and the Spanish-American War, the admission rates for typhoid fever were enormous. During the first year of the Civil War the annual admission rate was 70.69, with a death rate of 19.61, and it is likely that, in addition to this, a large number of unrecognized cases occurred. During the Spanish-American War and the Philippine Insurrection in the years 1898 to 1899, the annual admission was 91.22, and the death rate 9.67. During the last World War the method of vaccination used consisted in three inoculations at seven-day intervals of the salt solution suspension triple vaccine, containing typhoid "Rawlings," paratyphoid A and B, the first dose containing one-half billion bacilli, and the second and third containing a billion each. The typhoid rate was so low in the camps in the United States that a young man in the camp had forty-five times less opportunity of getting typhoid fever than did the same age group in civilian life during the same period. Although approximately three million men passed through the camps during the course of 1918, the actual admission rate for the United States was 0.17. In Europe, in spite of the most insanitary conditions in some of the battlefields during the summer, and with perhaps two million troops in France, there were only 488 cases with 88 deaths, and this, in spite of the fact, as we observed, that the opportunities for transmission were enormous in battle areas in which sanitation was practically impossible, and water supplies were bad and could not be corrected.

While there is no doubt of the fact that vaccination has reduced the incidence of typhoid fever, it is probable that the vaccine can be improved by the use of smooth virulent strains of typhoid bacilli. The experimental work of Grinnell showed that a vaccine made from a smooth virulent strain would cause the development of a relatively solid immunity in mice into which it was injected and that the serum of human beings vaccinated with this strain contained a high concentration of bactericidal substance and was protective. The vaccine made from a rough culture lacked this potency. Grinnell has pointed out that in 1930, most of the cultures of the Rawlings strain used for making vaccine in the different laboratories in this country were in the rough phase of dissociation.

Taking into consideration the importance of using virulent cultures for typhoid vaccine production, Colonel Siler and his colleagues at the U. S. Army Medical School have compared the effectiveness of a number of strains by large scale experiments on mice by the technique of Grinnell. They have set down as criteria for the production of potent vaccines the following conditions:

1. The strain used must be a highly virulent one.

2. The strain should be highly immunogenic as demonstrated by active and passive immunity tests on a selected breed of mice.

They selected, on the basis of their tests, a strain known as No. 58 for vaccination of U. S. Army personnel, and suggest that some form of chemical killing, either tricresol or formalin, is preferable to heat-killing since the latter appears to diminish the antigenic properties of the cultures.

While these investigations are of great practical importance, the principle underlying them and which surely must govern typhoid vaccine production in the future is the preservation of the "Vi" factor in the culture used by starting with a virulent culture, protecting it from dissociation during the period of its use and killing the vaccine suspensions by a method which will not destroy the antigenic properties of the "Vi" factor. The first two criteria can be accomplished by modern methods. The lability of the "Vi" factor, however, is such that, up to the present time, no certain method of preserving its antigenicity has been found. The problem here is not unlike that in analogous lability of the significant antigen of virulent hemolytic streptococci. Formalin seems to be the most useful bactericidal agent for this purpose to date. However, the investigations of the bactericidal effects of ultra-violet light and of the process of Loewenstein, that is, killing with temperatures just above the thermal death point may furnish useful improvements.

The question still remains as to how long typhoid vaccination can be regarded as efficient. There is no absolute information upon which opinions can be based. Vaccination is not a complete protection at any time, and a recently vaccinated individual may still occasionally contract the disease if he is infected with a large dose of virulent organisms. The protection, however, is very powerful and will prevent the disease from the ordinary chance infection. Repetition every two years ought to be sufficient for civilian purposes. For the armies in the field, we favor a first vaccination with three doses as stated above, and single or double doses repeated every six months.

Oral administration of dead typhoid bacilli with a dose of ox-bile was claimed by Besredka to produce *local immunity* of the small intestine, thus closing the portal of entry. The method has been used on a relatively large scale in some places in Europe and has been applied by Hoffstadt and her associates in this country. It is impossible to estimate whether or not this mode of vaccination is effective.

Specific Treatment.—Antisera against typhoid fever have been produced by a large number of workers, notably Chantemesse and Besredka both of whom used the serum of horses immunized with typhoid bacilli or "endotoxin," so-called. Garbat and Meyer believed that an improvement of results could be obtained by mixing the sera of animals that had been immunized with sensitized bacteria and of those treated with normal typhoid bacilli.

At the present time, however, practice has not sustained the hopes of a specific passive immunization in the treatment of typhoid fever.

Since 1893, various workers have tried to treat typhoid fever by injecting killed cultures or vaccines of typhoid bacilli. Ichikawa in 1914 injected dead typhoid bacilli, intravenously. Gay and Claypole and others have also taken up this method. The intravenous injection of vaccines in this way has usually resulted in a violent reaction, with often a chill and sudden drop of temperature, and, occasionally, definite improvement of the cases. Although this method was at first regarded as specific, Kraus in 1915 produced similar reactions in typhoid patients with colon bacilli, as well as with typhoid bacilli, and similar observations were made by Luedke and others. It is now quite clear that, whatever results are obtained by such treatment of typhoid patients, they cannot be regarded as specific reactions in the ordinary sense of the word.

Bacillus Faecalis Alcaligenes.—In 1896, Petruschky described a gram-negative bacterium which he had isolated from stale beer. Since then, many bacteriologists have reported the same bacillus in water, feces, and in the lower part of the small intestine and colon in man. Its habitat is that of an intestinal organism with saprophytic capacity. In recognition of this fact and of the production of alkali in milk cultures, Migula named the organism *Bacillus faecalis alcaligenes.*

Bacillus faecalis alcaligenes is an actively motile, gram-negative bacillus, possessing, like the typhoid bacillus, numerous peritrichal flagella. In size and shape, the organism is identical with the typhoid bacillus. On solid media and broth it grows like the typhoid bacillus. The organism does not produce indole, and does not liquefy gelatin. *B. faecalis alcaligenes* does not ferment any carbohydrate and produces a strongly *alkaline reaction in milk* after incubation of the culture at 37° C. for two to ten days. On the usual lactose agar-indicator plates employed for the isolation of pathogenic organisms of the typhoid-paratyphoid-dysentery group, the colonies of *B. faecalis alcaligenes* are colorless, due to its inability to ferment lactose. Hence, on first inspection of such plates this organism is apt to be mistaken for *B. typhosus.* Fermentation tests, the alkaline reaction in milk, and agglutination reactions readily differentiate this organism from *B. typhosus.* It is not agglutinated by antityphoid serum. The organism has been isolated from the feces of normal persons and also from those suffering from enteritis. A number of investigators have isolated it from the blood of febrile patients (Wilson). While the pathogenicity of *B. faecalis alcaligenes* is doubtful, it cannot be denied that some strains may cause disease.

Until about 1918, this organism was described as having a more or less indefinite relationship to the colon-typhoid bacilli and we are perpetuating that apparently natural arrangement by describing it in this place. In 1919, however, Castellani and Chalmers made it the type species of a new genus, and called the organism *Alcaligenes faecalis.* Bergey, in his *Manual of Determinative Bacteriology* (1934 edition), has adopted this classification and nomenclature. There may be good reason for a genus *Alcaligenes* for some of the gram-negative intestinal bacteria. *Bacillus bronchisepticus,* which we have mentioned in our discussion of pertussis, may sufficiently resemble *Alcaligenes faecalis* to be listed in a group with it. The organisms causing undulant fever in man and infectious abortion in animals, previously listed by Bergey with members of the *Alcaligenes* genus, have, in the fourth edition of Bergey's *Manual,* been given separate generic rank, under the name *Brucella.*

REFERENCES

ANDREWES, F. W.   J. Path. & Bacteriol., 1922, 25:505; 1925, 28:345.
ARKWRIGHT, J. A.   J. Path. & Bacteriol., 1921, 24:36; 1927, 30:345.
BAYNE-JONES, S.   Am. J. M. Sc., 1917, 154:55.
BESREDKA, A.   Ann. de l'Inst. Pasteur, 1895, 1896; 1902, 16:918.
——— Local Immunization, Williams and Wilkins Co., Baltimore, 1927, p. 133.
BIEN, Z.   Centralbl. f. Bakteriol., I Abt., 1924, 93:196.
BLUMER.   Johns Hopkins Hosp. Rep., 1895, 5.
BLUMENTHAL.   Arch. f. klin. Med., 1907, 88:509.
BRIEGER.   Deutsche med. Wchnschr., 1902, 27.

BUDD, W. Intestinal Fever, Lancet, 1856, 2:4, *et seq.*

BULLY. Ztschr. f. Hyg., 1911, 61:29.

CASTELLANI, A. Riforma med.. 1900.

CASTELLANI, A., and CHALMERS, A. Manual of Tropical Medicine, Wm. Wood & Co., London, 3rd ed., 1919, p. 936.

CHANTEMESSE. Progrès, Par., 1899, 7:245.

—— 14th Internat. Cong. Hyg., Berlin, 1907.

CHANTEMESSE and WIDAL. Arch. de physiol. norm. et path., Par., 1887.

—— Ann. de l'Inst. Pasteur, 1892.

CHIARI. Centralbl. f. Bakteriol., Orig., 15, 1894.

COLEMAN and BUXTON. Am. J. M. Sc., 1907, 133.

CONN. Med. Rec., 1894.

CONRADI and DRIGALSKI. Ztschr. f. Hyg., 1902, 34:283.

CONRADI. Centralbl. f. Immunit., 1910, 7:158.

DEAN. Am. J. Pub. Health, 1931, 21:390.

DOERR. Centralbl. f. Bakteriol., I Abt., 1905.

DREYER, G. J. Path. & Bacteriol., 1909, 13:331.

—— Committee upon Pathological Methods, Medical Research Council Spec. Rep. Ser. 51, London, 1920.

DRIGALSKI. Centralbl. f. Bakteriol., 1904, 35:776.

DRIGALSKI and CONRADI. Ztschr. f. Hyg., 1902, 39.

DULANEY, A. D., WINKLE, W. T., and TRIGG, R. Am. J. Pub. Health, 1932, 22:1033.

EBERTH, C. Archiv. f. path. Anat., etc., 1880, 81; 1881, 83:486.

EXNER and HEYWORSKI. Wien. klin. Wchnschr., 1908, 7.

FELIX, A. J. Immunol., 1924, 9:115.

—— J. Hyg., 1929, 28:418.

—— Lancet, 1930, 1:505.

FELIX, A., and PITT, R. M. Lancet, 1935, 2:186.

—— Brit. J. Exper. Pathol., 1934, 15:346.

FLEXNER. Johns Hopkins Rep., 1896, 5.

FOOTE. Med. News, 1895.

FRÄNKEL, E. Centralbl. f. klin. Med., 1886, 10.

—— Deutsche med. Wchnschr., 1899, 15:16.

—— Ztschr. f. Hyg., 1909, 34.

GAETHGENS. Deutsche med. Wchnschr., 1907, 1337.

GAFFKY, G. Mitt. a. d. kaiserl. Gsndhtsamte, 1884, 2:372.

GARBAT. J. Am. M. Ass., Nov. 1916, 1493.

—— Typhoid Carriers and Typhoid Immunity, Monogr., Rockefeller Inst. for Med. Res., No. 16, 1922.

GARBAT and MEYER. Ztschr. f. Exper. Path. u. Therap., 1910, 8:1.

GARDNER, A. D. J. Hyg., 1929, 28:376.

GAERTNER. Klin. Jahrb., 1902, 9.

GAY, F. P. Typhoid Fever, New York, 1918.

GAY, F. P., and CHICKERING. Arch. Int. M., 1916, 17:303.

GAY, F. P., and CLAYPOLE. Arch. Int. Med., 1912, 11.

—— Arch. Int. Med., 1913, 12:613.

GERONNE. Berl. klin. Wchnschr., 1915.

GRINNEL, F. B. J. Immunol., 1930, 19:457.

—— J. Exper. M., 1931, 54:577; 1932, 56:907.

GRUBER, M., and DURHAM, H. E. München. med. Wchnschr., 1896, 43:206.

GRÜNBAUM, A. S. Lancet, 1896, 2:806.

HADLEY, P. J. Infect. Dis., 1927, 40:1.

HAHN. München. med. Wchnschr., 1906, 23.

HARRISON. J. Roy. Army Med. Corps, 1907, 8.

HAVENS, L. C. The Bacteriology of Typhoid, Salmonella, and Dysentery Infections and Carrier States. New York, The Commonwealth Fund, 1935.

Hiss. Med. News, May, 1901.

Hoffstadt, R. E., and Thompson, R. L. Am. J. Hyg., 1929, 9:1, 20, 37.

Horgan, E. S. J. Hyg., 1932, 32:523.

Hort, E. C. J. Hyg., 1920, 18:369.

Houston and Irwin. Lancet, 1909, 1:311.

Houston and Thomas. Centralbl. f. Bakteriol., Ref., 1910, 45:390.

Ichikawa. Mitt. d. med. Gesellsch. zu Tokyo, 1914, 28.

Irwin and Houston. Lancet, 1909, 1:154.

Johnston. J. Med. Research, 1912, 27.

Kahlberlah. Med. Klin., 1915.

Karlinsky. Prag. Med. Wchnschr., 1890, 15.

Klein. Rep. Med. Off. Local Gov. Bd. London, 1894.

—— Johns Hopkins Hosp. Bull., 1907.

—— Rep. Med. Off. Local Gov. Bd., Lond., 1908.

Koch. Ver. a. d. Militarsanitätswesen, Heft 21, 1902.

—— Ztschr. f. Hyg. u. Infektionskr., 1909.

Kraus. Wien. klin. Wchnschr., 1897, 32; 1914, 27:1443; 1915, 29.

Kraus and Steinitzer. Quoted from Handbuch d. Techn., etc., 1, Fischer, Jena, 1907.

Krumwiede, Kohn and Valentine. J. Med. Research, 1918, 38:89.

Küster. Beitr. z. klin. d. Infektionskr., 1918, 7:98.

Kutscher in Kolle and Wassermann. Handbuch. d. Techn., etc., 2nd ed., Fischer, Jena, 1913.

Laubenheimer. Ztschr. f. Hyg., 1909, 58.

Luedke. München. med. Wchnschr., 1915, 321.

Macfadyen and Rowland. Centralbl. f. Bakteriol., 1901, 30; 1906, I.

Mayer and Ahreiner. Cited from Gay, J. Am. M. Ass., 1920, 75:498.

Metchnikoff, E., and Besredka, A. Ann. de l'Inst. Pasteur, 1911, 25:193.

Meyer, K. F., Neilson, N. M., Schoenholtz, P., Feusier, M. L. J. Infect. Dis., 1921, 28:381.

Migula. System du Bakterien, 1897–1900. Quoted from W. W. Ford, Textbook of Bacteriology, Phila., 1927, p. 546.

Morishima, K. J. Bacteriol., 1921, 6:275.

Mudd, S. J. Immunol., 1932, 23:81.

Nichols. J. Exper. M., 1916, 24:497.

—— J. Am. M. Ass., 1917, 68:958.

Nichols, H. J. J. Infect. Dis., 1921, 29:82.

Norris. J. Infect. Dis., 1904, 1:1, 472.

Neufeld. Ztschr. f. Hyg., 1899, 30.

Neumann. Berl. klin. Wchnschr., 1890, 27.

Petruschky, J. Ztschr. f. Hyg. u. Infektionskrankh., 1892, 12.

—— Centralbl. f. Bakteriol., I Abt., 1896, 19:187.

—— Centralbl. f. Hyg., 1898, 23.

Pfeiffer. Deutsche med. Wchnschr., 1894, 48.

—— and Kolle. Ztschr. f. Hyg., 1896, 21.

—— Deutsche med. Wchnschr., 1896, 22; 1898, 24.

Pratt. J. Bost. Soc. M. Sc., 1899, 3.

—— Am. J. M. Sc., 1901.

Prigge. Klin. Jahrb., 1909–1910, 20:245.

Prudden, T. M. Med. Rec. N. Y., 1887.

Rake, G. Proc. Soc. Exper. Biol. and M., 1935, 32:1523.

Richardson. J. Exper. M., 1898, 3.

—— J. Bost. Soc. M. Sc., 1900, 5.

Rosenau, Lumsden and Kastle. Treas. Rep. Pub. Health and Mar. Hosp. Serv.; Hyg. Lab. Bull., Wash., 1908, No. 52.

Russell, F. F. Am. J. M. Sc., 1913, 146.

—— J. Am. M. Ass., 1919, 73:1863.

SACQUEPÉE. Bull. de l'Inst. Pasteur, 1910, 8:521, 689.

SCHELLER. Centralbl. f. Bakteriol., I Abt., orig., 1908, 45:385.

SCHONE. München. med. Wchnschr., 1908, 1063.

SCHOTTMUELLER. Deutsche med. Wchnschr., 1900, 32.

———— Ztschr. f. Hyg., 1901, 36.

SCHUEDER. Ztschr. f. Hyg., 1901, 38:343.

SILER, J. F., et al., Military Surgeon, 1937, 80:91.

———— Am. J. Pub. Health, 1937, 27:142.

SMITH and TENBROECK, C. J. Med. Research, 1915, 31:503.

SOPER. Military Surgeon, 1919, 45:1.

STERN and KORTE. Berl. klin. Wchnschr., 1904, 10.

VEEDER. Med. Rec., 1898, 45.

WALKER, E. W. A., and MURRAY, W. Brit. M. J., 1904, 2:16.

WEIL, E., and FELIX, A. Wien. klin. Wchnschr., 1916, 29:33; 1917, 30:1509.

———— Ztschr. f. Immunitätsforsch, 1920, 29:24.

WELCH and BLACHSTEIN. Bull. Johns Hopkins Hosp., 1891, 2.

WHITE, P. B. Med. Res. Council. Spec. Rep. Ser. No. 103, London, 1926.

WIDAL, F. Bull. Soc. méd. Hôp. de Paris, 1896, 13.

WIDAL, F., and SICARD, M. A. Ann. de l'Inst. Pasteur, 1897; 11:353.

WILSON, W. J. A System of Bacteriology in Relation to Medicine, London, 1929, 4:299.

WINSLOW, KLIGLER and ROTHBERG. J. Bacteriol., 1919, 4:426.

WOLMAN and GORMAN. Am. J. Pub. Health, 1931, 21:115.

WRIGHT. Lancet, Sept. 1896.

———— Brit. M. J., 1901; Oct. 1903.

———— Lancet, Sept. 1902.

WRIGHT and LEISHMANN. Brit. M. J., Jan. 1900.

WRIGHT and SEMPLE. Brit. M. J., 1897.

ZINSSER. Proc. N. York Path. Soc., 1907.

ZINSSER, PARKER and KUTTNER. Proc. Soc. Exper. Biol. & Med., Nov. 1920.

CHAPTER XXXVIII

BACILLARY DYSENTERY AND THE DYSENTERY BACILLI

Family: *Enterobacteriaceae.* Tribe: *Salmonelleae.* Genus: *Shigella.* Type species: *Shigella dysenteriae.* Syn: Shiga bacillus.

DYSENTERY BACILLI

The dysenteries, which in sporadic cases or epidemic outbreaks, have afflicted man during centuries, are severe or mild inflammations of the lower intestinal tract. They are characterized by frequent and painful evacuations of fluid or mucopurulent bloody fecal discharges. Until the latter part of the nineteenth century, the inciting causes of these disorders grouped under the clinical term dysentery were not known. In 1875, Lösch discovered an ameba in the discharges of a patient with dysentery. Since then a group of dysenteries due to protozoa have been differentiated. The chief disease in this class is amebic dysentery. It was soon realized, after Lösch's discovery, that there was another large group of dysenteries that were not associated with amebae. This is the group of *bacillary dysenteries,* which we shall discuss in this chapter.

In 1898, Shiga discovered in the feces of patients suffering with dysentery in Japan the bacterial cause of the disease and described the organism which bears his name.

Many workers preceding Shiga had attempted to throw light upon this subject by isolations of bacilli from dysenteric stools, and by extensive animal inoculation. Shiga, following a suggestion made by Kitasato, approached the problem by searching for a micro-organism in the stools of dysentery patients which would be specifically agglutinated by the serum of these patients. He found, in 36 cases, one and the same micro-organism which showed uniform serum agglutinations. Further, he found that this bacillus was not present in the dejecta of patients suffering from other diseases nor in those of normal men, and that when tested against the blood serum of such people it was not agglutinated.

Immediately following Shiga's work, discoveries by Flexner in the Philippines and Kruse in Germany confirmed the observation that bacteria caused dysentery.

Flexner and others regarded his bacillus as identical with Shiga's. Kruse, however, recognized among the organisms isolated by him types that corresponded with the Shiga bacillus and others that differed from this type. He called the latter "pseudo-dysentery bacilli of insane asylums." The investigations of Martini and Lentz in 1902 disclosed serological differences between the bacteria in these two groups and brought out the very important fact that the Shiga bacillus was unable to ferment mannite, while the Flexner organisms fermented mannite, producing acid without gas. All subsequent investigations have confirmed this finding. The action of dysentery bacilli upon mannite is, therefore, a fundamentally important differential characteristic.

It was thus recognized that there were at least two groups of dysentery bacilli, those which fermented mannite and those which did not. Other investigators then

538

isolated and differentiated additional varieties of the mannite fermenters according to the abilities of the organisms to ferment various carbohydrates. Among these were the mannite-saccharose fermenting strain isolated by Strong and Musgrave in 1900 and the Y-bacillus isolated by Hiss and Russell in 1903, which fermented mannite but did not ferment maltose. In 1904, Hiss published a classification of dysentery bacilli based both upon fermentation reactions and agglutination tests. Hiss divided the organisms into four main groups and found that strains from many sources could be distributed among these groups. This classification was in general use, although recognized to be inadequate, until the completion of the studies of dysentery bacilli by the modern methods of serological analysis.

In addition to the Shiga and Flexner types, classified by Hiss, a third main class of dysentery bacilli was recognized as a group of organisms which had usually a slow, but sometimes rapid, action upon lactose. Lactose fermenting bacilli were isolated from dysenteric stools by Duval in 1904, by Kruse and his coworkers in 1907 (the Kruse E type) and by Sonne in 1915. Andrewes, in 1918, proposed the name *B. dispar* for this group, but the organisms are generally known as Sonne dysentery bacilli.

It is possible that a fourth main group of dysentery bacilli may exist, represented by the dulcite fermenting *B. alcalescens*. But the evidence that *B. alcalescens* is pathogenic is not convincing.

We may briefly summarize the dysentery group as follows:

CHIEF DIFFERENTIAL CHARACTERISTICS OF DYSENTERY BACILLI

Organism	Glucose	Mannite	Lactose	Dulcite	Indole	Toxin
B. dysenteriae, Shiga .... Syn: Shiga bacillus, Shigella dysenteriae	+	—	—	—	—	Neurotoxin (exotoxin) and enterotoxin (endotoxin)
B. ambiguus .... Syn: Schmitz bacillus, B. para-Shiga	+	—	—	—	+	
B. dysenteriae, Flexner ...... Syn: Flexner bacillus, Shigella paradysenteriae (many types)	+	+	—	—	±	Enterotoxin (endotoxin)
B. alcalescens	+	+	—	+	+	
Sonne dysentery bacillus ..... Syn: B. dispar, Kruse E.	+	+	+	—	—	

All these bacilli are Gram negative, non-motile, usually slender but sometimes short and plump, ranging between 1 to 3 μ in length and 0.3 to 0.6 μ in breadth. They do not form spores and have no flagella. They are aerobic and facultatively anaerobic. They do not liquefy gelatine. They produce acid but no gas in the fermentation of carbohydrates. All varieties produce acid from glucose; some produce indole.

They may be divided into two main groups: (1) Those which do not ferment mannite—the Shiga or Shiga-Kruse variety and (2) Those which ferment mannite. The former group consists only of the organism mentioned and is more common in the east and in tropical countries than in the temperate zones.

The mannite-fermenting group is made up of a considerable number of organisms of which the most common are the so-called Flexner, or Baltimore bacillus, the Hiss-Y bacillus, which differs from the Flexner group because of its failure to ferment maltose, the Strong bacillus, which ferments saccharose, and the Sonne bacillus which is chiefly characterized by its latent capacity for producing acid from lactose.

All these organisms are sometimes spoken of, in contrast to the Shiga or true dysentery group, as the "para-dysentery" bacilli.

Although this summarizes the dysentery bacilli as a whole, there may be a considerable number of sub-varieties of the main classes mentioned which show atypical fermentation and may be serologically differentiated.

We do not believe that these types represent all the variants of the dysentery bacilli. Numerous unclassified morphological variations have been described by Twort. Variability of the dissociative type occurs and the analysis of the smooth and rough transformations in this group has not been completed. In the epidemics of dysentery during the World War many investigators isolated nonmotile, gram-negative bacilli from the stools of mild dysenteroid cases which presented cultural peculiarities and did not agglutinate with type sera, and many organisms have been described by various observers which do not fit into any of the main subdivisions. The group of *Flexner dysentery bacilli* is notoriously heterogeneous, so much so that a doubled alphabet has been required to designate the races.

The *nomenclature* of the organisms in this group is unsatisfactory. The generic name was changed from *Eberthella* to *Shigella* within two successive editions of Bergey's *Manual of Determinative Bacteriology*.

Isolation.—The procedure for isolation of dysentery bacilli consists, briefly, in the plating of stool material as soon as possible after passage on eosin methylene blue lactose agar. Suspicious colonies are transferred to Russell's double sugar medium and run through fermentation tests and media containing dextrose, mannite, maltose, lactose, xylose, saccharose and dulcite. Rhamnose may be added to exclude doubtful paratyphoids which may have a depressed lactose fermentation capacity.

Resistance.—Not being spore-bearers, dysentery bacilli are not very resistant to heat and chemicals. They are destroyed at 60° C. within ten minutes, and the usual strength of the common chemical disinfectant kills them. Their resistance to the ordinary conditions in nature is the important feature of the epidemiology of the disease. We quote the following facts from Vincent and Muratet. In garden soil dysentery bacilli have been known to live from six to fifteen days, and up to forty-nine days at a depth of twelve inches. In damp sand they have been known to live as long as thirty-nine days. Cultures in broth have lived for twenty-five days, and they have lived more than thirty days in dejecta buried in the soil, and on linen folded up. In ice, they may live for longer than a month. Exposure to sunlight destroys them rapidly. Such statements must always be limited to the peculiar conditions of symbiosis, light, moisture, temperature, etc., existing under the particular conditions investigated. If we remember that non-spore-bearing organisms can be kept alive for very long periods if young agar growths are kept in sealed jars in a cool dark place, we may understand that under peculiarly favorable conditions in nature, organisms have survived far beyond anything suggested by knowledge of their general resistance under adverse conditions.

Poisonous Products.—The separate types of dysentery bacilli vary exceedingly in their powers to produce toxic substances. Of the various types which have been described, the strongest poisons have been produced with bacilli of the Shiga-Kruse variety, less regularly active ones with bacilli of the Flexner and of the "Y" type. Investigations carried out with the Shiga bacillus have tended to show that the disease itself is probably a true toxemia, its symptoms being referable almost entirely to the absorption of the poisonous products of the bacillus from the intestine.

The earliest investigations, carried on chiefly upon rabbits, which are more suscep- tible to this poison than any other animals, showed that even small doses of cultures of this bacillus administered intravenously or subcutaneously produce death within a very short time. Conradi, Vaillard and Dopter, and others came to the conclusion that the poisons of this bacillus were chiefly of the endotoxin type. Todd, Kraus, and Rosenthal, however, have shown that the Shiga bacillus produces a strong soluble toxin, similar in every way to diphtheria toxin. Kraus and Doerr, moreover produced specific antitoxins with these substances.

Olitsky and Kligler have extended the study of the *Shiga dysentery toxin* made by Todd. These writers differentiate definitely between a so-called exotoxin and an endotoxin. Their exotoxin they obtained by growing the Shiga bacilli for five days in alkaline-egg broth. Their endotoxin was produced by incubating agar growths in salt solution for two days and filtering. The exotoxin in small fractions of a cubic centimeter, after an incubation time of a few hours to four days, produces typical paralysis and severe nerve lesions in rabbits. This poison was destroyed by 75° C. after one hour, and powerful neutralization was obtained with the serum of horses immunized with it. Their endotoxin, so-called, produces loss of weight and diarrhea in the animals, but no paralysis. In general, their results agree with those of Kruse, Todd, Pfeiffer and Ungermann, and Bessau. They have produced far more potent toxins and more powerful antitoxins than previous workers.

The action of the dysentery toxin upon animals is characteristic and throws much light upon the disease in man. The injection of a large dose intravenously into rabbits causes a rapid fall in temperature, marked respiratory embarrassment, and a violent diarrhea. This is at first watery, later contains large amounts of blood. If the animals live a sufficient length of time, paralysis may occur, the animal may fall to one side or may drag its posterior extremities. Intravenous inoculation gives rise to intestinal inflammation of a severe nature, unquestionably due to the excretion of the poison by the intestinal mucosa and limited, usually, to the cecum and colon, rarely attacking the small intestine. Flexner believes it probable that most of the pathological lesions occurring in the intestinal canal of dysentery patients are referable to this excretion of dysentery toxin, rather than to the direct local action of the bacilli. The toxin causes a coagulative necrosis of the intestinal mucous membrane.

The characteristic action of the Shiga bacillus exotoxin is its effect upon the medulla and spinal cord in rabbits, where it produces lesions not unlike those seen in virus encephalitis and in lead poisoning. Peripheral neuritis also has been described in man.

Immunization.—The immunization of small animals, such as rabbits and guinea-pigs, against dysentery bacilli, especially those of the Shiga type, is attended with much difficulty, owing to the great toxicity of the cultures. Nevertheless, successful results may be achieved by the administration of extremely small doses of living or dead bacilli, increased very gradually and at sufficient intervals. Horses are more easily immunized. The serum of such actively immunized animals contains agglutinins in considerable concentration.

For diagnostic purposes in human beings, the agglutination reaction, according to the technic of the Widal reaction for typhoid fever, has been utilized by Kruse and others. According to most observers, normal human serum never agglutinates dysentery bacilli in dilutions greater than 1: 20, while the serum of dysentery patients will often be active in dilutions higher than 1: 50.

Bactericidal substances have been demonstrated in the serum of immunized animals as well as in that of diseased human beings. These have been determined, *in vitro*, by Shiga, and, by the intraperitoneal technic of Pfeiffer, by Kruse. Bacteriolysis may take place in high dilutions of the serum, and has recently been used for the differentiation of the types of the dysentery bacilli by Ohno.

True antitoxins in immune sera were described by Kraus and Doerr.

Todd has demonstrated that the mixture of such an immune serum with solutions of toxin and exposure of the mixture at 37.5° C. for a half hour would produce almost complete neutralization of the poison, thus demonstrating that at least a large part of the beneficial action of the immune sera was due to a true antitoxic process. Because of the different varieties of dysentery bacilli, polyvalent serum has been recommended.

The results of Olitsky and Kligler are even better than this, in that they have succeeded in protecting rabbits against one thousand lethal doses of the poison with antitoxic horse serum.

The production and standardization of Shiga *antitoxin* and *polyvalent anti-dysentery serum* for therapeutic purposes is now a routine practice in many state and commercial laboratories. The methods used in New York State have been described by Wadsworth. The standardization of dysentery serum was the subject of a special report by Shiga for the public health section of the League of Nations.

DYSENTERY IN MAN

The clinical term "dysentery" is a vague one and may signify violent diarrheal disturbances from almost any cause. Technically, the term dysentery should be restricted either to the amebic variety or the bacillary. Bacterial dysenteries have been attributed to many different organisms besides the true dysentery bacilli, such as some of the paratyphoid bacilli, *B. pyocyaneus*, the Morgan bacilli, etc.

Endemic in a large part of the world, especially in the warmer climates, the disease most frequently occurs in epidemics of more or less definite localization, usually under conditions which accompany the massing of a large number of human beings in one place, such as those which occur in the crowded quarters of unsanitary towns, in institutions such as insane asylums, or in military camps. The fatality of such epidemics may be very large. According to Shiga, the disease in Japan frequently shows a fatality of over 20 per cent.

The disease in human beings usually begins as an acute gastro-enteritis which is accompanied by abdominal pain and diarrhea. As it becomes more severe, the colicky pains and diarrhea increase, the stools lose their fecal character, becoming small in quantity and filled with mucus and flakes of blood. There is often severe tenesmus at this stage, and the bacilli are present in large numbers in the dejecta. Owing to the absorption of toxic products, symptoms referable to the nervous system, such as muscular twitching, may supervene, and if the disease is at all prolonged, there are marked inanition and prostration. In the course of convalescence arthritis is not uncommon.

At autopsy in early stages there may be found only a severe catarrhal inflammation of the mucous membrane of the large intestine. In the later stages there are extensive ulcerations, and the bacteria are found lodged within the depths of the mucosa and submucosa. Occasionally they may penetrate to the mesenteric glands, but as far as we know there is no penetration into the general circulation.

Although this acute disease represents the typical picture of clinical dysentery, it must not be forgotten that bacteria of the dysentery types may cause very much milder intestinal inflammations and even simple diarrheas. "Y" bacilli and Flexner bacilli have often been isolated from such mild conditions, especially during the hot weather.

Since about 1930 it has been found that *Sonne dysentery* is much more common in the United States than was formerly supposed. It has been described by Flexner, by Gilbert and Coleman, by Fothergill and by others in small epidemics, some of them occurring in infants' and children's hospitals. The disease caused by the bacillus may vary greatly in severity. A few of the cases may be violent and acute like those occasioned by the more virulent form of dysentery bacilli. The majority of cases, however, are fairly mild, characterized by sudden temperature of 102° F. or over, feebleness and loss of appetite. The fever is usually followed in 24 to 48 hours by diarrhea, sometimes, but not often, with blood in the stools.

Epidemiology and Prevention.—Bacillary dysentery is not limited to any particular part of the world. Unlike the amebic variety, it is probably just as common in temperate climates as it is in the tropical ones, though actual epidemic occurrence is probably a little more frequently observed in tropical communities where fly suppression and sewage and garbage disposal have not been developed.

Dysentery epidemics also are more apt to occur during the hot and dry parts of the year when flies are prevalent. It is a mistake to think of the disease only as occurring in epidemics, since organisms of the dysentery group probably cause a great many sporadic cases and small group attacks of diarrheal diseases which in their clinical manifestations cannot be strictly classified as dysentery. Thus, numerous small group outbreaks have been studied in America and Europe, occurring either in cities sometimes, as in those studied by Kruse and others, or in public institutions as insane asylums and orphanages, and in connection with such outbreaks a great many dysentery-like organisms have been described. In the Orient the disease has caused widespread epidemic outbreaks. Great epidemics occurred in Europe in 1538, 1779, and 1834. In its epidemic form it is particularly a disease of armies. Vincent and Muratet state that a destructive epidemic took place in the English Armies in 1415 after the battle of Agincourt. There were serious epidemics in the armies of the allies during the Crimean War, during the American Civil War, during the Franco-Prussian War, the Russo-Turkish and the Russo-Japanese War. Considerable dysentery morbidity occurred in the South African War, and during the World War [1] the disease was prevalent among all the armies fighting on the eastern and western fronts. It is likely that large epidemics are rarely caused by a single dysentery type. In 1905 Amako studied the epidemics which occurred in the town of Kobe and from 743 cases isolated dysentery bacilli in 526. During this single epidemic he found five different types of dysentery bacilli, the first being the typical Shiga bacillus, the second being a mannite fermenter, the fourth and fifth fermenting maltose and dextrin, the third having no effect upon maltose and dextrin but fermenting saccharose like the fourth and fifth. He found the first type in 108 cases, the second in 202, the third type in 9, the fourth in 109, and the fifth in 16 cases. In one case he found two different types in the same patient. Studying family epidemics at the same time, he usually found one and the same type in a single family, but in six families in which there were 25 patients he found two different types.

Dysentery is transmitted by much the same agencies which are responsible for transmission of other intestinal diseases, typhoid, paratyphoid, etc., and in consequence, sanitary and other conditions which bring about one disease give rise to cases of the other. It is a noticeable feature of the outbreaks of intestinal disease which occurred in the Allied Armies during the World War that every outbreak of dysenteric maladies was accompanied by enormous numbers of mild diarrheal conditions. This is mentioned by Vincent and Muratet for the French and British Armies, and was noticed during the outbreak of similar conditions among the American troops in July, 1918. At such times the intestinal disturbances are almost universal among troops, taking, in most, the form of a mild temporary and recurring diarrhea, in others a more severe diarrhea with fever, and in others, again, severe symptoms of typical dysentery. All the known varieties of intestinal invaders, typhoid, paratyphoid and the various dysentery bacilli, played a rôle in the outbreaks. It is not at all impossible that many of the mild cases may have been true dysentery or even true typhoid, modified by increased natural resistance and by vaccination in the men. On the other hand, it is also quite likely that the large majority of the mild cases which constituted perhaps 90 per cent of the total, represented infections by various other bacterial agencies originating in the massive infection of food and water with fecal organisms.

The most severe epidemics are those due to the Shiga bacillus. However, the Flexner bacilli have been known to cause considerable epidemics in southeastern Europe and in parts of Asia, in the Philippines, Japan, China, and Ceylon. The Strong bacillus has been known to cause disease in the Philippines and the "Y" bacillus has been found rather frequently in milder outbreaks and in sporadic cases especially in the United States.

---

[1] For a thorough study of dysentery outbreaks as they occurred during and after the war see Special Reports, Series No. 6, 1917; Series Nos. 7 and 15, 1918, of the British Medical Research Committee, Reports by Fildes, Dobell and associates, and Glynn and Robinson.

The Shiga type of dysentery bacillus does not appear to have been responsible for any large proportion of the cases of dysentery in this country. Outbreaks of dysentery due to Flexner bacillus infection have been more numerous and are apt to occur in asylums and prisons. It seems likely that many of the cases of so-called "summer diarrheas" of infants are due to infection with Flexner bacilli.

The *Sonne type* of dysentery bacillus has caused several small epidemics of dysentery in New York State and elsewhere since 1928. These have been reported by Gilbert and Coleman and Leahy. The organisms in the Sonne group were found to be somewhat varied, as indicated by Koser. The pathogenicity of the organisms was attested by the two fatal cases of Sonne enteritis described by Hay.

In many countries there seem to be endemic foci of dysentery. This has been studied in France where outbreaks of dysentery seem often to have started in the central part in the neighborhood of Tours, and it is not unlikely that in our own country there may be scattered dysentery foci in the large cities of the north and in some parts of the south.

In consequence, transmission from man to man by hands and indirect contamination of food, etc., is common during epidemics. The organisms may remain alive for a considerable period in the soil and under camp conditions, infected latrines may contaminate water supplies and by the intervention of flies, scatter the organisms to the food. Fly transmission is of the utmost importance. It was probably the most important means of transmission during the American Army epidemic spoken of above. Large water-born epidemics, as described in the case of typhoid fever, do not occur.

Dysentery carriers unquestionably exist. The organisms may persist for months in the intestinal canals of convalescents and have been described in the stools of individuals who give no history of having had the disease. The carrier problem in dysentery is a very difficult one because the isolation of small numbers of dysentery bacilli from stools is even more difficult than that of typhoid bacilli. It has been suggested that chronic carriers may harbor the organisms in the gallbladder, but this is doubtful. The carrier state appears to be more chronic after infection with the Shiga bacillus; more transient in those infected with the Flexner type.

Shiga is of the opinion that the chief element in the spread of dysentery is the carrier. The first positive carrier examination was made by Conradi who isolated dysentery bacilli from the stools of three healthy children during the occurrence of a contact epidemic in Metz. Martha Wollstein found dysentery bacilli at autopsy in the intestines of children who had presented none of the symptoms of dysentery before death, and similar isolations were made by Duval and Shorer in connection with epidemics of summer diarrhea. Shiga claims that in every dysentery epidemic a great many contact cases can be traced epidemiologically. His belief is that it is contact which keeps the disease going almost entirely during the interepidemic periods in Japan, and that this is largely due to the carrier condition in healthy people, mild sporadic diarrheas and convalescents of typical dysentery cases. Water, he thinks, can play a part, but in his accounts of water epidemics this implies rather gross carelessness in the care of water. It was suggested during epidemics in the British Army that dried feces carried about by dust may have contributed to the spread of epidemics.

Whether or not domestic animals may act as carriers is not certain, but it has been suggested that dogs may be spontaneously infected with bacillary dysentery and transmit it to human beings.

Kruse and Bowman have reported spontaneous bacillary dysentery in monkeys in which Flexner bacilli were isolated, and Messerschmidt found "Y" bacilli in the feces of healthy rabbits. Indirect transmission by means of food is, of course, to be expected. A small epidemic occurring in a hospital in New York city and caused by the bacillus "Y," was indirectly traced to milk.

The length of time during which the bacilli may live in the soil has been mentioned as a source of danger. Vincent and Muratet describe an instance of this. Dysentery had been common at the Chalons Military Camp in 1889. A year later, troops coming to this camp pitched their tents over the site of the old latrines. Dysentery appeared among this particular troop unit, whereas other troops remained free.

Preventive measures must center chiefly upon disinfection of dejecta, closure of latrines, fly-proofing of latrines and kitchens, and early recognition of suspicious cases. Food-handlers should be proved not to be carriers. Hands should be washed before and after defecation. Care of water supplies and food supplies is indicated. It is important to inquire into the possibility of recent intestinal disturbances however mild, among the kitchen personnel and others in contact with food. It is not uncommon in armies to find that company cooks are suffering from mild intestinal disturbances to which they, themselves, have paid little attention.

Prophylactic Vaccination.—Shiga believes that the periodical appearance of epidemics in Japan indicates the acquisition of immunity by the community. He states that in the thirty years preceding 1908, two great epidemics passed through Japan from the south to the north. The epidemic remained in a single region from one to three years, rapidly reaching a maximum and gradually declining. After a period varying from ten to twenty years, these great epidemics reappeared and he believed that the interval could be explained by acquired immunity. His attempts at vaccination are based on these considerations. His method consists very largely in injecting, simultaneously, killed suspensions of agar cultures with specific serum (or in other words, sensitized cultures), following this first injection with killed agar suspensions without serum. This has the advantage of not giving the severe reactions which follow the injections of cultures alone. By these methods he vaccinated ten thousand Japanese in epidemic regions without striking results as far as the morbidity was concerned, but with considerable lowering of the mortality.

Castellani inoculated 0.5 c.c. of a peptone water culture, killed by heating at 55° C. for one hour, following this, after a week, with a second inoculation of 1 c.c. Most observers have worked with killed suspensions of agar cultures taken up in salt solution. Vaccination by mouth has been tried, and favorable results reported. This method has not had a critical test (Enlows). The available evidence does not warrant recommendation of the use of dysentery vaccines as a general prophylactic measure.

Serum Treatment.—Sera, both monovalent and polyvalent, have been made by a large number of observers and extensive attempts at treatment have been carried out. Shiga himself used a multivalent dysentery serum. He obtained encouraging results in thousands of cases in Japan, and believed that there was a definite therapeutic advantage to be gained by use of the serum. Other reports have been conflicting.

LEAHY, A. D. Am. J. Pub. Health,
LENTZ, O. Ztschr. f. Hyg. u. Infek
LOVELL, R. J. Path. & Bact., 1929
MARTINI, E., and LENTZ, O. Ztschr
MORGAN, H. DE R. Brit. M. J., 190
——— J. Hyg., 1911, 11:1.
NEISSER and SHIGA. Deutsche med
OHNO. Philippine J. Sc., 1906, 1.
OLITSKY and KLIGLER. J. Exper. N
PFEIFFER and UNGERMANN. Centra
ROSENTHAL. Deutsche med. Wchn
SHIGA, K. Centralblt. f. Bakt., I A
——— Deutsche med. Wchnschr.,
——— Ztschr. f. Hyg., 41.
SHIGA, K., KAWANURA, N., and TSU
    League of Nations, Health Or
STRONG, R. P., and MUSGRAVE, W.
TODD. J. Hyg., Cambridge, 1904,
——— Brit. M. J., 1903, 2:1456.
TWORT, F. W. Brit. J. Exper. P
VAILLARD and DOPTER. Ann. de
VINCENT and MURATET. Military
WADSWORTH, A. B. Standard Me
    York State Department of He
WELCH, H., and MICKLE, F. L. A
WHITE, P. B. A System of Bacte
WOLLSTEIN, M. Stud. Rockefelle
ZINSSER, H. Proc. N. York Path.

Dysentery serum is most valuable in the Shiga types of the disease in which an exotoxin occurs.

THE MORGAN BACILLI

In 1905 and 1906 Morgan isolated several atypical varieties of gram-negative bacteria from the feces of children suffering from diarrhea. These organisms obviously belonged to the general "enteric" group, but their systematic position has not been definitely determined. Morgan described four types of these organisms. Of these, we shall discuss only the Morgan bacillus No. 1, as this strain is the only one of the four which seems to have pathogenicity and is the one which has received the greatest attention from investigators.

COLON-TYPHOID-PARATYPHOID DYSENTERY GROUPS

COMPOSITE TABLE OF MOST IMPORTANT TYPES

Bacillus	Dextrose	Mannite	Maltose	Lactose	Xylose	Sucrose	Dulcite	Lead acetate agar	Indol	Motility
B. coli communis	⊕	⊕	⊕	⊕	×	—	⊕	varies	+	+
B. coli communior	⊕	⊕	⊕	⊕	×	⊕	⊕	varies	......	+
B. acidi lactici	⊕	⊕	⊕	⊕	×	—	—	...	......	+
B. lactis aërogenes	⊕	⊕	⊕	⊕	×	⊕	—	...	......	+
B. paratyphosus A	⊕	⊕	⊕	—	—	—	slow	—	Generally no indole though literature not consistent on this point	+
B. paratyphosus B	⊕	⊕	...	—	⊕	—	+	+		+
B. enteritidis	⊕	⊕	...	—	⊕	—	+	+		+
B. abortus equi	⊕	⊕	...	—	⊕	—	+	—		+
B. suipestifer	⊕	⊕	...	—	⊕	—	irreg.	—		+
B. typhi murium	⊕	⊕	...	—	⊕	—	+	+		+
B. typhosus	+	+	+	—	slow	—	slow	+		+
B. dysenteriæ Shiga	+	—	—	—	×	—	—	×		—
B. dysenteriæ Flexner	+	+	+	—	×	—	—	?×	+.	
B. dysenteriæ Y (Hiss-Park)	+	+	—	—	×	—	×	×	+	—
B. dysenteriæ Strong	+	+	—		×	+	×	×	+	—
B. sonnei	+	+	+	+ slow	—	+ slow	—	—	—	—
B. fæcalis alcaligenes	—	×	×	×	×	×	×	×	......	+
B. morgani, No. 1	⊕ + slight gas	—	—		?			?×	+	+

⊕ = acid and gas   — = negative
+ = acid, no gas   × = not needed for identification

The Morgan bacillus No. 1 is a gram-negative rod, motile, and similar in morphology to other colon bacilli. It does not ferment lactose or mannite. It *ferments glucose* with the production of *acid and gas*, and *produces indole*. It does not liquefy gelatin. It is apparent that the inability of the organism to ferment lactose differentiates it from typical colon bacilli, that it differs from the paratyphoids in producing indole and in being unable to ferment mannite and maltose and that it differs from the dysentery bacilli in producing gas from dextrose. A number of strains of organisms regarded as the Morgan No. 1 bacillus have shown considerable variability. The strains are serologically heterogeneous and the agglutination reactions do not indicate that the organism is closely related to either the paratyphoid or dysentery group.

Morgan regarded th
Bergey and others h
(1934) of Bergey's
Salmonella morgani
Although we are pl
clinical reasons. In
than to the typhoid,

The pathogenicit
diarrheal stools of
Havens and Mayfiel
disease resembling
The serum of each
feces, urine, or blo
feces of 2798 health
tors classify *B. mo*
organism has been
logical garden.

AMAKO. Ztschr. f. H
ANDREWES, F. W., and
    Dysentery Bacilli,
ANDREWES, F. W. Lai
BESSAU. Centralbl. f.
CASTELLANI and CHAL
CONRADI. Deutsche m
———Festschr. z. 60.
    mann, 2 ed., Vol.
DOERR. Das Dysenter
DUVAL, C. W. J. Am
DUVAL and SHORER.
ENLOWS, E. M. A. U
FLETCHER, W., and M
    Carriers, Med. R
FLEXNER, S. J. Exper
———Phila. Med. J.,
———Bull. Johns H
———J. Am. M. As
GARDNER, A. D. A S
GILBERT, R., and COI
HAVENS, L. C., and N
HAY, H. R. J. Hyg.,
HISS, P. H., and RUS
———J. Med. Resea
KENAI, S. Brit. J. E
KOSER, S. A. J. Prev
KRAUS. Monatschr.
KRAUS and DOERR.
KRUSE, W. Deutsch
———Deutsche med
———RITTERSHAUS,

CHAPTER XXXIX

ASIATIC CHOLERA AND THE CHOLERA VIBRIO

Family: *Pseudomonadaceae*. Tribe: *Spirilleae*. Genus: *Vibrio*. Type species: *Vibrio comma*.
Synonyms: *Spirillum cholerae asiaticae*: Comma Bacillus

The organism of Asiatic cholera was unknown until 1883. In this year, Koch, at the head of a commission established by the German government to study the disease in Egypt and India, discovered the "comma bacillus" in the defecations of patients, and determined its etiological significance.

In 1892 Pettenkofer, then in his seventy-fourth year, a skeptic of the bacterial etiology of cholera, put the question to the test of experiments on human beings. He, Emmerich and several of their pupils swallowed broth cultures of the cholera vibrio. Pettenkofer had only a slight diarrhea with a great proliferation of the vibrios in the stool. Two of the others suffered from severe enteritis which appears to have been typical mild cholera. None died. On account of the unknown degree of virulence of the culture used and the undetermined degree of susceptibility or immunity of the subjects, this test was not the *experimentum crucis* that Pettenkofer thought it was. Apart from the constant association of the cholera spirillum with the disease, the etiological relationship has been clearly demonstrated by several accidental infections in bacteriologists.

Morphology and Staining.—The vibrio or spirillum of cholera is a small curved rod, varying from 1 to 2 μ in length. The degree of curvature may vary from the slightly bent, comma-like form to a more or less distinct spiral with one or two turns. The spirals do not lie in the same plane, being arranged in corkscrew fashion in three dimensions. The spirillum is actively motile and owes its motility to a single polar flagellum. Spores are not formed. In young cultures the comma shapes predominate, in older growths the longer forms are more numerous. Strains which have been cultivated artificially for prolonged periods without passage through the animal body have a tendency to lose the curve, assuming a more bacillus-like appearance. The spirilla are stained with all the usual aqueous aniline dyes. They are gram-negative. In histological section they may be demonstrated by staining with alkaline methylene blue.

Cultivation.—The cholera spirillum grows easily upon all the usual culture media. Moderate alkalinity of the media is preferable, though slight acidity does not prevent growth.

In *gelatin stab cultures* fluidification begins at the surface, rapidly giving rise to the familiar funnel-shaped excavation.

Upon *agar plates,* within eighteen to twenty-four hours, grayish, opalescent colonies appear, which are as a rule differentiated to some extent by their transparency from the other bacteria apt to appear in feces.

Coagulated blood serum is liquefied by the cholera vibrio. On *potato*, growth is

profuse and appears as a brownish coarse layer. In *milk*, growth is rapid and without coagulation. In *broth*, general clouding and the formation of a pellicle result. The rapidity and luxuriance of growth of the cholera spirillum upon *alkaline peptone solutions* render such solutions peculiarly useful as enriching media in isolating this micro-organism from the stools of patients. In peptone solu-
tion, the cholera spirillum gives rise to abundant indole, demonstrated in the so-called "cholera-red" reaction. This reaction has a distinct diagnostic value, but is by no means specific. In the case of the cholera spirillum the mere addition of strong sulphuric acid suffices to bring out the color reaction. This is due to the fact that, unlike some other indole-producing bacteria, the cholera organism is able to reduce the nitrates present in the medium to nitrites, thus itself furnishing the nitrite necessary for the color reaction. The medium which is most suit-

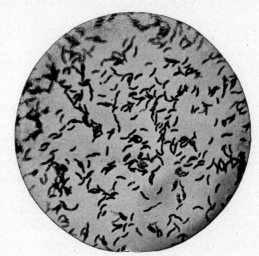

Fig. 50.—Cholera Vibrio.
(After Fränkel and Pfeiffer.)

able for this test is that proposed by Dunham, consisting of a solution of 1 per cent of peptone and 0.5 per cent sodium chloride in water.

Hemolysis.—The cholera vibrio is nonhemolytic. We base this statement partly upon our own observation of the growth of stock cultures, which is admittedly not a true index of the action of freshly isolated strains, and largely upon the work of Kraus and Fukuhara, of von Loghem and Greig. Greig showed that there was no hemolysis around colonies of *Vibrio comma* on blood agar plates during the first twenty-four hours' incubation at 37° C., but that on prolonged incubation a zone of hemolysis appeared. The supernatant fluid of a three-day old alkaline broth culture did not hemolize red corpuscles when mixed with them in a test tube. Von Loghem had suggested that the liberation of hemoglobin from red corpuscles under the influence of cholera vibrios was due to "hemodigestion." It seems as if this were the correct explanation. The El Tor strain isolated by Gotschlich is actively hemolytic. Many investigators have reported contradictory results in studies of the hemolytic properties of these vibrios. No correlation has been established between hemolytic activity and toxicity or virulence.

Fermentation Reactions.—Glucose, maltose, and saccharose are usually fermented. Acid is produced without gas. Xylose is not fermented. Most of the strains ferment mannite. Lactose is not fermented within the first forty-eight hours and many strains have no action on this substance. Slow or late fermentation of lactose has been reported. Because of variability in the biochemical activities of cholera vibrios, the fermentation reactions do not suffice to differentiate the members of this group. Taylor, Read and Paudit found that the fermentation of mannose was a characteristic of typical *v. cholerae*.

Variability.—The variations in the characteristics of the colonies of the cholera vibrio, in morphology, motility and biochemical activity have been noticed by many observers. The older observations particularly those of Eisenberg and Baerthlein were reviewed by Balteanu in the paper reporting his cultural and serological analysis

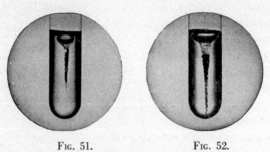

FIG. 51.   FIG. 52.

FIG. 51.—CHOLERA VIBRIO.
Stab culture in gelatin, three days old.

FIG. 52.—CHOLERA VIBRIO.
Stab culture in gelatin, six days old. (After Fränkel and Pfeiffer.)

of this organism and cholera-like vibrios. Balteanu dissociated the cultures into three types of colonies: (1) a rugose circumballate type, with a central nodule, a thin zone and a thickened edge; (2) white ring type, composed of a dense center and a thin clear bordering zone; and (3) an opaque, round hemispherical type with a regular surface. These do not exactly correspond to the usual smooth-rough transformations. The organisms in the opaque colonies were nonmotile. The morphology of the vibrios in the various colonies was not strikingly different.

During the growth of a culture of *Vibrio comma*, the organisms pass through coccoid, bacillary, long spiral, and budding or branching forms in addition to the typical curved shapes. The large irregular forms appear in both young and old cultures, although the older cultures contain numerous irregular forms and giant coccoids. Some investigators have interpreted this sequence of forms as evidence of a life cycle. Henrici, on the other hand, correlated the cell changes with the rate of growth and expressed the opinion that the irregular forms were not stages in a life cycle.

Serological Analysis.—It is to be recalled that the Pfeiffer phenomenon of specific lysis through the agency of an antibody was discovered in the course of studies of immunity to cholera. This test is relatively specific, but does not differentiate between the hemolytic El Tor strain and the nonhemolytic *Vibrio comma*. The agglutination test shows the usual group specificity. Many freshly isolated strains of the cholera vibrios are inagglutinable, presenting an important problem for further investigation.

Balteanu clearly demonstrated that Weil and Felix were in error in stating that motile cholera vibrios lacked the H, or flagellar antigen. The vibrio possesses only a single flagellum and hence carries only a small amount of flagellar material. By suitable methods, Balteanu obtained the flagella in concentration and showed that they were composed of the usual thermolabile loose flocculating H antigen, with specific properties. The bodies of the motile vibrios and the nonmotile forms contained the stable O-group antigen. Antigenic analysis has been carried further by Gardner and Venkatraman and by White. Serological analysis of the whole group of vibrios and the variants has not been completed.

In 1927, Landsteiner and Levine isolated a carbohydrate haptene from *Vibrio cholerae* and found that this polysaccharide had specific immunological properties.

Biological Considerations.—The cholera spirillum is aerobic and facultatively anaerobic. It does not form spores. The optimum temperature for its growth is about 37.5° C. It grows easily, however, at a temperature of 22° C. and does not cease to grow at temperatures as high as 40° C. Frozen in ice, these bacteria may live for about three or four days. Boiling destroys them immediately. A temperature of 60° C. kills them in an hour. In impure water, in moist linen, and in foodstuffs, they may live for many days. Associated with saprophytes in feces and other putrefying material, and wherever active acid formation is taking place, they are destroyed within several days. Complete drying kills them in a short time. The common disinfectants destroy them in weak solutions and after short exposures (carbolic acid, 0.5 per cent in one-half hour; bichloride of mercury, 1:100,000 in ten minutes; mineral acids, 1:5,000 or 10,000 in a few minutes).

Isolation from Feces and Water.—The principles of the special methods devised to isolate the cholera vibrio from feces and water are: (*a*) provision of aerobic conditions for surface growth and (*b*) an alkaline reaction of the medium, pH 8 to 9.

Dieudonné has recommended a selective medium upon which cholera spirilla will grow well, but upon which the colon bacillus will grow either very sparsely or not at all. Cocci will produce minute pinpoint colonies only and other common bacilli like those of the proteus group will grow hardly more easily than bacillus coli. Its preparation is very simple.

To seventy parts of ordinary 3 per cent agar, neutralized to litmus, there are added thirty parts of a sterile mixture of equal parts of defibrinated beef blood and normal sodium hydrate.

The latter is sterilized by steam before being added to the agar. This pure alkali agar is poured out in plates and allowed to dry several days at 37° or five minutes at 60° C.

The material to be examined is smeared upon the surface of these plates with a glass rod. If the blood-alkali mixture is prepared beforehand and allowed to stand for four or five weeks, the plates may be used immediately after pouring (Teague).

The principle of this medium is that cholera will grow in the presence of an amount of alkali which inhibits other fecal bacteria.

The best results in the practical isolation of the cholera spirilla from stools are obtained by making use of both of these properties from the beginning.

A portion of the stool is seeded directly into alkaline-peptone water. The broth used should be distinctly alkaline, titrated to pH 8 to 9. After six to twelve hours, a loopful from the surface of these peptone water tubes is plated upon plates of Dieudonné's medium, and is also transferred to a second series of alkaline-peptone water tubes. Once isolated, the spirilla are identified by their morphology and motility, by the appearance of their colonies, by their manner of growth upon gelatin stabs, by the cholera-red reaction, and, finally, by agglutinative tests in immune sera. Owing to the existence of other spirilla morphologically and culturally similar, the serum reactions are the only absolutely positive differential criteria.

For isolation of the vibrios from water, it is, of course, necessary to use comparatively large quantities. Fluegge and Bitter advise the distribution of about a liter of water in ten or twelve Erlenmeyer flasks. To each of these they add 10 c.c. of sterile peptone-salt solution (peptone 10 per cent, sodium chloride 5 per cent). After eighteen hours at 37.5° C. the surface growths in these flasks are examined both microscopically and culturally as before.

Cholera in Man.—In man the disease is contracted by ingestion of cholera organisms with water, food, or any contaminated material. The disease is essentially an intestinal one. The bacteria, very sensitive to an acid reaction, may often, if in small numbers, be checked by the normal gastric secretions. Having once passed into the intestine, however, they proliferate rapidly, often completely outgrowing the normal intestinal flora. Fatal cases, at autopsy, show extreme congestion of the intestinal walls. Occasionally ecchymosis and localized necrosis of the mucosa may be present and swelling of the solitary lymph follicles and Peyer's patches. Microscopically the cholera spirilla may be seen to have penetrated the mucosa and to lie within its deepest layers close to the submucosa. The most marked changes usually take place in the lower half of the small intestine. The intestines are filled with the characteristically fluid, slightly bloody, or "rice-water" stools, from which often pure cultures of the cholera vibrio can be grown. The micro-organisms can be cultivated only from the intestines and their contents, and the parenchymatous degenerations taking place in other organs must be interpreted as being purely of toxic origin.

There is at the same time a profound toxemia due, in part at least, to the absorbed cholera substances.

The incubation time of the disease is usually short, lasting from a few hours to several days. The disease usually begins with diarrhea which gradually becomes more violent until the colorless typical, rice-water stools appear. Castellani and Chalmers describe the further course as follows:

Vomiting generally appears early, food being first expelled, followed later by watery fluid with which bile and occasionally blood may be mixed. As the purging and vomiting persist the urine diminishes and may stop, and fluid departs from the subcutaneous tissues, which therefore contract so that the face alters, the nose becoming sharp, the cheekbones prominent, and eyes sunken and the skin of the fingers becomes wrinkled like that of a washerwoman.[1]

A considerable rôle is played in the subsequent course of the disease by the depletion of water, with consequent anuria, low blood pressure, cyanosis, acidosis, etc. The therapeutic effect of saline infusions is said to be astonishing.

Animal Pathogenicity.—In animals, cholera never appears as a spontaneous disease. Nikati and Rietsch succeeded in producing a fatal disease in guinea-pigs by opening the peritoneum and injecting cholera spirilla directly into the duodenum. Koch succeeded in producing a fatal cholera-like disease in animals by introducing infected water into the stomach through a catheter after neutralization of the gastric juice with sodium carbonate. At the same time, he administered opium to prevent active peristalsis. A method of infection more closely analogous to the infection in man was followed by Metchnikoff, who successfully produced fatal disease in young suckling rabbits by contaminating the maternal teat.

Subcutaneous inoculation of moderate quantities of cholera spirilla into rabbits and guinea-pigs rarely produces more than a temporary illness. Intraperitoneal inoculation, if in proper quantities, generally leads to death. It will be remembered that

1 Castellani and Chalmers, *Manual of Tropical Medicine*, Wm. Wood & Co., New York, 1919.

when working with intraperitoneal cholera inoculations the phenomenon of bacteriolysis was discovered by Pfeiffer.

Different strains of cholera spirilla vary greatly in their virulence. The virulence
of most of them, however, can be enhanced by repeated passages through animals.
Most of our domestic animals enjoy considerable resistance against cholera infection,
though under experimental conditions successful inoculations upon dogs, cats, and
mice have been reported. Doves are entirely insusceptible.

Cholera Toxin.—The absence of the cholera spirilla from the internal organs of
fatal cases, in spite of the severe general symptoms of the disease, points distinctly
to the existence of a strong poison produced in the intestine by the micro-organisms
and absorbed by the patient. It was in this sense, indeed, that Koch first interpreted
the clinical picture of cholera. Numerous investigations into the nature of these
toxins have been made, the earlier ones defective in that definite identification of the
cultures used for experimentation was not carried out.

Pfeiffer, in 1892, was able to show that filtrates of young bouillon cultures of
cholera spirilla were but slightly toxic, whereas the dead bodies of carefully killed
agar cultures were fatal to guinea-pigs even in small quantities. In consequence, he
regarded the cholera poison as consisting chiefly of an endotoxin. The opinion as to
the endotoxic nature of the cholera poison is not, however, shared by all workers.
Metchnikoff, Roux, and Salimbeni, in 1896, succeeded in producing death in guinea-
pigs by introduction into their peritoneal cavities of cholera cultures enclosed in
celloidin sacs. Brau and Denier, and Kraus, claim that they have succeeded not only
in demonstrating a soluble toxin in alkaline broth cultures of cholera spirilla, but
in producing true antitoxins by immunization with such cultures. It appears, therefore, that the poisonous action of the cholera organisms may depend both upon the
formation of true secretory toxins and upon endotoxins. Which of these is paramount
in the production of the disease cannot be definitely stated. In favor of the great importance of the endotoxic elements is the failure, thus far, to obtain successful therapeutic results with supposedly antitoxic sera.

Epidemiology.—Cholera is essentially a disease of man. Endemic in India and
other eastern countries, it has from time to time epidemically invaded large territories
of Europe and Asia, not infrequently assuming pandemic proportions and sweeping
over almost the entire earth. Five separate cholera epidemics of appalling magnitude
occurred during the nineteenth century alone; several of these, spreading from India
to Asia Minor, Egypt, Russia, and the countries of central Europe, reached even to
North and South America. Before 1892 there were four pandemics of cholera during
each of which the disease spread from India to Europe and thence throughout a large
portion of the inhabited world. These pandemics occurred during the periods: 1817
to 1823, 1826 to 1837, 1846 to 1863 and 1865 to 1875.

An important epidemiological fact is the existence of certain endemic foci where
cholera is always going on and from which epidemics and pandemics originate. The
chief endemic focus seems to be located in Lower Burma, and it is, as yet, an unsolved puzzle as to why the disease should remain smoldering in such regions and
spread widely only at certain periods, five, ten or more years apart. Important
epidemics have occurred between the years 1879 and 1910. In 1879 an epidemic spread
to Europe through Egypt and this outbreak is notable because in 1883 in Egypt,

Koch, as head of the German Cholera Commission, isolated the cholera spirillum. In 1891 another great epidemic, originating in India, is stated by Castellani as having started on the occasion of a bathing festival held on the Ganges. It spread among pilgrims and reached Europe in 1892, appearing with particular virulence in Hamburg. From there it spread to America and Africa by ocean commerce. During this epidemic it is said that 800,000 people fell victims in Russia alone. Violle records that in 1908, 1909, and 1910 there were a series of epidemics in Russia. In 1908 there were about 30,000 cases with 14,000 deaths; in 1909, there were 21,000 cases with 9,700 deaths, and in 1909 to 1910 there were 13,000 deaths. During the Balkan War in 1912 cholera appeared among the armies. During the World War there were cases of cholera in Galicia in the Austrian Army, and there were outbreaks in Bulgaria, Greece and Turkey, and in Mesopotamia.

The prevalence of cholera as an important epidemic disease may be estimated by the following chart of cholera epidemics of the last hundred years which is taken from Violle's work on cholera (1918) to which numerous references have been made.

EPIDEMICS OF CHOLERA IN VARIOUS PLACES

Place	Date	Deaths	Place	Date	Deaths
Havana	1833	8,000	Kashmir	1892	5,000
Malta	1837	4,000	England	1854	20,000
London	1832	4,000	France	1854	140,000
Paris	1832	7,000	Italy	1854	24,000
Basra	1821	5,000	Egypt	1865	60,000
Lahore	1845	22,000	Egypt	1883	50,000
Tabriz	1852	12,000	Egypt	1831	150,000
Teheran	1852	15,000	Cairo	1831	36,000
Bagdad	1852	2,000	Cairo	1892	33,000
Bellary and Mysore,			Russia	1908–10	144,000
India	1865	40,000	Rosetta	1865	2,168
Province of Bombay	1865	84,000			

The disease always originates from the dejecta of cholera patients and carriers. At times of epidemic, infection of the water and food supplies naturally plays an important rôle, and in such epidemics, as the one in Hamburg, the water supply was primarily responsible. The distribution of the disease here followed definitely the distribution of the infected water supply and the organisms were isolated from the water. This epidemic is one of the classical water epidemics and has served more than any other water epidemic in impressing medical and health authorities with the importance of water supply supervision. In countries like India and Egypt, etc., where water supplies are often taken from collecting tanks not properly supervised, and from individual wells, and where the supervision of feces disposal is not strict, it is quite natural that distribution by water supplies should be extremely important. Violle adds a number of interesting instances of water transmission which occurred in France in 1885, in which the source was soiled linen washed in a stream with distribution of the disease further downstream in other villages, but not in any of the villages higher up the river. It is also probable that in countries such as India, the custom of throwing dead bodies into rivers may contribute materially to the constant presence of the disease.

In endemic centers, it is more than likely that the cholera carrier is a very important factor of distribution. The existence of the carrier is proven beyond doubt, and, as in typhoid, individuals may remain carriers for very long periods. Greig has shown that the organisms may live in the gallbladders of human beings as in the typhoid carrier state. McLaughlin has found as many as 7 per cent of the population of an infected district to be cholera carriers.

Again, as in typhoid, distribution of fecal material to food by flies probably plays a very important rôle, and according to Barber the organisms may live for some time in the intestines in such insects as cockroaches. Whether or not domestic animals can act as distributers of the organisms is uncertain. Violle quotes Haffkine as stating that he had found the spirilla in the intestines of cattle, and that they were found by Hahn in the intestines of cows during cholera epidemics. The importance of this, however, is still quite uncertain.

In nature the cholera spirilla may, under favorable conditions, remain alive for considerable periods. In drinking water they have been found alive after several days and they may remain alive for weeks in water supplies. From the investigations of Wernicke, Shirnoff and others it would appear that under favorable conditions the spirilla may remain alive in river water and other natural waters for weeks or even months. In milk and other foods, the longevity of the cholera spirilla seems to depend particularly upon the nature and numbers of other bacteria present and on the production of an acid reaction. In cholera stools they will remain alive until considerable putrefaction has taken place and, therefore, may be assumed under favorable conditions to live at least one day, or perhaps three days or longer. In cold weather when bacterial growth is more or less inhibited, they may remain alive much longer than this.

Cholera Immunization.—One attack of cholera confers protection against subsequent infection. Active immunization of animals may be accomplished by inoculation of dead cultures, or of small doses of living bacteria. In the serum of immunized animals specific bacteriolytic and agglutinating substances are found. The discovery of bacteriolytic immune bodies, in fact, was made by means of cholera spirilla. Both the bacteriolysins and the agglutinins, because of their specificity, are of great importance in making a bacteriological diagnosis of true cholera organisms.

Prophylactic Vaccination.—Active immunization of cholera was one of the first methods of prophylactic vaccination attempted in the bacteriological era of infectious disease study. In 1884, a Spanish bacteriologist, Férran, who had been a pupil of Pasteur, carried out immunization experiments with cholera on guinea-pigs. In accordance with the methods prevalent at that time, he worked with attenuated cholera cultures. He tried this method on human beings in Spain in 1885 with results which seemed to him encouraging. Subsequent to this many different vaccines have been developed. Haffkine worked intensely on the subject and observed the results of vaccination on an enormous number of people in India, over a period of more than ten years. Haffkine's vaccine has undergone a number of modifications since he first used it. He made use of living cultures, beginning his experiments with attenuation of cholera spirilla by cultivation at a temperature of 40° C., using, at first, a less virulent and next a more virulent strain. Later, it was found that the cultures attenuated by cultivation at increased temperatures were not necessary. The extensive experimental work in India mentioned above seems to have shown that there is a distinct prophylactic value in the use of Haffkine's virus.

Other observers have made use chiefly of killed cultures. The French vaccine made at the Pasteur Institute consists of broth cultures killed at 50° C. Kolle grows his cholera spirilla on agar, suspending them in salt solution, killing at 56° C. for one hour, then adding 0.5 per cent carbolic acid. Other observers, like Nicoll and Vincent, killed without heat, by the addition of carbolic acid. Extracts of the cholera spirilla have also been used in various ways. Strong grows cholera organisms on agar, takes them up in salt solution, kills at 60° C. and then allows the suspensions to stand in the incubator for about five days, subsequently filtering through a Berkefeld candle. This filtrate is used for inoculation, after its sterility has been determined by culture. Wassermann has used materials prepared by precipitation of cultures with alcohol. Castellani during the last ten years has prepared what he calls a T.A.B.C., or tetravaccine, which is made by mixing agar cultures of typhoid, paratyphoid A, paratyphoid B, and cholera in saline emulsion. The emulsion is killed with 0.5 per cent carbolic acid, preserved for twenty-four hours in this form at room temperature and then standardized by the usual counting chamber method so that 1 c.c. should contain five hundred thousand typhoid, two hundred and fifty thousand paratyphoid A, two hundred and fifty thousand paratyphoid B, and two thousand million cholera spirilla. Five-tenths c.c. of this is injected, three doses being given within two weeks. This is the vaccine which we used on the Serbian Army during the War.

According to Teague salt solution suspensions of vibrios killed by heating for one hour at 53° C. are as efficacious as any other form of vaccine. The suspension, containing eight billion organisms per cubic centimeter, is administered by subcutaneous injection in two doses, the first of 0.5 c.c., the second of 1 c.c.

As far as the available statistics show at the present time, cholera vaccination is of distinct value. This has been the judgment of those who have scrutinized Haffkine's immunization experiments, as well as those who have observed more recent army experiences.

Bacteriophage.—D'Herelle, Asheshov, Morison and others have used bacteriophage in the prevention and treatment of cholera. The results have been said to be highly satisfactory, but evaluation cannot be made until adequate statistical analysis has been made.

CHOLERA-LIKE SPIRILLA

The biological group of the spirilla, to which the cholera spirillum belongs, is a large one, numbering probably over a hundred separate species. Most of these are of medical bacteriological importance chiefly because of the difficulties which they add to the task of differentiation, for while some of them simply bear a morphological resemblance to the true cholera vibrio, others can be distinguished only by their serum reactions and pathogenicity for various animals. Additional difficulty, too, is contributed by the fact that within the group of true cholera organisms occasional variations in agglutinability and bacteriolytic reactions may exist. Certain strains, too, the six El Tor cultures isolated by Gotschlich, while in every respect similar to true cholera spirilla, are considered as a separate subspecies by Kraus, because of their ability to produce hemolytic substances, a function lacking in other cholera strains.

Spirillum Metchnikovii.—This spirillum was discovered by Gamaleia in the feces and blood of domestic fowl, in which it had caused an intestinal disease. Morphologically and in staining reactions it is identical with *Spirillum cholerae asiaticae*. It possesses a single polar flagellum, and is actively motile. Culturally it is identical with *Vibrio cholerae* except for slightly more luxuriant growth and more rapid fluidification of gelatin. It gives the cholera-red reaction in peptone media.

It is differentiated from the cholera vibrio by its power to produce a rapidly fatal septicemia in pigeons after subcutaneous inoculation of minute quantities. It is much more pathogenic for guinea-pigs than the cholera vibrio. It is not subject to lysis or agglutinated by cholera immune sera.

Spirillum Massaua.—This organism was isolated at Massaua by Pasquale in 1891 from the feces of a clinically doubtful case of cholera. Culturally and morphologically it is much like the true cholera vibrio, but in pathogenicity is closer to *Spirillum metchnikovii*, in that small quantities produce septicemia in birds. It possesses four flagella. It does not give a specific serum reaction with cholera immune serum.

Spirillum of Finkler-Prior.—Isolated by Finkler and Prior from the feces of a case of cholera nostras. Morphologically it is like the true cholera spirillum, though slightly larger and less uniformly curved. Culturally it is much like the cholera vibrio, but grows more rapidly and thickly upon the usual media. It does not give the cholera-red reaction, nor does it give specific serum reactions with cholera immune serum.

Spirillum Deneke.—A vibrio isolated by Deneke from butter. Much like that of Finkler-Prior. It does not give the cholera-red reaction.

REFERENCES

ASHESHOV, I. N., *et al.* Studies on Cholera Bacteriophage. Indian J. M. Res., 1933, 20:1101.

BAERTHLEIN, K. Berl. klin. Wchnschr., 1911, 48:373.

BALTEANU, J. J. Path. & Bacteriol., 1926, 29:251.

BRAU and DENIER. Compt. rend. Acad. d. sc., 1906.

CASTELLANI, A., and CHALMERS, A. J. Manual of Tropical Medicine, Wm. Wood & Co., New York, 1919.

COMMITTEE UPON PATHOLOGICAL METHODS. The Laboratory Diagnosis of Acute Intestinal Infections, etc., Med. Res. Council, Spec. Rep. Ser. No. 51, London, 1920, p. 88.

DENEKE, C. Deutsche med. Wchnschr., 1885, 11:33.

DIEUDONNÉ, A. Centralbl. f. Bakt., I Abt., 1909, 50:107.

DUNHAM, E. K. Ztschr. f. Hyg. u. Infectionskrankh., 1887, 2:337.

——— Am. J. M., Sc., 1893, 105:72.

EISENBERG, P. Centralbl. f. Bakteriol., I Abt., 1912, 56:1.

FÉRRAN, J. Compt. rend. Acad. d. sc., 1885.

FINKLER, D. and PRIOR, J. Centralbl. f. allg. ges. Phys., 1884, 1:279.

GARDNER, A. D., and VENKATRAMAN, K. V. J. Hyg., 1935, 35:262.

——— Lancet, 1935, 1, 265.

GOTSCHLICH, F. Egypt. Sanit. Dept. Sci. Rep., 1906, p. 17.

——— Ztschr. f. Hyg. u. Infectionskrankh., 1906, 53:281.

GREIG, E. D. W. Indian J. M. Research, 1914–15, 2:623.

HAFFKINE, W. M. Bull. med. Par. 1892, 7:113.
HEIBERG, B. J. Hyg., 1936, 36:118.
HENRICI, A. T. J. Infect. Dis., 1925, 37:75.
HUME, E. E. Max von Pettenkofer, P. B. Hoeber, Inc., New York, 1927.
KOCH, R. Deutsche med. Wchnschr., 1883, 9:615, 743; 1884, 10:63, 111, 191, 221, 725.
KOLLE and SCHURMANN. In Kolle and Wassermann's Handbuch, etc., 2nd ed., Vol. IV.
KRAUS, R. In Kraus and Levaditi, Handbuch, etc., Vol. I, p. 186.
———— Centralbl. f. Bakteriol., 1906.
———— and FUKUHARA, Y. Ztschr. f. Immunitätsforsch. u. exper. Therap., 1909, 3:33.
LANDSTEINER, K., and LEVINE, P. J. Exper. M., 1927, 46:213.
LINTON, R. W., and MITRA, B. N. Ind. J. M. Res., 1936, 24:323.
MCLAUGHLIN. Quoted from Rosenau's Preventive Medicine and Hygiene, D. Appleton-Century Co., New York.
METCHNIKOFF, E., ROUX, E., and SALIMBENI. Ann. de l'Inst. Pasteur, 1896, 10:257.
MORISON, J. Bacteriophage in the Treatment and Prevention of Cholera. H. K. Lewis & Co., Ltd., London, 1932. Quoted from Topley and Wilson.
NICOLL and VINCENT. Cited from Violle, le Choléra, Paris, Masson Frères, 1919.
NIKATI, W., and RIETSCH, M. Deutsche med. Wchnschr., 1884, 10:634.
PASQUALE, A. Gior. med. d. r. esercito, etc., Roma, 1891, 39:1009.
PFEIFFER, R. Ztschr. f. Hyg., 1892, 11, 393.
———— Ztschr. f. Hyg. u. Infectionskrankh., 1894, 18:1.
———— and ISSAEFF, V. I. Ztschr. f. Hyg. u. Infectionskrankh., 1894, 17:358.
———— Deutsche med. Wchnschr., 1894, 20, 305.
———— and NOCHT. Ztschr. f. Hyg., 1889, 7:259.
———— and WASSERMANN, A. Ztschr. f. Hyg., 1893, 14:46.
SEAL, S. C. Ind. J. M. Res., 1936, 24:991.
SHIRNOFF. Centralbl. f. Bakteriol., 1908, 41:797.
STRONG. J. Exper. M., 1905, 8:229.
TAYLOR, J., READ, W. D. B., and PAUDIT, S. R. Ind. J. M. Rec., 1936, 24:349, 931.
TEAGUE, O. J. Am. M. Ass., 1921, 76:243.
VIOLLE, H. Le Choléra, Paris, 1919.
VON LOGHEM, J. J. Centralbl. f. Bakteriol., I Abt., 1910, 57:289; 1912 67:410.
WASSERMANN. Festchr.... Robert Koch, Jena, 1903.
WEIL, E., and FELIX, A. Ztschr. f. Immunitätsforsch. u. exper. Therap., 1920, 29:24.
WERNICKE, E. Hyg. Rundschau, 1895, 5, 736.
WHITE, P. B. J. Hyg., 1935, 35:347, 498.
———— Brit. J. Exper. Pathol., 1936, 17:229.
ZIMMERMANN, E. Ztschr. f. Immunitätsforsch., 1933, 79:219.
———— J. Pathol. and Bacteriol., 1938, 46:1.

CHAPTER XL

THE PYOCYANEUS GROUP AND PURULENT INFECTIONS

Family: *Pseudomonadaceae.* Tribe: *Pseudomonadeae.* Genus: *Pseudomonas.* Type species: *Pseudomonas aeruginosa.* Syn: *Bacillus pyocyaneus*

Most of the chromogenic gram-negative bacteria encountered by the medical bacteriologist are nonpathogenic. Some of the products of their growth in artificial media are toxic when injected into animals, but the vast majority of these organisms are unable to establish themselves in the tissues of animals. The medical bacteriologist usually puts them aside as "air contaminants" and has been taught by long experience to view with skepticism any claims that the *Flavobacteria* and certain other related chromogens produce disease in man or animals.

Among the pigment-producing organisms, there is one group which contains at least one member whose pathogenic capacity is established. This is the group of motile, gram-negative bacteria which produce fluorescent green, yellowish and blue pigments. Medical bacteriologists have been accustomed to refer to these organisms as members of the *pyocyaneus* group, taking the name from the long-known type species, *Bacillus pyocyaneus*, or "bacillus of blue pus." Organisms with these characteristics are widely distributed in nature, being found in water, soil, and intestinal contents of man and animals. The genus, which is, therefore, of general interest, has been finally set apart by Bergey under the designation *Pseudomonas* and the medically important species has been named *Pseudomonas aeruginosa*, adopting the nomenclature of Schröter and Migula.

Bacillus Pyocyaneus.—Many suppurating wounds, especially sinuses of long standing, discharge pus which is of a bright green or blue color. The fact that this peculiar type of purulent inflammation is due to a specific chromogenic microorganism was first demonstrated by Gessard in 1882.

Morphology and Staining.—*B. pyocyaneus* is a short rod, usually straight, occasionally slightly curved, measuring, according to Fluegge, about 1 to 2 μ in length by about 0.3 μ in thickness. The bacilli are thus small and slender, but are subject to considerable variation. While ordinarily single, the bacilli may be arranged end to end in short chains of two and three. Longer chains may be formed upon media which are especially unfavorable for its growth, as very acid media or those containing antiseptics. Spores are not formed. The bacilli are actively motile and possess each a single flagellum placed at one end.

B. pyocyaneus is stained easily with all the usual dyes. It is gram-negative. Irregular staining of the bacillary body is common. The organisms sometimes contain granules which stain deeply with Neisser's and Ljubinsky's stains and therefore may resemble diphtheria bacilli.

Cultivation.—The pyocyaneus bacillus is aerobic and facultatively anaerobic. It can be adapted to absolutely anaerobic environments, but does not produce its

561

characteristic pigment without the free access of oxygen. The bacillus grows readily upon the usual laboratory media and grows equally well upon moderately alkaline or acid media. Development takes place at temperatures as low as 18° to 20° C., more rapidly and luxuriantly at 37.5° C.

On *agar slants*, growth is abundant and confluent, the surface of the agar being covered by a moist, grayish or yellowish, glistening, even layer. The pigment which begins to become visible after about eighteen hours soon penetrates the agar itself and becomes diffused throughout it, giving the medium a bright green fluorescent appearance, which grows darker as the age of the culture increases. Portions of the surface of the growth may have a metallic sheen.

In *gelatin stabs*, growth takes place much more rapidly upon the surface than in the depths. A rapid liquefaction of the gelatin takes place, causing a saucer-shaped depression. As this deepens, pigment begins to form in the upper layers, often visible as a greenish pellicle.

In *broth*, growth is rapid and chiefly at the surface, forming a thick pellicle. Below this, there is moderate clouding. The pigment is formed chiefly at the top. In old cultures there is a heavy flocculent precipitate. In fluid media containing albuminous material, strong alkalinity is produced.

On *potato*, growth develops readily and a deep brownish pigment appears, which is not unlike that produced by B. mallei upon the same medium.

Milk is coagulated by precipitation of casein and assumes a yellowish green hue. In older cultures the casein is usually digested and liquefied.

Fermentation Reactions.—The production of large amounts of alkali by B. pyocyaneus may obscure the simultaneous acid fermentation of carbohydrates by the organism growing in a peptone solution. No gas is formed from any carbohydrate. B. pyocyaneus ferments only dextrose, with the production of acid.

Indole has not been produced by the pathogenic strains we have studied.

Pigments.—Bacillus pyocyaneus produces two sorts of pigment. One of these is greenish-yellow or green, soluble in water and diffuses through solid agar medium and broth. This pigment is insoluble in chloroform and has been called *fluorescin*. The other pigment is blue-green, pyocyanine, soluble in chloroform and also soluble in water. Pyocyanine can be crystallized from the chloroform solution in the shape of needle-like crystals in stellate arrangements. It is a complex aromatic compound. The base is unstable, but the picrate and other salts are stable. These have been studied chemically by McCombie and Scarborough.

A third brown pigment, described by Gessard and called pyoxanthose, was shown by Jordan to be a decomposition product of fluorescin.

It is probable that a third pigment, a red substance, does exist. Gessard in 1919 described erythrogenic varieties of B. pyocyaneus and in 1925, Meader, Robinson, and Leonard found that all their strains of B. pyocyaneus produced this red pigment, *pyorubin*, in addition to fluorescin and pyocyanine.

The extraction of broth cultures with chloroform may occasionally serve to distinguish the pyocyaneus bacilli from other similar fluorescent bacteria. The test is easily performed by adding about 1 to 2 c.c. of chloroform to 5 c.c. of the broth culture, shaking the mixture and noting the color of the chloroform layer which settles in the bottom of the tube.

Several *proteolytic* and *lipolytic* enzymes are produced by *Bacillus pyocyaneus*. One of these, *pyocyanase* has definite antibacterial properties.

Variability.—The morphological variations of *B. pyocyaneus* were described in considerable detail by Schürmayer, in 1895, and the organism has been classed among the "pleomorphous schizomycetes." The coccoid and branched forms, observed particularly in old cultures, are interpreted as involution or degenerated forms by one group of bacteriologists and as stages in a life cycle by the other. The questions at issue cannot be settled by means of the evidence at hand.

Dissociation takes place in several directions, producing rough and smooth, pigmented and nonpigmented, motile and nonmotile, lytic and nonlytic varieties, and a large number of intermediate or intricate secondary types of colonies, such as those studied especially by Hadley. Sonnenschein has described a mucoid encapsulated variety of *B. pyocyaneus*.

Serology.—The organisms in the fluorescent-pyocyaneus group may have antigens in common and agglutinins for *B. pyocyaneus* may agglutinate other organisms in this group, without any correlation with their source. In general the pyocyaneus bacilli are antigenically heterogeneous. Pribram and Pulay found that antiserums against *B. pyocyaneus* and *Proteus vulgaris* cross-agglutinated these organisms. Wilson has shown that, like Proteus X_{19}, certain "Z" strains of *B. pyocyaneus* are agglutinated by the serum of patients with typhus fever.

Pathogenicity.—*B. pyocyaneus* is one of the less virulent pathogenic bacteria. It is widely distributed in nature and may be found frequently as a harmless parasite upon the skin or in the upper respiratory tracts of animals and men. It has, however, occasionally been found in connection with suppurative lesions of various parts of the body, often as a mere secondary invader in the wake of another incitant, or occasionally as the primary cause of the inflammation. In most cases where true pyocyaneus infection has taken place, the subject is usually one whose general condition and resistance are abnormally low. Thus pyocyaneus may be the cause of chronic otitis media in ill-nourished children. It has been cultivated out of the stools of children suffering from diarrhea, and has been found at autopsy generally distributed throughout the organs of children dead of gastro-enteritis. It has been cultivated from the spleen at autopsy from a case of general sepsis following mastoid operation. The bacillus has been found, furthermore, during life in pericardial exudate and in pus from liver abscesses. Ewell describes a case of *B. pyocyaneus* bacteremia secondary to pyelo-nephritis and prostatic abscess.

Brill and Libman, as well as Finkelstein, have cultivated *B. pyocyaneus* from the blood of patients suffering from general sepsis. Wassermann showed the bacillus to have been the etiological factor in an epidemic of umbilical infections in newborn children. Similar examples of *B. pyocyaneus* infection in human beings might be enumerated in large numbers, and there is no good reason to doubt that, under given conditions, fatal infections may occur.

Many domestic animals are susceptible to experimental pyocyaneus infection, chief among these being rabbits, goats, mice, and guinea-pigs. Guinea-pigs are killed by this bacillus with especial ease. Intraperitoneal inoculation with a loopful of a culture of average virulence usually leads to the death of a young guinea-pig within three or four days.

Toxins and Immunization.—Emmerich and Loew have shown that filtrates of old broth cultures of *B. pyocyaneus* contain a ferment-like substance which possesses the power to destroy some other bacteria, apparently by lysis. They have called this substance "pyocyanase" and claim that, with it, they have succeeded in protecting animals from anthrax infection. During recent years pyocyanase has been employed locally for the removal of diphtheria bacilli from the throats of convalescent cases. Broth-culture filtrates evaporated to one-tenth their volume *in vacuo* are used for this purpose.

Pyocyanase is exceedingly thermostable, resisting boiling for several hours, and is probably not identical with any of the other toxins or peptonizing ferments produced by *B. pyocyaneus*.

The toxins proper of *B. pyocyaneus* have been the subject of much investigation, chiefly by Wassermann. Wassermann found that filtrates of old cultures were far more poisonous for guinea-pigs than extracts made of dead bacteria. He concludes from this and other observations that *B. pyocyaneus* produces both an endotoxin and a soluble secreted toxin. The toxin is comparatively thermostable, resisting 100° C. for a short time. Animals actively immunized with living cultures of *B. pyocyaneus* give rise in their blood-serum to bacteriolytic antibodies only. Immunized with filtrates from old cultures, on the other hand, their serum will contain both bacteriolytic and antitoxic substances. The true toxin of *B. pyocyaneus* never approaches in strength that of diphtheria or of tetanus. Active immunization of animals must be done carefully if it is desired to produce an immune serum, since repeated injections cause great emaciation and general loss of strength.

Hemolytic action by filtrates of old broth cultures of *B. pyocyaneus* was observed first by Bulloch and Hunter in 1900. They showed that these filtrates hemolyzed the red corpuscles of dogs, rabbits, sheep, and man. This substance, called "pyocyanolysin," was thermostable, resisting heat at 100° C. for 15 minutes. It was not known at first whether this substance was the alkali in the culture, a product of autolysis of the cells or a genuine lysin. Landsteiner and Raubitchek recovered a hemolytic substance from the residue of evaporated alcoholic extracts of cultures. This was confirmed by Fukuhara. Wilson stated that the organism produces both a genuine thermostable hemotoxin for which an antihemolysin can be prepared and a thermostable hemolysin, lipoidal in nature, soluble in alcohol and ether and non-antigenic.

A leukocyte-destroying ferment elaborated by *B. pyocyaneus* was described by Ghéorghiewski.

REFERENCES

BRILL and LIBMAN. Am. J. M. Sc., 1899.
BULLOCH, W., and HUNTER, W. Centralbl. f. Bakteriol., I Abt., 1900, 28:865.
CHARRIN. La maladie pyocyanique, Paris, 1889.
EISENBERG. Centralbl. f. Bakteriol., I Abt., 1900.
EMMERICH, R., and LOEW, O. Ztschr. f. Hyg. u. Infectionskrankh., 1899, 31:1.
EWELL, G. H. Urol. and Cutan. Rev., 1936, 50:10.
FINKELSTEIN. Centralbl. f. Bakteriol., 1899.
FUKUHARA, Y. Arch. f. Hyg., 1909, 71:387.
GESSARD, C. Thèse, Paris, 1882; Compt. rend. Acad. d. sc., Paris, 1882, 94:536.
——— Compt. rend. Soc. de biol., 1919, 82:795.

GHÉORGHIEWSKI. Ann. de l'Inst. Pasteur, 1899, 13:298.
HADLEY, P. J. Infect. Dis., 1924, 34:260.
JORDAN, E. O. J. Exper. M., 1899, 4:627.
——— J. Med. Research, 1903, 10:31.
KLINE, B. S., and MASCHKE. J. Am. M. Ass., 1932, 98:528.
KRAUNHALS. Ztschr. f. Chir., 1893, 37.
LANDSTEINER, K., and RAUBITCHEK, H. Centralbl. f. Bakteriol., I Abt., 1908, 45:660.
PRIBRAM, E., and PULAY, E. Centralbl. f. Bakteriol., 1915, 76:321.
McCOMBIE, H., and SCARBOROUGH, H. A. J. Chem. Soc., 1923, 123:3279.
MEADER, P. D., ROBINSON, G. H., and LEONARD, V. Am. J. Hyg., 1925, 5:682.
NEUMANN. Jahrb. f. Kinderh., 1890.
SCHÜRMAYER, B. Ztschr. f. Hyg. u. Infectionskrankh., 1895, 20:281.
SONNENSCHEIN, C. Centralbl. f. Bakteriol., I Abt., 1927, 104:365.
TROMMSDORFF, R. Centralbl. f. Bakteriol., I Abt., 1916, 78:493.
WASSERMANN, A. Ztschr. f. Hyg. u. Infectionskrankh., 1896, 22:263.
——— Virchow's Arch., 1901, 165.
WILSON, W. J. Lancet, 1922, 1:222.

CHAPTER XLI

THE BRUCELLA GROUP—UNDULANT FEVER AND INFECTIOUS ABORTION

Family: *Parvobacteriaceae.* Tribe: *Brucelleae.* Genus: *Brucella.* Species: *Brucella melitensis* and *Brucella abortus*

Undulant fever or Malta fever in man and infectious abortion in cattle, horses and swine, together with an intermediate type of infection in goats, are communicable diseases caused by a group of closely related bacteria. Along the lines of transmission by contact and by the ingestion of contaminated milk, these organisms pass back and forth between their human and animal hosts. The parasites show a tendency toward election of one or another animal host and it seems as though types or species were emerging in correspondence with these relationships. In typical instances, species or races can be differentiated, but in many other cases differential characteristics are not clearly shown and the distinctions made are difficult and often uncertain.

The organisms which cause these diseases are small, gram-negative, nonmotile cocco-bacillary forms, which are not acid-fast and do not form endospores. They have such distinctive characteristics that they deserve separate groupings, and a specific designation setting them apart. In line with the tendency to split up the huge genus *Bacterium*, the generic name *Brucella*, derived by Meyer and Shaw from the name of the discoverer of the cause of Malta fever, Sir David Bruce, has been adopted almost universally. The generic name *Alcaligenes*, proposed by Castellani and Chalmers and used by Bergey until 1934 has little to recommend it as a designation for these organisms. Under the term *Alcaligenes* are grouped organisms having in common chiefly the property of producing alkali in milk. We have already expressed our belief that the type species, *Alcaligenes faecalis* (*B. faecalis alcaligenes*), has little in common with the other organisms in this genus.

Although Malta fever in man and infectious abortion in cattle are diseases with long histories, it was not until 1918 that they were brought together. In that year, Alice Evans compared the organisms said to be the causes of these different infections and found them to be closely similar. This has been confirmed by all subsequent investigations.

The separate histories of the bacteriology of these diseases up to the year 1918 is briefly as follows:

In 1887, Bruce isolated the causative organism of Malta fever from the spleens of persons in the Island of Malta who had died of the disease. He named the organism *Micrococcus melitensis.* During the years 1904 to 1907, the same organism was found in goats and in the milk of infected goats, and the passage of the parasite from goats to man was demonstrated. The disease was and is widespread in Europe, with a concentration of incidence around the Mediterranean Sea. True Malta fever seems to have been introduced into the United States with a shipment of goats. The etiological agent of Malta fever, formerly called *Micrococcus melitensis*, was later recognized to be a small rod form and hence was called *Bacillus* or *Bacterium*. The name for it in current usage is *Brucella melitensis*.

In 1897, in Denmark, Bang discovered a small bacterium in the uterine discharges of cows which had aborted. He isolated this organism and proved its etiological importance in infectious abortion of cattle. Bang, noticing particularly the rod-forms, named the organism *Bacillus abortus*.

For more than twenty years these diseases were described separately as medical and veterinary entities and the distinctions were consolidated by the emphasis placed by monomorphists on morphological differences.

In 1918, Evans showed that the organisms were very similar morphologically and culturally. The chief differences found by her and by Meyer and his associates were serological. By agglutination tests and absorption of agglutinins a *melitensis* type could be distinguished at one extreme and an *abortus* type at the other, with intermediate forms and a *paramelitensis* group between these two. These serological distinctions have been on the whole practical and useful.

Experimental abortion in a cow was produced by Evans by inoculating the pregnant animal with *Brucella melitensis*. Carpenter caused pregnant heifers to abort by inoculating them with cultures of *Brucella abortus* isolated from man. Carpenter and Boak isolated *Brucella abortus* from a human fetus, thus confirming an earlier suggestion of de Forest who had observed a rare relationship between abortion in women and cattle.

The first bacteriologically proved case of human infection with *Brucella abortus* in man was reported by Keefer in 1924. This confirmed the suggestion made by Evans, on the basis of a serological study of human sera that cattle might be a source of Malta fever in this country. Additional confirmatory evidence was provided by Carpenter, and others in this country and abroad, who isolated the *abortus* organism from the blood, tonsils, feces and lesions of numerous patients.

The results of many investigations have shown that *Brucella abortus*, causing a widespread disease of cattle in this and other countries, is shed by the infected cow in the milk and that raw milk is undoubtedly a source of the infection in man.

The infectious abortion of swine is caused by a variety of *Brucella abortus* which is pathogenic for both man and cattle. In Iowa and in districts where the raising of hogs is an industry, this animal is an important source of human infections. This porcine organism, called by some *Brucella suis*, is more pathogenic for man than the bovine variety.

In addition to these three chief types or species of *Brucella* there is a multiplicity of types and sub-types.

The *incidence of the undulant fever* of man in the United States is probably greater than the official statistics indicate, as there are no doubt numerous unrecognized and unreported cases. Hasseltine collected reports of 1305 cases for the year 1929 and 1385 cases for the year 1930. He estimated that in 1930 the incidence rate of the disease in this country was 2 per 100,000, or about one-tenth that of typhoid fever. Routine agglutination tests of blood serum sent to laboratories for any purpose indicate that the incidence of the infection may be approximately 0.8 to 1.7 per cent among persons who for one reason or another seek medical advice. The statistics of agglutination tests differ in different sections of the country, as the exposure to and incidence of the infection is not evenly distributed. A positive reaction in a 1:80 or higher dilution of the patient's serum is strong evidence of past or existing infection with an organism of this group.

The age group and sex incidences show the peculiarities that more males are infected than females, that children under ten years of age are relatively exempt, and that the greatest number of patients are in the age group twenty to forty years.

True Malta fever, due to the caprine variety *Brucella melitensis*, is less common in this country than undulant fever due to *Brucella abortus*. It occurs in goat-raising districts, where goats' milk is consumed, chiefly in some of the southwestern states.

Hasseltine has divided cases of undulant fever into three groups according to the chief sources of infection, as follows:

1. The milk group: composed chiefly of professional and business persons, students, and those not directly exposed to contact infection who contract the disease by drinking raw milk.

2. The meat group: composed of packing house employees, butchers, and others who handle infected meat.

3. The farm group: composed of veterinarians and farmers who are directly in contact with infected cattle and swine. These are exposed also to infection through milk.

Clinical Features of Undulant Fever.—The fever is characterized by irregular and sometimes prolonged febrile periods with intervening periods of normal temperature. Undulant fever is at times septicemic. Blood cultures, therefore, should be made with a view to isolating *Brucella abortus* or *Brucella melitensis*. According to Amoss a blood culture should be incubated for at least eighteen days before it is discarded as negative. The organism localizes in the body producing focal necrotic and granulomatous lesions. From these sites it can be isolated sometimes by direct culture, but usually by the use of a "passage" guinea-pig into which the material is injected and from which after death the organism can be cultivated from the blood, spleen, lymph nodes, or liver. Occasionally the organism localizes in the appendix or intestine. In these cases it can be recovered from the feces by the use of the modification of Eyre's method described by Amoss and Poston. This method consists of adding an anti-abortus agglutinating serum to a suspension of the bacteria obtained from a sample of feces. By gentle centrifugation the clumps of abortus bacilli are sedimented before the unagglutinated bacteria can be removed in a mass from the bottom of the tube for plate cultures and inoculation of animals.

Additional aids to diagnosis in man are skin tests with *brucellin* and Huddleson's phagocytosis test. A positive skin test is indicative of acute or chronic infection, or a past infection. The phagocytosis test is apt to be positive in immune states; negative when active infection exists. Both the skin test and phagocytosis test are negative in normal individuals.

Description of Organisms and Differential Characteristics.—The general characteristics of all the *Brucella* organisms are:

Small cocco-bacillary forms, 0.5 μ wide by 0.5 μ to 2 μ long. They are gram-negative, nonmotile, and do not form endospores.

They stain readily with the analine dyes and are not acid-fast.

They are aerobic, micro-aerobic, and some varieties (the *abortus* types) grow best in an atmosphere of 10 per cent CO_2.

They do not produce indole, do not liquefy gelatin, and do not cause gross fermentation of carbohydrates. They produce no change in the reaction of milk or render it alkaline. The colonies are round, hemispherical, usually smooth and opaque, whitish or dull cream colored. The growth is somewhat tenacious. In broth culture they form a viscous sediment. On potato, these organisms develop a yellowish brown color. The optimum temperature for growth is 37° C. and the optimum reaction of the medium is pH 7.2 to 7.4.

All the organisms of this group are killed by heat at 60° C. in 10 to 15 minutes.

Utilization of glucose by *Brucella melitensis* was shown to occur by McAlpine and Slanetz by chemical analysis of the cultures. *Brucella abortus*, porcine type, has the same capacity to utilize glucose, while the bovine type is unable to do so. Huddleson has confirmed these findings.

In a medium containing organic sulphur, *Brucella abortus*, particularly *Brucella suis*, the porcine variety, liberates detectable H_2S while *Brucella melitensis* does not.

CO_2 Requirement.—Five to 10 per cent CO_2 in the atmosphere of a culture of *Brucella abortus* is in some cases essential and in all cases favorable for growth of this variety of the organism. *Brucella melitensis* does not require CO_2, and may be inhibited by concentrations of 5 to 10 per cent of this gas.

Selective Action of Dyes.—Huddleson found that thionin, 1 : 25,000, inhibited the growth of *Brucella abortus*, but did not inhibit *Brucella melitensis* or the porcine *abortus* strain. Methyl violet or basic fuchsin, 1 : 30,000, inhibited the growth of the porcine strain, but only slightly reduced the growth of *Brucella melitensis* and *Brucella abortus* (bovine). Pyronin, 1: 100,000, inhibited the growth of the porcine strains but did not interfere with the growth of the bovine strain and permitted only slight growth of *Brucella melitensis*.

These differential points may be summarized as follows:

TABLE I

DIFFERENTIATION OF THE SPECIES OF THE GENUS *Brucella*

| | REQUIRE-MENT FOR CO_2 | PRODUCTION OF H_2S DAYS | | | | UTILIZA-TION OF GLUCOSE | GROWTH INHIBITED † | |
		1	2	3	4		Thionin	Methyl Violet, Basic Fuchsin or Pyronin
Brucella melitensis	—	—	—	—	—	+	—	—
Brucella abortus	+ *	3 +	2 +	1 +	1 +	±	+	—
Brucella suis	—	4 +	4 +	4 +	4 +	+	—	+

* Laboratory strains that have become aerobic do not require CO_2 for isolation from inoculated animals.
† Specified dilutions of dyes should be used to obtain differentiation.

Pathogenicity.—The pathogenicity of the caprine, bovine, and porcine strains is different for monkeys, guinea pigs and for man and other animals. Theobald Smith observed that the lesions produced in guinea-pigs by the caprine and porcine strains were distinctly different from those due to the bovine strain.

Serological Differentiation.—Since the earlier work of Evans and Meyer, the opinion has been held that distinctions could be made between the *melitensis* and *abortus* types on the basis of agglutination and agglutinin absorption with specific antiserums. The reinvestigation of this subject in 1931 by Francis, however, led him to conclude that the facts did not support this contention.

Wilson attributes the remaining confusion in antigenic analysis to the failure to recognize that differentiation can be satisfactorily accomplished only with strains in the completely smooth state. The use of the absorption of agglutinins test in its original form does not provide a distinction between the three chief members of the *Brucella* group—*Br. melitensis, Br. abortus* and *Br. suis*. Each organism, in sufficient dosage, is able to absorb the agglutinins completely from a serum prepared against either of the other organisms. If, however, a small absorbing dose is used, and is adjusted to the titer of the serum to be absorbed, it is possible to distinguish between *Br. melitensis* on the one hand, and *Br. abortus* and *Br. suis* on the other. It is probable that the organisms contain qualitatively the same antigens though distributed in different proportions. *Br. melitensis* contains a small amount of A antigen and a large amount of M antigen. In *Br. abortus* and *Br. suis* there is a large amount of A and a small amount of M.

Prozones in agglutinin tests with these organisms are commonly encountered. Cross-agglutination reactions occur with *Bacterium tularense* and *anti-abortus* serum.

Products of Growth and Hypersensitivity.—The filtrates of cultures do not contain an exotoxin. The bacterial substances in these filtrates and the bodies of the organisms are capable of eliciting reactions of hypersensitiveness in man and animals. These products, known as "*abortin,*" are used for diagnostic purposes since they give rise on intradermal or subcutaneous injection to local and general allergic reactions. Severe reactions may occur.

Immunity.—It is the general belief that one attack of Malta fever or undulant fever protects against a second attack. It is difficult, however, to be certain that the first attack is cured. There are a great many cases, notably the cases of those investigators who have contracted the disease in the course of their work, in which the fever recurs several times in the same individual in the form of relapses and recrudescences. The intermissions between such attacks often last for months.

Prophylactic vaccination in man has not demonstrated its usefulness; nor has it been carried out on a sufficiently large scale to permit the formulation of conclusions.

Vaccination of cattle with living or dead cultures has been used extensively (Smith and Little). The practice of using live organisms as a vaccine has been largely abandoned because it spread the infection. Vaccination with killed cultures has not given results that can be readily interpreted.

Infected animals and human beings develop *agglutinins* against these organisms, often in high titer. Hence, agglutination reactions are useful for *serological diagnosis.* Experience has indicated that a titer of 1 to 80 is suggestive and that a titer of 1 to 100 or above is good presumptive evidence of infection with *Brucella abortus*. A continuation of the discussion of the diagnostic agglutination test will be found in the following chapter on Tularemia.

Treatment.—Many attempts have been made to treat undulant fever or Malta fever with specific antiserum or vaccines. Our impression is that these methods are not therapeutically effective.

Leavell, Poston, and Amoss, taking advantage of the knowledge of the bacteriostatic action of dyes, administered thionin and methyl violet by mouth to patients with intestinal brucellosis. Favorable results were reported by them.

Excellent therapeutic results have been reported for the use of sulfanilamide in the treatment of brucellosis, particularly in the usual type of undulant fever in man.

Control of Undulant Fever.—The measures which should be used to control and decrease Malta fever, and undulant fever, or the group of diseases which may properly be called brucellosis are indicated by the facts relating to the sources of infection and modes of transmission. As the disease rarely, if ever, is transmitted from an infected individual to another human being, the control measures are directed chiefly toward eradication of the disease among domesticated animals, chiefly goats, cattle and swine, and the killing of the *Brucella* organisms in meat and milk handled or consumed by man. Without attempting to list the detailed procedures of this enormous task, we may briefly summarize these measures as follows:

1. Eradication of the disease in herds of goats, cattle and swine. This is a large, difficult, expensive, and uncertain method.

2. Avoidance of contact with infected animals. In practice this contact cannot be avoided by farmers, veterinarians and meat handlers, but its risks can be diminished.

3. Pasteurization of milk.

4. Disinfection or safe disposal of urine and feces of patients.

Since 1921, the papers and monographs published on undulant fever and infectious abortion have been numerous and voluminous. Undoubtedly this literature will grow, as there are many problems yet to be solved. The disease is world wide in distribution. We may be witnessing the transference on a large scale of a disease of animals to man. Charles Nicolle has prophesied that undulant fever is apt to become one of the most frequent and stubborn of maladies. In his opinion it is a "disease of the future."

BACILLUS BRONCHISEPTICUS

A bacterium related in some respects to the *Brucella* group is an organism generally known as *Bacillus bronchisepticus*. In 1913, Theobald Smith pointed out the similarity between *Bacillus bronchisepticus* and *Bacillus abortus*. *Bacillus bronchisepticus* is antigenically related to *B. pertussis* and has been found associated with infections of the respiratory tract in guinea-pigs, dogs, and man. Once thought to be the cause of canine distemper, it is now regarded as only a frequent secondary invader since that disease has been proved to be due to a filtrable virus. It is capable of causing pneumonia and like *B. pertussis* and *B. abortus* elicits a monocytic type of cellular response.

Bacillus bronchisepticus (Brucella bronchiseptica) was first isolated and described by Ferry and, independently, by McGowan, in 1910–1911. Its characteristics were studied thoroughly by Torrey and Rahe in 1912. The organism is a short, gram-negative bacterium, occasionally coccoid, and *slowly motile*. It does not form endospores. It is an aerobe and does not require CO_2 for its growth. When first isolated it grows slowly, the colonies being hardly visible on agar in twenty-four hours but definitely visible in forty-eight hours. It grows well on glycerin agar. The optimum temperature for growth is 37° C., but growth occurs at 20° C. It produces a uniform turbidity in broth and no pellicle. No acid or gas is formed on carbohydrate media, but alkali is produced. Milk is rendered definitely alkaline. Indole is not formed. On potato, the growth has a yellowish brown color. The organism produces a hemolysin. The relations of this motile member of the *Alcaligenes* group to the organisms of undulant fever and infectious abortion, and to *B. pertussis* have not been completely worked out. It occurs to us, from a review of the facts, that the assignment of *B. pertussis* to the *Hemophilus* genus may be incorrect and that its natural position is among the *Brucella* organisms.

B. caviae septicus, the cause of guinea-pig pneumonia, isolated by Theobald Smith in 1914, is regarded by him as being identical with *B. bronchisepticus*.

REFERENCES

Amoss, H. A., and Poston, M. A. J. Am. M. Ass., 1930, 95:482.
Bayne-Jones, S. Am. J. Pub. Health, 1930, 20:1313.
Bruce, D. Practitioner, London, 1887, 39:161, 1888, 40:241.
—— Ann. de l'Inst. Pasteur, 1893, 7:289.
Bruce, D., Eyre, *et al.* Mediterranean Fever Commission Report, London, 1905–1907. Quoted from Duncan, J. T., *et al.*, A System of Bacteriology in Relation to Medicine, London, 1930, 5:386.
Burnet, E. Bull. de l'Inst. Pasteur, 1925, 23:369, 417.
Carpenter, C. M. J. Infect. Dis., 1926, 39:220.
—— J. Am. Vet. M. Ass., 1927, 70:459.
—— J. Am. M. Ass., 1931, 96:1212; 1932, 99:296.
Carpenter, C. M., and Boak, R. A. Am. J. M. Sc., 1933, 185:97.
de Forest, H. P. Am. J. Obst. 1917, 76:No. 2.
Evans, A. C. J. Infect. Dis., 1918, 22:576, 580.
—— Nomenclature of the Melitensis—Abortus Group, etc., U. S. Pub. Health Rep., 1923, p. 3.
—— U. S. Public Health Rep., 1923, 28:23; 1923, 28:825; 1924, 29:501.
—— J. Am. M. Ass., 1927, 88:630.
—— and Baumgartner, L. U. S. Pub. Health Rep., 1938, 53:1507.
Eyre, J. W. H. Lancet, 1908, 1:1747.
Ferry. J. Infect. Dis., 1911, 8:399.
Francis, E. U. S. Pub. Health Rep., 1931, 46:2416.
Gould, S. E., and Huddleson, G. F. J. Am. M. Ass., 1937, 109:1971.
Hardy, A. V. J. Am. M. Ass., 1929, 93:891. See also: Symposium on Undulant Fever, Am. J. Pub. Health, 1931, 21:491–525.
Hasseltine, H. E. U. S. Pub. Health Rep., 1931, 46:1519.
—— Am. J. Pub. Health, 1931, 21:519.
Huddleson, I. F. Am. J. Pub. Health, 1931, 21:491.
Huddleson, I. F. Brucella Infections in Animals and Man. Commonwealth Fund. New York, 1934.
Huddleson, I. F., Halsey, and Torrey. J. Infect. Dis., 1927, 40:352.
Huddleson, I. F., and Johnson, H. W. J. Am. M. Ass., 1930, 94:1905. See also: Burnet, E., Arch. d. l'Inst. Pasteur de l'Afrique du Nord, 1922, p. 187, cited by Huddleson.
Keefer, C. S. Bull. Johns Hopkins Hosp., 1924, 35:6.
Leavell, H. R., Poston, M. A., and Amoss, H. J. Am. M. Ass., 1930, 95:860.
McAlpine, F. G., and Slanetz, C. A. J. Infect. Dis., 1928, 42:73.
McGowan. J. Path. & Bacteriol., 1911, 15:372; 1916, 20:257.
Meyer, K. F., and Feusier, M. L. J. Infect. Dis., 1920, 27:185.
Meyer, K. F., and Shaw, E. B. J. Infect. Dis., 1920, 27:173.

Otero, P. M.   Puerto Rico J. Pub. Health & Trop. Med., 1929, 5:144.
—— J. Infect. Dis., 1933, 52:54.
—— and Gonzalez, L. M.   Proc. Soc. Exper. Biol. and M., 1939, 40:10.
Schoenholz, P., and Meyer, K. F.   J. Infect. Dis., 1927, 40:453.
Smith, T.   J. Exper. M., 1926, 43:207.
—— J. Med. Research, 1914, 29:291.
Smith, T., and Little, R. B.   Monogr. Rockefeller Inst. for Med. Research, No. 19, 1923.
Torrey and Rahe.   J. Med. Research, 1912, 27:291.

CHAPTER XLII

BACTERIUM TULARENSE AND TULAREMIA [1]

TULAREMIA

Tularemia is an infectious disease caused by *Bacterium tularense*. *Primarily* it occurs in nature as a fatal septicemia of wild rodents, especially rabbits and hares. In these animals, the lesions are chiefly focal, necrotic areas or nodules in the liver, spleen, lungs, bone marrow, and other organs, giving the gross appearance shown in Figure 53. *Secondarily* tularemia is a disease of man, transmitted to man by the bite of an infected, blood-sucking fly or tick, or by contamination of the hands or conjunctival sac with the internal organs or body fluids of infected rodents, flies or ticks. Accidental laboratory infections have occurred in investigators of the disease.

The disease in rodents was first recognized by McCoy in 1911 as a "plague-like disease" of ground squirrels (*Citellus beecheyi*) in California. McCoy and Chapin in 1912, after failures with the use of ordinary media, succeeded in cultivating the

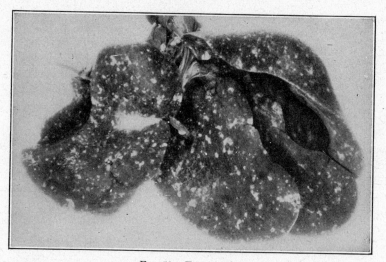

FIG. 53.—TULAREMIA.

Liver of rabbit showing focal lesions. (Army Medical Museum. Courtesy of Edward Francis, U.S.P.H.S.)

organism on a medium composed largely of egg yolk. They reproduced the disease with pure cultures of this organism, which they named *Bacterium tularense* after Tulare County, California, where the infected animals were found. The peculiar growth requirements of the organism, noticed from the beginning, have shown that *Bacterium tularense* is different from plague bacilli and organisms of the hemorrhagic septicemia

[1] We are indebted to Edward Francis for much of the material and for the illustrations used in the preparation of this chapter.

ment of this bacterium (
these phases of growth a
organism but also are
Rickettsiae.

The disease has a *sea.*
flies (June to September
the game laws, the open

The average *incubati*
Clinical Features of
have been recorded:

Ulceroglandular Typ
and is accompanied by
pulmonary and meninge:

Oculoglandular Type
by enlargement of the re

Glandular Type.—Th
is enlargement of the re

Typhoid Type.—Ther

Ingestion Type.—Co
fected animal.

In addition, a fatal
and MacLachlan and Tu

A few cases run the
of the patient to bed.

Isolation.—The only
from the blood and lesi
rabbit or white mouse. I
the patient, is injected
animals should die with
spleen, lymph nodes, an
glucose cystine agar. (S

In rare instances the
week of the disease. Wh
quantity of physiologica
rabbit.

The organism has be
this is not as dependabl
In the words of Francis
cultures taken directly fr

The morphological a
organism is a small, pled
it exists in a coccoid f
dominant but coccoid for

group. It was finally determined by Francis in 1922 that cystine is an essential ingredient for the growth of this organism on media.

With the insight afforded by modern investigations, cases can be recognized by the descriptions in the older clinical literature. Francis, in 1925, reported that in 1907, Martin, an ophthalmologist in Arizona, called attention by correspondence to 5 cases which he had seen. Pearse, in 1911, described 6 cases of the disease in Utah, where it was known as "deer-fly fever." The first case in man, proved bacteriologically to be due to *Bacterium tularense,* was reported in 1914 by Vail and by Wherry and Lamb. Francis, who took up the investigation in 1919, named the disease "tularaemia." Independently of these workers, Ohara, in Japan in 1925, described the clinical characteristics of the disease and correctly noted the source and mode of transmission by contact with tissue of infected wild rabbits.

Since 1924, clinicians and bacteriologists, made aware of the existence of tularemia by the publications of Francis, have recognized increasing numbers of cases in man in this country. This is clearly shown by the table on page 576 reported by Francis.

It is obvious that a disease of this nature, somewhat difficult to recognize and occurring in large rural areas as well as in cities, providing upwards of 1000 reported cases a year with a mortality of about 5 per cent, presents a serious public health problem in this country.

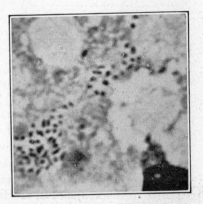

Fig. 54.—Bacterium Tularense in Smear from Bone Marrow of Black-tailed Jack-rabbit Dead on Fifth Day. Army Medical Museum. Courtesy of Edward Francis, U.S.P.H.S. × 2280.

Distribution.—In the United States, cases of tularemia in man have been reported from 46 states and from the District of Columbia. In most of the states the infection had been transmitted from diseased animals in the locality. In a few, the infection was contracted only from dressing wild rabbits shipped into markets from other states. The disease was recognized in Japan in 1925 by Ohara, in Russia in 1928, in Norway in 1929 by Thjötta, in Canada in 1930, and by Granström in Sweden in 1931, and in Austria in 1935.

The following animals have been found to be naturally infected with *Bacterium tularense:* ground squirrels in California and Utah; *wild rabbits and hares,* widespread in the United States; wild rats of Los Angeles; wild mice of California; quail and grouse in Minnesota; sheep in Idaho; wild rabbits in Japan, Norway and Canada; water rats in Russia; sage hens and grouse; wood ticks in California, Montana and Minnesota. Many other animals are known to be susceptible to infection, in varying degrees. Domesticated rabbits kept under domestic conditions have not been found to be naturally infected.

Degrees of susceptibility are noted as follows: (1) High susceptibility in man, monkey, ground squirrels, rabbits, guinea-pigs, mice, woodchucks, opossums, young coyotes, pocket gopher, porcupine and chipmunk. (2) Slight susceptibility in rats, cats, sheep and goats. (3) Nonsusceptibility in horse, cattle, hog, dog, fox, chicken and pigeon.

* The total p
at first glance ap
to 1924 and from

Transmis

human cases.
rabbits, skinn
these tissues (
material into
luck charms h
in fact, nearl
experimental
unbroken skir
may have led
highly infecti

The inges
infection of m

Contagion
a case of tula

The diseas
(ticks, flies, li
The transmiss
discalis (Fran
(Parker, Sper
onstrated that
tick, *Dermace*
nymph, and o
minute form.
epithelial cells
The intracellu
is of the great

2 E. Francis

(1) That, on account of the frequent cross agglutination between *tularense*, on the one hand, and *abortus* and *melitensis*, on the other, serums from suspected cases of tularemia and undulant fever should be tested for agglutination of *tularense* and either *abortus* or *melitensis*, unless the clinical history points definitely to a recognized source of infection for tularemia or undulant fever.

(2) That a serum which shows a marked difference in titer for *tularense*, on the one hand, and for *abortus* or *melitensis*, on the other, can usually be classed by the higher titer as due either to tularemia or to one of the varieties of *Brucella melitensis*.

(3) That a serum which agglutinates all three organisms to the same or nearly the same titer should be subjected to agglutinin absorption tests.[3]

Detailed instructions and materials for the performance of the agglutination test in tularemia can be obtained from the National Institute of Health, Washington, D. C.

Immunity.—Susceptible laboratory animals (guinea-pigs, rabbits and white mice) have not exhibited evidence of immunity to virulent infection, according to Francis in *Medicine*. It is not clear from published reports that the vaccines and antisera have been found either effective or of no value.

One attack of tularemia confers immunity in man. No instance of a second attack has been recorded and the long persistence of agglutinins in the blood of recovered patients may be an indication of their immunity. It has been suggested, but not proved, that this may be a superinfection type of resistance as the actual date of termination of an infection has not been definitely established. We have been informed by one investigator [4] of tularemia who contracted the disease in 1919 in the first month of his experiments, that he has had repeated subsequent local infections, each being at the site of a cut or crack on a finger into which infected animal tissue found entrance. A papular lesion forms, and virulent organisms can be recovered from the lesion by guinea-pig inoculation of blood from the incised papule. The regional epitrochlear lymph nodes become slightly enlarged and the overlying skin becomes flushed. But there is no spread of the infection nor any systemic symptoms. The local lesion then heals rapidly. He regards this process as similar to the reaction of immunity in smallpox vaccination.

There is no specific therapy for the disease. Foshay's antiserum has not been proved to be effective, although good results were obtained from its use in certain cases.

Systematic Position of Bact. Tularense.—Bergey, in his *Manual of Determinative Bacteriology*, 1939, has listed this organism under the name *Pasteurella tularensis*, classifying it with *B. pestis* and organisms of the hemorrhagic septicemia group. McCoy, Francis and others who have studied *Bact. tularense* have expressed the opinion that this is an unnatural assignment. The organism differs from *B. pestis* in its growth requirements, cultural characteristics, and also antigenically. Antigenically and in minor respects it resembles organisms in the *Brucella* group, perhaps being most closely related to *Brucella abortus*. On the whole, however, *Bact. tularense* differs in so many characteristics from plague bacilli on the one hand and from the abortus-undulant fever organisms on the other that it seems best to place it in a semi-independent position in recognition of its unique properties. This is undoubtedly the wiser course to follow until the many obscure relationships among bacteria have been more fully explored.

3 E. Francis and A. Evans, *U. S. Pub. Health Rep.*, 1926, 41:1273.
4 Francis, personal communication.

REFERENCES

CRAWFORD, M. J. Am. M. Ass., 1932, 99:1497.

FOSHAY, L. Am. J. M. Sci., 1934, 187:235.

———— Ohio State M. J., 1935, 31:21.

———— J. Am. M. Ass., 1937, 109:504. Report of Council on Pharm. and Chem.

FRANCIS, E. Medicine, 1928, 7:411.

———— U. S. Pub. Health Rep., 1921, 36:1731; 1923, 38:1396; 1927, 42:2763; 1932, 47:1287; 1933, 48:1127.

———— Proc. 4th Internat. Congress of Entomology, 1928, 2:929.

———— U. S. Hyg. Lab. Bull., 1922, No. 130.

———— J. Am. M. Ass., 1925, 84:1243; 1928, 91:1155.

———— De Lamar Lectures, Johns Hopkins University, Baltimore, 1927.

———— In Cecil's Textbook of Medicine, 1937, 4th ed., p. 350.

FRANCIS, E., and EVANS, A. U. S. Pub. Health Rep., 1926, 41:1273.

FRANCIS, E., LILLIE, R. D., and PARKER, R. R. The Pathology of Tularaemia. Bull. No. 167, National Institute of Health, Washington, D. C., 1937.

FRANCIS, E., and MAYNE, B. U. S. Pub. Health Rep., 1921, 36:1738.

FRANCIS, E., and MOORE, D. J. Am. M. Ass., 1926, 86:1329.

FREESE, H. L. U. S. Pub. Health Rep., 1926, 41:369.

GRANSTRÖM, K. O. Acta Ophth., 1932, 10.

LEDINGHAM, J. C. G., and FRASER, F. R. Quart. J. Med., 1924, 17:365.

MARTIN, A. Southwest. Med., 1925, 9:232.

McCOY, G. W. U. S. Pub. Health Bull., 1911, No. 43.

McCOY, G. W., and CHAPIN, C. W. J. Infect. Dis., 1912, 10:61.

OHARA, H. Jikken Iho (Japan), 1925.

———— Kinsei Igaku, 1925, 12.

PARKER, R. R., and SPENCER, R. R. U. S. Pub. Health Rep., 1926, 41:1341, 1403.

PARKER, R. R., SPENCER, R. R., and FRANCIS, E. U. S. Pub. Health Rep., 1924, 39:1057.

PEARSE, R. A. Northwest. Med., 1911.

PERMAR, H. A., and MacLACHLAN, A. W. G. Ann. Int. Med., 1931, 5:673.

THJÖTTA, T. J. Infect. Dis., 1931, 49:99.

TUREEN, L. L. J. Am. M. Ass., 1932, 99:1501.

VAIL, D. T. Ophth. Rec., 1914, 23:487.

WHERRY, W. B., and LAMB, B. H. J. Infect. Dis., 1914, 15:331.

CHAPTER XLIII

PLAGUE AND BACILLUS PESTIS

Family: *Parvobacteriaceae.* Tribe: *Pasteurelleae.* Genus: *Pasteurella.* Species: *Pasteurella pestis.*
Syn: *Bacillus pestis*

PLAGUE

The history of epidemic diseases has no more terrifying chapter than that of plague (Hirsch). Sweeping, time and again, over large areas of the civilized world, its scope and mortality were often so great that all forms of human activity were temporarily paralyzed. In the reign of Justinian almost 50 per cent of the entire population of the Roman Empire perished from the disease. The "black death" which swept over Europe during the fourteenth century killed about twenty-five million people. Smaller epidemics, appearing in numerous parts of the world during the sixteenth, seventeenth and eighteenth centuries, have claimed innumerable victims. In 1893 plague appeared in Hongkong. During the epidemic which followed, *Bacillus pestis,* now recognized as the etiological factor of the disease, was discovered by Kitasato and Yersin, independently of each other. By both observers the bacillus could invariably be found in the pus from the buboes of afflicted persons. It could be demonstrated in enormous numbers in the cadavers of victims. This evidence was strengthened, by accidental infections, which occurred in Vienna in 1898, with laboratory cultures.

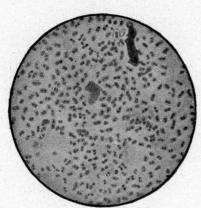

FIG. 57.—BACILLUS PESTIS.
(After Mallory and Wright.)

Morphology and Staining.—*Bacillus pestis* is a short, thick bacillus with well-rounded ends. Its length is barely two or two and a half times its breadth (1.5 to 1.75 μ by 0.5 to 0.7 μ). The bacilli appear singly, in pairs, or, more rarely, in short chains of three or more. They show distinct polar staining. In size and shape these bacilli are subject to a great degree of variation. In old lesions or in old cultures the bacilli show involution forms which may appear either as swollen coccoid forms or as longer, club-shaped, diphtheroid bacilli. Degenerating individuals appear often as swollen, oval vacuoles. All these forms, by their very irregularity, are of diagnostic importance. They appear more numerous in artificial cultures than in human lesions. A very important property of the plague bacillus is the formation within twenty-four to forty-eight hours of vacuolated and swollen forms upon salt agar, that is, agar to which 3 per cent of salt is added. Such a medium is of value in diagnostic work.

According to Albrecht and Ghon, the plague bacillus may be shown to possess a capsule. It does not possess flagella and does not form spores.

The plague bacillus is easily stained with all the usual aniline dyes. Diluted aqueous fuchsin and methylene blue are most frequently employed. With these stains the characteristically deeper staining of the polar portions of the bacillus is usually easy to demonstrate. Special polar stains have been devised by various observers. Most of these depend upon avoidance of the usual heat fixation of the preparations, which, in some way, seems to interfere with good polar staining. Fixation of the dried smears with absolute alcohol is, therefore, preferable. The bacillus is gram-negative.

Isolation and Cultivation.—The bacillus is easily isolated in pure culture from the specific lesions. Smears from buboes and other plague lesions will often show the typical bacilli in very small numbers only, possibly because of the ease with

which they undergo degeneration. The bacillus grows readily and luxuriantly upon the meat-infusion media. The optimum temperature for its cultivation is about 30° C. Below 20° C. and above 38° C., growth is sparse and delayed, though it is not entirely inhibited until exposed to temperatures below 12° C., or above 40° C. The most favorable reaction of culture media is neutrality or moderate alkalinity, though slight acidity does not prevent development.

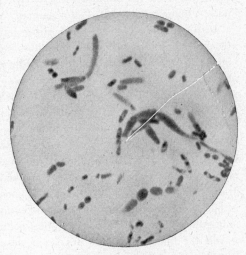

On *agar,* growth appears within four hours as minute colonies with a compact small center surrounded by a broad, irregularly indented, granular margin.

On *gelatin,* similar colonies appear after two or three days at 4° to 22° C. The gelatin is not liquefied.

FIG. 58.—BACILLUS PESTIS, INVOLUTION FORMS.
(After Zettnow.)

In *bouillon,* the plague bacilli grow slowly. They usually sink to the bottom or adhere to the walls of the tube as a granular deposit and may occasionally form a delicate pellicle. Chain formation is not uncommon. In broth cultures a peculiar stalactite-like growth is often seen, when the culture fluid is covered with a layer of oil and the flasks are incubated in a place where shaking or vibration can be prevented. Delicate threads of growth hang down from the surface of the medium into its depths.

Characteristic involution forms are brought out best when the bacilli are grown upon agar containing 3 per cent sodium chloride.

Milk is not coagulated. In litmus milk there is slight acid formation. On *potato* and on *blood serum* the growth shows nothing characteristic or of differential value. On *peptone media* no indole is formed.

Fermentation Reactions.—*B. pestis* produces acid without gas from glucose levulose, maltose, galactose and mannite. The organism does not ferment lactose, saccharose, dulcite, raffinose or inulin.

Biological Considerations.—*B. pestis* is aerobic. Absence of free oxygen is said to prevent its growth, at least under certain conditions of artificial cultivation. It is nonmotile. Outside of the animal body the bacilli may retain viability for months and even years if preserved in the dark and in a moist environment. In cadavers they may live for weeks and months if protected from dryness. In pus or sputum from patients they may live eight to fourteen days.

Complete drying in the air kills the bacilli within two or three days. Thoroughly dried by artificial means, they die within four or five hours.

Plague bacilli suspended in broth or saline are killed by heat at 50° C. in one hour, although exceptions have been reported. Heat at 80° C. kills organisms in thirty minutes.

Dry heat at 100° C. kills the bacillus in one hour. Live steam or boiling water is effectual in a few minutes. The bacilli possess great resistance against cold, surviving a temperature of 0° C. for as many as forty days.

Direct sunlight destroys them within four or five hours. The common disinfectants are effectual in the following strengths: carbolic acid, 1 per cent kills them in two hours, 5 per cent in ten minutes; bichloride of mercury 1:1000 is effectual in ten minutes.

Wilson reported that plague cultures which he had kept sealed for as long as ten years in the ice chest were found living and virulent at the end of this time.

In regard to the viability of plague bacilli in air at different atmospheric temperatures and conditions of humidity, there are many important sanitary problems involved which are of particular significance in connection with the spread of pneumonic plague. Teague and Barber worked on this subject in connection with the Manchurian epidemic of pneumonic plague, and found that plague bacilli contained in fine droplets of pneumonic plague sputum would die from drying in a few minutes unless they were suspended in an atmosphere with a very small water deficit; in other words, the humidity or the degree of saturation of the atmosphere with water is a very important factor in determining the length of time for which plague bacilli will remain alive in such droplet-spray. Such atmospheres under ordinary circumstances are common in cold climates and droplets of sputum will, therefore, remain infectious longer in cold, wet climates than in warm ones.

Animal Pathogenicity.—*B. pestis* is extremely pathogenic for rats, mice, guinea-pigs, rabbits and monkeys. The most susceptible of these animals are rats and guinea-pigs, in whom mere rubbing of plague bacilli into the unbroken skin will often produce the disease. This method of experimental infection of guinea-pigs is of great service in isolating the plague bacillus from material contaminated with other micro-organisms. For the same purpose, infection of rats subcutaneously at the root of the tail may be employed. Such inoculation in rats is usually fatal.

McCoy noted the surprising fact that, in San Francisco a considerable percentage of wild rats—especially old ones—showed a high degree of natural immunity to plague.

The careful studies of McCoy of the U. S. Public Health Service upon guinea-pigs and white rats show that individual plague cultures may vary considerably in virulence. The size of the dose, always excepting enormous quantities such as a whole agar culture, seems to make little difference in the speed with which the animals die. There may be considerable variation in the susceptibility of individual animals. Prolonged cultivation on artificial media may gradually reduce the virulence of plague bacilli.

In rats, spontaneous infection with plague is common and plays an important rôle in the spread of the disease. The pneumonic type of the disease is common in these animals and has been produced in them by inhalation experiments. During every well-observed plague epidemic, marked mortality among the domestic rats has been noticed.

Although it was formerly supposed that rat infection took place because of the gnawing of dead cadavers by other rats, the work of the British Indian Plague Commission has shown that rats, like man, are infected by means of fleas which pass from the infected to the uninfected animal.

In his work in California McCoy showed that the weasel and chipmunk are susceptible to plague infection, and, therefore, potential means of spread if once infected.

Toxin Formation.—The systemic symptoms of plague are largely due to the absorption of poisonous products of the bacteria. Albrecht and Ghon, Wernicke, and others were unable to obtain any toxic action with broth-culture filtrates and concluded that the poisons of *B. pestis* were chiefly endotoxins. The prevailing opinion is that the organism does not form an exotoxin. Hemolysin is not produced.

Immunization.—A single attack of plague usually protects human beings from reinfection. A second attack in the same individual is extremely rare. Immunization in animals produces specific agglutinating and bacteriolytic substances which are of great importance in the bacteriological diagnosis of the bacillus. The agglutinating action of the serum of patients is clinically important in the diagnosis of the disease, even in dilutions of 1 : 10, since undiluted normal human serum has no agglutinating effect upon plague bacilli.

The curative plague serum prepared by Yersin and others by the immunization of horses with plague cultures has been extensively used in practice. The sera are standardized by their protective power as measured in white rats. Therapeutic studies under the British Plague Commission were disappointing. Antiplague sera, either antibacterial or antitoxic, do not have any beneficial effect.

Antigenic analysis has been made by Schütze who described a somatic antigen of the O type and an ectoplasmic antigen of the H type.

The question of prophylactic vaccination and active immunization will be taken up in connection with plague prevention below.

Disease in Man.—There are two chief methods by which the disease is acquired by man. The first is by entrance of the bacilli through the skin as a consequence of the bite of an infected flea. During the act of biting, the flea may either regurgitate blood, or, as is usually the case, deposit feces on the skin. The infection may take place through the lesion caused by the fleabite, but more likely is rubbed in by the clothing or by scratching.

The other method by which plague is transmitted to man is by direct inhalation of sputum spray, a mode of infection which causes pneumonic plague. According to Castellani and Chalmers and others, about 2.5 per cent of the cases occurring during epidemics of bubonic plague are of the pneumonic variety, and there may be special epidemics of pneumonic plague like the one studied by Strong, Teague and others in Manchuria.

The incubation time of the disease is usually less than ten days, and may be no longer than two or three. The organisms entering through the skin may cause a localized lesion at the point of entrance. This may be of negligible size or may show a considerable inflammatory reaction. The organisms enter the lymphatics and cause the so-called bubo. The primary buboes are situated in the glands into which the infected area drains. The most common seat for these lesions is in the glands of the groin, but they also may be first seen in the axillary, cervical or other glands. Secondary buboes may arise in other parts of the body. The organisms rapidly enter the blood stream, causing septicemia.

The onset is usually sudden, with high fever and the general symptoms of a severe toxemia. Castellani states the bacilli can be found in blood cultures in about 30 per cent of the cases.

The disease may take a considerable number of forms which depend very largely upon the virulence of the organisms. It may be relatively mild, or may take an acute septicemic form which is rapidly fatal.

The pneumonic type is very severe and apt to kill rapidly. The onset of the pneumonic type, according to Strong and Teague, is abrupt, without prodromal symptoms. There is often a chill, headache, and fever which reaches 103° or 104° F. within a day of the onset, accompanied by a very rapid pulse. Cough appears within twenty-four hours. The expectoration soon becomes abundant and consists of blood-tinged mucus. When later it becomes thick and bright red, it contains enormous numbers of plague bacilli. There are marked signs of cardiac involvement, and delirium and coma frequently appear. Plague bacilli may frequently be found in the blood in such numbers that simple microscopical examination suffices for their detection. In the Manchurian epidemic not a single case in which bacteriological diagnosis was complete was known to have recovered.

The pathology of the lungs in this condition consists of general engorgement and edema. There are hemorrhages under the pleura, often fresh fibrinous pleurisy, and if a case lasts long enough there may be pneumonic infiltration. The distribution of the pneumonic areas may be either lobar or lobular. Bacteria are found in enormous numbers in the peribronchial lymph spaces and in the adjoining alveoli. They may also be present in large numbers in the interlobular septa and under the pleura.

Epidemiology.—The disease was prevalent in ancient times. Through the Middle Ages a number of plague epidemics swept through Europe and frequently reached the commercial ports of Italy, Asia Minor and other parts of eastern Europe from the Orient. In India it has long been known as a fatal form of epidemic disease and since the early part of the nineteenth century, has probably been endemic there. It was introduced into China probably in the first half of the eighteenth century by Mohammedans returning from Mecca *via* Burma to the province of Yunnan. Here it has been epidemic ever since. In 1894 the study of the Hongkong epidemic revealed the causative agent of the disease. There was a very serious epidemic in 1894 which started in China, spread through Bombay to other parts of India, thence to Madagascar, into the Malay States, the Philippine Islands, other islands of the Pacific, reaching North and South America and Europe; finally in 1900, it appeared in Cape Town and on the British Isles. In 1900 plague was endemic in Mongolia, southern China, the Himalayas, Mesopotamia, Persia, Uganda, parts of Russia and northern Africa. In Africa there are two endemic areas, one in Tripoli and the other in Uganda, from which occasional African epidemics take origin.

The disease is a constant menace in many different parts of the world and must remain an important source of concern to national public health organizations. In the United States the problem is perhaps more important than is appreciated. In 1903 it appeared in California and for several years after that human cases occurred, though it never took on the menace of an epidemic. This was prevented probably by the energetic work of the United States Public Health Service under Rupert Blue, McCoy, Curry, and Wherry who instituted energetic methods of rat extermination, rat proofing and other necessary measures. Foci have appeared in Texas and New Orleans and it must never be forgotten that the conditions of climate, etc., are not by any means unfavorable to the development of plague in some parts of America.

In 1923, there occurred an outbreak of plague in Los Angeles, California. Up to and including November 20, 1924, there had occurred 39 cases with 33 deaths, 5 of them being bubonic in type, all the rest being pneumonic. Since 1934 it has not been reported in the United States outside of California and Nevada.

Public health reports indicate that plague continues to be widespread throughout the world.

Plague is primarily a disease of rodents. The bacillus is pathogenic for rats, mice, guinea-pigs, rabbits, for the California ground squirrel (McCoy, 1909), and for various species of ground moles such as the Manchurian tarbagan (*Arctomys bobac*) (Wu Lien Teh).

The spread of plague by rats has long been recognized and even in ancient times mortality in rats has been associated with large epidemic outbreaks. The British Indian Plague Commission at Bombay demonstrated the relationship between rats and plague infection in carefully conducted experiments. According to the Commission, the most important species of rats are the *Epimys norvegicus* and *Epimys rattus*. Over thirteen hundred of some seventeen hundred rats found infected, belonged to these two species. Other rats can also be infected and the danger of plague exists wherever rats are found.

The rat problem is a very important one, not only in connection with plague, but in connection with economic loss as well. Creel of the United States Public Health Service has called attention to the necessity of rat extermination for economic reasons alone. The distribution and number of rats in the world is much greater than any one ordinarily supposes. Creel states that in the cane-producing tropical and semitropical countries, Puerto Rico, the West Indies, the Hawaiian Islands and the Philippines, there is an enormous rat population. He states that on one cane plantation in Puerto Rico where there were less than five hundred people, twenty-five thousand rats were killed in six months. He estimates that in the United States the rat population is probably as great as the human population, and the annual economic cost per rodent is higher than $1.00 apiece. Computing the upkeep of rats as one-half cent per day and estimating their number as above, Creel says that a sum of $167,000,000 is lost annually to the country by rat depredations.

According to the British Plague Commission, the usual way by which rats are infected from others is by means of fleas, and this, as first suggested in 1898 by Simond, is the method by which the disease is carried to man. In the British Indian Plague Commission experiments, when healthy and infected rats, entirely free from fleas were placed together, no plague developed, even when these rats were in contact with the urine and feces of the infected ones and with polluted food. But when fleas were introduced, infection occurred. The most common flea found on rats is the *Xenopsylla cheopis*. The disease can also be transmitted by *Ceratophyllus fasciatus* and by *Pulex irritans*. Fleas habitually infesting dogs and cats may also infest rats, which means that flea extermination must be general. It also indicates that the climatic and geographical distribution of fleas, as well as that of rats, must be taken into account in dealing with the disease.

In rats the first development is a generalized blood infection during which enormous numbers of bacilli may be present in the blood. These are then taken into the intestine of the flea where they can live for a long time, and may be deposited upon the skin of the victim during feeding, since the flea is apt to regurgitate blood and to deposit feces at this time.

The exact manner in which the flea infects has been a little in doubt. Pest bacilli undoubtedly appear in the feces of the flea and these may be deposited on the skin and rubbed in by the scratching, but a number of observers have succeeded in infecting rats by allowing fleas to bite through gauze and direct infection during the sucking of the flea has been considered likely because of regurgitation. Bacot and Martin investigated this in 1914 and found that in many fleas the growth of the plague bacilli in the blood that is sucked in produces a plug which occludes the preventriculus. Such fleas are not prevented from sucking. The esophagus is infected with plague bacilli and, in the repeated act of sucking, if the pharyngeal pump ceases for a minute, some of the blood, by elastic recoil, is driven back into the wound, together with its plague bacilli.

Fleas suffering from such obstruction do not necessarily die, since in a few days autolysis may occur and the plug disappear.

The same writers have studied the survival of the plague flea away from its host and find that this depends very largely upon the ratio between temperature and moisture. It is proportional to the rate with which they lose water. Under similar conditions with constant saturation deficiency their length of life is reduced to between one-half and two-thirds by a 10 degree rise in temperature. Climatological conditions, therefore, are shown to have a definite effect upon plague transmission in determining the length of time that a flea may live between the rodent and the human hosts.

It is thus established with considerable certainty that while contact infection and other means of direct and indirect transmission may, of course, occur, the usual manner of spread of plague is from rat to rat, rat to man, or man to man, by the agency of fleas. It is the *Epimys rattus* which lives in closest relationship to man, and is perhaps the most dangerous for this reason. The ordinary rat flea leaves the body of the rat within about three days of its death and is capable of remaining alive about three or four weeks. The plague bacilli may multiply tremendously in the intestine of the flea during the period between feedings. In the California outbreak infection from ground squirrels to man was definitely shown in a number of cases, and in Manchuria the tarbagan mentioned above has also been suspected of being the direct source.

McCoy, in 1921, stated that in the United States natural infection has taken place among ground squirrels of California, the black rats of Hawaii, and a species of wood rat and field rodent in Louisiana. Human cases have been unquestionably traced to ground squirrels, and almost always, he says, have the peculiarity of showing the primary buboes in the axillae, because the fleas in the course of the infection, attack the upper extremities, whereas when the disease is contracted from rats, the fleas are more apt to bite on the legs.

Such transmission does not hold good, however, for the pneumonic form of the disease. Studies made on the pneumonic form by Strong, Teague, Crowell and Barber, who observed the Manchurian epidemic during the winter of 1910 to 1911, showed that the infection here is not as formerly supposed primarily a septicemic condition, during which the lungs become secondarily involved, but occurs by direct inhalation into the bronchi. The organisms either pass along the bronchioles into the alveoli, or through the walls of the bronchioles into the lungs, giving rise first to peribronchial inflammations and later to more diffuse processes, followed by pneumonic changes of the lobar or lobular type. After this, the blood becomes quickly infested and bacteremia is, therefore, secondary to pneumonia. The organisms are coughed out with the droplets of sputum, and sprayed into the atmosphere. If the atmosphere is dry, they will rapidly die out. If, however, the weather is cold and the atmosphere charged with moisture the organisms may remain alive for considerable periods. According to the same writers, the organisms are not usually exhaled by the expired air during ordinary respiration or even during the labored respirations of the pneumonic case, but only during coughs when they may be sprayed out in enormous numbers. In this form of plague, then, the transmission is very largely direct.

McCoy states that pneumonic plague rarely occurs from rat infection, and that it is an interesting and perhaps significant fact that in plague squirrels there seems to be a definite tendency to localize in the lungs, a thing which rarely happens in rats. From a study of the plague cases in the United States, he states that except for one single focus of 13 cases, this form of the disease has not occurred. This pneumonic outbreak originated from a bubonic case of squirrel origin which developed secondary pneumonia and spread through four transmission generations in man in the autumn of 1919. In 1924, however, there was another small outbreak of pneumonic plague in California.

Sylvatic Plague.—There is a vast reservoir of plague in the wild rodents of the western mountainous states of this country. In 1938 Meyer presented a summary of data collected by the Committee on Sylvatic Plague, in coöperation with state health officers and the U. S. Public Health Service, concerning the extent of human and rodent plague as well as *Pasteurella pestis* infection of fleas and other insects on the American continent. In the surveys mass inoculations from pooled material from many animals were made. Latent and chronic plague was discovered. Examination of the cadavers of flying squirrels and field mice often failed to show inflammatory lesions, yet guinea-pigs succumbed to plague produced by inoculation with materials from these animals. It was concluded that the plague bacillus was present as an inapparent, invisible infection in an undiminished state of invasiveness.

Pooled samples of thousands of fleas likewise showed the great prevalence of plague bacilli in these insect parasites of wild rodents.

Plague Prevention.—From what has been said in regard to the transmission of the disease it is apparent that the prevention of plague becomes very largely a question of rat extermination and protection against fleas. Vigilance in observation of the mortality among rats in endemic centers, for the discovery of early rodent foci, is important. International precautions depend upon quarantine against rats which may easily be carried, and have been carried from country to country, by ships and by rail. The disinfestation of ships by sulphur dioxide by means of the Clayton apparatus, and by hydrocyanic acid gas as described by Creel and Faget of the United States Public Health Service, are among the important methods in use for the disinfestation of ships, sleeping cars, etc. Quarantine regulations and the supervision of incoming ships are important. In the United States a quarantine of seven days is imposed on ships arriving from plague ports. Precautions must be taken to prevent the travel of rats along hawsers when ships are docked at a wharf. This is usually accomplished by the application of large circular shields along the course of the hawsers in such a way that rats cannot cross.

When foci of plague are discovered in any community, wholesale rat destruction and isolation of the focus, by destruction of buildings, rat proofing of cellars, etc., must be resorted to. Blake has introduced a system of which Castellani and Chalmers speak very highly, the principle of which is that the rat extermination and other precautionary measures are started in a wide circle about the focus, working in toward the center, since work beginning at the focus itself in an outward circle may easily serve to scatter rats. In the Philippines and in villages in which natives live in primitive huts, actual burning of the houses has been resorted to, but this, too, may easily result in merely scattering the rat population into the neighboring districts. On a large scale, rat extermination is usually carried out by poisons in which phosphorus paste is perhaps the most important method. Of especial importance is the protection of food stores, and particular attention to all depositories of food, grain, etc., about which rats are apt to accumulate.

Bacteriological Diagnosis.—Since the bacteriological diagnosis of the earliest cases that occur is one of the most important problems of prevention, various governments have laid down methods of collection and shipment of material that should be followed in the case of suspected cases in man and rats. Public Health Report, Volume 35, Number 37, lays down the method in which material is to be collected for the United States. This we quote *in toto* from this bulletin as follows:

To the Officers of the Public Health Service and State and Local Health Officers:

Owing to the appearance of plague in several American ports it is important that all cases of suspected plague, both in man and animals, be subjected to a bacteriological examination.

1. The following material from persons or rodents suffering from plague may be sent to laboratories:

HUMAN CASES (LIVING)

(*a*) Pus or gland fluid from buboes aspirated by syringe or collected after incision, on agar slants

(*b*) Portions of tissues affected, removed at operation, in sterilized bottles, securely stoppered

(c) Blood specimens, in sterilized sealed glass ampules or test tubes

(d) Cultures of suspected organisms, on agar slants

HUMAN CASES (NECROPSY)

(a) Portions of the affected tissues—preferably bubo, lung and spleen—in sterilized glass bottles, securely stoppered

RODENTS

(a) The whole rodent carcass, in fruit preserving jar

2. Do not place tissues or rodents in a preservative. The bacteriological diagnosis of plague rests upon the production of the disease in laboratory animals, and the isolation and growth of the causative organism, *Bacillus pestis*. Any preservative that kills this organism will defeat the purpose of the examination. If decomposition of the specimen is feared, it may be placed in a tight container and this in turn surrounded by ice in a larger container, preferably of wood. Every specimen should be plainly marked, preferably by ordinary pencil, showing the date and the exact location from which it was taken.

3. The shipper must make certain that the specimen is packed in such manner as to prevent possible danger to those handling the same, providing the package is properly handled.

In this connection it is necessary that specimens be wrapped in sufficient cotton or other absorbent material, to prevent leakage of fluid from the container should the glass be broken.

The following instructions should be *explicitly observed.*

1. *Ship by express*—Federal laws prohibit the shipping of plague-infected material, or cultures, by mail.

2. Do not make packages too small, as small packages are more likely to be lost in transit, or overlooked.

3. Each package should be marked as follows:

NOTICE

This package contains perishable specimens
for bacteriological examination
Please Expedite [1]

Careful autopsy must of course be made on all cases, animal or man, and the lesions studied. Cultures are taken on agar and smears taken from buboes or sputum, stained by Löffler's methylene blue, the bipolar appearance and degeneration forms of the organisms looked for. Cultural diagnosis is then made by the appearance of the growing organisms, and their colonies, the staining properties, appearance on salt agar, agglutination in immune sera, and, above all, inoculation of rats and guinea-pigs with observation of the characteristic lesions in these animals.

Since the examination of rats for plague is an important phase of the study of epidemics, it may be well to review the typical lesions in these animals. There is engorgement of the subcutaneous vessels and a pink coloration of the muscles. The bubo when present is sufficient for diagnosis. Marked injection surrounds it and sometimes there is hemorrhagic infiltration. The gland itself is firm but usually caseous or occasionally hemorrhagic. In the liver there is apparent fatty change, but this is due to necrosis. Pin-point spots give it a stippled appearance as though it had been dusted with pepper. Pleural effusion is an important sign. The spleen is large, friable, and often presents pin-point granules on the surface. One or two per cent of rats may present no gross lesions. Cultures should of course be made. The method of examina-

[1] *U. S. Pub. Health Rep.*, Vol. 35, 37.

tion consists in immersing the rat in any convenient antiseptic to kill fleas and other ectoparasites. The rats are nailed by their feet to a shingle and the skin is reflected from the whole front of the body and neck so as to expose the cervical, axillary, and inguinal regions. The thoracic and abdominal cavities are then opened and examined.

A bulletin published by the United States Public Health Service in November, 1920 (35, No. 45), has laid down ordinances for rat-proofing. These we quote *in toto* directly from this bulletin.

The rat-proofing of buildings is generally secured either by elevation of the structure, with the underpinning open and free, or by marginal rat-proof walls of concrete or of stone or brick laid in cement mortar, sunk two feet into the ground, and fitting flush to the floor above. The wall must fit tightly to the flooring and not merely extend to the joists or supporting timbers, as this would result in open spaces, permitting the entrance of rodents. Groceries, stables, warehouses, markets, and food depots in general are best rat-proofed by having a concrete floor in addition to concrete walls. In these structures, untenanted as they are at night, rats might well enter by a doorway or window carelessly left open, or be introduced concealed in merchandise, and, gnawing through plank flooring, obtain a well-protected hiding place.

In addition to concrete floor and walls, these food depots must have tight-fitting doors, and all windows and other openings should be properly screened. A 12-gauge wire is preferable on account of its strength and durability, and the mesh should not be larger than one-half inch.

Rat-proofing by elevation of the building is chiefly applicable to small and medium sized frame dwellings. The purpose is to have a sufficient elevation, about two feet, so that the ground area beneath will be as exposed and free from covert as land unbuilt upon. Marginal rat-proofing will suffice in more pretentious dwellings where sufficient care can be exercised to prevent rats from gnawing through the floors.

Chicken pens can be protected by marginal concrete walls, sunk into the ground two feet or more, and by covering the sides and top with ½-inch mesh wire netting. Garbage cans should be made of serviceable metal and should have properly fitting tops.

Plank sidewalks and plank coverings for yards should be avoided. Cinders and concrete should be used instead. The latter should have marginal protection to prevent rats from burrowing beneath it.

Double walls, with a dead space between, should be avoided, or, if used, they should be rat-proofed at the top and bottom with heavy wooden timbers, 4 by 4-inch fillers, or by a concrete fill. Attics should be well opened and kept free of rubbish or other refuge for rats.

These precautions against rat harborage and for the protection of food supplies, in connection with careful trapping and poisoning, will be attended with considerable success in the destruction of rats.

The appended model ordinance is applicable, with perhaps slight modifications, to any urban community. It should be examined by competent local counsel for changes in form, or in substance if necessary, as dictated by special constitutional, legislative, or charter considerations.[2]

Vaccination.—The immunization of animals with suspensions of plague bacilli, killed by moderate heating, 50° C. for one hour, was first attempted by Yersin, Calmette and Borrel in 1897. A great many different vaccines have been introduced since then. The one most extensively used, with good results, is that of Haffkine, which consists of cultures grown in broth in shallow bottles for four weeks at room temperature and shaken once a day. At the end of this time they are sterilized at 55° C. for 15 to 30 minutes. The material then consists of degenerated organisms and extracts of the organisms. Phenol is added to make a 0.5 per cent solution. The modern plague vaccines contain from 1000 to 2000 million heat-killed organisms per c.c.

2 *Ibid.*, Nov. 1920, Vol. 35, 45.

Strong, believing that attenuated living bacilli might be more efficient than dead cultures, produced vaccines from a three years old laboratory culture, subsequently cultivated at temperatures above 41° C. These living cultures after such treatment had lost their virulence for guinea-pigs and monkeys almost completely. He vaccinated 42 individuals with these cultures without harm, and with resulting development of specific antibodies. The method is probably quite efficient but because of the possible danger involved in it, has not been extensively employed.

Antitoxin.—By injecting horses with filtrates of plague bacillus cultures, or extracts of the organisms containing bacterial protein an antitoxin can be produced (Naidu, Jung, and Kamakaka). Presumably, these preparations have been antiendotoxic and antibacterial. Antitoxins of this nature have been used in the treatment of bubonic plague but their efficacy has not been established.

BACTERIA OF THE HEMORRHAGIC SEPTICEMIA GROUP AND DISEASES OF ANIMALS

In many of the lower animals there occur violently acute bacterial infections characterized by general septicemia, usually with petechial hemorrhages throughout the organs and serous membranes and severe intestinal inflammations. These diseases, spoken of as the "hemorrhagic septicemias," are caused by a group of closely allied bacilli, first classified together by Hueppe in 1886. Some confusion has existed as to the forms which should be considered within Hueppe's group of hemorrhagic septicemia, a number of bacteriologists including in this class bacilli such as Löffler's *Bacillus typhi murium*, and Salmon and Smith's hog cholera bacillus, micro organisms which, because of their motility and cultural characteristics, belong more properly to the Gaertner, enteritidis, or paratyphoid group, intermediate between colon and typhoid.

The organisms properly belonging to this group are short bacilli, more plump than are those of the colon type, showing a marked tendency to stain more deeply at the poles than at the center. They are nonmotile, possess no flagella, and do not form spores. They grow readily upon simple media, but show a very marked preference for oxygen, growing but slightly below the surface of media. By some observers they are characterized as "obligatory aerobes," but this is undoubtedly a mistake.

While showing considerable variations in form and differences in minor cultural characteristics, the species characteristics of polar staining, decolorization by Gram, immobility, lack of gelatin liquefaction, and great pathogenicity for animals, stamp alike all members of the group. Its chief recognized representatives are the bacillus of chicken cholera, the bacillus of swine plague (*Deutsche Schweineseuche*), and the *Bacillus pleurosepticus* which causes an acute disease in cattle and often in wild game.

The dividing line is not sharp between the plague bacillus, *Bacillus pseudotuberculosis rodentium*, and the organisms which cause hemorrhagic septicemia and a variety of acute and chronic diseases in animals. For clinical, epidemiological, and public health reasons, we have followed the sound practice of discussing plague and tularemia in separate sections apart from the other hemorrhagic septicemias of animals. The generic name *Pasteurella*, however, has been adopted for the whole group of these bacteria, and Bergey has listed *Pasteurella avicida* as the type species. The organisms producing hemorrhagic septicemias in animals differ from the plague bacilli in general by the production of indole, by their specific infectiousness and in their serological reactions. The closest relative to the plague bacillus is the so-called *B. pseudotuberculosis rodentium*.

Bacillus Pseudotuberculosis Rodentium (Bacillus Pseudopestis).—Every one will agree with Meyer in his statement that "the designation of any disease characterized by pathological-anatomical lesions similar to those produced by the tubercle bacilli as *pseudotuberculosis* has led to a great deal of confusion." [3] The formation of "pseudotubercles" in guinea-pigs can be provoked by the introduction of inert substances, toxins, parasites, and various bacteria into the tissues of the animals. This lesion, therefore, is too nonspecific to point to a single etiological factor. Furthermore, the proneness of guinea-pigs ill with one type of infection to succumb to a secondarily acquired pathogenic organism, particularly some member of the paratyphoid or hemorrhagic septicemia groups, has introduced another element of confusion. It is not astonishing, therefore, that the so-called *Bacillus pseudotuberculosis rodentium* should appear in the literature under many different forms. It would seem to us advisable to drop the term *pseudotuberculosis* from the designation of any of these organisms. The organism with which we are concerned in this chapter is more appropriately called *Bacillus pseudopestis*, or *Pasteurella pseudopestis*, or preferably by some name which would avoid the pseudonyms of plague and tuberculosis altogether. It seems an error to list the organism in the diphtheria group, under the name *Corynebacterium pseudotuberculosis*, as done by Bergey.

The so-called *Bacillus pseudotuberculosis rodentium* is a small gram-negative organism resembling the plague bacillus in many respects. It is *nonmotile*, does not form spores, grows like *B. pestis* in broth and on agar, and does not produce indole. It produces a progressively fatal disease in guinea-pigs. This disease may be epidemic and appear in three clinical types (Ramon): septicemic, gastro-intestinal, and lymphadenopathic. The organism is said to have only slight pathogenicity for rats, producing mild chronic lesions.

There is a close serological relation between this organism and the plague bacillus. Cross-agglutination and cross-protection tests have not yet clearly distinguished between *B. pestis* and the pseudoplague bacillus from guinea-pigs (MacConkey, Rowland).

Most of those who have studied *B. pseudotuberculosis rodentium* have found the organism to be *nonmotile* in cultures incubated at 37° C. (Kakehi, Römisch, Meyer and Batchelder). Arkwright, however, has confirmed certain earlier observations that the organism is motile when grown at 18° to 26° C. This point, and other problems connected with this organism, require further investigation.

Bacillus of Chicken Cholera (Bacillus Avisepticus).[4]—The bacillus of chicken cholera was first carefully studied by Pasteur in 1880. It is a short, nonmotile bacillus, measuring from 0.5 to 1 μ in length. Stained with the ordinary aniline dyes, it displays marked polar staining qualities, which often give it the appearance of being a diplococcus. It is decolorized by Gram's method. It does not form spores, but may

---

[3] K. F. Meyer, *The Newer Knowledge of Bacteriology and Immunology*, Chicago, 1928, p. 614.
[4] Species: *Pasteurella avicida*.

occasionally form vacuolated degeneration forms, not unlike those described for *Bacillus pestis.*

The bacillus is easily cultivated from the blood and organs of infected animals, it grows well upon the simplest media at temperatures varying from 25° to 40° C. In *broth,* it produces uniform clouding with later a formation of a pellicle. Upon *agar* it forms, within twenty-four to forty-eight hours, minute colonies, white or yellowish in color, which are at first transparent, later opaque. Upon *gelatin,* it grows without liquefaction. Upon *milk,* the growth is slow and does not produce coagulation. Indole is formed from *peptone bouillon.* Acid, but no gas, is formed by the fermentation of a number of carbohydrates.

Among barnyard fowl, this disease is widely prevalent, attacking chickens, ducks, geese and a large variety of smaller birds. The infection is extremely acute, ending fatally within a few days. It is accompanied by diarrhea, often with bloody stools, great exhaustion, and, toward the end, a drowsiness bordering on coma. Autopsy upon the animals reveals hemorrhagic inflammation of the intestinal mucosa, enlargement of the liver and spleen, and often bronchopneumonia.

The specific bacilli may be found in the blood, in the organs, in exudates, if these are present, and in large numbers in the dejecta. Infection takes place probably through the food and water contaminated by the discharges of diseased birds.

Subcutaneous inoculation or feeding of such animals with pure cultures, even in minute doses, gives rise to a quickly developing septicemia which is uniformly fatal. The bacillus is extremely pathogenic for rabbits, less so for hogs, sheep, and horses, if infection is produced by subcutaneous inoculation. Infection by ingestion does not seem to cause disease in these animals.

Historically, the bacillus of chicken cholera is extremely interesting, since it was with this micro-organism that Pasteur carried out some of his fundamental researches upon immunity, and succeeded in immunizing chickens with attenuated cultures. The first attenuation experiment made by Pasteur consisted of allowing the bacilli to remain in a broth culture for a prolonged period without transplantation. With minute doses of such a culture (Vaccine I) he inoculated chickens, following this, aften ten days, with a small dose of a fully virulent culture. Although enormously important in principle, the practical results from this method, as applied to chicken cholera, have not been satisfactory. It was with this bacillus, furthermore, that Pasteur was first able to demonstrate the existence of a free toxin which could be separated from the bacteria by filtration.

Bacillus of Swine Plague (Bacillus Suisepticus, Schweineseuche).[5]—This micro-organism is almost identical in form and cultural characteristics with the bacillus of chicken cholera. It is nonmotile, forms no spores, is gram-negative, and does not liquefy gelatin. The bacillus causes an epidemic disease among hogs, which is characterized almost regularly by a broncho-pneumonia followed by general septicemia. There is often a serosanguineous pleural exudate, a swelling of bronchial lymph glands and of liver and spleen. The gastro-intestinal tract is rarely affected. The bacilli at autopsy may be found in the lungs, in the exudates, in the liver and spleen, and in the blood. In young pigs, the disease is almost uniformly fatal (T. Smith).

5 Species: *Pasteurella suilla.*

It is probable that spontaneous infection usually occurs by inhalation. Experimental inoculation is successful in pigs, both when given subcutaneously and when administered by the inhalation method. Mice, guinea-pigs and rabbits are also susceptible, dying within three or four days after subcutaneous inoculation of small doses.

Active and passive immunization of animals against *Bacillus suisepticus* has been attempted by various observers. Active immunization, if carried out with care, may be successfully done in the laboratory. Passive immunization of animals with the serum of actively immunized horses has been practised by Kitt and Mayr, Schrieber, and Wassermann and Ostertag. The last-named observers, working with a polyvalent serum produced with a number of different strains of the bacillus, have obtained results of considerable practical value.

Infection with the bacillus of swine plague, in hogs, is often accompanied by an infection with the hog cholera bacillus (*Schweinepest*). The latter, as we have seen, is a micro-organism belonging to the enteritidis group, intermediate between *B. coli* and *B. typhosus*, and differing from *suisepticus* in being actively motile, possessing flagella, not showing the polar staining, having a more slender morphology, and producing gas upon dextrose broth. A confusion between the two bacilli frequently occurs because of their nomenclature. Bacteriologically and pathogenically, they are quite distinct. *Bacillus suisepticus* produces an acute septicemia, accompanied by bronchopneumonia and usually not affecting the gastro-intestinal canal. The bacillus of hog cholera produces an infection localized in the intestinal canal.

Other important species in this group are: *Pasteurella boviseptica*, the cause of hemorrhagic septicemia in domestic cattle, deer and horses. *Pasteurella vituliseptica*, the cause of septic pneumonia in calves, is probably identical with *boviseptica*. *Pasteurella oviseptica* is the cause of pneumonia and enteritis in sheep (Schütze).

Pasteurella cuniculicida is the cause of *snuffles* and septicemia in rabbits. The older, more familiar, name of this organism was *Bacillus lepisepticum*. It has played an important rôle in bacteriology. De Kruif discovered dissociation of bacterial species while studying this organism. Webster has used it in investigations on experimental epidemiology and a relationship has been shown to exist between this organism and *Bacillus bronchisepticus* (Bull and McKee).

REFERENCES

ABEL, R.   Centralbl. f. Bakteriol., I Abt., 1897, 21:497.
ALBRECHT, H., and GHON, A.   Denkschr. d. k. Akad. d. Wissensch., Wien, 1898, 66.
ARKWRIGHT, J. A.   Lancet, 1927, 1:13.
BACOT, A. W., and MARTIN, C. J.   J. Hyg., 1914, Plague Supp., 423; 1924, 23:98.
BULL, C. G., and MCKEE, C. M.   Am. J. Hyg., 1927, 7:110.
CASTELLANI and CHALMERS.   Manual of Tropical Medicine, New York, 1919.
CREEL, R. H.   Pub. Health Rep., 1913, 28:No. 27.
DE KRUIF, P.   J. Exper. M., 1921, 33:773 *et seq.*
German Plague Com. Rep., 1899.
HAFFKINE.   Indian M. Gaz., 1897.
HIRSCH, A.   Handb. d. histor.-geograph. Pathologie, Stuttgart, 1881.
HUEPPE, F.   Berl. klin. Wchnschr., 1886, 23:753, 776, 794.
KAKEHI. S.   J. Pathol. & Bacteriol., 1916, 20:269.

KITASATO, S. Lancet, 1894, 2:428.

KITT, T., and MAYR, J. Monatschr. f. prakt. Tierh., 1897, 8:529.

KOLLE and OTTO. Ztschr. f. Hyg., 1903, 45.

KOSSEL and OVERBECK. Arb. a. d. k. Gsndhtsamte., 1901, 18:114.

LISTON. Bombay Bacteriol. Lab. Rep., 1913–1916.

MACCONKEY, A. T. J. Hyg., 1908, 8:335.

McCoy, G. W. Am. J. Hyg., 1921, 1:182.

———— Pub. Health Rep., Wash., July, 1912; July, 1913, No. 37.

———— J. Infect. Dis., 1909, 6:170, et seq.

MEYER, K. F. The Newer Knowledge of Bacteriology and Immunology, Chicago, 1928.

———— Am. J. Pub. Health, 1938, 28:1153.

MEYER, K. F., and BATCHELDER, A. J. Infect. Dis., 1926, 39:383.

NAIDU, B. P. B., JUNG, S., and KAMAKAKA, K. H. Indian J. M. Research, 1930, 17.

PASTEUR, L. Compt. rend. Acad. d. sc., Paris, 1880, 90:239.

Pub. Health Rep., Wash., 1924, 39:47.

RAMON, G. Ann. de l'Inst. Pasteur, 1914, 28:568.

RÖMISCH. Ztschr. f. Infectionskr. d. Haustiere, 1920, 21:138, 212.

ROSENAU. Preventive Medicine and Hygiene, New York, 1921.

SCHRIEBER. Berl. tierärztl. Wchnschr., 1899, 10.

SCHÜTZE, H. A System of Bacteriology in Relation to Medicine, London, 1929, 4:446.

———— Brit. J. Exper. Pathol., 1932, 13, 293.

SIMOND, P. L. Ann. de l'Inst. Pasteur, 1898, 12:625.

SMITH, T. U. S. Dep. Agric. Bureau animal indust., 1886.

STRONG. Philippine J. Sc., 1907, 1912, Sec. B.

STRONG, TEAGUE, CROWELL and BARBER. Philippine J. Sc., 1912, Sec. B, 7.

TEAGUE, O., and BARBER, M. A. Philippine J. Sc., Sec. B., 1912, 7:257.

WAYSON, N. E. Pub. Health Rep., Wash., 1925, 40, No. 38, 1975.

WEBSTER, L. T. J. Exper. M., 1924, 39:843, 40:109; 1926, 43:55, 573.

WEBSTER, L. T. and BURN, C. J. Exper. M., 1926, 44:343, 359.

WERNICKE. Centralbl. f. Bakteriol., 1898, Ref., 24.

WHERRY. J. Infect. Dis., 1908, 5.

WU LIEN TEH. J. Hyg., 1913, 13.

———— A Treatise on Pneumonic Plague, League of Nations, Health Organization, Geneva, 1926.

YERSIN, S. Ann. de l'Inst. Pasteur, 1894, 8:662.

CHAPTER XLIV

BACILLUS ANTHRACIS AND ANTHRAX (MILZBRAND, CHARBON)

Family: *Bacillaceae*. Genus: *Bacillus*. Species: *Bacillus anthracis*.

Anthrax is primarily a disease of the herbivora, attacking especially cattle and sheep. Infection not infrequently occurs in horses, hogs and goats. In other domestic animals it is exceptional. Man is susceptible to the disease and contracts it either directly from the living animals or from the hides, wool, or other parts of the cadaver used in the industries.

The history of the disease dates back to the most ancient periods and anthrax has, at all times, been a severe scourge upon cattle- and sheep-raising communities. Of all infections attacking the domestic animals no other has claimed so many victims as anthrax.

In Austria-Hungary, Germany, France, and the eastern countries, each year thousands of animals and numerous human beings perish of anthrax. In England and America the disease is relatively infrequent. No quarter of the globe, however, is entirely free from it.

Especial historical interest attaches to the anthrax bacillus in that it was the first micro-organism proved definitely to bear a specific etiological relationship to an infectious disease. The discovery of the anthrax bacillus, therefore, laid the corner-stone of modern bacteriology. The bacillus was first observed in the blood of infected animals by Pollender in 1849, and, independently, by Brauell in 1857. Davaine, however, in 1863, was the first one to produce experimental infection in animals with blood containing the bacilli and to suggest a direct etiological relationship between the two. Final and absolute proof of the justice of Davaine's contentions was not brought until the further development of bacteriological technic, by Koch who, in 1877, isolated the bacillus upon artificial media and reproduced the disease experimentally by inoculation with pure cultures.

Morphology and Staining.—The anthrax bacillus is a straight rod, 5 to 10 μ in length, 1 to 3 μ in width. It is nonmotile. In preparations made from the blood of an infected animal, the bacilli are usually single or in pairs. Grown on artificial media, they form tangles of long threads. Their ends are cut off squarely. The corners are often sharp and the ends of bacilli in contact in a chain often touch each other only at these points, leaving in consequence an oval chink between the ends of the organisms. The appearance of a chain of anthrax bacilli has been not inaptly compared to a rod of bamboo. On artificial media, in the soil, and in material from dead animals the anthrax bacillus forms spores. Oxygen is necessary for the formation of these spores and they are consequently not found in the blood of infected subjects. The spores are located in the middle of the bacilli and are distinctly oval. They are difficult to stain, but may be demonstrated by any of the usual spore-staining procedures, such as Möller's or Dorner's methods. The bacilli themselves are easily stained by the usual aniline dyes, and gentian violet or fuchsin in aqueous solution may be conveniently employed. The organism is gram-positive.

The gram-positive material in the anthrax bacillus has been shown by Churchman to form a cortical layer of the cell body. Gram-negative forms, lacking this cortex, are only about one-half the thickness of the gram-positive organisms.

In preparations from animal tissues or blood, stained by special procedures, the anthrax bacillus may occasionally be seen to possess a capsule. In chains of anthrax bacilli, the capsule when present seems to envelop the entire chain and not the individual bacteria separately. The organism may form a capsule in artificial media, especially in media containing serum.

Isolation.—Isolation of the anthrax bacillus from infected material is comparatively simple, both because of the ease of its cultivation and because of the sharply characteristic features of its morphological and cultural appearance.

Cultivation.—The anthrax bacillus is an aerobic, facultatively anaerobic bacillus. While it may develop slowly and sparsely under anaerobic conditions, free oxygen is required to permit its luxuriant and characteristic growth.

The optimum temperature for its cultivation ranges about 37.5° C. It is not, however, delicately susceptible to moderate

Fig. 59.—Bacillus Anthracis.
From pure culture on agar.

variations of temperatures and growth does not cease until temperatures as low as 12° C. or as high as 45° C. are reached. By continuous cultivation at some of the temperatures near either the higher or the lower of these limits, the bacillus may become well adapted to the new environment and attain luxuriant growth. (Dieudonné).

The anthrax bacillus may be cultivated on all of the usual artificial media. It may be cultivated also upon hay infusion, various other vegetable media, sugar solutions and urine. While moderate acidity of the medium does not prevent the growth of this bacillus, the most favorable reaction for media is neutrality or slight alkalinity.

In *gelatin stab cultures,* growth appears at first as a thin white line along the course of the puncture. From this, growth proceeds in thin spicules or filaments diverging from the stab, more abundantly near the top than near the bottom of the stab, owing to more active growth in well oxygenated environment. The resulting picture is that of a small inverted Christmas tree. Liquefaction begins at the top, at first a shallow depression filled with an opaque mixture of bacilli and fluid. Later the bacilli sink to the bottom of the flat depression, leaving a clear supernatant fluid of peptonized gelatin.

In *broth,* growth takes place rapidly, but does not lead to an even general clouding. There is usually an initial pellicle formation at the top where the oxygen supply is greatest. Simultaneously with this a slimy mass appears at the bottom of the tube, owing to the sinking of bacilli to the bottom. Apart from isolated flakes and threads the intervening broth is clear. Shaken up, the tube shows a tough, stringy mass, not unlike a small cotton fluff, and general clouding is produced only by vigorous mixing.

Upon *agar plates*, growth at 37.5 C. is vigorous and colonies appear within twelve to twenty-four hours. They are irregular in outline, slightly wrinkled, and show under the microscope a characteristic tangled-thread appearance. The colonies are slightly glistening and tough in consistency.

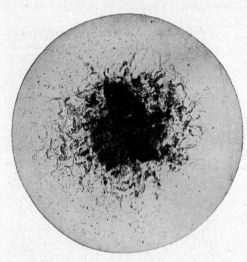

Fig. 60.—Anthrax Colony on Gelatin.
(Guenther)

On *agar slants*, the colonies usually become confluent, the entire surface soon being covered by a grayish, tough pellicle which, if fished, has a tendency to come away in thin strips or strands.

On *potato*, growth is rapid, white, and rather dry. Sporulation upon potato is rapid and marked, and the medium is favorable for the study of this phase of development.

Milk is slowly acidified and slowly coagulated. This action is chiefly upon the casein; very few, if any, changes being produced either in the sugars or in the fats of the milk. The acids formed are chiefly formic, acetic and caproic acids.

If anthrax bacilli are cultivated for prolonged periods upon media containing hydrochloric or rosolic acid or weak solutions of carbolic acid (Chamberland and Roux), cultures may be obtained which do not sporulate and which seem permanently to have lost this power, without losing their virulence to the same degree. Similar results may be obtained by continuous cultivation at temperatures above 42° C. By this procedure, however, virulence, too, is considerably diminished.

Resistance.—Because of its property of spore formation, the anthrax bacillus is extremely resistant toward chemical and physical environment. The vegetative forms themselves are not more resistant than most other nonsporulating bacteria, being destroyed by a temperature of 54° C. in thirty minutes. Anthrax spores may be kept in a dry state for many years without losing their viability (Surmont and Arnould). While different strains of anthrax spores show some variation in their powers of resistance, all races show an extremely high resistance to heat. Dry heat at 140° C. kills them only after three hours. Live steam at 100° C. kills them in five to ten minutes. Boiling destroys in about ten minutes. Destruction of anthrax spores in furs, hides and brushes is difficult. Blue states that for brushes the best method is soaking for four hours in 10 per cent formalin solution at 110° F. Hair and bristles may be sterilized before using in the autoclave at 15 pounds for three hours, but this ruins many materials.

Spores may retain their viability after exposure to 5 per cent carbolic acid for forty days, or may be destroyed by the same solution in two days. Corrosive sublimate, 1 : 2000, kills most strains in forty minutes.

Direct sunlight destroys anthrax spores within six to twelve hours.

Variability.—The nonspore-bearing variants of *B. anthracis* breed true. These organisms remain asporogenous and have reduced virulence. The range of morphological appearances in cultures at different ages is amazing, coccoid, filamentous, and spirillary forms occurring in addition to the typical rods. Some of these forms, such as the gonidia described by Haag, are said to have reproductive significance. But the actual relationship of forms to a life cycle other than that represented by the endospore have not been determined with any certainty.

Dissociation of the species into S (smooth) and R (rough) colony variants occurs, as described by Markhoff, Gratia, and Nungester. It is said that the rough forms of *B. anthracis* are more virulent than the smooth.

Pathogenicity.—The anthrax bacillus is pathogenic for cattle, sheep, guinea-pigs, rabbits, rats and mice. The degrees of susceptibility of these animals differ greatly, variations in this respect existing even among different members of the same species. Thus, the long-haired Algerian sheep show a high resistance, while the European variety are highly susceptible; and, similarly, the gray rat is much more resistant than the white rat. Dogs, hogs, cats, birds and the cold-blooded animals are relatively insusceptible. For man the bacillus is definitely pathogenic, though less so than for some of the animals mentioned above.

While separate races of anthrax bacilli may vary much in their degree of virulence, a single individual strain remains fairly constant in this respect if preserved, dried upon threads or kept in sealed tubes, in a cold, dark place. Virulence may be reduced (Toussaint) by various attenuating laboratory procedures which are of importance in that they have made possible prophylactic immunization. Heating the bacilli to 55° C. for ten minutes considerably reduces their virulence. Similar results are obtained by prolonged cultivation at temperatures of 42° to 43° C., or by the addition of weak disinfectants to the culture fluids (Chamberland and Roux). Once reduced, the new grade of virulence remains fairly constant. Increase of virulence may be artificially produced by passage through animals.

Experimental infections in susceptible animals are most easily accomplished by subcutaneous inoculations. The inoculation is followed, at first, by no morbid symptoms, and some animals may appear perfectly well and comfortable until within a few hours or even moments before death, when they suddenly become visibly very ill, rapidly go into collapse, and die. The length of the disease depends to some extent, of course, upon the resistance of the infected subject, being in guinea-pigs and mice from twenty-four to forty-eight hours. The quantity of infectious material introduced, on the other hand, has little bearing upon the final outcome, a few bacilli, or even a single bacillus, often sufficing to bring about a fatal infection. Although the bacilli are not demonstrable in the blood until just before death, they nevertheless invade the blood and lymph streams immediately after inoculation, and are conveyed by these to all the organs. This has been demonstrated clearly by experiments where inoculations into the tail or ear were immediately followed by amputation of the inoculated parts without prevention of the fatal general infection. The bacilli are probably not at first able to multiply in the blood. At the place of inoculation and probably in the organs they proliferate, until the resistance of the infected subject is entirely overcome. At this stage of the disease, no longer held at bay by any antagonistic qualities of the blood, they enter the circulation and multiply within it. Autopsy upon such animals reveals an edematous hemorrhagic infiltration at the point of inoculation. The spleen is enlarged and congested. The kidneys are congested, and there may be hemorrhagic spots upon the serous membranes. The bacilli are found in large numbers in the blood and in the capillaries of all the organs.

The mode of action of *B. anthracis* is as yet an unsettled point. It is probable that death is brought about to a large extent by purely mechanical means, such as capillary obstruction. Neither a true secretory toxin nor an endotoxin has been demonstrated for the anthrax bacillus. The decidedly toxemic clinical picture of the disease, however, in some animals and in man, precludes concluding that such poisons do not

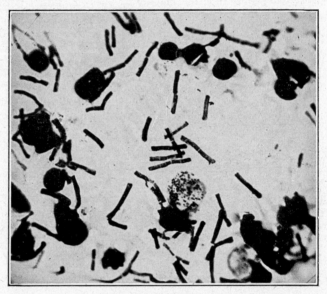

FIG. 61.—BACILLUS ANTHRACIS.
In smear of spleen of animal dead of anthrax.

exist. It is a matter of fact, however, that neither culture filtrates nor dead bacilli have any noticeable toxic effect upon test animals and exert no appreciable immunizing action.

Spontaneous infection of animals takes place largely by way of the alimentary canal, the bacilli being taken in with the food. The bacteria are swallowed as spores, and therefore resist the acid gastric juice. In the intestines they develop into the vegetative forms, increase, and gradually invade the system. The large majority of cattle infections are of this type. Direct subcutaneous infection may also occur spontaneously when small punctures and abrasions about the mouth are made by the sharp spicules of the hay, straw, or other varieties of fodder.

When infection upon a visible part occurs, there is formed a diffuse, tense local swelling, not unlike a large carbuncle. The center of this' may be marked by a black, necrotic slough, or may contain a pustular depression.

Infection by inhalation is probably rare among animals. Transmission among animals is usually by the agency of the excreta or unburned carcasses of infected animals. The bacilli escaping from the body are deposited upon the earth together with animal and vegetable matter, which forms a suitable medium for sporulation. The spores may then remain in the immediate vicinity, or may be scattered by rain and wind over considerable areas. The danger from buried carcasses, at first suspected by Pasteur, is probably very slight, owing to the fact that the bacilli cannot sporulate in the anaerobic environment to which the burying process subjects them. The disease, in infected cattle and sheep, is usually acute, killing within one or two days. The mortality is extremely high, about 80 per cent.

In man the disease is usually acquired by cutaneous inoculation. It may also occur by inhalation and through the alimentary tract.

Cutaneous inoculation occurs usually through small abrasions or scratches upon the skin in men who habitually handle live stock, and in butchers, or tanners of hides. Infection occurs most frequently upon the hands and forearms. The primary lesion, often spoken of as "malignant pustule," appears within twelve to twenty-four hours after inoculation, and resembles, at first, an ordinary small furuncle. Soon, however, its center will show a vesicle filled with serosanguineous, later seropurulent fluid. This may change into a black central necrosis surrounded by an angry red edematous areola. Occasionally local gangrene and general systemic infection may lead to death within five or six days. More frequently, however, especially if prompt excision is practised, the patient recovers. The early diagnosis of the condition is best made bacteriologically by finding the bacilli in the local discharge.

The pulmonary infection, known as "wool-sorter's disease," occurs in persons who handle raw wool, hides, or horse hair, by the inhalation or by the swallowing of spores. The disease is rare in this country. The spores, once inhaled, develop into the vegetative forms and these travel along the lymphatics into the lungs and pleura. The disease manifests itself as a violent, irregular pneumonia, which, in the majority of cases, leads to death. The bacilli in these cases can often be found in the sputum before death.

During and since the War anthrax infection of the skin from shaving brushes has been recognized both in England and America (Coutts, Symmers and Cady, and Jacobsohn).

Infection through the alimentary canal may rarely occur in man, from ingestion of uncooked meat of infected animals. The clinical picture that follows is one of violent enteritis with bloody stools and great prostration. Death is the rule. The diagnosis is made by the discovery of the bacilli in the feces.

General prophylaxis consists chiefly in destruction of infected animals, the burying of cadavers, and the disinfection of stables, etc. The practical impossibility of destroying the anthrax spores in infected pastures, etc., makes it necessary to resort to prophylactic immunization of cattle and sheep.

In connection with his studies of local immunity and local tissue susceptibility, Besredka published the results of experiments which seemed to demonstrate that the skin was the only tissue susceptible to infection with the anthrax bacillus. In guinea-pigs and rabbits the contamination of the skin with *B. anthracis* produced the disease, but no infection occurred when the organisms were introduced into the subcutaneous tissues, peritoneal cavity or veins by means which avoided placing the bacilli in the skin. These findings have been corroborated by some and denied by others. Our impression is that while the skin is the tissue of greatest susceptibility, anthrax will occur if a sufficiently virulent strain enters the body by any other route, including, in some instances, the gastro-intestinal tract as a portal of entry. Local differences in the resistance of tissues and differences in the virulence of cultures probably account for the contradictory results of many experiments performed to test Besredka's hypothesis of local specific tissue susceptibility.

Serology.—The antigenic analysis of *B. anthracis* and its variants has not been carried forward as far as this method of study has been pushed in the case of some of the other bacteria. The agglutinins produced by the injection of whole organisms of one culture into animals have had general group properties. The difficulties encountered in obtaining homogeneous suspensions for agglutination tests can be overcome, according to Noble, by using a sporeless strain of *B. anthracis*, obtained by cultivating the organism at 42.5° C. A vigorously growing eighteen-hour culture of the nonsporogenous variety is washed off agar plates with physiological saline containing 0.5 per cent phenol, thoroughly shaken, allowed to stand until the large clumps settle and then is strained. This emulsion of bacilli is said to be stable and to give sharp agglutination reactions with antianthrax serum.

The anthrax bacillus in the animal body is encapsulated and hence contains specific polysaccharides. It is probable that material of this nature constitutes the heat stable antigen obtained by Ascoli in the extracts of organs of animals dead of anthrax for use in his diagnostic precipitin test. These extracts give a precipitate with antianthrax serum. Ascoli's precipitin reaction is helpful in making a rapid diagnosis when the work has to be done with putrid material from dead animals, or with tissues preserved in formalin or alcohol, or with hides. To make the extract, a small piece of the spleen is boiled in 5 to 10 c.c. of saline, cooled, filtered clear and layered on the antiserum. A zone of precipitate occurs at the junction of the extract and antiserum in positive tests. Suitable controls should be made at the same time. The ordinary antianthrax therapeutic serum may not be potent in precipitins. The serum most useful in Ascoli's test should be prepared by immunizing animals (rabbits) against encapsulated anthrax bacilli (Rosenberg and Romanow).

Immunity.—Minute quantities of virulent anthrax cultures usually suffice to produce death in susceptible animals. Dead cultures are inefficient in calling forth any immunity in treated subjects. It is necessary, therefore, for the production of *active immunity* to resort to attenuated cultures. The safest way to accomplish such attenuation is the one originated by Pasteur, consisting in prolonged cultivation of the bacillus at 42° to 43° C. in broth. Nonspore-forming races are thus evolved.

The longer the bacilli are grown at the above temperature the greater is the reduction in their virulence. Koch, Gaffky, and Löffler, utilizing the variations in susceptibilities of different species of animals, devised a method by means of which the relative attenuation of a given culture may be estimated and standardized. Rabbits are less susceptible than guinea-pigs, and virulent anthrax cultures, grown for two or three days under the stated conditions, lose their power to kill rabbits, and are less virulent for guinea-pigs. After ten to twenty days of further cultivation at 42° C. the virulence for the guinea-pig disappears, but the culture is potent against the still more susceptible mouse. Even the virulence for mice may be entirely eliminated by further cultivation at this temperature.

The method of active immunization first practised by Pasteur, and still used extensively, is carried out as follows:

Two anthrax cultures of varying degrees of attenuation are used as *vaccins*. The *premier vaccin* is a culture which has lost its virulence for guinea-pigs and rabbits, and is potent only against mice. The *deuxième vaccin* is a culture which is still definitely virulent for mice and guinea-pigs, but not potent for rabbits. Forty-eight-hour broth cultures of these strains, grown at 37.5° C., form the *vaccin* actually employed. Vaccin I is subcutaneously injected into cattle in doses of 0.25 c.c., sheep receiving about half this quantity. After twelve days have elapsed similar quantities of Vaccin II are injected.[1]

Pasteur's method has given excellent results and confers an immunity which lasts about a year.

Chauveau modified Pasteur's method by growing the bacilli in bouillon at 38° to 39° C., at a pressure of eight atmospheres. Cultures are then made of races attenuated in this way, upon chicken bouillon and allowed to develop for thirty days. Single injections of 0.1 c.c. each of such cultures are said to protect cattle.

Active immunization of small laboratory animals is very difficult, but can be accomplished by careful treatment with extremely attenuated cultures.

Investigations of local susceptibility and resistance, along the lines of Besredka's hypothesis are providing evidence that cutaneous vaccination is a more effective means of inducing immunity than the subcutaneous injection method. Velu and Nevodoff have reported that a single intracutaneous injection of "Vaccin I" produced a high degree of immunity in guinea-pigs and other animals. This has not been extensively confirmed, but it is in accord with what has been determined with respect to the value of intracutaneous vaccination in other infections, such as tuberculosis, smallpox, and certain staphylococcus diseases.

Passive immunization by means of the serum of actively immune animals was first successfully accomplished by Sclavo in 1895.

Sobernheim introduced the treatment of animals simultaneously with immune serum and the "deuxième vaccin" of Pasteur. Eichhorn, in order to safely produce more severe reactions, developed a spore vaccine from carefully tested strains which maintained its activity in glycerin salt solution and could be standardized. The vaccine as developed by him induces reactions with great regularity and can be combined with immune serum for rapid immunization. In 1925 he distributed 50,000 doses of his more virulent spore vaccine, which induced reactions in 95 per cent of the animals vaccinated. Horses give more pronounced reactions than mules and cattle. Direct vaccination losses are insignificant and the method of combination of spore vaccine and serum can be used for hyperimmunization in serum production.

Eichhorn also has concentrated anthrax serum by a method analogous to that used with diphtheria antitoxin. Such serum, as prepared by the Bureau of Animal Industry of the United States, has been increasingly used in infections of man. In Jacobsohn's series of 61 cases, administration of the Eichhorn type of serum systematically and subcutaneously around the lesions was often followed by sterility of the blood stream,

---

[1] Pasteur, Chamberland and Roux, *Compt. rend. Acad. d. Sc.*, Paris, 1881, 92.

diminution of local lesions and recovery in 29 out of 36 treated cases. Regan lays stress on the importance of the local injections around the pustule.

The "barrage" of locally injected antianthrax serum around the lesion does not seem to be essential for the treatment of the disease in man. Sabolotnyi has obtained good results following subcutaneous or intravenous injection of the serum. The antianthrax therapeutic sera on the market in this country are usually given in doses of 30 to 100 c.c. by subcutaneous or intravenous injection. By the use of anti-anthrax serum the mortality from anthrax in man has been reduced from about 25 per cent to 8 per cent.

AEROBIC SPORE-BEARING BACILLI

The anthrax bacillus is the only pathogenic member of a large genus of gram-positive and gram-negative spore-bearing rod-shaped bacteria. The other members of this group, while nonpathogenic, are important for studies in general bacteriology and on account of their active metabolic processes when growing in soil and dead materials. These organisms, highly resistant to heat and chemicals when they are in the spore stage, dictate the methods used for the sterilization of culture media, the canning of foods, and other preservative processes. The products of their growth have valuable uses in the industries.

The custom of dividing spore-bearing bacteria into two genera on the basis of their oxygen requirements is gaining ground, although the intermediate micro-aerophilic forms and the range of tolerance of oxygen access and oxygen deprivation by all these organisms makes a sharply drawn dividing line unnatural. The generic name *Bacillus* is now usually applied only to the spore-bearing aerobes. The genus of spore-bearing anaerobes is called *Clostridium*.

The types of spore-bearing aerobes selected for mention in a textbook on medical bacteriology are those which resemble the anthrax bacillus. As many others are encountered in exudates, or superficial wounds or as contaminants of cultures, a general acquaintance with these bacilli is essential. For a description of them, the reader is referred to the serviceable and thorough studies of Ford and his associates.

The most important aerobic spore-bearers resembling *B. anthracis* are: *B. anthracoides, B. ramosus* and *B. subtilis.*

B. anthracoides (Hueppe and Wood).—A gram-positive bacillus, morphologically different from *B. anthracis* in that the ends are more rounded. Culturally, somewhat more rapid in growth and more rapid in gelatin fluidification. Nonpathogenic. Otherwise indistinguishable from *B. anthracis.*

B. ramosus (Wurzel Bacillus).—Cultivated from water—city water supplies. Morphologically somewhat larger than *B. anthracis,* and the individual bacilli more irregular in size. Very rapid liquefaction of gelatin and growth most active at room temperature. Nonpathogenic.

B. subtilis (Hay Bacillus).—Although not very closely related to the anthrax group, this bacillus is somewhat similar and conveniently described in this connection. It is of importance to workers with pathogenic bacteria, because of the frequency with which it is found as a saprophyte or secondary invader in chronic suppurative lesions.

Morphology and Cultivation.—Straight rod, 2 to 8 μ long, 0.7 μ wide. Spores formed usually slightly nearer one pole than the other. Grows in long chains and only in such chains are spores found. It does not decolorize by Gram's method. It is *actively motile* in young cultures in which the bacilli are single or in pairs. In older cultures chains are formed and the bacilli become motionless. Gelatin is liquefied. On gelatin and agar the bacilli grow as a dry corrugated pellicle. Microscopically, the colonies are made up of interlacing threads, being irregularly round with fringed edges. There is a tendency to confluence. The bacillus is found in brackish water, infusions of vegetable matter, etc., and is practically nonpathogenic, occurring only occasionally as a saprophyte in old sinuses and infected wounds.

Although *Bacillus subtilis* is the type species of the genus, there is still some disagreement as to what are its characteristics. The difficulties of taxonomy are clearly brought out in the papers of Soule and Conn, discussing the characteristics of *B. subtilis* and *B. cereus.*

REFERENCES

Ascoli, A. Ztschr. f. Immunitätsforsch. u. exper. Therap., 1911, 11:103.

Besredka, A. Ann. de l'Inst. Pasteur, 1921, 35:421.

————— Local Immunization; Specific Dressings. Translated by H. Plotz, Baltimore, 1927.

Blue. Pub. Health Rep., Wash., 1919, 35.

Chamberland and Roux. Compt. rend. Acad. d. sc., Paris, 1882, 96.

Chauveau. Compt. rend. Acad. d. sc., 1884.

Churchman, J. W. J. Exper. M., 1927, 46:1007.

Conn, H. J. J. Infect. Dis., 1930, 46:341.

Coutts. Reports to Local Gov. Board, London, 1917, N. S. 112.

Davaine. Compt. rend. Acad. d. sc., 1863, 57.

Dieudonné. Arb. a. d. k. Gsndhtsamte, 1894.

Eichhorn, A. U. S. Dep. Agric. Bull., 1915, 34:16.

————— J. Agric. Research, 1917, 8:37.

————— J. Am. Vet. M. Ass., 1925, 68:276.

Eppinger. Wien. med. Wchnschr., 1888.

Erilow, A. P., and Golotina, Z. J. Ztschr. f. Hyg. u. Infectionskrankh., 1926, 105:509.

Ford, W. W. Textbook of Bacteriology, Philadelphia, 1927, pp. 659–712.

Ford, W. W., *et al.* J. Bacteriol., 1916, 1 (series of papers).

Gratia, A. Compt. rend. Soc. de biol., 1924, 90:369.

Haag. Centralbl. f. Bakteriol., I Abt., orig., 1927, 104:463.

Hueppe and Wood. Berl. klin. Wchnschr., 1889, 16:347.

Iwanoff. Ann. de l'Inst. Pasteur, 1892.

Jacobsohn. Month. Bull. N. Y. City Dep. Health, 1923–24, 14:Nos. 3, 7.

Koch, R. In Cohn's Beitr. z. Biol. d. Pflanz, 1877, 2:277.

Koch, Gaffky, and Löffler. Mitt. a. d. k. Gsndhtsamte., 1884.

Koch and Wolffhuegel. Mitt. a. d. k. Gsndhtsamte., 1881.

Lebre, A. Ztschr. f. Immunitätsforsch. u. exper. Therap., 1912, 12:428.

Markhoff. Ztschr. f. Infectionskr. d. Haustiere., 1912, 12:Fasc. 2. Quoted from Gratia.

Momont. Ann. de l'Inst. Pasteur, 1892.

Nevodoff. Ann. de l'Inst. Pasteur, 1925, 29:888.

————— Compt. rend. Soc. de biol., 1926, 94:170.

Noble, A. J. Immunol., 1919, 4:105.

Nungester, W. J. J. Infect. Dis., 1929, 44:73.

Ottolenghi, D. Ztschr. f. Immunitätsforsch. u. exper. Therap., 1911, 9:769; 1912, 12:386.

Pasteur, Chamberland and Roux. Compt. rend. Acad. d. sc., Paris, 1881, 92.

Regan, J. C. Am. J. M. Sci., 1921, 162:406.

Rosenberg, R., and Romanow, D. Centralbl. f. Bakteriol., I Abt., 1929, 110:102.

SABOLOTNYI, S. S.   Centralbl. f. Bakteriol., I Abt., 1926, 99:53.

SCHOCKAERT, J.   Compt. rend. Soc. de biol., 1928, 99:1242.

SCLAVO, A.   Centralbl. f. Bakteriol., I Abt., 1895, 18:744.

SOBERNHEIM, G.   Ztschr. f. Hyg. u. Infectionskrankh., 1897, 25:301; 1899, 31.

———— In Kolle and Wassermann, Handbuch, etc., Vol. II.

SORDELLI, A.   Compt. rend. Soc. de biol., 1928, 99:1423.

SOULE, M. H.   J. Infect. Dis., 1925, 42:93; 1932, 51:191.

SURMONT and ARNOULD.   Ann. de l'Inst. Pasteur, 1894.

SYMMERS, D.   Ann. Surg., 1922, 75:663.

SYMMERS, D., and CADY, B. W.   J. Am. M. Ass., 1921, 77:2120.

TOUSSAINT.   Compt. rend. Acad. d. sc., Paris, 1880, 91.

VELU, H.   Ann. de l'Inst. Pasteur, 1927, 41:615.

CHAPTER XLV

ANAEROBIC BACILLI AND WOUND INFECTIONS— THE TETANUS BACILLUS AND TETANUS

Family: *Bacillaceae*. Genus: *Clostridium*. Species: *Clostridium tetani*

Lockjaw or tetanus, though a comparatively infrequent disease, has been recognized as a distinct clinical entity for many centuries. The infectious nature of the disease, however, was not demonstrated until 1884, when Carlo and Rattone succeeded in producing tetanus in rabbits by the inoculation of pus from the cutaneous lesion of a human case. Nicolaier, not long after, succeeded in producing tetanic

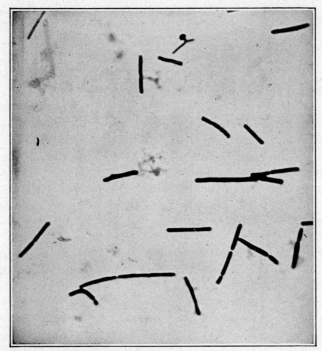

Fig. 62.—Bacillus Subtilis. (*See page 606*)

(Hay bacillus.)

symptoms in mice and rabbits by inoculating them with soil. From the lesions produced at the point of inoculation, Nicolaier described a bacillus which may have been *Bacillus tetani*, but which he was unable to isolate in pure culture. Kitasato, in 1889, definitely solved the etiological problem by obtaining from cases of tetanus pure cultures of bacilli with which he was able again to produce the disease in animals.

Kitasato succeeded where others had failed because of his use of anaerobic methods and his elimination of nonspore-bearing contaminating organisms by means of heat. His method of isolation was as follows: The material containing tetanus bacilli was smeared upon the surface of agar slants. These were permitted to develop at incubator temperature for twenty-four to forty-eight hours. At the end of this time the cultures were subjected to a temperature of 80° C. for one hour. The purpose of this was to destroy all nonsporulating bacteria, as well as aerobic spore-bearers which had developed into the vegetative form. Agar

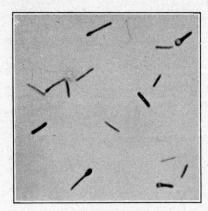

FIG. 63.—CLOSTRIDIUM TETANI.

Gram stain. × 1200. From culture seventy-two hours old, showing spores.

plates were then inoculated from the slants and exposed to an atmosphere from which oxygen had been completely eliminated and hydrogen substituted. On these plates colonies of tetanus bacilli developed.

Morphology and Staining.—The bacillus of tetanus is a slender bacillus, 2 to 5 μ in length, and 0.3 to 0.8 μ in breadth. The vegetative forms which occur chiefly in young cultures are slightly motile. They possess numerous peritrichal flagella. After twenty-four to forty-eight hours of incubation, the length of time depending somewhat on the nature of the medium and the degree of anaerobiosis, the bacilli develop spores which are characteristically located at one end, giving the bacterium the diagnostic drumstick appearance. As the cultures grow older the spore-bearing forms completely supersede the vegetative ones.

The tetanus bacillus is easily stained by the used aniline dyes. It is gram-positive. Flagella staining is successful only when very young cultures are employed.

Distribution.—The tetanus bacillus occurs in the superficial layers of the soil. The earth of cultivated and manured fields seems to harbor this organism with especial frequency, probably because of its presence in the feces of some of the domestic animals.

Biological Characteristics.—The bacillus of tetanus is generally described as an obligate anaerobe. While it is unquestionably true that growth is ordinarily obtained only in the complete absence of oxygen, various observers, notably Férran and Belfanti, have successfully habituated the bacillus to aerobic conditions by the gradual increase of oxygen in cultures. Habituation to aerobic conditions has usually been accompanied by diminution or loss of pathogenicity and toxin formation. Anaerobic conditions may likewise be dispensed with if tetanus bacilli be grown in symbiosis with some of the aerobic bacteria. The addition to culture media of suitable carbohydrates, and of fresh sterile tissue, has also been found to render it less exacting as to mechanical anaerobiosis.

Anaerobically cultivated, *B. tetani* grows readily upon meat infusion *broth*, which it clouds within twenty-four to thirty-six hours.

Upon meat infusion gelatin at 20° to 22° C. the tetanus bacillus grows readily, growth becoming visible during the second or third day. There is slow liquefaction of the gelatin

On *agar*, at 37.5° C., growth appears within forty-eight hours. Colonies on agar plates present a rather characteristic appearance, consisting of a compact center surrounded by a loose meshwork of fine filaments, not unlike the medusa-head appearance of subtilis colonies, but more delicate, translucent and fern-like. In agar stabs, fine radiating processes growing out in all directions from the central stab tend to give the culture the appearance of a fluff of cotton. Blood agar is hemolyzed. On fresh blood agar the growth spreads over the surface like a delicate sprig of maiden-hair fern. *Milk* is a favorable culture medium and is not coagulated. On *potato,* growth is delicate and hardly visible.

The most favorable temperature for the growth of this bacillus is 37.5° C. The optimum reaction for growth is pH 7.0 to 7.6. No growth occurs at pH below 6.4 or above 9.2. All the media named may be rendered more favorable still by the addition of 1 or 2 per cent of glucose, maltose, or sodium formate. In media containing certain carbohydrates, tetanus bacilli produce acid. In gelatin and agar, moderate amounts of gas are produced, consisting chiefly of carbon dioxide, but with the admixtures of other volatile substances which give rise to a characteristically unpleasant odor, not unlike that of putrefying organic matter. This odor is due largely to hydrogen sulphide and methylmercaptan. Cooked meat medium is very satisfactory for cultivation of the organism.

The vegetative forms of the tetanus bacillus are not more resistant to heat or chemical agents than the vegetative forms of other micro-organisms. Tetanus spores, however, will resist dry heat at 80° C. for about one hour, live steam for about five minutes; 5 per cent carbolic acid kills them in twelve to fifteen hours; 1 per cent of bichloride of mercury in two or three hours. Direct sunlight diminishes their virulence and eventually destroys them. Protected from sunlight and other deleterious influences, tetanus spores may remain viable and virulent for many years. Henrijean has reported success in producing tetanus with bacilli from a splinter of wood infected eleven years before.

During the years 1924 to 1927, Fildes made a thorough investigation of the biology of *Bacillus tetanus* and the pathogenesis of tetanus. The results of these studies with a review of the older literature were brought together by him in 1929 in a valuable summary, on which we have drawn in the preparation of material for this chapter and which should be consulted by the student of this subject on account of its wealth of factual detail.

The *germination of spores* occurs only under conditions of oxygen tension lower than that in normal tissues. The failure of spores to germinate in normal tissues and the rôle played by necrotic tissue in forming a favorable nidus for the development of tetanus spores in the body are thus explained.

The organism is slightly *saccharolytic.* Only a few strains produced detectable acidity from glucose (Reddish and Rettger).

Dissociation.—Smooth and rough colonies, motile and nonmotile variants were obtained.

Serology.—By agglutination and absorption of agglutinins, strains of tetanus bacilli were divisible into 9 types. (Gunnison.)

Types I, III, and V were markedly specific. In the agglutination reactions, coarse loose clumps were formed with some strains, finely granular compact clumps with others. These differences could be correlated with the H, flagellar, antigens of the motile strains, and the O, somatic, antigens of the nonmotile varieties. The H type of coarse agglutination was often strictly specific, while the O, fine flocculating reaction, was in this case as in others, indicative of broader group relationships.

Isolation.—For the isolation of *Bacillus tetani* from an infected wound, Fildes recommended the following method:

1. Excise tissue of the wound. Material taken on swabs or pipets is unsatisfactory.
2. Place the tissue in a tube of Tulloch's medium (meat infusion exhausted by growth of bacteria). [See section on Technic.] Heat this for 1½ hours at 65° C. in order to destroy vegetative forms of aerobes. Incubate this culture containing the piece of tissue for 3 or 4 days at 37° C. An anaerobic jar is not necessary.
3. Transfer a drop of this culture to the bottom of a slanted tube of Fildes' influenza medium (peptic-blood digest agar. See section on Technic). The medium selected for this should be so dried that the apex of the slant is hard. Incubate this for 24 hours at 37° C. under anaerobic conditions.
4. After 24 hours a film of growth, with characteristic filamentous upper edge, appears in a positive case. A pure culture of the tetanus bacillus can at times be secured from the edge of this filamentous spreading growth.[1]

Toxin.—The pathogenicity of the tetanus bacillus depends entirely upon the soluble toxin (*tetanospasmin*) which it produces. This toxin is produced in suitable media by all strains of virulent tetanus bacilli. While partial aerobiosis does not completely eliminate toxin formation, anaerobic conditions are by far more favorable for its development.

The medium most frequently employed for the production of tetanus toxin is neutral or slightly alkaline beef-infusion bouillon containing 0.5 per cent sodium chloride and 1 per cent peptone. Glucose or sodium formate may be added, but while these substances increase the speed of growth of the bacilli they do not seem to enhance the degree of toxicity of the cultures. Glucose is said even to be unfavorable for strong toxin development. It is important, too, that the bouillon shall be freshly prepared. There does not seem to be any direct relationship between the amount of growth and the degree of toxicity of the cultures. Under anaerobic conditions in suitable bouillon and grown at 34° to 35° C., the maximum toxin content of the cultures is reached in from ten days to two weeks. After this time the toxin deteriorates rapidly.

Tetanus toxin, in solution in the bouillon cultures, may be separated from the bacteria by filtration through Berkefeld or Chamberland filters. Since the poison in such filtrates deteriorates very rapidly, much more rapidly even than diphtheria toxin, various methods have been devised to obtain the toxin in the solid state. The most useful of these is precipitation of the toxin out of solution by saturation with ammonium sulphate. Very little of the toxin is lost by this method and, thoroughly dried and stocked in vacuum tubes, together with anhydrous phosphoric acid, it may be preserved indefinitely without deterioration. The precipitate thus formed is easily soluble in water or salt solution, and therefore permits of the preparation of uniform solutions for purposes of standardization.

Brieger and Boer precipitated the toxin out of broth solution with zinc chloride. Vaillard and Vincent have procured it in the dry state by evaporation *in vacuo*.

---

[1] P. Fildes, *Brit. J. Exper. Pathol.*, 1925, 6:62.

Brieger and Cohn, Brieger and Boer, and others have attempted to isolate tetanus poison, removing the proteins from the ammonium sulphate precipitate by various chemical methods. The purest preparations obtained by them were in the form of fine yellowish flakes, soluble in water, insoluble in alcohol and ether. Solutions of this substance have failed to give the usual protein reactions.

The toxin when in solution is extremely sensitive to heat. Kitasato states that exposure to 68° C. for five minutes destroys it completely. Dry toxin is more resistant, often withstanding temperatures of 120° C. for more than fifteen minutes. Exposure to direct sunlight destroys the poison in fifteen to eighteen hours. Flexner and Noguchi found that 5 per cent eosin added to the toxin would destroy it within one hour. This action is ascribed to the photodynamic power of the eosin. Jungeblut found that vitamin C (l-ascorbic acid) inactivated tetanus toxin *in vitro* but failed to confer complete protection against tetanus intoxication *in vivo*.

Tetanus toxin is one of the most powerful poisons known to us. Filtrates of broth cultures in quantities of 0.000005 c.c., will often prove fatal to mice of 20 grams weight. Dry toxin obtained by ammonium sulphate precipitation is quantitatively even stronger, values of 0.000001 gram as a lethal dose for a mouse of the given weight not being uncommon. Brieger and Cohn succeeded in producing a dry toxin capable of killing mice in doses of 0.00000005 gram.

In 1936 Eaton purified tetanus toxin by modification of procedures he had used for the isolation of diphtheria toxin. Approximately 99.5 per cent of the impurities were removed. The final preparation gave biuret, Millon's, xanthoproteic, diazo and sulphur reactions. It appeared to be a protein, but this is not certain. In the purest preparation the M. L. D. for a 500 gram guinea-pig containing 0.000009 to 0.000018 mgm. N.

Different species of animals vary greatly in their susceptibility to tetanus toxin. Human beings are extremely susceptible. We have heard of cases of general and sometimes fatal tetanus occurring in men who were only scratched by a needle which had been used for the injection of the toxin into a horse. Man is said to be as susceptible as the horse. The hen, on the other hand, is extremely resistant to the toxin— approximately 360,000 times more resistant than the horse. A useful table of relative susceptibilities of animals is quoted from Fildes [2] as follows:

RELATIVE AMOUNT OF TOXIN REQUIRED TO KILL 1 GRAM OF ANIMAL

Horse	1	Goat	6
Guinea-pig	2	Rabbit	24
Monkey	3	Dog	300
Mouse	4	Cat	2400

After the inoculation of an animal with tetanus toxin there is always a definite period of incubation, from 8 to 24 hours, before the toxic spasms set in. The site of injection, species of animal and amount of toxin injected influence the length of the incubation period. This period may be shortened by increase of the dose, but never entirely eliminated. When the toxin is injected subcutaneously, spasms begin first in the muscles nearest the point of inoculation. Intravenous inoculation, on the other hand, usually results in general tetanus of all the muscles. The feeding of toxin does

2 P. Fildes, *A System of Bacteriology in Relation to Medicine*, London, 1929, vol. 3, p. 308.

not produce disease. The toxin is destroyed by the acid of the gastric juice and by proteolytic enzymes in the gastro-intestinal tract.

The harmful action of tetanus toxin is generally attributed to its affinity for the central nervous system, where it exerts a strychnin-like action. Wassermann and Takaki showed that tetanus toxin was fully neutralized when mixed with brain substance. Other organs—liver and spleen, for instance—showed no such neutralizing power. The central origin of the tetanic contractions was made very evident by the work of Gumprecht, who succeeded in stopping the spasms in a given region by division of the supplying motor nerves.

The manner in which the toxin is transported to the central nervous system has been extensively investigated. Marie and Morax, followed by Meyer and Ransom, provided a great deal of experimental evidence which appeared to show that the toxin reached the cells of the central nervous system by way of the motor nerves. According to this theory, the toxin is absorbed by the endings of the motor nerves and thence passes to the cells in the cord or brain via the axis cylinders. Teale and Embleton, among others, demonstrated that the supposed transport of the toxin through perineural lymph spaces could not occur. Before 1934, almost all investigators of this problem appeared to accept the opinion that the cells of the central nervous system could not absorb toxin from the blood stream, but were affected by the toxin only when it was conveyed to them through the axis cylinder of a motor nerve.

An attack upon all the older conceptions of the transport of tetanus toxin by way of the nerves was begun by Abel in 1934. With his associates Hampil, Firor and others he has supplied much experimental evidence to show that (1) tetanus toxin, absorbed by lymphatics is carried by the blood stream to the central nervous system and (2) there are probably two components in the toxin, one which acts upon the cells of the central nervous system, producing clonic spasm and another which acts directly upon the muscles, producing tonic contractions. Firor, in 1938, found that tetanus toxin is changed to an even more poisonous substance in the spinal cord of dogs.

Tetanolysin.—Tetanus bouillon contains, besides "tetanospasmin" another substance discovered by Ehrlich and named by him "tetanolysin." Tetanolysin has the power of causing hemolysis of the red blood corpuscles of various animals, and is an entirely separate substance from tetanospasmin. It may be separated from tetanospasmin by treating the toxic broth with red blood cells. The lysin is more thermolabile than the tetanospasmin. It gives rise to an antihemolysin when injected into animals. Oxidation of the lysin by exposure to air rapidly inactivates it (Neill).

Pathogenicity.—The comparative infrequency of tetanus infection is in marked contrast to the wide distribution of the bacilli in nature. Introduced into the animal body as spores, and free from toxin, they may often fail to incite disease, easily falling prey to phagocytosis and other protective agencies before the vegetative forms develop and toxin is formed. The protective importance of phagocytosis was demonstrated by Vaillard and Rouget who introduced tetanus spores inclosed in paper sacs into the animal body. By the paper capsules the spores were protected from the leukocytes, not from the body fluids. Nevertheless, tetanus developed in the animals. The nature of the wound and the simultaneous presence of other micro-organisms seem to be important factors in determining whether or not the tetanus bacilli shall be enabled to proliferate. Deep, lacerated wounds, in which there has been consider-able tissue destruction, and in which chips of glass, wood splinters, or grains of dirt have become embedded, are particularly favorable for the development of these germs. The injuries of compound fractures and of gunshot wounds are especially liable to supply these conditions, and the presence in such wounds of the common pus cocci, or of other more harmless parasites, may aid materially in furnishing an environ-ment suitable for the growth of the tetanus bacilli. Apart from its occurrence fol-lowing trauma, tetanus has been not infrequently observed after childbirth, and iso-lated cases have been reported in which it has followed diphtheria and ulcerative lesions of the throat.

A definite *period of incubation* elapses between the time of infection with tetanus bacilli and the development of the first symptoms. In man this may last from five to seven days in acute cases, to from four to five weeks in the more chronic ones. Experi-mental inoculation of guinea-pigs is followed usually in from one to three days by rigidity of the muscles nearest the point of infection. This spastic condition rapidly extends to other parts and finally leads to death, which occurs within four or five days after infection.

Autopsies upon human beings or animals dead of tetanus reveal few and insig-nificant lesions. The initial point of infection, if at all evident, is apt to be small and innocent in appearance. Further than a general and moderate congestion, the organs show no pathological changes. Bacilli are found sparsely even at the point of infection, and have been but rarely demonstrated in the blood or viscera. Nicolaier succeeded in producing tetanus with the organs of infected animals in but 11 out of 52 cases. Tizzoni and Creite have succeeded in cultivating tetanus bacilli out of the spleen and heart's blood of infected human beings.

Spores may be transported from the site of inoculation to the liver, spleen, and other organs, and there lie dormant for as long as fifty-one days. If injury of the organ is experimentally produced and dead tissue or blood clot produced, the spores may develop and tetanus ensue. These experiments may explain cases of so-called cryptogenic tetanus.

In man tetanus may take either an acute or chronic form, the word "chronic" here meaning simply that the onset is less abrupt, the incubation time longer, the symptoms slower in development and the prognosis more favorable. In the acute form, the incubation time ranges from three or four days to ten or fourteen days, the common, very rapid cases taking about seven. In the so-called chronic form the incubation time may occasionally exceed a month. The first symptoms usually consist in headache and general depression followed rather rapidly by difficulty in swallow-ing and in opening the mouth, due to spasms or trismus of the masseters. There is slight stiffness of the neck which makes it difficult for the patient to bring the chin forward on the chest. Gradually there develops a spasm of the muscles of the cheeks which results in a drawing up of the tissues about the mouth, giving a curious and characteristic expression, the so-called *risus sardonicus*. Gradually the spasms extend to the trunk and back, with the development of opisthotonos after several days. Increased difficulty in swallowing may ensue, and there may be involuntary evacuation of urine and feces. The localization of the symptoms to some extent follows the location of the injury. Tetanus may occur in the newborn, occasionally, developing soon after birth. For differential diagnosis, it is best to refer to books on general medicine and surgery.

Many types of atypical tetanus in untreated and in prophylactically treated cases have been reported, a description of which can be found *in extenso* in the volume on *The Abnormal Forms of Tetanus* by Courtois-Suffit and Giroux in the British Medical War Manuals, published in 1918. They speak of splanchnic tetanus characterized especially by the involvement of the muscles of deglutition and respiration, with great dysphagia. Simple cephalic tetanus in which the infection may be confined to the head, is a type in which dysphagic and paralytic symptoms are never present, and which result most frequently from wounds of the head. It may be characterized only by unilateral and bilateral trismus, or by contraction of muscles of the face. There is, however, a dysphagic form of this in which pharyngeal spasms precede trismus. Rarely they have noticed a so-called hydrophobic form in which convulsions accompany the spasms.

Prophylactic Use of Tetanus Antitoxin.[3]—The most important use for tetanus antitoxin which has been found hitherto, is its prophylactic administration. The methods of applying this have varied in different parts of the world and in different armies. That it is of great value was demonstrated by the almost immediate reduction of tetanus in wounded soldiers after the universal introduction of prophylactic tetanus antitoxin in all the armies in the field. The wounds which are particularly dangerous as far as tetanus is concerned are those in which there is considerable laceration, especially injury to bone, and in which dirt, and especially manured soil or soil from cultivated fields, and feces, are likely to be present. The growth of tetanus bacilli is favored by the presence of dead tissue and other infected organisms. Studies by members of the United States Public Health Service have shown that tetanus can be produced with regularity if staphylococcus infection is added to the infection with tetanus spores, and injury of tissue by the injection of small quantities of such substances as quinine, may start the growth of latent tetanus spores with subsequent development of the disease. Tetanus spores pass through the intestinal canals of animals and man without injury, and are distributed in the soil where they can live for almost unlimited periods. Wounds inflicted upon men in the field, especially by the blunt and ragged projectiles of high explosives, and by any injury passing through soil- and filth-covered clothing, through unwashed skin, furnish an ideal nidus for infection. In consequence, in practically all the Allied Armies every wounded man was given an injection of about one thousand to fifteen hundred units of tetanus antitoxin as soon after the injury as he came under medical observation. In civilian life, the wounds that require similar prophylactic treatment are those inflicted with much traumatism and under dirty conditions, especially those in which compound fractures are involved.

We refrain from giving any set rules for prophylactic treatment. The principles involved are that the injection of from five hundred to fifteen hundred or even up to five thousand units should be made subcutaneously as soon as possible after the injury. It should be remembered that the first injection may not be sufficient. The antitoxin gradually disappears in the course of about twelve days, and wounds that are slow in cleaning up or cases in which secondary interference, such as removal

[3] The preparation and standardization of tetanus antitoxin have been described in Section II.

of sequestrum, resetting of bones, etc., becomes necessary, may call for a second injection after six to eight days, with due precautions to prevent anaphylaxis. In such cases, according to the judgment of the surgeon, second injections should become almost the rule since experience in the World War showed that after two injections tetanus is very rare in appearance.

Treatment of Developed Tetanus.—To speak of the specific treatment of tetanus without saying a few words about the surgical treatment would be taking the risk of conveying a false impression. Therefore, though our business here is concerned largely with specific treatment, we wish to emphasize that surgical treatment must always be carried out whatever method of serum therapy be employed. This must consist in thoroughly cleansing the wound, removal of foreign bodies, fragments of projectiles, clothing, gross dirt, etc., and, as the late War has shown, it is perhaps best whenever possible to carry out débridement or excision of the wound. From Tulloch's studies it would appear that no dressing is particularly superior to any other and we doubt very much whether oxidizing agents, like the insufflation of oxygen, peroxides, etc., are of much use, because of the reducing powers of tissues.

As to specific serum treatment, it must be admitted that earlier results were very disappointing, and the mere subcutaneous injection even of large doses of tetanus antitoxin has usually been disappointing in the acute forms of the disease. This has perhaps been largely due to the fact that the injected antitoxin could have no possible influence on the toxin which had already become united with the substances of the nerve tissues. A great many modifications in the method of injection have been employed, such as injection directly into the central nervous system and into the nerve trunks, themselves. It may be stated that the relative acuteness of the tetanus infection very definitely influences the results of serum therapy. The following table [4] gives a general idea of the usefulness of serum therapy in this disease:

Incubation (days)	Recoveries	Deaths	Mortality (per cent)	Mortality before the Introduction of Serotherapy, according to Brunner (per cent)
1 to 5	3	7	70	90
5 to 10	20	7	29	70
10 to 12	7	1	13.3	....
Over 12	15	1	6.6	....

Various methods of administering tetanus antitoxin have been tried. Intraspinous administration of tetanus antitoxin was advised some years ago by Park and Nicoll and by Doyen in France. A spinal puncture was made, a moderate amount of spinal fluid taken out and then, 3000 to 5000 units slowly injected. This was combined with intravenous or intramuscular injection. Experience of the last few years indicates that intraspinous administration is not effective and should not be recommended. Success

4 This table cited from Courtois-Suffit and Giroux, Military Medical Manuals, University of London Press, London, 1918, p. 193.

CHAPTER XLVI

ANAEROBIC BACILLI AND WOUND INFECTIONS

BACILLUS WELCHII AND ANAEROBIC BACTERIA ASSOCIATED WITH TRAUMATIC INJURIES

Family: *Bacillaceae*. Genus: *Clostridium*

The anaerobic bacilli which infect wounds were studied extensively during the World War, and the literature which has appeared on this subject since 1914 is voluminous. Unfortunately much that has been written is inaccurate, due to the fact that in many instances the work was carried on in poorly equipped laboratories and under difficulties. The two most important sources of confusion in this field are: the nomenclature and the impurity of cultures. During the War many previously described bacilli were rediscovered and given new names, and the literature is full of papers claiming or disclaiming that certain organisms isolated from wounds are identical with organisms described by earlier workers. Even such a well-known species as *B. welchii* appears in the literature under four names.

Most of the early descriptions of anaerobic bacilli cannot be relied upon, because of the extreme difficulty of isolating the anaerobes in pure culture. Many investigators even during the first year of the War were describing a mixture of two or more anaerobes when they thought they were dealing with a pure culture. It was not until the development of the newer anaerobic methods which made surface growths feasible that the purity of anaerobic cultures could be relied upon. It is only by repeated plating of these anaerobic spore-bearing bacilli, as emphasized repeatedly by English workers, that pure cultures can be obtained. Barber's technic for the isolation of a single bacillus has applied also to the problem of the purification of the anaerobic bacilli.

Anaerobic bacilli in war wounds can always be traced to the contamination of the wound either directly or indirectly with fecally contaminated soil. Most of the anaerobic bacilli have been shown to be normal inhabitants of the intestinal tract of man or animals, and are present in great numbers in cultivated ground.

In civilian practice gas gangrene is generally attributed to the presence of *B. welchii*. In war wounds, however, it was found that although *B. welchii* was isolated from the majority of the cases of gas gangrene, it practically never occurred in pure culture, and was usually associated, besides aerobes, with other anaerobic bacilli which in many instances proved to be more pathogenic than *B. welchii*.

In this book only the most important and frequently occurring anaerobic bacilli will be discussed. The reader is referred for more detailed description to the book of Weinberg and Seguin, and to the Report of the British Medical Research Committee (Douglas, Fleming and Colebrook). In this country, Hall and Heller (1921) have succeeded in purifying many cultures of these and other anaerobic bacilli and have contributed valuable information on the bacteriology of the organisms. The classifications of Hall have been used with modifications by Ford, Bergey and others.

The anaerobic bacilli found in war wounds can be divided into two general groups, as first suggested by von Hibler in his book on anaerobes, published in 1908: the saccharolytic and the proteolytic.

The saccharolytic group includes as its most important members: *B. welchii*, *vibrion septique*, *B. oedematiens*, *B. fallax*.

The proteolytic group includes: *B. sporogenes*, *B. histolyticus*, *B. putrificus*.

This classification, like most others, is not a rigid one. It merely means that members of the saccharolytic group have a much greater avidity for carbohydrates than have members of the proteolytic group.

It may be possible to demonstrate proteolytic activity of the organisms included in the saccharolytic group on special media from which all carbohydrate has been removed, but on the ordinary culture media the difference between the two groups is striking.

Members of the proteolytic group can be distinguished from the saccharolytic group by the fact that they liquefy coagulated horse serum. Organisms of the saccharolytic group fail to liquefy this medium even after prolonged incubation. In milk the saccharolytic bacilli produce acid and varying amounts of gas. The proteolytic bacilli digest milk with the production of alkali.

The organisms of the proteolytic group are not in themselves pathogenic, but complicate wounds by their intense proteolytic action. They are saprophytes, they have no power of invading the tissues and if present without members of the saccharolytic group usually do not interfere with the healing of the wound.

Whether the organisms of the saccharolytic group are saprophytes or not, is an open question. De Kruif concludes that *B. welchii* cannot be classified as a pure saprophyte, because a twice washed bacillary emulsion of some strains in doses of 0.1 c.c. to 1 c.c. will kill a guinea-pig. But in this case even the most careful intramuscular injection will kill some of the tissue at the point of inoculation, and with even a very small amount of dead tissue, *B. welchii* can produce a toxin which has tremendous aggressive action and has the property of killing the tissue with which it comes in contact. This makes possible the further invasion of *B. welchii*.

A review of the serological relations among the toxigenic anaerobes was published by McCoy and McClung in 1938. The serological relationships are not always in harmony with present taxonomic schemes.

B. Welchii.[1]—*B. welchii* is the organism most frequently found in gas gangrene. It was present in about 72 to 80 per cent of the cases of gas gangrene studied during the World War, and has been consistently associated with civilian cases of gas gangrene. It is generally considered the most important etiological factor in this disease. On the other hand, it must also be stated that *B. welchii* was frequently present in wounds which never developed gangrene. Taylor reports that *B. welchii* was found in 80 per cent of all wounds examined and that only 10 per cent of these developed gas gangrene. The development of gas gangrene depends on the virulence of the strain of *B. welchii*, the amount of dead tissue present, and the anaerobic conditions in the wound. In war wounds *B. welchii* was practically never present in pure culture.

1 Species: *Clostridium perfringens.*

It was usually associated with anaerobes of the saccharolytic and the proteolytic type.

B. welchii was discovered independently in three countries. It was first discovered by Welch and Nuttall in 1892, and called by them *Bacillus aerogenes capsulatus,* a name still used by the majority of English writers. In this country this organism is usually called *B. welchii.* Welch isolated it from the blood and organs of a cadaver dead eight hours. In 1893 Fränkel isolated a similar organism in Germany from several cases of gaseous phlegmons, calling it *B. phlegmonis emphysematosae,* but soon recognized that he was working with the same bacillus previously described by Welch. However, this organism is still referred to as the Fränkel bacillus in German literature. In 1897, without having heard either of Welch's or Fränkel's work, this organism was again described by Veillon and Zuber in France and called by them *B. perfringens. B. welchii, B. aerogenes capsulatus,* Fränkel bacillus, *B. perfringens* are all names for the same organism.

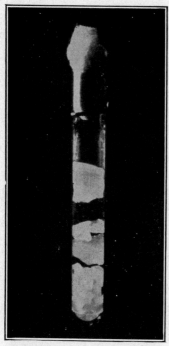

FIG. 64.—CLOSTRIDIUM WELCHII.

Culture in dextrose infusion agar showing fragmentation of the medium by gas after twenty-four hours' incubation at 37° C.

B. welchii is a short, plump gram-positive bacillus, occurring singly or in pairs. Chains are not formed as a rule. It is nonmotile and has a capsule. It grows best under strictly anaerobic conditions, but its requirements for anaerobiosis are less rigid than those of *B. tetani.* It grows well in media containing tissue such as cooked meat medium after simple boiling. With milk boiling is not always sufficient to obtain good growth, and it is best to put milk tubes in anaerobic jars. The majority of strains do not form spores readily. Alkaline sugar-free media rich in protein, such as alkaline egg, are necessary to demonstrate spore formation with the majority of strains. The spore of *B. welchii* is large, oval, and central or subterminal. *B. welchii* is the most active fermenter in the saccharolytic group. It ferments all the common sugars with the production of large amounts of gas. Lactic and butyric are the two acids most frequently formed, the latter often giving cultures of *B. welchii* a characteristic odor. Glucose agar is sometimes fragmented to such an extent that the plug is blown off the tube. Simonds has been able to divide the *B. welchii* group into subdivisions depending on the ability to ferment either glycerin or inulin, or both, or neither, and this classification has been confirmed by Henry. In wounds, *B. welchii* ferments the muscle sugar producing gas in the tissues and for this reason is commonly called the "gas" bacillus. The crepitation thus produced is characteristic of gas gangrene and indicates the extent of the infection. The rapid fermentation of the lactose in milk gives a characteristic reaction in this medium which is diagnostic for *B. welchii.* The acid clot torn by gas bubbles and the separation of the milk into coagulum and whey is easily recognized and is not given by other anaerobes. The inoculation of a mixed culture from a wound into milk makes possible the diagnosis of B. welchii within twelve to eighteen hours.

Opinions as to the ability of B. welchii to liquefy gelatin vary greatly. B. welchii does not grow well on sugar-free gelatin and it is, therefore, difficult to draw conclusions as to its action on gelatin. B. welchii, as pointed out by Rettger in 1906, never attacks proteins if carbohydrates are present and even in the absence of carbohydrate shows only a very slight proteolytic activity. No indole is formed from broth, and coagulated serum is not liquefied or blackened. The organism is definitely not proteolytic.

Verder has described five distinct colony types of B. welchii. Among these the smooth types resembled colonies of smooth motile varieties of Salmonella. The rough colonies were of a spreading type, with finely fimbriated edges or deep corrugations. The morphology of the organisms varied considerably.

The hemolytic power and pathogenicity of different strains of B. welchii vary greatly. B. welchii is particularly pathogenic for guinea-pigs and pigeons, the latter being used in the standardization of B. welchii toxin. B. welchii in fatal cases usually invades the blood stream shortly before death, and can usually be isolated from the blood after death. Spores are never formed in the animal body. Rabbits and mice are much less susceptible.

Agglutinin production in response to injections of B. welchii in rabbits and horses is extremely poor (Robertson). Simonds obtained a serum in rabbits which agglutinated the homologous strain in a dilution of 1:80. Ten strains of B. welchii failed to agglutinate with this serum, and ten others agglutinated only in a dilution of 1:20. The agglutination reaction for the identification of anaerobes has so far proved unsatisfactory.

Toxin Production.—Klose in 1916 reported the isolation of a toxin from B. welchii prepared by growing B. welchii for fourteen days in a 5 per cent glucose broth. The antitoxin produced by injections of this toxin only protected guinea-pigs against three lethal doses of B. welchii cultures. The antigenic properties of this toxin were too feeble to consider it a true toxin. The most important contribution to the bacteriology of B. welchii was made in 1917 by Bull and Pritchett who were able to prepare a soluble toxin which, when injected into a suitable animal, produced a potent antitoxin possessing protective and curative properties against B. welchii infections in animals. One c.c. of antitoxin per 100 grams body weight injected subcutaneously protected guinea-pigs against three hundred lethal doses of culture. The production of a powerful toxin (0.3 c.c. to 3 c.c. being the M. L. D. for a pigeon of 300 grams injected intramuscularly) depended on the virulence of strain, a short incubation period, twenty-one to twenty-four hours, and the presence of fresh muscle and glucose in the broth. Bull and Pritchett found no variations in the ability of different strains of B. welchii, irrespective of the source of the culture, to produce toxin. The toxin production of less active strains could be increased by raising the virulence of the culture by animal passage. Caulfield found that he did not get good toxin production unless the virulence of his strain was such that 0.02 c.c. of supernatant fluid of a young broth culture would kill a 300-gram pigeon. Caulfield also emphasized the importance of fresh muscle in the culture medium, although De Kruif and the Hygienic Laboratory in Washington obtained good results by substituting chopped veal, which can be autoclaved, for the fresh muscle tissue. The most potent toxins, however, seem to be obtained by inoculating the infected muscle of a pigeon dying of a *B. welchii* infection directly into the medium to be used for toxin production, or, at most, allowing one short culture generation (ten hours) to intervene between the last animal passage and the inoculation of the broth for toxin. By preparing a toxin in this way, Bengtson of the Hygienic Laboratory has been able to prepare a *B. welchii* antitoxin in which 1 c.c. of serum contains one unit, one unit neutralizing one thousand M. L. D. of *B. welchii* toxin. It is now recognized that different types of *B. welchii* produce somewhat different toxins and that the toxins themselves are complex.

In laboratory animals infected with pure cultures of *B. welchii*, the antitoxin gives complete protection. Protection in laboratory animals is also afforded by injections of antimicrobial sera prepared by injections of whole broth culture of *B. welchii* by Weinberg and Seguin, but the antitoxin content of these sera has not been determined.

Bull and Pritchett in their original paper state that the toxin produced by *B. welchii* is comparable to the toxins produced by tetanus and diphtheria, and judged by its antigenic properties it must certainly be classified as a true exotoxin. It differs from the classical toxins in that toxin production varies directly with the virulence of the strain and that it has no definite incubation period. *B. welchii* antitoxin cannot protect against mixed infections where *B. welchii* is associated with either vibrion septique or *B. oedematiens*. In this case the animal always dies of the vibrion septique or *B. oedematiens* infection. However, since both these organisms occur in a smaller percentage of cases and have rarely been isolated from civilian cases of gas gangrene, *B. welchii* antitoxin will probably prove of great value.

Isolation.—*B. welchii* is a normal inhabitant of the intestinal tract of adults and may be found in the stools of infants. Simonds found *B. welchii* present in 8 out of 19 stools of babies under one year of age. It can be easily isolated from stools by the following procedure:

Five c.c. of a fecal suspension in saline are inoculated into a tube of milk which has been freshly boiled and cooled. The tube is heated at 80° C. for one hour to kill off the vegetative forms of the fecal flora, and is then incubated. The development of the stormy fermentation described above indicates the presence of *B. welchii*. Purification is best completed by plating anaerobically from the milk culture.

Animal inoculation is also useful in the isolation of *B. welchii*. The material suspected of containing *B. welchii* is injected intravenously into a rabbit. After five minutes the rabbit is killed and placed in the incubator for five to eight hours. At the end of this time, the animal is usually distended with gas. At autopsy gas bubbles will be found distributed throughout the organs, especially in the liver. *B. welchii*, if present, can usually be isolated from the liver and the heart's blood. Cultures can also be identified by injecting them intramuscularly into two guinea-pigs, one normal, the other protected by a dose of *B. welchii* antitoxin. If both pigs die, and an anaerobic organism is isolated from the heart's blood, it indicates the presence of some other pathogenic anaerobe, not *B. welchii*. If the normal pig dies with an anaerobic, capsulated, nonmotile gram-positive bacillus in the heart's blood, and the antitoxin pig survives, it is a fairly sure indication that the organism in question is *B. welchii*.

B. welchii is an important micro-organism in medical bacteriology for several other reasons besides its pathogenic action in wounds.

It has been suggested that the constant absorption of the hemolysin liberated by the Welch bacillus in the intestine might produce pernicious anemia. Reed and his associates have shown that repeated injection of this hemolysin into rabbits produces anemia and blood cell changes resembling those seen in pernicious anemia. But the progressive disease has not been reproduced in this manner.

Kendall has described an intestinal intolerance for carbohydrates associated with overgrowth of the Welch bacillus in the intestine. It is not improbable that certain cases of intestinal distention associated with frothy diarrhea are due to the action of *B. welchii* upon fermentable material in the intestines, producing considerable volumes of gas, (Simonds).

The toxic symptoms of intestinal obstruction have been attributed to the absorption of poisons elaborated by the Welch bacillus in the closed intestinal loop (Williams). Stabins and Kennedy found a great increase in the numbers of *B. welchii* in closed jejunal loops of dogs, confirming the occurrence of the organism in obstructed intestines.

B. welchii has been used as a commercial "bread starter" on account of its vigorous fermentation of dough (Koser). Occasionally it occurs in public water supplies. When taken by mouth, in bread or water, the organism does not appear to exert any pathogenic action.

Vibrion Septique.[2]—Vibrion septique, according to Weinberg and Seguin, occurred in 12 per cent of the wounds examined by them. Henry isolated it in 16 per cent of his cases. Before the World War, cases of human gas gangrene due to vibrion septique alone were very few in number. Such cases were described by Ghon and Sachs, by von Hibler, Gould, and by Muir and Ritchie. During the War, vibrion septique was usually associated with other anaerobes, notably *B. welchii.* Weinberg and Seguin cite only one case of gas gangrene in which vibrion septique was the only anaerobe present.

Vibrion septique was first described by Pasteur in 1877, who isolated it from the blood of a cow dead three days, and from the blood of a horse dead one day, both animals having supposedly died of anthrax. Pasteur called this organism a vibrion, although it is in reality a bacillus, because it is extremely motile in animal exudates and may look slightly curved when in motion. In 1881, Koch, in studying the etiology of anthrax, isolated an organism which he called the bacillus of malignant edema. Koch considered his organism identical with Pasteur's vibrion septique, although the bacillus of malignant edema had marked proteolytic properties, which Pasteur did not mention in the description of vibrion septique. A great amount of confusion has arisen out of this controversy and the literature is full of papers discussing whether or not Pasteur and Koch were working with the same organisms and with attempts to identify organisms isolated from wounds with one or the other of these bacilli. The majority of workers now consider that Pasteur was working with a strictly saccharolytic organism which is identical with what we call vibrion septique at the present time. The bacillus of malignant edema of Koch is thought by most investigators to belong to the proteolytic group and is fairly definitely identified with *B. sporogenes.*

Vibrion septique is a motile, slender gram-positive bacillus with slightly rounded

2 Synonyms: bacillus of Ghon and Sachs and bacillus III of von Hibler. Species: *Clostridium septicum.*

ends. It is a strict anaerobe. It forms spores readily in most media. The spore is oval, occurring either centrally or subterminally, and appears at the end of twenty-four to forty-eight hours. It has no capsule. It ferments the common sugars with the exception of saccharose. It produces a loose clot in milk in one to four days. Gelatin is liquefied, but coagulated serum is not attacked. Vibrion septique is hemolytic. It is always pathogenic for laboratory animals and guinea-pigs, mice, pigeons and rabbits are all susceptible. It invades the blood stream, producing a septicemia. The occurrence of long filamentous forms in the livers of guinea-pigs dying of a vibrion septique infection is characteristic and is used in the identification of vibrion septique.

Robertson divided the vibrion septique group into four serological types, based upon the agglutination reaction. Robertson again stresses the necessity of minute care in purifying cultures and points out that impure cultures fail to agglutinate. It is difficult, however, to attach much importance to variations in agglutinin production of different strains, since there is no difference in toxin production, and since the antitoxin produced by the injection of the toxin of strains belonging to one serological type neutralizes the toxins produced by members of the other types. The agglutination reaction in the case of vibrion septique subdivides strains that agree in every other respect, and may in this instance be regarded as ultraspecific, as Robertson suggests. She was able to obtain agglutinating sera with a titer of 1: 25,000.

Toxin Production.—A powerful soluble toxin is produced by all strains of vibrion septique and does not depend on the virulence of the culture. According to Robertson, as potent toxins are produced by old laboratory strains of vibrion septique as by recently isolated cultures. The toxin, like that of *B. welchii,* has no incubation period. The toxin of vibrion septique often fails to produce death in guinea-pigs when injected subcutaneously or intramuscularly, merely producing local necrosis. Toxin production is tested both in rabbits and guinea-pigs by intravenous injection: 0.5 c.c. of toxin injected intravenously kills a guinea-pig in five minutes: 0.1 to 1 c.c. injected into rabbits intravenously kills them without a latent period, with symptoms of respiratory disturbance, paralysis and convulsions. It is difficult to establish an M. L. D. for rabbits of the same weight owing to individual variation. In some instances, death is produced immediately in one rabbit, whereas another rabbit of the same weight will show severe symptoms followed by recovery. These tests, however, have not been made with genetically uniform animals.

METHOD OF PRODUCTION.—The Hygienic Laboratory obtains a powerful toxin using a 0.2 per cent glucose broth containing 10 per cent horse serum. Robertson recommends using liver of a pig dying of a vibrion septique infection with which to inoculate the broth, but the difficulties of obtaining a liver without gross contaminations are such that the former method is preferable. The broth is incubated twenty-four to forty-eight hours. Care should be taken in the selection of the filter since certain filters seem to hold back a large percentage of the toxin. This point is emphasized both by Weinberg and Seguin and by Robertson. Antitoxins are prepared by injecting the toxin into horses or sheep. The French standard requires that 0.001 c.c. of the antitoxin should neutralize two fatal doses of the toxin after thirty minutes' incubation of the mixture at room temperature. The vibrion septique antitoxin is specific; it does not protect against *B. oedematiens.*

Occurrence.—Vibrion septique has been isolated from milk. Heller in 1920 in an excellent summary of anaerobic infections in animals has shown that spontaneous infections by vibrion septique occur in sheep, horses and hogs. Meyer in 1915 reported the isolation of typical vibrion septique from two cases of symptomatic anthrax in hogs. Cattle, according to Heller, are less susceptible to vibrion septique infections than the other animals mentioned. Herbivorous animals are subject to infections with vibrion septique, both following and not following demonstrable wounds, whereas infections in man seem to occur only as the result of wounds.

Differentiation of Vibrion Septique and B. Chauvei (Bacillus of Symptomatic, Anthrax Blackleg).[3]—*B. chauvei* was in no instsance isolated from wound cultures, and has never been known to cause an infection in man. Vibrion septique, on the other hand, frequently infects animals and a bacteriological differentiation between vibrion septique and *B. chauvei* must be made. These two organisms are closely related and very similar, and a reliable differentiation is difficult even for a bacteriologist familiar with anaerobic bacilli. Robertson distinguishes between *B. chauvei* and vibrion septique by the fact that the former ferments saccharose and not salicin, whereas vibrion septique ferments salicin and not saccharose. Long snake-like filaments are demonstrable in smears from the liver of guinea-pigs dead of vibrion septique infection; these are entirely lacking in *B. chauvei* infections. Vibrion septique is more pathogenic for laboratory animals and produces more gas in the tissues than *B. chauvei*. *B. chauvei* grows more slowly than vibrion septique. Vibrion septique is gram-positive, whereas most investigators consider *B. chauvei* gram-negative. Protection tests with a known vibrion septique antitoxin ought to prove the most reliable way of identifying vibrion septique.

B. Oedematiens.[4]—Weinberg and Seguin claim to have isolated this organism in 34 per cent of the wounds examined by them. This is a higher proportion than that obtained by other workers. Henry found *B. oedematiens* in 5 out of 50 cases examined. *B. oedematiens* was isolated in 1915 by Weinberg and Seguin. In 1916 a similar organism was isolated by Sacquepée under the name *"bacille de l'oedeme gazeuse malin."* Later Sacquepée called this organism *B. bellonensis*. *B. bellonensis* and *B. oedematiens* are now considered to be the same organism by the majority of workers. According to Heller, *B. oedematiens* is closely related to but not identical with a bacillus discovered in 1894 by Novy and called by him *B. oedematiens maligni II*. *B. oedematiens* is a strict anaerobe. It is a large gram-positive bacillus, resembling anthrax in appearance. It is only sluggishly motile. It forms chains in culture and often shows curved forms after two or three days. Filaments are not formed in the animal body. It forms oval subterminal spores readily in all media. It ferments most of the common sugars, and forms a loose clot in milk in three or four days. It liquefies gelatin, but does not attack coagulated serum.

Pathogenicity.—*B. oedematiens* is usually pathogenic, although Weinberg and Seguin report the isolation of two nonvirulent strains; rabbits are less susceptible than guinea-pigs. Mice are also susceptible. It may or may not enter the blood stream. The lesion in the animal is characterized by a whitish gelatinous exudate and the absence of gas. The production of agglutinating sera with *B. oedematiens* has not

---

3 Bacillus of symptomatic anthrax = *Clostridium chauvoei*.
4 Species: *Clostridium novyi.*

been satisfactory, because *B. oedematiens* tends to agglutinate spontaneously. It is feebly hemolytic, much less so than vibrion septique and *B. perfringens*.

Toxin.—*B. oedematiens* forms a soluble toxin. Different strains vary in their toxin production. With a potent strain 0.01 c.c. of toxin injected intravenously kills a 300 to 400 gram guinea-pig in forty-eight hours. This toxin differs from those of vibrion septique and *B. welchii* in that it never kills acutely on intravenous injection. The toxin is prepared according to Weinberg and Seguin, by growing *B. oedematiens* in broth containing chopped veal for six to ten days.

Antitoxin.—Rabbits, sheep and horses have been used to produce antitoxic sera. Immunization is difficult and small doses must be used at first. Weinberg and Seguin prepared an antitoxin in a horse of such a titer that 1:10,000 dilution neutralized two lethal doses (guinea-pig).

B. Fallax.[5]—*B. fallax* was discovered during the World War by Weinberg and Seguin. It is a much less important factor in gas gangrene than the members of the saccharolytic group already described. It is usually associated with other pathogenic anaerobes. Weinberg and Seguin cite one case in which it invaded the blood stream and caused death. It was isolated by Henry in 3 cases out of a series of 50.

It is an anaerobic gram-positive bacillus, resembling vibrion septique in appearance. It has a capsule and is slightly motile. It does not form spores readily in most culture media. Spores are formed on coagulated serum. The spores are central or slightly subterminal.

B. fallax coagulates milk slowly. It does not liquefy gelatin or coagulated serum.

B. fallax is not hemolytic. It is only slightly pathogenic and soon becomes avirulent on artificial cultivation.

Proteolytic Group.—The organisms of this group can never produce gas gangrene without the presence of one or more bacilli of the saccharolytic group. The members of the proteolytic group digest milk without the formation of a clot and liquefy and often blacken coagulated serum. These two characteristics together with the fact that cultures of the proteolytic organisms usually have a very offensive odor, make it comparatively easy to distinguish them from the saccharolytic group. Sugars are fermented by the proteolytic type, but much less rapidly and with the production of less acid and gas than in the case of the saccharolytic group. The members of the proteolytic group produce spores readily in all media. None of these organisms are very pathogenic and produce no general picture of toxemia in spite of the tremendous liquefaction of tissue caused by them. The ferments of several of the proteolytic anaerobes have been isolated and have been found to split proteins to amino-acids so rapidly that there is no time for the intermediate products to intoxicate the animals. The separation of the proteolytic anaerobes from the saccharolytic is extremely difficult. The members of the two groups are usually present together, and what will seem to be a pure culture of a saccharolytic organism if held for any length of time, will often show a contamination with a proteolytic organism. The best methods for separation of the two groups are: by rapid transplantation in sugar media, where the saccharolytic organisms outgrow the proteolytic, combined with frequent plating, or by animal inoculation. The latter is the more satisfactory. In the animal body after intramuscular injection, the more pathogenic organisms belong-

5 Species: *Clostridium fallax.*

ing to the saccharolytic group frequently invade the blood stream and may be isolated from the heart's blood.

B. Sporogenes.[6]—This organism was next to *B. welchii* most frequently found in wound cultures. Weinberg and Seguin isolated it in 27 per cent of their cases. *B. sporogenes* was the anaerobe usually responsible for the foul odor of wounds. According to most authors, the pathogenicity of this organism is negligible. Weinberg and Seguin claim to have isolated a few toxic strains, but these may possibly have been mixed with members of the saccharolytic group. Heller has not found any proteolytic anaerobes that are pathogenic for animals.

B. sporogenes was definitely described by Metchnikoff in 1908. Whether *B. sporogenes* is identical or not with Koch's bacillus of malignant edema, will probably never be definitely settled. It is considered identical by many workers, although this is emphatically denied by others. *B. sporogenes* is a gram-positive, anaerobic bacillus, actively motile, forming oval subterminal spores readily in all media and in the animal body. It is intensely proteolytic, liquefying gelatin and coagulated serum, and digesting and blackening meat. Most strains of *B. sporogenes* are not hemolytic. Occasionally a feebly hemolytic strain has been isolated. It does not produce a soluble toxin and is not pathogenic for laboratory animals unless injected in large quantities.

B. Histolyticus.[7]—This organism was discovered by Weinberg and Seguin and isolated by them from eight wound cultures. Like *B. sporogenes*, it is intensely proteolytic and is of interest chiefly because of the striking lesion it produces in the animal body. It is a gram-positive anaerobic, motile bacillus with rounded ends. Sporulation takes place in all media, different strains varying in the time required for spore formation. The spores are large and oval and occupy a terminal position. No gas is formed in cultures of *B. histolyticus* and no putrid odor develops. Gelatin and coagulated serum are liquefied. It does not produce a soluble toxin. It is not hemolytic. The injection of large doses, 2 to 3 c.c. intramuscularly into guinea-pigs, of the whole culture digests the tissues so rapidly that at the end of twelve to twenty-four hours, the bone may be exposed. The picture is striking, one of the characteristics of *B. histolyticus* infection being that in spite of a tremendous local lesion, the animal appears well.

B. Putrificus.[8]—*B. putrificus* was first discovered in 1884 by Bienstock in the intestine of a cadaver. It is a gram-positive anaerobe, motile, forming terminal oval spores in all media. It is actively proteolytic, producing a foul odor. No pathogenic strains have been isolated. It has been studied by Tissier and Martally, who found it in putrid meat. Klein worked with a similar organism which he called *B. sporogenes cadaveris*. Hibler considers *B. putrificus* and *B. sporogenes cadaveris* the same.

A variety of anaerobes have been described under the name *putrificus* and it has been difficult to identify any of them with Bienstock's organism. Hartsell and Rettger, after an exhaustive reinvestigation of the group have concluded that *Clostridium putrificum* (Reddish and Rettger) is a distinct species. They have proposed the name *Clostridium lentoputrificum* for this organism.

---

6 Species: *Clostridium sporogenes.*
7 Species: *Clostridium histolyticum.*
8 Species: *Clostridium lentoputrescens.*

Identification of Anaerobes Present in Wound Cultures.—Polyvalent mixtures of gas-gangrene antitoxins are now available. For the strictly specific serum treatment of infected wounds, the prompt identification of the members of saccharolytic group, *B. welchii*, *B. oedematiens* and vibrion septique, is most important. The process of purification and identification by cultural methods is at best slow, and Henry has, therefore, suggested the inoculation of the unknown material into immunized guinea-pigs as the quickest and most reliable method. The procedure he outlines is as follows: inoculate the unknown mixed culture into cooked meat medium, and incubate. The next day inoculate the supernatant fluid into milk, and inject intramuscularly into two immunized guinea-pigs, one pig having received a mixture of *B. welchii* and vibrion septique antitoxin, the other a mixture of *B. welchii* and *B. oedematiens*. The stormy fermentation of milk is diagnostic for *B. welchii* and this reaction takes place within twenty-four hours. If the pig that was protected against vibrion septique (the *B. welchii* factor having been eliminated in both pigs) dies, it indicates the presence of some other pathogenic anaerobe, probably *B. oedematiens*. The diagnosis of *B. oedematiens* is further indicated if the guinea-pig that received the *B. oedematiens* combination of sera survives. If the animal inoculations come out in the opposite way, the presence of vibrion septique is indicated. The pathogenic organism can usually be isolated from the heart's blood of the animal that succumbs. By using a "filter" of protected guinea-pigs in this way, the pathogenic organisms can be separated out and the specific serum injected into the patient within forty-eight hours.

SURGERY AND BACTERIOLOGY IN THE MANAGEMENT OF TRAUMATIC WOUNDS (WAR WOUNDS)

The extensive experience gained by surgeons, during the World War, in connection with infected wounds, has developed a number of important bacteriological methods which are likely to remain as parts of the routine work of civil hospitals, especially those in which traumatic cases are handled. The most complete treatise on the entire matter may be found in the book by Carrel and De Helly, *The Treatment of Infected Wounds.*

The usual type of war wound, or, for that matter, any kind of traumatic wound, presents conditions in regard to the possibilities of infection which are quite different from those ordinarily encountered in aseptic surgery. From the skin and clothing bacteria, both aerobic and anaerobic, are carried by the projectiles or other foreign bodies into the tissues. Tissues are destroyed to a variable degree, and such devitalized tissues furnish an excellent medium for bacterial growth. There is always an interval or latent period between contamination of the wound and proliferation and penetration of the organisms. The duration of this latent period varies, but usually approximates six hours.

The immediate aim of treatment is the prevention or limitation of infection, and, for this reason, the rational method of determining whether this purpose is being accomplished and what the next procedure should be is bacteriological control. This is carried out by examination of smears and by cultures.

The first step in limiting infection in such wounds is accomplished by débridement, that is, excision of the tract with removal of all the devitalized and contaminated tissues, together with foreign bodies, bits of projectile, clothing, etc. Bacteria are greatly diminished though not eradicated by this procedure.

Bacteriological control of the original infection of the wound and its progress under treatment is carried out by a method of systematic smear examination of the wound, supplemented by cultures, first practically developed by Carrel.

The smear method, introduced by Carrel and employed since that time by many surgeons on a large material, is simple, can be carried out by any well trained assistant or technician without the aid of a highly trained bacteriologist, and has apparently yielded results of value. Our description is taken almost entirely from Carrel's own writings. Wounds should be examined every two or three days, and when the time for secondary closure appears, perhaps every day. The principle consists in the examination of the secretions of the wounds by means of smears in such a way that an approximate estimate of the number of bacteria contained in the wounds can be made. Although the method is very inaccurate, its value does not depend upon its revealing slight differences, the significant variations being so widely apart that the necessary error in the comparative enumerations does not render the method useless.

The examination need not begin earlier than twelve hours after the infliction of the wound, since up to that time few bacteria will be found. At the end of this time, when hemorrhage has completely stopped, smears are taken with a platinum loop from different parts of the wound. The points from which cultures are taken should always be those in which bacteria are most likely to be present in large numbers. Thus, Carrel chooses points in contact with foreign bodies, necrotic bits of bone, and from deep in the sinuses and crevices of the wound. Specimens should never be taken from bleeding points. Specimens should always be taken from a considerable number of different places in the same wound. Care should be exercised to avoid taking smears from the skin adjacent to the wound. With the end of a small platinum loop small amounts of secretion are picked up, and smeared upon slides in such a way that approximately the same area is covered by the different loopfuls of secretion. With loops of uniform size and a little practice, a surprising uniformity of technic can be developed.

These smears are allowed to dry, and may be stained in a variety of ways. Carbol thionin has been extensively used, but we believe that a Gram stain which is almost as simple, will give a little more useful information. It is desirable at all times to make approximate estimates of the relative prevalence of various types of organisms.

The stained slides can now be examined under the microscope and the number of bacteria per field counted. If the number exceeds 50 or more to the field, more accurate counting will yield no valuable information because the wound still contains too many bacteria to warrant closure or relaxation of the local therapy that is being applied.

Gradually, as the wound improves, fewer and fewer bacteria will appear in the daily series of slides, and when the number has dropped below 50 per field, careful counting may give an index of daily variations. Eventually, the number will decrease to only one microorganism per 5, 10 or 20 fields, in which case the daily report can be expressed in fractions, as $\frac{1}{5}$, $\frac{1}{10}$, or $\frac{1}{20}$, etc. The daily counts can, in this way, be numerically charted, and constructed into a curve which will show the surgeon by glance the numerical progress of the bacterial infection.

Carrel states that it is useless to take any smears as long as hemorrhage exists. If the wound is being irrigated with Dakin's solution or other antiseptic fluids, the treatment must be omitted for at least two hours before the smears are taken. Smears taken from the surface of smooth muscles are practically useless, since smooth muscle becomes sterile early in the healing process. Therefore, the choosing of the point of smear is of the utmost importance. The depth of the wound may begin to become sterile at times when individual little foci around necrotic bone, small pockets, etc., may still contain numerous bacteria. This must be borne in mind and an intelligent survey of the wound made by the bacteriologist who takes the smear. To overlook such dangerous points would seriously imperil the life of the patient, were the wound closed. When absolutely no bacteria are found in such smears, it does not mean that the wound is completely sterile. It is still possible that cultures might reveal organisms, and when the period of secondary closure approaches, especially when streptococci have been present at a previous time, we would regard it of the greatest importance to take a culture aimed particularly at the demonstration of hemolytic streptococci, before the actual suture is carried out.

Cultural examinations should be made at the beginning by taking specimens from parts of the wound selected as indicated above, and smearing them upon fresh blood-agar plates (without glucose). This is primarily aimed at determining whether cocci, and especially hemolytic streptococci or staphylococci, are present. If the smears show a great many bacilli resembling the ordinary anaerobes, it may be well, too, to make anaerobic cultures, but anaerobic analysis is not of great immediate value to the surgeon as far as further procedure is concerned because of the long time consumed by such examinations. Suture is not carried out if hemolytic cocci of any kind are present, and for this reason, with a smear as a preliminary indication, frequent culture upon blood plates should be undertaken during the progress of the treatment.

In discussing the subject, it is not possible to give an intelligent survey of the bacteriological methods, without, to some extent, entering into the surgical considerations involved. For this reason we quote from Pool, whose experience with this type of wound has been extensive.

Débridement should be carried out as soon as possible after infliction of the wound. Primary suture may be employed only during quiet periods in case of war, and in hospitals where the patient may be retained for careful observation. Otherwise suture of the wound may lead to enclosure, within an imperfectly débrided wound, of various micro-organisms, including those which produce gas gangrene. In regard to delayed primary and secondary suture, the following observations of E. H. Pool are not without interest:

The determination as to when a wound may be sutured depends on bacteriologic findings and clinical observation. It must be emphasized that the coöperation of a bacteriologist is indispensable in making a decision as to the indications for delayed primary and secondary sutures. The practical function and indisputable importance of the bacteriologist in war surgery lies in this. In the consideration as to whether a wound is suturable or not, reliance must be placed chiefly on cultures, the important feature being the determination of the presence or absence of hemolytic cocci. For this, a routine blood-agar examination is essential.

Bacterial counts are far from exact, yet they give an indication as to the degree of bacterial contamination of a wound, especially the progress from day to day, and are of value especially for one untrained in estimating clinically the indications and contraindications for suture.

From eighteen to forty-eight hours after the original operation of débridement or excision of tissues, the wound is dressed and a culture and a smear are made. A report is returned as soon as possible. This contains the approximate number of organisms per field and the varieties of organisms. If no organisms are found, suture is indicated. If hemolytic cocci are present, suture is not considered. In the absence of hemolytic cocci, if the wound is clinically suturable, the presence of a few anaerobes or other organisms (approximately one in two fields) does not contraindicate suture. A considerable number of organisms of any kind indicates delay of suture, until the bacterial growth declines. A culture and a smear should be repeated at the following dressing; the results of this examination will determine suturing or further delay. If the wound is left open for a considerable period, e.g., over a week, or is definitely infected, a smear is made every two days. It is also advisable to make a culture occasionally. Care must be taken not to touch the skin surface in making the smear, since skin contamination vitiates the value of the report. From the smear a bacterial curve is plotted according to Carrel's plan. When the organisms in two successive counts are few, that is, approximately one per two fields, and a culture shows an absence of hemolytic cocci, the wound is considered susceptible of secondary suture except when the wound has contained hemolytic cocci at any time. In that case careful cultures are made from granulation tissue and from the discharge from all parts of the wound, and absence of hemolytic cocci should be established by two successive negative cultures before suture is made. It has been observed that streptococci are prone to lie dormant in small numbers, but to flare up and cause virulent infection after closure of the wound.[9]

In compound fractures the same principles apply, except that, as stated by Pool, expedition, thoroughness, and early closure are particularly important because it means the conversion of open into closed fracture. In such fractures of the long bones, delayed primary suture, that is, suture not later than six days after the infliction of the wound, should be aimed at. He states that it has been demonstrated repeatedly that severe fractures of long bones, except the femur, may be closed in from three to six days after débridement. If this cannot be done, secondary suture may often be made successfully under proper bacteriological control.

In joints, the principle of treatment consists in complete débridement of the wound tract into the soft parts and bone, the removal of foreign bodies and irrigation of the joint, followed by absolute closure of the joint by suture, with or without closure of the superficial parts.

If a joint becomes distended after the operation and infection is suspected, the effusion should be aspirated and examined by smear and culture. If such examination indicates infection, the joint should be reopened and treatment for suppurative arthritis begun.

In civil surgery the principles worked out with war wounds can be applied with still greater hope of success, since here the nature of the trauma and infection is apt to be less extensive.

As to serological treatment in civilian surgery, this will be applicable chiefly in cases in which there has been a considerable delay in the proper surgical treatment of the wound after its infliction. It seems most probable at the present time that the most hopeful prospect for future therapy will lie in the combination of antitoxic sera against B. welchii, B. oedematiens and Vibrion septique, with tetanus antitoxin, prophylactically injected in the same way in which tetanus antitoxin alone has been used hitherto.

9 E. H. Pool, J. Am. M. Ass., 1919, 73.

BACILLUS OF SYMPTOMATIC ANTHRAX AND BLACKLEG IN CATTLE

Family: Bacillaceae. Genus: Clostridium. Species: Clostridium chauvoei

Bacillus of Symptomatic Anthrax (*Bacillus anthracis symptomatici, Rauschbrand, Charbon symptomatique, Sarcemphysematis Bovis*).—Symptomatic anthrax is an infectious disease occurring chiefly among sheep, cattle, and goats. It is spoken of as "quarter-evil" or "blackleg." The disease has never been observed in man. It was formerly confused with true anthrax, because of a superficial similarity between the clinical symptoms of the two maladies. Bacteriologically, the two micro-organisms are in entirely different classes.

Symptomatic anthrax is of wide distribution and infection is usually through the agency of the soil in which the bacillus is present, in the form of spores which may retain viability for several years.

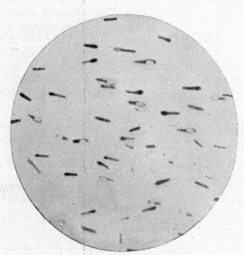

FIG. 65.—CLOSTRIDIUM CHAUVOEI.
(After Zettnow.)

Morphology and Staining.—The bacillus of symptomatic anthrax is a bacillus with rounded ends, being about 4 to 6 μ long, and 0.5 to 0.6 μ wide. It is usually seen singly and never forms long chains. The bacillus in its vegetative form is actively motile and possesses numerous flagella placed about its periphery. In artificial media it forms spores which are oval, broader than the rod itself, and placed near, though never actually at, the end of the bacillary body. This gives the bacillus a racket-shaped appearance.

It is readily stained with the usual aniline dyes, but is easily decolorized by Gram's method of staining. However, von Hibler claims that when very carefully stained the bacillus can be shown to be gram-positive—at least when taken from the animal body. It is gram-positive in young cultures.

Cultivation.—The bacillus is a strict anaerobe. It was obtained in pure culture first by Kitasato. Under anaerobic conditions it is easily cultivated upon the usual laboratory media, all of which are more favorable after the addition of glucose, glycerin or nutrose. In all media there is active gas formation, which, owing to an admixture of butyric acid, is of a foul, sour odor. The bacillus is not very delicate in its requirements of a special reaction of media, growing equally well on those slightly acid or slightly alkaline.

Surface colonies upon *agar plates* are circular and made up of a slightly granular compact center, from which a thinner peripheral zone emanates, containing microscopically a tangle of fine threads.

In *agar stabs*, at 37.5° C., growth appears within eighteen hours, rapidly spreading from the line of stab as a diffuse, fine cloud. Gas formation, especially near the bottom of the tube, rapidly leads to the formation of bubbles and later to extensive splitting of the medium. In *gelatin stab cultures* growth is similar to that in agar stabs, though less rapid. Liquefaction is produced in *gelatin* stab cultures.

Fermentation of Carbohydrates.—*Clostridium chauvoei* ferments glucose, maltose, lactose and saccharose with the production of acid and gas. It does not ferment mannite or salicin.

Indole is not produced.

Pathogenicity.—Symptomatic anthrax bacilli are pathogenic for cattle, sheep, and goats. By far the largest number of cases, possibly the only spontaneous ones, appear among cattle. Guinea-pigs are very susceptible to experimental inoculation. Horses are very little susceptible. Dogs, cats, rabbits and birds are immune. Man also appears to be absolutely immune. Spontaneous infection occurs by the entrance of infected soil into abrasions or wounds, usually of the lower extremities. Infection depends to some extent upon the relative degree of virulence of the bacillus—a variable factor in this species. Twelve to twenty-four hours after inoculation there appears at the point of entrance a soft, puffy swelling, which on palpation is found to emit an emphysematous crackling. The emphysema spreads rapidly, often reaching the abdomen and chest within a day. The course of the disease is extremely acute, the fever high, the general prostration extreme. Death may result within three or four days after inoculation.

At autopsy the swollen area is found to be infiltrated with a thick exudate, blood-tinged and foamy. Subcutaneous tissue and muscles are edematous and crackle with gas. The internal organs show parenchymatous degeneration and hemorrhagic areas. The bacilli, immediately after death, are found but sparsely distributed in the blood and internal organs, but are demonstrable in enormous numbers in the edema surrounding the central focus.

If carcasses are allowed to lie unburied for some time, the bacilli will attain a general distribution, and the entire body will be found bloated with gas, the organs filled with bubbles. Practically identical conditions are found after experimental inoculation.

Toxins.—According to the investigations of Leclainche and Vallée, the bacillus of symptomatic anthrax produces a soluble toxin. It is not formed to any extent in ordinary broth, but is formed in considerable quantities in broth containing blood or albuminous animal fluids.

The best medium for obtaining toxin, according to the same authors, is the bouillon of Martin, made up of equal parts of veal infusion and a peptone solution obtained from the macerated tissues of the stomachs of pigs.

The toxins in the filtrates of cultures of *Clostridium chauvoei* were reinvestigated in 1923 and 1925 by Kojima and Bassett. The review of their work by Robertson indicates that there are two toxins in these filtrates, a lethal toxin and a hemolytic toxin. These toxins were destroyed by heat at 52° C. in thirty to sixty minutes. These bacteria-free filtrates, like the "agressin" obtained by Schöbl in filtrates of fluid from infected tissues, are antigenic and are useful for the prophylactic immunization of animals which may be exposed to infection.

Immunity.—Active immunization against the bacillus of symptomatic anthrax was first accomplished by Arloing and his collaborators by the subcutaneous inoculation of cattle with tissue-extracts of infected animals. The work of these authors resulted in a practical method of immunization which is carried out as follows:

Two vaccines are prepared. Vaccine I consists of the juice of infected meat, dried and heated to 100° C. for six hours. Vaccine II is a similar meat juice heated to 90° C., for the same length of time. By the heating, the spores contained in the vaccines are attenuated to relatively different degrees. Vaccine I in quantities of 0.01 to 0.02 c.c. is emulsified in sterile salt solutions and injected near the end of the tail of the animal to be protected. A similar quantity of Vaccine II is injected in the same way fourteen days later.

This method has been retained in principle, but largely modified in detail by various workers. Kitt introduced the use of the dried and powdered whole meat instead of the meat juice, and made only one vaccine, heated to 94° C., for six hours. This method has been largely used in this country. Passive immunization with the serum of actively immunized sheep and goats has been used in combination with the methods of active immunization.

Two other methods have been used for active immunization. In one of these methods, the filtered juice expressed from infected muscle is injected subcutaneously. This bacteria-free filtrate contains the so-called "agressin." In the second method, the bacteria-free filtrates of the toxic broth cultures are used. These toxins stimulate the production of a high degree of immunity. In the opinion of Robertson *immunization by injection of toxin* will probably displace all other methods.

REFERENCES

BARBER. J. Exper. M., 1920, 32:295.
BASSETT, J. Bull. Soc. centr. de méd. vét., 1925, 78:393.
BENGTSON. Pub. Health Rep. U. S. Mar. Hosp. Serv., Wash., 1920, 122.
BLANC and POZERSKI. Compt. rend. Soc. de biol., 1920, 87:29.
BULL and PRITCHETT. J. Exper. M., 1917, 26:867.
CARREL and DE HELLY. The Treatment of Infected Wounds, New York, 1919.
CAULFIELD. J. Infect. Dis., 1920, 27:151.
DE KRUIF. J. Infect. Dis., 1917, 21:6.
DOUGLAS, S. R., FLEMING, A., and COLEBROOK, L. Studies in Wound Infection, Medical Research Council, Spec. Rep. Ser. No. 57, London, 1920.
FRÄNKEL. Centralbl. f. Bakteriol., 1893, 13:13.
GHON and SACHS. Centralbl. f. Bakteriol., 1909, I Abt. orig., 48:396.
GOULD. Ann. Surg., 1903, 38:481.
HALL, I. J. Infect. Dis., 1922, 30:445.
——— J. Bacteriol., 1926, 11:407.
HARTSELL, E., and RETTGER, L. F. J. Bacteriol., 1934, 27:19.
HELLER, H. H. J. Bacteriol., 1921, 6:445, 521.
——— J. Infect. Dis., 1920, 27:385.
HENRY. J. Path. & Bacteriol., 1917, 21:244.
HENRY and LACY. J. Path. & Bacteriol., 1920, 32:3.
KENDALL, A. I. J. Am. M. Ass., 1926, 86:731.
KITASATO, S. Ztschr. f. Hyg. u. Infectionskrankh., 1889, 6.
KLOSE. München. med. Wchnschr., 1916, 63:723.
KOCH. Mitt. a. d. k. Gsndhtsamte., 1881, 1:53.
KOJIMA, J. Ztschr. f. Immunitätsforsch. u. exper. Therap., 1923, 37:170, 185.
KOSER, S. A. J. Infect. Dis., 1923, 32:208.
LECLAINCHE and VALLÉE. Ann. de l'Inst. Pasteur, 1900, 14:590.

MARTIN. Ann. de l'Inst. Pasteur, 1898.

McCoy, E., and McLung, L. S. Bacteriol., Rev., 1938, 2:47.

McIntosh and Fildes. Lancet, 1916, 1:768.

Metchnikoff. Ann. de l'Inst. Pasteur, 1908, 22:419.

Meyer. J. Infect. Dis., 1915, 12:458.

Muir and Ritchie. Manual of Bacteriology, 2nd ed., Edinburgh, 1899.

Novy. Ztschr. f. Hyg., 1894, 17:209.

Pasteur and Jourbet. Bull. Acad. med. Par., 6:793.

Pool, E. H. J. Am. M. Ass., 1919, 73.

Reddish, G. F. J. Bacteriol., 1924, 9:320.

Reddish, G. F., and Rettger, L. F. J. Bacteriol., 1922, 7:505; 1923, 8:375.

Reed, G. B., Orr, J. H., et al. J. Infect. Dis., 1927, 41:283, 289.

———— Canad. M. Ass. J., 1926, 16: 525.

Rettger. J. Biol. Chem., 1906, 11:71.

Robertson, M. J. Path. & Bacteriol., 1920, 23, 153.

Robertson, M. A System of Bacteriology in Relation to Medicine, London, 1929, 3:270. References 46, 47 and 49 quoted from this work.

Sacquepée. Ann. de l'Inst. Pasteur, 1916, 30:76.

Schöbl, U. Centralbl. f. Bakteriol., I Abt., 1910, 56:395; 1912, 62:296.

Simonds, J. P. Monogr. No. 5, Rockefeller Inst. M. Research, 1915.

Stabins, S. J., and Kennedy, J. A. Arch. Surg., 1929, 18:753.

Veillon and Zuber. Arch. de méd. exper., 1898, 10:517.

Verder, E. Proc. Soc. Exper. Biol. & Med., 1933, 30:547.

Von Hibler. See Kolle and Wassermann, Handbuch, etc., 2nd ed., Vol. IV, 792.

———— Untersuchungen über die pathogenen Anaeroben, Jena, 1908.

Weinberg, M., and Seguin, P. La gangrène gazeuse, Paris, 1918.

Welch and Nuttall. Johns Hopkins Hosp. Bull., 1892, 3:81.

Williams, B. W. Brit. J. Surg., 1927, 14:295.

Wolf. J. Path. & Bacteriol., 1920, 23:254.

CHAPTER XLVII

ANAEROBIC BACILLI AND FOOD POISONING

BOTULISM AND CLOSTRIDIUM BOTULINUM

Family: *Bacillaceae.* Genus: *Clostridium.* Species: *Clostridium botulinum*

Meat poisoning was formerly regarded as entirely dependent upon putrefactive changes in infected meat, resulting in the production of ptomaines or other harmful products of bacterial putrefaction. It was not until 1888 that certain of these cases were definitely recognized as true bacterial infections, in which the preformed poison probably aided only in establishing the infection. Gaertner, in that year, discovered the *Bacillus enteritidis,* a micro-organism belonging to the group of the paratyphoid bacilli, and demonstrated its presence both in the infecting meat and in the intestinal tracts of patients.

There is another type of meat poisoning, however, which is not only much more severe, but is characterized by a profound systemic toxemia. The etiological organism causing this type of food poisoning was first demonstrated by Van Ermengem, in 1896, and named *Bacillus botulinus.* Van Ermengem isolated the bacillus from a pickled ham, the ingestion of which had caused disease in a large number of persons. Of the 34 individuals who had eaten of it, all were attacked, about 10 of them very severely. Van Ermengem found the bacilli in large numbers lying between the muscle fibers in the ham, and was able to cultivate the same micro-organism from the stomach and spleen of one of those who died of the infection. The results of Van Ermengem were confirmed by Roemer, and others. As a rule the organism does not invade the tissues of man or of living animals.

Morphology and Staining.—*Bacillus botulinus* is a gram-positive rod with rounded ends, 4 to 6 μ in length by 0.9 to 1.2 μ in thickness. The bacilli are either single or grouped in very short chains. Involution forms are numerous on artificial media. The bacillus is slightly motile and possesses from four to eight peripheral flagella. Spores are formed, most regularly in glucose gelatin of alkaline titer. The spores are oval and situated near the end of the bacillus, rarely in its center. Spores are formed at 20° to 25° C., and are usually absent at higher temperatures. Botulismus bacilli may be divided into several types which, though culturally very similar to each other, are differentiable by the *individual specificity of their toxins* and, therefore, their antitoxins. The usual types found in this country are those designated by the nomenclature of Types A, B, and C (Bengtson). This division of types was first suggested by G. S. Burke, in 1919. A Type D was added after investigation of botulism or lamsiekte of cattle in South Africa and Type E toxin from an organism isolated from spoiled fish in Russia. (Meyer and Gunnison.) Five types of botulinus toxin are now recognized.

Cultivation.—The bacillus is a strict anaerobe. In anaerobic environment it is easily cultivated on the usual meat-infusion media. It grows most readily at temperatures about 25° C., less luxuriantly at temperatures of 35° C. and over.

The bacillus is delicately susceptible to the reaction of media, growing only in those which are neutral or moderately alkaline.

In deep stab cultures in 1 per cent *glucose agar*, growth is at first noticed as a thin, white column, not reaching to the surface of the medium. Soon the medium is cracked and split by the abundant formation of gas. On agar plates, the colonies are yellowish, opalescent, and round, and show a finely fringed periphery.

On *gelatin*, at 20° to 25° C., growth is rapid and abundant, and differs little from that on agar, except that, besides the formation of gas, there is energetic fluidification of the medium. On glucose-gelatin plates, Van Ermengem describes the colonies as round, yellowish, transparent, and composed of coarse granules which, along the periphery in the zone of fluidification, show constant motion. The appearance of the surface colonies on glucose-gelatin plates is regarded by the discoverer as diagnostically characteristic.

In *glucose broth* there is general clouding and large quantities of gas are formed. At 35° C. and over, the gas formation ceases after four or five days, the broth becoming clear with a yellowish white flocculent sediment. At lower temperatures this does not occur.

Milk is not coagulated and *disaccharides* and *polysaccharides* are not fermented.

The gas formed in cultures consists chiefly of hydrogen and methane. All cultures have a sour odor, like butyric acid, but this is not so offensive as that of some of the other anaerobic organisms.

Isolation.—The isolation of *B. botulinus* from infected material is often quite easy, since as Burke states, few other organisms may be present in the canned or pickled food products. Often anaerobic shake cultures in agar made directly, serve to isolate the organisms. In most contaminated material, however, she recommends inoculation from the original material into Van Ermengem's broth, inoculating quite richly, duplicate cultures being made and heated at 60° C. for one hour, to destroy nonspore-bearers. These cultures are then incubated at 28° C. after which parts of them are filtered, and the filtrate in quantities of 1 c.c. injected into 250 gram guinea-pigs. If the guinea-pigs die within four days, other guinea-pigs are tested with specific botulismus antitoxin. The presence of the organisms having been thus proven in the broth, isolation is now carried out by careful plate cultures, incubated anaerobically, or by shake cultures.

Resistance.—The heat resistance of the spores of types A and B of *Clostridium botulinum* is greater than that of any other anaerobes. Esty and Esty and Meyer found that the heat resistance of the spores of 112 strains of this organism varied from 3 to 110 minutes when heated at 105° C. in a phosphate solution of pH 7.0. The maximum survival times of spores in this solution were 330 minutes at 100° C., 110 minutes at 105° C., 33 minutes at 110° C., 11 minutes at 115° C., and 4 minutes at 120° C. The spores of Type C are less resistant to heat. Jordan has suggested that "it is perhaps for this reason that in the outbreaks of botulism in the United States—which are mostly due to heat preserved foods—Type C has not been found." [1] The earlier observers, notably Van Ermengem, reported that the spores were killed at 80° C. It is not unlikely

[1] E. O. Jordan, *The Newer Knowledge of Bacteriology and Immunology*, Chicago, 1928, p. 448.

that the sausage and smoked meat from which the cultures were isolated provided chiefly Type C.

Pathogenicity.—*Clostridium botulinum* is primarily a saprophyte. It grows under anaerobic conditions in decaying vegetable or animal material, in incompletely sterilized cans or jars of meat, beans, asparagus, olives and other foodstuffs which have been contaminated with the organism. In these places, in the absence of oxygen, it produces its extraordinarily potent toxins. These toxins, swallowed by the animal or man consuming the food, produce the disease known as botulism. It was customary to state that the organism had no invasive power and did not elaborate its toxins in the animal body. This is not correct. Coleman and Meyer, and Starin and Dack have shown that detoxified spores injected into an animal may germinate in the tissues, that the bacilli can grow in the tissues and that in these situations they can produce a fatal toxic effect. It is thought that it is highly improbable that man is ever infected in this manner.

Botulismus Toxin.—The five recognized types of botulismus toxin (types A to E) have been mentioned. The following discussion deals with the general properties of the toxins.

Botulismus toxin is produced under conditions of strict anaerobiosis on any medium on which the organism will grow readily. According to Dickson the toxin is much more potent if the organisms are grown on an alkaline medium and in the dark. Van Ermengem obtained his best toxin by growing the organisms on the beef infusion broth to which he added 1 per cent sodium chloride, 1 per cent peptone and 2 per cent glucose. Leuchs used a pork infusion with 0.5 per cent sodium chloride, 1 per cent glucose and 1 per cent peptone. Landmann claimed that animal protein was necessary for good toxin production. According to Dickson this is not essential. He has produced toxin in media made from string beans and from peas, and found that, although an alkaline reaction is favorable, an acid reaction does not prevent toxin formation. According to Burke toxin is produced as readily at 37.5° as it is at 28° C. The toxin is destroyed at temperatures of about 80° C. Thom, Edmonson and Giltner claim that their toxin was destroyed by ten minutes' heating at 75° C. Van Ermengem's original report was that heating at 56° C. for three hours killed it, as does heating at 80° C. for one-half hour. According to Dickson, it is rapidly destroyed by exposure to sunlight and to air, but will maintain its potency for six months if kept in the dark as it would be in preserved foods. It is not affected by drying and is insoluble in alcohol, ether and chloroform. Normal soda, 20 per cent by volume, is stated by Dickson to destroy it, though similar amounts of acid do not reduce its virulence in twenty-four hours.

Its potency is considerable. Dickson produced his strongest toxin in pork and beef infusions, but also obtained potent preparations in media of string beans, peas, green corn, and less virulent toxin in media prepared from asparagus, artichokes, peaches and apricots. Brieger and Kempner obtained a toxin of which 0.000001 of a c.c. would kill a 250 gram guinea-pig in four days, and (we quote from Dickson), Van Ermengem found in one of his outbreaks that 200 grams of the poisonous ham caused the death of one patient. He quotes another case in which a piece of preserved duck the size of a walnut was sufficient to cause a disease lasting six weeks, and in his own series, a patient died after tasting a small spoonful of spoiled corn, another died after "nibbling a portion of a pod of the spoiled string beans." A third was quite ill after tasting, but not swallowing a pod of beans.

Botulinus toxin is remarkable in its ability to withstand the acids and alkalis of the gastro-intestinal tract and its capacity to exert its effect after absorption from the alimentary canal. According to Bronfenbrenner and Schlesinger (1920–21), the poison is about one hundred times less toxic when administered by mouth than when injected into an animal. Bronfenbrenner and Schlesinger (1924) found that HCl increased the potency of the toxin in a mixture with a reaction of pH 4.0. Dack and his coworkers showed that the small intestine is permeable to the toxin.

The effect of the poison is a paralysis of deglutition and respiration, occulomotor paralysis and constipation. It is possible that the toxin acts upon centers in the mid-brain, but Jordan, quoting Dickson and Shevky, expressed the opinion that the paralysis of the muscles of respiration was due to the action of the toxin upon the peripheral endings of the motor nerve fibers.

The toxin is potent for monkeys, rabbits, guinea-pigs, cats and various birds. Dickson found chickens highly susceptible, and also found that dogs were not as resistant as formerly thought to be. The most susceptible animals seem to be mice, guinea-pigs and monkeys. Rabbits, cats, dogs and rats are relatively resistant. The reasons for these differences in susceptibility are not known.

A number of characteristic paralytic diseases of birds and mammals are due to these toxins which the animals ingest with their food. The best known examples are grass or fodder sickness (Tocher, Tocher, Brown and Buxton) of horses, silage disease in cattle and *limberneck* (Graham and Schwarze, Dickson) in chickens, *lamsiekte* (Theiler, Scheuber) of cattle in South Africa, and *duck sickness* (Kalmbach) in this country.

Pathology.—In animals, according to Van Ermengem, there is a general hyperemia of the organs and especially of the nervous system. Dickson, who made a thorough review of the pathological work done by Van Ermengem, Vander Stricht, Marinesco and others, summarized the pathology as follows: In the central nervous system the meninges at the base of the brain, especially around the pons and the medulla, are usually more markedly congested than at the cortex, and there may be hemorrhage in the upper part of the cord and at the base of the brain. The lungs may be hyperemic, heart muscles flabby, but nothing characteristic. An important and regular lesion found by Ophuls and Wilbur was multiple thrombosis in both the arteries and veins of the central nervous system. Ophuls believes this is due to a certain vasodilatation with slowing of the blood stream due to a powerful paralyzing effect of the poison on the unstriped muscles. The thromboses are particularly common at the base of the brain. Ophuls, too, differs from others in believing that the specific action of the toxin on the nerve cells themselves has been very much exaggerated in that his histological examinations of the brains of fatal cases did not bear out this earlier opinion.

Transmission and Occurrence.—Kempner and Pollack in 1897 isolated *B. botulinus* from the intestines of a normal hog, but Dickson was unable to find the organism in the intestinal canals of 250 grain-fed hogs in the slaughterhouses of San Francisco. He also collected soil from gardens, but in a considerable series of specimens did not find organisms. Burke obtained seven cultures of the *B. botulinus* from moldy cherries, leaves touched with droppings of insects, bush-bean plants, manured bush beans, manure from a hog and moldy hay. These investigations seem to indicate that the *B. botulinus* is common in nature, and may be present in the intestines of domestic animals. It may possibly be disseminated by insects and birds.

Van Ermengem's first isolations were from pickled meat, thus showing that ordinary salting or brine preservation does not kill botulinus spores. The epidemics that have occurred are summarized by Mayer, and by Dickson. At the time of Mayer's publication (in 1913), 800 European cases had been observed since 1882, 200 of which had been fatal. Of 64 cases collected by Dickson for the United States during twenty-five years, 54 occurred in California. Wilbur and Ophuls reported an outbreak in 1914 due to the eating of canned beans. In U. S. Public Health Bulletin 127 (1922), Geiger, Dickson and Meyer have studied 91 reports. Among these were 51 outbreaks due to home-preserved products including vegetables, cheese, fish, sausage, pork, beef and chicken, and 31 outbreaks attributable to commercially canned products. In this report it is suggested that certain forms of forage poisoning, especially in horses, are instances of true equine botulism. These writers also state that the bacillus may be present in certain localities as an inhabitant of the intestinal tract of cattle, and that botulismus in hogs, dogs, cats and goats, though very rare, has been noted following the ingestion of home-canned vegetables. Geiger, in a subsequent report in 1924 (U. S. Public Health Bulletin Reprint 911) adds the fact that positive findings in the cultures of garden soil are the rule in western states, and positive cultures were obtained from the stools of recovered cases. He believes that many soils contain both A and B types of *B. botulinus*, the Type B being found predominating both in garden and virgin soil in a particular area. This is probably the source of infection of vegetables used for canning.

Armstrong carefully studied an outbreak in 1919 which was traced to ripe olives. It is impossible in this space to do justice to the large and valuable botulismus literature which has developed during the last few years, since the studies of Dickson, Meyer and others have renewed the interest of laboratory workers in the disease. The mortality of the disease has been high, and for the United States generally, as stated by Dickson, it has been over 64 per cent.

Clinical Manifestations.—Botulismus is characteristic in its clinical manifestations and should not present great diagnostic difficulties, once the disease is suspected. Since the toxin is preformed before ingestion, the symptoms are not long in following the eating of infected food, coming on usually within twenty-four hours or less. Delays of two or three days, however, may occur, and should not throw out possible positive diagnosis. The earliest symptoms usually consist in a general weakness and lassitude, with fatigue and some headache. Characteristic is the frequent lack of any symptoms pointing to the gastro-intestinal canal. Constipation is the rule. Very early in the disease, disturbances of vision may occur which are due to impairment of the muscles of the eyeball. There is, particularly, involvement of the third cranial nerve, with blepharoptosis, mydriasis, impaired light reflex and diplopia. There may be photophobia. For a detailed discussion of the symptomatology, the reader is referred to the monograph of Dickson. Impairment of the pharyngeal muscles may produce difficulties in swallowing with inability to chew, and sluggishness of the tongue with thickness of speech. Absence of fever is an important feature, and in the early stages there is usually no fever and no change in the heart rate. Fatal cases usually end in death within three to seven days, due either to cardiac failure or terminal asphyxia. In discussing the differential diagnosis, Dickson mentions particularly, poliomyelitis, cerebrospinal syphilis, early stages of bulbar paralysis, belladonna poisoning and methyl alcohol poisoning.

Specific Therapy.—Potent antitoxins may be produced by the treatment of susceptible animals with toxin. Kempner in 1897 was the first to experiment on this extensively, using the Van Ermengem strain, and producing antitoxin in goats. The immunization of small laboratory animals is comparatively difficult, unless minute doses and attenuated toxin is used. The chief studies on these phases of the problem have been made by Forssman and Lunstrom and by Leuchs. More recently, Dickson and Howitt have produced potent antitoxins in goats, though their products, they state, were not as powerful as those reported by Kempner and some other observers. It is very important to note that in these experiments antitoxin produced against one series of strains had no appreciable effects upon the toxins of three other strains. This brings out the great importance of producing curative sera by the use of toxins from the three common types, A, B, C, occurring in this country, and in some cases against all five types.

Dickson advises intravenous injection and states that his procedure would be as follows: The usual precautions for the administration of horse serum should be observed, and the patient tested for skin sensitiveness. If no such sensitiveness is found, the serum should be injected immediately into a vein at the rate of not more than 1 c.c. a minute. Comparatively large doses should be given, since the amount of toxin ingested may be quite large.

Prevention.—Deducing preventive measures from the facts cited in the above paragraphs, it would seem that, in the first place, all people in the habit of preparing canned food should be thoroughly alive to the possibilities of contamination and know that *B. botulinus* spores may be present on fruit, vegetables, etc., before they are preserved. It should be well understood that food may be contaminated with botulinus, without being changed in any way in its gross appearance, and that not even the slightest rancid odor which sometimes indicates its presence, need be apparent. The sterilization of canned food, sausages, preserved meat, etc., should be thoroughly attended to and no home-canned preparation be eaten under any circumstances unless cooked before eaten.

REFERENCES

ARMSTRONG. Pub. Health Rep., Wash., Dec., 1919, 54.

BENGTSON, I. A. Pub. Health Rep., Washington, 1922, 37:164.

BRIEGER and KEMPNER. Deutsche med. Wchnschr., 1897, 23:521.

BRONFENBRENNER, J., and SCHLESINGER, M. J. Proc. Soc. Exper. Biol. & Med., 1920–21, 18:254.

———— J. Exper. M., 1924, 39:509.

BURKE, G. S. J. Bacteriol., 1919, 4:541, 555.

———— J. Infect. Dis., 1923, 32:433.

COLEMAN, G. E., and MEYER, K. F. J. Infect. Dis., 1922, 31:662.

DACK, G. M., et al. J. Infect. Dis., 1926, 38:174; 1926, 39:173, 181; 1927, 40:585.

DICKSON, E. C. J. Am. M. Ass., 1915, 65:492.

———— Monogr. Rockefeller Inst. M. Research, July 31, 1918, No. 8.

DICKSON, E. C., and SHEVKY, E. J. Exper. M., 1923, 38:327.

DICKSON and HOWITT. J. Am. M. Ass., 1919, 74:718.

ESTY, J. R. Am. J. Pub. Health, 1923, 13:108.

ESTY, J. R., and MEYER, K. F. J. Infect. Dis., 1922, 31:650.

Forssman and Lunstrom. Ann. de l'Inst. Pasteur, 1902, 16:294.

Graham, R., and Schwarze, H. J. Bacteriol., 1921, 6:69.

Gunnison, J. B. J. Immunol., 1934, 26:17.

Gunnison, J. B., Cummins, J., and Meyer, K. F. Proc. Soc. Exper. Biol. & Med., 1936, 35:278.

Jordan, E. O. The Newer Knowledge of Bacteriology and Immunology, Chicago, 1928.

Kalmbach, E. R. Science, 1930, 72:658; 1932, 75:57.

Kempner. Ztschr. f. Hyg., 1897, 26:481.

Kempner and Pollack. Deutsche med. Wchnschr., 1897, 23:505.

Landmann. Quoted from Dickson.

Leuchs. In Kolle and Wassermann, Handb., etc., 2nd ed., Vol. IV, p. 932.

———— Ztschr. f. Hyg., 1910, 65:55.

Mayer. Deutsche Vrtljschr. f. öff. Gsndhtspflg., 1913, 35:8.

Meyer, K. F., et al. J. Infect. Dis., 1922, 31:501, 541, 556.

Meyer, K. F., and Gunnison, J. B. J. Inf. Dis., 1929, 45, 106, 119.

Ophuls and Wilbur. Arch. Int. Med., 1914, 14:589.

Roemer. Centralbl. f. Bakteriol., 1900, 27.

Scheuber, J. R. 15th Rep., Vet. Res. South Africa, 1929.

Starin, W. A., and Dack, G. M. J. Infect. Dis., 1925, 36:383.

Theiler, A, et al. 11th and 12th Reps., Vet. Res. South Africa, 1927.

Thom, Edmonson and Giltner. J. Am. M. Ass., 1919, 73:901.

Tocher, J. F., Tocher, J. W., Brown, W., and Buxton, J. B. Vet. Rec., 1923, 3:37, 75. Quoted from R. T. Hewlett, A System of Bacteriology in Relation to Medicine, London, 1929, 3:373.

Van Ermengem. Centralbl. f. Bakteriol., 1896, 19:443.

———— Ztschr. f. Hyg., 1897, 26.

———— Quoted from Kolle and Wassermann, Handb., etc., 2nd ed.

CHAPTER XLVIII

MISCELLANEOUS BACTERIA OF MEDICAL IMPORTANCE

In addition to the organisms described in the preceding chapters, there are many other bacteria which are of importance in medicine. Some of these are nonpathogenic, but have an influence upon the state of health of human beings, some are of doubtful pathogenicity, others are pathogenic but rarely encountered. As we cannot afford to provide a chapter on each of these organisms in a book of this character, we shall present only brief notes on a miscellaneous group of these bacteria.

TRACHOMA AND BACTERIUM GRANULOSIS

Trachoma is a specific type of chronic granular conjunctivitis, characterized by the infiltration of the subepithelial tissue with lymphocytes, by necrosis in these nodules, and scar formation. In the course of the disease the cornea becomes clouded, and scars form on the inside of the lid pulling it inward. Partial or complete blindness may result. The disease has an ancient history and is world wide in distribution. It is an infectious disease, transmissible from person to person. Stringent quarantine regulations are in force to prevent the admission of trachomatous immigrants into this country. The disease is prevalent in the United States, particularly in the states of West Virginia, Kentucky, eastern Tennessee, western Virginia, Missouri, Arkansas, and Oklahoma. It is endemic among some of the tribes of American Indians (Mossman, Kerr).

While poverty and dietary deficiency may be contributory causes, it is generally believed that a virus or bacterium is the etiological agent of the disease. The *virus theory* was based upon the interpretation placed by Halberstädter and von Prowazek upon so-called "elementary bodies" or "inclusion bodies" found in the epithelial cells scraped from the lesions. Bengtson concluded that these intracellular formations are probably due to engulfed bacteria or are products of cellular degeneration. Julianelle has produced trachoma-like lesions in monkeys with bacteria free Berkefeld filtrates of material from lesions in man. In his opinion the disease is caused by a virus.

The *bacterial theory* of the cause of trachoma has received a great deal of attention. Many types of bacteria have been isolated from trachomatous eyes and from cases of follicular conjunctivitis that were certainly not cases of trachoma. There are difficulties in clinical diagnosis and in the interpretation of pathological specimens which introduce uncertainties in the observations on both the natural and experimentally produced follicular conjunctival lesions. The Koch-Weeks bacillus, and various cocci and diphtheroids have at one time or another been supposed by some one to be the cause of trachoma. The organism, which since 1928 has been of the greatest interest, is a bacterium isolated by Noguchi from trachoma cases among American Indians in the region of Albuquerque, New Mexico.

Noguchi named this organism *Bacterium granulosis*. Noguchi, Olitski and others produced a chronic follicular conjunctivitis in *Macacus rhesus* monkeys by inoculation of the conjunctiva with this organism. Others, notably Mayou and Morax, failed to isolate the organism or to produce the disease with Noguchi's culture. We agree with Woods' estimate of the evidence in his statement made in 1933, that "it appears impossible at present to accept any etiological relation between *B. granulosis* and trachoma." The description of this organism is as follows.

In some respects *Bacterium granulosis* resembles *Bacterium monocytogenes*, but differs from *B. monocytogenes* in fermentation reactions and pathogenicity for rabbits. *Bacterium monocytogenes* is virulent for rabbits while *Bacterium granulosis* is nonpathogenic for rabbits.

THE LISTERELLA GROUP

Infectious Mononucleosis—Meningitis

Several pyogenic diseases of man and lower animals appear to be related through the inflammatory and destructive actions of bacteria included in the group recognized by Bergey in 1934 as a genus under the name *Listerella*. The limits of the group are not well defined and species distinctions are still uncertain. But of the pathogenic importance of the organisms there is no doubt.

The organisms are short rods 0.5 μ broad and 1 to 4 μ long, occurring singly, in pairs and in short chains. Some forms are coccoid, others resemble diphtheroids. They are gram-positive, motile by means of a single polar flagellum, aerobic, capable of fermenting a variety of carbohydrates, producing acid without gas. The optimum temperature for growth is 37° C. Growth is slow. After 48 hours the colonies are usually 2 mm. in diameter, round, transparent, smooth or rough. On blood agar or liver extract agar with dextrose the growth becomes opaque and somewhat viscid. On blood agar the organisms produce clear, beta-type, hemolysis.

The type species is *Bacterium* or *Listerella monocytogenes*. This variety was isolated by Murray, Webb and Swan (1926) from rabbits having a generalized infection associated with increase in the numbers of large mononuclear lymphocytes. Glandular fever in man (Pfeiffer, 1889), or infectious mononucleosis (Sprunt and Evans, Longcope, Scheer) may have a similar cause. Nyfeldt has isolated a strain of this organism from the blood of a patient suffering from this disease. Positive cultures have not been obtained from the blood of patients seen at the New Haven Hospital.

Observations on the pathogenicity of organisms of the *Listerella* group were made by Burn (1935), who in 1933 and subsequent years, isolated strains from the lesions of individuals dying of a disease, of which sepsis, focal necrosis of the liver and meningitis were the predominant features. Other observers, as Seastone (1935) has noted, have isolated these organisms from suppurative meningitis in cattle and sheep, and from myocardial infection in fowls. Schultz isolated the organism from a case of meningo-encephalitis in man.

Fusiform Bacteria.—The aerobic or anaerobic bacteria with elongated spindle-shaped cells constitute a genus *Fusobacterium* in Bergey's classification. As Smith has pointed out, the definition of the group is not satisfactory; the knowledge of these organisms is incomplete and probably many bacteria classified as fusiforms are unrelated to each other. These organisms occur in the mouth, around the teeth, in the tonsils, and in preputial and labial secretions. They are numerous in putrid purulent and gangrenous lesions of the lungs, genitalia and other parts of the body. In these places they are often associated with spirochetes. In our discussion of *Vincent's angina* we shall consider in greater detail the evidence presented to support the view that the fusiform bacteria and spiral forms in that infection are the same organism. There are great differences in opinion among bacteriologists as to the forms which should be assigned to this group. The organisms are difficult to cultivate and variable in morphology. Abundant growth occurs in the potato extract medium of Slanetz and Rettger. For primary isolation gentian violet is added to this medium in a final concentration of 1 : 20,000.

Rettger and his associates, Slanetz and Spaulding, have contributed a great deal to the knowledge of fusiform bacteria and have cleared away some of the confusion concerning this genus. Eighty strains of *Fusobacterium* were divided into two groups by their biochemical and serological behavior. Group II is distinguished from Group I by (a) its ability to produce approximately twice as great an acidity from carbohydrates as the latter and (b) its property of fermenting maltose and trehalose, and (3) its inability to form indole, produce hydrogen sulfide and reduce nitrates. Each of the two groups is made up of two important fermentative sub-groups. They noted that spiral forms occurred rarely. On the other hand, Tunnicliff and Hammond, after studying rough colonies of fusiform bacilli, presented additional evidence to support the opinion that fusiform bacilli and spirilla are different forms in the life cycle of one organism.

NECROBACILLOSIS

A disease of cattle, sheep, horses and mules, characterized by coagulative necrosis, ulcers of the skin, foot rot, and multiple infarction abscesses in the lungs has been known to veterinarians for a long time as "calf diphtheria," "grease heal," and in general, necrobacillosis (Jensen, Weinberg and Ginsbourg, Albrecht). The causative organism was isolated by Schmorl in 1891 and named by him *Streptothrix cuniculi*, and later called *Actinomyces necrophorus*.

A few human infections with this organism were recorded before 1925, of which the cases described by Stemen and Shaw and Shaw are typical of the localized vesicular and gangrenous dermatitis produced by the organism. In 1927, Harris and Brown isolated a hemolytic variety of this organism from vaginal and uterine cultures of women after childbirth and suggested that it might be a factor in the causation of puerperal infection. Cunningham described 2 fatal cases of the infection in man. His paper contains an account of the micro-organism as we have seen it and is well illustrated. Shaw and Bigger have reported a case of necrobacillosis of the lung in man. Dack has recovered the organism from cases of ulcerative colitis.

Actinomyces Necrophorus.—*Actinomyces necrophorus* is an extraordinarily pleomorphic anaerobe, growing in long filaments, clusters of clubbed cells, or small coccobacillary forms. True branching was seen occasionally. The organism resembles some of the anaerobic fusiform bacteria even more than the actinomycetes and its pathogenic action is like that of some of the fusiforms. In the tissues only small coccoid or bacillary forms were seen. The pus from lesions and cultures have a characteristic pungent foul odor. Hemolytic and nonhemolytic varieties occur.

OROYA FEVER AND BARTONELLA BACILLIFORMIS

From ancient times, the inhabitants of Peru have suffered from a disease characterized by fever, anemia and a nodular warty eruption. Many have died from this disease. In one form of the disease the eruption is conspicuous and this type was called *Verruga peruviana;* the type distinguished by fever and severe anemia was called *Oroya fever.* For years the question as to whether these were two diseases or different manifestations of one disease was unsettled. In 1885, Daniel Carion, a medical student in Lima, inoculated himself with blood from a verruga nodule. He died, presumably of Oroya fever, twenty-three days later. Strong has expressed the opinion that the record is insufficient to show that Carion died of Oroya fever, and has presented evidence that Oroya fever and verruga are different diseases. Bacteriological and transmission investigations, to which we shall refer, seem to indicate that the diseases are actually different manifestations of the same infectious process. In other words, they have the same etiology.

In 1905, Barton found a small cocco-bacillus in the *red corpuscles* and sometimes outside the cells in the blood of patients with Oroya fever. Strong, in 1913, named this organism *Bartonella bacilliformis.* In 1926, Noguchi cultivated the organism from the blood of patients with Oroya fever. Inoculation of the organism into *rhesus* monkeys produced a disease resembling verruga. The organism can be transmitted by the wood tick, *Dermacentor andersoni,* and in nature is transmitted by the gnat, *Phlebotomus* (Noguchi), as shown by Townsend and Shannon. This is another important example of insect transmission of a pathogenic bacterium and is reminiscent of phenomena of the *Rickettsia* diseases.

There is a form of *Bartonella* disease in white rats which appears only after removal of the spleen. Evidently the spleen holds the disease in check, perhaps through a protective activity of the reticulo-endothelial cells. The organism causing the disease in rats is known as *Bartonella muris.* This disease and some of the immunological problems presented by it have been studied by Ford and his associates.

As this subject is too large to be dealt with adequately here, the reader is referred particularly to the reviews by da Rocha-Lima and Lauda.

THE LACTOBACILLI

Transformation of the Intestinal Flora.—The *lactobacilli* are pleomorphic, gram-positive bacteria, usually appearing as long slender rods, nonmotile and generally aerobic. They do not form endospores. Their conspicuous characteristic is their ability to produce considerable amounts of lactic acid in the fermentation of carbohydrates and their ability to survive in an acid medium (pH 3.0–4.5). On account of this property they were formerly regarded as acidophilus. While they survive in a relatively acid environment, a reaction nearer neutrality is more favorable for their growth. Hence they are more correctly termed "aciduric." We shall not describe these organisms in detail but refer the reader to the descriptions of Topley and Wilson, and to the works of Rettger and Cheplin, Kopeloff, Rogers and the annotated bibliography of Frost and Hankinson.

Lactobacillus Therapy.—These organisms are of especial interest to medical bacteriologists because of their occurrence in the intestines, mouth and genitalia, their use as a form of therapy for constipation and other intestinal disorders and their possible etiological rôle in the production of dental caries.

Three organisms in this group require only passing mention in this place. They are *Lactobacillus bifidus, Döderlein's bacillus* and *Bacillus acidophilus.*

Lactobacillus bifidus, a gram-positive organism appearing often in Y-shape, isolated first by Tissier from the feces of breast-fed infants. Tissier believed that this organism was different from *Bacillus acidophilus* of Moro. This organism is related to *B. acidophilus* but not identical with it.

The taxonomic relationships of *Lactobacillus bifidus* and *Bacteroides bifidus* have been discussed by Weiss and Rettger. They regard this organism as a *Lactobacillus* and are of the opinion that it does not belong in the group *Bacteroides.*

Döderlein's bacillus is the large and pleomorphic gram-positive organism commonly seen in smears from the vagina. It is probably identical with *Bacillus acidophilus* (Cruickshank).

The Boas-Oppler bacillus, found in stomach contents in gastric stasis is a variety of *Bacillus acidophilus.*

The remaining important members of this aciduric group are *Lactobacillus bulgaricus* and *Lactobacillus acidophilus.* Kendall, Rettger, Kopeloff, and others in this country and investigators abroad have repeatedly studied these organisms with a view to differentiating them and noting their biochemical actions and ecological relationships. The differentiation is difficult and often uncertain. A most important point for the considerations to follow is that *B. bulgaricus* is normally a saprophyte which produces souring of milk and has no capacity to establish itself in the intestinal tract, while *Bacillus acidophilus* occurs often in the intestinal tract of man and animals and under certain conditions can establish itself there when administered by mouth. Certain strains of *Bacillus acidophilus* are preëminently intestinal strains. The so-called rough type is most suitable for implantation in the intestine, as Rettger has shown.

Bacillus bulgaricus came into prominence about 1908, when Metchnikoff popularized his theory that longevity could be gained and many ills cured or avoided by the drinking of sour milk, after the fashion of certain vigorous Bulgarians. Much uncritical, clinical literature grew up around this fad and *B. bulgaricus* was consumed in many dosage forms, in milk and in cultures, by patients with many ailments. The chief virtue attributed to the organism was an ability to displace a putrefactive intestinal flora with its own acid-producing fermentative progeny. Many troubles were supposed to be due to "auto-intoxication" from the absorption of putrefactive products formed in the intestine. Constipation was one of the important symptoms relievable by *B. bulgaricus,* but certain diarrheas also were said to yield to its beneficent action.

Many absurdities were cleared away by the scientific investigations of Rettger, Kendall, Torrey and others in this country on the transformability of the intestinal flora. The gist of much careful bacteriological and clinical work seems to us to be this:

Lactobacillus bulgaricus cannot establish itself in the intestine and therefore can have no effect upon the intestinal flora. Some strains of *Bacillus acidophilus* can establish themselves in the intestinal tract of man and when supplied with carbohydrates, lactose or dextrin ingested with food or milk, can produce a reaction or condition in the intestine unfavorable for the development of the putrefactive bacteria. This is the basis of modern acidophilus therapy. Selected strains cultivated in milk are prescribed for and ingested in sour milk by patients who suffer from constipation, diarrhea, and a variety of intestinal disorders. This form of therapy has a limited value. The administration of lactic acid in milk in many cases seems to be as beneficial as the administration of this organism. The evaluation of the clinical reports of the results of acidophilus therapy is difficult. Many unsuitable and inactive preparations of *Bacillus acidophilus* have been used. The best results have been obtained by those who have been most careful to control all the details of the preparation of the product and the regimen of the treatment. This form of therapy has much less vogue than it had during the period 1920 to 1930 and, in our opinion, its use will be limited in the future to relatively few cases. *Lactobacillus acidophilus* was defined in 1932 by a committee of bacteriologists in this country appointed by A. E. Woods, Director of Scientific Work of the U. S. Department of Agriculture at the request of the National Acidophilus Milk Coöperative Association. The committee, composed of L. A. Rogers, A. C. Hunter, John C. Torrey, Nicholas Kopeloff, Stewart M. Farr, and Leo F. Rettger, reported the following authentic description of the organism:

LACTOBACILLUS ACIDOPHILUS

Habitat.—Occurs normally in the intestines of warm-blooded animals and under suitable conditions cultures may be implanted by artificial means.

Morphology.—Gram-positive rods, single, or in short or long chains, occasionally filamentous. Dimensions variable, depending on environment but fairly uniform in 20–24 hour milk culture, in which medium the individual cells measure 0.6–0.8 μ in thickness and 2–8 μ in length. Longer cells and even filaments may be seen at times.

Oxygen Requirements.—Microaerophile or facultative anaerobe. Some strains require added carbon dioxide for normal growth.

Temperature Relations.—Optimum temperature is 37–40° C. Maximum temperature limit is usually 43° C. but a few cultures grow at 46° or even 48° C. Growth rarely occurs at temperatures as low as 20° C.

Colony Formation.—Colonies on tomato juice peptone agar or other suitable media have delicate filamentous outgrowths giving the colony a rough or woolly appearance. These may be mixed with smooth round colonies and in exceptional cases all colonies may be smooth.

Milk.—Milk is curdled, in some cases very slowly, with a firm curd. Litmus, if present, is reduced.

Fermentation.—In the fermentation of lactose a mixture of acids is formed which includes volatile acids usually in the proportion of between 12 and 20 per cent of the total acid. The volatile acids are formic, acetic and butyric.

The lactic acid is entirely of the inactive type.

Small amounts of CO_2 are formed but this is not enough to be evident in milk or the ordinary fermentation tubes.

Maltrose, sucrose, and raffinose are almost always fermented. Mannitol is rarely fermented, and about one-half the cultures ferment salicin.

Growth in Carbohydrate Broth.—Granular precipitate at 35–37° C. with little or no clouding of the medium.

Phenol and Indole.—Cultures are usually tolerant of indole and phenol and in a suitable medium will grow in the presence of indole in concentrations of 1:1100 to 1:1900 and phenol of 1:250 to 1:400.

Dental Caries.—The etiology of dental caries is complex. The carbohydrate constituents of diet are important factors and the vitamins and hormones which regulate the calcium-phosphorus metabolism undoubtedly influence the susceptibility or resistance of the teeth to decay. Carious lesions of the teeth, however, invariably contain lactic-acid producing organisms and much evidence has been brought forward by Bunting and Jay, McIntosh, James and Lazarus-Barlow which indicates that certain varieties of *Bacillus acidophilus* cause dental caries. Although this organism may not be the sole cause of dental caries, it is, in our opinion, an important factor in the production of the decay of teeth. Other acidogenic and aciduric bacteria of the mouth also may be of etiological importance in dental caries. Anderson and Rettger regard streptococci as agents capable of producing these lesions.

REFERENCES

ALBRECHT, B. In Kolle, Kraus and Uhlenhuth, Handb. d. path. Mikroorg., 1929, 6:673.
ANDERSON, T. G., and RETTGER, L. F. J. Dental Res., 1937, 16:489.
BENGTSON, I. U. S. Pub. Health Rep., 1928, 43:2210, 2217.
BUNTING, R. W., HALLEY, F. D., JAY, P., and HARD, D. G. Am. J. Dis. Child., 1930, 40:536.
BURN, C. J. Bacteriol., 1935, 30:573.
CRUICKSHANK, R. J. Hyg., 1931, 31:375.
CUNNINGHAM, J. S. Arch. Path., 1930, 9:843.
DACK, G. M., DRAGSTEDT, L. R., and HEINZ, T. E. J. Am. M. Ass., 1936, 106:7.
———— J. Infect. Dis., 1937, 60:335.
———— JOHNSTON, R., and McCULLOUGH, N. B. J. Exper. M., 1938, 62:169.
DA ROCHA-LIMA, H. In Kolle, Kraus and Uhlenhuth, Handb. d. path. Mikroorg., 1930, 8:1049.
FORD, W. W., and ELIOT, C. P. Am. J. Hyg., 1930, 12:669.
FROST, W. D., and HANKINSON, H. Lactobacillus Acidophilus, Milton, Wisc., 1931.
HALBERSTÄDTER, L., and VON PROWAZEK, S. Deutsche med. Wchnschr., 1907, 33:1285.
———— Arch., f. Protistenk., 1907, 10:335.
HARRIS, J. W., and BROWN, J. H. Bull. Johns Hopkins Hosp., 1927, 40:203.
JAY, P. J. Am. Dental Ass., 1929, 16:230.
———— Am. J. Pub. Health, 1938, 28:759.
JENSEN, C. O. In Kolle and Wassermann, Handb. d. path. Mikroorg., 2nd ed., 1913, 6:234.
JULIANELLE, L. A. The Etiology of Trachoma. Commonwealth Fund. New York, 1938.
————, HARRISON, R. W., and MORRIS, M. C. J. Exper. M., 1937, 65:735.
KENDALL, A. I. J. Med. Research, 1910, 22:153.
———— Bacteriology, General, Pathological and Intestinal, Philadelphia, 1931.
KERR, J. W. U. S. Pub. Health Rep., 1915.
KOPELOFF, N. Lactobacillus Acidophilus, Baltimore, 1926.
LAUDA, E. In Kolle, Kraus and Uhlenhuth, Handb. d. path. Mikroorg., 1930, 8:1073.
LONGCOPE, W. T. Am. J. M. Sc., 1922, 164:781.
MAYOU, M. S. A System of Bacteriology in Relation to Medicine, 1930, 7:244.
———— J. Exper. M., 1932, 55:803.
METCHNIKOFF, E. Prolongation of Life, New York, 1908.
McINTOSH, J., JAMES, W. W., and LAZARUS-BARLOW, P. J. Exper. Pathol., 1922, 3:138; 1924. 15:175.
MORAX, V. Rev. internat. du trachome, 1931, 8:133.
MORO, E. Jahrb. f. Kinderh., 1900, 52:38.
MOSSMAN, P. D. U. S. Pub. Health Rep., 1931, 48:2940.
MURRAY, E. G. D., WEBB, R. A., and SWAN, M. B. R. J. Pathol. & Bacteriol., 1926, 29:407.

Noguchi, H. J. Exper. M., 1926, 43:851; 1926, 44:543; 697, 715, 729; 1928, 48:Supplement No. 2, 1–53.

Nyfeldt, A. Compt. rend. Soc. de biol., 1929, 101:590.

Olitsky, P. K. Tr. Am. Acad. Ophth. Oto-Laryngol., 1930, 225.

Pfeiffer, E. Jahrb. f. Kinderh., 1889, 29:257.

Rettger, L. F. Yale J. Biol. & Med., 1932, 4:485.

Rettger, L. F., and Cheplin, H. A. Treatise on the Transformation of the Intestinal Flora with Special Reference to the Implantation of Bacillus Acidophilus, New Haven, 1921.

Rettger, L. F., Weinstein, L., Deiss, J. E., and Levy, M. N. Arch. Int. M., 1933, 52:384.

Rogers, L. A., Curran, H. R., and Whittier, E. O. J. Bacteriol., 1933, 25:595.

Scheer, K. Monatschr. f. Kinderh., 1930, 48:59.

Schmorl, G. Deutsch. Ztschr. f. Thiermed., 1891, 17:375.

Seastone, C. V. J. Exper. M., 1935, 62:203.

Shannon, R. C. Am. J. Hyg., 1929, 10:78.

Shaw, F. W. Bull. Med. Coll. Virg., March, 1925.

———Zentralbl. f. Bakteriol., I Abt., 1933, 129:132.

Shaw, F. W., and Bigger, I. A. J. Am. M. Ass., 1934, 102:688.

Shultz, E. W., Terry, M. C., Bryce, A. T., Jr., and Gebhardt, L. P. Proc. Soc. Exper. Biol. & Med., 1938, 38:605.

Smith, D. T. Oral Spirochetes and Related Organisms in Fuso-Spirochetal Disease, Baltimore, 1932, 14–20.

Slanetz, L. A., and Rettger, L. F. J. Bacteriol., 1933, 26:599.

Spaulding, E. H., and Rettger, L. F. J. Bacteriol., 1937, 34:535, 549.

Sprunt, T. P., and Evans, F. A. Bull. Johns Hopkins Hosp., 1920, 31:410.

Stemen, C. M., and Shaw, F. W. J. Kansas M. Soc., 1910, 10:405.

Strong, R. P. Harvey Lectures, New York, 1913–14, 204–223.

Strong, R. P., Tyzzer, E. E., Sellards, A. W., Brues, C. T., and Gastiaburu, J. C. Report of First Expedition to South America, Harvard School Trop. Med. Rep., 1915.

Tissier, H. Étude sur la flore intestinale normale et pathologique chez le nourrison, Paris, 1900.

Topley, W. W. C., and Wilson, G. S. The Principles of Bacteriology and Immunity, New York and London, 1929, 1:470.

Townsend, C. H. T. J. Am. M. Ass., 1913, 61:1717.

Tunnicliff, R., and Hammond, C. J. Infect. Dis., 1937, 61:26.

Weinberg, M., and Ginsbourg, R. Monogr. de l'Inst. Pasteur, 1927, No. 211.

Weinstein, L. Yale J. Biol. and M., 1938, 10:247.

Weiss, J. E., and Rettger, L. F. J. Infect. Dis., 1938, 62:115.

Witts, L. J. J. Pathol. & Bacteriol., 1928, 31:249.

Woods, A. C. Allergy and Immunity in Ophthalmology, Baltimore, 1933, 49.

Preparatio
in the air,
in a funne
citric acid
washed wi
methylene
method gi
the cellula
effective i
reliable te

The
In maki
cerned ii
organisn
Rickettsi
Rickettsi
animal
successft
and Sch
cultures
vello. P
many g
Cultures
utilized
of the (
render
Ricketts
cytopla
tissue c

A r
Wei de
adjuste
or beel
tissue a
diffusic
environ
propert

Th
technic

1. A
v
c

2. A
f
c
v
f
1

SECTION IV

THE RICKETTSIA DISEASES

CHAPTER XLIX

TYPHUS FEVER (ROCKY MOUNTAIN SPOTTED FEVER, TRENCH FEVER, TSUTSUGAMUSHI FEVER)

The diseases brought together in this section, though occurring in many different parts of the world, resemble each other in so many important biological attributes that we are justified in assuming a close relationship between them. With the exception of trench fever which stands somewhat apart in this particular, they are very much alike in clinical manifestations. They all show the Weil-Felix reaction with *Proteus X$_{19}$* or *Proteus XK*. They are all insect-borne. In some of them an intermediate animal host (a rodent) has been demonstrated, and in those in which this has not been accomplished, epidemiological data render likely the existence of such a host. Recent years have revealed, within the typhus-spotted fever division, a number of subvarieties which shade into each other in such a gradual manner that a development of one type of disease from another, by adaptations of the virus to different insect and animal hosts, suggests itself. This phase of the problem cannot be profitably discussed until we have considered the conditions prevailing in the best-known of the group, typhus fever.

Although there are still occasional publications in which causation by true bacteria or by a filtrable virus is suggested, it is quite generally accepted by students of these diseases that they are caused by a class of micro-organisms spoken of as *Rickettsia*.

THE RICKETTSIAE

The name *Rickettsia* was given to the organism under consideration by da Rocha-Lima in 1916, when he designated the bodies now recognized as the causative agents of typhus fever *Rickettsia prowazeki*, in honor of Ricketts and of Prowazek, both of whom had died in the course of typhus investigations. In 1909, Ricketts had described bacillary bodies which he had seen in the blood of patients with Rocky Mountain spotted fever. Guided by this observation, together with Wilder in 1910, Ricketts described similar micro-organisms in typhus blood smears and in smears from lice that had fed on typhus patients. Von Prowazek made similar observations in Serbia in 1913; Sergent, Foley and Vialatte in North Africa in 1914. Thorough study of the organism was then made by da Rocha-Lima, and extensive confirmatory observations were published for both Rocky Mountain spotted fever and typhus fever, by Wolbach and his associates in 1922. For a short time, confusion in regard to the etiological importance of the *Rickettsiae* was caused by the observation of similar bodies seen extracellularly in uninfected lice. Da Rocha-Lima's investigations satis-

washed disks are dried slowly in the incubator and then sterilized in the holders in the autoclave.

The Tyrode-serum mixture, as given above, after filtration, is warmed to 45° C. and mixed at this temperature with the 300 c.c. of the 3% agar. The mixture is then poured into 6 x 1 inch test tubes with sterile precautions, using a sterile siphon system, in 10 c.c. amounts. The tubes are slanted and left at room temperature to harden. Then they are stoppered with sterile #4 stoppers. The final reaction should be about pH 7.8. The slants should be kept upright at room temperature for two or three days so that the water of condensation may sink to the bottom to be removed with a capillary pipette before the tubes are planted, since excessive moisure interferes with growth. They are kept at room temperature for an additional check on possible contamination and after this can be kept in the ice chest until used.

Infected mouse embryo cells, finely minced, are gently deposited on these slants so as to cover about one-third of the surface. *Rickettsiae* become plentiful in from 6 to 10 days at 37° C.

It is not unlikely that the *Rickettsiae* are, originally, insect parasites—a surmise which is suggested by the frequency of similar organisms in a variety of insects and the fact that, in tissue culture, they are most easily grown at a temperature somewhat lower than that of the mammalian body. In the Mexican disease, the initial accumulation of the organisms in the tunica vaginalis is perhaps favored by the fact that the temperature of the testis is several degrees lower than that of the body as a whole.

Hereditary transfer of *Rickettsiae* in their insect hosts appears to take place in Rocky Mountain spotted fever. Wolbach in 1919 recorded the occurrence of the organisms in the spermatozoa of infected male ticks, and the transmission of the disease from infected males to uninfected female ticks has been observed by Philip and Parker. The presence of the organisms in the ova of ticks had been previously observed (Parker), and for these reasons, in the case of Rocky Mountain spotted fever, the assumption of an intermediate animal host for the perpetuation of the disease is not necessary. In typhus fever and other diseases of the group, however, the infection is apparently not carried in the ova and is not inherited through insect generations.

Eventually, *Rickettsiae* may be included in the bacteria. For the present, their peculiarities of habitat, appearance, staining properties, intracellular position and resistance to cultivation appear sufficient reason to separate them in a special class. We consider that any organism which grows on ordinary media without cells cannot at the present time be regarded as a true *Rickettsia*. Added to this is the fact that, although there is no question about minor differences between the *Rickettsiae* causing the several diseases we are about to discuss, their epidemiological cycles and modes of attack mark them as forming a homogeneous group. Of great interest is their apparent selective affinity for specific types of cells. Though found in the blood and in all the organs of sick animals and men, they accumulate visibly in cells of mesothelial origin, particularly in the lining cells of the serous cavities, such as the tunica vaginalis, and, under experimental conditions, in the peritoneum and in the intima of blood vessels.

The species of *Rickettsia* that have particular importance for the student of infectious diseases are the following:

Rickettsia prowazeki (da Rocha-Lima, 1916). The organism of European typhus fever; closely related to but not serologically identical with the *Rickettsia* causing New World typhus fever. The latter was first described with full realization of differentiation between the diseases, by Mooser. Whether or not the Mooser bodies should be separately named remains to be seen.

Rickettsia pediculi (da Rocha-Lima, 1916). This organism was for a time regarded as a normal parasite on the louse, with no pathogenic significance. Da Rocha-Lima favors the view that this organism is identical with the *Rickettsia quintana* which is regarded as the causative agent of trench fever.

Dermacentroxenus rickettsii (Wolbach, 1919). This organism causes Rocky Mountain spotted fever.

The following table of some of the more commonly observed *Rickettsiae* has been tentatively constructed by Wolbach.

WOLBACH'S TENTATIVE CLASSIFICATION

Insects	*Mallophaga*	*Melophagus ovinus* (sheep "louse" or "tick")		
		Rickettsia melophagi	Nöller	1917
	Corrodentia	*Psocus Sp.?* (dust louse)		
		Unnamed rickettsia...............Sikora		1918
	Hemiptera	*Pediculus humanus* (human louse)		
		Rickettsia prowazeki..............Hegler and Von Prowazek....		1914
		Da Rocha-Lima..............		1916
		Rickettsia (rocha-lima)?........Weigl, oral statement........		1920
		Rickettsia pediculi..............Munk and Da Rocha-Lima....		1917
		Rickettsia quintana..............Munk and Da Rocha-Lima....		1917
		Rickettsia wolhynica............Toepfer		1916
		Cimex (Acanthia) lectularius (bedbug)		
		Rickettsia lectularius...........Bacot		1921
	Diptera	*Culex pipiens* (mosquito, Europe)		
		Unnamed rickettsia..............Nöller, quoted by Sikora......		1920
	Siphonaptera	*Ctenocephalus felis* (cat flea)		
		Rickettsia ctenocephali...........Sikora		1918
		Ctenopsylla musculi (mouse flea)		
		Unnamed rickettsia..............Sikora		1918
	Arachnida, Acarina	*Dermacentor venustus* (wood tick, U. S.)		
		Dermacentroxenus rickettsii......Ricketts		1909
		Leptus (Tromibidium) akamushi (harvest mite, Japan)		
		Unverified quotation by Sikora..............................		1920
		Dermanyssus Sp.? (bird mite, Europe)		
		Unnamed, Nöller; quoted by Sikora.........................		1920

The *R. melophagi* is not pathogenic and is the only one that has been cultivated upon glucose blood agar. We question its proper inclusion in this group. The *R. corrodentia* of the dust louse is, likewise, not associated with any mammalian host. It lives extracellularly in the stomach of the louse and is apparently non-pathogenic. The *R. pediculi, quintana* and *wolhynica* are probably identical, according to Wolbach and Todd. They are more uniform in morphology than the *Rickettsia* of typhus and are easier to stain. They occur extracellularly in the louse's stomach,

adhere to the cuticular epithelium, and may invade the epithelial cells. They are transmitted to the egg. Their etiological association with trench fever has been suggested.

The *R. prowazeki* is pleomorphic and seems to be exclusively intracellular in the
louse.

The *R. lectularius* of the bedbug is nonpathogenic, but morphologically resembles
R. prowazeki.

The ones occurring in mosquitoes and in cat and mouse fleas are nonpathogenic.

The *R. orientalis* supposed to have been cultivated by Sellards from Tsutsugamushi disease was without doubt a contaminating bacterial organism not related to
the disease.

We may set down the main groups of Rickettsia diseases as follows:

Typhus—of which there are at present two determinable varieties which immunize one against the other and which can both be transferred from man to man by
the human louse. In this group the vascular histopathology is an angeitis without
invasion of the deeper layers of the vessels and without the thrombonecrotic lesions
seen in the spotted fever group. The *Rickettsiae* are intracytoplasmic (Pinkerton)
and do not appear to invade the nuclei.

Spotted Fever—of which there are a number of varieties, all of which cross
immunize and are conveyed by ticks. In all of them the histopathology is of the
thromboangeitic type, often with necroses, and in all of those so far studied (Pinkerton), the *Rickettsiae* may have an intranuclear position.

The Tsutsugamushi Group—all conveyed by *Acarina* or mites. Gross immunity
exists within the group, but relationships with other groups is unsatisfactory in this
respect, owing to difficulties of animal experimentation.

TYPHUS FEVER

Clinical Manifestations.—The earliest clinical description which can be regarded as reliably recognizable as the disease we now call typhus fever is that
written by Fracastor in 1554. That the disease occurred long before this is unquestionable but we deduce this from a combination of available epidemiologic and incomplete clinical data. Fracastor described the typical course including the type of
fever and the rash in such a manner that no mistake is possible. Later classical descriptions which were particularly important for differential diagnosis were those of
Jenner and of Murchison. In America the important studies of Gerhard of Philadelphia contributed much to the clear differentiation of this disease from typhoid fever.

The incubation time may range from five to twenty-one days. A case of autopsy
infection published during the World War took exactly twelve days to develop.

The onset may vary from extreme abruptness to a more gradual one. As a rule
the onset resembles closely that of a severe case of influenza. We take the main
points of our description from a study by George C. Shattuck on cases observed during the Serbian epidemic.

The temperature rises rapidly, often to from 103° to 104° F., with chills, great
depression, weakness, pains in the head and limbs. The eruption appears on the fourth
or fifth day after the onset and, except in times of epidemic, the diagnosis is extremely difficult in the preëruptive stage. As the eruption appears the fever is apt to

rise. The rash begins to appear usually on the shoulders and trunk, extending secondarily to the extremities, the backs of the hands and feet, and sometimes to the palms and soles. It becomes more abundant during the subsequent second and third days, but it is seen very rarely on the face and forehead. The rash is at first composed of pink spots which disappear on pressure, but soon it becomes purplish, more deeply brownish red and finally fades into a brown color. Hemorrhagic centers may later develop which persist for considerable lengths of time. There are no eruptions on the mucous membranes of the mouth and pharynx. It is important to remember (a thing which Shattuck points out and which we have confirmed) in connection with the differential diagnosis between typhus and purpura haemorrhagica that in the purpura eruption the spots are hemorrhagic from the beginning and are more sharply defined than those of typhus. Fresh fleabites are sometimes hard to distinguish from the typhus eruption.

The heart is usually rapid and may become irregular. The blood pressure is apt to be low and Shattuck believes that myocardial weakness often occurs. Epistaxis may occur at the height of the disease. Bronchitis often occurs during the later stages and cough is almost regularly present. Nervous symptoms of various kinds are important accompaniments of the disease. In many cases a state of lethargy resembling that of typhoid fever is present. There may be twitching of the muscles during this stage of stupor. Delirium occurs in all but the very mild cases. The most constant and troublesome subjective symptom is the very severe headache.

The leukocytes, as worked out by Sellards, are rarely increased in number, ranging in number from three thousand to fifteen thousand, the average being between five thousand and seven thousand. Differential counts show approximately normal percentages.

The most common complications are parotitis, suppurative otitis and mastoiditis, and a peculiar gangrene of the extremities, especially of the feet, is particularly associated with cases occurring during the cold weather. This gangrene is probably associated with the vascular changes incident to the localization of the virus. Bronchitis is almost a regular complication. Albuminuria is present, and the urine gives a diazo reaction.

For a thorough discussion of the pathology of the disease we refer the reader to Wolbach's Harvey Lecture. (Series 1920-1921, New York Harvey Society.)

The diagnostic *Weil-Felix reaction* is considered in a separate section.

Epidemiology.—It is quite impossible to undertake an adequate description of the epidemiology of typhus fever in the space available in this book. The disease has been one of the most deadly in the history of human epidemics. Extensive discussions of its occurrence from earliest times may be found in Hirsch's *Handbook of Geographical and Historical Pathology*, in Murchison and in a number of the more modern works on epidemiology. The earliest reference to an outbreak of disease which has a definite resemblance to typhus fever dates from the eleventh century, and deals with an epidemic which took place in 1083 in a monastery near Salerno. From that time on, the disease is associated with military campaigns and with human misery in general. Hirsch writes "The history of typhus is written in those dark pages of the world's story which tell of the grievous visitations of mankind by war, famine and misery." Reasons for this are now well understood in the light of the information we possess concerning the conditions under which the disease is transmitted. The earliest precise description of typhus is found in Fracastor's book *De Contagione*, which was published in 1546. From that time on information is more reliable because of the accurate descriptions both of the movement of the disease in its epidemics and of the clinical condition in man given by Fracastor. In its early history the disease was apparently frequent both endemically and epidemically in all parts of Europe and, in connection with almost all the wars and sieges of importance, typhus outbreaks decimated the troops and probably had an important influence upon the outcome of campaigns. During the siege of Granada, where it killed many thousands of the besieging army, it received its name "tabardillo" from the mantle-like spotted rash which covered the bodies of its victims. It is the disease of the Black Assizes which occurred in Oxford in 1577 and at Exeter in 1586. Throughout the Thirty Years War it was perhaps the most serious cause of death among the many that killed off the European populations during this unhappy period. It ravaged the Napoleonic army on its return from Russia and swept through western Europe in repeated epidemics before and after this period. Since 1846 no great epidemics have occurred in western Europe, but the disease has remained prevalent in Ireland and in southeastern Europe and Russia. The latter regions form the great endemic center of typhus at the present day. The most important recent epidemics have been those which took place during the World War in the Balkans and in Russia. In the winter of 1914–15, a severe outbreak began in Serbia, a detailed description of which may be found in the report of the American Red Cross Commission published by Strong in 1920.

The Serbian epidemic of 1915 was so severe that it interfered materially with military activities, and it was probably because of the epidemic that the Austrian Armies delayed their second attack upon Serbia. A detailed description of this epidemic is found in the article by Strong in the *Red Cross Report* referred to above. Typhus appeared in the Serbian Army in October and November of 1914, and it is said by Strong to have been introduced from Albania. It is also believed that typhus was present in the Austrian Army during its first invasion of Serbia, and there may well have been endemic cases in Serbia before the invasion. After the Austrian repulse of the late summer of 1914, typhus broke out among Austrian prisoners and Serbian soldiers. Owing to the fighting in the north the Serbian civilian population was forced southward and conditions of personal hygiene, housing, etc., were made particularly difficult.

Until 1917 it was the prevailing opinion that there was but one type of typhus virus responsible for this disease in many different parts of the world. At that time, Neill described, in guinea-pigs intraperitoneally inoculated with blood from cases that occurred in Texas, the development of pronounced scrotal swellings not hitherto observed in the experimental disease. These observations made no impression until Mooser, in 1928, recognized such swellings as characteristic of the infection of guinea-pigs with Mexican virus and found, in the tunica vaginalis of such animals, small Giemsa-staining bodies which he regarded as Rickettsiae. This was the beginning of a differentiation between the classical European typhus and a Mexican, or New World variety.

It was subsequently found by a number of observers that the virus obtained from the sporadic typhus cases of the southern United States corresponded, in regard to scrotal swellings and tunica lesions, to the Mexican variety. In an epidemiological study of these cases, Maxcy, in 1926, suggested the possibility that the responsible virus was kept alive in an animal reservoir, possibly rodent, and was transmitted to man by some insect other than the louse. This suspicion was corroborated in 1931, when Dyer and his associates of the United States Public Health Service isolated a virus of this type from the fleas of rats trapped in typhus foci in Baltimore; and Mooser, Castaneda and Zinsser obtained a similar virus from the brains of rats caught in the Belem Prison in Mexico City during an epidemic.

Since that time, a large amount of work has been done in many parts of the world on the differentiation of the two types of virus. It is no longer accurate to speak of an "endemic" as contrasted with an "epidemic" virus since both types can occur both endemically and epidemically. It is, further, no longer correct to designate the two varieties respectively as "European" and "New World," because a "Mexican" type of virus has been found in rats in the Mediterranean basin, isolated strains from Mexico have behaved like the European type, and the Brill's disease virus isolated by us in Boston has shown all the characteristics of the agent which causes the classical European disease.

There is an unquestionably close relationship between the two types which is of fundamental importance in theoretical and practical immunological investigations. There are, however, experimentally determinable differences which forbid absolute identification.

Brill's disease, which is a mild typhus that was observed first by Brill among southeastern European and Jewish immigrants in New York, occurs in isolated cases in many of the large cities of the Atlantic coast. It is the opinion of Zinsser and Castaneda that the condition known as Brill's disease is the imported European typhus fever introduced into the large cities of the north Atlantic seaboard by immigrants from the typhus foci of southeastern Europe. This view is based upon the fact that they isolated three strains of virus from typical cases of Brill's disease occurring in Boston, and these have conformed, in the course of guinea-pig passage, to the European type. In addition to such experimental evidence, epidemiological studies remove all doubt about the European origin of this infection.

Typhus is also constantly prevalent and occasionally epidemic along the North African coast, where the studies of Nicolle revealed the fundamental fact of louse transmission and of the susceptibility of laboratory animals.

Typhus is also present constantly and often epidemic throughout China and probably in other parts of Asia, where it appears from descriptions that the Chinese typhus has many of the characteristics of the European disease, whereas the Manchurian variety resembles the Mexican and American types. It has also been described from the Malayan Peninsula, but data by which this variety can be accurately classified are not yet available.

In a subsequent section we will discuss the differentiation of varieties of human *Rickettsia* diseases, correlating these with the epidemiological data.

Transmission.—The group of *Rickettsia* diseases includes a number of varieties about some of which we have accurate data of transmission, whereas in regard to others there are still considerable gaps in our knowledge. Although the suspicion that typhus fever was insect-transmitted dates far back into the history of typhus, the question was not solved until Nicolle, Comte and Conseil proved in 1909 that the disease is transmitted by body lice. Reasoning from epidemiological observations, they fed body lice upon a typhus-fever-infected *Macacus sinicus*, and then allowed these insects to feed upon healthy monkeys. That the head louse, which is closely related to the body louse, can also transmit the disease, was later demonstrated by da Rocha-Lima. The virus develops in the intestinal lining cells of the lice, which become infectious within four, five or six days, but reach their highest degree of infectiousness between the eighth and the eleventh day. The virus seems to grow more virulent in the lice and passage through lice can be used in laboratories to step up a virus when it seems to be losing potency. Infected lice invariably die in which they differ from other insects—a fact which possibly indicates that a louse is a relatively recent vector. It is not certain whether the virus is deposited in the human victim with the bite, or whether it gets into the wound of the bite with the feces. The louse feces always contain *Rickettsiae* and the louse regularly deposits feces while it feeds. Unlike Rocky Mountain fever in ticks, which is transmitted from generation to generation of infected ticks, the typhus virus is not hereditary in lice. Many other means of transmission of typhus fever from man to man have been suspected, but so far as we know at the present time, the European disease cannot be acquired except by a louse bite or by direct and penetrating contact with blood or organs of a patient. A typhus fever patient who has been completely deloused is, therefore, not dangerous. A few autopsy infections have been described, but they are unquestionably rare, since the virus does not live long in dead bodies. The very large number of laboratory infections which have occurred in the study of these diseases have been the consequence either of accidents with infected lice or fleas or with the blood and exudates of infected guinea-pigs. Although we know nothing further than the louse transmission for the European disease, analogy with the New World variety would make it seem likely that here also we may eventually find that there is an animal reservoir and that other insects may be involved.

With the New World variety we have gained a considerably more complete story of the cycle of transmission since 1926.

Maxcy in 1926 studied cases corresponding to the Mexican disease in the southeastern United States and concluded that its origin could not, in the American variety, be traced to lice. Like Hone and Wheatland in Australia, he suspected an animal reservoir, mentioning particularly rats and mice, and suggested an insect vector other than lice which might convey the virus from the unknown animal reservoir to man.

The search for other insects that could harbor the typhus virus was undertaken by many investigators. Zinsser and Castaneda succeeded in infecting bedbugs and three varieties of ticks with the Mexican virus by intrarectal injections; and, in the case of bedbugs, by allowing the insects to feed on heavily infected rats. Since they did not succeed in transmitting the infection to new animals by the bites of such insects, they attached minor epidemiological importance to these findings.

Dyer and his associates in 1931 reported the discovery of the typhus virus in rat fleas collected from rats trapped in a typhus focus. Shortly after this Mooser, Castaneda and Zinsser, examining domestic rats in Mexico City during a small epidemic of typhus fever, discovered the virus in the brains of rats trapped in the Belem Prison, where the epidemic was supposed to have originated. Following the discovery of the virus in rats it was found that the rat louse, *Polyplax spinulosus,* was easily infected in the natural manner from rats and could transmit the disease to other rats. Subsequently, Dyer and his associates as well as Mooser and Castaneda, succeeded in transmitting the disease from rat to rat by the flea, *Xenopsylla cheopis.* The epidemiology of the Mexican and American variety of the disease, therefore, is almost entirely cleared up.

The disease is maintained in a reservoir of rats, among which it is kept going in the interepidemic periods, probably by both the *Polyplax* and the flea. This explains the important problem of interepidemic survival of the virus, which was not explicable on the human louse transmission alone, for the reason that the *Pediculus* succumbs with regularity to typhus infection and therefore cannot maintain the virus for any length of time. After a human case has occurred in a louse community, the disease passes from man to man by the human body louse and, quite surely, by the head louse as well, and this is the reason for epidemics; but in communities not infested with lice, the disease occurs sporadically and is probably acquired directly from the animal reservoir.

The question of the vector by which typhus fever passes from rats to man has probably been settled by the flea discovery; for the rat flea will on occasion bite man and the flea does not die of the disease, as does the louse, but may retain the virus for a month or longer.

As far as other insects are concerned, while bedbugs and ticks have been experimentally infected, the former by the natural method of feeding, and the disease produced by injecting all of these infected insects into guinea-pigs, nevertheless, it was never possible to infect from such insects by the natural method of bite. Moreover, about 1000 bedbugs collected in Mexico City shortly after the time of our rat discovery did not harbor the virus.

The flea is thus the most likely vector from rat to man, although there is still a difficulty—which is the fact that the rat does not die of typhus fever, and that unless the association of the patient with rats is a very close one, there is little possibility of the rat flea leaving the rat for man. It is still possible, however, that the first infections may occur in prisons or in places where rats are trapped or where there is very close rat-man association.

In the European disease the epidemiological data have not been so fully worked out as in the American variety, and the diseases are sufficiently different to prevent us from drawing conclusions by analogy. There is, however, a certain amount of evidence in favor of the older view to the effect that the interepidemic reservoir of European typhus fever is, certainly in part, in human beings, either carriers or late recrudescences. Studies on Brill's disease in Boston and New York definitely exclude the propagation of this variety of typhus by rats and rat fleas, and comparative studies of the virus of the European disease and that of the Mexican or American type indicate that passage of the murine, Mexican virus through man modifies it in the direction of the more or less fixed European characteristics. This suggests that possibly the common origin of the two types is in rodents but that an irreversible adaptation to man has taken place in Central Europe.

The rat studies in Mexico led European observers to make similar investigations in various parts of the Mediterranean basin where typhus fever was prevalent. Marcandier and Pirot discovered a virus not unlike the American variety in rats on the battleships at Toulon. A similar observation was made by Lepine in rats at Athens and Piraeus. The latter obtained similar results with rats captured at Bayreuth and with Caminopetros and Pangalos found the virus in rat fleas. Although preliminary investigations of a similar sort have been carried out in Tunis and on the European continent, no evidence has been uncovered that would connect the classical European disease with a rodent reservoir.

The so-called "exanthematous typhus" of São Paulo described by Monteiro is tick-transmitted, and belongs to the Rocky Mountain spotted fever group. Parker and Davis have proved by cross-immunity tests the identity of the São Paulo disease with Rocky Mountain spotted fever. The sera of guinea-pigs recovered from Rocky Mountain spotted fever had protective value against the São Paulo virus, and guinea-pigs that had recovered from the Brazilian virus remained afebrile when reinoculated with Rocky Mountain spotted fever virus.

The Manchurian typhus belongs to the murine group.

Tsutsugamushi fever, which is most likely a close relative of true typhus fever, has a mouse reservoir and is transmitted by the harvest mite, *Trombicula akamushi*.

Experimental Typhus Fever in Man and Animals.—Laboratory accidents and accidents in the field have amply demonstrated that typhus fever can be transmitted from animals to man, and transmission from man to man with blood has been experimentally carried out. The transmission to man by lice, discovered by Nicolle, has been many times confirmed by laboratory accident since the time of its discovery. Autopsy infections seem to be rare. From infected guinea-pigs the disease may be transferred to man with blood, with brain emulsion and, in the Mexican variety, most virulently with tunica scrapings.

One of the most important steps in etiological study of an infectious disease is the production of the disease in animals. In the cases of typhus this was first accomplished by Nicolle.

In 1909 Nicolle successfully inoculated an anthropoid ape, and Anderson and Goldberger in the same year succeeded in inoculating lower monkeys, rhesus and capuchin. Successful monkey inoculations were then made by Ricketts and Wilder, and by Gavino and Girard. In these animals inoculation with blood from active cases is followed by a rapid rise of temperature after an incubation time of five days or more, and the fever remains high for three to five days, after which it comes down by lysis. Occasional recrudescences have been noticed in monkeys. Goldberger and Anderson had a mortality of 2 per cent in their monkeys. The disease may be transmitted from monkey to monkey with the blood, which is infectious during the febrile period and may remain so for as long as thirty-two hours after the temperature returns to normal.

Efforts to inoculate other animals were at first unsuccessful, but in 1911 Nicolle, Conseil and Conor succeeded in transferring the disease to guinea-pigs both with the blood of human patients, during the acute stages of the disease, and with louse virus. Guinea-pigs are regularly susceptible and have become the chief instruments not only for typhus fever experimentation but for differentiation between the varieties of diseases of this group. The most effective method of inoculating guinea-pigs is by the intraperitoneal route, but the disease can also be produced by subcutaneous inoculation, though with less regularity and severity.

With the European virus, the course of guinea-pig typhus after intraperitoneal inoculation is, within limits of variation, as follows: After an incubation time of eight to twelve days, the temperature of the animals rises to over 104° F., sometimes reaching 105° to 106° F. This temperature is maintained for from three to six days, after which it comes down to normal within about forty-eight hours. The proof of typhus fever in a guinea-pig, however, must be based on more than the temperature curve alone. Positive criteria are as follows:

1. The typical temperature.

2. The reproduction of the disease in other guinea-pigs by intraperitoneal injection of blood or brain emulsion during the height of the febrile period. The brain emulsion is apt to be virulent slightly longer than the blood and can be used up to the fourteenth day with success.

3. The development of a specific immunity to further virus inoculations in the guinea-pig. Such immunity becomes apparent immediately after defervescence and may persist for six months or longer, whereas the protective bodies in the blood of recovered guinea-pigs disappear in between two to three weeks.

4. The development, in the brains of guinea-pigs, of the typical typhus lesions first described by Otto and Dietrich and very thoroughly studied by Wolbach.

5. The sterility of ordinary bacterial cultures from the organs.

As a general rule in experimentation the criteria regularly applied and indispensable are passage, immunity and brain lesions.

In the case of the Mexican variety, guinea-pig inoculation is followed, even in the first passage from man to guinea-pigs by a slight swelling of the scrotum, first described in 1917 by Neill and recognized as a differential characteristic by Mooser in 1928. The incubation time between inoculation and the development of the scrotal swelling shortens as the strain becomes adapted to the guinea-pigs, and eventually occurs, according to the size of the dose, in from five to seven days after peritoneal inoculation. It does not occur, even with this virus, upon subcutaneous inoculation, when the Mexican infection is more closely similar to the European. The scrotal swelling, unlike that occurring with Rocky Mountain spotted fever, is not associated with vascular lesions, thrombosis and necrotic edema, but is due to an inflammatory reaction of the mesothelium lining the tunica vaginalis. In this lesion Mooser was the first to find *Rickettsiae*, sometimes in great numbers, lying at first entirely within the cytoplasm of the cells, and later appearing extracellularly as a consequence of the bursting of the cells themselves. The temperature rises on the fifth or sixth day with the first reddening of the scrotum, usually comes down on the day after the preliminary swelling, and on the next day rises again to from over 104° to 106° F. At this time the swelling is prominent, the scrotum red and the tunica adherent so that the testicles do not easily reduce. These symptoms, together with the temperature, subside in the course of three, four or five days. The guinea-pigs never die of the uncomplicated disease. In the Mexican guinea-pigs, immunity is established to the European disease, and *vice versa*. As far as symptoms in guinea-pigs are concerned, the Mexican variety is identical with that of the Eastern United States, except in the case of Brill's disease which has been shown to be the imported European disease. Brain lesions are less frequent in the New World than in the Old World variety, possibly—as Mooser has suggested—because the animals are immunized by the early development of the scrotal lesions. In other respects, the Mexican virus acts similarly to the European. Guinea-pig organs and blood are universally infectious, but the tunica scrapings are many times more virulent than is the blood of the same animal. A peculiarity that seems to be alike for these diseases as well as for Rocky Mountain spotted fever and possibly for trench fever, and has led to much early experimental difficulty is the fact that, in the blood, the virus seems to adhere firmly to the red blood cells.

The use of the guinea-pig in differentiating the various *Rickettsia* diseases is dealt with in another section.

Next to the guinea-pig, the most useful animal for typhus experimentation is the rat. Rats were formerly regarded as resistant, but as Nicolle and Le Bailly have shown, the European virus produces, in rats and mice, an *inapparent* infection, without fever, demonstrable only by the fact that the virus can be carried through generations of rats and mice and back to guinea-pigs and monkeys.

The American variety of typhus is more virulent for rats and produces a definite febrile curve. Scrotal swelling is occasionally seen and *Rickettsia,* under suitable experimental conditions, can be obtained in large amounts from rats. Nicolle and Laigret as well as Savoor have further shown that the American-Mexican virus will remain alive and unattenuated through a considerable number of mouse passages, whereas the European virus rapidly attenuates and dies out within two or three generations of mouse transmission.

Rabbits are susceptible, though they do not show any regularity of temperature curve. This at least is true of the European variety. Pinkerton has shown that the Mexican virus produces temperatures in rabbits (personal communication).

It is of considerable interest that rabbits recovered from typhus virus develop agglutinins against the *Proteus* X_{19}, that is, a Weil-Felix reaction. Rats will occasionally develop a Weil-Felix, but guinea-pigs never develop such agglutinins.

It is not impossible that a true mild typhus fever infection may result from living virus injections into horses and donkeys.

Many other animals have been experimented upon, but have no particular significance for typhus investigations.

Insect susceptibility lies chiefly with lice. The human body-louse and head-louse, as well as *Polyplax spinulosus,* the rat-louse, become regularly infected and die of the disease within less than two weeks. Fleas become easily infected but recover and may retain the virus for over four weeks. Ticks and bedbugs have been infected artificially, but the virus does not appear to increase in them, nor have they any proven epidemiological significance.

Etiological Theories and Reasons for Regarding the Rickettsiae as the Causative Agents of Typhus Fever.—In the opinion of most students of typhus fever, and certainly in our own, the *Rickettsia* bodies are the etiological agents which cause typhus fever and the other diseases mentioned in the chapter heading. The following reasons may be advanced in justification of this opinion:

Typhus fever virus is not filtrable in the sense in which this is true of a filtrable virus. This has been the conclusion of all who have studied the question with proper controls, including ourselves.

In the European disease, the *Rickettsia* bodies are found to occur regularly in lice from typhus fever patients and are absent in the uninfected insects. They appear with regularity in lice artificially infected with typhus virus in regions in which no typhus exists and, with such artificially infected lice, the typical disease in all necessary criteria can be produced in laboratory animals.[1] There has been, throughout, a parallelism between the presence of *Rickettsia* and the infectiousness of the insects and no effort to separate the virus and the *Rickettsia* has succeeded either in the hands of European or American investigators.

In connection with the Mexican variety of the disease it has been possible to establish the etiological relationship of the *Rickettsia* by more direct methods, because it has been easier, with this variety, to obtain large amounts of the organisms separate from the animal or insect body cells or fluids. Mooser first described the presence of true *Rickettsia* in the cells of the tunica vaginalis of guinea-pigs infected with Mexican typhus in 1928. These organisms have the same staining reactions as the European *Rickettsia*, are not cultivable except in the presence of living cells and are in every way comparable to the *Rickettsia prowazeki* seen in lice infected with the European virus. Pinkerton and we ourselves have shown similar though less numerous organisms can be found in the tunica cells of guinea-pigs intraperitoneally infected with the European virus if the examinations are made within six or seven days after infection, before the temperature has gone up. The tunica material containing the *Rickettsia* in the Mexican typhus animals is many times more virulent than is the blood of the same animal. Lice infected with Mexican tunica material by the Weigl method develop *Rickettsia* identical in every respect to those seen in lice similarly injected with the European virus, and lice injected by the Weigl method with virulent suprarenal and spleen tissue from Mexican typhus guinea-pigs develop *Rickettsia* identical with those described above, even if, in the injected material, *Rickettsia* cannot be found. Guinea-pigs infected with such lice develop the typical disease. Indeed, the virulence of the virus is stepped up by the procedure, and lice infected in this way with the Mexican *Rickettsia* succumb to the disease in from eight to thirteen days, as do the European typhus lice.

Rat lice (*Polyplax*) allowed to feed on Mexican typhus rats develop the organisms characteristically and can convey the disease to other rats by their bites. Also, injection of such lice into guinea-pigs reproduces the typical disease. Fleas feeding on Mexican typhus rats develop *Rickettsia* similar to those in the lice and can transmit the typical disease to other rats by bite or to guinea-pigs by injection.

By methods of reducing the resistance of rats by benzol injections and by x-ray treatment, it has been possible to obtain enormous quantities of the Mexican *Rickettsia* in the peritoneal cavities of such animals. It has been possible to wash suspensions obtained in this way free from cells and plasma and with such washed

1 The artificial infection of lice with typhus virus is readily accomplished by the method first developed by Weigl in which virus in the form of blood, tunica scrapings or tissue suspensions is injected through fine capillary tubes under a binocular microscope into the rectum of lice. The insects are then fed on an immune for eight to twelve days, when they are found to resemble in every respect, including the presence of *Rickettsia* crowded in the intestinal cells, lice that have been fed on a typhus patient. Lice invariably die, falling victim to the disease even as does man. There is no point in describing the technic in a book of this sort, since while it is not very difficult, it must be seen and practiced in order to be carried out.

suspensions the disease has been reproduced. Animals so infected with washed Mexican *Rickettsia* have proved to be immune both to the Mexican and the European virus.

Tissue cultures in which the *Rickettsiae* have been made to grow by a variety of methods, including plasma cultures, Maitland cultures and fertile egg cultures, have been successfully used to infect laboratory animals.

Added to this array of proof, there are further unquestionable arguments derived from immunological experiments which will be dealt with below.

Immunology.—Patients who have recovered from typhus fever become immune. It was formerly believed that such immunity persisted through life, but recent information contradicts this. Second and third attacks have been observed, and we have heard of deaths from such subsequent infections. Repeated infections in the laboratory have also been reported. It is probable, however, that in most cases a certain amount of immunity persists for many years. It is in this way that we can explain the milder course of typhus in populations in which the disease is constantly prevalent and in which outbreaks of epidemic extent occur frequently. The disease is relatively mild in children, and in such populations a certain amount of immunization in the young is constantly taking place.

Guinea-pigs that have recovered from the disease may remain immune for six months or a year, but relative susceptibility seems to develop after that. After convalescence, the blood serum develops definite protective powers against the virus.

Nicolle and Conseil, studying these conditions in man, found that such viricidal powers remained active for probably more than fourteen days and less than three months.

Our own experiments on guinea-pigs (Zinsser and Batchelder) showed that the blood was protective from the first day of defervescence up to the end of the second week, but that such protective effects disappeared between the third and the fourth weeks.

Convalescent serum from man appears, according to Weil, Breinl and Gruschka, to possess some prophylactic value, and the use of such serum is prevalent in European typhus regions.

Active immunization both in animals and man was extensively experimented upon even before the *Rickettsia* etiology of the typhus disease was accepted.

Nicolle, Sparrow and Conseil succeeded in immunizing a small number of people by a preliminary treatment with minute doses of brain virus from guinea-pigs, and minute doses of infectious guinea-pig serum have been used in the same way with some success, but living virus for immunizing purposes is too dangerous to lead to any practical methods of production. Da Rocha-Lima was probably the first one to suggest serovaccine—that is, the injection of a combination of virus with immune or convalescent serum—in other words, a neutralized, living virus. That such a method may be practical was shown by results obtained by Zinsser and Batchelder in which guinea-pigs treated with a single dose of virus neutralized with convalescent serum developed a solid active immunity.

Active immunization with the dead virus of typhus fever was not successful until da Rocha-Lima suggested and Weigl perfected a method of producing suspensions rich in *Rickettsia* by the trituration of the intestines of typhus-infected lice. The method has been studied with excellent results in animals by Breinl and by Rosenberger and a vaccine of this kind is now being produced for immunization against the European disease by Weigl. Production consists in artificially infecting large numbers of lice by the Weigl method of rectal injection, feeding them on immunes until the accumulation of *Rickettsia* is considerable, and then triturating their intestines in a weak carbolic acid salt solution. The indications from the studies of many observers are that such vaccines possess a considerable immunizing power. It is obvious, however, that production of such a protective substance on a large scale is fraught with many practical difficulties and dangers. Nevertheless, Weigl's experiments have demonstrated for typhus a principle that for Rocky Mountain spotted fever has been indicated by Spencer and Parker and by Connor—namely, that active immunization with dead virus is successful in proportion to the amounts of dead virus that can be concentrated in the vaccine. For the Mexican disease, in which *Rickettsiae* are more easily obtained without the use of insects, Zinsser and Castaneda have produced a vaccine containing large numbers of *Rickettsiae* of the Mooser type by intraperitoneally infecting rats whose resistance has been lowered by x-ray radiation. With such vaccines it has been possible to immunize guinea-pigs against the Mexican disease and to obtain about 30 per cent immunization against reasonable doses of the European virus. The use of these formalinized suspensions in man is being studied in Mexico, but no final judgment as to their practical value in man can as yet be formulated.

The active prophylactic immunization of animals against typhus fever with killed *Rickettsiae* has therefore been established in principle. For the murine type the preparation of *Rickettsia* suspensions by the x-ray rat method of Zinsser and Castaneda fulfills all the necessary criteria. In regard to the classical European type the Weigl method is effective but since it depends upon the individual rectal injection of not less than 50 laboratory-bred lice for each dose of vaccine and since these lice must then be fed for ten days on immune human beings and their intestines subsequently dissected out for emulsification, the method can never lend itself to large-scale practice. For this reason we are making vaccines against the classical disease by cultivating the organism on the agar-tissue culture slants described in a preceding paragraph. In such cultures, *Rickettsia* grow in enormous numbers and retain all their characteristics of virulence and immunizing power for several years. They can be obtained in enormous amounts with relatively little labor or expense. This method is being tried out in China by Dr. Samuel Zia.

Passive immunization in typhus fever has been studied largely with convalescent serum, and such serum, if taken early in the convalescence, appears to have a certain amount of prophylactic value. Nicolle and Blaizot have produced a serum by injection of a donkey with large quantities of organ emulsions and blood of typhus animals. Their results in the serum therapy of man were indeterminate. Da Rocha-Lima had negative results with the serum of a similarly immunized horse. Zinsser and Castaneda have immunized a horse with a long series of large quantities of *Rickettsia* obtained by the x-ray rat method. The serum of this horse eventually developed a Weil-Felix reaction in dilutions up to 1:160 and, incomplete, up to 1:320. The serum protected guinea-pigs against ten to fifty times the infectious dose, even when the serum was administered subcutaneously as long as forty-eight hours

MAXCY. U. S. Pub. Health Rep., 1926, 41:296?
MONTEIRO. Brazil-med., 1931, 35:805; 1932, 16
MOOSER. Arch. f. Schiffs- u. Tropen-Hyg., 192
—— J. Infect. Dis., 1928, 43; 1929, 44:186.
MOOSER and CASTANEDA. Medicina (Mexico),
MOOSER, CASTANEDA and ZINSSER. J. Exper. M
—— J. Am. M. Ass., 1931, 97:231.
MOOSER and DUMMER. J. Exper. M., 1930, 51
NEILL. U. S. Pub. Health Rep., July, 1917, 11
NIGG and LANDSTEINER. J. Exper. M., 1932, 5!
NICOLLE. Compt. rend. Acad. d. sc., 1909, 157
—— Ann. de l'Inst. Pasteur, 1910, 1911, 191
NICOLLE and BLAIZOT. Ann. de l'Inst. Pasteu
NICOLLE, COMTE and CONSEIL. Compt. rend.
NICOLLE and CONSEIL. Compt. rend. Acad. d.
NICOLLE, CONSEIL and CONOR. Compt. rend.
NICOLLE, C., and LAIGRET, J. Arch. de l'Inst.
NICOLLE and LE BAILLY. Compt. rend. Acad.
NICOLLE, SPARROW and CONSEIL. Presse méd.
OLITSKY. J. Infect. Dis., 1917, 20:349.
OTTO and DIETRICH. Centralbl. f. Bakteriol.,
OTTO and MUNTER. Kolle u. Wassermann Ha
PARKER. Bull. Montana State Board of Health
PARKER, R. R., and DAVIS, G. E. U. S. Pub.
PHILIP and PARKER. U. S. Pub. Health Rep.,
PINKERTON. J. Infect. Dis., 1929, 44:337.
PINKERTON and HAAS. J. Exper. M., 1931, 54
RICKETTS. J. Am. M. Ass., 1909, 52:379.
RICKETTS and WILDER. J. Am. M. Ass., Feb
    1373; July 23, 1910, 309.
ROSENBERGER. Cited from Otto and Munter.
SELLARDS. Typhus Fever, etc. (Serbian Epide
SERGENT, FOLEY and VIALATTE. Compt. rend.
SHATTUCK. Typhus Fever, etc. (Serbian Epic
SPENCER and PARKER. U. S. Pub. Health Rep
VON PROWAZEK. Beitr. z. Klin. d. Infektionsl
WEIGL. Med. Klin., 1924, 1046.
WEIL, BREINL and GRUSCHKA. Ztschr. f. Imn
WHEATLAND. Med. J. Australia, 1926, 5:261.
WILDER. J. Infect. Dis., 1911, 9.
WOLBACH. J. Med. Research, 1919, 41:1.
WOLBACH, PINKERTON and SCHLESINGER. Pro
WOLBACH and SCHLESINGER. J. Med. Researc
WOLBACH, SCHLESINGER and PINKERTON. J.
WOLBACH, TODD and PALFREY. Etiology and
ZINSSER and BATCHELDER. J. Exper. M., 193
ZINSSER and CASTANEDA. J. Exper. M., 1930,
—— New England J. Med., 1933, 209:815.
—— Proc. Soc. Exper. Biol. & Med., 1932,
ZINSSER, H., FITZPATRICK, F., and WEI, H. C

the ea
those
per cer
exists
find di
of spo
variabi

De
fever
wester
thing
virus
Maryl
animal
inocul
lesions
strain
on a f
vestiga
bite o
in full
Simila

Th
fever
heredi
heredi
have
experi
of dis
Rhipi
Bouto
easter
fever
carrie
Derm
theref
edge
States
by a
in do
throu
varia
The
muri
has t
of p

after the virus was given intr[a...]
upon the European virus. It[s...]
disease is now under investig[...]

The immunological facts
similarity between the Europ[ean...]
typhus fever, there are still
relations, as indicated by the
summarized as follows: Guir[...]
New World typhus develop
World disease as obtained fr[om...]
disease. Quantitative relatior[...]
lapping, there is also a diffe[...]
develop agglutinins for both
Weil-Felix reaction. Rabbits
tinins for the x-ray rat vaccir[...]
the rabbit sera develop a We[...]
of the type of group reactic[...]
two types of *Rickettsia*.

Such facts explain the pa[...]
with our Mexican vaccines
explain the complete failure
European virus. The fact tha[t...]
types possess a solid immunit[y...]
success by sufficiently high
immunized animal.

ANDERSON and GOLDBERGER. J. [...]
—— J. Am. M. Ass., 1912, 49.
—— N. York M. J., 1912, 976.
—— U. S. Hyg. Lab. Bull., 191[...]
ANIGSTEIN. Trans. 8th Cong. Fa[...]
BREINL. Ztschr. f. Immunitätsfor[...]
CASTANEDA. J. Infect. Dis., 193C[...]
CASTANEDA and ZINSSER. J. Exp[...]
CONNOR. J. Immunol., 1924, 9:[...]
DA ROCHA-LIMA. Centralbl. f. F[...]
—— Berl. klin. Wchnschr., 191[...]
—— München. med. Wchnschr[...]
—— Kolle u. Wassermann Han[...]
—— Cited from Otto and Mu[...]
DYER, CEDER, et al. U. S. Pub. [...]
DYER, RUMREICH and BADGER. [...]
FRACASTORII, HIERONIYMI. De [...]
    Wright, 1930.
GAVINO and GIRARD. Cited from[...]
HONE. Med. J. Australia, Sydn[...]
LEPINE. Compt. rend. Acad. d. [...]
LEPINE, CAMINOPETROS and PAN[...]
MARCANDIER and PIROT. Compt.[...]

1915. Later Fletcher and Field reported a number of typical cases admitted to the hospital at Kuala Lumpur from neighboring states. The disease is transmitted by the larval form of a mite, *Trombicula akamushi,* in Japan; and in Formosa and Sumatra by the *Trombicula deliensis.* From the investigations, chiefly by Miyajima, Kawamura, and others, it appears that in Japan the animal reservoir is a small rodent, a vole [1] (*Microtus montebelli*). In Formosa, the animal reservoir is the common house rat, *Mus rattus rufescens.* In Sumatra, on the other hand, Walch and Keukenschrijver are of the opinion that the animal hosts are the house rat, *Mus concolor,* and the field rat, *Mus diardii.* The rats show no obvious disease when inoculated with blood of patients, but are found on autopsy to have considerable splenic enlargement. As far as the insect carriers, the *Trombiculae,* are concerned, the adult and nymph forms are not dangerous because they are entirely vegetable feeders. The larvae of the two known responsible mites feed on a variety of animals, and Fletcher has suggested that birds may play an important part in disseminating the disease by transporting the mites over large distances. The larvae, according to Nagayo, pass the virus on through the nymph and adult forms.

In man, the symptoms resemble those of typhus and spotted fever, but are characterized by small ulcers at the points of insect bite, followed by swelling and tenderness of the local lymphatics.

Unlike the spotted fever and typhus groups, the transmission of the Tsutsugamushi virus to laboratory animals has met with a great deal of difficulty. The *Orang* and the *Macacus fuscatus* have been successfully infected by Nagayo and others by the injection of human material; and Walch succeeded in infecting a gibbon. Until recently, guinea-pigs—though capable of harboring the virus in inapparent form—have shown no characteristic reactions, but Ishiwara and Ogato found that the virus could be carried in testicular passage in rabbits. The most certain method of animal inoculation appears to be the intraocular inoculation of rabbits and guinea-pigs, first thoroughly studied by Nagayo and his associates. Within three to five days, when the inflammatory reaction is at its highest point, examination of Descemet's membrane reveals numerous *Rickettsiae* in the endothelial cells. Tissue cultures made with Descemet's membrane material have been successfully carried out and the subcultures have remained infectious.

As far as we have any information, the mite fever, or *Mijtekoorts,* of Sumatra, transmitted by the *T. deliensis* (a form very closely related to the *T. akamushi*) is identical with the Japanese disease.

On the other hand, the so-called "Rural Typhus" of Malaya seems to be a variant, similar to but not identical with Tsutsugamushi. As indicated by the recent investigations of Lewthwaite and Savoor, this disease in man is "practically identical" with the true Tsutsugamushi of Malaya except that the primary ulcer is lacking.

Guinea-pig inoculations carried out with "Rural Typhus" by Fletcher and Lesslar in 1925 produced febrile reactions in a few animals, but transmission in passage failed. Lewthwaite and Savoor employed a method described by the writer with Castaneda and Seastone in typhus experiments with guinea-pigs, namely the inoculation of animals rendered susceptible by a vitamin deficient diet, and in this

[1] The voles are a sub-family of the mouse group—the Microtinae. They include short tailed field mice and are characterized chiefly by their dentition.

way they managed to establish a strain of "Rural Typhus" in two animals from
which they were able to carry the virus in passage. After the ninth passage, the use
of vitamin deficient animals was no longer necessary. Incubation was 9 to 18 days,
with a febrile reaction lasting 5 to 6 days, and a 90 per cent mortality of the
animals. A strange symptom in the guinea-pigs inoculated with their first strain was
the occurrence of ascites, usually on the third day of the fever. It is not clear from
their report whether this symptom, which is totally different from anything one
sees in guinea-pigs inoculated with any of the other Rickettsia diseases, was peculiar
to the vitamin deficient animals, a surmise which we make only because in their
subsequent isolations of "Rural Typhus" virus from wild rats there is no mention of
ascites. Moreover, in this first strain there was no scrotal swelling in any of 300
or more male guinea-pigs infected.

Circumstantial evidence had pointed to the rat as the reservoir of true Tsutsugamushi disease in Malaya. Fletcher, Lesslar and Lewthwaite, in 1928, examined
130 rats trapped in endemic and non-endemic foci of the disease and found the
larval mite, *Trombicula deliensis,* only on rats from the endemic areas. Investigations
of similar significance were made by Gater in 1930. Lewthwaite and Savoor, sus-
pecting that rats might be the reservoir of the "Rural Typhus" as well as of the
Tsutsugamushi disease, succeeded in isolating a virus by the inoculation of brain,
spleen and testes suspensions of a wild, brown rat trapped in an endemic area of
rural typhus. A guinea-pig so inoculated showed a febrile reaction and scrotal
swelling; a rat similarly infected showed no reactions whatever. From these two
animals guinea-pigs were inoculated, at first into vitamin deficient animals, later
into normal guinea-pigs. Study of this virus and another one, similarly isolated,
revealed properties which persuaded the writers that they were dealing with a virus
closely related to that of Tsutsugamushi Fever. A large proportion of the guinea-pigs
died towards the end of the febrile reaction, and in 70 per cent—unlike the animals
observed in the strain started from the human case—there was redness and tenderness
of the scrotum. Intraocular inoculation of rabbits with guinea-pigs' tunica and
heart's blood gave rise to reactions similar to those seen in infections with the
virus of "Rural Typhus" of human origin and with that of Tsutsugamushi disease.
The two rat strains isolated in this way were not identical, in that one of them died
out in rabbits, while the other one was carried on in passage. Cross immunity tests
in rabbits between one of the rat strains, six strains of "Rural Typhus" of human
origin and a strain of Tsutsugamushi showed complete cross immunity in five
strains and partial in the sixth. These results indicated that these diseases are closely
related.

Since the investigators mentioned were unable, in previous attempts, to establish
a true Tsutsugamushi strain in guinea-pigs, even when they used vitamin deficient
animals, and since the rat strains of rural typhus differed somewhat from the human
strain previously described, the relationship of these several viruses does not appear
entirely clear. Cross immunity with Tsutsugamushi virus maintained by intraocular
inoculations in rabbits points, of course, to a close interrelationship of these infectious
agents. We have not, however, as yet, any reliable experimental information about
cross-immunization between Tsutsugamushi infection and either Spotted Fever or the
Typhus groups.

TSUTSUGAMUSHI GROUP

Conveyed by mite larvae. Cross-immunity with other groups not determined nor within the group except as below mentioned.

Disease	Insect Vectors	Natural Animal Reservoir	Remarks
Tsutsugamushi	Larva of *Trombicula akamushi*	Field mouse in Japan. Wild rats in Malaya.	Transmissible to rabbits by intraocular route. Febrile reaction in monkeys.
Rural typhus of Malaya	*Trombicula deliensis*	Wild rats. Strains isolated from rats by L e w t h w a i t e and Savoor.	Disease differs from preceding only in absence of primary larvae. Transmitted to vitamin-deficient guinea-pigs. Cross-immunity with Tsutsugamushi.
Mite fever of Sumatra, "Mijtekoorts"	*Trombicula deliensis*	No information.	

Trench Fever (Wolhynian Fever).—In 1915 there appeared among the armies at the front a disease which did not clinically resemble the ordinary well-known febrile diseases. Cases of this condition were seen among British troops by Graham and by Herringham and on the German front in Poland and Wolhynia similar ones were described by His and by Werner. The disease had been noticed by Graetzer as early as 1914. Cases appeared in enormous numbers and because the disease seemed to arise almost entirely from the front areas it was spoken of as *trench fever*.

Work on the clinical differentiation of the disease was done by a great many army surgeons. An accurate report was made by McNee, Brunt and Renshaw, by a number of German workers, and finally by a British and by an American commission, the American group organized under Strong. In a Harvey Lecture by Swift printed in the *Archives of Internal Medicine*, July, 1920, an accurate summary of available facts concerning this disease may be found.

The disease is sudden in onset with fever, headache and pains in the muscles. The onset resembles that of influenza. In a few days, pain and tenderness of the joints appear, and the temperature shows peculiar remissions which Swift characterizes as being of the "spiky" type.

Characteristic of the disease are the bone pains which are not accompanied by any signs of inflammation. There may be continued hyperesthesia. There may be sensory disturbances with increase of the tendon reflexes. The fever curves are very irregular, some showing the intermittent "spiky" type referred to above, others developing the typhoid-like ladder type. Another characteristic is the frequency of relapses, in which, after remissions of varying intervals, a second rise of temperature comes on. The relapses may come on after weeks or months. A case of which we have personal knowledge has developed two relapses in the course of two years after the original attack. In other cases Swift states that the manifestations may assume a subacute or chronic form with low grade fever which may continue for months.

Transmission and Etiology.—McNee, Brunt and Renshaw, in 1916, succeeded in transferring the disease from man to man by intravenous and intramuscular injections of whole blood. In these early experiments they found that the plasma if entirely free from hemoglobin, was not infectious, but that the red cells contained the virus even after repeated washings. This observation is identical with that of Spencer and Parker in Rocky Mountain spotted fever and with our own on typhus, and undoubtedly signifies close absorption of the virus to the surfaces of the cells. They did not succeed in passing the virus through a Berkefeld filter. In 1917, Werner, whom we quote from Swift, allowed himself to be bitten by lice that had previously fed on trench fever patients, and contracted a mild form of the disease. A similar observation was made by Kuczynski on himself. Davies and Weldon in the same year carried out a similar experiment, allowing themselves to be bitten by lice immediately after the lice had fed on trench fever patients. One of them developed trench fever twelve days later. A similar experiment on a volunteer was successfully made by Pappenheimer and Mueller in 1917. In 1918 two commissions were formed for the purpose of studying the disease. The American commission was aided by a British entomologist, Captain Peacock. The first result of these investigations was that McNee's observation about transmission with whole blood was confirmed, but it was found, in contrast to McNee's results, that the plasma as well as the red blood cells was infectious. It seemed that the blood taken as early as the fourth day of the disease was more infectious than that obtained later. Transmission after filtration through Berkefeld filters did not succeed at first, but Swift records that later, when infectious urine was used, filtration was successful. In view of the nonfiltrability of other *Rickettsiae* this observation may require revision.

Experiments were made with lice, all of which were reared from eggs and fed on normal subjects, and the noninfectiousness of these lice was proven by allowing them to feed on eleven different uninfected people. Such lice were allowed to feed several times on trench fever patients and subsequently allowed to feed on 23 volunteers, 78 per cent of whom developed trench fever. It did not seem necessary for the lice to be in contact with the skin while feeding, nor was it necessary to produce scarification. In two instances the mere bite of the louse through the meshes of gauze covering the box produced the disease. The incubation time in these louse transmitted cases varied from fourteen to thirty-eight days, the average being twenty-one. Meanwhile, the British commission found that the excreta of infected lice applied to scarified skin could also produce the disease, thus showing that the excrement of lice that have bitten trench fever patients may be infectious when it comes in contact with lesions on the skin.

Byam showed that as late as three hundred to four hundred days after the onset of the disease, trench fever patients can still infect lice. This is of great importance in appraising the epidemiological possibilities of carriers. Lice could also be infected by patients during the periods of remission.

Both the British and the American commissions showed that the virus is probably not transmitted through the eggs of the louse. The British commission reported that the head louse can transmit the disease through its excreta in the same way as the body louse. Other insects, however, did not seem to carry the disease.

Although complete proof is still lacking, it seems most probable that trench fever is a *Rickettsia* disease. Toepfer, da Rocha-Lima and other German observers who have studied *Rickettsia* bodies in typhus fever were encouraged to undertake similar studies in connection with trench fever because of the similarity of the means of conveyance of the two diseases. These observers, as well as Jungmann succeeded in finding *Rickettsia* bodies in the intestines of lice fed on trench fever patients. Da Rocha-Lima, comparing lice that had bitten individuals who did not have trench fever with those fed on trench fever patients, found that 72 per cent of the insects found on the trench fever patients showed *Rickettsia* bodies, but 20 per cent of those fed on normal people showed similar ones. Arkwright, Bacon and Duncan found similar *Rickettsia* bodies in a large number of lice that had fed several times on 64 trench fever patients. They found the bodies in only one out of many lots of insects fed on normal people. Their experiments seem to indicate that when *Rickettsia* bodies appeared in the excrement of lice after feeding, these excrements were infectious.

Experimentation which might bring conclusive proof of *Rickettsia* etiology is rendered difficult owing to failure to produce the disease in laboratory animals.

Prevention of trench fever, like the prevention of typhus, depends upon delousing.

The Weil-Felix Reaction.—The so-called Weil-Felix reaction has attained extraordinary importance in the diagnosis of typhus fever and considerable significance for the differentiation of the several groups of *Rickettsia* infection. The three most important varieties of *Proteus* bacilli in use at the present time are those known as Ox 19, Ox 2 and Ox K. The history of these strains is as follows:

In 1915, Weil and Felix cultivated from the urine of a typhus patient in Roumania an organism belonging to the proteus group. This bacillus, X 1, was agglutinated by the serum of the patient and by those of nine other typhus cases in dilutions of 1-200. In the same epidemic, these investigators again cultivated a Proteus, X 2, with agglutinating properties similar to the first one. In the following year, they obtained a third strain of *Proteus*, which they called X 19, which had the property of being agglutinated by typhus sera in titers much higher than those observed with X 1 and X 2. With this organism, they were able actually to make diagnoses of typhus fever at the stages of the disease so early that X 1 and X 2 were not yet agglutinated. Felix at about this time commented on the infrequency of *Proteus* isolation from typhus cases, but obtained the organism from two autopsies.

In subsequent studies of the antigenic structure of the various *Proteus* bacilli, Weil and Felix dissociated their organisms into the H and O types. Antiserum produced with the O forms agglutinated its homologous O form in small granular clumps, but the H form in heavy flakes. In reactions with typhus serum, the *Proteus* agglutinations corresponded to the O type. Subsequently, the same investigators found that the O agglutinogens were more type specific than the H, and by means of the O variants OX 2 and OX 19 could be differentiated, being related to each other in much the same way as are different types of meningococcus. Rabbits intensely immunized with OX 19 and OX 2 developed only very slight cross agglutination for the heterologous types. Since that time, the OX forms have been generally used for typhus diagnoses.

The origin of the OX K or OX Kingsbury is a curious one. This strain was supplied in 1921 to the Bland Sutton Institute by the National Type Culture Collection as a typical Proteus X 19 and was taken to the Straits Settlements by

A. N. Kingsbury in 1923. It was used by Fletcher and Lesslar in 1925 in investigations which led to the discovery of the nature of the endemic tropical fevers of Malaya. Other X 19 strains were then obtained and used in agglutination tests, with the result that two serological groups, K and W, were obtained. Comparison of the K strain with eight cultures of X 19 from various sources revealed that it differed from these in agglutination and absorption tests and in certain cultural properties. The K strain was the only one which agglutinated with the blood of the tropical cases.

In regard to the theory of the Weil-Felix reaction, nothing precise can be said at the present time. A good many investigators have been tempted to explain the reaction by assuming that the *Proteus* bacilli represent dissociation forms of *Rickettsia*. Others have even assumed that *Rickettsia* forms and *Proteus* bacilli are phases in a cycle which also includes an ultramicroscopic virus. There is no experimental evidence to justify such opinions. The involvement of an ultramicroscopic form has been, we believe, finally disposed of by our own experiments on filtration, and on suspensions of washed *Rickettsia*.

WEIL-FELIX REACTIONS *

	O X 19	O X 2	O X K
Classical Typhus	+ + +	+	—
Tabardillo	+ + +	?	—
Fièvre Nautique	+ + +	?	—
Australian Endemic	+ + +	+	—
Tropical (Urban?) Malayan	+ + +	+	—
Tropical Scrub	—	—	+ + +
Tsutsugamushi (Sumatra)	—	—	+ + +
Tsutsugamushi (Japan)	—	—	+ + +
Rocky Mountain Spotted	+	+	+
Fièvre Boutonneuse	+	+	—
South African Tick Bite	+	+	+
Indian Tick Typhus	?	?	?
São Paulo Typhus †	+ + +	+	+

* This table taken from a paper by Felix, A., Trans. Royal Soc. Trop. Med. and Hyg., 1935, 29:113.
† Very likely wrong. This disease belongs to the Spotted Fever group.

REFERENCES [2]

ARKWRIGHT, BACOT and DUNCAN. Proc. Roy. Soc. Med., 1919, 13:23.
BADGER, L. F. U. S. P. H. Rep., 1932, 47:2365.
BALZ and KAWAKAMI. Virchow's Arch., 1879:78.
BLANC, G. and CAMINOPTEROS, J. Bul. Acad. Med., April 14, 1931.
BYAM. Proc. Roy. Soc. Med., 1919, 13:19.
BYAM, et al. Trench Fever, Brit. War Office Comm. Rep., 1919.
CASTANEDA and ZIA. J. Exper. M., 1933, 58:55.
COMBIESCO, D. Arch. Roum. Path. Exp., 1932, 5:23.

[2] For a complete review of the literature see: Zinsser, H. Am. J. Hyg., 1937, 25:430.

Da Rocha-Lima. München. med. Wchnschr., 1917:64.
Davies and Weldon. Lancet, 1917, 1:183.
Fejgin. J. Prev. M., 1929, 3:311.
—— Compt. rend. Soc. de biol., 1927:96.
Felix, A. (Br.) J. Hyg., 1931, 31:225.
Foot. J. Med. Research, 1919, 39.
Graetzer. Wien. klin. Wchnschr., 1916, 29:295.
Graham. Lancet, 1915, 2:703.
Herringham. Lancet, 1916, 9:429.
His. Berl. klin. Wchnschr., 1916, 53:738.
Ishihara and Ogata. Tr. 6th Cong. Far Eastern Ass. Trop. Med., Tokyo, 1925.
Jungmann. Deutsche med. Wchnschr., 1917, 64:359.
Kawamura. Kolle u. Wassermann Handb., etc., 3rd ed., 1930, 8:1387.
Kuczynski. Reported from Jungmann, Deutsche med. Wchnschr., 1917, 64:359.
Lewthwaite, R., and Savoor, S. Br. J. Exp. Path., 1936, 17:23.
Maxcy, K. U. S. P. H. Rep., 1929, 44:1935.
McClintic. Pub. Health & U. S. Mars.-Hosp. Serv., Weekly Bulletin, No. 20, 27:1912.
McNee, Brunt and Renshaw. Brit. M. J., 1916, 1:295.
Monteiro, J. L. Mem. Inst. Butantan, Monogr. 6, 1931.
Mooser, H. J. Inf. Dis., 1928, 43:241.
Mooser, H., Castaneda, M. R., and Zinsser, H. J. Am. Med. Ass., 1931, 97:231.
—— J. Exp. Med., 1931, 54:567.
Mooser, H., and Dummer, C. J. Exp. Med., 1930, 51:189.
Nagayo, M. Practice of Med. in Tropics, Byam and Archibald, London, 1923.
Nagayo, et al. Am. J. Hyg., 1921, 1:569.
—— Jap. J. Exper. M., 1931, 9:87.
Neill, M. H. U. S. P. H. Rep., 1917, 32:1105.
Nicolle and Comte. Bull. Soc. path. exot., 1910, 3:214.
Otto and Munter. Kolle u. Wassermann Handb., etc., 3rd ed., 1930, 8:1192, et seq.
Palm. Quoted from Kawamura, Kolle u. Wassermann Handb., etc., 3rd ed., 1930, 8:1387.
Parker, R. R. U. S. P. H. Rep., 1933, 48:839.
Philip and Parker. U. S. Pub. Health Rep., 1933, 48:266.
Pinkerton, H. J. Inf. Dis., 1929, 44:337.
Pinkerton, H. and Hass, G. J. Exp. Med., 1936, 64:601.
Reimann, H. A. and Fisher, L. C. J. Am. Med. Ass., 1932, 98:1875.
Ricketts. J. Am. M. Ass., 1906, 46; 47:33, 358, 1067; 1907, 49:25, 1278.
—— Tr. Chicago Path. Soc., 1907.
—— J. Infect. Dis., 1907, 4:141; 1908, 5:221.
—— Med. Rec., N. Y., 1909, 76:842.
Rumreich, A., Dyer, R. E. and Badger, L. F. U. S. P. H. Rep., 1931, 46:463, 470.
Spencer and Parker. Pub. Health Rep., Wash., 1925, 60, No. 41.
Swift. Harvey Lecture, Harvey Society, New York, Jan. 10, 1920.
Toepfer. München. med. Wchnschr., 1916, 63:1495.
Weigl. Ztschr. f. Hyg., 1923, 99:302.
Weil and Felix. Wien. klin. Wchnschr., 1916, 31:33, 974; 1917, 1509; 1918, 637, 1158.
Weil, E. and Felix, A. Wien. klin. Woch., No. 36, 1918.
Werner. München. med. Wchnschr., 1916, 63:402.
Wilson. Brit. J. Hyg., 1909, 9:317.
Wilson and Chowning. J. Am. M. Ass., 1902, 39.
Wolbach. J. Med. Research, 1919–1920, 41:1, 3.
Zinsser, H. Am. J. Hyg., 1937, 25:430.
Zinsser, H., and Castaneda, M. R. J. Exper. M., 1932, 56:455.

SECTION V

THE SPIROCHETES

CHAPTER LI

CLASSIFICATION OF SPIROCHETES

Order: *Spirochaetales*

Spirochetes are slender, undulating, corkscrew-like, relatively flexible, filamentous organisms. They are ubiquitous, occurring in nature in soil, water, decaying organic materials, and in and upon the bodies of plants, animals and man. Some of the spirochetes are saprophytes, some are commensals, and others are pathogenic, causing a number of the most serious and severe diseases of human beings and of the lower animals. Among the pathogens are the spirochetes which cause syphilis, yaws, relapsing fever, hemorrhagic jaundice, and other diseases of man, and various spirochetal septicemias of birds and mammals.

The spirochetes were among the first micro-organisms to be seen and pictured. In 1681, Leeuwenhoek wrote that he had seen in his own feces very small animalcules with the figure of "river eels" which "had a very nimble motion, and bent their bodies serpent-wise, and shot through the stuff as quick as a pike does through the water." [1] Dobell, from whom this quotation is made, expressed the opinion that "it can hardly be doubted that these organisms were spirochetes." Figure G in Leeuwenhoek's drawing of animalcules seen in scrapings from the teeth, which we have reproduced as Figure 2 in Chapter I of this book, was published in 1695. It is a clear picture of a spirochete, which Dobell regarded as probably *Spirochaeta buccalis*. Donné saw spirochetes in 1837 in smears from the genitalia and from lesions of venereal disease.

The scientific name *Spirochaeta* was applied by Ehrenberg in 1838 to a large free-living spiral organism, whose protoplasm appeared to be wound around an axial filament. The next important observations on these organisms were those of Obermeier, in 1873, recording the occurrence of filamentous spiral forms in the blood of patients with relapsing fever. Other investigators saw and studied spirochetes from time to time. But as the spiral forms are much more difficult to see, stain, and cultivate than are the bacteria, progress in acquiring knowledge of their nature and properties was slow and uncertain. The modern period of the investigation of spirochetes began only about 1904 when Schaudinn and other protozoologists entered this field.

Up to this time the tendency had been to classify the spirochetes with the bacteria. The protozoologists, however, noticed that a small protozoan parasite appeared to have a spiral filamentous stage in the body of the insect host, a mosquito, which transmitted it. They concluded, therefore, that spirochetes were protozoan in nature and

---

[1] C. Dobell, *Antony van Leeuwenhoek and His "Little Animals,"* Harcourt, Brace and Co., New York, 1932.

when Schaudinn and Hoffmann in 1905 discovered the spirochetal cause of syphilis, which they called *Treponema pallidum*, they regarded it as a protozoon. Many other protozoologists have followed Schaudinn in placing spirochetes among the protozoa.

Nature of Spirochetes.—Those who are most competent to express opinions on the nature of spirochetes have not agreed as to whether the organisms are bacteria or protozoa. The spirochetes have characteristics common to both great groups of micro-organisms and individual properties distinguishing them as a class. The consensus of opinion at present is that spirochetes are more nearly related to the bacteria than to the protozoa.

General Characteristics of Spirochetes.—The most important general features of these organisms are the following (Ford, Noguchi):

Morphology.—These organisms have short or long spirals with the twists in three dimensions. The size varies greatly, from 2 μ to 500 μ in length. The organisms are unicellular. Some forms have an elastic axial filament, but in the small forms this filament has not been proved to exist. The cell body is usually cylindrical and round on cross section. The *spirals* are relatively fixed, but are somewhat extensible. The number of spirals in some forms has diagnostic importance, but varies. The distance between the crests of the spirals, the amplitude or distance from the crest of the spiral to the midline, and the pitch or sharpness of angle of the spirals are important diagnostic anatomical features. Large curves of the whole body are superimposed upon these fundamental spirals. Except in *Spirochaeta plicatilis,* there is no cell wall, but a thin elastic membrane is present. No definite nucleus has been demonstrated. Some of the forms, particularly the larger varieties, contain volutin granules. The large organisms of the genera *Saprospira* and *Cristispira* have a chambered structure. It was once thought that spirochetes had an undulating membrane, and that their relationship to protozoa, especially to trypanosomes, was indicated by the presence of this structure. It has been shown that spirochetes do not have undulating membranes.

Flexibility.—All spirochetes are more flexible than bacteria, but flexibility of these organisms varies with different species. One of us found an organism in the testis of the rabbit so inflexible that the name *Treponema rigidum* was proposed for it. The pathogenic spirochetes are all very flexible.

Spore and Granule Formation.—The spirochetes do not form resistant endospores. In old cultures, in some lesions, and in the eggs of insect vectors, only minute granular forms can be found. Occasionally a few spirochetes may be found along with these granules, which makes it difficult to be certain that the granules alone are capable of reproduction or causing infection. Undoubtedly some spirochetes have a granular stage.

Filtrability.—Infectious filtrates of spirochetes of the relapsing fever types and the leptospiral types have been obtained by various observers. These organisms either in a granular form or in spiral form pass through Berkefeld V and N filters. Noguchi and others did not succeed in obtaining Berkefeld filtrates containing *Treponema pallidum*. This question is concerned quite as much with the physics of filtration as it is with the form and nature of the organism. A slow passage through a filter by growth along the channels has been demonstrated for *Treponema pallidum*.

Motility.—Spirochetes are motile. They progress by sinuous and rotating movements of the body and not by means of flagella. A chief differential point between true spirochetes and bacteria is that the spirochetes do not have flagella. Some of them have delicate terminal filaments, but these are not organs of locomotion. However, the organism which causes rat-bite fever, resembling spirochetes in many ways, has one flagellum at each end.

Division.—Spirochetes divide exclusively by transverse fission, usually into two equal parts. The figures interpreted as indicating longitudinal division are now regarded as V or Y forms produced by bending at the point of division or partially intertwined spirals.

Resistance.—The resistance to the solvent or lytic action of saponin and bile varies with the different species. As the same variations are found among the bacteria, this property has no special differential significance. Resistance to plasmolysis and plasmoptysis is the same as that observed for bacteria. The range of resistance to heat is within that of the bacteria. Most of the spirochetes are killed by heat at a temperature of 60° C. in one-half hour. We shall refer to this property later in connection with *Treponema pallidum.* As these organisms do not form endospores, their resistance to injurious substances and physical agents is like that of the non-sporogenous bacteria.

Susceptibility to chemotherapeutic agents is notable among the organisms in this group and the spirochetes differ from the bacteria in being especially susceptible to destruction by arsenical, antimony, bismuth and mercury compounds when they are within the bodies of animals. The most conspicuous example of this is the successful arsenical chemotherapy of syphilis based on the use of heavy metals, particularly arsenic, in compounds of the salvarsan type.

Staining Reactions.—Some spirochetes stain readily with the ordinary aniline dyes. Most of the pathogenic varieties are difficult to stain. Stains used for blood cells and for the demonstration of protozoa give the best results. These are the polychrome methylene blue stains of Wright, Giemsa, and others based upon the Romanowsky method. Spirochetes are gram-negative. Impregnation of the organisms with silver nitrate, followed by reduction of the silver in the organisms is a procedure of great utility in the demonstration of spirochetes in tissues and smears. The Levaditi method is usually applied to tissues; the Fontana-Tribondeau method to smears. (See section on Technic.)

The pathogenic spirochetes, usually thin, 0.1 to 0.2 μ in thickness, are best seen in the living state by dark ground illumination. *Dark field illumination* is and should be a routine procedure in the examination of material for spirochetes.

Cultivation.—Nearly all the varieties of spirochetes have been cultivated in artificial media. Usually serum, blood, or pieces of tissue are necessary for the growth of the organisms. Some spirochetes are aerobic, other anaerobic. Cultivation of these organisms is difficult and the organisms often change their properties in culture, rapidly losing pathogenicity. Differential cultural features have not thus far served as a discriminating basis for classification.

Nomenclature.—For discussions of the classification and nomenclature of spirochetes, reference should be made to the larger systematic texts and handbooks of bacteriology and protozoology. These matters are still in dispute and there is no single classification or terminology used by all the workers in this field. One cause of the difficulties is that the scientific term *Spirochaeta* is properly applied only to the large free-living form described by Ehrenberg in 1838 which has little in common with the pathogenic spiral forms which the medical bacteriologist is accustomed to call spirochetes. Another source of confusion in nomenclature has come through the shifting of the spirochetes from the bacteria to the protozoa and again to the bacteria. For example, the term *Spironema*, valid for spirochetes when they were classed as bacteria became invalid when they were classed as protozoa because a protozoon had previously been designated *Spironema*. With the return of the spirochetes to the class of *Schizomycetes*, *Spironema* would become again available as a generic name. The classification and nomenclature which we shall use will be a combination of several systems which seem to us to be convenient. We shall follow Noguchi's (1928) system chiefly, but make no pretense of authoritative selection.

A primary classification can be based on habitat, parasitism and pathogenicity, although parasites, commensals and saprophytes occur in the same genus. These distinctions are:

    I. Large free-living forms.
   II. Spirochetes living in mussels.
  III. Tissue spirochetes. These are chiefly pathogens which are parasitic in or upon the tissues of animals. Occasionally they may occur in the blood. Some of these forms exist on the mucous membranes and in the intestines and in these cases are not pathogenic. In this group we place chiefly *Treponema*, the parasites of syphilis and yaws, and *Leptospira*, the cause of hemorrhagic jaundice. Leptospiral forms occur also in water.
  IV. Blood spirochetes. The organisms of this group are the causes of various types of relapsing fever in man and spirochetal septicemia in animals. They exist chiefly in the blood but may have a residence in tissue or cells at times. They are usually loosely coiled organisms with long indefinite spirals.

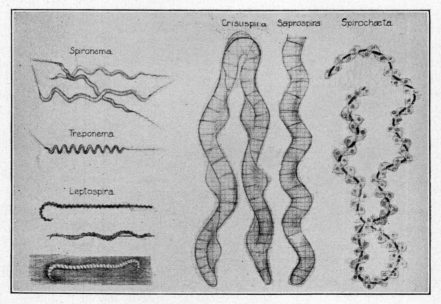

FIG. 67.—TYPES OF SPIROCHETES.

Diagram showing the characteristic features and relative proportions of *Spirochæta*, *Saprospira*, *Cristispira*, *Spironema*, *Treponema*, and *Leptospira*.   (From Noguchi, 1918.)

The first classification proposed by Noguchi in 1918 was modified by him in 1928. These classifications were based chiefly on morphology. The morphological types of spirochetes are shown in Noguchi's diagram, reproduced here as Figure 67. It will be noted that the names *Spironema* and *Treponema* appear on this diagram. We think that this indicates an advisable separation of the blood-spirochete (*Spironema*) from the tissue spirochetes (*Treponema*), although Noguchi and others have found so many intergrading forms between these two groups that they regard a wide separation as forced and unnatural. In Bergey's *Manual of Determinative Bacteriology* (1934), these differences are recognized and the group called *Spironema* by Noguchi is given generic rank under the name *Borrelia*. There is an increasing use of the name *Borrelia*, which was proposed in 1907 by Swellengrebel. The classification of spirochetes summarized from Bergey's *Manual*, 1939, is as follows:

I. *Spirochaeta.*—Large forms, 100–500 μ long by 0.5–0.75 μ broad, 50 to 250 spirals, usually saprophytic, free-living in water, protoplasm spirally wound around an elastic axial filament. Type species: *Spirochaeta plicatilis* (Ehrenberg).

II. *Saprospira.*—Large forms, 100–120 μ long, no spirals but curves, usually saprophytic, free-living in water, cross section circular. Type species: *Saprospira grandis* (Gross).

III. *Cristispira.*—Large forms, 45–90 μ long, 1–1.5 μ in diameter, few wavy spirals, usually parasitic in mussels, has a chambered structure and possesses a crest or ridge. Type species: *Cristispira balbiani.*

IV. *Borrelia.*—Small flexible forms, 8–15 μ long by 0.25–0.3 μ broad, with terminal filaments and large wavy spirals, usually parasitic. Formerly called *Spironema* (and before that: *Spirillum*). The "blood spirochetes" of the relapsing fever group are in this genus. Type species: *Borrelia gallinarum* (Swellengrebel).

V. *Treponema.*—Small, thin (or relatively thick) forms, 8–15 μ long by 0.1 to 0.3 μ broad, 8 to 14 regular rigid spirals with or without tapering ends and filaments, numerous small regular spirals, flexible or semi-rigid, usually parasitic. The organisms of syphilis and yaws and other "tissue spirochetes" are in this group. Type species: *Treponema pallidum* (Schaudinn and Hoffmann).

VI. *Leptospira.*—Thin, closely twisted cylinders, 7–14 μ long, 0.25 μ broad, flexible, with ends which curve to form "hooks." Usually parasitic, but may occur as saprophytes. The organism causing Weil's disease (hemorrhagic jaundice) is in this genus. The type species is: *Leptospira icterohaemorrhagiae* (Inado and Ido), Noguchi.

In this classification there is no place for the spiral organism which causes rat-bite fever. This organism was called *Spirochaeta morsus-muris* by its discoverer. It is a small rigid spiral form with one or more flagella at each end. English authorities, particularly, regard this organism as predominantly bacterial and have named it *Spirillum minus* (Carter). In our opinion the organism is very closely related to the spirochetes. Other similar organisms have been found in the stomach contents and intestines of animals, and for these the generic name *Spirella* was proposed by Dubosq and Lebailly in 1912. In 1928, Noguchi applied this name to the rat-bite fever organism. We think this usage is preferable to the practice of forcing a somewhat unnatural assignment of this spirochete-like parasite to the group of vibrios.

Artifact Spirochetes.—A great many mistakes have been made by those unfamiliar with the appearances of blood, pus, and cultures under dark-field illumination in identifying as spirochetes wavy filamentous structures of heterogeneous origin. Forms extraordinarily like spirochetes are given off by red corpuscles in a drop under a cover glass (Schultz). Fibrin filaments may resemble spirochetes. Cilia (May and Goodner), bacterial flagella (Florence) and numerous pieces of cellular débris (Nägler) often have a deceptive spirochetal appearance. They can usually be distinguished from spirochetes by repeated *controlled* observations.

REFERENCES

Dobell, C.   Antony van Leeuwenhoek and His "Little Animals," New York, 1932, pp. 225 and plate XXIV facing p. 239.

Donné, A.   Recherches microscopiques sur la nature des mucus, Paris, 1837.

Dubosq, O., and Lebailly, C.   Compt. rend. Acad. d. sc., Paris, 1912, 154:535.

Ehrenberg, C. G.   Die Infusionsthierchen, etc., Leipzig, 1838.

Florence, L.   J. Bacteriol., 1921, 6:371.

Ford, W. W.   Textbook of Bacteriology, W. B. Saunders Co., Philadelphia, 1927, 925.

Gage, S. H.   The Microscope, Ithaca, N. Y., 15th ed., 1932.

May, H. G., and Goodner, K.   Tr. Am. Micr. Soc., 1926, 45:302.

Nägler, K.   Centralbl. f. Bakteriol., 1912, 65:112.

Noguchi, H.   J. Exper. M., 1918, 27:575.

——— The Spirochetes, in The Newer Knowledge of Bacteriology and Immunology, Chicago, 1928, Chap. XXXVI, pp. 452–497.

Obermeier, O. H. F.   Centralbl. f. d. med. Wissensch., 1873, 11:145.

Schaudinn, F., and Hoffmann, E.   Arb. a. d. k. Gsndhtsamte., 1905, 22:527.

Schultz, E. W.   J. Lab. & Clin. M., 1923, 8:2.

Siedentopf.   Ztschr. f. wissensch. Mikr., 1908, 25.

Swellengrebel, N. H.   Ann. d. l'Inst. Pasteur, 1907, 21:448, 562.

CHAPTER LII

TREPONEMA PALLIDUM AND SYPHILIS; TREPONEMA PERTENUE AND YAWS

TREPONEMA PALLIDUM AND SYPHILIS

Syphilis is an infectious disease, with protean manifestations, caused by a spiro-chete, *Treponema pallidum* (synonym, *Spirochaeta pallida*). Under natural conditions, syphilis occurs only in man and the infection is transmitted from one human being to another, usually by direct contact, generally through sexual intercourse. Monkeys, rabbits and guinea-pigs can be infected experimentally by inoculation with material from syphilitic lesions in man. In monkeys and rabbits, the disease produced by experimental infection closely resembles that seen in man. Other animals are insus-ceptible. Transmission by indirect means, or fomites, may occur rarely. Syphilis is one of the most prevalent and important of all infectious diseases (Parran). Vonderlehr and Usilton state that the probability that a person in the U.S.A. will acquire syphilis at some time of life is one in ten.

Syphilis in man usually progresses through a number of stages. These are ir-regular and very varied. The most important are:

1. An incubation period of four to six weeks.
2. The primary stage, or stage of the development of the chancre. This lesion starts as a papule at the point of infection, enlarges, becomes indurated, and ulcerates, forming an ulcer with a firm base and hard edge in some cases—*but not always*. Spirochetes can be found in fluid expressed from this chancre. Exudate from every chancre should be examined by dark field illumination.
3. The secondary stage, characterized by skin rashes, mucous patches, and a variety of super-ficial lesions. *Treponema pallidum* can usually be found in material from these lesions.
4. Tertiary stages, with lesions of viscera, bones, and central nervous system. Spirochetes are usually scanty and difficult to find in sections from these pathological tissues.

In addition, there are latent forms of syphilis, varieties of congenital syphilis and syphilitic phenomena which simulate the whole gamut of medical disorders.

Historical.—The medical and sociological history of syphilis is full of interest, but cannot be recounted in detail here. The disease may have existed in Europe prior to 1495, as the mercurial recipes for the treatment of "grosse vérole" and "mal-franzoso" discovered by Sudhoff (Garrison) to have been in use by physicians in the twelfth century indicated that mercury was a cure for skin disease resembling syphilis. After the return of the sailors of Columbus to Europe about 1494, syphilis became almost epidemic in Europe and was one of the great scourges of the middle ages. The lack of convincing evidence that syphilis existed in Europe before the discovery of the New World, its virulence and extreme contagiousness suggested that the disease was an importation from America. There has been much osteological research upon the remains of the early Central and South American peoples in the

Distilled water rapidly immobilizes and finally causes fragmentation of the organism.

Drying destroys the spirochete.

Saponin (10 per cent), immobilizes and causes fragmentation in thirty minutes to two hours.

Heat.—The thermal death time of *Treponema pallidum in vitro* was determined by Boak, Carpenter and Warren by exposing emulsions of testicular tissue of experi-mentally infected rabbits, containing numerous spirochetes, to different tempera-tures for different periods of time. The heated material was then injected intratesti-cularly into rabbits and observations made on the ability or inability of the material to produce lesions. The Zinsser-Hopkins, and Nichols strains of *Treponema pallidum* were used. The Nichols strain was somewhat the more resistant. The thermal death times were: five hours at 39° C., three hours at 40° C., two hours at 41° C., and one hour at 41.5° C. These observations form a rational basis for the treatment of syphilis by induced fever, such as the malarial therapy of Wagner-Jauregg and the febrile state induced by high frequency electrical currents shown by Carpenter and his associates to be effective in curing experimental syphilis in rabbits.

attempt to determine whether or not syphilis existed among them before Columbus visited this hemisphere and the Spaniards invaded the West Indies, Mexico and Peru. The evidence that pre-Columbian syphilis existed among these Aztec and Inca aborigines has been increasing. The question has not been settled, but the New World origin of syphilis seems more than likely (Williams, Pusey).

That syphilis was contagious was readily apparent to those who had contracted it, and in the eighteenth and nineteenth centuries, John Hunter, Ricord, and other physicians proved that syphilis was infectious by inoculating men with material from syphilitic sores. Clinical discrimination of syphilitic lesions was such a highly developed art among these physicians that it cannot be doubted that their judgment that they had reproduced the disease in this manner was correct. Unfortunately, they were not aware of the other varieties of pathogenic bacteria

FIG. 68.—TREPONEMA PALLIDUM.

Viability.—The spirochete loses its viability rapidly in desiccated materials. In tissues it may retain viability and infectivity for several days, or longer. Zurhelle and Strempel found virulent spirochetes in syphilitic tissue up to three and a half days and Shaffer found syphilitic rabbit testicular material kept in storage in the cold infective up to one week.

Cultivation.—In 1912, Noguchi reported that he had isolated *Treponema pallidum* in pure culture and had produced syphilitic lesions in monkeys by inoculating them with the growth. This statement was accepted and a number of investigators have reported similar success (Schereschewsky, Hilgermann). The media commonly employed are Noguchi's ascitic fluid agar or liquid medium in a deep tube with a piece of tissue, Schereschewsky's coagulated serum. Anaerobiosis is essential. In these cultures, spirochetes resembling *Treponema pallidum* proliferate. We believe, however, that although the organism cultivated may have been the spirochete of syphilis, the proof of its virulence is not convincing. The transitory lesions produced by Noguchi, and by others are not clearly the lesions of progressive transmissible syphilis, or may have been due to a residue of spirochetes carried over with material of the original inoculation. One of us, working with Hopkins and Gilbert (Zinsser, Hopkins and Gilbert) obtained cultures similar to

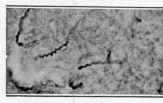

those described by Noguchi and found on study that they were completely avirulent and had no serological relationship whatever with the virulent *Treponema pallidum*. The culture treponemata were neither killed nor agglutinated by the serum of syphilitic human beings or rabbits, and virulent treponemata were not affected in the slightest degree by immune sera produced with the culture treponema. A serum which agglutinated the culture treponema in dilutions of 1 : 5000 had no protective effect whatever against the virulent treponema. It was our conclusion that the

FIG. 70.—TREPONEMA PALLIDUM.

Photograph of section of liver, congenital syphilis stained by Levaditi method.

culture treponema either had no relationship to syphilis or represented a nonvirulent dissociation form. Incidentally, these studies seemed to exclude any possible specific value of the luetin reaction. In 1929, Kast and Kolmer published an extensive compilation of many of the media used in attempts to cultivate this organism and presented a critical review of the reports on its cultivation. They concluded that the cultivation of virulent *Treponema pallidum* had not been generally accomplished. Gammel and Ecker recorded only failure after several years spent in attempts to cultivate the organism. It is our opinion that virulent *Treponema pallidum* has not been cultivated in artificial media.

Demonstration and Isolation.—The demonstration of *Treponema pallidum* in the lesions of syphilis is accomplished by dark field illumination in the microscopic examination of unstained material, and by the application of Giemsa's or Wright's stain or the silver impregnation methods which we have referred to. (See section on Technic.) The most certain bacteriological diagnosis of syphilis is made through the use of these methods, particularly the method of dark field illumination.

Isolation of the organism cannot be accomplished, at present, by the use of culture media. The organism can be transferred to rabbits or monkeys by inoculation and maintained by passage in these animals. The rabbit is especially useful for this purpose.

Pathogenicity.—Syphilis is a natural infection of man only. All races of human beings appear to be susceptible, although there are racial and individual differences in reaction to the organism. *Treponema pallidum* is a strict parasite, with special adaptation to man.

The organism is pathogenic for monkeys. In 1903, Metchnikoff and Roux were the first who succeeded in producing the disease in a lower animal. They infected a female chimpanzee by inoculating the animal with material from a human lesion. A short time later Nicolle succeeded in infecting lower monkeys (*Macacus*) and since then it has been determined that all monkeys are susceptible. Inoculation of monkeys is best accomplished by the insertion of a small piece of human syphilitic tissue in a subepidermal pocket.

Bertarelli transferred the disease to rabbits in 1906. The rabbit has been used extensively in much subsequent experimental investigation of syphilis. Intratesticular inoculation of an emulsion of human syphilitic tissue or scrapings from a chancre usually serves to establish the infection in the rabbits, although not all inoculations "take." Rabbits thus inoculated developed in the course of two weeks an induration of the testis. This increases until the sixth or seventh week, and the testis appears swollen, firm and nodular. The skin over the point of inoculation, or into which spirochetes have been placed, ulcerates during this period and has the characteristics of a chancre. Brown and Pearce succeeded in producing almost all types of syphilis in rabbits by appropriate methods of inoculation.

Guinea-pigs were shown by Kolle and Evers to be susceptible to experimental infection, but these animals have not been used extensively in investigations of syphilis.

The transmission of syphilis to llamas in Peru, reported by Jáuregui and Lance-otti in 1924 has not been confirmed.

The pathogenic properties of the spirochete become altered to only a slight extent by passage through animals. No marked increase in virulence for rabbits has been noted by the rabbit passage strains. Neurotropic properties are said to be displayed by the Nichols strain. Chesney summarized the evidence showing that the spirochete did not become attenuated by its residence in rabbits and cited the reports of accidental infections of laboratory workers as evidence that the spirochetes in rabbit lesions are pathogenic for man (Graetz and Delbanco, Gahylle).

Immunity.—A second attack of syphilis in a human being may occur, but this is a relatively rare event. It has been evident for a long time that the patient with active or latent syphilis is refractory to a second inoculation and it has been established that immunity may persist for an indefinite time after the disease has been cured.

Antibodies.—Nearly all investigators have failed to find antispirochetal antibodies in the sera of syphilitic patients. Syphilitic serum does not agglutinate the spirochetes in material from lesions and does not contain treponemacidal substances. Syphilitic serum does not agglutinate cultures of *Treponema pallidum*. Rabbits injected with these cultures develop agglutinins for the culture-spirochetes but these sera have no protective action when injected into rabbits along with virulent organisms. It is concluded from the results of our experiments and the work of others, that the serum of a syphilitic individual does not contain the usual type of anti-spirochetal antibodies and, therefore, that humoral antibodies have no significance in immunity in syphilis.

Active immunization with inanimate products derived from natural and experimental syphilitic lesions is unsuccessful.

Passive immunization likewise has not been achieved. The blood of a syphilitic person in a refractory state is neither protective nor curative.

There is neither an effective vaccinal prophylactic procedure nor a specific serum therapy for syphilis.

Nevertheless, the blood of syphilitic patients and animals contains substances which react in a practically specific manner with the lipoidal fractions of muscle and other tissues from normal animals. The normal heart muscle of the ox is the most commonly used source of these lipoids. These reactions are demonstrable by *complement fixation* and *precipitation* tests. The two highly developed and standardized procedures for the serodiagnosis of syphilis, the Wassermann reaction and its modifications and various precipitation tests, notably the *Kahn test,* are based upon the capacity of syphilitic sera to react with tissue lipoids. From our present point of view, these reactions appear to be nonspecific phenomena, although a lipoid-haptene combination may be involved in an incompletely understood specific antigen-antibody reaction in this case. While these tests indicate infection, they are not an index of immunity. Saline solution extracts of syphilitic organs, such as the original "antigen" prepared by Wassermann from the liver of a syphilitic fetus, and extracts of culture-spirochetes are not specifically serviceable as antigens for complement fixation and precipitation tests.

Acquired immunity or a resistant state from the natural or experimental infection becomes apparent with the development of the primary chancre and persists, in greater or less degree, throughout the course of the disease. The earlier investigators used the reinoculation test as an index of their state of resistance. If reinoculation did not produce a local lesion, the man or animal was said to be resistant. Chesney and others, however, have shown that, both naturally and experimentally, infection on reinoculation can occur without the production of a local lesion. Hence a search for the spirochetes in the lymph nodes and organs of an animal is required to determine whether or not infection exists.

Two main theories have been proposed to account for the resistant state of syphilitics. The first was Neisser's theory that the animal or man was resistant only as long as infection existed. Superinfection is usually impossible in syphilis as it is in a number of other spirochetal, virus, and bacterial diseases. With complete cure the animal or man gradually returns to a state of susceptibility. In the resistant stage, the immunity to various strains of spirochetes is not identical, at least in rabbits. The resistance is greatest against the homologous strain of the organism.

The results of Wassermann reactions have shown that the latent infections in both the mother and child account for the laws of Colles and Profeta.

Chesney has found that Neisser's theory is controverted by the fact that rabbits acquire during the course of syphilis an immunity which will persist after the infection has been abolished, and he expressed the opinion that in man also an acquired immunity persists in the absence of the disease.

The mechanism of immunity in syphilis has not been elucidated. States of anergy or hypersensitivity may exist, through which the cells are unresponsive or protectively overactive against the spirochetal parasite.

Hypersensitiveness.—There have been many attempts to apply the principle of the tuberculin reaction to syphilis. The eliciting of local reactions of hypersensitiveness by the intradermal injection of extracts of syphilitic lesions has been employed for diagnosis, but the results have been irregular. In 1911, Noguchi prepared "luetin" from cultures of the organism supposed to be *Treponema pallidum*. This, when injected intradermally in patients with tabes and cerebrospinal syphilis, produced local reactions. It was found later that a number of nonspecific substances will produce the same effect in syphilitics and Sherrick showed that the administration of iodides may lead to a positive luetin reaction in normal persons. The "organic luetins" extracted from lesions have not been satisfactory.

Chemotherapy.—Before the time of Ehrlich, mercurial compounds were used during centuries for the treatment of syphilis. Ehrlich's discovery of salvarsan brought the organic arsenical compounds to the fore as possible sterilizing therapeutic agents to destroy all spirochetes in a patient and cure the disease. Neither salvarsan nor any of a host of arsenical compounds has accomplished this as promptly as expected. But cures have been effected by the use of these drugs. Bismuth compounds also have value as antisyphilitic remedies. Reference should be made to the books on therapeutics, pharmacology and syphilis for the large amount of information which has been accumulated on the proper use of these drugs.

Serodiagnosis.—The blood serum of a syphilitic person or animal is capable of reacting with the lipoidal extracts of normal tissues, chiefly the lipoids extracted from normal beef heart. This reactivity can be made apparent in two ways: by complement fixation and by precipitation. While it may be that flocculation, invisible in one case and visible in the other, is the basic process in both of these reactions between syphilitic serum and lipoidal tissue extracts, two distinct types of diagnostic tests have been developed. The varieties of the complement fixation tests are generally known as the "Wassermann reaction" (Kolmer and Boerner). There have been numerous flocculation tests proposed for use in the serum diagnosis of syphilis. In our opinion the best of these is the Kahn test. The flocculation and precipitation tests of Hinton, Kline, and Eagles are also important diagnostic procedures.

Unless a lipoidal haptene is the mediator of these reactions, neither the complement fixation tests nor the precipitin reactions are immunologically specific. Nevertheless, these procedures have been so skilfully adjusted that they have a high degree of practical specificity (Wadsworth, Maltaner).

There are two stages in syphilis when all of these tests may be negative. (1) The initial stage, during the first two weeks of the developing chancre. A dark field examination of material from the lesion is essential in this stage. (2) In latent syphilis following treatment. The tests may become negative under treatment before the patient is cured.

The reader is referred to other books on syphilis (Kolmer) for notes on the percentage of positive reactions to be expected in each clinical stage of syphilis. We can sum up the physicians' expectations by saying that in our experience in working in a serodiagnostic laboratory the physician demands the explanation of two events:

(1) the failure of the complement fixation or Kahn test to be positive in a known case of syphilis and (2) the occurrence of a positive reaction with either test in cases thought by the physician or pathologist not to be syphilis. In many other cases, which might or might not be syphilis, physicians tend to accept the results of these tests, whether positive or negative, as having great diagnostic force. Occasionally, through errors in technic or nonspecific weakly positive tests, nonsyphilitics have been treated for a Wassermann reaction and syphilitics left without benefit of arsenic or mercury because their tests were negative.

Neither of these tests is absolutely diagnostic of syphilis. A positive test does not always indicate syphilis and a negative test does not exclude syphilis. The results of the test are to be interpreted by the clinician and pathologist in the light of their complete knowledge of the case.

The decision as to whether the complement fixation test is better than the Kahn test or whether the Kahn test is superior to some modification of the Wassermann test is made as a rule in two ways. First, the judgment may be based upon the results of competitive examination of serum by workers highly skilled in the use of each test and second, by the experience of the individual worker using both tests in a routine manner.

According to the results achieved by Kahn at Montevideo and elsewhere, in competitive tests conducted under the auspices of a committee of the League of Nations, his test *is more specific and sensitive* than any other test, complement fixation procedure or flocculation test. The Kahn test or a precipitation reaction has supplanted the Wassermann reaction as a primary serological diagnostic procedure.

In the experience of one of us, the Wassermann reaction carried out according to the New York State Health Department method, has been more sensitive than the routine Kahn test, but has given nonspecific reactions at times. Nonspecific complement fixation reactions were rare, but those with the Kahn test were fewer than those occurring with the complement fixation test. The Kahn test occasionally failed to give positive reactions in treated cases when the complement fixation test provided essential evidence upon which a history of syphilis was drawn from the patient.

TREPONEMA PERTENUE AND YAWS

In a disease known as "framboesia tropica," or popularly "yaws," occurring in tropical and subtropical countries and much resembling syphilis, Castellani, in 1905, was able to demonstrate a species of spirochete which has a close morphological resemblance to *Treponema pallidum*. The micro-organism was found in a large percentage of the cases examined both in the cutaneous papules and in ulcerations. Confirmatory investigations on a larger series of cases were later carried out by Von dem Borne.

The micro-organism is from 7 to 20 μ in length with numerous undulations and pointed ends. Examined in fresh preparations, it has an active motility similar to that of *Treponema pallidum*. In smears it is easily stained by means of the Giemsa method (Turner).

Both the clinical similarity between yaws and syphilis, as well as the similarity between the micro-organisms causing the diseases, has opened the question as to the identity of the two micro-organisms. According to most clinical observers, however, yaws, which is a disease characterized chiefly by a generalized papular eruption, is unquestionably distinct, clinically, from lues, and experiments of Neisser, Baermann, and Halberstadter, as well as of Castellani himself, have tended to show that there is a distinct difference between the immunity produced by attacks of the two diseases. The disease is transmissible to monkeys and rabbits, as is syphilis.

Epidemiological studies on yaws have proven that yaws is not transmitted in the same way as lues, probably passing from individual to individual by casual contact. Whether or not insects are involved is still uncertain. It yields readily to arsphenamine, more readily than lues, and complete cure seems to be more easily attained than in the other disease.

The Wassermann reaction is usually positive in yaws. Syphilis occurs in patients with yaws and Jahnel and Lange produced yaws in a paretic. Schöbl and his collaborators have shown that inoculation of monkeys with heated material from lesions of yaws protects against *Treponema pertenue* and modifies the course of experimental inoculated syphilis in these animals.

VENEREAL SPIROCHETOSIS OF RABBITS

The occurrence of a spirochete indistinguishable from *Treponema pallidum* in a natural venereal disease of rabbits was reported by Ross in 1912 and Bayon in 1913. The organism is identical morphologically with the spirochete of syphilis, and was called *Treponema cuniculi* by Noguchi in 1928.

In the rabbit, the lesions produced by this organism are slightly elevated, scaly areas about the genitalia, superficial and not indurated (Warthin). The organism has none of the invasiveness of *Treponema pallidum* and does not produce a generalized disease. Its occurrence in animals used for experimental studies of syphilis might lead to confusion if the examinations were limited to morphology alone. Appropriate inoculation tests will differentiate the organism from the spirochete of syphilis. Rabbits with natural venereal spirochetosis do not give a positive Wassermann reaction (Kolle, Ruppert and Möbus, Turner).

REFERENCES

Bayon, H. Brit. M. J., 1913, 2:1159.

Bertarelli, E. Centralbl. f. Bakteriol., 1906, 41:320.

Boak, R. A., Carpenter, C. M., and Warren, S. L. J. Exper. M., 1932, 56:741.

Brown, W., and Pearce, L. J. Exper. M., 1921, 33.

Carpenter, C. M., Boak, R. A., and Warren, S. L. J. Exper. M., 1932, 56:751.

Castellani, A. Brit. M. J., 1905, 2:1280.

——— J. Hyg., 1907, 7:558.

Chesney, A. M. Immunity in Syphilis, Medicine, 1926, 5:463; published also in Medical Monographs, Vol. XII, Baltimore, 1927.

Gahylle, E. Compt. rend. Soc. de biol., 1924, 91:911.

Gammel, J. A., and Ecker, E. E. Arch. Dermat. & Syph., 1931, 23:439.

Garrison, F. H. An Introduction to the History of Medicine, Philadelphia, 4th ed., 1929, pp. 189–192, with a review of Sudhoff's historical investigations.

Graetz, F., and Delbanco, E. Med. Klin., 1914, 375.

HILGERMANN, R. Deutsche med. Wchnschr., 1931, 57:488.

JAHNEL, F., and LANGE, J. München. med. Wchnschr., 1927, 74:1487.

JÁUREGUI, F., and LANCEOTTI, L. Bull. Acad. de méd., 1924, 92 (Cited by Chesney.)

KAHN, R. L. The Kahn Test, A Practical Guide, Baltimore, 1928.

——— J. Am. M. Ass., 1929, 93:351.

——— Arch. Dermat. & Syph., 1932, 26:59.

——— Revista Argentina Dermasifilog., 1932, 16:319.

——— Reports of Laboratory Conferences on Serodiagnosis of Syphilis, League of Nations Health Organization, 1928 and 1931.

KAST, C. C., and KOLMER, J. A. Am. J. Syph., 1929, 13:417.

KOLLE, W., and EVERS, E. Deutsche med. Wchnschr., 1926, 53:1075.

KOLLE, W., RUPPERT, F., and MÖBUS, T. Arch. f. Dermat. u. Syph., 1921, 135:260. (Cited by Chesney.)

KOLMER, J. A. Practical Textbook of Infection, Immunity and Biologic Therapy, Philadelphia, 1923.

KOLMER, J. A., and BOERNER, F. Approved Laboratory Technic, New York, 2nd ed., 1938.

LUSTGARTEN, S. Wien. med. Wchnschr., 1884, 34:1389.

MALTANER, E. Am. J. Pub. Health, 1939, 29:104.

METCHNIKOFF, E., and ROUX, E. Ann. d. l'Inst. Pasteur, 1903, 1904, 1905.

NEISSER, BAERMANN, and HALBERSTADTER. München. med. Wchnschr., 1906, 53:1337.

NICOLLE, C. Ann. d. l'Inst. Pasteur, 1903.

NOGUCHI, H. J. Exper. M., 1911, 14:99, 557; 1912, 15:90.

——— The Newer Knowledge of Bacteriology and Immunology, Chicago, 1928, p. 478.

PARRAN, T. Shadow on the Land, Reynal and Hitchcock, New York, 1937.

PUSEY, W. A. The History and Epidemiology of Syphilis. Charles C. Thomas, Springfield, 1933.

ROSS, E. H. Brit. M. J., 1912, 2:1651.

RAIZISS, G. W. and SEVERAC, M. Arch. Dermatol. and Syphilol., 1937, 35:1101.

SCHAUDINN, F., and HOFFMANN, E. Arb. a. d. k. Gsndhtsamte., 1905, 22:527.

SCHERESCHEWSKY, J. Deutsche med. Wchnschr., 1909, 35:835, 1260, 1652.

SCHÖBL, O., and HASSELMANN, C. M. Arch. f. Schiffs- u. Tropen-Hyg., 1932, 36:Beiheft 2.

SCHÖBL, TANABE, and MIYAO. Philippine J. Sc., 1930, 12:219, 239.

SHAFFER, L. W. Arch. Path., 1926, 2:50.

SHERRICK, J. W. J. Am. M. Ass., 1915, 45:404.

TURNER, T. B. Am. J. Hyg., 1936, 23:431; 1937, 25:477.

VON DEM BORNE. J. Trop. M., 1907, 10:345.

VONDERLEHR, R. A., and USILTON, L. J. Ven. Dis. Information, U. S. Pub. Health Serv., 1938, 19:396.

WADSWORTH, A., MALTANER, F., and MALTANER, E. J. Immunol., 1938, 35:93, 105, 217.

WAGNER-JAUREGG, J. Psychiat.-neurol. Wchnschr., 1918, 20:132. (Quoted from Carpenter.)

WARTHIN, A. S., BUFFINGTON, E., and WANSTROM, R. C. J. Infect. Dis., 1923, 32:317.

WARTHIN, A. S., and STARRY, A. C. J. Am. M. Ass., 1921, 76:234.

——— J. Infect. Dis., 1922, 30:592.

WILLIAMS, H. U. Arch. Path., 1932, 13:779, 931.

ZINSSER, H. Resistance to Infectious Disease, New York, 4th ed., 1931, pp. 489-505.

ZINSSER, H., HOPKINS, J. G., and GILBERT, R. J. Exper. M., 1915, 21:213.

ZURHELLE, E., and STREMPEL, R. Arch. f. Dermat. u. Syph., 1927, 153:219.

CHAPTER LIII

THE SPIROCHETES OF RELAPSING FEVER, VINCENT'S ANGINA AND OTHER DISEASES

Genus: *Borrelia*, formerly *Spironema*

Authorities on the classification of spirochetes, Noguchi and Hindle, do not make a sharp distinction between the *Treponemata*, which we have considered in the last chapter on syphilis and yaws, and the large group of spiral organisms which cause blood infections in man and animals, and are associated with superficial inflammations and gangrenous processes in man. These organisms, however, are morphologically quite different from the treponemes. They are long or short flexible spirals with loose irregular coils in place of the regular and relatively rigid spirals of the species of *Treponema*. The pathological lesions which they produce differ from those caused by the tissue parasites of syphilis and yaws. Some of them have become adapted to insects as well as to man and animals and are transmissible by insect vectors. The spirochetes of the Vincent type are semisaprophytic and form a close link with the fusiform bacteria. While we shall avoid calling them treponemes, we hold no brief for any special name. The names *Spironema* and *Borrelia* appear to us to be useful designations, and we shall use them without intending to imply that our selection of the name is based on competent studies in taxonomy and nomenclature.

RELAPSING FEVER

Family: *Spirochaetaceae*. Genus: *Borrelia*. Species: *Borrelia duttoni, novyi* and *recurrentis*.

The micro-organisms causing relapsing fever were first observed in 1873, by Obermeier, who demonstrated them in the blood of patients suffering from this distinct type of fever. Since his time extensive studies by many other observers have proven beyond question the etiological connection between the disease and the organisms.

Morphology and Staining.—The spirochete of Obermeier is a delicate spiral thread measuring from 7 to 9 μ in length (Novy), and about 1 μ in thickness. While this is its average size, it may, according to some observers, be considerably longer than this, its undulations varying from four to ten or more in number. Compared with the red blood cells among which they are seen, the micro-organisms may vary from one-half to nine or ten times the diameter of a corpuscle. In fresh preparations of the blood, very active corkscrew-like motility and definite lateral oscillation are observed. In stained preparations no definite cellular structure can be made out, the cell body appearing homogeneous, except in degenerated individuals, in which irregular granulation or beading has been observed. Terminal filaments have been described by various observers. Novy and Knapp believe that the organisms possess only one terminal filament. Zettnow, on the other hand, claims to have demonstrated lateral flagella by special methods of staining. Norris, Pappenheimer and Flournoy, in smears stained by polychrome methods, have described long, filamentous tapering ends which they interpreted as bipolar, terminal flagella, never observing more than one at each end. Spores are not found.

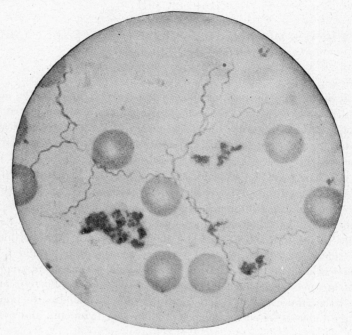

FIG. 71.—SPIROCHETE OF RELAPSING FEVER.
(After Norris, Pappenheimer, and Flournoy.)

Cultivation.—Novy and Knapp succeeded in keeping the micro-organisms alive and virulent in the original blood for as long as forty days. They do not, however, believe that extensive multiplication, or, in other words, actual cultivation, had taken place in their experiments. Norris, Pappenheimer and Flournoy, on the other hand, have obtained positive evidence of multiplication of the spirochetes in fluid media. They obtained their cultures by inoculating a few drops of spirochetal rat blood into 3 to 5 c.c. of citrated human or rat blood. Smears made from these tubes, after preservation for twenty-four hours at room temperature, showed the micro-organisms in greater number than in the original infected blood. A similar multiplication could be observed in transfers made from these "first-generation" tubes to other tubes of citrated blood. Attempts at cultivation for a third generation failed.

Noguchi in 1913 successfully cultivated the spirochete of Obermeier in ascitic fluid containing a piece of sterile rabbit's kidney and a few drops of citrated blood under anaerobic conditions.

Four different, probably distinct varieties of spirochete have been described in connection with relapsing fever, all of which have been cultivated by Noguchi by means of this method. The first is known as the spirochete of Obermeier mentioned above. Probably distinct are the *Spirochaeta duttoni* of West African tick fever described by Dutton and Todd in 1905, the *Spirochaeta kochi,* and the *Spirochaeta novyi* (Novy and Fränkel), the organism studied by Norris and Pappenheimer and Flournoy, and regarded as a different species by them.

Pathogenicity.—Inoculation with blood containing these spirochetes produces disease in monkeys, rats and mice. Attempts to transmit the disease experimentally to dogs, rabbits and guinea-pigs have so far been unsuccessful. The subcutaneous inoculation of monkeys is followed after from two to four days by a rise of temperature which occurs abruptly, and may last several days. During this time the spirochetes can be found in the blood of the animals. The temperature subsides after a day or more, when it again rapidly returns to normal. As a rule, the paroxyms are not repeated. Occasionally, however, two or three attacks may supervene before immunity is established. In rats, an incubation time of from two to five days occurs. At the end of this time the spirochetes may be found in large numbers in the blood, and the animals show symptoms of a severe systemic infection. The attack lasts from four to five days, at the end of which time the micro-organisms again disappear. Occasionally even in these animals relapses have been observed. Gross pathological changes are not found, with the exception of an enlargement of the spleen.

In man the disease caused by the spirochete of Obermeier and allied organisms, commonly known as relapsing fever, is common in eastern Europe, India, Africa, and most of the warmer countries. It has, from time to time, been observed epidemi-

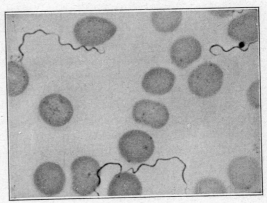

Fig. 72.—Spirochete of Relapsing Fever.
(From preparation furnished by Dr. G. N. Calkins.)

cally in Europe, especially in Russia, and a few epidemics have occurred in the United States (Francis and Porter, Beck and Stevens). The disease comes on abruptly, beginning usually with a chill accompanied by a sharp rise of temperature and generalized pains. Together with the rise of temperature, which often exceeds 104° F., there are great prostration and occasionally delirium. Early in the disease the spleen becomes palpable and jaundice may appear. The spirochetes are easily detected in the blood during the persistence of the fever, which lasts usually from three to ten days. At the end of this time the temperature usually drops as suddenly as it rose, and the general symptoms rapidly disappear. After a free interval of from one to three weeks a relapse may occur, which is usually less severe and of shorter duration than the original attack. Two, three, or even four attacks may occur, but the disease is not often fatal. When patients do succumb, however, the autopsy findings are not particularly characteristic. Apart from the marked enlargement of the spleen, which histologically shows the changes indicating simple hyperplasia, and a slight enlargement of the liver, no lesions are found. The diagnosis is easily made during the febrile stage by examination of a small quantity of blood under a cover-slip or in the hanging-drop preparation.

Several types of relapsing fever have been described. In Africa the disease has long been prevalent in many regions. The investigations of Ross and Milne, Koch, Dutton and Todd, and others have brought to light the fact that many conditions occurring among the natives, formerly regarded as malarial, are caused by a species

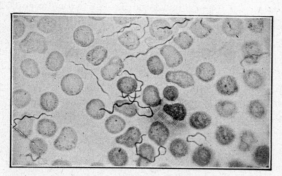

FIG. 73.—SPIROCHETE OF DUTTON, AFRICAN TICK FEVER.
(From preparation furnished by Dr. G. N. Calkins.)

of spirochete. Whether or not the micro-organisms observed in the African disease are exactly identical with the spirochete observed by Obermeier is yet a question about which several opinions are held. Dutton and Todd believe that the same micro-organism is responsible for both diseases. Koch, on the other hand, believes that the slightly smaller size of the African spirochete and the milder course of the clinical symptoms indicate a definite difference between the two.

Animal experiments made with the African organism, furthermore, usually show a much more severe infection than do similar inoculations with the European variety. The spirochete found in the African disease is usually spoken of at present as *Spirochaeta duttoni*. Novy and Knapp came to the conclusion that, although closely related, definite species differences exist between the two types.

The mode of transmission of this disease is not clear for all types. Dutton and Todd, however, were able to show satisfactorily that, in the case of the African disease at least, transmission occurs through a species of tick. The tick (*Ornithodorus moubata*) infects itself when sucking blood from an infected human being. The spirochete may remain alive and demonstrable within the body of the tick for as long as three days. Koch has shown, furthermore, that they may be found also within the eggs laid by an infected female tick. He succeeded in producing experimental infection in monkeys by subjecting the animals to the bites of the infected insects. For the European variety of the disease no such intermediate host has as yet been demonstrated with absolute certainty. It is known, however, that the organism can live in the bodies of bedbugs and it has also been suggested that lice may be the carriers. Lice also are regarded as the transmitting agent of a similar relapsing fever prevalent in North Africa caused by the *Spiroschaudinnia berberi*.

Immunity.—It has long been a well-known fact that recovery from an attack of relapsing fever usually results in a more or less definite immunity. The blood of human beings, monkeys, and rats which have recovered from an attack of this disease shows definite and specific bactericidal and agglutinating substances, and Novy and Knapp have demonstrated that the blood serum of such animals may be used to confer passive immunity upon others.

SPIROCHETOSIS OF FOWLS [1]

An acute infectious disease occurring among chickens, chiefly in South America, has been shown by Marchoux and Salembeni to be caused by a spirochete which has much morphological similarity to the spirochete of Obermeier.

The disease comes on rather suddenly with fever, diarrhea, and great exhaustion, and often ends fatally. The spirochete is easily demonstrated in the circulating blood of the animals by staining blood smears with Giemsa's stain or with dilute carbolfuchsin.

Experimental transmission from animal to animal is easily carried out by the subcutaneous injection of blood. Other birds, such as geese, ducks, and pigeons, are susceptible; mammals have, so far, not been successfully inoculated. According to the investigation of Levaditi and Manouelian, the spirochetes are found not only in the blood but thickly distributed throughout the various organs.

Under natural conditions, infection of chickens seems to depend upon a species of tick which acts as an intermediate host and causes infection by its bite. The spirochete, according to Marchoux and Salembeni, may be found in the intestinal canal of the ticks for as long as five months after their infection from a diseased fowl.

In the blood of animals which have survived an infection, agglutinating substances appear and active immunization of animals may be carried out by the injection of infected blood in which the spirochetes have been killed, either by moderate heat or by preservation at room temperature. The serum of immune animals, furthermore, has a protective action upon other birds.

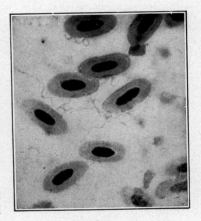

FIG. 74.—SPIROCHAETA GALLINARUM.

(From preparation furnished by Dr. G. N. Calkins.)

It is not impossible that the *Spirochaeta gallinarum* may be identical with the *Spirochaeta anserina* previously discovered by Sacharoff. This last-named microorganism causes a disease in geese, observed especially in Russia and northern Africa, which both clinically and in its pathological lesions corresponds closely to the disease above described as occurring in chickens. The spirochete is found during the febrile period of the disease in the circulating blood, and is morphologically indistinguishable from the spirochete of chickens. The similarity is further strengthened by the fact that *Spirochaeta anserina* is pathogenic for other birds, but not for animals of other genera. Noguchi, in 1912, succeeded in cultivating *Spirochaeta gallinarum* by the same method by which he has cultivated the organisms of relapsing fever. Ascitic fluid tubes with a piece of sterile rabbit kidney were inoculated with a few drops of blood containing the spirochetes and cultivated at 37.5° C. under aerobic conditions.

[1] Species: *Borrelia gallinarum.* Syn: *Spirochaeta gallinarum.*

VINCENT'S ANGINA AND FUSOSPIROCHETAL DISEASES

VINCENT'S ANGINA

Species: *Borrelia vincentii*

The condition known as Vincent's angina consists of an inflammatory lesion in the mouth, pharynx or throat, situated most frequently upon the tonsils. The disease usually begins as an acute stomatitis, pharyngitis or tonsillitis, which soon leads to the formation of a pseudomembrane, which, at this stage, has a great deal of resemblance to that caused by the diphtheria bacillus. At later stages of the disease there may be distinct ulceration, the ulcers having a well-defined margin and "punched-out" appearance, so that clinically they have often been erroneously diagnosed as

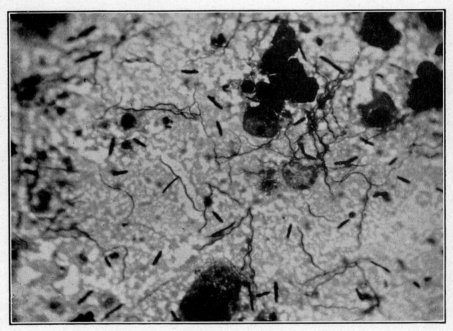

FIG. 75.—THROAT SMEAR FROM VINCENT'S ANGINA SHOWING FUSIFORM BACTERIA AND SPIROCHETES.

(Photograph by Stella Zimmerman, Syracuse University School of Medicine.)

syphilis. Apart from the localized pain, the disease is usually mild, but occasionally moderate fever and systemic disturbances have been observed. Unlike diphtheria and syphilis, this peculiar form of angina usually yields to local treatment. Intravenous injections of neoarsphenamine and preparations of antimony are also said to be curative.

The nature of lesions of this peculiar kind was not clear until Plaut, Vincent and others reported uniform bacteriological findings in cases of this description. These observers demonstrated in smears from the lesions a spindle-shaped or fusiform bacillus, together with which there is usually found a spirillum not unlike the spirillum of relapsing fever. The two micro-organisms are almost always found together in this form of disease and were regarded by the first observers as representing two distinct forms dwelling in symbiosis.

The *fusiform bacilli* described by Vincent, Plaut, Babes and others, are from 3 to 10 μ in length, and have a thickness at the center varying from 0.5 to 0.8 μ. From the center they taper gradually toward the ends, ending in blunt or sharp points. The length of these bacilli may vary greatly within one and the same smear preparation. They are usually straight, sometimes slightly curved. They do not stain very easily with the weaker aniline dyes, but are readily stained by Löffler's methylene blue, carbolfuchsin, or better, by Giemsa's stain. Stained by Gram, they are usually decolorized, though in this respect the writers have found them to vary. Stained preparations show a characteristic inequality in the intensity of the stain, the bacilli being more deeply stained near the end, and showing a banded or striped alternation of stained and unstained areas in the central body. Their staining qualities in this respect are not unlike those of the diphtheria bacillus, and according to Babes the dark areas are to be interpreted as metachromatic granules. The bacilli are usually reported as being nonmotile. Smith (1932), however, has found his Type I fusiform bacillus to be motile. In the 4th edition (1934) of Bergey's *Manual* this organism is listed as *Fusiformis dentium*, Hoelling.

The *spirilla* found in Vincent's angina are usually somewhat longer than the fusiform bacilli, and are made up of a variable number of undulations, shallow and irregular in their curvatures, unlike the more regularly steep waves of *Treponema pallidum*. They are stained with even more difficulty than are the bacilli and usually appear less distinct in the preparations. The stain, however, is taken without irregularity, showing none of the metachromatism observed in the bacilli. The spirals are gram-negative.

By the earlier observers cultivation of these micro-organisms was attempted without success. It has been shown, however, that cultivation could be carried out under anaerobic conditions. Tunnicliff has cultivated the organisms anaerobically upon slants of ascitic agar at 37.5° C. This observer found that in such cultures, before the fifth day, bacilli only could be found, that after this time, however, spirilla gradually appeared and finally constituted the majority of the organisms in the culture. It appeared to Tunnicliff from this study that the spirilla might be developed out of the fusiform micro-organisms.

The micro-organisms of Vincent's angina, when occurring in the throat are rarely present alone, being usually accompanied by other micro-organisms, such as staphylococci, streptococci, and not infrequently diphtheria bacilli. When occurring together with diphtheria, they are said, by some German observers, to aggravate the latter condition considerably. This frequent association with other micro-organisms renders it impossible to decide conclusively that the fusiform bacilli and spirilla are the primary etiological factors in these inflammations. It has been frequently suggested that they may be present as secondary invaders upon the soil prepared for them by other micro-organisms.

The genus *Fusobacterium* has been studied systematically by Rettger, Slanetz and Spaulding.

Before we continue the discussion of the relation between fusiform bacteria and spirochetes, it will be advantageous to comment briefly on the rôle of these organisms

in numerous pathological processes which may be listed under the heading fusospirochetal disease.

Fusospirochetal Disease

Vincent's first paper describing these organisms dealt with hospital gangrene, or,
as he called it, "pourriture d'hôpital." Fetor has been noted as a characteristic of the
many types of putrid inflammation and gangrenous processes in which fusiform
bacilli and spirochetes have been found in association in the lesions. There have
been many clinical, pathological and bacteriological studies of these conditions. In
1932, Smith brought together in a most valuable monograph a review of the work
of many investigators with a summary of the results of his own researches in this
field.

Smith has found no evidence that the spirochetes of the mouth can by themselves
produce disease in man. He considers them the most important member "in a symbiotic group of anaerobic organisms which is capable of initiating a severe and fatal
disease." This group produces disease in the tonsils, gums, cheeks, tongue, pharynx,
larynx, eyes, ears, trachea, bronchi, lungs, esophagus, appendix, colon, genitalia,
and when carried in emboli in the blood stream they initiate disease in the brain and
other internal organs. The chief characteristics of the lesions produced by them are
necrosis and destruction of tissue, pseudomembrane formation in superficial lesions
and a fetid odor.

These organisms are, as a group, responsible for such diseases as noma, the
bronchial spirochetosis of Castellani, and fusospirochetal pulmonary gangrene and
abscess (Smith, 1927), tropical ulcer, and pseudomembranous and phagedenic infections of the male and female genitalia. Undoubtedly, they are important in the progress of pyorrhea alveolaris.

Smith (1932) has clearly demonstrated the pathogenicity of this group of spirochetes, fusiform bacilli, vibrios and cocci, and has directed a renewal of attention to
the fact that a number of natural infections of man have a multiple etiology.

The mucocutaneous spirochetes in this group have been listed under various
names, reflecting the uncertainties of nomenclature and classification. Lesions have
been produced by inoculation with mixtures of fusiform bacilli (and other bacteria),
and *Treponema microdentium*, *Treponema macrodentium*, or *Spirochaeta buccalis,*
Spirochaeta phagedenis, and *Spirochaeta calligyrum*. The organism called here *Treponema macrodentium* was cultivated by Noguchi in 1912 and believed by him to be
identical with the spirochete found in Vincent's angina.

Relation of Fusiform Bacilli to Spirochetes.—The genus *Fusobacteriu* is defined in Bergey's *Manual* (1939) as follows: "Gram-negative, anaerobic rods usually
with tapering ends. Usually non-motile. Stain with more or less distinct granules." [2]
The type species is *Fusobacterium plauti-vincenti*. Fusiforms and spiral forms are
found in association in the lesions of Vincent's angina, ulcerative stomatitis, gangrene
and in wounds.

All of the fusiform bacteria found in the mouth do not meet this definition, as
some varieties are motile. There are many types of anaerobic fusiform bacilli. Var-

---

[2] D. H. Bergey, *Bergey's Manual of Determinative Bacteriology*, Baltimore, Williams and Wilkins Co.,
5th ed., 1939.

ney, who isolated and studied 18 strains, has described these and has found that they can be classified serologically. Smith (1932), on the basis of his own experience, classified the fusiform bacilli in three types, according to their morphology. These types are:

TYPE I. This is the large fusiform bacillus found in Vincent's angina. Length 3 to 20 μ, with 0.6 to 0.8 μ. Ends tapered and pointed. Actively motile in material from lesions and in some young cultures. Produces a rancid odor in cultures. It is suggested by Smith that this fusiform bacillus is identical with the so-called *Spirochaeta buccalis*. Has a double contour in dark field illumination. It is susceptible to arsenic.

TYPE II. Very similar to Type I, thinner (0.3 μ wide), appearing as a single line in dark field illumination. Actively motile when taken from lesions. Susceptible to arsenic. Smith suggests that in its spiral form it may be identical with Vincent's spirochete.

TYPE III. Small straight form, 2 to 5 μ long, 0.3 to 0.4 μ wide. Nonmotile. Common in lung abscesses and chronic bronchiectasis.

There has been a long continued controversy on the question of whether fusiform bacteria develop into spirochetes and spirochetes into fusiform bacilli. Tunnicliff cultivated fusiform bacilli anaerobically upon slants of ascitic fluid agar at 37.5° C. and found that in such cultures before the fifth day only bacilli could be found, but that after this time spiral forms appeared and finally constituted the majority of the organisms in the culture. Krumwiede, who isolated and studied a number of these organisms, was among those who maintained that fusiform bacilli and spirochetes were totally different organisms. In 1927, Sanarelli, studying the "Héliconèmes" of Vincent, obtained the transformation of a spirochete into a fusiform bacillus by growing it in a medium containing a filtrate of a culture of *Bacillus mesentericus*. His opinion was that certain fusiform bacilli are spirochetes which are unable to coil. Smith (1932) has reported that he has repeatedly seen spiral forms take the place of fusiform bacilli in pure culture and has seen fusiform bacilli develop into spiral forms.

In our opinion, Smith has proposed a sensible solution of this problem of the morphological relation of spirochetes to fusiform bacilli. He pointed out that there are two points of confusion. One is the existence of several types of fusiform bacilli, and that undoubtedly different investigators have been studying different types of these organisms. The second source of confusion is that there is no generally accepted agreement as to the meaning of the term "spirochete." Furthermore, dissociative phenomena may occur as a basis of the observed morphological changes. It is certain that fusiform bacilli do not develop into some of the specific, well-defined spirochetes, but the assumption of a spiral form by some of the fusiform bacilli produces loosely coiled spirochete-like organisms which might be classified morphologically as a species of *Borrelia*.

REFERENCES

BABES. In Kolle and Wassermann, Handb., etc., 1907.
CASTELLANI, A. J. Trop. M., 1905, 8:253.
DUTTON and TODD. J. Trop. M., 1905.
——— Lancet, 1905.
——— Brit. M. J., 1905.
FRANCIS, E. Tr. Ass. Am. Physicians, 1932, 47:143.

HINDLE, E. A System of Bacteriology in Relation to Medicine, London, 1931, 8:101, *et seq.*, esp. pp. 142, 145, 147–184.

HOELLING. Arch. f. Protistenkunde, 1910, 19:240.

KOCH. Deutsche med. Wchnschr., 1905, 31.

———— Berl. med. Wchnschr., 1906.

KRUMWIEDE, C., and PRATT. J. Infect. Dis., 1913, 13:438.

LEVADITI and MANOUELIAN. Ann. de l'Inst. Pasteur, 1906.

MARCHOUX and SALEMBENI. Ann. de l'Inst. Pasteur, 1903.

NOGUCHI, H. J. Exper. M., 1912, 16:199, 620; 1913, 17:89.

———— The Newer Knowledge of Bacteriology and Immunology, Chicago, 1928, Chap. 36, pp. 452–497.

NORRIS, PAPPENHEIMER and FLOURNOY. J. Infect. Dis., 1906, 3.

NOVY and FRÄNKEL. Cited from Noguchi.

NOVY and KNAPP. J. Infect. Dis., 1906, 3.

OBERMEIER. Centralbl. f. d. med. Wissensch., 1873, 11.

PLAUT, H. C. Deutsche med. Wchnschr., 1894, 20:920.

PORTER, G. S., BECK, M. D., and STEVENS, I. M. Am. J. Pub. Health, 1932, 22:1136.

ROSS and MILNE. Brit. M. J., 1904.

SACHAROFF. Ann. de l'Inst. Pasteur, 1891.

SANARELLI, G. Ann. de l'Inst. Pasteur, 1927, 41:679.

SLANETZ, L. A., and RETTGER, L. F. J. Bacteriol., 1933, 26:599.

SMITH, D. T. Am. Rev. Tuberc., 1927, 15:352; 1927, 16:584.

———— Oral Spirochetes and Related Organisms in Fuso-Spirochetal Disease, Baltimore, 1932.

SPAULDING, E. H., and RETTGER, L. F. J. Bacteriol., 1937, 34:535, 549.

TURNBULL. Indian M. Gaz., 1905.

TUNNICLIFF, R. J. Infect. Dis., 1906, 3:148; 1911, 8:316; 1923, 33:147; 1933, 53:280; 1934, 55:380.

VARNEY, P. J. Bacteriol., 1927, 13:275.

VINCENT, H. Ann. de l'Inst. Pasteur, 1896, 10:488.

———— Bull. et mém. Soc. méd. d. hôp. de Par., 1898, 15:244.

ZETTNOW. Deutsche med. Wchnschr., 1906, 32.

CHAPTER LIV

THE LEPTOSPIRA GROUP—INFECTIOUS JAUNDICE (WEIL'S DISEASE) AND OTHER LEPTOSPIROSES

Order: *Spirochaetales*. Family: *Spirochaetaceae*. Genus: *Leptospira*. Type Species: *Leptospira icterohaemorrhagiae*

Since 1914, it has been determined that several long-known infectious diseases, characterized by fever, jaundice and petechial hemorrhages are caused by various types of distinctive spirochete, now called *Leptospira* (Noguchi, 1917). The most important of these diseases are infectious hemorrhagic jaundice, or Weil's disease, and the seven day fever of Japan and leptospirosis in the United States (Meyer.)

LEPTOSPIRA

During the ten-year period, from 1918 to 1928, much evidence was presented by Noguchi and his associates in support of the opinion that a species of *Leptospira*, known as *Leptospira icteroides* was the cause of yellow fever. This opinion, though widely accepted, was not adopted by Agramonte and others on the grounds that a leptospiral etiology of yellow fever was not in accord with the known natural history of the disease. The proof by Sellards and Theiler and Schüffner in 1927–28 that *Leptospira icteroides* was identical with the leptospira of Weil's disease, the failure of competent investigators to find *Leptospira* in cases of yellow fever, and the reproduction of yellow fever with filtrates which did not contain *Leptospira* caused the abandonment of the conception of yellow fever as a leptospiral disease. Yellow fever is caused by a filtrable, ultramicroscopic virus.

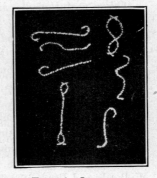

FIG. 76.—LEPTOSPIRA ICTEROHAEMORRHAGIAE.

Diagrammatic sketch of appearance of organisms in the dark field.

The spirochetes in this genus are tightly coiled, thin, flexible organisms, 7 to 14 μ long and 0.25 to 0.3 μ in diameter (Noguchi, 1928). The individual spirals are composed of such closely wound coils that they are difficult to distinguish, the organism under dark field illumination often appearing as a chain of minute cocci. The terminal thirds of the body of the spirochete are more flexible than the middle portion and are usually bent in the form of a hook. The organism is motile, progressing by undulatory movements and by a rapid spinning on the long axis. During this spinning motion, one end may be curved in a hook while the other end remains straight. The organism then progresses slowly in the direction of the straightened end. Often both ends are hooked, usually in opposite directions, while the organism spins rapidly on its long axis. (Figure 76.) Division occurs by transverse fission. Occasionally chains of the organisms are produced.

709

course and symptoms and many etiological guesses were made. For a time it was

the training which should be required of writers on "pathogenic fungi." Our effort

1 A. Castellani, *Fungi and Fungous Diseases*, Am. Med. Ass., Chicago, 1928, reprinted from *Arch. Dermat. & Syph.*, 1927, 17:383, 571, 714; 1928, 18:61, 194, 354.

719

The same term is, however, often loosely used for any rounded cell of a fungus, whether it be a part of the body of the organism, or an encysted resting form, or a true reproductive form. The function of a cell in these rudimentary plants is often hard to define. One which seems at first to be merely a component unit of the thallus may if it becomes detached reproduce an entire organism. We may, however, divide all these rounded cells into two classes: (*a*) True spores, the sole function of which is reproduction; and (*b*) *vegetative spores*, remembering that the latter may also serve to reproduce the species.

Spores differ in their mode of origin and in their arrangement on or within the thallus. Almost every species of fungus produces several types. There are two groups of reproductive spores, one sexually produced, the other asexually. Of the many names given to different forms we will attempt to define only those which it will be necessary to use in this chapter. It will be found that many of these are used in a somewhat varying sense by different writers.

Reproductive Spores.—An *oospore* is a sexual type produced by the fertilization of a female cell by a differentiated male cell.

A *zygospore* is a sexual type produced by the fusion of two undifferentiated cells. Zygospores occur only on those forms having no cross walls.

Conidium is a general term applied to all asexual reproductive spores. The term is by some writers restricted to exospores or those formed by a bud which protrudes from the membrane of the parent cell.

Endospore is a general term applied to any spore formed within the membrane of the parent cell.

Ascospores are a special class of endospores which are formed in a membrane known as the ascus, the number of spores in the sac being limited to two, four, or eight, and constant for the particular species producing them. The parent cell from which ascospores are produced has originally two nuclei which fuse into one before again dividing to form the ascospores. This fusion is regarded as a rudimentary sexual process. It has also been shown that in certain species the parent cell is the result

All varieties of *Leptospira* are dissolved by trypsin and bile, but are completely

and stains. The organism has rarely been detected with certainty in the blood of man. It may be found in material from the lesions. Wright's and Giemsa's stains are satisfactory. The flagella can be demonstrated best by the use of the Tribondeau-Fontana silver stain.

will be directed to the presentation of a review of authoritative statements of others, arranged and criticized according to our admittedly limited experience.

A general setting and classification of the groups of forms, with indications of relationships, is shown in the following summary:

Classifications.—The fungi belong to the group of plants known as *Thallophyta.* These are filamentous plants which do not develop a complex body. Thallophytes do not produce roots, stem or leaves.

There are two large subdivisions of the *Thallophyta: Algae,* containing chlorophyl; *Fungaceae,* lacking chlorophyl.

The *Fungaceae* include the fungi, of which three large groups may be recognized: (*a*) *Schizomycetes,* or bacteria. (*b*) *Eumycetes,* molds and fungi in the ordinary sense of the term, unicellular or multicellular filamentous plant-like organisms, usually larger than bacteria, with definite cell walls, which multiply by cell fission, budding, and usually by means of *asexual* and *sexual* spores. This group contains the *pathogenic fungi.* (*c*) *Myxomycetes,* a multinucleated naked protoplasmic plasmodial body. No species of this group is pathogenic for man. These organisms may be protozoa.

The next stage in classification, namely the subdivision of the fungi, presents difficulties, insuperable at present. Putting aside confusion due to the misuse of terminology, a fundamental difficulty exists in the incomplete knowledge of these organisms. A second difficulty is the lack of harmony between botanical classifications and clinical-pathological groupings. From the medical point of view, the inconvenience of systematic mycology is its grouping together of organisms which have very dissimilar effects upon animal tissues. The fault of a clinical-pathological classification is its grouping together of unrelated fungi under the captions of similar diseases.

Typical fungi are made up of cylindrical cells, joined into filaments, from which smaller rounded cells called spores are developed. From these two elements, filaments and spores, the fungi build up a structure that differs in complexity in the different species. The unicellular types such as the common yeasts grow in easily dissociated masses like bacteria and each cell combines the functions of absorbing foodstuffs, of building them up into its own substance and of reproducing new individuals. In the molds, which represent simpler multicellular fungi, the filaments lie distinct in a loose meshwork, without definite arrangement except that certain of them are thrust up vertically and develop spores.

The gross appearance, the microscopic structure and especially the type of spores produced are relied on for the identification and classification of the various species

rations of fungi usually obscure details which are clearly visible in the unstained specimens.

The methods to be employed depend upon the type of the fungus, the material in which it occurs and on the source, whether from a lesion in an animal or from a culture.

For *direct examination* of material from a lesion, skin scrapings, pus, pseudomembrane, sputum or exudate: Place the material in a drop of 20 per cent sodium or potassium hydroxide on a slide and cover with a cover-glass. The hydroxide dissolves the tissue cells or renders them transparent in fifteen to thirty minutes, but does not, as a rule, dissolve the fungus. Mycelia, spores, clubs and other structures are thus rendered plainly visible.

Cultivation.—Most of the pathogenic fungi grow on media containing peptone, glucose, agar or broth, with an acid reaction, pH 5.5 to 6.5. For many varieties room temperature (20° to 25° C.) is most favorable for growth. Some varieties, especially those associated with generalized infection, grow best at 37° C. when first isolated. The most commonly employed medium is Sabouraud's agar, one form of which is described in the section on Technic. Enrichment of the medium with serum and a reaction of pH 7 to 7.4 are required for the cultivation of some of the actinomycetes,

Most of these fungi are aerobic. Some of the pathogenic actinomycetes are anaerobic, or, at least, micro-aerophilic.

As these organisms grow slowly, the media should be protected against drying during incubation of the cultures. The tubes or plates may be closed with rubber caps or placed in a moist chamber.

For numerous technical details of cultivation, the preparation of media, microculture chambers, staining, and methods for demonstrating fungi in tissue sections, reference may be made to the useful chapter on these subjects in Henrici's book. Tests of pathogenicity and serological reactions will be considered later.

THE MOLDS

In this place we shall describe briefly typical members of the groups of *Phycomycetes* and *Ascomycetes,* mentioning their medical significance and omitting discussion of their much greater importance in agriculture, industry—and in the loss of food products and manufactured articles which they cause by their growth.

Phycomycetes.—Members of the genus *Mucor* belonging to this order frequently appear in agar plates which have been opened. They develop as a mesh of delicate consists in the fusion of the tips or lateral processes of two neighboring hyphae, which form a large spore covered with a warty membrane, known as a *zygospore*. No exospores are formed by the mucors but chlamydospores are numerous.

The common laboratory contaminants are *Mucor mucedo*, a constant inhabitant of horse dung, and *Rhizopus nigricans*, which can usually be obtained by allowing a piece of moistened bread to stand in a covered Petri dish.

Mucor corymbifer (*Lichtheimia corymbifera*) differs from the preceding species in having pear-shaped instead of spherical sporangia borne in loose clusters on hyphae which are not raised above the surface of the medium. This species is pathogenic for rabbits, and has been reported as the cause of inflammations of the auditory canal and of other infections in man (Whalen).

There are numerous genera and species of the *Mucoracae*. Among these, the most common of all the molds belonging to this group is *Rhizopus nigricans*. This black-

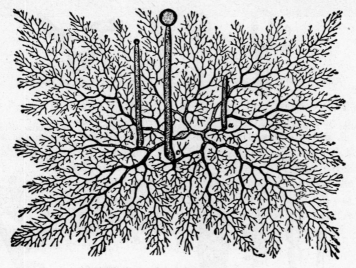

FIG. 78.—MUCOR MUCEDO.

Single-celled mycelium with three hyphae and one developed sporangium. (After Kny, from Tavel.)

spored mold is a frequent air contaminant of bacteriological plates and is often found on moldy bread. *Rhizopus* produces *stolons*, or runners, which are branches of the mycelium which extend outward from the growing mold and give rise to a new complete fungus where their tips come in contact with the medium. By means of these runners, or stolons, the mold rapidly covers the surface of a Petri dish.

Ascomycetes.—In this group are included all fungi which form ascospores. The majority have a mycelium made up of septate filaments and reproduce by means of conidia which are frequently borne on characteristic structures. In the lower types met with as laboratory contaminants ascospore formation is rarely observed.

The Yeasts.—The simplest forms of ascomycetes are the exo-asci of which the yeasts or saccharomycetes are familiar examples. These develop on laboratory media as moist masses of separate round or oval cells usually from 10 to 20 μ in diameter. These send out buds (blastospores) which gradually assume the size of the parent

antineuritic vitamin B and of ergosterol, from which the antirachitic vitamin D is obtained by radiation with ultraviolet light.

Many observers include in the yeast family certain pathogenic fungi causing thrush and blastomycosis. These will be described in the section on the hyphomycetes.

The powdery molds which so frequently appear in Petri dish cultures and which even grow through cotton plugs and invade tube cultures also belong to the ascomycetes. The two commonest genera, *Penicillium* and *Aspergillus*, have characteristic conidiophores which make their identification easy.

In *Penicillium glaucum* and other species of this mold, the fertile hyphae branch toward their upper extremities and terminate in a radiating group of flask-shaped cells (phialides) from the tips of which the conidia or spores develop. The spores are formed consecutively by division of this terminal cell and are pushed outward in chains, the oldest spore being at the outward end of the chain, the youngest next cells from which they quickly separate. When grown on a dry surface some of the cells divide into ascospores which remain for a while inclosed in the membrane of the parent cell or ascus. Typical yeasts are unicellular but in some species the cells successively produced by budding adhere to the parent cells and form mycelial fila-

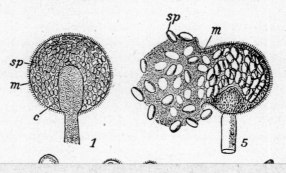

to the spore-producing cell. These spores in chains give the head of the mold the appearance of a tassel or brush, from which the name *Penicillium* is derived. This mode of spore formation is an important differential character, distinguishing *Penicillium* from *Monilia* (in which spores are formed by a budding process in a manner which places the youngest spore at the outer end of the chain). Cultures of *Penicillium* have various colors, due to pigment in the spores. Thom has recognized 600 species of this mold.

The *Aspergilli* (Thom and Church) are equally common and troublesome contaminants. They appear on culture media as a white feltwork often thickly dotted with black points becoming in older cultures diffusely black or yellow or green. The conidia are borne on hyphae which terminate in a large rounded head from which phialides project in all directions. From the tips of these extend chains of conidia, often so densely packed together that the supporting structure is hidden and the whole appears as a spherical mass of pigmented spores. These molds are active producers of oxalic and other organic acids. The *sterigmocystis* differs from the aspergillus in that secondary phialides each bearing a chain of spores project from each primary phialide.

The commonest species is *Aspergillus niger*, the spores of which contain a black pigment. In an optical cross-section of the rough head of this mold the appearance is that of a minute sunflower with a pale center and black tipped petals.

Pathogenicity of Aspergilli.—Many species of these molds are pathogenic for laboratory animals if the spores are injected intravenously. A number of human infections have also been ascribed to them. So-called pulmonary aspergillosis is a condition clinically resembling tuberculosis, in which an aspergillus, usually the species *fumigatus*, is found abundantly in the sputum. In most cases the fungus merely invades tissue previously infected with tuberculosis, in other cases (notably in the infection which has been described in the pigeon feeders of Paris by Dieulafoy and by Chantemesse and Widal) the disease is apparently primary and spontaneous cure may result. Madura foot, a disease which will be referred to in discussing the actinomyces group, has been in certain cases attributed to infection with these molds.

FIG. 82.—PENICILLIUM GLAUCUM.

B, end of a hypha—branching into two conidiophores from which are given off the sterigmata. From the ends of these are developed the round conidia (*c*). (After Zopf.)

Pinta or Craaté, a disease of tropical America characterized by superficial colored patches on the skin, is thought to be caused in some cases by aspergilli, in others by a species of trichophyton. Aspergilli have also been reported as infecting the eye, nosé, auditory canal and wounds in various regions.

Aspergilli have been found to be associated with and probably the cause of miliary lung disease (Sayers and Meriwether), infections of the nails of the toes and fingers (Rockwood), and a definite type of mycosis of the spleen (Jaffé and Hill).

Various fungi, without infecting the tissues, may cause disease in man. Disorders of this nature may be due either to the consumption of the toxic products of the fungi or to hypersensitivity to the spores or mycelium.

Ergotism.—Ergot is composed of several alkaloidal poisons produced by the ascomycete, *Claviceps purpurea,* growing in the grain bearing heads of barley, rye and wheat. When bread made from infected grain is eaten, the poisons are absorbed from the gastro-intestinal tract and produce contraction of smooth muscles of the blood vessels and viscera. The results are the familiar effects of ergot poisoning, gangrene, chiefly of the extremities, and abortion due to the ability of ergot to cause

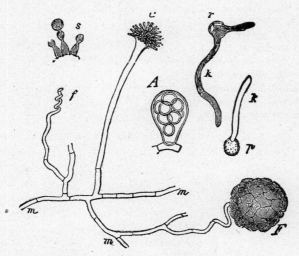

Fig. 83.—Aspergillus Glaucus.

A, ascus. C, sterigmata on conidiophore. F, perithecium. k, mycelial filament. m, septate mycelium. p, germinating conidium. r, ascospore. s, sterigmata. (After De Bauj.)

contraction of the uterus. In the middle ages, ergotism was a pandemic scourge and was one of the forms of "Saint Anthony's fire."

The fungus grows in the grains, which enlarge, and become replaced by the mycelium. Finally a large black, hard, horn-like mass known as the *sclerotium* is formed. This is known as the "ergot grain" and contains the poison.

Asthma.—Human beings can become hypersensitive to mold spores and probably parts of the mycelium inhaled with the dust of the atmosphere. Van Leeuwen and his associates have presented convincing evidence that asthma, urticaria and eczema of millers may be due to inhalation of the spores of molds in flour. Hopkins, Benham and Kesten described a case of asthma and eczema due to the inhalation of and contact with the spores of a species of *Alternaria* and Bernton reported a case of asthma due to *Aspergillus fumigatus.*

REFERENCES

BERNTON, H. S. J. Am. M. Ass., 1930, 95:189.

CALANDRUCCIO, S. Agostino Bassi, di Lodi, Il Fondatore della Teoria Parisitica, Catania, 1892.

COCA, A. F., WALZER, M., and THOMMEN, A. A. Asthma and Hay Fever, Springfield, 1931.

DOBELL, C. Antony van Leeuwenhoek and His "Little Animals," New York, 1932, p. 112 et seq.

HENRICI, A. T. Molds, Yeasts and Actinomycetes, New York, 1930.

HOPKINS, J. G., BENHAM, R. W., and KESTEN, B. M. J. Am. M. Ass., 1930, 94:6.

———— Proc. Soc. Exper. Biol. & Med., 1930, 27:342.

JACOBSON, H. P. Fungus Diseases, Springfield, Ill., 1932.

JAFFÉ, R. H., and HILL, L. R. Arch. Path., 1928, 6:196.

RAISTRICK, H., et al. Phil. Trans. Royal Soc. of London, 1931, Ser. B., 220, 1.

———— Enzymforschung, 1932, 1:345.

ROCKWOOD, E. M. Arch. Dermat. & Syph., 1930, 22:395.

SAYERS, R. R., and MERIWETHER, F. V. U. S. Pub. Health Rep., 1930, 45:2994.

SCHOENLEIN. Arch. f. Anat., Physiol., u. Wissenschflt. Med., 1839, p. 82.

THOM, C. The Penicillia, Baltimore, 1930.

THOM, C., and CHURCH, M. The Aspergilli, Baltimore, 1926.

VAN LEEUWEN, S. Allergic Diseases, Philadelphia, 1925.

WHALEN, E. J. Arch. Otolaryngol., 1936, 24:436.

CHAPTER LVII

THE DERMATOMYCOSES AND FUNGI OF THE RINGWORM GROUP

Infections of the skin and its appendages with fungi are very common. The diseases thus produced may be trivial or may have serious consequences on account of their distressing chronicity, the occasional production of destructive lesions of the skin and general systemic and allergic effects. Under the title of *dermatomycoses*, are included a number of clinically distinct diseases, all of which, however, are related by the fact that the invasion of the fungi rarely penetrates deeper than the epidermis and its appendages—the hair and nails. The common name for these maladies is "ringworm," although many of them are not characterized by the typical rings due to the spreading of the infection at the peripheries of areas on the skin. These infections are contagious and are communicable by means of contaminated clothing and structures such as floors of rooms.

The fungi producing these diseases are numerous, variable, and difficult to classify. In general they are placed in the order of *Hyphomycetes*, or *fungi imperfecti*, because the perfect sexual stages do not exist or have not been demonstrated. The various fungi show little resemblance to each other and the so-called "dermatophytes" as a group are defined not by any common botanical characteristics but by the type of lesions they produce.

Our knowledge of the dermatophytes dates from Schoenlein's discovery of the favus fungus in 1839. Two years later Gruby discovered the fungus of ringworm and distinguished between the large and small spored types. Since then many workers have contributed to our knowledge of these parasites. For general considerations of the subject, the reader is referred to the monographs of Sabouraud, Castellani, Jacobson and Henrici.

Methods of Study and Diagnosis.—The lesions of the dermatomycoses may be scaly, crusted (scutula), vesicular, papular or ulcerated. The experienced clinician is able to recognize the types of the diseases in many cases from the color, shape, characteristics and distribution of the lesions, and can form an estimate of the probable nature of the infecting fungus from observations of the lesions and their location on the smooth, glabrous skin, in the axillae and pubic regions or in the scalp.

The *mycological diagnosis* is to be made from: (1) demonstration of the forms of the fungus in skin scrapings, fluid from vesicles or the coverings of vesicles or in the crusted scutula, and (2) cultivation and study of the fungus on artificial media.

The preparations for *demonstration of the fungus in material from lesions* are made by placing the skin scrapings or other material in a drop of 20 per cent sodium or potassium hydroxide on a slide, covering this with a cover glass, and examining the *unstained* specimen microscopically after the tissue cells have been

731

attached by a pointed tip (*Botrytis* type). Often they are scattered irregularly along the hyphae, but occasionally show a characteristic arrangement. Groups of conidia formed along the sides of an unbranched terminal hypha Sabouraud calls *thyrses*, larger groups borne on branched conidiophore clusters (*grappes*).

dissolved or cleared, which usually takes twenty to thirty minutes after the application of the alkali (Moore).

The forms of the dermatophytes occurring in the lesions, skin scrapings, hairs, etc., are branched segmented mycelial filaments, or spores (fragmented mycelium).

Pectinate bodies are swollen and usually curved ends of hyphae which give off a row of abortive branches from one side—the structure vaguely resembling a comb.

Spirals.—These are simply convoluted hyphae which may take all the forms of a tendril from a spirillum-like form to a close-set coil.

Nodular Organs.—These are chains of large rounded cells knotted together into small dense masses suggesting the sclerotia of higher fungi.

Cultural Characteristics.—The more important varieties of dermatophytes have been cultivated and show certain common characteristics. All of them grow as leathery masses of closely interwoven hyphae. From a point of inoculation on solid media they spread out symmetrically over the surface at the same time sending down numerous short branches which penetrate the substrate and bind the growth firmly to it. As the membranous disk extends peripherally the central mycelium continues to grow, increasing in thickness and forcing the less adherent portions upward. This produces on the surface a series of humps and ridges, with corresponding hollows and grooves on the under side, which often form striking geometrical patterns. The surface may be smooth and hard but most species sooner or later develop a *duvet*— a covering of aerial hyphae which according to their length give the surface a powdery or velvety or hairy appearance. The majority develop a yellow or brown pigment and some are characterized by brilliant red and violet colors which appear late and are most marked in those portions of the membrane which are raised above the surface of the medium.

The rapidity of growth varies greatly in the different species but their evolution is always a matter of weeks. Some varieties such as the microspora attain a diameter of 10 centimeters or more. Others do not extend beyond 1 or 2 centimeters from the center, but may pile up a mass a centimeter in thickness.

On broth they usually form a thick membrane which spreads over the surface, but if the fragment planted sinks, it develops a thick mesh of filaments in the bottom of the tube. On potato growth is less vigorous, frequently forming a moist streak on the center of the medium, the appearance of which is of aid in identification of some species.

Gelatin is liquefied by most strains. Glucose and mannite are fermented with the production of acid but no gas. Media containing peptone as well as fermentable sugar are usually not acidified, but it can be shown that the sugar is destroyed by the growth of the fungus. On synthetic media containing one of the fermentable sugars distinct but transient acidification occurs. Fungi of the ringworm group can be distinguished from fungi of similar morphology by the fact that they do not ferment lactose or saccharose. The rapidity with which they ferment glucose and mannite may be used as an aid in differentiation (Hopkins and Iwamoto).

The optimum reaction is somewhat more acid than that for bacteria, about pH 7.0; but they develop readily throughout a range of reaction from pH 4.0 to 8 and above. Although obligate aerobes, they will grow feebly with scanty oxygen supply as in the depth of a broth culture. They develop well at room temperature and most species also in the incubator.

Pathogenicity.—The ringworm fungi are found with such regularity and in such profusion in many of the human lesions as to leave little doubt as to their causative relationship to the disease. Many of the same species are found, too, in similar lesions of domestic animals. These latter will also induce lesions in guinea-pigs with more or less regularity if culture fragments are inserted in the skin. Such experimental lesions are often transitory but resemble somewhat the spontaneous disease. Other species such as the *Microsporon audouini* and *Epidermophyton inguinale,* mentioned below, although found abundantly in characteristic human lesions, have not been found in animals and are innocuous when experimentally injected.

Concerning the power of the dermatophytes to produce systemic disease we have little information. Their entire lack of invasive power in the spontaneous infections is quite striking. The production of tuberculoid lesions produced by intravenous injections of cultures of these fungi have little significance in view of the fact that many types of foreign bodies produce similar results.

Immunity and Hypersensitivity.—Patients who have recovered from deep ringworm infections are relatively immune from subsequent attacks. A number of experimental observations, especially those of Bloch and Massini and of Kusunoki bear out this clinical observation. It appears that animals which have been infected with the more virulent types of dermatophytes, causing suppurative lesions, resist reinoculation and that the protection is valid against other species than those first injected. On the other hand, both clinical and experimental observations show that infections with less virulent species induce no immunity.

Active immunization by injections of killed spores and mycelium has not been successful. There is no effective vaccine available for prophylactic immunization. The whole cells of these fungi are apparently only feebly antigenic. Antibodies occur. ring in the blood serum of animals treated by injections of these fungi are low in potency and have little specificity. Kesten, Cook, Mott and Jobling were unable to induce the formation of precipitins for saline extracts of *Trichophyton gypseum* by injecting rabbits with the whole organism.

On the other hand, there is definite evidence that the tissues of man resist the spread of dermatophytes and become hypersensitive to the substance of these fungi. The condition, an example of nonspecific tissue resistance, is illustrated by the generalization of a dermatomycosis which may occur in a weakened anergic subject. An illustration of this is the case of almost universal dermatomycosis due to *Trichophyton gypseum* described by Bloch in a man fifty years old who had several other diseases and lacked an allergic reaction to products of the fungus.

Hypersensitivity of patients with ringworm can be demonstrated by intracutaneous injections of extracts of trichophytons and filtrates of broth cultures. Products of this nature are called in general *trichophytin* (Sulzberger and Lewis). The reactions elicited by injection of trichophytin into the skin are group-specific, but not species-specific. They are useful as aids in the diagnosis of obscure skin lesions, and as an indication of the reactivity of the patient. Trichophytin has been used with encouraging results for the treatment of chronic dermatomycosis.

The vesicular and squamous changes on the hands which accompany so many cases of epidermophytosis of the feet are apparently manifestations of allergy. They occur in persons hypersensitive to trichophytin. The fungi are not found in these lesions and the lesions on the hands disappear only after the focus of infection in the feet is cured. These secondary lesions called *epidermophytids,* according to the investigations of Peck, Highman and others, are elicited by the hematogenous transport of living fungi from the primary lesion. It is conceivable that the products of the fungi may produce the same conditions. Sulzberger and Wise have attempted to desensitize patients by injections of trichophytin. Desensitization was produced but the condition was not always improved. Epidermophytids appeared occasionally after the injection of trichophytin.

FAVUS

Favus is a disease usually limited to the scalp but which occasionally attacks the glabrous skin and the nails. It is characterized by the formation at the mouths

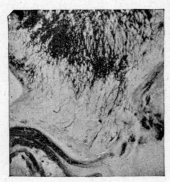

of the hair follicles of small yellow cup-shaped crusts known as *scutula*. It is found in adults as well as in children and in this country occurs chiefly among immigrants from eastern and southern Europe where it is endemic.

Achorion Schoenleinii.—Favus of the scalp is caused by one species of fungus the *Achorion schoenleinii*. A scutulum when crushed in alkali is found to be composed almost entirely of the fungus. The central portion is made up of rounded spore-like bodies of varying size without definite arrangement. Toward the periphery similar elements are seen strung out in filaments, and mixed with them hyphae of thicker elongated elements with irregular contours. Within the diseased hairs are filaments, sometimes of cubical, sometimes of elongated elements. They differ from those found in the hairs of ringworm, chiefly in that cells of different sizes and forms are found in the same case.

FIG. 85.—ACHORION SCHOENLEINII.

Section of favus crust. Stained by Gram. (After Fränkel and Pfeiffer.)

The isolation of the achorion is rendered difficult by its frequent association in lesions with pyogenic cocci and molds. It develops slowly on agar and the growth attains a maximum diameter of 2 to 3 centimeters in three to four weeks. It forms a remarkably tough brownish membrane with deep irregular folds the general outline being rounded upward toward the center. The surface is waxy at first and later shows a whitish powdery duvet. In most strains, however, after long cultivation on artificial media subcultures grow more rapidly, attain a larger size and become covered with a white velvety layer of aerial hyphae (pleomorphism). On gelatin a small surface growth quickly liquefies the medium. The *Achorion* utilizes sugars slightly if at all.

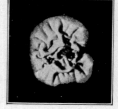

FIG. 86.—ACHORION SCHOENLEINII.

Eight weeks culture on Sabouraud's test medium, one-half natural size. (Hopkins.)

Microscopically the growth is made up of crooked hyphae of irregular contour often composed of chains of oval cells. Pear-shaped conidia may be found scattered on the sides of the more delicate filaments but never in clusters. Chlamydospores are always numerous, sometimes attached singly to the clubbed tips of hyphae but more often occurring in chains in their course. These chains may be knotted into a small nodular mass.

About the periphery of a culture are numerous clubs either pear-shaped or notched at the tip. These may occur singly (*têtes de clous*) or in clusters (*chandeliers faviques*).

Inoculation of fragments of scutula into the skin of guinea-pigs produces transitory ringworm-like lesions. With some culture strains similar results have been obtained, with others inoculation has been unsuccessful.

Other species of Achoria.—Fungi have also been cultivated from favus-like lesions in animals. The *Achorion quinckeanum* which frequently infects house mice has occasionally been found in human cases of favus of the body. In culture these so-called achoria show little in common with Schoenlein's parasite but resemble somewhat trichophyta of the gypseum group (*vide infra*). Plaut concludes that there is no reason for placing them in this genus except that they form scutula in lesions.

RINGWORM OR TINEA

The common form of this disease is tinea of the scalp which affects only children. It is highly contagious and in children's schools and institutions may assume epidemic proportions. The infection begins in the epidermis where it is often transitory but the parasite soon invades the hairs and there remains.

There is usually slight evidence of inflammation but some species of the ringworm fungi cause suppuration in and about the hair follicle. This may result in the formation of large indolent subcutaneous abscesses known as *kerions*.

Tinea of the body may occur secondarily to scalp lesions in children or as a primary infection at any period of life. The lesions often assume a circular form—the disease progressing at the periphery and clearing at the center. There may be only slight thickening and desquamation of the epidermis but usually there are superficial vesicles which quickly dry into crusts, and occasionally follicular pustules and kerions. Some species invade the nails.

Ringworm is also a common disease in domestic animals and human cases can often be traced to infection from these sources. The fungi of animal origin when they infect man either directly from a diseased animal or indirectly from another human case, usually produce more inflammatory lesions than do those species which affect man only.

MICROSPORON

The small-spored ringworm fungi are in this locality the commonest cause of ringworm of the scalp. The species of animal origin also attack the glabrous skin especially in children. In the epidermis of the diseased scalp they appear as curved branching hyphae made up of elongated elements. The stumps of the diseased hairs are covered with a mosaic of small round spores of uniform diameter (about 2 μ) which completely envelops the hair. If the hair is crushed, mycelial threads are also seen which grow along the medulla. From these central filaments branches project out through the cortex and give rise to the sheath of spores. The spores give the infected hairs a frosted appearance.

Cultures.—These parasites are easily cultivated. They grow rapidly on Sabouraud's agar producing large flat colonies which from the first are covered with a duvet of aerial hyphae. At the center is a raised papilla and from this folds in the membrane radiate out. The color of the duvet varies from snow white to deep buff and of the membrane from buff to brilliant orange or a russet brown. The pigment, which is well developed only on glucose-containing media, is diffusible. Gelatin is very slowly liquefied.

Morphology.—In young cultures, long straight coarse trunks radiate out from the center giving off frequent branches which later form an inextricable tangle of threads running in all directions. Some terminal branches bear conidia attached to their sides by a flattened facet (*Acladium* type). They also form chlamydospores and fuseaux.

Sabouraud describes eleven species of microspora which he divides into two groups: one affecting man only and one affecting both animals and man.

Microsporon Audouini.—This is the type species of the group affecting man only. In gross appearance the cultures are distinguished by their slower growth, their velvety white or faintly buff duvet and less active pigment production. *Microsporon audouini* produces only occasional and atypical fuseaux but numerous chlamydospores which are frequently subterminal, the hypha projecting beyond them like a spine. It also produces typical pectinate bodies. Animal inoculation has been unsuccessful. Closely allied to this species are: *Microsporon umbonatum*, *M. tardum* and *M. velveticum*.

Microsporon lanosum (*M. audouini, var. canis*).—This is the type species of the microspora of animal origin. It produces ringworm in the dog. The cultures grow very rapidly and on glucose are deeply pigmented. The duvet is long, shaggy, and in older growths assumes a dark tan color. The upper surface is covered with a thick crop of typical lenticular fuseaux which alone serve to identify cultures as belonging to this group. Experimental lesions in the guinea-pig can be produced by the inoculation of cultures. Other members of this group are: *Microsporon felineum*, *M. equinum*, *M. fulvum*, *M. villosum*, *M. pubescens* and *M. tomentosum*.

FIG. 87.—MICROSPORON LANOSUM.

Six weeks culture on Sabouraud's test medium, one-half natural size. (Hopkins.)

FIG. 88.—FUSEAUX OF MICROSPORON LANOSUM. × 200.

TRICHOPHYTON

The trichophyta, like the microspora, may produce ringworm of the scalp but they also produce lesions on the glabrous skin and nails. The genus is defined chiefly by the fact that its members produce lesions without scutula and appear in infected hairs as chains of spore-like elements. This alignment of the so-called spores (which are in reality short mycelial elements) distinguishes them from those of the preceding genus. In most trichophyta, too, the spores are large but in a few days they are of about the same size as those of the microspora (3 μ). In culture most species produce conidia attached to the hyphae by pointed tips and frequently arranged in clusters. A few species (*T. violaceum*) which bear no conidia are, however, included in the genus. On artificial media the growths are much buckled and raised as compared to the flat cultures of the microspora. The cultures, however, vary so greatly among themselves in appearance that no description can be given which would apply to the genus as a whole.

Classification.—Sabouraud lists thirty species. His classification is based primarily on the appearance of the parasite in the infected hairs. Such a scheme has the disadvantage that it groups together forms which have diverse cultural characteristics and separates others which culturally are similar. He divides them first into three divisions:

I. The *Trichophyton endothrix* in which the fungus is found only within the medulla of the hair
II. The *Trichophyton neo-endothrix* in which some infected hairs show also a few filaments on their surface
III. The *Trichophyton ectothrix* in which besides invading the substance of the hair the fungus proliferates actively on its surface

Of this third division there are two groups:

A. The microid ectothrices, of which the spore-like elements about the infected hairs are from 3 to 4 μ in diameter. They are again divided into two sub-groups, differing culturally: (*a*) the gypseum group and (*b*) the niveum group.
B. The megalospora, of which the rounded elements are from 6 to 8 μ in diameter. These Sabouraud again divides into: (*a*) a group forming downy cultures, and (*b*) a group in which the cultures are faviform.

The typical members of the endothrix group (*T. crateriforme* and *T. acuminatum*) form small raised colonies less than 4 centimeters in diameter. They are white or slightly yellowish and are covered from the first with a short powdery or velvety duvet but show little tendency to pleomorphic change. They produce numerous conidia in thyrses or small clusters but show no other characteristic structures. Sabouraud describes many variants of these species which differ in the contour of their colonies or in pigment production.

Trichophyton violaceum, which is also an endothrix is a very different organism. It develops slowly, forming small wrinkled colonies with a hard glistening surface, which slowly develop a black-violet color. The mycelium is made up of short crooked elements and no conidia are formed. It is found with relative frequency in tinea of the scalp, body and nails. A variant (*T. glabrum*) differs only in the absence of pigment.

Trichophyton cerebriforme, the type of the neo-endothrix group, resembles in culture the *T. crateriforme*.

The gypseum group (*T. asteroides, radiolatum*, etc.) grow more vigorously, forming large colonies up to 10 centimeters in diameter. The surface is powdery or plaster-like, but the parasites soon become pleomorphic and produce a long velvety duvet. They produce conidia in large clusters, rudimentary fuseaux and numerous spirals. The lesions are inflammatory, with folliculitis and kerion formation. They cause ringworm in horses.

The niveum group resembles the pleomorphic forms of the gypseum group. They form conidia only.

Trichophyton rosaceum (the type of the downy megalospora) forms a colony of medium size resembling a folded disk of white velvet. The deep portion develops a crimson or violet pigment with gives a rose tint as seen through the white duvet. It forms long thyrses and rudimentary fuseaux.

The faviform strains (*T. ochraceum, T. album,* etc.) resemble culturally the *Achorion schoenleinii.* They are grouped with the trichophyta chiefly because they form no scutula in lesions.

ECZEMA MARGINATUM AND POMPHOLYX

Eczema marginatum or ringworm of the groin is a common dermatosis. In the lesions Castellani and Sabouraud found a fungus to which the latter gave the name *Epidermophyton inguinale.* More recently Ormsby and Mitchell and others in this country have found the same fungus in eczematous lesions of the hands and feet and also in the vesicular eruptions in these regions formerly called pompholyx. Sabouraud has also found various species of trichophyta in palmar eczemas.

Epidermophyton Inguinale
(*Trichophyton cruris*)

In the epidermis the parasite is seen as long interlacing filaments made up of oblong or oval cells with double contours. It develops slowly in culture as a greenish

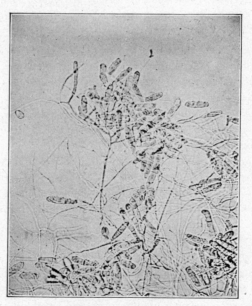

Fig. 89.—Fuseaux of Epidermophyton Inguinale. × 200.

buff colony with folds radiating from a central or slightly eccentric peak, attaining a diameter of perhaps 2 centimeters in a month. The surface at first is dry and powdery, but on sugar media it quickly becomes pleomorphic, developing a thick white duvet. Related varieties are also found which form large crateriform colonies.

The cultures form no conidia but are readily identified by the innumerable blunt fuseaux which are borne on aerial hyphae. These are often in clusters which has been compared to a hand of bananas. Older cultures show also many intercalary chlamydospores. The fuseaux are not found in cultures which have become downy.

TINEA VERSICOLOR

(Pityriasis versicolor, Chromophytosis)

Tinea versicolor appears as large fawn-colored patches on the covered parts of the body. These show slight superficial scaling but no evidence of inflammation. The causative fungus is found abundantly in the horny epidermis where it seems to grow as a saprophyte.

Microsporon furfur (Malassezia furfur).—This fungus bears little resemblance to the microspora which cause ringworm. It appears as septate filaments of very irregular contour 3 to 4 μ wide. They are usually unbranched but interlace, forming a meshwork in which are found masses of spore-like bodies. In 1937 Moore succeeded in cultivating the organisms. He reproduced the disease by inoculating the skin of human volunteers with pure cultures.

ERYTHRASMA

Erythrasma is a superficial infection of the epidermis which produces round scaling patches usually located in the axillae or groins. There is no evidence of inflammatory reaction except a hyperemia which gives the lesions a characteristic red color. A parasite is found in the epidermis which appears as minute twisted threads which are easily broken up into elements about the size of bacilli. Cultures have been described by Michele and by Ducrey and Reale but according to others the organism cannot be cultivated. It has been given various names: *Microsporon minutissimum, Sporothrix minutissimum*, and *Nocardia minutissimum*.

INTERDIGITAL RINGWORM

Ringworm disease, or dermatomycosis, of the hands and feet is a widely distributed and old type of skin infection. In the past it has occurred sporadically among people, and fairly commonly on the hands of those whose business is the washing of dishes. In more recent times, the increased common use of gymnasiums, locker-rooms, swimming pools, and bath-rooms by groups of persons has been accompanied by a greater and at times almost epidemic prevalence of fungous infections of the skin between the fingers and toes. The prevalence is said to be as great as 80 per cent in some communities (Sharp and Taylor, Gilman). The association of the disease with various sports has been the source of its common name, "athlete's foot."

The lesions are often vesicular, erosive, exfoliative and exudative. They are at times incapacitating, and always uncomfortable on account of itching and painful cracks in the skin. Allergic lesions occur frequently.

Various fungi have been isolated from the lesions of interdigital ringworm. Trichophytons of various sorts have been obtained, the most common, according to Peck, being several types of the Kaufmann-Wolf *Epidermophyton*. Hopkins and Benham isolated several varieties of *Monilia* from lesions of *erosio interdigitalis* and paronchyia.

It is difficult to *control* the spread of this type of infection. General hygiene of the foot and sanitation of floors have not aided greatly in reduction of the incidence. Medical inspection of the feet and hands of persons using gymnasiums, locker-rooms, etc., exclusion of the infected from the group of noninfected, treatment of the lesions with the usual fungicides, notably the sodium thiosulphate preparation of Gould, and routine foot baths in solutions of hypochlorides or sodium thiosulphate are relatively effective control measures.

REFERENCES

BLOCH, B. Arch. f. Dermat. u. Syph., 1932, 165:149.

BLOCH and MASSINI. Ztschr. f. Hyg. u. Infectionskrankh., 1909, 73:68.

CASTELLANI, A. Fungi and Fungous Diseases, Am. M. Ass., Chicago, 1927–28.

EMMONS, C. W. Arch. Dermat. & Syph., 1932, 25:987.

GILMAN, R. L. J. Am. M. Ass., 1933, 100:715.

GOULD, W. L. J. Am. M. Ass., 1931, 96:1300.

HENRICI, A. T. Molds, Yeasts and Actinomycetes, New York, 1930.

HIGHMAN, W. J. J. Am. M. Ass., 1930, 95:1158.

HOPKINS, J. G., and BENHAM, R. W. N. York State J. M., 1929, 29:793.

HOPKINS and IWAMOTO. Arch. Dermat. & Syph., 1923, 8:619, 838.

JACOBSON, H. P. Fungous Diseases, Springfield, Ill., 1932.

KESTEN, H., COOK, D., MOTT, E., and JOBLING, J. J. Exper. M., 1930, 52:813.

KUSUNOKI. Arch. f. Dermat. u. Syph., 1912, 114:1.

MACCARTHY. Ann. de dermat. et syph., 1925, 6:19.

MOORE, M. Mycopathologica, 1938, 1, 53.

———— Arch. Dermatol. & Syph., 1936, 34, 880.

ORMSBY and MITCHELL. J. Am. M. Ass., 1916, 67:711.

PECK, S. M. Arch. Dermat. & Syph., 1930, 22:40.

SABOURAUD, R. Les Teignes, Paris, 1910.

———— Ann. de dermat. et syph., 1928, 9:656, 669, 769.

SHARP, W. B., and TAYLOR, E. K. J. Prevent. Med., 1928, 2:485.

SULZBERGER, M. B., and LEWIS, Y. M. Arch. Dermat. & Syph., 1930, 22:410.

SULZBERGER, M. B., and WISE, F. J. Am. M. Ass., 1932:99, 1759.

WEIDMAN, F. D., and McMILLAN, T. M. Arch. Dermat. & Syph., 1921, 4:451.

WEIDMAN, F. D., and SPRING, D. Arch. f. Dermat. u. Syph., 1928, 18:829.

CHAPTER LVIII

MYCOSES OF SKIN, MUCOUS MEMBRANES AND INTERNAL ORGANS

Moniliasis, Torula Infection, Blastomycosis, Coccidioidal Granuloma and Sporotrichosis

The fungi which cause the diseases to be considered in this chapter have little in common except that they represent orders of the *Hyphomycetes* or *fungi imperfecti* and that they usually cause primary lesions in the skin and mucous membranes and often produce secondary lesions in the internal organs and bones. The lesions are often ulcerative and granulomatous, resembling slightly in gross appearance and in finer structure the lesions of tuberculosis and syphilis. In fact, it is usually necessary to consider the differential diagnosis between some of these diseases and syphilis and tuberculosis in cases in which it is difficult to demonstrate fungi in the lesions. The grouping of the fungi to be discussed in this chapter is entirely one of convenience and has no botanical sanction.

MONILIASIS

Monilia is still an ill-defined genus of the hyphomycetes and the species are not clearly known. Systematic investigations are in progress, notably by Martin and by Wickerham and Rettger.

The organisms are yeast-like fungi which reproduce (1) by budding in the form of yeast, (2) by the production of a segmented branched mycelium under certain conditions, parts of the mycelium being capable of independent growth, and (3) by the formation of spores or conidia. The spores are produced by successive budding of specialized cells arising at mycelial nodes or at the ends of filaments. The youngest spore occurs at the outer end of a group or chain of spores. Chlamydospores also are produced within resting cells.

In growth on media, *Monilia* in surface colonies resembles the homogeneous culture masses of yeast, but is tougher. Budding forms occur chiefly in the surface growth. When oxygen is reduced, as in a stab culture in agar, or beneath the surface of colonies on solid medium, the mycelium is developed and penetrates the medium in delicate processes. Extracts of carrots are among the materials which may be added to a liquid medium to induce the production of abundant mycelium by *Monilia.*

In the lesions, the yeast forms are common, but mycelial filaments also are formed.

Numerous species of *Monilia* have been recognized by Castellani on the basis of cultural and biochemical reactions, especially the fermentation of carbohydrates. Unfortunately, as Jacobson has noted, these fermentation reactions are inconstant and vary with the pleomorphism or physiological alterations of the fungi of this

743

group. Some of the distinctions made by these methods are artificial and do not indicate natural species.

Serological reactions are useful to a certain extent in differentiating species of *Monilia*. In 1929 Hopkins and Benham found it possible to differentiate species of *Monilia* by agglutination and absorption of agglutinin. Kesten, Cook, Mott and Jobling, however, noted that the polysaccharides isolated from *Moniliae* exhibited only partial specificity, giving frequent cross-precipitin reactions. Benham, continuing immunological studies in connection with a general investigation of moniliae parasitic on man, concluded that agglutination reactions, when used in conjunction with other

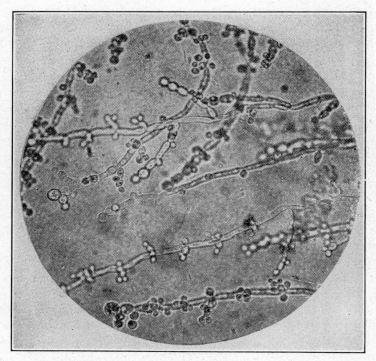

Fig. 90.—Monilia Albicans, Unstained, Showing Mycelium Spores and Yeast-like Cells. (From Benham.)

methods, were fairly satisfactory for the identification of the organisms. Benham found that *Monilia albicans* was a very inclusive species, containing the organisms of thrush (*Monilia* or *Oidium albicans*), the organism of sprue (*Monilia psilosis*), and several moniliae isolated from interdigital erosion. The other species of pathogenic *Monilia* which appeared to be distinct were *Monilia candida, Monilia parapsilosis* and *Monilia krusei.*

Pathogenicity for Man.—The *Moniliases* are a large group of diseases in which the lesions are usually limited to the skin and mucous membranes, but in which also granulomatous, or suppurative, lesions may be produced in the lungs, kidneys and other organs. Space does not permit a detailed discussion of these conditions here. Allergic eruptions are associated with the infections (Owen, Anderson and Henrici). A list of the diseases are as follows:

1. *Cutaneous Moniliasis.*—Interdigital erosions, exfoliative dermatitis, parony-chia, and skin eruptions in nursing infants and patients kept in continuous water baths are usually due to *Monilia albicans*. In this connection, allergic lesions called *moniliids* were found by Hopkins to be important accompaniments of interdigital and gastro-intestinal moniliasis. His investigations indicate that a patient may become hypersensitive to moniliae through the gastro-intestinal tract as well as through the skin.

2. *Moniliasis of Mucous Membranes.*—ORAL.—White patches on buccal surfaces of lips and cheeks, on the gums and tongue; diffuse whitish or black (*lingua nigra?*) pseudomembrane formed on the tongue; pseudomembrane on tonsils, and pharynx (thrush), are characteristic. *Monilia albicans* is commonly found in these lesions.

Vaginal moniliasis occurs, with the forma-tion of a thrush-like pseudomembrane on the vaginal mucosa and the production of more or less purulent exudate.

3. *Bronchial and Pulmonary Moniliasis.*—Castellani, in 1905, first described the infections of the respiratory tract due to *Monilia* and since then many investigators have recognized these conditions. The symptoms vary from those of mild respiratory infection to severe forms re-sembling tuberculosis, with cough, occasional hemoptysis and purulent sputum. Undoubtedly a number of *Moniliae* found in sputum are sec-

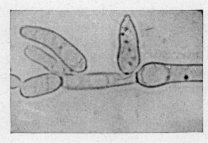

FIG. 91.—MONILIA ALBICANS, UNSTAINED.
(After Zettnow.)

ondary invaders or contaminants. Nevertheless, there is considerable evidence that these organisms are important causes of pulmonary disease.

4. *Gastro-intestinal Moniliasis.*—A specific type of frothy diarrhea, known as *sprue*, has been attributed to infection with *Monilia psilosis*. This condition and the accompanying anemia will be discussed later.

THRUSH

Thrush is a localized disease of the mouth, occurring most frequently in children suffering from malnutrition, but also in cachetic adults. It is characterized by the development of creamy patches on an area of catarrhal inflammation, usually on the tongue.

Monilia Albicans

(*Oïdium albicans,* Robin; *Saccharomyces albicans,* Rees; *Endomyces albicans,* Vuillemin)

The micro-organism which causes thrush was first described by Langenbeck in 1839. It is found abundantly in the false membrane covering the lesion where it appears as a mass of simple or branched mycelial filaments made up of irregular units of about 4 by 20 μ. Oval cells of somewhat larger diameter are also found, attached to the ends of the filaments, or lying free and throwing out buds.

BLASTOMYCOSIS

Busse in 1894 reported a case of fatal, generalized yeast infection beginning in an abscess of the tibia. Pus from the lesions contained numerous giant cells in which he observed round or oval, double-contoured bodies surrounded by a wide capsule. They varied in size from that of a red corpuscle to that of a liver cell. Many showed small cells projecting as buds from the larger parasites. The parasite grew readily on ordinary media in budding forms, often surrounded by a capsule as in the tissues. It was pathogenic for laboratory animals, especially for white mice. In glucose solutions it produced carbon dioxide and alcohol. In 1896 Gilchrist described a similar organism isolated from a patient with a severe chronic cutaneous disease which he described as pseudo lupus vulgaris. This organism also was found in giant cells, was capsulated, and showed budding forms. In culture, however, it produced mycelia and conidia and did not ferment glucose. Oxalic acid crystals were seen in the cultures. In the same year Curtis in France isolated a similar parasite from a myxomatous tumor of the leg.

Numerous cases of infection with yeast-like organisms have since been described. In a case reported by Zinsser the lesion was an abscess of the back involving the spine. The parasite corresponded morphologically to Busse's. Animal inoculation in rabbits and guinea-pigs proved positive and the organism seemed to show a selective preference for the lungs and spleen. In the lungs of the animals, especially, lesions were found with surprising regularity even when the inoculation was made intraperitoneally.

The parasite grows readily on all ordinary media. On agar it forms a creamy layer, in broth a flocculent deposit. It forms gas on certain sugars. Most strains do not liquefy gelatin or clot milk. Commonly it develops as a mass of oval cells reproducing by budding but often, especially in fluid media, forms filaments like those seen in the lesions, with terminal or lateral spores. Large globoid chlamydospores at the end of short lateral branches are also found.

SPRUE

Sprue is an important disease of subtropical countries which is characterized by progressive wasting with profuse anemia and a white frothy diarrhea. There is an inflammation of the entire intestinal tract and the lesions on the tongue are frequently characteristic.

Monilia Psilosis

Ashford has made an elaborate study of cases occurring in Puerto Rico. He isolated from the tongue and stools of 200 patients an organism which he calls *Monilia psilosis*. This is apparently identical with the *Monilia enterica* of Castellani.

Ashford's monilia is a large round organism 4 to 7 μ in diameter with a granular and usually vacuolated protoplasm. On Sabouraud's agar it grows as a faintly greenish creamy elevated mass with mycelium which usually penetrates the medium.

In gelatin it invariably produces hyphae which spread laterally from the stab and give the growth an appearance which Ashford describes as that of an inverted Christmas tree. *Monilia psilosis* produces acid and gas on dextrose, levulose, maltose

Clinically there are two distinct types of this disease, the blastomycetic dermatitis of Gilchrist and the systemic blastomycosis. The former is by far the more common. Of the latter a collection of 47 cases was made in 1916 (Wade and Bel). The portal of entry in many of these has seemed to be the respiratory tract, the earlier lesions being in the lungs. In other cases the general infection has followed a cutaneous lesion. The skin and subcutaneous tissues show the most numerous secondary lesions but the bones, liver, spleen, kidney and brain have each been involved in several instances (Martin and Smith).

Blastomycosis, and coccidioidal granuloma are chronic granulomatous diseases caused by several varieties of related fungi. As Moore and others have shown there are different types of these diseases in North America, South America and in Europe, and the organism concerned in each type of disease has special characteristics.

BLASTOMYCES HOMINIS

(*Saccharomyces Hominis*, Busse; *Cryptococcus Gilchristi*, Vuillemin; *Zymonema Gilchristi*, De Buermann and Gourgerot; *Mycoderma dermatitis*, Brumpt; *Oïdium Hektoenii*, Ricketts)

The parasites causing this disease probably represent a group of allied organisms rather than an individual species. As seen in the tissues or exudates they have shown a marked similarity in all cases. In the abscesses of the generalized form they are

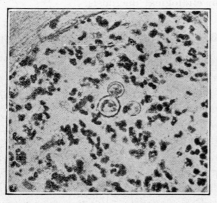

FIG. 92.—BLASTOMYCES, SHOWING BUDDING FORMS IN PUS FROM A LESION IN MAN.
(From Gilchrist.)

very numerous, in the cutaneous form somewhat more difficult to find and are best sought in the small epidermal abscesses which border the lesion. In an unstained moist film of pus spread out between a cover-slip and slide they appear as round or occasionally oval highly refractive bodies containing granules of various sizes and often vacuoles and surrounded by a hyaline capsule. They vary greatly in diameter usually from 10 to 20 μ. *Budding forms and pairs united in a figure eight can usually be found.* They stand out more definitely if the pus is cleared by mixing with a 20 per cent potassium hydrate solution. They stain irregularly. As a rule with the stronger aniline dyes they are overstained so that the details are obscured. With hemotoxylin eosin the capsule usually remains unstained and the body takes a pale stain with deep blue granules but in some cells the capsule may stain deeply. Thionin, polychrome methylene blue, and Wright's blood stain have been recommended. In tissue sections stained with hemotoxylin and eosin, or better with thionin, or methylene blue, the clean-cut, circular parasites are easily recognized, lying, as a rule, within multinuclear giant cells.

Isolation.—The isolation of the organism is rendered difficult by the frequent presence in the lesion of bacteria which develop more rapidly than the fungus.

Gilchrist and Zinsser encountered gram-positive cocci, others diphtheroid bacilli. No special methods for facilitating isolation have been devised but success will often attend painstaking and repeated plating of the cultures in high dilution. The most favorable medium is glucose agar and the organisms develop well at room or at incubator temperature.

Cultural Characteristics.—On agar or glucose agar the colonies appear after two to four days as minute glistening white hemispherical spots which are not unlike colonies of *Staphylococcus albus*. In older cultures the appearance of different strains shows marked variations, some remaining smooth and pasty, others changing to a tough, wrinkled membrane firmly adherent to the agar, and still others becoming covered with white aerial hyphae. All become brown with age. In agar stab cultures the organisms show their preference for a well oxygenated environment by growing but slightly along the course of the stab and by heaping up a thick creamy layer on the surface of the medium. Most strains fail to liquefy gelatin. In broth cultures the medium remains clear, the organisms growing as a stringy sediment, as a pellicle, or as tufted masses in the depth of the medium. On blood serum, potato and bread growth is easily obtained. Some strains ferment carbohydrates but most do not.

Morphology.—In freshly isolated cultures the growth consists of large round cells with blastospores like those seen in the tissues. Capsules are often formed. Most strains sooner or later develop coarse, irregular, branching mycelial filaments. These are divided by septa and produce chains of arthrospores and terminal or lateral conidia. Hamburger, in a careful culture study of four strains from systemic infections was impressed with the effect of the temperature of incubation on the morphology of the organism. All of his strains grown in the incubator tended to multiply by budding, while at room temperature all were filamentous, and two produced aerial hyphae.

Pathogenicity.—All strains which have been tested have proved pathogenic for laboratory animals. White mice seem the most susceptible.

Classification.—Cultures from the various cases have shown little uniformity. It is impossible to be certain that they represent distinct species as they are somewhat pleomorphic and change their morphology with varying cultural conditions and after long preservation on artificial media.

The most serious attempt to systematize their varying characteristics is that of Ricketts. He considered the seventeen strains on which he based his report all to be closely related species of one genus. He described three main types under which in spite of minor differences he grouped the various strains.

His classification is not, however, satisfactory. Stober has observed the three types of agar growth to occur successively in the same strain.

A definite classification of these organisms is as yet impossible but there seem to be two types which the various strains more or less closely resemble.

1. The fermenting type described by Busse and called *Cryptococcus hominis* by Vuillemin, Brumpt and Castellani. These organisms resemble the true yeasts in their morphology and zymogenic properties.

2. The nonfermenting types described by Gilchrist and called *Cryptococcus gilchristi* by Vuillemin, *Cryptococcus dermatitidis* by Castellani and *Mycoderma dermatitis* by Brumpt. These usually produce mycelium and reproduce by means of

thallospores and conidia. They are related to the sporothrices and the trichophyta. There is no correlation between the type of organism and the type of lesion it produces.

COCCIDIOIDAL GRANULOMA

There is a group of cases resembling closely systemic blastomycosis, the first observation of which was that of Wernicke and Posadas.

Their case presented numerous pea-sized cutaneous tumors and clinically resembled mycosis fungoides. In the lesions they discovered intracellular spherical hyaline bodies which they thought to be protozoan cysts. These cysts were surrounded by hyaline capsules and some of the larger forms contained a great number of the daughter cysts. Later Rixford and Gilchrist reported a similar case and since then

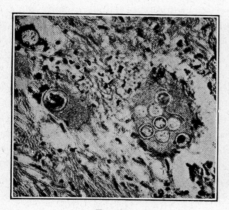
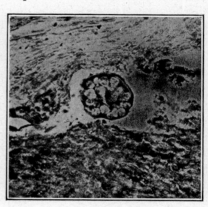

Fig. 93.   Fig. 94.

Fig. 93.—Coccidioides, Round and Sporulating Forms in a Giant Cell in a Lesion in Man.
(From Rixford and Gilchrist.)

Fig. 94.—Coccidioides, Sporulating Form in Lesion.
(From Rixford and Gilchrist.)

a number of other cases have been reported, most of them from the San Joaquin Valley, California.

Ophuls described three clinical types: (1) with primary cutaneous lesions, and later generalization; (2) with primary pulmonary lesions and later generalization but no skin lesions; (3) with primary pulmonary lesions and secondary subcutaneous lesions.

The disease runs a more acute and severe course than blastomycosis and of 24 cases collected by MacNeal and Taylor, but 2 recovered. The cutaneous lesions consist of large rather painless granulomatous abscesses; there is usually marked lymphadenitis and the lungs, bones, liver, kidneys and meninges have been found to be involved. Histologically, the lesions both in man and in experimentally infected animals very closely resemble those of tuberculosis.

CHROMOBLASTOMYCOSIS

Chromoblastomycosis, first described by Medlar and Lane in Boston in 1915, has been recognized in many countries. The disease is characterized by the occurrence of numerous, large cauliflower-like growths on the skin, chiefly on the legs and feet. Sections of the lesions show proliferation of the epithelium, and, in the corium, tuberculoid foci with brownish yeast-like bodies in the granulomata. Carrión, Koppisch and Emmons have described the cases seen in Puerto Rico. Carrión has shown that the causative fungus is a new species, *Hormodendrum compactum*.

COCCIDIOIDES IMMITIS

(*Oïdium coccidioides*, Ophuls; *Mycoderma immite*, Brumpt)

The distinction between this parasite and that of blastomycosis is recognized by Ophuls, Wolbach and MacNeal. The parasite seen *in the tissues* resembles the blastomyces, but *does not show buds and reproduces by the formation of endospores.* These appear as a mass of minute round bodies—each of which may be capsulated— within the membrane of the parent cell. The parasites vary greatly in size and some are much larger than those usually found in blastomycosis, reaching 50 μ in diameter.

Cultures.—The colonies appear in surface plants in from two to seven days as small slightly raised disks distinctly penetrating the media. Older cultures, with a leathery mycelium, become covered with a dusty white layer of aerial hyphae. The cultures become brown with age. In broth they grow as a fluffy mass which sinks to the bottom. Sugars are not fermented. Gelatin is slowly liquefied and milk slowly peptonized.

Morphology.—In culture the spherical bodies immediately throw out filaments 2 to 8 μ in diameter which are branched and septate. In older cultures they develop large chlamydospores and also conidia which are usually arranged in chains at the end of the hyphae. In anaerobic cultures in Noguchi's ascitic agar-rabbit kidney medium, MacNeal and Taylor observed the formation of endospores like those found in the lesions. The organism is pathogenic for dogs, rabbits and guinea-pigs.

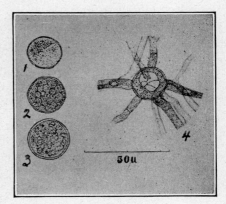

FIG. 95.—COCCIDIOIDES.

1, granular form; *2*, *3*, sporulating form. These types of cells occur in the lesions. *4*, development of mycelial filaments in culture. (From MacNeal and Taylor.)

Cooke has studied the immune reactions in a human case of this disease and found precipitins which reacted up to 1 : 160 dilution of the serum against extracts of the cultures. The serum did not react with extracts of cultures of blastomyces. He was unable to obtain complement fixation or positive skin reactions with his extracts. Immunological methods are not satisfactory for diagnosis.

Rhinosporidium seeberi, a sporulating fungus of undetermined nature, is an etiological agent in nasal polyps. It is well described by Pasternack and Alexander.

SPOROTRICHOSIS

Sporotrichosis is a chronic infection usually limited to the skin, the subcutaneous tissues, and lymphatics, occasionally involving the muscles, bones, joints and lungs (Forbus). The lesions resemble closely syphilitic gummata and in typical cases occur in a chain extending up the arm, connected by thickened lymphatic vessels. They slowly soften and ulcerate.

The first cases described were those of Schenck and of Hektoen and Perkins in this country. It is a rare infection in the eastern United States (Hopkins and Benham, 1932, Weise), but apparently endemic in the upper Mississippi valley and the southwestern states (Hamburger, Moore). In France and Switzerland it is relatively common and our present knowledge of the disease is based chiefly on the work of De Beurmann and Gougerot. It may be caused by several species of hyphomycetes belonging to the genus *Sporotrichum*.

Sporotrichum

It is difficult and often impossible to demonstrate the parasites by direct examination. When found in smears of the pus, or in sections of the lesions, they appear as oval or cigar-shaped cells varying in length from 10 to 2 μ and in breadth from 3 to

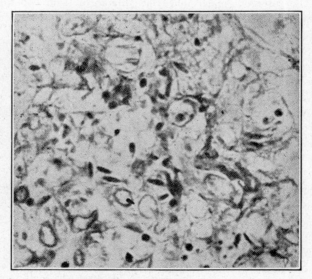

Fig. 96.—Sporotrichum Schenki, Spores in Lesion in Testis of Rat.
(From Hopkins.)

1 μ. These are frequently within large mononuclear phagocytes. The parasites may be demonstrated by clearing the pus with 20 per cent sodium hydroxide or by staining with thionin or other basic stains. They are gram-positive.

Cultural Characteristics.—As a rule the organism can be found only by making cultures from the pus or from the bloody fluid aspirated from firmer lesions. Tubes of Sabouraud's test medium or of 4 per cent glucose agar should be heavily inoculated on the surface and incubated at room temperature. Taylor recommends glycerin glucose-agar to which acetic or citric acid (1 : 1500) is added. The colonies appear in four days or more as minute gray flecks, soon surrounded by a delicate fringe. The centers as they enlarge become raised and wrinkled and darken to a buff, or chocolate, or in some species to a black color. In flask cultures they may attain a diameter of 10 centimeters and more. At the periphery is a smooth flat zone with delicate radiating outgrowths, which, if they reach the side of the tube, grow upward along the dry glass. The surface is usually hard and glistening, but in old cultures may show hairy or powdery outgrowths from the surface.

The sporothrix grows on media of very simple composition but more luxuriantly on those containing sugar. On glucose broth it forms a thick membrane. It liquefies glucose gelatin, but does not clot or digest milk. On hexoses it forms lactic acid

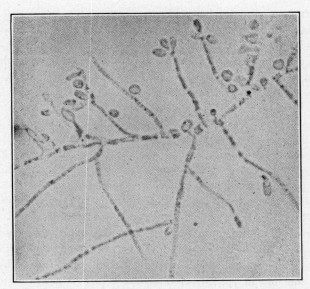

Fig. 97.—Sporotrichum Schenki in Hanging Drop Culture, Showing Typical Clusters of Spores at the Ends of Short Lateral Branches.
(From Hopkins.)

but does not ferment mannite or dulcite. Species vary in their action on disaccharides.

Morphology.—This is best studied in hanging-drop cultures. The growth is made up of interlacing, branching septate hyphae. These are delicate (about 2 μ) and of uniform diameter. The spores are oval or pear-shaped (about 3 or 4 μ) and are found on any part of the hyphae to which they are usually attached by short sterigmata. In De Beurmann's species they are very numerous and form thick clusters at the tips of the hyphae or sheaths along their course. Chlamydospores are also found.

Species.—*Sporotrichum schenki* is the species found in most American cases. The cultures are white or slightly brownish. They ferment lactose but not saccharose. The spores are not numerous and have no sterigmata.

Sporotrichum beurmanni is the commonest species in France. The cultures soon darken to a chocolate brown. They ferment saccharose but not lactose. Spores are very numerous and often provided with short sterigmata.

Five other pathogenic varieties are listed by De Beurmann and there are many saprophytic species. Wolbach has described a species isolated from an arthritis of the knee which he named *S. councilmani*.

Pathogenicity.—Spontaneous infections due to the *Sporotrichum beurmanni* have been observed in rats, dogs and horses. Experimentally cultures have been shown to be virulent for rats and other laboratory animals.

The pathogenic species seem capable also of saprophytic existence. De Beurmann recovered his species from the normal throats of patients with sporotrichosis and of others who had recovered from the disease. Gougerot found in oat grains, and in other plants sporothrices which he regarded as identical with the human species and which were virulent for rats.

Kesten and Martenstein, reinvestigating problems of experimental sporotrichosis, showed that cutaneous inoculation of sporotrichum spores produces in rats an eruption composed of minute papules, with extension of the infection to regional lymph nodes. Following intracardial injection of the spores, a similar papular eruption develops in the skin of rats, especially on previously irritated areas. A generalized sporotrichosis in rats follows intracardial inoculation.

This fungus is unusual in its pathogenicity for both plants and animals. Benham and Kesten transmitted sporotrichosis to carnations by inoculation of the plants with a culture of *Sporotrichum schenki* derived from an infection in man. The "human disease" produced in carnations a bud rot similar to that caused by the plant pathogen *Sporotrichum poae*. After living saprophytically or parasitically in plants, *Sporotrichum schenki* retained its virulence for animals.

The successful experimental inoculation of barberry thorns with *Sporotrichum schenki*, accomplished by these investigators, adds to the evidence that plants may be the natural source of this infection for man and that the disease may be contracted by puncture wounds with infected thorns or other pieces of plant tissue.

Immunity.—Widal and Abrami found that suspensions of sporothrix spores were agglutinated by the sera of patients in dilutions 1:200 or above and have used this reaction in diagnosis. They also obtained fixation of complement. Others report that patients give skin reactions with culture extracts. In human cases there is no evidence of the development of an immunity but in animals successful immunization, both active and passive, has been reported.

REFERENCES

ASHFORD. Am. J. M. Sc., 1917, 154:159.
BENHAM, R. W. J. Infect. Dis., 1931, 49:183.
BENHAM, R. W., and KESTEN, B. J. Infect. Dis., 1932, 50:437.
BUSSE, O. Centralbl. f. Bakteriol., I Abt., 1894, 16:175.
CARRIÓN, A. L. and KOPPISCH, E., Puerto Rico. J. Pub. Health and Trop. M., 1933, 9:169.
CARRIÓN, A. L. *Ibid.*, 1935, 10:543; 1936, 11:663; 1938, 13:37.
COOKE, J. V. Arch. Int. Med., 1915, 15:479.
CRONE, J. T., DE GROAT, A. F., and WAHLIN, J. G. Am. J. Pathol., 1937, 13:863.
CURTIS. Ann. d. l'Inst. Pasteur, 1896, 10.
DE BEURMANN and GOUGEROT. Les Sporotrichoses, Paris, 1912.

EMMONS, C. W., and CARRIÓN, A. L.   Mycologia, 1937, 29:327.

——— Puerto Rico, J. Pub. Health and M., 1935, 11:114; 1936, 11:703.

FORBUS, W. D.   Am. Rev. Tuberc., 1927, 16:598.

GILCHRIST, T. C.   Johns Hopkins Hosp. Rep., 1896, 1:269.

HAMBURGER, W. W.   J. Am. M. Ass., 1912, 59:1590.

——— J. Infect. Dis., 1907, 4:201.

HARRISON, F. C.   Tr. Roy. Soc. Canada, 1928, 22:Sect. V, 187.

HEKTOEN, L., and PERKINS, C. F.   J. Exper. M., 1900, 5:77.

HIRSCH, E. R., and COLEMAN, G. H.   J. Am. M. Ass., 1929, 92:437.

HOPKINS, J. G.   Arch. Dermat. & Syph., 1932, 25:599.

HOPKINS, J. G., and BENHAM, R. W.   New York State J. M., 1929, 29:793; 1932.

KESTEN, H. D., COOK, D. H., MOTT, E., and JOBLING, J. W.   J. Exper. M., 1930, 52:813.

KESTEN, B., and MARTENSTEIN, H.   Arch. Dermat. & Syph., 1929, 20:441.

LANE, C. F.   J. Cutan. Dis., 1915, 33:840.

MACNEAL, W. J., and TAYLOR, R. M.   J. Med. Research, 1914, 25:261.

MARTIN, D. S., and SMITH, D. T.   Am. Rev. Tuberc., 1939, 39:275; 488

MASSEE, J. C., and ROONEY, J. S.   J. Am. M. Ass., 1930, 94:1650.

MEDLAR, E. M.   J. M. Res., 1915, 32:507.

MOORE, M.   Arch. Dermatol. & Syph., 1935, 31:672; 1938, 38:163.

OPHULS, W.   J. Exper. M., 1905, 6:443.

PASTERNACK, J. G., and ALEXANDER, C. S.   Arch. Otolaryngol., 1938, 27:746.

RICKETTS.   J. Med. Research, 1901, 6:373.

RIXFORD, E., and GILCHRIST, T. C.   Johns Hopkins Hosp. Rep., 1896, 1:209.

SCHENCK, B. R.   Bull. Johns Hopkins Hosp., 1898, 9:286.

STOBER.   Arch. Int. Med., 1914, 13:509.

STODDARD, J. L. and CUTLER, E. C.   Monog. Rockefeller Inst. M. Research No. 6, 1916.

TAYLOR, K.   J. Am. M. Ass., 1913, 60:1142.

WADE and BEL.   Arch. Int. Med., 1916, 18:103.

WEISE, E. C.   N. Eng. J. M., 1931, 205:951.

WERNICKE, R.   Centralbl. f. Bakteriol., I Abt., 1892, 12:859.

WIDAL and ABRAMI.   Quoted by De Beurmann and Gougerot.

WOLBACH, S. B.   J. Med. Research, 1904, 8:53.

WOOD, E. J.   Am. J. M. Sc., 1926, 169:28.

ZINSSER, H.   Proc. New York Path. Soc., 1907, 7.

CHAPTER LIX

ACTINOMYCETES AND ACTINOMYCOSIS WITH NOTES ON CLADOTHRIX AND LEPTOTHRIX

Standing midway between the true bacteria and the more complex molds, there are a number of pathogenic micro-organisms, now generally designated *Actinomycetes*, which offer great difficulties in classification. The cultures of these organisms resemble those of the hyphomycetes in gross characteristics, being usually dry, tough, wrinkled and sometimes covered with a down of aerial outgrowths. These mold-like fungi are characterized by a *delicate mycelium*, usually less than 1 μ in diameter and hence within bacterial dimensions. The mycelium is septate and shows a marked tendency to branch. The component parts of the mycelium often stain unevenly but do not contain recognizable nuclei. The mycelial filaments fragment into bacillary and coccoidal forms, and some varieties under special conditions grow in diphtheroid forms. The actinomycetes reproduce by the formation of spores, or conidia, in clusters and chains at the tips of aerial hyphae. These spores have the general dimensions of micrococci.

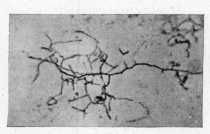

Fig. 98.—Actinomyces (Strepto-thrix), Showing True Branching.

Many classifications of the group have been proposed according to the opinions held by investigators with respect to the phylogenetic relations of these organisms. Some regard them as degraded fungi, others as a primary stock from which both bacteria and fungi have developed, and still others call them "higher bacteria." In all these opinions, there is a general agreement that the actinomycetes are in an intermediate position between bacteria and fungi. The arrangement in Bergey's *Manual of Determinative Bacteriology* (1934) seems as satisfactory as any, although it definitely assigns the *Actinomycetes* to the class of *Schizomycetes*, in which the bacteria are included. Certainly the actinomycetes are more than "fission fungi," but it is possible that the bacteria also have other forms of reproduction than simple binary fission. In Bergey's *Manual*, the order: *Actinomycetales* contains two families: 1, the *Actinomycetaceae*, which includes the actinomycetes, and leptothrix, which we shall consider in this chapter and 2, the *Mycobacteriaceae*, which includes the tubercle bacilli, the diphtheria bacillus and other bacteria.

This broad classification gives the general setting of the group. The further subdivisions into genera and species present almost insuperable difficulties in the present state of the knowledge of these organisms and few bacteriologists are in agreement upon either the names or characters of the genera and species. We shall not enter upon a discussion of those vexed questions of taxonomy and nomenclature.

Our point of view is briefly summarized with respect to the generic names of these filamentous organisms by the statement that:

Leptothrix is the name we shall use for all the *unbranched* filamentous forms; *Actinomyces* is the generic name we shall use for those forms which have septate and *branched* mycelium, with reproduction by formation of aerial spores (conidia). The characters of club formation, oxygen tension requirements, and pathogenicity seem to us to be of subgeneric importance. Hence, we shall use the name *Actinomyces* for all those organisms called *Nocardia, Streptothrix, Cladothrix* (a notoriously in-correct appellation), *Oöspora,* and *Discomyces.* As far as species distinctions are concerned, we are not competent to decide the questions. Many of the listed "species" appear to us to be artificial. For a discussion of some of these names, the reader is referred to the paper by Breed and Conn.

The actinomycetes are enormously important in the economy of nature. They are ubiquitous and active in bringing about changes in organic matter in soil, water, and in and upon the bodies of man and animals. The medical bacteriologist encounters the saprophytic forms as contaminants of culture media, and nonpathogenic organisms in feces, sputum contaminated with saliva, and exudates from some open lesions. A few species are pathogenic. These cause *Actinomycosis*, Madura foot, and various lesions in man and animals.

ACTINOMYCOSIS

Actinomycosis is an infectious granulomatous disease, characterized by destruc-tion of tissue, suppuration, and an overgrowth of fibrous tissue. The term, compounded from mycological, clinical and pathological conceptions of the disease, originally expressed the definite idea that the process was caused by the ray fungus. Increasing knowledge, however, has indicated that approximately the same type of clinical symptoms and pathological changes can be brought about by a variety of actino-mycetes, some of which do not form radiating masses of clubs in the tissues, by other fungi such as the ascomycetic molds found in Madura foot, and even by the *Actinobacillus* of Lignières and Spitz. The point of view that the clinical-pathological entity actinomycosis may have a multiple etiology has been adopted by Henrici, Jacobson, and others, and our experience has led us to the same belief.

Actinomycosis is usually chronic. The fungi and other organisms causing the disease may invade the skin, subcutaneous tissue, lymph nodes, lungs, any of the viscera and bones. Large or small granulomatous masses and the formation of sinuses are common features of the disease. From these groups of conditions, three distinct types are to be considered.

1. *Actinomycosis.*—True actinomycosis of man and cattle (called "lumpy jaw" in cattle), is due to one or more species of *Actinomyces* possessing the property of forming in the lesions masses of radiating clubs at the outer surfaces of globular clus-ters of mycelium. The parasites of this form of the disease have been given a great variety of names: *Nocardia, Streptothrix, Discomyces,* and *Cohnistreptothrix.* We shall refer to the species as *Actinomyces hominis* and *Actinomyces bovis.* Aerobic and anaerobic or micro-aerophilic varieties are found in both the animal and human types of the disease.

2. *Maduramycosis, or Mycetoma.*—This is usually a fibrous and suppurating granuloma of the foot, known as Madura foot. Jacobson lists 19 species of fungi from 2 classes and 8 genera which have been isolated from cases of maduramycosis. Most of these are of the actinomyces type, but some are aspergilli and penicillia. Apparently club formation in the granules of fungi is not as common as in cases of true actinomycosis, but the filamentous fungi with branched mycelium, the actinomycetes, are no doubt the most important etiological agents of maduramycosis.

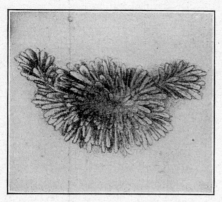

FIG. 99.—CLUSTER OF CLUBS OF ACTINO-
MYCES FROM A SULPHUR GRANULE.
(From Kolle and Hetsch.)

3. *Actinobacillosis.*—This is primarily a disease of cattle, occurring chiefly in Argentina, with lesions like those of actinomycosis, but due to a small gram-negative, club-forming bacillus, first described by Lignières and Spitz in 1902. Griffith found the organism in cases of the disease in cattle in England. Ravaut and Pinoy and others have reported cases of the infection in man. This organism may be related to the *Bacillus actinoides*, described by Smith in 1918 as a cause of pneumonia in calves.

Among the diseases caused by the trichomycetes or higher bacteria, the most important is actinomycosis. Occurring chiefly in some of the domestic animals, notably in cattle, the disease is observed in man with sufficient frequency to make it of great clinical importance. In cattle the specific micro-organism which gives rise to the disease was first observed by Bollinger in 1877. In the following year Israel discovered a similar micro-organism in human cases.

The parasites appear in the pus from discharging lesions as *small granular bodies*, plainly visible to the naked eye and somewhat resembling *sulphur granules*, of a grayish or of a pale yellow color. In size they measure usually a fraction of a millimeter. Ordinarily they are soft and easily crushed under a cover-slip, but occasionally, especially in old lesions, they may be quite hard, owing to calcification.

Microscopically they are most easily recognized in fresh preparations prepared by crushing the granules upon the slide under a cover-slip

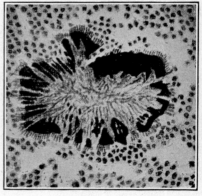

FIG. 100.—ACTINOMYCOTIC GRANULE IN
PUS, STAINED TO SHOW THE MYCELIUM.
(From Kolle and Hetsch.)

and examining them without staining. They may be rendered more clearly visible by the addition of a drop or two of 20 per cent potassium hydrate. When the granules are calcareous, the addition of a drop of concentrated acetic acid will facilitate examination. Dried preparations may be examined after staining with Gram's stain. Observed under the microscope, the granules appear as rosette-like masses, the centers of which are quite opaque, and dense, appearing to be made up of a closely meshed network of filaments. Around the margins there are found radially arranged striations which in many cases end in characteristically club-shaped bodies. Inside of the central network there are often seen coccoid or spore-like bodies which have been variously interpreted as spores, as degeneration products, and as separate cocci fortuitously found in symbiosis with the actinomyces.

About the periphery of the granules the free ends of the filaments become gradually thickened to form the so-called actinomycosis "clubs." These clubs, according to most observers, must be regarded as hyaline thickenings of the sheaths of the threads and are believed to represent a form of degeneration and not, as some of the earlier observers believed, organs of reproduction. They are homogeneous, and in the smaller and presumably younger granules are extremely fragile and soluble in water. In older lesions, especially in .those of cattle, the clubs are more resistant and less easily destroyed.

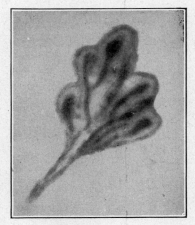

Characteristic clubs are seldom seen in cultures but were observed by Wright in cultures containing animal serum or whole blood and by Bayne-Jones in glucose broth without serum.

The coccus-like bodies found occasionally lying between the filaments of the central mass, most observers now agree, do not represent anything comparable to the spores of the true hyphomycetes. In many cases they are unquestionably contaminating cocci; in others again they may represent the results of degeneration of the threads.

FIG. 101.—CLUBS OF ACTINOMYCES FROM "LUMPY JAW."

Gram stain. Shows the filaments within thickened sheaths.

In tissue sections, the micro-organisms may be demonstrated by Gram's method of staining or by a special method devised by Mallory. This is as follows for paraffin sections:

1. Stain in saturated aqueous eosin ten minutes.
2. Wash in water.
3. Aniline gentian violet, five minutes.
4. Wash with normal salt solution.
5. Gram's iodine solution one minute.
6. Wash in water and blot dry.
7. Cover with aniline oil until section is clear.
8. Xylol, several changes.
9. Mount in balsam.[1]

Cultivation.—The isolation of actinomyces from lesions may be easy or difficult according to whether the pus is free from contamination or whether it contains large numbers of other bacteria. In the latter case it may be almost impossible to obtain cultures. The descriptions of methods of isolation and of cultural characteristics given by various writers have shown considerable differences. The most extensive cultural

[1] Mallory, in Mallory and Wright, *Pathological Technique*, Philadelphia, 1908.

work has been done by Bostroem, Wolff and Israel, and by J. H. Wright. Bostroem has described his cultures as aerobic, but Wolff and Israel and Wright agree in finding that the micro-organisms isolated by them from actinomycotic lesions grow but sparsely under aerobic conditions and favor an environment which is entirely free from oxygen, or at least contain it only in small quantities. The method for isolation recommended by Wright is, briefly, as follows:

Pus is obtained, if possible, from a closed lesion and washed in sterile water or broth. The granules are then crushed between two sterile slides and examined for the presence of filaments. If these are present in reasonable abundance, the material is distributed in tubes of glucose agar, which are then allowed to solidify. If these first cultivations show a large number of contaminations, Wright recommends the preservation of other washed granules in test tubes for several

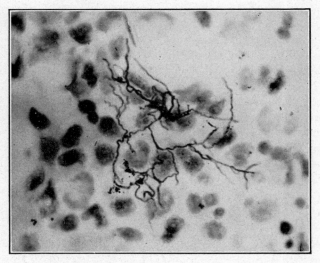

Fig. 102.—Branching Filaments of Actinomyces in Pus.
(Photograph by Stella Zimmerman, University of Syracuse School of Medicine.)

weeks, in the hope that contaminating micro-organisms may thus be killed by drying before the actinomyces lose their viability.

If cultivation is successful colonies will appear, after two to four days at 37.5° C. as minute white specks, which, in Wright's cultures, appeared most abundantly within a zone situated 5 to 10 millimeters below the surface of the medium. Above and below this zone they are less numerous, indicating that a small amount of oxygen furnishes the best cultural environment. Upon the surface of agar slants, growth, if it takes place at all, is not luxuriant.[2]

In alkaline meat-infusion broth growth takes place in the form of heavy, flocculent masses which appear at the bottom of the tubes. Surface growth and clouding do not take place.

Milk and potato have been used as culture media but are not particularly favorable.

Pathogenicity.—Actinomycosis occurs naturally most often in cattle and human beings. It may occur also in sheep, dogs, cats and horses.

Its locations of predilection are the various parts adjacent to the mouth and

2 J. H. Wright, *J. Med. Research*, 1905, 13:349.

pharynx. It occurs also, however, in the lungs, in the intestinal canal and upon the skin. When occurring in its most frequent location, the lower jaw, the disease presents, at first, a hard nodular swelling which later becomes soft because of central necrosis. It often involves the bone, causing a rarefying osteitis. As the swellings break down, sinuses are formed from which the granular pus is discharged. The neighboring lymph nodes show painless, hard swellings. Histologically, about the filamentous knobs or granules, there is a formation of epithelioid cells and a small round-cell infiltration. In older cases there may be an encapsulation in connective tissue and a calcification of the necrotic masses, leading to spontaneous cure. As a rule, this process is extremely chronic. Infection in the lungs or in the intra-abdominal organs is, of course, far more serious. When death occurs acutely, it is often due to secondary infection.

On account of the frequent occurrence of spicules of straw and grain in the actinomycotic lesions of the jaws of cattle, and because of the opinion of Bostroem and others that the actinomycetes isolated from grains were the same as those found in lesions, the opinion was widely accepted that the infection was introduced by punctures with pieces or spines of fungus-bearing plants. In recent years, however, this view has been shown to be almost untenable. The actinomycetes from plants are usually nonpathogenic for animals and the varieties cultivated from plants do not correspond in their oxygen requirements and other characters with many of the forms isolated from the lesions of man. It must be admitted that while lesions can be produced, typical actinomycosis has not been established experimentally in lower animals by inoculation with any of the culture strains.

In place of the opinion that the actinomycosis is contracted by wounds with vegetable material, Colebrook and others would substitute the theory that the disease is brought about by the penetration into wounds of actinomyces of human or animal origin. Actinomycetes are known to occur in the intestines, mouth and tonsillar crypts. Colebrook observed several cases of actinomycosis beginning on the hands of men who had wounded their hands in fist-fights when striking the teeth of their opponents.

B. actinomycetum comitans.—As in other mycoses the isolation of the parasite in actinomycosis is made difficult by the presence in the lesions of numerous bacteria which overgrow primary cultures. The contaminants are frequently pyogenic cocci and saprophytic intestinal bacilli. One unusual type of organism has, however, been found in these lesions with sufficient frequency to deserve mention. Wolff and Israel mention the presence in the granules of numerous pleomorphic bodies resembling micrococci. Similar organisms have been noted by Klinger, Colebrook and Goldworthy. In the granules they appear as minute gram-negative coccobacilli fused together into sheets. In culture they grow aerobically or anaerobically as minute coherent colonies which on agar are smooth and glistening, in broth, starlike and frequently adherent to the sides of the tubes. They grow on simple media but quickly die out in culture. They form acid but no gas on sugars. Guinea-pigs and rabbits may be killed by large injections but no lesions resembling actinomycosis are produced. It is doubtful if these bacteria play an important rôle in spontaneous cases of the disease. One of us (Bayne-Jones) isolated *B. actinomycetum-comitans* together with the micro-aerophilic actinomycete from the pus aspirated from a cervical lymph node of a patient with actinomycosis in Baltimore.

MYCETOMA (MADURA FOOT)

The disease known by this name is not unlike actinomycosis. It is more or less strictly limited to warmer climates and was first recognized as a clinical entity in India, by Carter. Clinically it consists of a chronic productive inflammation most frequently attacking the foot, less often the hand, very infrequently other parts of the body. Nodular swellings occur, which break down in their centers, leading to the formation of abscesses, later of sinuses. Often the bones are involved and a progressive rarefying osteitis results. From the sinuses a purulent fluid exudes, in which are found characteristic granular bodies. These may be hard, brittle, and black, resembling grains of gunpowder, or may be grayish white or yellow and soft and grumous. According to the appearance of these granules different varieties of the disease have been described as mycetoma with black, white, yellow, or red granules. These different varieties of the disease though clinically similar may apparently be produced by a large number of different parasites all belonging to the fungi or higher bacteria. We will mention below the few cases from which aspergilli and allied molds have been isolated. In the majority of cases organisms similar to the nocardia or actinomycetes have been found. Brumpt divides them into two genera: the *madurella* having septate mycelia and the *discomyces* which is without septa, but this distinction is not generally recognized. For a discussion of the characteristics of the various strains one should refer to the works of Brumpt and of Castellani.

The parasite of the commoner black variety which certainly seems to be a distinct disease has been carefully studied by Wright from whose description the following points are taken.

The small, brittle granules observed under the microscope show a dark, almost opaque center along the edges of which filaments, or hyphae, may be seen in a thickly matted mass. By crushing the granules under a cover-slip in a drop of sodium hypochlorite or of strong sodium hydrate, the black amorphous pigment is dissolved and the structural elements of the fungus may be observed. They seem to be composed of a dense meshwork of mycelial threads which are thick and often swollen, and show many branches. Transverse partitions are placed at short distances and the individual filaments may be very long. Spores were not observed by Wright. In a series of over fifty cultivations on artificial media from the original lesion, Wright obtained a growth in a large percentage.

In *broth*, he obtained at first a rapid growth of long hyphae which eventually formed a structure which he compares in appearance to a powder puff.

On *agar*, growth appeared within less than a week and spread over the surface of the medium as a thick meshwork of spreading hyphae of a grayish color. In old cultures black granules appeared among the mycelial meshes.

On *potato*, he observed a dense velvety membrane, centrally of a pale brown, white at the periphery. Small brown droplets appeared on the growth in old cultures.

Animal inoculation with this micro-organism has so far been unsuccessful.

FARCY AND OTHER INFECTIONS WITH ACTINOMYCETES

An aerobic genus of these filamentous fungi has been known for a long time under the name *Nocardia*—and other names applied with almost equal frequency to the organisms of actinomycosis. Whatever the proper name may be for these varieties of this group of fungi, a knowledge of them is essential for the medical bacteriologist, as the group contains pathogenic members.

In 1888, Nocard described a member of this group as the etiological agent of a glanders-like disease, *farcin du bœuf*, occurring in Guadeloupe. Nocard called the organism *Actinomyces farcinica*.

Eppinger cultivated from a brain abscess in man an organism which he called *Cladothrix asteroides* on account of the star-like appearance of the young colonies on agar. He also found the organisms in sections of the bronchial lymph nodes and believed the invasion had occurred through the respiratory tract. Since then a number of fatal systemic infections due to similar organisms have been described by Petruschky, Berestnew, Flexner, MacCallum, Norris and Larkin and others, and an apparently identical organism was isolated by Musgrave and Clegg in a case of Madura foot. A summary of the various cases up to 1921 has been made by Henrici and Gardner. In most of these cases the portal of entry was the respiratory tract, but a few began as wound infections. Strains from various cases have been considered by some to be identical, by others to represent a number of closely related species. The organism is now known as *Actinomyces asteroides*.

Morphology.—Morphologically the nocardiae (*Actinomycetes*) show considerable variation. In material from infectious lesions they have most often appeared as rods and filaments with well-marked branching. Occasionally the filaments are long and intertwined, and branches have shown bulbous or club-shaped ends. In Norris and Larkin's case, the young cultures in the first generations seem to have consisted chiefly of rod-shaped forms not unlike bacilli of the diphtheria group, showing marked metachromatism when stained with Löffler's methylene blue. They are easily stained with this dye or with aqueous fuchsin. Many strains are acid-fast, but decolorize somewhat more readily than do tubercle bacilli. In tissue sections they may be demonstrated by the Gram-Weigert method.

Cultivation.—These organisms develop slowly on ordinary agar or gelatin plates, forming visible colonies in from two to five days. Later they form a membrane somewhat adherent to the surface which soon becomes wrinkled. It is at first white but later turns yellow or even a brilliant orange. On broth they grow as a thick pellicle or, occasionally as a flocculent precipitate. Most strains have not liquefied gelation or altered litmus milk, but liquefying strains have been described. All strains have proved highly virulent for guinea-pigs and somewhat less so for rabbits, producing in the animals abscesses or lesions resembling tuberculosis.

CLADOTHRIX

The only definite species of *Cladothrix* is Cohn's *Cladothrix dichotoma*. This is a filamentous organism which grows within a sheath and shows false branching. The mycelial filaments are not actually dichotomous, but lie at angles to each other. This organism is one of the "iron bacteria," occurring in water. As Henrici has said: "No one acquainted with this organism would consider it closely related to the actinomycetes." Eppinger named the actinomycete discovered by him *Cladothrix asteroides* under the mistaken impression that it showed false branching. Since that time, this misnomer has appeared in many classifications and texts on medical mycology. In our opinion, the genus is as false as the supposed branching—and we mention it here in order to dismiss it from further consideration. The genus is not recognized in the 4TH (1934) edition of Bergey's *Manual*.

LEPTOTHRIX AND LEPTOTRICHOSES

The forms originally called *Leptothrix* were straight or curved, unbranched filamentous organisms isolated from water. These are members of the group of "iron bacteria."

The name, carried over into medical mycology, was applied to delicate unbranched filamentous forms found by Robin, in 1847, in scrapings from the teeth of horses. In Bergey's *Manual* (1934) two species are recognized, *Leptotrichia buccalis* (Robin) and *Leptotrichia placoides* (Dobrzyniecki) isolated from a filling in a tooth canal. Filamentous organisms, swollen ends and peculiar lateral clusters of oval coccoid bodies are common in the tartar on teeth. A number of species were described, without cultures, by Miller in his book on the bacteriology of the mouth.

Pathogenic species of *Leptothrix* have been described from time to time. They have been isolated from abscesses of internal organs, abscesses of the brain, from meningitis, and in inflammation of the mouth. Reviews of the literature and bibliographies have been provided by Mackenzie and Harris and by Wherry and Oliver.

These organisms in culture are pleomorphic, forming coils and spirals, and, most commonly, bacillary forms. It seems to us that the validity of this genus (*Leptotrichia*) is questionable. Many bacteria grow in filaments and all the varieties of leptothrix grow in bacillary forms, the shorter rods often predominating over the filaments. The genus needs reinvestigation.

REFERENCES

BABES. Virchow's Arch., 1886, 105.
BAYNE-JONES, S. J. Bacteriol., 1925, 10:569.
BERESTNEW. Ztschr. f. Hyg., 1898, 29.
BOLLINGER. Deutsche Ztschr. f. Tiermed., 1877, 3.
BOSTROEM. Beitr. z. path. Anat., 1890–91, 9:1.
BREED, R. S., and CONN, H. J. J. Bacteriol., 1917, 4:585.
CARTER, V. Mycetoma, etc., London, 1874.
COLEBROOK, L. Brit. J. Exper. Pathol., 1920, 1:197.
ELLIS, D. Proc. Roy. Soc. Lond., Ser. B., 1912, 85:344.
EMMONS, C. W. U. S. Pub. Health Rep., 1938, 53:1967.
EPPINGER. Wien. klin. Wchnschr., 1890.
FLEXNER. J. Exper. M., 1896, 3.
GOLDWORTHY, W. E. J. Pathol. and Bacteriol., 1938, 46:207.
GRIFFITH, F. J. Hyg., 1916, 15:195.
HARRIS, P. N. Am. J. Pathol., 1933, 9:71.
HENRICI, A. T. Molds, Yeasts and Actinomycetes, New York, 1930, p. 257.

HENRICI and GARDNER. J. Infect. Dis., 1921, 28:232.

ISRAEL. Virchow's Arch., 1878, 74; 1879, 78:421.

JACOBSON, H. P. Fungous Diseases, Springfield, 1932.

KLINGER, R. Centralbl. f. Bakteriol., I Abt., 1912, 62:191.

LAWRENCE, W., NEUHAUSER, I., and HOWELL, K. J. Am. M. Ass., 1932, 99:300.

LIGNIÈRES, J., and SPITZ, G. Centralbl. f. Bakteriol., I Abt., 1904, 35:294, 452.

——— Rev. Soc. méd. argent., 1902, 10.

MacCALLUM, W. G. Centralbl. f. Bakteriol., I. Abt., 1902, 31:529.

MARTIN, D. F., JONES, C. P., YAO, K. F., and LEE, L. E. J. Bacteriol., 1937, 34:99.

NOCARD, E. Ann. de l'Inst. Pasteur, 1888, 2:293.

NORRIS and LARKIN. Proc. N. York Path. Soc., March, 1899.

PETRUSCHKY. Verhandl. d. Kong. f. innere Med., 1898.

RAVAUT and PINOY. Presse Méd., Paris, 1911, 19:49.

ROBIN, C. Arch. Physiol., Vol. 186 (cited from Bergey's *Manual*, 1931).

——— Des Végétaux qui croissent sur les animaux vivants, Paris, 1847, cited from I. Mackenzie.

——— A System of Bacteriology in Relation to Medicine, London, 1931, 8:91.

SMITH, T. J. Exper. M., 1918, 28:333.

THOMPSON, L., and WILLIUS, F. A. J. Am. M. Ass., 1932, 99:298.

WHERRY, W. B., and OLIVER, W. W. J. Infect. Dis., 1916, 19:299.

WICKERHAM, L. J., and RETTGER, L. F. Systematic investigation of the genus Monilia, 1938 (in press).

WOLFF, M., and ISRAEL, J. Arch. f. path. Anat., 1891, 126:4, 11.

WRIGHT, J. H. J. Med. Research, 1905, 13:349.

SECTION VII

DISEASES CAUSED BY ULTRAMICROSCOPIC VIRUSES. THE EXANTHEMATA AND DISEASES OF UNCERTAIN ETIOLOGY

CHAPTER LX

GENERAL CONSIDERATIONS OF ULTRAMICROSCOPIC VIRUSES AND VIRUS DISEASES

THE NATURE OF VIRUSES

In this section we shall consider agents of disease which are invisible under the microscope with ordinary illumination, usually able to pass through the pores of porcelain filters and which have not been cultivated *in vitro* in the absence of living susceptible cells. These are the agents of disease which for lack of more appropriate names are called *filtrable viruses*, or *ultramicroscopic viruses*. Rivers, in a review of the knowledge of the nature of viruses points out that invisibility, failure to be retained by filters, and inability to propagate themselves in the absence of living susceptible cells are negative properties, somewhat unsatisfactory for the definite characterization of these agents. Their positive characters are those which emphasize the fact that viruses have a most intimate relation with their host cells. They multiply only in the presence of susceptible cells, they are often specifically adapted to one or a few animal or plant hosts, they produce marked stimulation or destruction of cells, they often produce intracellular inclusion bodies and they usually lead to the production of lasting immunity in animals which survive their attacks. Filtrable viruses cause numerous diseases of man, animals, plants, insects and bacteria. Virus diseases range from dangerous and fatal to harmless conditions. Spectacular symptoms occur in most of the virus infections of man and animals, yet some viruses do not produce any clinical symptoms, giving rise to inapparent diseases (Cowdry).

Although Pasteur suspected that the cause of rabies might be an invisible organism smaller than bacteria, the first definite evidence that such agents of disease actually existed came in 1892 through the experiments of Iwanowski and Beijerinck on the transmission of mosaic disease of tobacco with cell-free filtrates of the juice of diseased plants. In 1897–98 Löffler and Frosch showed that the cause of foot and mouth disease was a filtrable virus. Since about 1920 there has been a great deal of active investigation in this field. Upwards of 100 diseases of plants and as many more diseases of animals and man are considered to be due to viruses.

Filtration.—The viruses were discovered by means of bacteria-retaining filters. Hence, filtrability has been so prominent a characteristic of the viruses that they have been generally designated "filtrable viruses." This is an unsatisfactory term, as it places too much emphasis upon a physical means of separating electrically charged particles, which gives no fundamental information as to the nature of the particles. We have attempted to avoid this term, preferring the less objectionable, though still unsatisfactory, designation "ultramicroscopic virus." The term "virus" is becoming sufficient as a name for these agents. But whatever term is used, it is necessary for a comprehension of this subject to discuss *filtration*.

Two types of filters have been used: (1) candles or disks of diatomaceous earth, or unglazed porcelain, and (2) collodion membranes of determinable porosity. Most of the work with viruses has been done with the first type of filter, the well-known Berkefeld, Chamberland and Mandler filters. The second type of filter has been useful in indicating the possible range of the sizes of virus particles.

The Berkefeld filters, in grades W, N and V are said to have pores or channels of approximately the following diameters: W, 3 to 4 μ; N, 5 to 7 μ; V, 18 to 12 μ. Mudd found that the intergranular spaces of Berkefeld filters were of the order of 3.8 μ to 7.1 μ. It is apparent from these figures that the pores of filters which retain bacteria are wider than the diameters of the organisms. As the channels in these filters are angular, it has been suggested that bacteria are retained in them because the rigid cylindrical organisms cannot turn the corners. This may be true to some extent and may explain why a very flexible spirochete like *Leptospira* can slip through a filter. But this explanation does not hold for the spherical bacteria, 1 μ or less in diameter, which are retained by these filters. Evidently other factors come into play in the filtration process.

The factors influencing filtrability have been studied by many investigators abroad and in this country, notably by Mudd, Kramer, Holman, Bronfenbrenner, Grinnell, Ward and Tang, and Varney and Bronfenbrenner.

These investigators have shown that: The walls of the capillary pores of a filter are electrically charged and will absorb particles carrying a charge of opposite sign (Kramer). Motile and flexible organisms may pass through or grow through the walls of filters. The period of the filtration process and the pressure upon the fluid have an influence on the result; organisms retained from fluids which pass through filters in a short time under pressures of 20 to 50 mm. Hg. may traverse filters when the process is carried on for an hour or more under greater pressures. The reaction of the fluid containing the particles is important with respect to the electrical charges upon the particles and the walls of the filter pores. Filters coated with paraffin oil permit the passage of colloidal particles which the unoiled filter would retain (Holman). It is possible that lipoidal coatings of filter pores may have a similar effect. Meat infusion broth (Bronfenbrenner) and hormone medium (Grinnell, Ward and Tang) will change the retentiveness of Berkefeld filters. Hence this type of suspending fluid aids filtrability of particles which would not be filtrable when suspended in saline solution. Kendall's medium was found to be a material of the type which renders filters permeable or traversable (Varney and Bronfenbrenner).

The older tests of filters made by noting the rate of flow of distilled water through them or the pressure required to bubble air through a filter under water are useful to detect gross leaks, but are not safe guides as to whether or not the filter will hold back bacteria.

Tests of the retentiveness of a filter by adding bacteria to the material to be filtered are useful when the bacteria are held back but inconclusive when the bacteria pass through. Grinnell found that an old culture of *B. prodigiosus* would pass through a filter impermeable to a young culture. Perhaps there were filtrable forms of the bacterium in the old culture. Young cultures of *B. prodigiosus* passed through Berkefeld V and N filters when suspended in a modified hormone broth or alkaline extracts of animal or vegetable cells.

The conclusion to be drawn from these facts is that filtration through Berkefeld filters and similar candles is a physical process, and that filtrability is determined more by electrical charge, surface forces, time, pressure, and plasticity of the organism than by actual size of the organism. All of this tends to tear down the fence which the walls of filters at one time placed between fields of knowledge and conceptions of the nature of organisms. Filters remain as apparatus of great utility, but lose their old definitive significance.

Filtration through *collodion membranes of graded porosity*, long studied by Bechhold, have been used by a number of investigators as a means of determining the sizes of particles. A valuable contribution to the knowledge of the sizes of the pores and of the processes of filtration in ether-alcohol collodion membranes and films of acetic acid collodion has been made by Elford in the course of his studies of the ultramicroscopic structure and methods of preparation of these filters. Directions for the preparation of ultrafilters have been published also by Krueger and Ritter.

Sizes.—The suggestion of Beijerinck that a virus was a fluid—a "contagium fluidum virum"—was soon displaced by the belief that a virus is particulate. This is the predominant opinion. The size of a virus particle is not known with certainty. It is likely that the viruses in material from lesions are adsorbed on colloidal particles or aggregates. The measurements of these sizes, made by ultrafiltration, and by sedimentation rates vary from 10 mμ for the virus of foot and mouth disease to 175 mμ for vaccine virus. This enormous range of differences in size (diameter) indicates that the investigators may have been measuring particles on which virus was adsorbed. It is generally accepted, however, that the range of sizes of viruses is relatively enormous. They grade down from the elementary bodies of vaccinia, fowl pox, infectious myxomatosis of rabbits, infectious fibromas and psittacosis, with diameters of 150 to 250 mμ to the minute viruses of poliomyelitis and foot and mouth disease, with diameters of 10 to 12 mμ. The larger viruses may or may not be gigantic protein macromolecules. The smaller viruses, represented by the rod-shaped particle of tobacco mosaic virus may be macromolecules of nucleo-protein. Comparative sizes of viruses are shown in Figure 103, a chart prepared by Dr. W. M. Stanley and used as an illustration for this Sigma Xi lecture on virus proteins.

Electrical Charge.—Under ordinary biological conditions, in tissue fluids, virus particles carry a negative charge and can be concentrated at the anode by cataphoresis. At least the virus-bearing particle has a negative charge. The actual charge on the virus itself cannot be determined until a "pure virus" is available.

Purification.—The chief methods used to purify viruses are those of selective adsorption on aluminum hydroxide or other absorbents followed by elution with phosphate solutions. The methods of enzyme chemistry are applicable here.

In 1935 Stanley crystallized the virus of tobacco mosaic. He discovered that it is a gigantic molecule, a macromolecule of weight of the order of 17,000,000. By salt-

COMPARATIVE SIZES OF VIRUSES

	Molecular weight X 10⁻⁶ (Particle weight X6.06 X 10¹⁷)	Diam. or length X width in mμ
Red blood cells*	173 000 000	7 500
Bacillus prodigiosus*	173 000	750
Rickettsia*	11 100	300
Psittacosis*	8 500	275
Vaccinia*	2 300	
Myxoma*	2 300	175
Canary pox*	2 300	
Pleuro-pneumonia organism*	1 400	
Pseudo rabies	1 400	150
Ectromelia	1 400	
Herpes simplex	1 400	
Rabies fixe'	800	125
Borna disease	800	
Influenza	700	120
Vesicular stomatitis	410	100
Staphylococcus bacteriophage †	300	90
Fowl plague	300	
C₁₆ bacteriophage	173	75
Chicken tumor I *	142	70
Tobacco mosaic *	43	430 X 12.3
Cucumber mosaics 3 and 4 *	43	
Gene (Muller's est. of max. size) *	33	125 X 20
Latent mosaic of potato *	26	430 X 9.8
Rabbit papilloma (Shope)*	25	40
Equine encephalitis	23	38
Megatherium bacteriophage	23	
Rift valley fever	11	30
Tomato bushy stunt *	9	28
Tobacco ring spot *	7.4	26
Hemocyanin molecule (Busycon)*	6.7	59 X 13.2
Yellow fever	4.3	22
Louping ill	2.8	19
Hemocyanin molecule (Octopus)*	2.8	64 X 8
Poliomyelitis	0.7	12
Staphylococcus bacteriophage†	0.4	10
Foot-and-mouth disease	0.4	
Hemoglobin molecule (Horse) *	0.069	2.8 X 0.6 [¹⁄₁₀ th these sizes]
Egg albumin molecule*	0.040	1.8 X 0.6

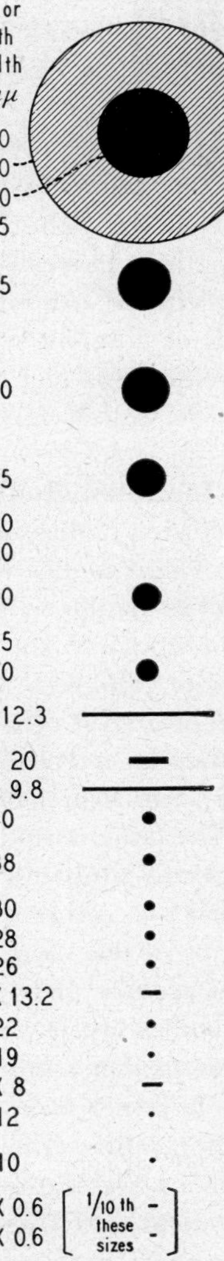

FIG. 103.—COMPARATIVE SIZES OF VIRUSES.

A chart showing the relative sizes of several selected viruses, including bacteriophages, as compared to those of red blood cells, Bacillus prodigiosus, rickettsia, pleuropneumonia organism, and protein molecules. The figures for size have been arbitrarily selected from data available in the literature. Particles known to be asymmetric are so indicated and the estimated length and width and the molecular weight in accordance with the asymmetry are given. In other cases where the particles are known or assumed to be spherical, the diameter and the molecular weight based on a sphere of density 1.3 are given. *, Evidence regarding shape available. †, Large size from filtration and sedimentation of concentrated solutions and small size from diffusion of dilute solutions. (Reproduced from Science in Progress, The Yale University Press, 1939, by permission of Dr. W. M. Stanley and The Yale University Press.)

ing-out and by the use of the ultracentrifuge Stanley isolated other viruses having the same general physical and chemical properties. For these substances he introduced the designation *"virus proteins."* According to his hypothesis, elaborated in 1938, a virus protein reproduces itself from the materials of a living cell by a process resembling autocatalysis, an enzymatic reaction catalyzed by the same kind of molecules that are introduced.

Cultivation.—The only proved instances of propagation or increase of virus in materials outside the body of an animal or plant are those in which living cells have been present in the culture medium. Tissue cultures and emulsions of cells have been used for these purposes.

Adaptation.—Viruses exhibit changes in their properties in passage through susceptible animals of different species. Examples of this are the conversion of small-pox virus into vaccine virus and the acquisition of the power to produce encephalitis in monkeys gained by yellow fever virus when "passed" by intracerebral inoculation through mice.

Intracellular Inclusion Bodies.—Cells of plants, animals and man infected by viruses develop inclusion bodies in the cytoplasm or in the nucleus. Examples of these formations are the Negri bodies of rabies, the coccoid bodies of Borrel in fowl pox, the polyhedral bodies in the wilt disease of caterpillars, and others which will be mentioned in connection with the specific diseases. The nature of these bodies is not known with certainty, although their presence usually indicates that the cells are under the influence of a virus. Three theories have been proposed to account for them. The inclusion bodies have been regarded as (1) products of degeneration of the cell substance, (2) virus aggregates, and (3) virus particles mantled or clothed with cellular material. The last conception was the origin of the name *Chlamydozoa* applied to the viruses. It seems probable that these inclusions are not always simply products of mitochondrial or cellular degeneration. It is equally probable that they are not the visible forms of the virus. Inclusions may or may not contain virus. In most cases, the inclusion appears to be composed of both virus and cellular material. The sizes of inclusion bodies are usually larger than the viruses.

Inclusion bodies have a number of specific characteristics and are valuable aids in diagnosis. They have not been found in all virus diseases. For example, none has been found in poliomyelitis. Their presence or absence was regarded by McKinley as a main basis for a classification of virus diseases.

Effects of Physical and Chemical Agents.—The resistance of viruses to ultraviolet light, disinfectants, heat and cold is almost the same as that of the vegetative forms of bacteria. The degrees of resistance and susceptibility of viruses to these agents are, in general, within the range of bacterial resistance. The viruses are less resistant than bacterial spores.

Immunity.—After recovery from most of the virus diseases animals and man usually have a strong and lasting immunity to reinfection. The sera of recovered animals and patients are capable of neutralizing the homologous virus. Complement fixing, precipitating and agglutinating antibodies for viruses have been demonstrated by Schultz and others. It is well established, therefore, that the viruses are active antigens, with specific properties. Immunization with "killed" virus has not been successful.

Viruses and Filtrable Forms of Bacteria.—In the chapter on variation of bacteria we have discussed the evidence for the existence of filtrable forms of bacteria. It is admitted that bacteria may pass through filters under certain conditions and that these filtrable forms may be small viable particles of bacterial protoplasm—either viable fragments or especially small forms, gonidia perhaps—developed during the growth phases of the organisms. We have indicated in this chapter that filtrability through Berkefeld filters has lost its fundamental significance as a measure of size, since the physics of bacterial filtration has been more fully understood. The existence of filtrable forms of bacteria does not prove that these forms are a phase of a life cycle, and we have expressed the opinion that while the evidence on the supposed life cycles of bacteria is increasing and improving in quality, it is not yet convincing. The point of this discussion is that several investigators, notably Rosenow and Kendall in this country, have advanced the thesis that the ultramicroscopic viruses are the invisible, filtrable cyclo-stages of ordinary bacteria. Rosenow has drawn his evidence from his frequent discovery of streptococci in the lesions or in cultures from poliomyelitis and encephalitis. Others suggest that the virus of yellow fever is the invisible filtrable stage of *Leptospira icteroides*; that the virus of hog cholera is the filtrable stage of *B. suipestifer*. Kendall's experiments on the reduction of gross bacteria to ultramicroscopic dimensions and to a filtrable state in his special medium and the development of bacterial forms by transfers from filtrates may or may not be acceptable proof of the filtrability of bacteria. These experiments do not provide convincing evidence that the viruses which we are considering here are the same as ultramicroscopic, filtrable forms of ordinary bacteria. In 1932, Hadley wrote that no adequate proof had been brought forward to show that the virus-like stages of bacteria were related to the filtrable viruses. We are not convinced by any of the evidence presented to support the conception of viruses as having a bacterial origin. In fact we regard this as highly improbable.

The Problem of the Nature of Viruses.—Are the viruses, and bacteriophage, living or inanimate? It is generally accepted that the fundamental attributes of life are metabolic assimilation of heterogeneous substances which are built up into the substance of the organism, reproduction and adaptation. Viruses appear to have these properties. They have antigenic, and therefore chemical, specificity, they increase in numbers, and they change in response to differences in environment. All these properties, however, are exhibited only when the virus is associated with a living cell. Hence it is not possible to state definitely whether the virus is acting independently or whether the cell, under the stimulus of an inanimate substance, elaborates more of the same substance from its own materials. Many investigators are of the opinion that viruses are enzymes and that their minute size precludes their being living things. Crystalline viruses obtained by Stanley from tobacco mosaic and by Bawden and Pirie from bushy stunt of tomatoes are non-living according to the usual understanding of the word. Reproduction of virus proteins may explain the way in which protoplasm grows.

As Rivers and others have pointed out, there are three main possibilities as regards the nature of viruses. Some viruses may be extremely small living organisms, "the midgets of the microbial world," possessed of a nature like that of familiar living organisms; others may represent forms of life unrecognized at present; and finally others may be inanimate transmissible agents of disease. The evidence does not compel a choice of one or the other of these views. In the end it may be found that all three are true. In the ingenious arguments over the nature and origin of viruses the old doctrine of spontaneous generation has emerged with vitality under the guise of conceptions of "autocatalysis." (Rivers.)

Classification.—As viruses are known chiefly by their effects upon living plants and animals the classifications which have been proposed have been based upon the special affinities of the viruses for tissues of animals, plants, insects and bacteria. A classification according to relationships to hosts would list the viruses as "parasites" of plants, insects, fishes, fowls, various lower animals and man. While host-specificities are numerous and strict, there is considerable overlapping in such a classification. Levaditi and others have classified the viruses according to their ectodermotropic, mesodermotropic and neurotropic propensities in animals and man. The viruses, however, are not so strictly limited in their affinities as to be classifiable in this manner. McKinley's classification takes into consideration items of cell inclusions, filtrability and transmissibility and is a classification of virus diseases. They may be classified also in accordance with their effects, as neoplastic necrotizing or lytic agents. There is no generally accepted classification of the viruses.

Topley and Wilson classify the viruses in the following groups:

Group A, characterized by lesions of the skin: variola, vaccinia, herpes, etc.

Group B, characterized by lesions of the central nervous system: poliomyelitis, encephalitis, rabies, etc.

Group C, characterized by catarrhal or generalized infections: influenza, measles, yellow fever, etc.

Group D, characterized by tumor formation: Rous sarcoma, fowl leukemia, papillomatosis and fibromatosis of rabbits, warts, etc.

In the subsequent chapters we shall deal briefly with typical virus diseases of plants and animals and consider in some detail the more important virus diseases of man.

The diseases of man caused by viruses are measles, German measles, mumps, herpes febrilis, herpes zoster, varicella, small pox, Alastrim, vaccinia, rabies, psittacosis, common colds, influenza, encephalitis (St. Louis, Japanese, and equine and epidemic types), lymphocytic choriomeningitis, poliomyelitis, lymphogranuloma inguinale, Australian X disease, louping ill, Rift valley fever, yellow fever, pappataci fever, dengue fever, warts, foot and mouth disease, pemphigus, and molluscum contagiosum.

REFERENCES

BAWDEN, F. C., and PIRIE, N. W. Nature, 1938, 141:513.
BRONFENBRENNER, J. J. J. Exper. M., 1927, 45:873.
COWDRY, E. V. Scientific Monthly, 1937, 45:266.
ELFORD, W. J. Proc. Roy. Soc., Lond., Ser. B., 1930, 106:216; 1933, 112:384.
——— Brit. J. Exper. Pathol., 1929, 10:126.
GRINNELL, F. B. J. Bacteriol., 1929, 18:175.
HADLEY, P. Proc. Inst. Med. Chicago, 1932, 9:62, esp. p. 78.
HOLMAN, W. L. Am. J. Pathol., 1926, 2:483.
——— J. Lab. & Clin. M., 1926, 12:158.

KENDALL, A. I. Northwestern Univ. Bull., 1931, 32: No. 5 and No. 8.
—— Science, 1931, 74:129; 1932, 75:295.
KRAMER, S. P. J. Gen. Physiol., 1926, 9:811.
—— J. Infect. Dis., 1927, 40:343.
—— The Newer Knowledge of Bacteriology and Immunology, Chicago, 1928, 557.
KRUEGER, A. P., and RITTER. J. Gen. Physiol., 1930, 13:409.
—— Science, 1933, 77:288.
LEVADITI, C. Presse méd., 1938, No. 102:1889.
LIPSCHÜTZ, B. Chlamydozoen, etc., in Handb. d. path. Mikroorg. ed. by Kolle, Kraus and Uhlen-
    huth, 3rd ed., Berlin, 1930, 8:311–418.
MCKINLEY, E. B. Science, 1932, 76:449.
—— Filtrable Virus and Rickettsia Diseases, Bureau of Science, Manila, 1929.
—— Philippine J. Sc., 1929, 39.
MUDD, S. Am. J. Physiol., 1922, 63:429.
—— J. Bacteriol., 1923, 8:459.
RIVERS, T. M. Physiol. Rev., 1932, 12:423.
—— Ann. Int. M., 1936, 9:1466.
—— J. Ann. M. Ass., 1936, 107:206.
—— J. Bacteriol., 1937, 33:1.
—— Bull. New York Acad. M., 1938, 14:383.
RIVERS, T. M., et al. Filtrable Viruses, Williams and Wilkins Co., Baltimore, 1928.
STANLEY, W. M. Science, 1935, 81:644.
—— J. Biol. Chem., 1937, 117:733.
—— J. Phys. Chem., 1938, 42:55.
—— J. App. Physics, 1938, 9:148.
—— Am. Naturalist, 1938, 72:110.
—— The Isolation and Properties of Tobacco Mosaic and Other Virus Proteins. The Harvey
    Lectures, 1937–38.
VARNEY, P. L., and BRONFENBRENNER, J. J. Proc. Soc. Exper. Biol., 1932, 29:804.
VINSON, C. G., and PETRE, A. W. Contributions from Boyce Thompson Institute, 1931, 3:131, 147.
Virus Diseases, by various authors, Vol. 7, in A System of Bacteriology in Relation to Medicine,
    London, 1930.
WARD, H. K., and TANG, F. J. Exper. M., 1929, 49:1.

CHAPTER LXI

VIRUS DISEASES OF PLANTS AND ANIMALS

The virus diseases of plants and animals are numerous and important. Several of the diseases of animals are transmissible to man. Investigations of them have yielded most of the fundamental knowledge of the viruses. As the subject is too large to be treated in detail in this book, the reader is referred to the comprehensive reviews of Rivers.

Mosaic Disease of Plants.—The plant disease known as tobacco mosaic was first recognized by Swieten in 1857. In 1892 Iwanowski discovered that the disease was caused by a filtrable virus. This was the first demonstration of an ultramicroscopic virus and this virus has continued to be one of great importance for scientific studies. In 1898 Beijerinck confirmed Iwanowski's findings and emphasized the great difference which exists between viruses, which he regarded as a "contagium fluidum vivum" and ordinary bacteria.

In 1935 Stanley crystallized this virus, discovering that it is a macromolecule of protein of rod shape, with a weight of approximately 17,000,000 and a diameter of 33 mμ. The virus retained its infection, antigenic, physical and chemical properties through numerous fractional crystallizations and recrystallizations. It appears to reproduce itself by a process of autocatalysis.

Bawden and Pirie have obtained the virus of bushy stunt of tomatoes in true crystalline form.

Silkworm Jaundice.—This is a disease which affects the caterpillar of the silkworm moth. It is characterized by the development of patches in the skin which may become edematous, decolorized, yellowish and dry. It has been extensively studied by von Prowazek, who proved its filtrability and described small, shining spots, which were present in large numbers in the blood, and which he was able to stain by Giemsa. In tissue sections he found similar bodies by the Levaditi method in the nuclei of some of the cells.

This is a type of the numerous "polyhedral diseases" of insects. The polyhedral bodies are regarded as arising in various cells from the nuclear changes produced by the virus. They do not contain the virus.

Leukemia of Chickens.—This is a disease closely analogous to human leukemia in which similar blood changes, alterations of the bone marrow and enlarged spleen are present. It was shown to be transmissible in series with blood and to be filtrable, by Ellermann and Bang in 1908.

Furth studied simple strains of leucosis virus and sarcoma as well as complex strains which produced both erythroleukosis and sarcoma.

Chicken Diphtheria.—This disease, which was at first believed to be caused by a bacillus not unlike the diphtheria bacillus, was shown to be due to a filtrable virus by Uhlenhuth. Bordet has cultivated minute micro-organisms from chicken diphtheria on the same medium upon which he grows whooping-cough bacilli. Chicken diphtheria is one of a number of "croupous diseases" of fowls. It is different from fowl pox.

Fowl Pox (*Epithelioma Contagiosum of Chickens*).—This is a disease of chickens in which small knobs form about the combs and head. The filtrability of this disease was shown by Marx and Sticker in 1902. The virus has not been cultivated so far. Von Prowazek and Lipschütz have described small bodies which can be stained by the Löffler flagella stain in the cells of the affected tissues.

These "elementary bodies" of von Prowazek resemble the minute granules seen in molluscum contagiosum, variola and vaccinia. Borrel believed that they were the actual virus particles and this view was adopted by Paschen, Lipschütz, and others. Goodpasture, who has studied the specific granules of fowl pox and "other pox diseases," has furnished evidence that the minute particles are probably virus particles while the larger cell inclusions are colonies or masses of virus. Goodpasture has proposed the name *Borreliota* for the group of these organisms, with the designation *Borreliota avium* for the organism of fowl pox. Canary pox virus has been studied by Burnet.

In 1914 Sanfelice expressed the opinion that the cause of fowl-pox is an inanimate substance which acting upon normal cells causes these cells to produce more of the same material which in turn is capable of attacking other cells.

Fowl Plague (*La Peste aviaire, Huehner Pest*).—This is a rapidly fatal disease of chickens, the virus of which was first filtered by Centanni and Savonuzzi. The chickens show signs of weakness and sleepiness, the comb becomes violet, and death may occur in a few days or may take a slow form lasting a week or longer. The virus appears in the blood. Centanni infected by subcutaneous injection of minute amounts of blood and by feeding. The serum produces the disease as well as the whole blood. Marchoux claims to have cultivated the virus in a 2 per cent glucose, 1 per cent peptone agar inoculated with small amounts of blood. Landsteiner and Berliner by similar methods succeeded in infecting with the ninth subculture in amounts no greater than the original material. They believe that whole-blood cells are necessary in the culture medium and not merely a blood extract. The virus seems to concentrate in the nervous system at a time when it disappears from the blood.

Chicken Sarcoma.—The transplantable sarcoma of chickens was found to be due to a filtrable virus by Rous in 1910. The first tumor worked with was a spindle cell sarcoma with a tendency to myxomatous degeneration. Later, Rous obtained similar results with an osteochondroma of chickens.

Since 1911, Rous and his associates and others have discovered additional varieties of tumors of fowls which are transmissible by cell-free filtrates.

In 1925, Gye reported experiments indicating that the material causing this and certain other tumors was divisible into a virus fraction and an activating fraction. He claimed to have cultivated the virus in serum broth with chick embryo. Mueller was unable to confirm this work and Gye's theories of the nature of the tumor-producing agent have not been accepted. Barnard claimed to have photographed the virus particles by the use of ultraviolet light, but there is no certainty as to the nature of the small particles demonstrated by this means.

Murphy, who has obtained the Rous tumor agent in a relatively pure state by a series of precipitations, has expressed the opinion that the agent is not a living thing, but is a substance like an enzyme.

On the basis of studies of the virus induced tumors of fowls, leucosis of chickens and the carcinomas of rabbits which follow injections of the Shope virus of papillomatosis Rous, Gye and others have developed a theory that viruses may be the cause of cancer. Extremely important findings for the whole tumor problem are anticipated from further investigations along these lines. For a review of the subject the reader is referred to the Harvey lecture delivered by Rous in 1935 and the series of papers by him and his associates published in the Journal of Experimental Medicine since that year.

Distemper of Dogs.—Canine distemper is most common among young dogs, but ferrets, foxes, raccoons and other animals are susceptible to the disease. Man is insusceptible. The disease is characterized by fever, catarrhal and purulent secretions from the respiratory tract, diarrhea and sometimes nervous symptoms due to encephalitis. The disease causes severe losses in kennels and fox farms. It has always been known to be extremely infectious. The diseased animals are susceptible to secondary bacterial infection of the respiratory tract, chiefly with *B. bronchisepticus.*

Carré in 1905 showed that the agent of distemper was filtrable. Since then, Laidlaw and Dunkin, in England, have confirmed this, and have solved the problem of the etiology of the disease. They have contributed greatly to the knowledge of the virus of distemper and have prepared vaccines of attenuated and living virus which appear to be effective agents for prophylactic immunization.

African Horse-sickness.—The African horse-sickness has caused great ravages among horses, repeatedly occurring in epidemic outbreaks. It is transmitted by a filtrable virus and can be inoculated with filtrates obtained from diluted blood of tested animals. The virus is present in the peritoneal fluid and in the serous exudates of the lesions. Horses, mules and donkeys are susceptible. It does not seem to be contagious and is probably transmitted by insects. It was first filtered by Nocard and has been studied by M'Fadyan.

Pernicious Anemia of Horses.—This disease, widespread in Africa, was not recognized as a specific infection and clinical entity until Theiler and Kehoe in 1915 discovered it in the course of other experimentation. It appears in an acute and chronic form of which anemia is one of the minor symptoms, and is not, therefore, the most suitable name. The virus is present in the blood, which remains infectious even after the horse has recovered. The process of natural infection is not known, though insects are a possibility. Also, it was found that the disease can be passed from horse to horse not only with injections of the blood, but by administering urine by mouth. The virus is filtrable through Berkefeld candles, if the blood or urine is suitably diluted. The first active filtrates were obtained by Carré and Vallée.

Equine Encephalitis.—For many years horses in the eastern and western portions of the United States have been subject to a paralyzing or fatal disease of the central nervous system. This disease, known as encephalomyelitis is caused by a filtrable virus. It is apparently transmitted by contact and by mosquitoes. Pheasants also have the natural disease. (Tyzzerl.)

In 1938 the disease came into special prominence because cases of human infection appeared among persons attending horses sick with encephalomyelitis. Fothergill, Webster, Howitt, Feemster and others proved that the virus from the human lesions was identical with the virus from the horses.

Rinderpest.—The disease of cattle known by this name and spoken of by the French as *la peste bovine* has been a serious economic scourge for centuries. Clinically, it is characterized by catarrhal conditions of the nasal mucous membrane, with fever, conjunctival infection, profuse diarrhea and rapid emaciation. The animals die on the tenth or eleventh day. Autopsy findings, according to Nicolle, show congestion and sometimes ulceration of nasal and buccal mucous membranes and a marked intestinal inflammation in which the lymph follicles show alterations not unlike those of typhoid fever. The liver is particularly characteristic. Koch found that the disease can be transmitted from animal to animal with minute amounts of blood. The experimental methods in the study of this disease were worked out in great detail by Kolle and Turner. The virus is also present in the secretions and intestinal contents. A curious fact noticed by Kolle and Turner, as well as by Nicolle and Adil-Bey, is that there is no loss of infectiousness of the blood even in high dilutions. Filtration experiments are not uniformly successful. However, Nicolle and Adil-Bey succeeded in obtaining positive filtrations by various methods which depended upon a very high dilution of the virus. Their best results were obtained when they injected into the peritoneal cavity and filtered the peritoneal washings in high dilution. Direct filtration of the blood was unsuccessful.

As animals which recover from rinderpest have a solid and lasting immunity, many attempts have been made to prepare an effective prophylactic vaccine. Kelser succeeded in doing this by treating with chloroform a ground-up emulsion of the spleens and lymph nodes of animals killed in the acute stage of the disease. The use of this vaccine has effected great savings of valuable cattle, and has been applied with advantage on a large scale in the Philippines.

Catarrhal Fever of Sheep.—This disease is common in South Africa where it has been at times a serious economic problem. It is spoken of sometimes as "blue tongue." The most extensive articles available upon the condition are those of Spreull and of Theiler. Spreull determined that the disease is not contagious and suspects that there is an intermediate insect host, though the responsible insect has not been determined. The blood is virulent and the virus was filtrable through Berkefeld candles. By immunization of recovered sheep, a serum which has protective effects was produced.

Sheep Pox.—This is a pustular disease of sheep probably transmitted by direct and indirect contact. The infectious material has been filtered by Borrel who was able to transmit the disease with filtrate. The virus is found in the blood, in the pustular fluid, and sometimes in the milk. Borrel obtained virus from filtration in an interesting way, by inoculating into the pleura, obtaining, four or five hours later, a very virulent pleural fluid. He also obtained fluid by producing enormous pustules by subcutaneous inoculation into the axilla. *Clavelée*, or sheep pox, is a disease of great economic importance and Borrel did a considerable amount of work upon a method of sero-vaccination in this disease which has proved to be of value.

Agalactia of Sheep and Goats.—This is a condition in which the symptoms are chiefly connected with changes in amounts and nature of the milk. There is a local inflammatory reaction of the mammary glands followed by joint swellings and often accompanied by lesions of the eye, particularly a keratitis with a copious flow of tears and conjunctival inflammation. The cornea may ulcerate. The disease has been of great economic importance, especially in Italy and the Basses Alpes. Celli and Blasi first showed that the disease could be transmitted with a filtrable virus. The disease has been carefully studied by Carré.

Hog Cholera.—A very serious epidemic disease of hogs was formerly believed to be caused by the bacillus of hog cholera, a member of the paratyphoid group, and the bacillus is unquestionably found in a large percentage of the diseased hogs, but in 1903 De Schweinitz and Dorset showed that the virus causing it was filtrable and that the presence of the hog cholera bacillus was probably a purely secondary phenomenon. This disease has been the subject of extensive investigation by methods of immunization in which separate simultaneous injections of virus and serum of hyperimmunized animals are made.

Foot and Mouth Disease.—This malady occurs chiefly in cattle, sheep and goats, more rarely in other domestic animals. It is characterized by the appearance of a vesicular eruption localized upon the mucosa of the mouth and upon the delicate skin between the hoofs. In the females similar eruptions may appear upon the udders. With the onset of the eruption there may be increased temperature; refusal of food, and general depression. Usually the disease is mild; the vesicles become small ulcers and pustules. Occasionally the disease is complicated by catarrhal gastro-enteritis or an inflammation of the respiratory tract, and death may ensue.

The disease is transmitted from animal to animal by means of virus contained in the vesicular contents. Infection may also take place through the agency of milk.

Rarely the disease may be transmitted to man. Such infection, when it does take place, occurs usually among the milkers and attendants in dairies, and is transmitted by direct contact. The disease in man is usually very mild. Mohler states that the disease may be transmitted to man by the milk of infected animals.

The causative agent of foot and mouth disease is unknown. A number of organisms have been cultivated from the vesicles and mucous membranes of afflicted animals, but none of these could be shown to have etiological significance. Löffler and Frosch demonstrated that the virus contained in the vesicles may pass through the pores of a filter. The virus is easily destroyed by heating to 60° C. and by complete dessication. There are several types of viruses of foot and mouth disease and of vesicular stomatitis. Olitsky (1934) and others have shown that there is a generic relation between these viruses and the virus of equine encephalomyelitis.

One attack of foot and mouth disease protects against subsequent attacks. This immunity in most cases lasts for years, though rare cases of recurrence within a single year have been reported. Löffler has actively immunized horses and cattle with graded doses of virus obtained from vesicles and with the sera of such animals has produced passive immunity in normal subjects.

A serious outbreak of foot and mouth disease occurred in 1914 in the United States, extending to twenty-two states and the District of Columbia. During this epidemic the susceptibility of swine to the disease was thoroughly proved. Eradication of the disease is described by Mohler as depending upon the following measures:

1. *Immunization.*—Mohler states that while Löffler's work on serum treatment in

this disease is of great scientific interest, its practical value is problematical. Small doses do not protect, but larger doses do if repeated. Since the amounts to be given range from 30 to 200 c.c., treatment is expensive and even then 6 to 8 per cent of failures occur. Moreover, Mohler states as another disadvantage that the preparation of the serum requires the propagation of the virus in the country, which would be a constant menace to the stock industry.

2. *Quarantine and Disinfection.*—In general, Mohler is discouraging in regard to quarantine and disinfection without slaughter. A quarantine sufficiently isolated to be of value in a disease so easily transmitted presents great difficulties in connection with the domestic animals.

3. *Slaughter and Disinfection.*—This, according to Mohler, is the only satisfactory and economical method for controlling the disease in a country like the United States where the infection is not indigenous. The details of applying this method will be found in the circular by Mohler referred to above.

The following facts, taken from Table II of Mohler's articles on the 1914 outbreak, indicate the economic importance of the disease. In Illinois, which was apparently the center of the epidemic, from November, 1914, to May, 1916, the animals that had to be slaughtered were as follows: cattle, 31,074; swine, 45,500; sheep, 18,006; goats, 57, and deer, 9. There were fifty-four infected counties in the state. The appraised value of the animals slaughtered in the state was $2,509,102, and the appraised value of the animals slaughtered in the country as a whole from October, 1914, to May, 1916, was $5,865,720.

In 1924, Frosch and Dahmen claimed to have cultivated the virus of foot and mouth disease on ordinary media. This has not been confirmed by those who have repeated these experiments.

Virus of Guinea-pig Paralysis.—There is a disease in guinea-pigs which has superficial similarity to human poliomyelitis in that the virus is constantly present in the central nervous system of the spontaneously diseased animals. Römer succeeded in transmitting the disease by intracerebral injection of filtered brain. The disease appears nine to twenty days after inoculation, eventually developing paralysis before death.

Filtrable Rabbit Virus of Rivers.—In experiments in which he attempted to transmit chickenpox to rabbits by intratesticular injection, Rivers encountered a filtrable virus which caused local infiltration of the injected tissues with lymphocytic cells and local swelling. Papules and inflammation of the skin and upon the cornea can be produced with the material from lesions and nuclear inclusions in the endothelial cells and in the cells of the cornea were observed. This virus is chiefly of importance for investigators who are working on filtrable viruses in rabbits, since errors which Rivers avoided only by extreme care may be made by ignorance of the presence of this spontaneous disease in rabbits.

The virus is known as virus III. The spontaneous disease caused by the virus has not been recognized. Under experimental conditions it produces, in addition to lesions in the cornea, skin and testes, an encephalitis which is at times similar to that induced by herpetic virus. Virus III and herpetic virus, however, are not immunologically related.

Infectious Myxomatosis of Rabbits.—In 1898, Sanarelli described an infectious disease of laboratory or domesticated rabbits to which the name "infectious myxomatosis" has been given because the inflammatory lesions have some of the characteristics of tumors. Wild rabbits are insusceptible. Infection appears to take place through the upper respiratory tract or conjunctivae, and a discharging conjunctivitis is an early and noticeable symptom. Soon after the onset, nodules appear in the skin of different parts of the body. These are composed of proliferating and necrotic cells in large amounts of gelatinous matrix. The virus has been shown to be filtrable by Hobbs and others, although with the difficulties noted by Andrewes. Several types of inclusion bodies have been found in the cells in the lesion: (1) many small basophilic bodies within the cytoplasm of the tumor-like cells (Splendore and Lipschütz) and (2) acidophilic masses and granules in the cytoplasm of the epithelial cells overlying the lesions or involved in the vesicles. These were first described by Rivers who has obtained the elementary bodies in a relatively pure state.

Papillomatosis and Fibromatosis of Rabbits.—These two distinct diseases, occurring spontaneously in wild cottontail rabbits, were found by Shope in 1932 and 1933 to be caused by specific filtrable viruses.

Among the most important consequences of these discoveries has been the use of these viruses for the investigation of problems of cancer, particularly by Rous and Gye.

Encephalomyelitic Virus Diseases of Animals.—Some of the viruses have affinities for the central nervous system in man and animal and a most important group of diseases are the consequences of these neurotropic properties of viruses. Some of these diseases occur naturally in animals and are naturally transmissible to man. Others are transmissible from man to a few animals only with difficulty under experimental conditions. We have not space to discuss these diseases here, but will mention some of them which have not been previously discussed and cite references to articles dealing with them. Equine encephalitis has been mentioned above.

1. *Rabies.*—Rabies is probably the most important of this group. On account of its significance as a disease of man, we shall consider rabies in another chapter.

A rare disease of cattle, to which other animals are susceptible, is characterized by intense itching of some part of the skin, frenzy, and death in thirty-six to forty-eight hours. The disease became known as *pseudorabies*, from the investigations of Aujeszky. It is due to a filtrable virus. A similar or identical disease is known in this country as *mad itch*. The viruses of the two diseases appear to be almost identical (Shope, 1931; Hurst, 1933).

2. *Fox Encephalitis.*—The involvement of the nervous system is one phase of the pathological process. The disease has been studied especially by Green and his associates. Rosenow's view that streptococci are etiologically related to fox encephalitis has not been established.

3. *Encephalitis of Rabbits.*—This is an important disease, partly because of the confusion it has caused by its occurrence in animals used for the experimental investigation of other virus diseases of man. Levaditi, Nicolau, and Schoen, Doerr and Zdansky have described a sporulating protozoon in the lesions. This "body," named *Encephalitozoon cuniculi,* is supposed by them to be the parasitic cause of the disease. For general descriptions of the brain lesions of domestic rabbits and of spontaneous encephalitis of rabbits, the reader is referred to the papers of McCartney and DaFano

The coexistence of protozoan-like parasites and meningoencephalitis in mice has been noted by Cowdry and Nicholson.

4. *Borna's Disease.*—Borna's disease is an encephalomyelitis of horses, sheep and cattle. Kelser believes that the encephalitis prevalent among horses in the United States is a form of Borna's disease. The condition has been known to exist in the western and some of the southern and eastern states for over sixty years, and in the last few years has caused considerable economic losses in the west and southwest. It has been shown by Kelser that the virus of this disease can be experimentally transmitted by the *Aedes aegypti* mosquito, and epidemiological studies bear out the probable natural transmission by mosquitoes, although a number of different species may be responsible. The virus is infectious for guinea-pigs and monkeys and to a lesser degree for rabbits, rats and mice.

5. *Guinea-pig Paralysis.*—This is a disease showing some resemblance to poliomyelitis in man.

6. *Encephalitis of Sheep.*—There are apparently several kinds of virus infections of the central nervous system of sheep which may be transmissible to man. One of these may be related to the encephalitis of man known as Australian X disease. Another type is "louping ill," an encephalitis of sheep noted first in the border countries of England and Scotland. Pool, Brownlee, and Wilson showed that louping ill was due to a filtrable virus and Findlay transmitted the infection to monkeys. The virus produces meningoencephalitis with special involvement of the Purkinje cells of the cerebellum. From the report of Rivers and Schwenkter it seems probable that man is susceptible to this encephalitic virus of louping ill.

REFERENCES

ANDREWES, C. H. A System of Bacteriology in Relation to Medicine, London, 1930, Chap. XXV, p. 308.

AUJESZKY, A. Centralbl. f. Bakt., I Abt., 1902, 32:353.

BARNARD, J. E. Lancet, 1925, 2:117.

BAWDEN, F. C., and PIRIE, N. W. Nature, 1938, 141:513.

BEIJERINCK, M. W. Centralbl. f. Bakt., II Abt., 1899, 5:29.

BORDET, J. Ann. de l'Inst. Pasteur, 1910, 24:161.

BORDET, J., and FALLY, V. Ann. d. l'Inst. Pasteur, 1910, 24:563.

BORREL, A. Compt. rend. Soc. de biol., 1904, 57:642.

———— Etude experimentale de la clavelée, Ann. de l'Inst. Pasteur, 1903, 7:123, 732.

BORREL and SALIMBENI. Ann. de l'Inst. Pasteur, 1898, 12:240.

BURNET, F. M. J. Path. & Bacteriol., 1933, 37:107.

CARRÉ, H. Bull. Soc. centr. de méd. vét., 1905, 335.

———— Ann. de l'Inst. Pasteur, 1912, 26:937.

CARRÉ and VALLÉE. Compt. rend. Acad. d. sc., Paris, 1904, 139:331, 1239.

CELLI and BLASI. Ann. d'ig. sper., 1906, Fasc. 2, cited from Carré.

CENTANNI, E. Centralbl. f. Bakt., I Abt., 1902, 31:145.

CENTANNI, E., and SAVONUZZI. Acad. di Scienza, Ferrara, 1901.

COWDRY, E. V., and NICHOLSON, F. M. J. Exper. M., 1924, 40:51.

DaFANO, C. J. Path. & Bacteriol., 1924, 27:333.

———— Med. Sc. Abstr. & Rev., 1924, 10:355.

DE SCHWEINITZ. 20th Annual Report, U. S. Bureau animal indust., Wash., 1903.

DOERR, R., and ZDANSKY, E. Ztschr. f. Hyg. u. Infectionskrankh., 1924, 101:239.

DUJARDIN-BEUMETZ. Thèse, Paris, 1900.

———— Ann. de l'Inst. Pasteur, 1906, 20:449.

ELLERMANN, V., and BANG, O.   Centralbl. f. Bakteriol., I Abt., 1908, 46:595.

———— Ztschr. f. Hyg. u. Infectionskrankh., 1909, 63:231.

FEEMSTER, R. F.   Am. J. Pub. Health, 1938, 28:1403.

FERRY, N. S.   J. Infect. Dis., 1911, 8:399.

FINDLAY, G. M.   Brit. J. Exper. Path., 1928, 9:28; 1932, 13:230.

FOTHERGILL, L. D., DINGLE, J. H., FARBER, S., and CONNERLY, M. L.   New England J. M., 1938, 219, 411.

FROSCH and DAHMEN, H.   Berl. tierärztl. Wchnschr., 1924, 40:273.

———— Lancet, 1924, 1:962.

FURTH, J.   J. Exper. M. 1932, 55:465, 479, 495; 1933, 58:253.

———— J. Bact., 1936, 31:47.

GOODPASTURE, E. W.   Science, 77:119.

GOODPASTURE, E. W., and WOODRUFF, C. E.   Am. J. Pathol., 1929, 5:1; 1930, 6:7, 13; 1931, 7:1.

GREEN, R. G., ZIEGLER, N. R., GREEN, B. B., and DEWEY, E. T.   Am. J. Hyg., 1930, 12:109.

GYE, W. E.   Lancet, 1925, 2:109.

———— Brit. M. J., 1925, 2:291.

HOBBS, J. R.   Am. J. Hyg., 1928, 8:800 (quoted from Andrewes).

HOWITT, B.   J. Immunol., 1937, 33:235.

———— Science, 1938, 88, 455.

HURST, E. W.   J. Exper. M., 1933, 58:415.

IWANOWSKI, D.   Bull. d. Acad. imp. d. Sci. d. St. Pétersbourg, 1892, 13:237 (quoted from Centralbl. f. Bakteriol., II Abt., 1899, 5:250).

———— Centralbl. f. Bakteriol., Botan. Beihft., 1893, 3.

JOEST, E.   Ergeb. d. Allg. Path. u. path. Anat., I Abt., 1915, 18:359.

KELSER, R. A.   Philippine J. Sc., 1928, 36:373.

———— Manual Vet. Bact., 2nd ed., Baltimore, 1933.

KNEEBONE, J. LE M., and CLELAND, J. B.   Australian J. Exp. Biol. & Med. Sc., 1926, 3:119.

KOCH, R.   Centralbl. f. Bakteriol., I Abt., 1897, 21:526.

KOLLE, W., and TURNER, G.   Ztschr. f. Hyg. u. Infectionskrankh., 1898, 29:309.

KUNKEL, L. O.   Virus Diseases of Plants, Chap. IX, p. 335, in Filtrable Viruses, by T. M. Rivers, et al., Baltimore, 1928.

LAIDLAW, P. P.   A System of Bacteriology in Relation to Medicine, 1930, 7: Chap. XV, p. 232.

LAIDLAW, P. P., and DUNKIN, G. W.   J. Comp. Path. & Therap., 1926, 39:201, 213, 222; 1928, 41:1, 209.

LANDSTEINER, K., and BERLINER.   Centralbl. f. Bakteriol., I Abt., 1912, 67:165.

LEDINGHAM, J. C. G.   J. Path. & Bacteriol., 1933, 37:393.

LEVADITI, C., NICOLAU, S., and SCHOEN, R.   Ann. de l'Inst. Pasteur, 1924, 38:651.

LIPSCHÜTZ, B.   Wien. klin. Wchnschr., 1927, 40:1101.

LÖFFLER and FROSCH.   Centralbl. f. Bakteriol., I Abt., 1897, 22:257; 1898, 23:371.

MARCHOUX.   Compt. rend. Acad. d. sc., Paris, 1908, 147:357.

MARX, E., and STICKER, A.   Deutsche med. Wchnschr., 1902, 28:893.

McCARTNEY, J. E.   J. Exper. M., 1924, 39:51.

McKINLEY, E. B.   Filtrable Virus and Rickettsia Diseases, Bureau of Science, Manila, 1929.

———— Science, 1932, 76:1977.

M'FADYAN, J.   J. Comp. Path. & Therap., 1900, 13:1; 1901, 14:103.

MOHLER, J. R.   U. S. Dep. Agric., Circular No. 325, 1924.

———— Bull. No. 41, Pub. Health & U. S. Mar.-Hosp. Serv., Washington, 1908.

MUELLER, H.   J. Exper. M., 1927, 45:243.

MURPHY, J. B.   Tr. Ass. Am. Phys., 1931, 46:182.

NAKAMURA, N., FUTAMURA, H., and WATANUKI, T.   Proc. Pan-Pacific Congr., 1926, 2:2623, 2636.

NICOLLE, M., and ADIL-BEY.   Ann. de l'Inst. Pasteur, 1899, 13:237; 1901, 15:715; 1902, 16:56.

NOCARD and ROUX.   Ann. d. l'Inst. Pasteur, 1898, 12:240.

OLITSKY, P. K., and BOÏZ, L.   J. Exper. M., 1927, 45:673, 685.

OLITSKY, P. K., COX, H. R., and SYVERTON, J. T.   J. Exper. M., 1934, 59:159.

OLITSKY, P. K., and FORSBECK, F. C.   Science, 1931, 74:483.

OLITSKY, P. K., TRAUM, J., and SCHOENING, H. W.   U. S. Dept. Agric., Techn. Bull., No. 76, 1928.

OLITSKY, P. K.   J. Exper. M., 1925, 41:129.

ONO, S.   Jap. Soc. Vet. Sc., 1925, 4:45.

POOL, W. A., BROWNLEE, A., and WILSON, D. R.   J. Comp. Path & Therap., 1930, 43:253.

RIVERS, T. M.   Proc. Soc. Exp. Biol. & Med., 1927, 24:435.

—— J. Exper. M., 1930, 51:965.

—— Infections of the Central Nervous System, Baltimore, 1931, Chap. 2, p. 49, from Proc. Ass. for Res. in Nervous and Mental Disease.

—— et al., Filtrable Viruses, Baltimore, 1928.

—— Physiol. Rev., 1932, 12:423.

—— Ann. Int. M., 1936, 9, 1466.

—— and SCHWENKTER, F. F.   J. Bacteriol., 1934, 27:65.

—— and STEWART, F. W.   J. Exper. M., 1928, 48:603.

—— and TILLETT, W. S.   J. Exper. M., 1924, 40:281; 1925, 41:185.

—— and WARD, S. M.   J. Exper. M., 1937, 66:1.

RÖMER, P. H.   Deutsche. med. Wchnschr., 1911, 37:1209.

—— Centralbl. f. Bakteriol., I Abt. Ref., 1911, 50: Beilage, 30.

ROSENOW, E. C.   J. Infect. Dis., 1931, 48:304.

ROUS, P.   J. Exper. M., 1910, 12:696; 1913, 18:416; see also 1935 to 1938.

—— J. Am. M. Ass., 1912, 59:1793.

—— The Virus Tumors and the Tumor Problem (Harvey Lecture). Am. J. Cancer, 1936, 28, 233.

ROUS, P., and MURPHY, J. B.   J. Exper. M., 1914, 19:52.

SANARELLI, G.   Centralbl. f. Bakteriol., I Abt., 1898, 23:865.

SCHMEISSER, H.   J. Exper. M. 1915, 22:820.

SHOPE, R. E.   J. Exp. M., 1931, 54:233; 1932, 56:793, 803; 1936, 63:33, 43, 173.

SPLENDORE, A.   Centralbl. f. Bakteriol., I Abt., 1909, 48:300.

SPREULL.   J. Comp. Path. & Therap., 1925, 18:321.

STANLEY, W. M.   Science, 1935, 81:644.

—— Science, 1935, 81:644; 1938, 87:469.

—— The Isolation and Properties of Tobacco Mosaic and Other Virus Proteins. Harvey Lectures, 1937–38.

—— Ergeb. du Physiologie, etc., 1937, 36:294.

—— J. Physical Chem., 1938, 42:55.

—— J. Biol. Chem., 1937, 117:57, 325, 755; 1938, 123:507.

SUTTON and O'DONNELL.   J. Am. M. Ass., 1916, 66:947.

TANIGUCHI, T.   Japan Med. World, 1927, 7:7.

THEILER, A.   Sc. Bull., Union South Africa, Dept. Agric., 1921, No. 19.

THEILER, A. and KEHOE.   Third and Fourth Reports, Director of Vet. Res., Pretoria, South Africa, 1915.

TYZZER, E. E., SELLARDS, A. W., and BENNETT, B. L.   Science, 1938, 88:506.

UHLENHUTH and MANTEUFEL.   Arab a.d. kaiserl. Gsndhtsamte., 1910, 288.

VINSON, C. G.   Science, 1927, 66:357.

VINSON, C. G. and PETRE, A. W.   Contrib. from the Boyce Thompson Inst., 1931, 3:131, 147.

—— Botan. Gaz., 1929, 87:14.

—— Phytopathol., 1932, 22:965.

VON PROWAZEK, S.   Centralbl. f. Bakteriol., I Abt., 1912, 67:268.

VON PROWAZEK, S. and LIPSCHÜTZ, B.   Centralbl. f. Bakteriol., I Abt., 1908, 46:609.

—— Handb. d. pathog. Protozoen, Leipzig, 1911–12, 1:230.

WEBSTER, L. T., and WRIGHT, F. H.   Science, 1938, 88:305.

CHAPTER LXII

VIRUS DISEASES OF MAN
SMALLPOX, VACCINIA AND OTHER EXANTHEMATA

SMALLPOX AND VACCINIA

Smallpox or variola is one of the most virulent of infectious diseases. Throughout history it has been a severe scourge of mankind, prevailing in China and other eastern countries many centuries before Christ and sweeping through medieval Europe, especially at the time of the Crusades, in a series of severe epidemics. All races of men are susceptible and no age from childhood to senility is exempt. In modern times the disease is endemic in most uncivilized countries, especially those of the East, and occurs sporadically in all parts of the globe. Owing to rigid enforcement of vaccination and of quarantine laws, however, the disease has been greatly reduced in civilized countries.

The etiological agent which causes smallpox is a virus.

It has been suggested by Goodpasture that the Guarnieri bodies are composed of aggregates of the minute "elementary bodies" of vaccinia described first by Paschen. The minute cocci are regarded by some investigators as virus particles and the larger cell inclusions as colonies of virus. The granules and the larger bodies are infectious, but their actual nature has not been definitely determined. The name proposed for these organisms of variola by Goodpasture is *Borreliota variolae hominis*.

The results of attempts to cultivate a virus of this nature will be summarized in the paragraphs on vaccinia.

Smallpox is transmitted with extreme ease. While we have no certain knowledge of the portal of entry through which the virus invades the human body, many considerations have made it seem plausible that this may take place through the mucosa of the upper respiratory tract.

Knowledge of the means of defense against the malady is fortunately well advanced. It has been known for centuries that one attack of smallpox protects against subsequent attacks. This knowledge was made use of by the physicians of ancient China and India, who, during mild epidemics, exposed healthy children to infection, hoping that mild attacks would result which would confer immunity. While dangerous in the extreme, such "variolation," nevertheless, was not without some benefit and was even introduced into Europe in the eighteenth century by Lady Mary Wortley Montagu.

Such practices, however, were made unnecessary by the classical investigations of Jenner published in 1798. Jenner, as a student, had been impressed with the fact that country people who had been infected with a disease known as cowpox, were usually immune against smallpox. His studies and observations came to a practical issue when, in 1796, he inoculated a boy, James Phipps, with pus from a cowpox lesion on the hand of an infected dairymaid. Two months later the same boy was inoculated with material from a smallpox pustule without subsequent disease. With this experiment the principles of vaccination as in use at the present time were founded.

The question as to the identity of cowpox and smallpox has been the basis of a long controversy. Many observers claimed from the beginning that the two diseases, though closely related to each other, were essentially different. Others, on the contrary, and this seems to be the prevailing opinion among scientists at the present day, maintain that cowpox or vaccinia, as it is called when inoculated into a human being, represents merely an altered and attenuated variety of variola. This latter view is based on the following considerations, which we take from Haccius as quoted by Paul.

1. Variola is invariably transmissible to cattle, when proper methods of inoculation are employed.

2. Variola carried through several animals, in the above way, becomes altered in character, approaching in nature typical vaccinia or cowpox.

3. Such virus, reinoculated into man, gives rise to purely local lesions which are mild and unlike smallpox.

4. Inoculation with such virus protects both man and animals against subsequent inoculation with cowpox, and, in the case of man, against smallpox as well.[1]

Kolmer has carried out complement fixations, using as antigens salt solution suspensions of cowpox and smallpox virus, and has demonstrated close biological relationship between the two.

It has been claimed, moreover, that cowpox originally was transmitted to cattle by human beings affected with smallpox. This seems likely both because of the comparative rarity of the former disease and because of its spontaneous occurrence almost invariably upon the teats of cows, although both males and females are equally susceptible to experimental inoculation.

The relationship of variola to chickenpox or varicella has been more easily determined. Chickenpox does not protect against smallpox nor is this the case *vice versa*. The two diseases are unquestionably quite distinct.

Vaccinia and the Production of Vaccine.—During the early days of vaccination, it was customary to inoculate human beings with the matter obtained from the pustules of those previously vaccinated. While this method was perfectly satisfactory for the immediate purposes in view, practical difficulties and the occasional accidental transmission of syphilis have rendered this practice undesirable. In consequence, at all institutes at which vaccine is produced for use upon man, the virus is obtained from animals. Horses and mules, both extremely susceptible to vaccinia, have been employed, and goats have, at times, been chosen because of their insusceptibility to tuberculosis. Rabbits have also been used by Calmette and Guérin, and others. Rabbits are now used routinely for passage of the virus.

The animals almost exclusively employed at the present day, however, are calves, preferably at ages of from six months to two years. Very young suckling calves are unsuitable because of the great speed of development and small size of the lesions

[1] Paul, "Vaccination," in Kraus and Levaditi. *Handbuch, etc.*, Vol. I.

produced. The animals should be healthy and are subjected, before use, to the tuberculin test, although, according to Paul, this produces a hypersusceptibility to the
vaccine, and can be omitted without danger when careful supervision is observed.
Some observers prefer to use light-colored animals rather than dark-skinned or black
ones, both for reasons of greater ease of cleanliness and because the former are supposed to be more susceptible than the latter. This contention is denied by others. The
sex of the animals is immaterial.

During the period of use, the calves are fed, according to age, with either an
exclusive milk diet, or they are given, in addition, fresh hay. The greatest cleanliness
in regard to the bedding and stalls must be observed and separate stables should be
available for the animals under treatment and those under observation before treatment. These stables, if possible, should be so built that they can be easily scoured
and flushed with water, and stalls should be disinfected after occupation. If possible,
stables should be artificially heated and a comfortable temperature maintained.
Halters and fastenings should be so arranged that the animals can not lick the scarified
surfaces. Careful veterinary control before vaccination and during the period of
treatment must be observed in order to eliminate animals with systemic disease or
other complications.

The calves may be vaccinated with material taken from previously vaccinated
animals. Again, they may be inoculated with "seed virus" obtained from the vesicles
of human vaccinia. This method of using humanized virus for the inoculation of
calves for vaccine production is preferred by many workers and is spoken of as
"retrovaccination." At present the virulence of vaccine virus is maintained by passages through rabbits.

Park believes that the most efficient and reliable seed virus consists of what he
calls *human-calf-rabbit* seed virus. Crusts from healthy children, nineteen days after
vaccination, are collected. These are cut up and emulsified with sterile water. With
this an area of about six inches square is inoculated on a calf, the remainder of
which is vaccinated in the ordinary way. The virus from this space is separately
collected and, after being glycerinated, is used in dilution of $1 : 12\frac{1}{2}$ parts of salt
solution to vaccinate rabbits on the shaven skin of the back. The pulp from this
rabbit vaccination is then used for calf vaccination.

Actual vaccination of the animals is done as follows:

Calves which have been kept under observation for at least a week are thoroughly washed and
cleaned and the abdomen is clipped and shaved over an area extending from the ensiform cartilage
to the pubic region, including the entire width of the belly and the inner folds of the thighs. It
is best to shave the animal a day or two before vaccination so as to avoid fresh scratches and
excoriations. Just before actual operation the animal is strapped to a specially constructed operating table in such a way as to allow free access to the shaved area. This area is now thoroughly
washed with soap and water followed by alcohol, or, in some institutes, by a weak solution of
lysol. If the latter is used, the field of operation must again be thoroughly rinsed with sterile water.
About a hundred small scarifications are made in this area, preferably by crossed scratches, covering for each scarification an area of about 3 to 4 square centimeters. Into these areas the virus
is rubbed, using for each small area a quantity about sufficient to vaccinate three children. Two
to three centimeter spaces are left between the lesions. The lesions are then allowed to dry and
may be covered with sterile gauze or, as in Vienna, with a paste made up of beeswax, gum arabic,
zinc oxid, water, and glycerin. In some institutes the lesions are left entirely uncovered.

Ordinarily within about twenty-four hours after vaccination a narrow pink areola appears about the scratches. Within forty-eight hours the scratches themselves become slightly raised and papular, and within four or six days typical vaccina vesicles have usually developed.

To obtain the vaccine from such lesions, the entire operative field is carefully washed with warm water and soap, followed by sterile water. In some cases 2 per cent lysol is employed, but must again be thoroughly removed by subsequent washing with sterile water. Crusts, if present, are then carefully picked off and the entire contents of the vesicle, sticky serum, and pulpy exudate removed by the single sweep of a spoon curet. The curetted masses are caught in sterile beakers or tubes and to them is added four times their weight of a mixture of glycerin fifty parts, water forty-nine parts, and carbolic acid one part. German workers prefer a mixture of glycerin eighty parts, and water twenty parts, omitting the use of carbolic acid. The glycerinated pulp is allowed to stand for three or four weeks in order to allow bacteria, which are invariably present, to die out. After preservation for such a length of time, moreover, thorough emulsification is obtained more easily than when this is attempted immediately after curettage. At the end of three or four weeks, the glycerinated pulp is thoroughly triturated, either with mortar and pestle or by means of specially constructed triturating devices. Pulp so prepared should remain active for at least three months if properly preserved in sealed tubes in a dark and cool place.

From the serum oozing from the bases of the lesions, after curettage, bone or ivory slips may be charged for vaccination with dry virus. The glycerinated pulp is put up in small capillary tubes, sealed at both ends, and distributed in this form. Park states that a calf should yield about 10 grams of pulp (which when made up should suffice to vaccinate 1500 persons) and in addition about two hundred charged bone slips.

The virus may be tested for its efficiency by a variety of methods. Calmette and Guérin inoculated rabbits upon the inner surfaces of the ears and estimated the potency of the virus from the speed of development and extensiveness of the resulting lesions. Guérin has estimated the potency of virus quantitatively by a method depending upon the inoculation of rabbits with a series of dilutions:

Beginning with a mixture containing equal weights of glycerin and vaccine pulp, dilutions are made with sterile water ranging from 1 : 10 to 1 : 100. Rabbits are shaved over the skin of the back and 1 c.c. of each of these dilutions is rubbed into the shaved areas. Fully potent virus should cause closely approximated vesicles in a dilution of 1 : 500, and numerous isolated vesicles in a dilution as high as 1 : 1000.

Quantitative estimations of the bacteria in the glycerinated virus should be made by the plating method and the vaccine used only when after several weeks of preservation the numbers of the bacteria have been greatly diminished. In glycerinated pulp the bacteria will often disappear entirely in the course of a month. The vaccine should also be tested for the possible presence of tetanus bacilli, by the inoculation of white mice.

Tetanus following vaccination has been due in a few instances to tetanus spores in the vaccine. In others the tetanus spores have been in the bone-scarifiers, in pads placed over the vaccination lesion, or on the skin of the patient. The inclosure of the vaccine lesion within a dressing or shield was found by Armstrong to favor the development of tetanus.

Stock vaccine virus should be stored in the cold, at approximately 0° to 5° C.

Since 1933 extensive experiments have been conducted for the purpose of producing bacteria free vaccine virus in tissue cultures or in sterile tissues. The most significant of these attempts are those of Rivers and Ward, who have cultivated vaccinia virus in flasks containing minced chick embryo in Tyrode's solution, and the experiments of Goodpasture and his associates who have grown the virus on the chorio-allantoic membrane of the chick embryo. It is not improbable that vaccines of this type will replace the older calf-lymph virus.

Vaccination of human beings is performed by lightly scarifying the skin of the arm or leg with a sharp sterile needle or lancet and rubbing into the lesion potent vaccine virus. In this process the less blood drawn the better since mixture with blood to some extent neutralizes the virus. The virus was formerly dried upon wood, bone, or ivory slips. At present the glycerinated pulp is almost universally employed.

In order to be successful, vaccination should be done with careful attention to the details of the procedure. The methods found to be most satisfactory in the U. S. Public Health Service are described by Leake and Force, from whom we quote *verbatim,* as follows:

PREPARATION OF THE SITE FOR VACCINATION

The skin of the upper arm in the region of the depression formed by the insertion of the deltoid muscle should be gently but thoroughly cleansed with acetone on sterile gauze or cotton and wiped or allowed to dry for a few seconds. Acetone is suggested as a cleansing agent rather than alcohol for the following reasons: 1. It is a more efficient cleanser. 2. It is cheaper. 3. It is not denatured with substances which may possibly affect the vaccination result. 4. It evaporates more rapidly. 5. Approximately 200 vaccinations performed after the use of acetone and alcohol on alternate subjects resulted in more successful vaccinations with acetone than with alcohol.

METHODS OF VACCINATING

1. *The Multiple Pressure Method.*—In each package of capillary tubes there will be found a perforated rubber bulb with a diaphragm across the interior of the neck. Push an unbroken capillary tube through the neck of the bulb until about a quarter of an inch of the capillary tube appears beyond the bulb. Break the tip which has been pushed through and withdraw the tube until the broken end lies in the neck of the bulb. With sterile gauze, break the other tip of the capillary tube and drop the contents on the spot to be vaccinated by squeezing the bulb with the finger over the perforation.

The needle, which should be new, sharp, and sterile, is held parallel to the skin, with the forefinger and middle finger of the right hand above the needle and the thumb below, the needle pointing to the operator's left. The needle should be crosswise of the arm, so that the thumb of the operator does not interfere by hitting the skin. The *side* of the needle point is then pressed *very firmly* and rapidly into the drop about thirty times within five seconds (ten times for primary vaccinations), covering an area *not over one-eighth of an inch* in diameter. The area covered by the pressures can be kept small by steadying the last two fingers of one's hands against the arm of the person being vaccinated and by moving the hand from the wrist only. This rapid up-and-down motion of lifting the needle and pressing it against the skin should be quite perpendicular to the skin and needle and not in the direction of the long axis of the needle. The point is not driven into the skin, but at each pressure the elasticity of the skin will pull a fraction of an inch of the epidermis over the point of the needle so that the vaccine is carried into the deeper layers of the epidermis. If the skin has not been unduly rubbed in cleansing and if the pressure is entirely perpendicular to the needle, no signs of bleeding should occur and all evidence of trauma will fade out in less than six hours. Immediately after the pressures have been made, the remaining vaccine is gently wiped off the skin with sterile gauze and the sleeve pulled down, the whole operation of pressing and wiping taking less than 10 seconds—it is not necessary to rub the vaccine in, as with the other two methods.

The advantages of this method are its mildness and painlessness, the fact that it is more rapid than any other effectual and safe method, the very superficial implantation, the leaving of the epidermis nearly intact, the fact that no control site is necessary for estimating the amount of trauma in a reaction of immunity (since the evidence of trauma due to the operation has usually disappeared before the first observation for an early reaction is made), and the fact that the vaccine is wiped off immediately so that the uselessness of a dressing is obvious to the person vaccinated.

2. *The Method of Incision or Linear Abrasion.*—The vaccine is dropped on the skin as described for the multiple-pressure method. The underside of the arm is then grasped with the vaccinator's left hand, in order to stretch the skin where the vaccine has been dropped. This tension is maintained while the vaccine is being inserted. With the point of a sterile needle pressed through the drop of vaccine *"a very slight scratch, not exceeding the eighth part of an inch"* (Jenner), is made down the arm. With the side of the needle or the flat end of a sterile toothpick, the vaccine is then gently rubbed across the scratch for at least 15 seconds. The scratch should penetrate the epidermis, but not draw blood. The friction across the scratch may cause a slight oozing of blood-tinged serum, but this should not be sufficient to wash out the vaccine virus.

3. *The Drill Method.*—In the drill method the epidermis is perforated by a small drill with a sharp cutting edge 2 mm. in width. The drill is made of carbon steel and the tip can be sterilized by flaming. The drill method is preferable for quantitative investigations or where there is a tendency to vaccinate too large an area, because of the uniformity of size of insertion.

If in capillary tubes the vaccine is prepared for insertion as previously described, but is not dropped on the skin until after the derma has been exposed. The skin is tightly drawn and the drill pressed against it perpendicularly. A single rotary turn is then made without altering the pressure. This will detach a small flake of epidermis, which should be brushed off with the edge of the drill. This exposes a circle of derma about 2 mm. in diameter and, if skillfully done, should cause no bleeding. The vaccine is dropped on this circle of exposed derma and rubbed in with a sterile toothpick, as described under the method of incision.

If the number of persons being vaccinated is large enough to warrant the expenditure of all the vaccine in a vial container at one clinic period, the vaccine may be supplied in vials and transferred directly to the arm with the sterile toothpick.

NUMBER OF INSERTIONS

Multiple insertions should be used under the following conditions:

1. In case of exposure to smallpox.
2. In case of failure of previous vaccination.
3. In case there is any doubt as to the full potency of the vaccine on account of possible adverse conditions of transportation or storage.
4. In case the subject is not likely to return for revaccination in the event of failure.

When multiple insertions are used, they should be made not less than 2.5 cm. apart. A capillary tube should be used for each insertion.

PRECAUTIONS

The vaccination site should not be exposed to direct sunlight until dry. *Dressings are unnecessary and are harmful if permitted to remain on the arm.* The small vesicles produced by any one of the above methods are reasonably tough and will dry without rupturing unless macerated by the excessive heat and moisture present under a vaccination shield or other nonmobile covering. This maceration is not prevented by the presence of openings in the vaccination shield. Vesicles and crusts should be kept dry. If necessary to prevent the soiling of the clothing, a fold of sterile gauze may be attached to the garment, not to the skin. Very rarely a severe "take" may require a few days of antiseptic dressings.

All primary vaccinations should be observed at the end of 10 and 15 days, and *revaccinations* should be observed in 2 and 4 days, in order to detect a possible reaction of immunity. *The vaccination should be considered successful as soon as this reaction of immunity appears and begins to subside,* provided vaccine of full potency has been used. A test for full potency is that the vaccine should give more than 50 per cent of vaccinoid reactions in the group of people vaccinated more than 10 years previously.

Small insertions are insisted upon because the diameter of the lesion is dependent upon the area of the insertion, and the rapidity of healing is dependent upon the size of the lesion.

Studies by Wright have shown that the *intracutaneous injection* of 0.1 c.c. of the ordinary glycerinated virus diluted with one part of sterile distilled water, resulted in "takes" when the ordinary scarification methods were unsuccessful. He vaccinated 227 negro soldiers in this way, and obtained over 70 per cent successful vaccinations when only slightly over 8 per cent were obtained on the same series of cases previously, by the incision method.

Force, who has had extensive experience with his method of intradermal vaccinations, suggested that this procedure be used in cases in which the cutaneous method has failed to give either a take or the accelerated "reaction of immunity."

Reactions following Vaccination.—The types of reaction following vaccination are illustrated diagrammatically in the following chart: [2]

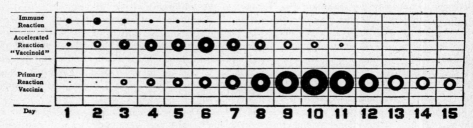

FIG. 104.—TYPES OF REACTION FOLLOWING VACCINATION.

The four types of reaction which may follow vaccination are briefly as follows:

1. *Vaccinia or Primary Reaction.*—Seen in those never previously vaccinated or whose immunity from previous vaccinia or smallpox has completely disappeared. The papule appears on the third to the fifth day and the vesicle reaches its greatest development on the eighth or tenth day, or later.

2. *Vaccinoid or Accelerated Reaction.*—Seen in those retaining partial immunity from a previous attack of smallpox or a previous vaccination. The papule appears on the third or fourth day, with vesicle formation by the fifth day. Pustulation is frequent. The height of the reaction occurs on the sixth or seventh day, after which it subsides rapidly.

3. *Reaction of Immunity or Immediate Reaction.*—Seen in persons possessing a high degree of immunity. A papule appears *within forty-eight hours* and subsides without forming a vesicle.

4. If none of the above reactions occurs or if there is delayed formation of a small papule after the third day, without further development, this is a negative reaction. The person should be revaccinated. Failures are nearly always due to deteriorated or impotent vaccine or to faulty technic.

The accelerated reactions were seen by Nash, Sutton, and Jenner before 1798 and were interpreted as the results of a "system disposed to reject" variolous matter. These were, no doubt, the first recorded observations on an allergic reaction. Force, particularly, called attention to the accelerated reaction as an evidence of immunity.

The first vaccination should be done in infants at about 6 months of age. Under ordinary circumstances a second vaccination should be performed when the subject

2 Reproduced from *Health News*, 1925, 2:165, New York State Department of Health.

is about 18 to 20 years old. Vaccination should always be repeated in the event of exposure to smallpox, an anticipated exposure or an outbreak of the disease in the community.

The benefits of vaccination are no longer a question of opinion, and opposition to the practice is explicable only on the basis of ignorance. Statistical compilations upon this point are very numerous. We select from the voluminous literature a single example, taken from Jürgensen, which embodies the statistics of death from smallpox in Sweden, during the periods immediately preceding and following the introduction of vaccination. In that country the first vaccination was done in 1801. By 1810 the practice was generally in use but not enforced. In 1816 it was legally enforced. The years from 1774 to 1855 can thus be divided into three periods.

Period	Smallpox Deaths, per Million Inhabitants	Death Rate, per Million
1. Prevaccinal, 1774–1801 (25 years)...............	2,050	20.00
2. Transitional, 1801–1810 (9 years)...............	680	....
3. Vaccination enforced, 1810–1855 (35 years)......	169	0.17

In considering the benefit of vaccination it must not be forgotten that revaccination is quite as important as the first vaccination, which confers immunity only for from seven to ten years. A child should therefore be vaccinated soon after birth or at least before the eighth month, and the process should be repeated about every seven years thereafter.

Smallpox vaccination is one of the few public health measures for which we believe compulsory legislation is justified. Relaxation of the laws has always led to outbreaks. We are sure that vaccination is responsible for the practical elimination of the scourge which was the most dreaded affliction of human beings in the Middle Ages and considerably later. As recently as 1921 an outbreak in Kansas City led to 1090 cases and 222 deaths, and it was necessary to vaccinate over 200,000 people before the epidemic ceased. In 1922 in Denver there were 805 cases with 247 deaths, a rate of over 30 per cent. No order requiring persons to be vaccinated in Denver was issued until November 21, 1922, with the result that as against 252 cases in November, there were only 81 in December.

Nature and Cultivation of Vaccine Virus.—The space available here is not sufficient to permit us to summarize the very numerous reports of experimental investigations of vaccinia virus. The virus is filtrable with difficulty from saline emulsions of lesions, but passes readily through Berkefeld V candles when emulsified in hormone broth, pH 7.6, as shown by Ward.

The virus appears to be particulate, as judged from the infectious properties of the elementary bodies of Paschen and their aggregates which may form the Guarnieri bodies. We have discussed these formations in previous paragraphs. MacCallum and Oppenheimer concentrated the virus by centrifugation and noted a great increase of these minute cocci.

The virus has been cultivated only in tissue cultures or in media containing living cells. The first success with this method of cultivation was gained by Steinhardt and Lambert in 1914, using guinea-pig cornea immersed in vaccine virus. Parker, in 1924, propagated the virus in tissue cultures of rabbit testis and plasma. In 1926, Cracuin and Oppenheimer cultivated the small bodies of vaccinia in tissue culture. The most successful results of cultivation of this virus have been those of Rivers and his associates (Rivers and Ward) and Maitland who have secured great increase of the virus in media containing minced chick embryo, serum, and Locke's solution. The bacteria-free culture virus produced typical lesions of vaccinia in rabbits and man and may be used for Jennerian prophylaxis in man.

Goodpasture has grown the virus on the chorio-allantoic membrane of the chick embryo. (Buddingh.)

Alastrim.—Closely related but not identical with smallpox is a disease called alastrim which occurs particularly in Brazil, the West Indies, Jamaica and other parts of the world. MacCallum mentions an epidemic in 1911, reported by Carini, Rebus and Aragao in which there were 250 cases with a mortality of 0.5 to 2 per cent. MacCallum has studied the disease in Jamaica. In character alastrim is similar to a mild attack of smallpox. The similarity is so close that MacCallum suggests that the mild form of smallpox which has been epidemic in various parts of Canada and in the United States may be more closely related to alastrim than to true smallpox.

Alastrim is easily communicable and therefore readily assumes epidemic form. Its close relationship to smallpox is apparent from the fact that the diseases show considerable mutual protection against each other, and ordinary vaccination seems to protect against alastrim as well as against smallpox. This protection, however, is not absolute and MacCallum mentions two cases reported by Deeks in which alastrim occurred in persons who had recovered from true smallpox. All that we know at the present time is that the disease, clinically so similar to smallpox, is probably a mild variety of this disease but not identical with it.

Laboratory Diagnosis of Smallpox.—In doubtful cases of pox-like disease it is sometimes useful to take advantage of laboratory tests of the virus. The available tests are:

Paul's Test.—This is carried out by scarifying the cornea of the rabbit and inoculating the scratch with material from the suspected lesion. In about 50 per cent of cases of smallpox a positive Paul's test is obtained. The positive results consist of the development of keratitis with a small umbilicated papule.

Intradermal Inoculation of Rabbits.—Normal rabbits are used as test-animals and rabbits previously immunized by vaccination are used as controls. The material from a lesion of the patient is injected intradermally into each animal. If the material contains smallpox or vaccine virus, a papular and crusted, or vesicular lesion develops in the skin of the normal rabbit in about four days, while the immune rabbit does not form any lesion, or shows an accelerated and transient reaction.

Serological Test.—The lesion of the patient is ground up in saline, gently centrifuged, and the supernatant fluid mixed with the serum of a vaccine-immune rabbit. In some cases a specific flocculant precipitate forms if the suspension contains variola or vaccine virus.

It is obvious that these tests do not differentiate between smallpox, alastrim, and vaccinia.

MOLLUSCUM CONTAGIOSUM

This is a contagious disease of the skin characterized by slight elevated knobs which usually present a small central depression and consist of a series of radially branching masses of epithelial cells separated by fibrous septa. It was long regarded by skin specialists as a mild form of neoplasm. Natural transmission is probably by contact. Juliusberg in 1905 succeeded in transmitting the growth to himself and to colleagues by rubbing up an excised growth with sand and filtering the diluted extracts through a Chamberland filter. Fifty days later typical molluscum growths developed which histologically showed the inclusion bodies, small, oval appearances which Lipschütz has described as characteristic. Leber later managed to obtain proliferation of what he believes to have been the filtrable virus in cultures made with human blood-serum. In these preparations he describes an increase in the Lipschütz bodies.

The cytoplasmic cell inclusions, or "molluscum bodies" have been restudied by Goodpasture and Woodruff. They found them very similar in structure and mode of development to the Borrel bodies of fowl pox. This work suggests that the minute bodies are virus particles and that the larger inclusion bodies are colonies or aggregates of the virus. Goodpasture has proposed the name *Borreliota mollusci* for the specific corpuscles (Lipschütz corpuscles) of molluscum contagiosum.

VERRUCA VULGARIS

Some forms of the common wart are said to be contagious and transmissible by injection of Berkefeld filtrates of the hyperplastic tissue. Ciuffo is said to have been the first investigator who succeeded in obtaining an active filtrate. Kingery and Wile appear to have proved that warts are due to a filtrable virus. The paraffin covering placed by them on their filters may have aided filtration. Certainly, no specific bacterium has been isolated from warts and inclusion bodies are found within the epithelial cells.

VARICELLA

Chickenpox, or varicella, is one of several highly contagious diseases of man characterized by a vesicular eruption on the skin. Varicella has been shown to be inoculable in man by Kling and others who have attempted to devise a method of prophylactic vaccination.

The reasons for placing varicella among the virus diseases are: (1) the disease itself or a specific type of infection can be produced in man or monkeys by inoculation with the bacteria free (as evidenced by cultures) fluid from vesicles; (2) intranuclear inclusions occur in the affected cells. These eosinophilic intranuclear bodies, first described by Tyzzer, resemble the cell inclusions seen in herpes and virus III infections.

There has been much discussion of the possible relationship between herpes zoster and varicella. This began from the clinical observations of Bokay that cases of herpes zoster followed exposure to chickenpox. Since 1909, there has been a considerable effort made to solve the problem thus presented. We agree with the conclusion reached by Rivers and Eldridge that in spite of the occasional production of indistinguishable clinical appearances, the cause of herpes zoster is different from the cause of varicella. It seems probable that herpes zoster is due to a virus, and that herpes simplex, herpes zoster, and varicella are caused by distinctly different viruses.

HERPES ZOSTER

Among the various types of infectious vesicular eruptions of the skin, there are three varieties of special interest. These are varicella, herpes zoster, and herpes simplex. We have discussed varicella in the preceding paragraph. Herpes simplex (or herpes febrilis) will be considered in connection with encephalitis. Herpes zoster, or "shingles" as one form of the disease is called, may be conveniently discussed here.

The etiology of zoster is obscure. Probably a number of irritants acting on posterior root ganglia can produce a vesicular eruption in the area of the cutaneous distribution of a nerve. Studies summarized by Rivers and Eldridge indicate that herpes zoster is caused by a virus and that this virus differs from the viruses of varicella and herpes simplex. An attack of herpes zoster usually renders the patient immune to another attack of zoster, but does not immunize against varicella and herpes simplex virus. Intranuclear cell inclusions occur, but the filtrates of material from zoster lesions have not been proved to contain a virus.

MEASLES

The causative agent of measles appears to be a virus. It has been cultivated by Plotz in media containing living cells.

It would be a thankless task to review the literature of all the many attempts to isolate micro-organisms from this disease, none of which has resulted in throwing any light on the etiology. The year 1926 brought a number of claims regarding measles causation which, in view of the recent work of the Dicks on scarlet fever, have attracted more attention than would have been given them otherwise. It is entirely uncertain, at the present time, whether these claims will develop into something more permanent than the many other etiological announcements that have been made in the past. Tunnicliff for some years has been publishing observations concerning the presence of a gram-positive, *viridans* type of diplococcus in the blood of measles patients during the early preeruptive and eruptive stages. With Hoyne, in 1926, she reported on the protection of human beings against measles with the serum of a goat that had been treated with these organisms. Ferry and Fisher, in 1926, described a similar streptococcus-like organism which differed from Tunnicliff's largely in being completely aerobic, while the Tunnicliff one is a facultative anaerobe. Ferry and Fisher claim that their organism produces a toxic substance which is nontoxic for measles convalescents but gives a reaction in susceptibles in a large majority of the cases. Neither of these organisms can as yet be definitely accepted, and no confirmations have been reported to date.

Attempts to produce the disease experimentally have frequently been made, the earliest recorded being those of Home of Edinburgh, published in 1759. Home took blood from the arms of patients afflicted with measles, caught it upon cotton, and inoculated normal individuals by placing this blood-stained cotton on wounds made in the arm. Home claimed that in this way he produced measles of a modified and milder type in fifteen individuals. Home's results, however, while at first accepted, were assailed by many writers and it is by no means certain that the disease produced by him was really measles. The individuals studied by Home may have contracted measles naturally.

A number of other observers after Home attempted experimental inoculation of this disease, and positive results were reported by Stewart of Rhode Island (1799), Speranza of Mantua (1822), Katowa of Hungary (1842), and McGirr of Chicago (1850).

The experiments of all these early writers, however, are unsatisfactory, owing to the necessarily unreliable technic of their methods.

In 1905 Hektoen succeeded in experimentally producing the disease in two medical students by subcutaneous injection of blood taken from measles patients at the height of the disease (fourth day). The experiments were carefully carried out and the symptoms in the subjects were unquestionable. They demonstrated that the virus of the disease is present in the blood. Attempts at cultivation carried out with the same blood were entirely negative. It was also shown by Hektoen's experiments that the virus of measles may be kept alive for at least twenty-four hours when mixed with ascitic broth.

Similar experiments were recently carried out by Sellards, both on monkeys and on eight volunteers, but entirely without success.

More important than the blood transfer experiments from the point of view of transmission are experiments in which inoculation has been attempted with secretions from the nose and throat. In 1852 Mayer reported the successful inoculation of human beings with mucus from the noses and throats of early measles cases, but complete failure in similar attempts at transfer with skin desquamations following the rash. Anderson and Goldberger claimed in 1911 that they were able to produce temperature reactions and mild skin changes in monkeys by the injection of nasal and pharyngeal secretions from early cases. This work has been elaborated and brought to more convincing conclusions by Blake and Trask. These writers inoculated monkeys (*Macacus rhesus*) intratracheally with filtered and unfiltered washings from patients in the early eruptive stages of measles and showed that the lesion which developed in the skin and buccal mucous membrane during the course of the monkey infection was histologically almost identical with that found in human measles. They successfully transmitted the infection from monkey to monkey and demonstrated that one attack of experimental measles conferred immunity upon the monkeys. Plotz obtained similar results with his cultures.

Epidemiology and Prevention.—There are few infectious diseases as common as measles. Crum has collected statistics which show that measles is responsible for about 1 per cent of all deaths occurring in the temperate zones. In statistical summaries of twenty-two countries extending over a period of four years preceding 1910, there were over 366,000 deaths attributable to measles of an aggregate population of 32,625,651. All races and ages seem to be susceptible, though children are more often infected, and the discrepancy between adults and children is probably due merely to the fact that most adults have had the disease before they attain adult life. Whenever young adults from rural districts come together in camps, epidemics will occur quite comparable with and more severe than those occurring among school children and asylum children at an earlier period of life. The disease is common all over the world and not apparently influenced by climatic conditions. Death following measles is usually due to bacterial bronchopneumonia.

When it appears first among aboriginal populations, it sweeps through them with a violence unknown among more civilized nations with whom the disease has been endemic for centuries. Such was the great epidemic in the Fiji Islands in 1874, and similar epidemics have occurred in the South Sea Islands and among American Indians and the Negro races. The disease occurs more commonly in cities than in rural districts.

Susceptibility of previously uninfected individuals seems to be practically universal. Interesting in this connection are the statistics of concentration camps in the United States during the World War such as those of Vaughan and Palmer made at Camp Wheeler. The population of this camp, like that of many others, was made up of young men from rural communities, many of whom had not had measles before. The sick rate week by week which followed the onset of the epidemic is tabulated by Vaughan and Palmer as follows:

For Week Ending		Annual Measles Morbidity Rate per 100,000
October	19	83
October	26	428
November	2	615
November	9	1760
November	16	2200
November	23	1120
November	30	248
December	7	240
December	14	19

We may assume that the definite exposure to measles of an uninfected human being will almost invariably result in an attack.

Since the disease is probably communicated by the secretions of the nose and throat, reasonable exposure may be taken to imply crowding in sleeping quarters, contact in public vehicles, places of amusement, at meals, at play, in schools and in the ordinary indoor association of work and recreation. Whether or not the disease can be conveyed indirectly to any degree is not certain, but it is very likely that infection from secretions on toys, food or other objects that are put into the mouth may take place, so long as the secretion is not dried. Judging from what we know of other filtrable viruses, moreover, the virus of measles may offer considerable resistance even to drying.

One of the most important epidemiological facts is the infectiousness of the secretions in the early preeruptive stages. The disease may be infectious as long as four days before the rash appears and since at this time the patients are rarely very sick, this is the dangerous period for transmission.

Uncomplicated measles in itself is not a very fatal disease, but, like influenza, measles seems to bring about a certain susceptibility to various respiratory infections, and measles epidemics are usually accompanied by many fatal postmeasles pneumonias. These pneumonias may take the form of pneumococcus or streptococcus infections, according to the nature of the most prevalent mouth and throat flora prevailing in the community. The conditions for a fatal measles epidemic, therefore, are fulfilled when measles breaks out in an industrial community, a camp, a school, etc., during the cold weather when coughs and colds prevail and when virulent pneumococci and streptococci are plentifully scattered about in mucus. By these means the secondary invaders are widely distributed.

The *prevention of measles,* in crowded communities or groups, is fraught with many difficulties. However, with vigilance and adequate discipline, much can be accomplished. In schools, industrial communities and in military units, the most important procedure in our opinion is constant inspection and early segregation of all individuals with catarrhal colds. In the army it has been the practice of sanitarians, a practice which we believe we have seen succeed to an unexpected degree, to inspect entire units once a day upon the appearance of a case of measles. The entire unit is made to pass an inspecting officer in single file in the morning, a few questions as to general health are asked, the conjunctivae and throats and the skin of the chest and arms are rapidly inspected, and individuals complaining of headache, a restless night, a cold or a cough, or those in whom the conjunctivae are inflamed, or the nose secreting, are made to step out and temperatures are taken. All those with a temperature of 100° F. or above are isolated and great care is taken to segregate catarrhal cases from the rest of the population. This method makes it possible to inspect a large group in a very short time and will accomplish far greater results than the mere isolation of individual suspicious cases which come to the sanitarian of their own accord. Munson has given this method particular attention in the army with astonishingly favorable results.

The incubation period of the disease is 10 to 14 days. During the prodromal stage, from about the tenth day after exposure to the fourteenth day, the patient is an active source of infection. The patient should be isolated from about the eighth day after exposure until the temperature has fallen, in incomplicated cases, and the rash has largely faded.

Specific Prophylaxis.—In 1918, Nicolle and Conseil showed that the serum of human beings convalescent from measles would protect children against the infection. As measles is such a common disease, nearly all adults are immune and contain protective substances in their blood. Hence, it has been possible to obtain passive immunization of children and other susceptibles by intramuscular injections of whole blood drawn from parents or other adults and injected into the recipient before the blood has coagulated. The dose varies from 3 to 15 c.c. By this means, a more or less controllable degree of passive immunity can be conferred upon the exposed child. An incomplete immunity is advantageous, as it permits the child to have a mild or modified attack of measles, recovery from which is followed by a solid active immunity. In the United States this method has been used extensively, following the experience of Park and Freeman and others.

McKhann and his associates have prepared an extract from human placenta with which measles may be modified or prevented. This extract contains the immune bodies present in the blood serum of the adult. The material, like convalescent's serum or the blood of adults is of considerable value as a prophylactic agent.

MUMPS

Mumps (*epidemic parotitis*) is one of the most difficult infections to circumscribe when once it has started in a crowded community. Mumps epidemics in the army spread with speed and without yielding to ordinary preventive measures. Ordinarily it is chiefly a disease of children among whom it spreads in schools and institutions.

Prevention is particularly difficult because the susceptibility among children is practically universal and since exposure need not be very close to give rise to infection. Also, difficulties are added to by the fact that it may be passed on to others during the incubation time before actual symptoms have appeared. Our impression from army experience is that there may be carriers.

Infection is direct, by the secretions of the mouth, nose and throat, and it enters the new victim probably by the same route. The incubation time after infection may be anywhere from five days to three weeks. Martha Wollstein has brought forward evidence which indicates that the saliva and secretions from mumps cases contain a filtrable virus. With such filtered secretions she obtained pathological changes in the testicles and parotid glands of cats which simulated human mumps. Johnson and Goodpasture (1934) produced typical mumps in *Macacus rhesus* monkeys by inoculating the parotid glands, through Stensen's duct, with saliva from patients with mumps. They have shown conclusively that the causative agent of mumps is a filtrable virus.

One attack usually protects, though not always. Prevention depends upon early recognition and isolation for two weeks after all symptoms have disappeared. When the disease spreads in a group, it should be remembered that it may be infectious for some time before symptoms occur and that the incubation time may last as long as three weeks. Protective measures, exclusion of contacts from school, and closure of schools if found necessary, must cover this period. Contagiousness is generally assumed to cease with complete disappearance of the lesion, though this is based purely on clinical observations.

LYMPHOGRANULOMA INGUINALE

A venereal disease, identical with tropical bubo, was described in Europe in 1913 by Durand, Nicolas and Favre. Since then it has been recognized in many countries throughout the world (Howard and Strauss) occurring in males and females, whites and Negroes. In the male the chief characteristic of the disease is acute and chronic inguinal lymphadenitis, which may or may not suppurate. In the female, in addition to the adenitis, elephantiasis of the vulva and stricture of the ampulla of the rectum are common.

Although the inguinal nodes are often secondarily infected with Ducrey's bacillus and other organisms, bacteria cannot be cultivated from the simple lesions. Hellerström and Wassén, Levaditi and others have shown that the infective agent is a filtrable virus. The virus is pathogenic for monkeys and mice, producing, after intracerebral inoculation, a characteristic meningo-encephalitis.

The chief advance in recognition of the disease has come through the application of the allergic skin test discovered by Frei. The original Frei test was performed by injecting intradermally 0.1 c.c. of a 1 to 10 dilution, in saline solution, of pus aspirated from a suppurating inguinal node. In persons having the disease, a papule surrounded by a red areola developed in 48 to 72 hours at the site of the injection. This test appears to be specific. Due to the difficulty of obtaining sufficient material from human subjects a substitute for the Frei antigen has been prepared in the form of a saline emulsion (1 to 5 or 1 to 10) of the brains of infected mice. This has been used with satisfaction by some observers, but Strauss and Howard, who have studied the problem carefully, report that Frei antigen made from the brains of mice gives false reactions and is not suitable for the routine diagnosis of lymphogranuloma inguinale.

REFERENCES

ANDERSON, J. F., and GOLDBERGER, J. J. Am. M. Ass., 1911, 57:1612.

ARMSTRONG, C. U. S. Pub. Health Rep., 1927, 42:3061.

BAUER, W. W. Am. J. Pub. Health, 1931, 21:285.

BLAKE, F. G., and TRASK, J. D. J. Exper. M., 1921, 33:385.

BUDDINGH, G. J. Am. J. Pub. Health, 1937, 27:1135.

CALKINS, G. N. J. Med. Research, 1904, 11:136.

CALMETTE and GUÉRIN. Ann. de l'Inst. Pasteur, 1902.

CHAPIN, C. V., and SMITH, J. J. Prevent. Med., 1932, 6:273.

CIUFFO. Giorn. ital. d. mal. ven., 1907. (Cited from Lipschütz.)

CLARKE, J. J. Brit. Med. J., 1894, 2:869.

COUNCILMAN, W. T., MAGRATH, G. B., and BRINCKERHOFF, W. R. J. Med. Research, 1904, 11:12.

CRACUIN, E. C., and OPPENHEIMER, E. H. J. Exper. M., 1926, 43:815.

CRUM. Am. J. Pub. Health, 1914, 4:289.

DOERR, R. Zentralblt. f. Haut-u-Geschlechtskrank, 1924, 13:417; 15:1, 129, 289; 1925, 16:481. (Quoted from Rivers.)

DURAND, NICOLAS, J. and FAVRE, M. *Bull. et Mem. Soc. Méd. des Hôp. de Paris*, 1913, 35:274.

EWING, J. J. Med. Research, 1905, 13:233.

FERRY, N. S., and FISHER, L. W. J. Am. M. Ass., 1926. 86:942.

FORCE, J. N. U. S. Pub. Health Rep., 1927, 42:1031.

FREI, W. *Klin. Wochnschr.*, 1925, 4:2148; 1927, 6:2042.

GOODPASTURE, E. W. Science, 1933, 77:119.

GOODPASTURE, E. W., and WOODRUFF, C. E. Am. J. Path., 1931, 7:1.

———, ———, and BUDDINGH, G. J. Am. J. Path., 1932, 8:271.

GRUENHAGEN. Arch. f. Dermat. u. Syph., 1892.

GUARNEIERI. Arch. per le sc. med., Torino, 1892, 16:403.

——— Centralbl. f. Bakteriol., I Abt., 1894, 16:299.

GUÉRIN, C. Am. de l'Inst. Pasteur, 1905.

HEKTOEN, L. J. Infect. Dis., 1905, 2:238.

HELLERSTRÖM, S. and WASSÉN, E. *C. r. Soc. de Biol.*, 1931, 83:802.

HOME. Medical Facts and Experiments, Edinburgh, 1759.

HOWARD, M. E. and STRAUSS, M. J. *New Eng. J. Med.*, 1935, 212:323.

HUDDLESTON. Quoted in Park, Pathogenic Bacteria, New York, 1908.

JOHNSON, C. D., and GOODPASTURE, E. W. J. Exper. M., 1934, 59:1.

JULIUSBERG, M. Deutsche med. Wchnschr., 1905, 31:1598.

KINGERY, L. B. J. Am. M. Ass., 1921, 76:440.

KLING, C. A. Berl. klin. Wchnschr., 1913, 50:2083.

KOLMER, J. A. J. Immunol., 1916, 1:51, 59.

LEBER. Centralbl. f. Bakteriol., I Abt., 1912, 67:58.

LEVADITI, C., RAVAUT, P., LÉPINE, P. and SCHOEN, R. Ann. de l'Inst. Pasteur, 1932, 48:27.

LI, C. P., and RIVERS, T. M. J. Exper. M., 1930, 52:465.

MacCallum, W. G. Am. J. Hyg., 1921, 1:38.

MacCallum, W. G., and Oppenheimer, E. H. J. Am. M. Ass., 1922, 78:410.

Maitland, H. B., and Laing, A. W. Brit. J. Exper. Path., 1930, 11:119.

Maitland, H. B., and Maitland, M. C. Lancet, 1928, 2:596.

McKhann, C. F., and Chu, F. T. Am. J. Dis. Children, 1933, 45:475.

————, Green, A. A., and Coady, H. J. Pediat., 1935, 6:603.

McKinnon, N. E., and Defries. Am. J. Hyg., 1928, 8:93, 107.

Monti. Centralbl. f. Bakteriol., I Abt., 1894, 16:300.

Nicolle, C. and Conseil, E. Bull. Soc. Méd. Hôp. de Paris, 1918, 42:336.

Park, W. H. and Freeman, R. G. J. Am. M. Ass., 1926, 87:556; 1930, 95:4.

Park and Williams. Pathogenic Microorganisms, New York, 1914, p. 569.

Parker, F. J. Med. Research, 1924, 44:645.

Parker, R. F., & Muckenfuss, R. S. Proc. Soc. Exper. Biol. & Med., 1932, 29:483.

Paschen, E. Deutsche med. Wchnschr., 1917, 43:746.

Pfeiffer, L. Ztschr. f. Hyg., 23.

Plotz, H. Bull. l'Acad. de M., 1938, 102:598.

Rivers, T. M., J. Exper. M., 1926, 43:275; 1931, 54:453.

Rivers, T. M., and Eldridge, L. A. J. Exper. M., 1929, 49:899, 907.

Rivers, T. M., and Ward, S. M. J. Exper. M., 1933, 58:635; 1935, 62, 549.

Steinhardt, E., and Lambert, R. A. J. Infect. Dis., 1914, 14:87.

Strausss, M. J. & Howard, M. E. J. Am. Med. Ass., 1934, 103:1830; 1936, 106:517.

Tunnicliff, R., and Hoyne, A. L. J. Infect. Dis., 1926, 38:48.

Tyzzer, E. E. J. Med. Research, 1905, 14:361.

Paul. Vaccination, in Kraus and Levaditi, Handbuch, etc., Vol. I.

Vaughan and Palmer. J. Lab. and Clin. Med., 1919, 4:647.

Van der Loeff. Monatschr. f. prakt. Dermat., 4.

Von Bokay, J. Wien. klin. Wchnschr., 1909, 22:1323.

Ward, H. K. J. Exper. M., 1929, 50:31.

Wile, U. J., and Kingery, L. B. J. Am. M. Ass., 1919, 73:970.

Wollstein, M. J. Exper., M., 1916, 23:353.

Wright. J. Am. M. Ass., 1918, 71:654.

CHAPTER LXIII

POLIOMYELITIS, ENCEPHALITIS AND RABIES

POLIOMYELITIS [1]

The disease known as acute anterior poliomyelitis has long been recognized as an acute infectious condition, both because of the characteristics of its clinical manifestations and of its epidemic occurrence. For these reasons it was classified with acute infectious diseases by Marie and by Strümpell long before any experimental evidence of infection was obtained.

The modern period of the study of the disease dates from 1840, the year in which Heine published his monograph on flaccid paralysis of the lower extremities in children. In 1887, Medin described an outbreak of the disease in Stockholm, during which he saw many cases of the febrile paralytic type. Wickman's careful study of more than a thousand cases in an epidemic in Sweden in 1905 indicated that poliomyelitis, or Heine-Medin disease, as Wickman named it, was contagious. Since then, there have been severe epidemics of poliomyelitis in Europe and America and investigation of the disease from all sides has been extensive.

Poliomyelitis is an acute inflammatory process localized chiefly in the anterior horns of the spinal cord. For this reason the disease was once called anterior poliomyelitis. But as lesions occur in other parts of the central nervous system, the adjective "anterior" has been dropped from the name. Another name, "infantile paralysis," is unsuitable because cases occur in adults as well as in children and it is now known that many (perhaps the majority) become affected without being paralyzed. Bulbar paralysis, some types of encephalitis, and the condition known as "Landry's paralysis" (Landry) may be the result of infection with the virus of poliomyelitis. Inclusion bodies have not been found in the affected cells.

The thorough clinical study of poliomyelitis, published by Peabody, Draper, and Dochez in 1912 contains observations which have been repeatedly confirmed. The *incubation period* varies, but appears to be about ten days. Amoss records that the stage of communicability extends from one week before the onset to two weeks after the onset. Carriers may remain infectious for months, although chronic carriers appear to be rare (Lucas and Osgood). Prodromal symptoms, if they appear at all, come on just before the onset of the disease. They may be very mild, consisting of slight fever, sweating, drowsiness, pain in the neck and head, and weakness. Intestinal symptoms are not uncommon. Again cases may begin without prodromal symptoms with sudden illness, chill and fever. This may be all that occurs in the so-called abortive cases which in Wickman's studies represent from 25 to 56 per cent of all cases.

1 For a thorough survey see: *Poliomyelitis*, a book by several authors under the auspices of the International Committee for the Study of Poliomyelitis, organized by Jeremiah Milbank. Williams and Wilkins Co., Baltimore, 1932.

During the early periods of the disease the cases may show various types of development. They may simply show signs of general infection, they may resemble influenza, the gastro-intestinal symptoms may be predominant, and others may show signs of meningeal irritation. The neck may be stiff, but not with the involuntary stiffness of meningitis, showing rather a reflex resistance when the attempt is made to move the head forward.

The best appreciation of the clinical condition in acute poliomyelitis may be had by considering the cases as (1) the abortive cases which never become paralyzed, (2) the cerebral group which is rare and in which involvement of the upper motor neurons with spastic paralysis is the chief characteristic, and (3) the bulbospinal group, which is the largest group, and in which motor neuron involvement and flaccid paralysis occur.

In the preparalytic stages the leukocytes are apt to be slightly increased in number and there is a definite increase of the polynuclears by 10 to 15 per cent. A leukocytosis of 15,000 to 30,000 is distinctively suggestive of the disease, especially if the polynuclears are increased at the expense of the lymphocytes.

The study of the spinal fluid is essential. During the first days of the disease, before the paralysis appears, there is an increase of the cellular contents with a total which may amount to 500 cells per cubic millimeter, but usually the cells number about 50 per cubic millimeter. In the later stages of the disease the cell counts come back to normal. During this early stage, most of the cells consist of lymphocytes, rarely showing predominant polynuclears. The globulin content of the spinal fluid during the early stages is practically normal, or slightly increased. This, however, increases later, as the cell counts drop. The fluid reduces Fehling's solution.

Etiology.—In 1909, Landsteiner and Popper reproduced the disease in monkeys (*Cynocephalus hamadryas* and *Macacus rhesus*) by inoculating the animals intraperitoneally with a saline emulsion of the spinal cord of a child that had died during the fourth day of an attack of poliomyelitis—during the stage of acute fever. Soon after this Knoepfelmacher, Flexner and Lewis, and Strauss and Huntoon independently obtained the same results.

Flexner and Lewis succeeded in transmitting the disease from monkey to monkey, and showed that the infection could be produced not only by intraperitoneal inoculation, but also by subcutaneous, intravenous, and intraneural injections. They proved also that the virus was present in the spinal fluid, blood, nasopharyngeal mucosa, and lymph nodes as well as in the brain and cord during the first days after inoculation of the animals. The virus has not been found in human cerebrospinal fluid or blood.

The discovery of Flexner and Lewis that the virus occurred in the nasopharyngeal mucus and that monkeys could be infected by intranasal application of virus containing material was most important in indicating the chief natural portal of entry and route of infection in man.

Monkeys can be infected by the gastro-intestinal route (Leiner and von Wiesner), and Aycock has reported the occurrence of milk epidemics which indicate further that the virus may enter by the ingestion of infected material. Contamination of the nasopharynx with the virus has not been excluded in these successful feeding experiments.

The filtrability of the virus was demonstrated by Landsteiner and Levaditi, and Flexner and Lewis, in 1909. The virus passes with relative ease through a Berkefeld V candle, but is largely withheld by the finer W filter. The size of the virus particle is variously estimated as of the order of 12 to 17 mμ.

The virus can be preserved for six years or more in nervous tissue in 50 per cent glycerin in the ice chest. It is killed by heat in 20 minutes at 60° C.; in 30 minutes at 45° to 50° C. Oxidizing agents destroy the virus and bile and bile salts are destructive to it.

Cultivation of the Virus.—The virus of poliomyelitis survives and multiplies in artificial media containing living cells (Long, Olitsky and Rhoads). It does not grow on lifeless media. The streptococci isolated by Rosenow and others from the cord and spinal fluid in cases of poliomyelitis are, in our opinion, unrelated to the disease and hence without etiological significance (Bull).

The "globoid bodies," found by Flexner and Noguchi in cultures containing human ascitic fluid and sterile rabbit kidney inoculated with virus containing brain or cord, were thought at one time to be the particles of the virus. These very small coccoid bodies were regarded by Amoss as being "undoubtedly organisms," but he states that "the relationship of the globoid bodies to poliomyelitis remains unsolved." Doubts have been expressed as to whether these "bodies" are actual organisms.

By adsorption of the virus on alumina gel and elution with M/15 Na$_2$HPO$_4$ solution, Sabin has purified and concentrated the virus.

The virus is resistant to freezing, drying, X-rays, sonic vibrations and protoplasmic poisons. It is extremely sensitive to ultraviolet light (Jungeblut).

Immunity.—Recovery from an attack of poliomyelitis confers immunity.

In monkeys, various degrees of immunity can be brought about by sublethal doses of virus, injection of attenuated virus (Flexner and Amoss), multiple intradermal injections of active virus, or injections of mixtures of virus and convalescent serum (Rhoads). Active prophylactic immunization of animals is therefore an established fact. Flexner, in summarizing much of this work on the *prevention of poliomyelitis* states that the virus, changed by passage from monkey to monkey, retains its immunizing properties while showing an alteration of infective power. Flexner concludes that whether or not use may be made of this transformation in securing active immunization of human beings, future study alone can determine.

Immune man and animals contain in their blood viricidal and protective antibodies. The ability of such sera to neutralize the virus *in vitro* and *in vivo* has been studied by many since this property was first noticed by Flexner and Landsteiner and many others who first investigated experimental poliomyelitis. These facts have led to an extensive use of convalescent serum for the treatment of disease, and as advised by Flexner and Stewart for *passive prophylactic immunization*.

No satisfactory antiserum has been prepared from goats or horses, as it appears to be difficult to immunize these naturally insusceptible animals. The antipoliomyelitis horse serum developed by Weyer, Park, and Banzhaf contained virus-neutralizing substances, but when used for treatment seemed to have about the same value as convalescent serum, which in our opinion is negligible.

The occurrence of protective antibodies in the blood of adult human beings is extraordinarily frequent, particularly among persons living in cities. Aycock and

Kramer found that 87 per cent of the mothers tested by them possessed virus-neutralizing substance in the blood.

Two main theories have been proposed to account for this great frequency of virus-neutralizing property of the blood of adult human beings. One of these, of which Aycock is the chief exponent, is that the neutralizing property of the blood serum is an expression of active immunity acquired from subclinical attacks of non-paralytic poliomyelitis. Flexner, Aycock and others are of the opinion that the infection is very widely disseminated and that there are thousands of minor or abortive cases for every case of paralysis. This opinion seems to us to be rational and to be supported by epidemiological facts. Opposed to this is the theory of "maturation immunity," of Jungeblut, which would account for resistance on the basis of age-changes in the animal, particularly the altered functions of the anterior lobe of the hypophysis and perhaps other glands of internal secretion which occur during adolescence. Whether the physiological factors of resistance to poliomyelitis will be found to be more important than the specific immunological factors remains to be determined.

Jungeblut has studied the relation of vitamin C to the resistance of monkeys to poliomyelitis virus. He showed that parenteral injection of natural vitamin C reduced the severity of the experimentally produced disease.

Serum Therapy.—In the absence of any effective antiserum produced by the immunization of horses against poliomyelitis virus (Weyer, Park and Banzhaf), recourse has been had to serum obtained from human beings convalescent or recovered from the disease for use as a therapeutic agent. All experimental work has shown that in infected monkeys, the serum must be given before the onset of symptoms in order for it to exert its protective action. It was shown that no benefit was gained by the administration of serum to animals after paralysis had appeared. The serum has no curative action.

It was hoped that by the administration of convalescent serum to infected human beings early in the disease, paralysis could be prevented and life saved. An extensive attempt to do this was made, particularly during the 1931 outbreak of the disease in New York. Serum was injected intraspinally as soon as the diagnosis was made in many cases. Although it was admittedly impossible to tell before the event which patients would have severe poliomyelitis with paralysis and death and which might survive with a mild or abortive infection, attempts were made to establish a controlled series of patients for test of the serum. We cannot review all the studies, but agree with Park in his estimate of results obtained under his observation that there was no statistical proof that the serum has any value after the cells of the nervous system are involved. This involvement occurs so early in the course of the disease that it is impossible to administer serum in time to do good. It seems to us that convalescent serum has not been established as an effective therapeutic agent, and, indeed, we believe that the intraspinal injection in some cases may be definitely harmful because the irritant action of the serum increases the edema of the cord.

The use of convalescent serum or whole blood for prophylactic immunization of children exposed to the disease was believed to have some value as a measure for protection. Blood drawn from parents is injected directly intramuscularly in doses of 30 c.c. into their children. This is not recommended for routine use.

CHEMICAL PROPHYLAXIS.—In 1935 Armstrong and Harrison found that the instillation of a 4 per cent solution of sodium aluminum sulfate into the upper parts of the noses of monkeys protected these animals against intranasal infection with the virus of poliomyelitis. Since then this solution, and solutions of tannic acid, zinc sulfate and other astringents have been applied intranasally to human beings. The assumption on which this form of chemical prophylaxis is based is that the substance applied coagulates or changes the bare terminations of the olfactory fibers, blocking the transmission of the virus. The method has had extensive trials, as in the epidemics in Toronto in 1936-37 (Tisdall) and elsewhere (Schultz). On the whole the results are discouraging. There is no satisfactory chemoprophylaxis at present.

Epidemiology.—The history and characteristics of epidemics of poliomyelitis have been summarized in the Survey referred to at the beginning of this chapter. A résumé of a few additional epidemiological facts may be placed here. Poliomyelitis virus is present in the mucous membranes of the nose and throat, in the excretions from these membranes and in the intestinal contents. It may also be present in the tonsils. It leaves the infected body with the discharges from the nose and throat and the intestines, and when swallowed from the throat can pass into the intestines, resisting the action of the gastric and intestinal secretions. Flexner, Clark and Dochez injected monkeys with filtrates from washings of the intestines after feeding monkeys with spinal cord material from infected monkeys and taking the intestinal fluid two hours after feeding. Outside the human body the virus probably can survive for some time, though the exact period is not known. Neustaedter and Thro claim to have been successful in infecting monkeys with dust taken from a sick room. Trask, Vignec and Paul have obtained strains of the virus from feces. Toomey has emphasized the gastro-intestinal tract as a portal of entry of the virus.

There is a great deal of evidence to show that poliomyelitis carriers exist. Experimental evidence of this carrier state has been advanced by Osgood and Lucas who found the virus in monkeys five months after convalescence. We ourselves have seen cases in which it could be definitely proven that they had not been in contact with a preceding case, two of them in country districts where the scantily populated surrounding area could be searched without danger of overlooking a case. It is also likely that at times of epidemic a great many very mild attacks of poliomyelitis may occur, which are mistaken for mild influenza or severe colds, and in connection with the occurrence of a recent case seen by us there were a number of indefinitely diagnosed cases of intestinal disturbance, with fever, in the neighborhood. It is not impossible that such cases may be true poliomyelitis of a mild type without paralysis but capable of passing on the virus. Peabody, Dochez and Draper have cited similar cases.

The virus probably gets into the new patient by direct and indirect contact, and can be carried from place to place, perhaps on the feet of flies, a fact which would be indicated by some experiments done by Flexner.

In 1911 epidemiologists of the State Public Health Service of Massachusetts established a parallelism between the distribution of poliomyelitis cases and the occurrence of the biting stable fly, stomoxys. Subsequently, M. J. Rosenau published experiments in which he obtained poliomyelitis infection by allowing infected stomoxys flies to bite monkeys. These observations were confirmed by Anderson and Frost, but all subsequent attempts to repeat the experiments have failed. The ordinary manner of infecting the human being is probably, then, through the nasopharynx. A great many cases begin with intestinal disturbances which may last a few days before the patient is ill enough to go to bed. It is more than likely, therefore, that the virus may also enter the body by ingestion and that infection of food may play a rôle.

The disease is usually present to some extent in crowded centers of the world, in the spring and summer months. The season of greatest prevalence is May to November. Most cases are in children below five, but adults also may have poliomyelitis.

Although a great many studies have been made to trace the infection of one case to exposure to another, such attempts have failed in most instances, and it seems fairly well established that there is great variation in the susceptibility of individuals to the disease. Whether this depends upon previous mild attacks of the variety spoken of above or whether it is a congenital difference, cannot be stated.

EPIDEMIC ENCEPHALITIS [2]

Epidemic encephalitis is one of the infections of the central nervous system which has come into prominence since 1917. Its older history is not ascertainable with certainty, although the descriptions of "sleepy sickness" by older writers and the long-known examples of Parkinsonian disease suggest that encephalitis existed before its more modern recognition (Flexner).

It is difficult to say whether the disease which we now speak of as *lethargic encephalitis* is identical with the conditions formerly described as "Schlaf Krankheit" or "sleeping sickness" (not to be confused with African sleeping sickness, due to trypanosomes). Camerarius, whom we quote from Smith, is said to have described an epidemic disease in Germany in 1712 which was probably encephalitis. In 1768 and 1835 similar epidemics seem to have occurred in the trail of outbreaks of influenza, a fact of considerable importance in view of the fact that renewed interest in the disease began with the occurrence of many cases of lethargic encephalitis following in the train of the pandemic of influenza in 1917–1918. After the influenza epidemic of 1889, relatively few typical cases of what we now speak of as lethargic encephalitis were reported, though nervous complications were apparently very common. During the later stages of the World War epidemic of influenza, cases began to appear in many different places which, at first, were either mistaken for poliomyelitis or were not diagnosed before death. We remember seeing two cases in soldiers during this period in which the diagnosis was doubtful and which we now believe to have been lethargic encephalitis. Although the occurrence of outbreaks of encephalitis has often been preceded by epidemic influenza, this relationship has not been constant.

One of the first systematic reports is that of von Economo who described an outbreak of the disease in Vienna in 1917. In 1918 an outbreak occurred in Great Britain which was studied and reported by Wilson, Hall, Herringham and others. In writing of the distribution of the disease during this epidemic, Smith stated that the first cases occurred in central Europe, in 1917, appeared in France, Great Britain

2 For a thorough review and bibliography, see J. B. Neal, *Epidemic Encephalitis, Report of a Survey by the Matheson Commission*, New York, 1929.

and Algeria in 1917 and early 1918, and reached North America during the latter half of 1918 and early in 1919 (editorial). The disease spread rapidly through the United States and by May, 1919, cases had been reported from twenty of the states. The largest number were reported from Illinois, New York, Louisiana and Tennessee, a fact which shows the apparent independence of the disease of climatic conditions. The disease spread through the United States from east to west. It has been recognized in this country repeatedly since 1919.

The outbreak of encephalitis in Japan in 1924 described chiefly by Kaneko, had features of acuteness, severity and seasonal incidence in the summer which have led Leake and others to consider the possibility that there is more than one type of disease passing under the name "epidemic encephalitis." The type described by von Economo, occurring at all seasons, has been referred to as Type A; the Japanese type, occurring chiefly in the summer, has been referred to as Type B. Whether or not these two types actually exist, there is evidence from etiological studies to be described below that epidemic encephalitis in man is caused by several distinguishable agents in the class of viruses.

There is also a good deal of reason to believe that the epidemic of encephalitis which occurred in St. Louis and Kansas City during August and September of 1933 represents a disease distinct from the encephalitis described by von Economo and others. According to Bredeck, the epidemic seems to have begun in St. Louis County on July 7 and in St. Louis City on July 30. It reached its peak in September. On October 10 a total of 1065 cases had been reported from the county and city. The case fatality rate was 18.5 per cent, approximating the 20 per cent mortality rate anticipated by Leake. The case incidence rate in age groups was approximately 13 per cent among children under fifteen years of age; 23 per cent among those sixteen to thirty-four years old; 29 per cent among those thirty-five to fifty-four years old. This incidence of cases among adults was greater than the proportion to be expected from the age-group composition of the population, showing that adults were more susceptible than children.

During the summer of 1932 similar cases of encephalitis occurred in Cincinnati, Ohio, and Paris, Illinois. Encephalitis occurred in New York City also during 1932 and 1933. The relationship of these infections will be discussed more fully in the paragraphs on etiology.

Evidence of direct communicability is as difficult to obtain as it is in poliomyelitis and meningitis. Most cases occur sporadically without obvious connection with previous cases. In St. Louis in 1933, however, there were a sufficient number of cases in families and with traceable contacts to warrant the establishment of control measures based on the assumption that encephalitis is a disease transmitted from person to person chiefly through droplet infection from nasal secretions (Bredeck). Stallybrass, Kling and Liljenquist and MacNalty had previously reported definite examples of communicability by contact. Food, water and milk were excluded as vehicles of the spread of infection in the St. Louis epidemic in 1933. Although the seasonal incidence and the limitation of the distribution of cases to regions in the United States below the 40th parallel of latitude suggested that encephalitis in the St. Louis outbreak might have been transmitted by insects, no evidence was obtained in proof of this supposition. Tests made in human beings by allowing mosquitoes which had been fed on patients with encephalitis to bite normal human men at various periods after the feeding with supposedly infected blood were negative.

The *incubation period* is probably 9 to 21 days (Leake).

The onset of encephalitis may be sudden, but is usually gradual, with headaches, lassitude and gradually increasing fever. Occasionally there are vomiting, vertigo and muscular pains. Disturbances of vision, diplopia, due to oculomotor palsy, may appear early. Following this there may be increased fever, intensified vomiting, disturbances of the cranial nerves, great general weakness and finally coma. Recovery may occur in two or three weeks or the coma may persist for a long time. Paralysis of muscular groups and facial paralysis, ptosis, disturbances of pupillary reflexes and other reflexes occur. Lethargy is not always a characteristic of the disease, as a number of patients suffer from excitability and insomnia.

The spinal fluid shows an increased number of cells in a certain percentage of cases, but this increase of cell-count is usually not very high. It is probable that the number of leukocytes in the spinal fluid may be related to the degree of meningeal involvement, being greatest in the cases of meningo-encephalitis.

The *mortality* has varied between 18.5 and 29 per cent. The average expected mortality appears to be about 20 per cent in acute cases. As many patients with encephalitis have died of bronchopneumonia or some coincident infection, the actual mortality due to encephalitis is not known with certainty.

The age distribution of encephalitis is entirely different from that of poliomyelitis, so much so that Smith believed that this alone would distinguish the two diseases. In poliomyelitis over 59 per cent of the cases occur before the fourth year of age, and 68 per cent of the cases occur below the age of five, whereas in epidemic encephalitis 58 per cent of the cases occur in persons twenty years of age or older.

In some epidemics, 60 per cent of the cases occurred in males. In the epidemic in St. Louis in 1933 no sexual or racial predilection was apparent.

Etiology.—The specific cause of epidemic encephalitis has been sought for among the bacteria and the viruses.

In encephalitis, as in most of the virus diseases, early investigations were confused by the isolation of a variety of bacteria. Strauss, Hirschfeld and Loewe isolated "globoid bodies." Von Wiesner, Rosenow, Maggiora and his associates, and Evans and Freeman obtained, from encephalitis tissues, various types of streptococci, usually of the diplo-streptococcus form, with a tendency to produce green discoloration of blood agar. In no case, in our opinion, have any of these organisms been shown conclusively to have any etiological relationship to the disease. Indeed, careful critical appraisal of the results obtained indicates that the organisms were the incidental contaminants so frequently isolated, in many conditions, from tissues after death. The theories promulgated by some of these investigators, that the isolated streptococci—as well as subtilis-like bacilli similarly obtained—represented bacterial stages in a pleomorphic cycle of which the filtrable form represents another phase must, for the present, be regarded as nothing but interesting speculations, without any basis in fact which would justify anything more than further experimentation in these directions. Our own experience, like that of others, indicates that bacteria are not etiologically related to encephalitis. Muckenfuss, Armstrong and McCordock, and others, did not recover bacteria from the brains of fatal cases of encephalitis in St.

Louis in 1933. We believe, therefore, that the causative agent of encephalitis is not a bacterium.

In the opinion of Rivers "the clinical picture, pathological changes observed in the brain, and epidemiological studies, by analogy warrant its (encephalitis) classification with the virus diseases." DaFano and Ingleby have described minute inclusion bodies in the nerve cells and McCordock found "intranuclear inclusion bodies in the cells of the tubular epithelium of the kidney in about one-quarter of the cases so far examined in St. Louis."

There has been a "vigorous effort" on the part of Levaditi and others to prove that the virus of herpes febrilis is the cause of epidemic encephalitis. The herpes-encephalitis problem will be discussed in the succeeding section. We may state here, however, that the occurrence of herpes virus in the brain tissue from cases of encephalitis appears to us to be coincidental. Those who investigated the outbreak in St. Louis in 1933 gave special attention to this point. They failed to obtain herpes from any of the encephalitis material.

The opinion that herpes virus might be responsible for certain forms of encephalitis in man seemed for a time likely, for the following reasons: the virus of herpes, as described in another section, produces an encephalitis, in rabbits and in certain varieties of monkeys, which has considerable resemblance to the human disease, both in clinical features and in pathological lesions. During the earlier years of encephalitis investigation, herpes virus was isolated from a small number of cases by the inoculation of suspensions of nervous tissue and spinal fluid into rabbits. Levaditi and Harvier inoculated brain suspensions from a case into a rabbit, obtaining a transmissible strain of virus indistinguishable from that of herpes. Doerr and Schnabel and Doerr and Berger obtained similar results with both spinal fluid and brain material. All told, not more than eight successful isolations of this kind can be found in the literature. In contradiction to these, there are records of many hundreds of unsuccessful attempts of the same kind and of occasional isolations of herpes virus from similar materials in cases that have never suffered from encephalitis. Most important among these are the results of Flexner's experiments, in which a herpes virus was obtained in two rabbits inoculated with spinal fluid from a case of tertiary syphilis.

Summarizing the evidence as a whole, it appears that the occurrence of herpes virus in the brain tissues of cases of encephalitis is coincidental in the sense that this virus is probably present in the tissue of a great many individuals, especially of those suffering frequently from herpetic lesions. Taken as a whole, we must conclude that—for the present—the herpes etiology of the type of encephalitis which began in 1917 cannot be accepted and is unlikely, but cannot be completely rejected as yet.

It is not so easy to interpret the results of Perdrau, who succeeded in obtaining a herpes virus from two acute cases of encephalitis only after the brain tissue had been preserved in glycerine in the ice-chest for several weeks, and only after he had employed special methods of inoculation too complicated to be detailed. Although Perdrau's work has not been confirmed by others, it was done under careful control by an experienced investigator and arouses the suspicion that the ordinary methods of inoculation, directly from the patient, do not suffice for transfer. Of similar importance are isolations of a herpes virus from post-measles encephalitis and ascending myelitis by skin inoculation carried out by Gay and his associates.

The discoveries of Muckenfuss, Armstrong and McCordock, and Webster and Fite show conclusively that the encephalitis which occurred in St. Louis in 1933 was due to a filtrable virus. Collateral studies support the assumption that other outbreaks of epidemic encephalitis have been caused by somewhat similar but distinguishable viruses.

During the St. Louis outbreak, Muckenfuss, Armstrong and McCordock first transmitted to *Macacus rhesus* a disease resembling encephalitis by giving these monkeys repeated intracerebral and intraperitoneal inoculations with suspensions of brain tissue from encephalitis cases. After a febrile period in which the animals showed muscular weakness, tremors and excitability, the monkeys recovered. The infection was passed through a series of monkeys and from monkeys to white mice. In mice the disease was usually fatal. *Cebus* and Java monkeys and rabbits were refractory.

Webster and Fite, by inoculating encephalitis brain emulsions intracerebrally into specially susceptible strains of white-face and Swiss mice produced a fatal disease in these animals. The symptoms were those of encephalitis, and the pathological lesions in the central nervous system, consisting of damage to nerve cells and perivascular accumulations of mononuclear cells, were similar to the lesions of encephalitis in man. Different samples of the virus produced identical effects in mice. Webster and Fite found that Berkefeld N filtrates in dilutions as high as 1:2000 produced fatal disease in mice when inoculated intracerebrally.

Webster and Fite and Cox and Fite found protective substances in the serum of monkeys which had been injected with the St. Louis encephalitis virus and in serum from the blood of human beings who were convalescent from the disease or who had recovered. The results of numerous carefully conducted protection tests with mixtures of virus and serum injected into mice indicated that: (1) a single type of virus was the cause of the epidemic of encephalitis in St. Louis and Kansas City in the summer of 1933 and in Paris, Illinois, in 1932; (2) the cases of meningo-encephalopathy in Indianapolis were probably different from the encephalitis in St. Louis; (3) while there were cases of encephalitis in New York City due to the St. Louis type of virus, other cases of encephalitis in New York and New Jersey were not due to this virus; (4) chronic cases of so-called epidemic encephalitis did not show protective properties in their sera against the St. Louis encephalitis virus; and (5) the viruses of poliomyelitis, herpes, equine encephalomyelitis and vesicular stomatitis are distinctly different from the virus of the acute encephalitis which occurred in St. Louis in 1933.

It is obvious that many problems remain to be solved before a complete knowledge of the etiology of epidemic encephalitis is obtained. The results of these investigations, however, have greatly clarified the atmosphere by showing that at least one clinically recognizable type of acute epidemic encephalitis is caused by a specific filtrable virus.

The transmission of *equine encephalitis* to human beings was recorded in the preceding chapter.

HERPES FEBRILIS

Löwenstein and Grüter in 1920 made the discovery that the common herpetic vesicles of man, which occur chiefly about the lips and face (cold sores) and have been considered by physicians as diagnostically significant in various febrile conditions, contain a virus which can be readily inoculated upon the cornea of rabbits. Such transmission is a simple procedure, and, provided the herpes vesicle is not too old and dry, is invariably successful. Since this observation was made the literature, largely inspired by Doerr's suggestion that herpes virus may be identical with that of encephalitis lethargica, has grown to such dimensions that we can find space only for a concise statement of facts and problems, and cite only a limited number of the more important publications in which references to other work may be found. The facts regarding herpes are as follows:

1. The virus is present in all herpetic vesicles with the exception of herpes zoster (separately dealt with). It is qualitatively the same wherever the original lesion may be localized. Apart from herpetic vesicles the virus can be found in the saliva of herpetic and nonherpetic individuals, and has been reported by Bastai and his associates in the blood serum and the spinal fluid of a number of human beings suffering from herpes. The virus has also been found in the spinal fluid of occasional individuals who have had no recent herpes and have apparently never had encephalitis (Flexner).

2. The virus can be transferred to the cornea of a rabbit and can be carried indefinitely by corneal series from rabbit to rabbit. Some of the animals (the fatal percentage depending upon the virulence of the particular virus) will die with recognizable and characteristic symptoms (fever, salivation, grinding of teeth, tremors, spastic contractions usually involving neck and back muscles and leading to a form of intermittent opisthotonos) just before death, which ensues in from four to seven days. In such animals the brain contains the virus and transmission in series from brain to brain is now possible. The virus can also be inoculated upon the skin of rabbits, where a papular and vesicular eruption is produced. Other animals that are susceptible, though less so than rabbits, are guinea-pigs, white rats and white mice. Monkey experiments have been contradictory and doubtful, and dogs, cats and birds are insusceptible. The virus can be preserved in neutral glycerin, one of our own strains remaining alive under such conditions for eleven months in the ice chest.

3. The virus is filtrable. Thus far it has not been cultivated on lifeless media. No microscopically visible particles have been identified as the causative agent. Pathologically characteristic are certain acidophilic nuclear inclusions described by Lipschütz in the epithelial cells of vesicles and in the corneal cells of rabbits, and found by Goodpasture and Teague in all the susceptible tissues of inoculated rabbits.

4. Following recovery from a corneal or skin inoculation rabbits are immune. The immunity lasts certainly six months, possibly longer, and the serum of such rabbits and, to a lesser degree, the extract of the brain tissue has a limited and irregular neutralizing power for the virus if incubated with it before inoculation.

It is likely from the work of Bastai and his associates that severe herpes may be merely a dermal symptom of a general infection which, in most cases at least, does little injury to other tissues. In herpes, therefore, we may be dealing with a virus which has, as Levaditi suggests, a neurodermal, or better, ectodermal affinity—an agent that may possess pathogenic relations with a number of conditions not yet fully understood.

The Herpes-Encephalitis Lethargica Problem.—When Strauss, Hirschfeld and Loewe first published their successful transmission of encephalitis from man to monkeys and rabbits, it seemed justifiable to believe that an important etiological problem had been solved. Unfortunately, however, subsequent developments have not led to uniform confirmation of their results and the problem is still a controversial one. To discuss this problem in full would be a formidable task, since new work has necessitated a complete revision of all the earlier studies. For this reason we will briefly summarize the arguments for and against the identification of the two viruses, and refer to the very full critical analyses published by Doerr who made extensive investigations of the problem.

The early reports of Strauss, Hirschfeld and Loewe presented the transfer of encephalitis virus with spinal fluid, brain, nasal washings, etc., of man to rabbits and monkeys as a relatively simple and almost uniformly successful process—sufficiently reliable to induce them to suggest such inoculation as a diagnostic procedure. They also reported successful culture. Somewhat later McIntosh and Turnbull reported success in similar transfer to monkeys, though with less regularity. Levaditi and Harvier then obtained a positive rabbit by inoculating with the brain tissue of a fatal case, and Doerr and Schnabel, who had been studying herpes virus and were the first to suggest the possible identity of the two infectious agents, succeeded in starting a strain of virus in a rabbit inoculated with 0.2 c.c. of the spinal fluid of a human case. At about the same time Schnabel obtained another strain of virus by similar methods. All these virus strains were easily carried on in series and developed properties indistinguishable from those of ordinary herpes virus. The ease with which these early strains were obtained, however, is in direct contrast to later developments. Kling and his coworkers in Sweden believed that they had obtained a virus in rabbits by inoculation of human material but, in their cases, the condition induced in the rabbits was chronic, rarely fatal; and except for certain histological changes found in the brains after the animals were killed, the inoculations were negative. We are inclined to regard the transfers of Kling as altogether doubtful and, for the time being, as having little bearing upon the etiology of encephalitis. Kling was dealing with the spontaneous encephalitis of rabbits.

Other observers, notably Flexner and Amoss in a large series, as well as we in 14 human cases, have never succeeded in transferring a typical herpetiform encephalitis to rabbits with human material from the central nervous system. Meanwhile, Doerr himself, in subsequent attempts, encountered difficulties not apparent at first. Of 44 attempts reported in 1924 only 1 was "positive" and there are at present only 5 or 6 virus strains in existence—those of Doerr and Schnabel and those of Levaditi and Harvier and Gay—which purport to originate from human encephalitis. This irregularity has engendered justified doubt which is considerably strengthened by the work of Bastai and Busacca. These investigators infected human beings with herpes virus intracutaneously, corneally, and intraspinously and determined that the virus in the spinal fluid persisted for many weeks. None of these individuals developed encephalitis. They also demonstrated the herpes virus in the spinal fluids of a number of individuals who had recovered from herpetic eruptions and suggest that herpes virus is a common and generalized infection of human beings which does not lead to encephalitis-like disease even when injected into the spinal canal, and that the occasional successful rabbit transfers, such as those recorded above, may have been due to the accidental presence of herpes virus in the central nervous system of an encephalitic patient. This point of view is also taken by F. T. Parker, Jr., largely upon the histological ground that the Lipschütz intranuclear herpes bodies which are characteristic of herpetic lesions in rabbits are absent in human encephalitis. The case reported by Flexner and Amoss gives further support to this view. They obtained a typical herpetic passage virus for rabbits from the spinal fluid of a tertiary luetic who had never had encephalitis and was not suffering from herpes at the time.

The alternatives which confront us in the herpes-encephalitis problem at the present time are, thus, the following:

1. Herpes virus is a widespread infectious agent which, with or without skin eruption, penetrates into the blood and certain nervous systems of human beings frequently and without causing any serious clinical symptoms. The earlier investigators of encephalitis happened, by a curious chance, to encounter encephalitis cases in which herpes virus had penetrated into the brain and spinal canal, perhaps more easily because of the encephalitic condition. In this case herpes has nothing to do with encephalitis.

2. On the other hand (as Doerr still believes), the two virus strains are closely related but the encephalitis variety has been greatly attenuated for rabbits by passage through man and direct transfer is, therefore, possible in exceptional cases only. This view is also favored by Perdrau, who claims to have obtained direct takes in rabbits with human material if he kept the brain substance in glycerin for two weeks before inoculating rabbits or if he injected it mixed with the brain substance (his "aggressin") of immune herpes rabbits. It is also favored somewhat by Breinl's experience and our own (Zinsser and Tang) that herpes virus in minute doses or injected into partially immunized rabbits leads to a slow comatose condition closely analogous to human encephalitis.

In the discussion of encephalitis in the preceding section we pointed out that the results of the investigations of Flexner and of one of us (Zinsser) were incompatible with the view that herpes virus causes epidemic encephalitis. We concluded that at present the herpes etiology of the type of encephalitis which began in 1917 cannot be accepted and is unlikely, but cannot be completely rejected. It has become certain from the discoveries of Muckenfuss, Armstrong and McCordock and of Webster and Fite that at least one type of acute epidemic encephalitis in man has a specific etiology. As we have noted in the previous section, these investigators showed not only that herpes virus did not occur in the brain tissue of fatal cases of encephalitis in St. Louis in 1933, but also that the outbreak of acute epidemic encephalitis in St. Louis and Kansas City was due to a specific filtrable virus (Webster and Fite).

The subject of encephalitis is further complicated by the clinical association of encephalitis with influenza, the occurrence of encephalitis following smallpox vaccination, and by a number of instances of *postinfection encephalitis*. These conditions will be dealt with in the succeeding section.

Encephalitis Following Vaccinia and Other Virus Infections

In 1872, Westphal clearly described an inflammatory and degenerative disease of the central nervous system under the name "acute disseminated encephalomyelitis." Instances of this condition following various infections were noticed from time to time, but its etiology was, and still is obscure. Since 1924, this nervous disorder has received a great deal of attention because of the relatively sudden and frequent occurrence of encephalomyelitis which followed smallpox vaccination in Holland, England, and to a less extent in this country. It is now generally recognized that an inflammatory and degenerative disease of the brain and spinal cord, characterized chiefly by *demyelinization of the nerve fibers* in areas near blood vesicles, the central ventricles, and the subarachnoid space, may follow a number of the infections caused by viruses and possibly some of the bacterial diseases (Flexner). The chief diseases with which the condition has been associated are smallpox, vaccinia, varicella, measles, rabies (vaccine treatment), influenza and canine distemper. Although some cases occur without obvious precedent infection, the available information is sufficient to warrant grouping all these instances of perivascular demyelinization of areas in the central nervous system under the term "postinfection encephalitis." In doing this, we are in agreement with the opinion that epidemic encephalitis, discussed in the preceding section of this chapter, is a separate and distinct disease.

As an example of the condition, *postvaccinal encephalomyelitis* is the most important. A brief summary of knowledge on this subject is as follows:

In 1924, Lucksch, in Prague directed attention to cases of encephalitis following vaccination against smallpox, and discussed the question of the possibility of a vaccinal encephalitis. Following this, Bastiaanse described an outbreak of the disease in Holland and several reports have been published on the cases occurring in England (Turnbull and McIntosh). A few cases have been reported from the United States (Flexner, Wilson).

The time between the vaccination and the onset of nervous symptoms has usually been 10 to 13 days, although a few cases have occurred within the first 10 days after vaccination and in the period from the 14th to the 34th day. The most common "incubation period" is eleven or twelve days. The age incidence among those affected has varied, but most of the cases have occurred in children 3 to 8 years of age. This concentration of incidence among children of "school age" suggests a correlation with first vaccinations.

Flexner (1930) noted three lines of conjecture which have been followed to account for the occurrence of numerous cases of postvaccinal encephalitis. (1) The disease may be due to vaccine virus with neurotropic properties. (2) Vaccine virus, introduced into the skin, has aroused to activity a second organism present in the body in a latent state. (3) The disease may be the manifestation of an allergic reaction to the vaccine virus. No single vaccine virus has been used in all these cases, and encephalitis has not followed vaccination with the Levaditi neurotesticular virus used widely in Spain, but did follow vaccination with this virus in Holland. There is no evidence that a second latent virus, activated by vaccination, is the cause of the disease. The allergic hypothesis is not supported by experimentally demonstrated facts or by the previous history of vaccination.

Flexner concludes, that so far as known data can be interpreted with probability, vaccine virus is not the specific incitant of postvaccinal encephalitis and that the etiology of the disease is unsolved.

LYMPHOCYTIC CHORIOMENINGITIS

Armstrong and Lillie, and Rivers and Scott proved that one form of so-called "aseptic meningitis" was caused by a virus. The virus occurs in the spinal fluid and can be transmitted to mice and guinea-pigs by intracerebral and intraperitoneal inoculation of spinal fluid from a patient suffering from the disease. Neutralizing antibodies are found in the serum of a patient during convalescence (Howard). Using a soluble specific antigen derived from the tissues of animals infected with the virus of lymphocytic choriomeningitis, Howitt, Smadel, Baird and Wald obtained positive complement fixation reactions with sera of patients who had recovered from the disease. In 1939 Howard published a discussion of the diagnosis of this disease in man.

RABIES

(Hydrophobia, Rage, Lyssa, Hundswuth)

Rabies is primarily a disease of animals, infectious for practically all the mammalia, but most prevalent among carnivora, dogs, cats, and wolves. It is said also to occur spontaneously among skunks of the southwestern United States, and is readily inoculable upon guinea-pigs, rabbits, mice, rats, and certain birds, chicken and geese. Infection of man occurs when the saliva of rabid animals gains entrance to wounds from bites or scratches. The disease is more or less widely prevalent in all civilized countries except England, where the careful supervision of dogs, enforcement of muzzling laws, and rigid enforcement of legislation regarding the importation of dogs, have caused a practical eradication of the disease. The incidence of rabies was decreasing in most countries before 1914. After the World War there was an increase in the number of rabid animals and in human rabies. With the restoration of control measures there has been a decrease of the incidence of rabies since 1924 (Rice and Beatty).

Experimental infection in susceptible animals is best carried out by injections of a salt-solution emulsion of the brain or spinal cord of an afflicted animal, subdurally, through a trephined opening in the skull, but may also be accomplished by injection into the peripheral nerves, the spinal canal, or the anterior chamber of the eye. Intravenous and intramuscular injections are also successful, though less regularly so.

The time of incubation after inoculation varies with the nature of the virus used, the location of the injection, and the quantity injected. In accidental infections of man and animals the incubation is shortest and the disease most severe when the wounds are about the head, neck, and upper extremities and are deeply lacerated. This is explained by the fact that the poison is conveyed to the central nervous system chiefly by the path of the nerve trunks. This was experimentally shown by Di Vestea and Zagari who inoculated animals by infection into peripheral nerves, and showed that the nerve tissue near the point of inoculation becomes infectious more quickly than the parts higher up; thus the lumbar cord of an animal inoculated in the sciatic nerve is infectious several days before virus can be demonstrated in the medulla.

In man, infected with "street virus," that is, with the virus of a dog or other animal not experimentally inoculated, the incubation period varies from about forty to sixty days. Isolated cases have been reported in which this period was prolonged for several months beyond this.

It is interesting to estimate how many people bitten by rabid dogs actually contract the disease unless treated (Cornwall). The estimate of whether the dog was rabid or not was made by the death of hydrophobia of one of the persons bitten. Cornwall's statistics are as follows:

> Number of persons bitten 423
> Death from hydrophobia 148
> Mortality per cent 35

The danger of the bites, of course, depends to a large extent upon whether the bite takes place through clothing or in such a way that a minimum amount of the dog's saliva comes in contact with the wound. Once symptoms develop, all cases die, therefore no omission of treatment in a case bitten by a proved rabid animal is ever justified.

The virulence of rabic virus may be markedly increased or diminished by a number of methods. By a repeated passage of the virus through rabbits, Pasteur was able to increase its virulence to a more or less constant maximum. Such virus which had been brought to the highest obtainable virulence, he designated as *virus fixe*. Inoculation of rabbits, dogs, guinea-pigs, rats, and mice with such virus usually results in symptoms within six to eight days. The same animals inoculated with street virus may remain apparently healthy for two to three weeks.

In dogs and guinea-pigs inoculation usually results first in a stage of increased excitability, restlessness, and sometimes viciousness. This is followed by depression, torpor, loss of appetite, inability to swallow, and finally paralysis. In rabbits the disease usually takes the form of what is known as "dumb rabies," the animals gradually growing more somnolent and weak, with tremors and gradual paralysis beginning in the hind legs.

In experimentally infected birds the disease is slow in appearing and may show a course of gradually increasing weakness and progressive paralysis extending over a period of two weeks after the appearance of the first symptoms.

In man, the disease begins usually with headaches and nervous depression. This is followed by difficulty in swallowing and spasms of the respiratory muscles. These symptoms occur intermittently, the free intervals being marked by attacks of terror and nervous depression. Occasionally there are maniacal attacks in which the patient raves and completely loses self-control. Finally, paralysis sets in, ending eventually in death.

Pathological examination of the tissues of rabid animals and human beings reveals macroscopically nothing but ecchymoses in some of the mucous and serous membranes. Microscopically, however, many abnormal changes have been observed and were formerly utilized in histological diagnosis of the condition. Babes described a disappearance of the chromatic element in the nerve cells of the spinal cord. This observation has been confirmed by others (Van Gehuchten), but is no longer regarded as pathognomonic of rabies. The same observer has described a marked leukocytic infiltration which occurs about the blood vessels of the brain and about the ganglia of the sympathetic system. These changes are not found in animals infected with fixed virus and are present only in animals and human beings inoculated with street virus.

Negri Bodies.—In 1903 Negri of Pavia described peculiar structures which he observed in the cells of the central nervous system of rabid dogs. While present in all parts of the brain, these "Negri bodies" are most regularly present and numerous in the larger cells of the hippocampus major and in the Purkinje cells of the cerebellum. The presence of these structures in rabid animals and man has been confirmed by a large number of workers in various parts of the world, and the specific association of these bodies with the disease is now beyond doubt. In consequence, the determination of Negri bodies in the brains of suspected animals has become an extremely important method of diagnosis—more rapid and accurate than the methods previously known.

The demonstration of Negri bodies in tissues is carried out as follows:

A small piece of tissue is taken from the cerebellum or from the center of the hippocampus major (cornu ammonis), and is fixed for twelve hours in Zenker's fluid. It is then washed thoroughly in water and dehydrated as usual in graded alcohols, embedded in paraffin, and sectioned. The sections are best stained by the method of Mann, as follows:

The sections, attached to slides in the usual way, are immersed in the following solution for from twelve to twenty-four hours:

Methylene blue (Gruebler OO), 1 per cent	35 c.c.
Eosin (Gruebler BA), 1 per cent	35 c.c.
Distilled water	100 c.c.

They are then differentiated in:

Absolute alcohol	30 c.c.
Sodium hydrate, 1 per cent in absolute alcohol	5 c.c.

In this solution blue is given off and the sections become red. After about five minutes the sections are removed from this solution, are washed in absolute alcohol, and are placed in water where they again become faintly bluish. It is of advantage to immerse them, now, in water slightly acidified with acetic acid. Following this they are dehydrated with absolute alcohol and cleared in xylol, as usual.

In preparations made in this way, the nerve cells are stained a pale blue, and in their cytoplasm, lying either close to the nucleus or near the root of the axis-cylinder process, are seen small oval bodies stained a deep pink. The bodies are variable in size, measuring from 1 to 10 μ in diameter. They are round or oval, show a more deeply stained peripheral zone which has been interpreted as a cell membrane, and, in their interior, often show small vacuole-like bodies. There may be more than one, often as many as three or four, in a single cell.

The Lentz stain is also useful for the demonstration of Negri bodies in brain sections.

An excellent method is the impression method of Frothingham who cuts the Ammon's horn transversely with scissors and gently presses a clean slide against the cut surface, lifting it rapidly. Five or six impressions can be made on one slide. Following this, the impressions are dried, fixed in Zenker and passed through water,

95 per cent alcohol, alcohol saturated with iodine. The iodine is washed out with 95 per cent alcohol followed by another washing in water. The slides are then stained in the usual manner. Frothingham recommends equal parts of Unna's stain and 5 per cent aqueous eosin, or saturated alcoholic eosin for fifteen minutes followed by five minutes in Löffler's methylene blue with careful differentiation in alcohol.

The rapid *demonstration of Negri bodies in smears* of brain tissue has become a routine procedure since the introduction of a modified Van Gieson stain by Williams and Lowden. The method used in the New York State Laboratory will be described in the section on Technic at the end of this book (Schleifstein).

Nature of Negri Bodies.—Negri bodies are round or oval structures 1 to 10 μ in diameter occurring in the cytoplasm of ganglion cells of the hippocampus, Purkinje cells of the cerebellum, and ganglion cells of the medulla, cord and posterior root ganglia. Several may occur in a single cell and the bodies are found along the processes of the cells as well as in the body of the cell.

Negri bodies are cytoplasmic inclusion bodies which present the same problems as other structures of similar characteristics found in other virus diseases. Calkins regarded them as sporulating protozoa, and the description of *Encephalitozoon rabei* or *Glugea lyssae* by Levaditi indicates that he considers these bodies to be protozoal in nature.

Other investigators, among whom is Goodpasture, believe that the Negri bodies are composed of degenerated mitochondria and neurofibrils.

While these questions are not settled, the evidence seems to us to be opposed to the theory of the protozoal nature of these structures, and to indicate that the Negri bodies may be a composite of virus and cellular material.

Diagnosis by Inoculation of Mice.—It has been known since 1887 that white mice are susceptible to rabies. After inoculation these animals develop furious and paralytic types of the disease. The use of mice for diagnostic purposes was neglected until 1935 when Webster and Dawson described an improved method. They employed a special strain of white mice selectively bred for susceptibility to neurotropic viruses. The technic as practised by Leach is as follows:

A small portion of the Ammon's horn of the brain of a dog or other animal, fresh or after preservation in full strength glycerin, is ground in a sterile mortar. Nine parts of broth (hormone or meat infusion) is added to 1 part of ground brain tissue. After thorough emulsification the suspension is centrifuged at 2000 to 2500 revolutions per minute for 5 minutes. With a 0.25 cc. tuberculin syringe, 0.03 cc. of the supernatant fluid is injected through the skull into the brain of an etherized white mouse, 4 to 6 weeks old. A 27 gauge needle ¼ inch long is used and the injection is made slightly to one side of the mid line of the skull and halfway between the eye and ear. As a rule, 4 mice are injected with material from each specimen of brain.

In positive cases, the inoculated mice show first sluggishness and roughening of the fur. This is followed by photophobia and conjunctivitis. Paralysis usually begins in the hind legs and the legs become extended. Convulsions may occur at this stage. Death is preceded by complete prostration and labored irregular respiration. Paralysis appears, as a rule, on the 8th to 10th day after inoculation and death occurs on the 10th or 12th day. Negri bodies are found in the brains of inoculated mice, sometimes as early as the 5th day after infection.

Rabies Virus.—Remlinger succeeded, with some difficulty in obtaining active Berkefeld V filtrates of rabies virus. The disease is transmissible by material in tissues and filtrates which do not contain any visible or cultivable micro-organism.

The report of the cultivation of Negri bodies by Noguchi is now regarded as being based upon a misinterpretation of the structure of materials found in smears of the cultures. The especially remarkable fact disclosed by Noguchi was that the virus remained active for nearly seven months, passing through 21 transfers, in a medium of ascitic fluid and kidney incubated at 37° C. This may indicate that the virus was multiplying in the presence of living cells in the medium.

Different strains of rabies virus differ in virulence and adaptation to specific hosts, but all of them are immunologically similar. By immunological and histological studies, the Kobayashi virus of encephalitis in Japan and the Koritschoner virus of encephalitis have been shown to be identical with rabies virus.

Webster and Clow cultivated rabies virus in serum—Tyrode solution containing embryo mouse brain or embryo chick brain. The virus reached a titer of 3×10^{-5} cc. after 4 days' incubation at 37° C., and survived for 2 months at 5° C. in the liquid or dry state.

Specific Therapy.—The treatment which is now prophylactically applied to patients infected with or suspected of infection with rabies has been but little altered either in principle or in technical detail since it was first worked out by Pasteur. In principle it consists of an active immunization with virus, attenuated by drying, administered during the long incubation period in doses of progressively increasing virulence.

By the repeated passage of street virus through rabbits, Pasteur obtained a virus of maximum and approximately constant virulence which he designated as *virus fixe*. By a series of painstaking experiments he then ascertained that such *virus fixe* could be gradually attenuated by drying over caustic potash at a temperature of about 25° C., the degree of attenuation varying directly with the time of drying. Thus, while fresh *virus fixe* regularly caused death in rabbits after six to seven days, the incubation time following the inoculation of dried virus grew longer and longer as the time of drying was increased, until finally virus dried for eight days was no longer regularly infectious and that dried for twelve to fourteen days had completely lost its virulence.

The method of active immunization which Pasteur used consisted in injecting, subcutaneously, virus of progressively increasing virulence, beginning with that derived from cords dried for thirteen days and gradually advancing to a strong virus. Thus the patient was immunized to a potent virus several weeks before the incubation time of his own infection had elapsed. Pasteur successfully proved the efficacy of his method upon dogs and finally upon human beings, the first human case being that of a nine-year-old child—Joseph Meister.

Technic.—The technic developed by Pasteur is still, in the main, followed by those who treat rabies to-day.

I. As a preliminary, it is necessary to prepare or obtain *virus fixe*. This may generally be procured from an established laboratory or may be prepared independently by passing street virus through a series of young rabbits (weighing from 700 to 1000 Gms.). According to Högyes the passage of the virus through 21 to 30 rabbits, in this way, will reduce its incubation time to seven or eight days. Babes claims to obtain a *virus fixe* more rapidly by passing the virus alternately through rabbits and guinea-pigs.

For purposes of inoculation, virus is prepared by emulsifying in sterile salt solution pieces of the medulla or cerebellum of animals dead of a previous inoculation. The brain tissue which is not emulsified may be preserved under sterile glycerin in a dark and cool place for further use.

II. Rabbits are inoculated with *virus fixe* by intracranial injection. A small incision is made in the shaved scalp in the median line, and the skin is retracted. With a small trephine or a round chisel, an opening is made in the skull and in the angle between the coronary and sagittal sutures. Through this opening about 0.2 to 0.3 c.c. of the *virus fixe* is injected, either directly into the brain substance or simply under the dura.

As soon as a rabbit so inoculated has died it is autopsied. The animal before dissection should be washed in a disinfectant solution—lysol or carbolic acid. The skin is then removed and the animal, lying on its ventral surface, is fastened to a dissecting board. The spinal canal is then laid open with a pair of curved scissors and the spinal cord carefully removed. This is accomplished by cutting across the cord in the lumbar region, and lifting this with a forceps while the nerve roots are divided from below upward.

The cord is suspended by a sterile thread within a large bottle into the bottom of which pieces of potassium hydrate have been placed. The bottle is then set away in a dark room or closet, the temperature of which is regulated so as to vary little above 25° C. Bacteriological controls as to the sterility of the cord should also be made.

After drying, pieces of the cord are prepared for injection. This is done in various ways. At the New York Department of Health 1 centimeter of the cord is emulsified in 3 c.c. of sterile salt solution, the dose for injection being usually 2.5 c.c. Marx emulsifies 1 centimeter of the cord in 5 c.c. of sterile bouillon or salt solution, using 1 to 3 c.c. of this for injection according to the age of the cord. For shipment 20 per cent of glycerin and 0.5 per cent of carbolic acid are added.

The scheme of treatment is also subject to variations according to the individual customs of various laboratories. The table given below represents the recommendations at present favored by many health departments.

TWENTY-ONE DAY SCHEME OF RABIES VACCINE TREATMENT

DAY	DAYS CORD DRIED	FACE CASES	NUMBER OF INJECTIONS	ADULTS	CHILDREN 6 to 10 years	CHILDREN 1 to 5 years
1	8—7—6	8—7—6	2	3 c.c.	3 c.c.	3 c.c.
2	8—7—6	8—7—6	2	3 c.c.	3 c.c.	3 c.c.
3	5—4	5—4	2	3 c.c.	3 c.c.	3 c.c.
4	5	5	1	2 c.c.	2 c.c.	2 c.c.
5	4	4	1	2 c.c.	2 c.c.	* 1½ c.c.
6	4	4	1	2 c.c.	2 c.c.	* 1½ c.c.
7	3	3	1	2 c.c.	* 1½ c.c.	* 1 c.c.
8	3	3	1	2 c.c.	* 1½ c.c.	2 c.c.
9	5	2	1	2 c.c.	2 c.c.	2 c.c.
10	4	4	1	2 c.c.	2 c.c.	2 c.c.
11	4	4	1	2 c.c.	2 c.c.	2 c.c.
12	3	3	1	2 c.c.	2 c.c.	* 1½ c.c.
13	3	2	1	2 c.c.	2 c.c.	* 1½ c.c.
14	4	4	1	2 c.c.	2 c.c.	2 c.c.
15	4	4	1	2 c.c.	2 c.c.	2 c.c.
16	3	3	1	2 c.c.	2 c.c.	* 1½ c.c.
17	3	2	1	2 c.c.	2 c.c.	* 1½ c.c.
18	4	4	1	2 c.c.	2 c.c.	2 c.c.
19	4	4	1	2 c.c.	2 c.c.	2 c.c.
20	3	3	1	2 c.c.	2 c.c.	2 c.c.
21	3	2	1	2 c.c.	2 c.c.	2 c.c.

* Face cases receive adult doses.

The severity or mildness of cases is estimated from the depth and degree of laceration of the wounds, also from their location—bites about the face and upper extremities being the most dangerous.

During the course of such treatment patients may show troublesome erythema about the point of injection and occasionally backache and muscular pains. Treatment need not be omitted unless these symptoms become excessive.

The efficiency of the Pasteur treatment in rabies is no longer problematical. According to Högyes, the average mortality from rabies of the victims of dog-bites who have received the Pasteur treatment is approximately 1 per cent.

Although the method described above is the one which is extensively used in all established institutes for the treatment of rabies, other methods have been elaborated and used to a slight extent. One of these is the "dilution method" of *Högyes*. A definite quantity of the spinal cord of a rabbit dead of *virus fixe* is emulsified in 100 c.c. of normal salt solution. Dilutions of this emulsion are made and the patient is injected at first with a dilution of 1:1000, subsequent injections being made of gradually increasing concentration until a concentration of 1:100 is reached. This method has not found extensive application.

Harris and *Shackell* describe an improved method of desiccating rabic virus which consists in placing the material to be dried in the bottom of a vacuum desiccating jar in the upper part of which is a separate dish containing sulphuric acid. The temperature is reduced by placing the jar in a salt and ice mixture, and after thorough solidification of the material has resulted, a rapid vacuum is produced by a vacuum pump to less than 2 millimeters of mercury. The virus so dried will retain its virulence for as long as four months, if guarded against moisture.

SEMPLE'S METHOD.[3]—The method which is most frequently employed is the one which depends upon the use of virus treated with carbolic acid at room temperature, and, therefore, possibly killed. This method was developed very largely by the efforts of Lieutenant Colonel D. Semple at the Indian Medical Service Research Institute at Kasauli, Calcutta. Semple's directions are as follows:

An 8 per cent dilution of rabies virus is made in normal solution and killed by exposure to 1 per cent carbolic acid at 37° C. for twenty-four hours. This fluid is diluted with an equal volume of normal saline, making a 4 per cent rabies virus in 0.5 per cent carbolic acid. Sterility tests are made.

Cornwall in 1923 reported upon the effects of treatment with a virus made by Semple's method, the actual preparation made being a 1 per cent fixed virus suspension in normal salt solution with 0.5 per cent phenol. Five c.c. of this were injected into each person daily for fifteen days. Injections were made in separate amounts of 2½ c.c. subcutaneously. He reports on the treatment of 28,898 people in India as follows:

Death during the treatment .... 0.15 per cent
Death less than 15 days after completion of the treatment .... 0.27 per cent
Death more than 15 days after completion of the treatment........ 0.7 per cent
Total mortality of those treated .... 0.1 per cent

Basing the estimate of efficiency upon statistics gathered in cases where a presumably rabid dog had bitten several persons of whom some accepted the treatment and some refused, he gathers the following information from a study of 2174 cases:

Deaths among the treated .... 2.9 per cent
Deaths among the untreated .... 6.2 per cent

3 We are indebted for the references to this method to John Reichel.

These percentages become more significant if we combine them with Cornwall's estimate above that only 35 per cent of untreated people bitten actually contract hydrophobia.

Modifications of the Semple method are being used and have been licensed by the Treasury Department of the United States.

Attempts to treat active rabies with the sera of immunized animals have so far been unsuccessful.

Prophylactic Immunization of Dogs.—This method has been recently introduced for the purpose of immunizing dogs by a modified active immunization. The method has consisted in single injections of phenolized rabies virus first practiced by Umeno and Doi, who immunized over fifteen thousand animals. Their statistical results are promising, though not absolutely conclusive. The matter has been taken up in this country and has been experimentally studied by Eichorn and Lyon, who obtained excellent though not absolutely conclusive results, and the method has been introduced by the public health departments of Connecticut and New Jersey with promising results. Case-reports will be found in papers by Bigelow and Webber, and Withington and Bigelow. The state of affairs at the present writing is that the prophylactic immunization in dogs will constitute an important addition to our methods of exterminating rabies as soon as the technic has been perfected and the rather difficult organization of the undertaking has been put upon a practical basis. Phillips, by an investigation in Ohio, concluded that the one day treatment of dogs is not reliable at present and that the number of injections will have to be increased, probably as in the Semple treatment for human beings.

In 1931, Schoening reported that a dog can be immunized by an injection of 1 c.c. of phenolized vaccine or of Kelser's chloroform treated vaccine. Schoening expressed the opinion that the immunization of the dog population is a step forward in the control of rabies, but that the rigid enforcement of the older measures is absolutely necessary for the solution of the rabies problem.

Paralysis Following Anti-Rabic Vaccination.—In the section of this chapter dealing with post-infection disseminated encephalomyelitis we have mentioned that disease of the nervous system sometimes follows injections of rabies vaccine in man (Bassoe and Grinker). Paralytic symptoms following this type of vaccination have been noticed since the time of Pasteur. McCoy, who reviewed cases occurring in the United States in 1930, collected records of only 3 cases in 20,000 Pasteur treatments. Hence, the condition is not common. The disease occurs only in adults and appears from the sixth to the twentieth day after the beginning of the injections. The cases have been associated with all the types of vaccine used, and are not due to a special rabies virus. As we have indicated, the etiology of the condition is not definitely known.

REFERENCES

Amoss, H. L. Quoted from Filterable Viruses, ed. by T. M. Rivers, Baltimore, 1928, Chap. V., p. 159.
Anderson, J. F., and Frost, W. H. U. S. Pub. Health Rep., 1912, 27:332; 1913, 28:833.
Armstrong, C. U. S. Pub. Health Rep., 1929, 44:2041.
—— J. Am. M. Ass., 1929, 92:392.
—— and Lillie, R. D. P. S. Pub. Health Rep., 1934, 49, 1019; 1935, 50:831.
—— and Harrison, W. T. U. S. Pub. Health Rep., 1935, 50:725; 1936, 51:203.

AYCOCK, W. L.   Am. J. Hyg., 1927, 7:791; 1928, 8:35.
——— J. Prevent. M., 1929, 3:245; 1930, 4:189, 201.
——— Am. J. Pub. Health, 1930, 20:41.
AYCOCK, W. L., and KRAMER, S. D.   J. Exper. M., 1930, 52:457.
BABES.   Virchow's Arch., 110.
——— Ann. de l'Inst. Pasteur, 1896, 6.
BASSOE, P., and GRINKER, R. R.   Arch. Neurol. & Psychiat., 1930, 23:1138.
BASTAI, P., and BUSACCA, A.   Klin. Wchnschr., 1924, 3:147, 442.
BASTIAANSE, F.   Nederl. Tijdschr. v. Geneesk., 1925, 69:I, 86.
BIGELOW and WEBBER.   Boston M. & S. J., 1924, 191:582.
BREDECK, J. F.   Am. J. Pub. Health, 1933, 23:1135.
BULL, C. G.   J. Exper. M., 1917, 25:557.
CALKINS, G. N.   Proc. N. York Path. Soc., 1906, 6.
CORNWALL.   Brit. M. J., 1923, 2:298.
COX, H. R., and FITE, G. L.   Proc. Soc. Exper. Biol. & Med. 1934, 31:499.
DAFANO, C., and INGLEBY, H.   Proc. Roy. Soc. Med., Sect. Path., 1919, 12:42. (Cited from J. McIntosh, A System of Bacteriology in Relation to Medicine, London, 1930, Vol. 7, Chap. XI, p. 172.)
DI VESTEA and ZAGARI.   Ann. d. l'Inst. Pasteur, 1889, 3:237.
DOERR, R.   Centralbl f. Haut. u. Geschlechtskrankh., vols. 13:417; 15:1, 289; 16:20; 1924, 16:481.
DOERR, R., and SCHNABEL, A.   Ztschr. f. Hyg. u. Infectionskrankh., 1921, 94:29.
Editorial, J. Am. M. Ass., 1919, 72:414.
EICHORN and LYON.   J. Am. Vet. M. Ass., 1924, 64:1.
EVANS, A. C.   U. S. Pub. Health Rep., 1932, 47:1723.
EVANS, A. C., and FREEMAN, W.   U. S. Pub. Health Rep., 1926, 41:1095.
FLEXNER, S.   J. Am. M. Ass., 1920, 74:865; 1923, 81:1688, 1785; 1928, 91:21; 1930, 94:305; 1932, 99:1244.
——— Science, 1933, 77:7.
FLEXNER, S., and AMOSS, H.   J. Exper. M., 1924, 39:191; 1925, 41:215, 233, 357.
FLEXNER, S., and CLARK, P. F.   J. Am. M. Ass., 1911, 56:1717.
FLEXNER, S., CLARK, P. F., and DOCHEZ, A. R.   J. Am. M. Ass., 1912, 59:272.
FLEXNER, S., and LEWIS, P. A.   J. Am. M. Ass., 1909, 53: 1639, 2095; 1910, 54:227, 253, 535, 1140; 1913.
FLEXNER, S., and NOGUCHI, H.   J. Exper. M., 1913, 18:461.
FLEXNER, S., and STEWART, F. W.   J. Am. M. Ass., 1928, 91:383.
——— New Eng. J. M., 1928, 199:213, quoted from S. Flexner, Science, 1933, 77:7.
FROTHINGHAM.   J. Med. Research, 1906, 14:471.
GAY, F. P.   Proc. Ass. Research in Nervous and Mental Diseases, 1932, 12:191.
GAY, F. P., and HOLDEN, M.   J. Infect. Dis., 1929, 45:415.
——— J. Am. M. Ass., 1931, 96:2028.
——— Proc. Soc. Exper. Biol. & Med., 1933, 30:1051.
GOODPASTURE, E. W.   Am. J. Pathol., 1925, 1:547.
GOODPASTURE, E. W., and TEAGUE, O.   J. M. Research, 1923, 44:121, 139.
GRÜTER.   Klin. Monatsbl. f. Augenh., 1920, 65:398.
HALL, A. J.   Brit. M. J., 1918, 2:461.
HARRIS.   J. Infect. Dis., 1913, 13:155.
HARRIS and SHACKELL.   J. Infect. Dis., 1911, 8:47.
HEINE, J.   Beobachtungen über Lähmungszustände der untern Extremitäten und deren Behandlungen, Stuttgart, 1840.
HOWARD, M. E.   J. Infect. Dis., 1939, 64:68.
HOWITT, B. F.   J. Immunol., 1937, 33:235.
JUNGEBLUT, C. W.   J. Exper. M., 1937, 66:459, 479.
——— Proc. Soc. Exper. Biol. & M., 1937, 37:160.
JUNGEBLUT, C. W., and ENGLE, E. T.   J. Am. M. Ass., 1932, 99:2091.

JUNGEBLUT, C. W., and SMITH, L. W.   J. Immunol., 1932, 23:35.

KANEKO, R.   Jap. M. World, 1925, 5:237.

KANEKO, R., and AOKI, Y.   Ergeb. d. inn. Med. u. Kinderhlk, 1928, 34:342.

KELSER, R. A.   J. Am. Vet. M. Ass., 1930, 30:595.

KLING, C., and LILJENQUIST, F.   Compt. rend. Soc. de biol., 1921, 84:521 (cited from MacNalty).

KLING, C., DAVIDE, H., and LILJENQUIST, F.   Compt. rend. Soc. de biol., 1922, 87:75, 77, 79.

KNOEPFELMACHER, W.   Med. Klin., 1909, 5:1671.

KOBAYASHI.   Jap. Med. World, 1925, 5:145 (quoted from E. V. Cowdry, J. Exper. M., 1927, 45:799).

KORITSCHONER, R.   Wien. klin. Wchnschr., 1923, 36:385.

——— Ztschr. f. Immunitätsforsch. u. exper. Therap., 1925, 42:217.

KRAMER, S. D.   J. Am. M. Ass., 1932, 99:1048.

LANDSTEINER, K., and LEVADITI, C.   Compt. rend. Acad. d. sc., 1909, 148:787.

——— Ann. de l'Inst. Pasteur, 1910, 24:833.

LANDSTEINER, K., and POPPER, E.   Ztschr. f. Immunitätsforsch. u. exper. Therap., 1909, 2:377.

LEACH, C.   Am. J. Pub. Health, 1938, 28:162.

LEAKE, J. P.   J. Am. M. Ass., 1933, 101:928.

——— Am. J. Pub. Health, 1933, 23:1140.

LEINER, C., and VON WIESNER, R.   Wien. klin. Wchnschr., 1910, 13:91, 323, 817.

LENTZ, O.   Centralbl. f. Bakteriol., I Abt., 1907, 44:375.

LEVADITI, C.   L'herpés et le zona, Paris, 1926.

LEVADITI, C., and HARVIER, P.   Compt. rend. Soc. de biol., 1920, 83:354, 385, 675, 1143.

LEVADITI, C., NICOLAU, S., and SCHOEN, R.   Compt. rend. Soc. de biol., 1924, 90:994.

LIPSCHÜTZ, B.   Arch. f. Dermat. u. Syph., 1921, 136:428.

LONG, P. H., OLITSKY, P. K., and RHOADS, C. P.   J. Exper. M., 1930, 53:361.

LÖWENSTEIN, A.   Klin. Monatsbl. f. Augenh., 1920, 64:15.

LUCAS, W. P., and OSGOOD, R. B.   J. Am. M. Ass., 1913, 60:1611.

LUCKSCH, F., Med. Klin., 1924, 20:1170.

——— Centralbl. f. Bakteriol., I Abt., 1925, 96:309.

MACNALTY, A. S.   Epidemic Diseases of the Central Nervous System, London, 1927; and sup-
    plement to 48th Ann. Rep. Local Gov. Bd., London, 1919, p. 71.

MAGGIORA, A., MANTOVANI, M., and TOMBOLATO, A.   Riforma med., 1920, 36:114.

MANOUELIAN, Y., and VIALA, J.   Ann. de l'Inst. Pasteur, 1924, 38:258.

MARX.   Deutsche med. Wchnschr., 1899, 1900.

McCORDOCK, H. A.   Am. J. Pub. Health, 1933, 1152.

McCOY, G. W.   U. S. Pub. Health Dept., 1930, 45:1888.

McINTOSH, J., and TURNBULL, H. M.   Brit. J. Exper. Pathol., 1920, 1:89.

MEDIN, O.   Verhandl. d. X internat. med. Kong., 1890, 2:Abt. 6, 37.

MUCKENFUSS, R. S.   Am. J. Pub. Health, 1933, 1148.

MUCKENFUSS, R. S., ARMSTRONG, C., and McCORDOCK, H. A.   U. S. Pub. Health Rep., 1933, 48:1341.

NEGRI, A.   Ztschr. f. Hyg. u. Infectionskrankh., 1903, 43:507; 44:519.

NEAL, J. B.   Am. J. Pub. Health, 1933, 23:1144.

NEUSTAEDTER, M., and THRO, W. C.   N. York M. J., 1911, 94, 613, 813.

NOGUCHI, H.   J. Exper. M., 1913, 18:314.

OLITSKY, P. K., RHOADS, C. P., and LONG, P. H.   J. Am. M. Ass., 1929, 92:1725.

OSGOOD, R. B., and LUCAS, W. P.   J. Am. M. Ass., 1911, 56:495.

OTTOLENGHI, D., TONIETTI, F., and D'ANTONA, S.   Policlinico, 1920, 27:1075.

PARK, W. H.   J. Am. M. Ass., 1932, 99:1050.

——— N. York State J. M., 1932, 33:91.

PARKER, F. T.   J. Med. Research, 1924, 44:289.

PASTEUR, L.   Series of papers on rabies, Compt. rend. Acad. d. sc., 1881, 1882, 1884, 1885, 1886.

——— Ann. d. l'Inst. Pasteur, 1887, 1888.

PEABODY, F. W., DRAPER, G., and DOCHEZ, A. R.   Monogr. Rockefeller Inst. M. Research, No. 4, 1912.

PERDRAU, J. R.   Brit. J. Exper. Pathol., 1925, 6:41, 123.

——— J. Path. & Bacteriol., 1928, 31:17.

PHILLIPS. Ohio's Health, 1922, 13, Nov., Ohio State Dept. Health.

Poliomyelitis. A book by several authors under auspices of the International Committee for the Study of Infantile Paralysis, organized by Jeremiah Milbank, Baltimore, 1932.

Report of Committee on Vaccination, Ministry of Health, London, 1928.

REMLINGER. Ann. de l'Inst. Pasteur, 1903, 17:834.

RHOADS, C. P. J. Exper. M., 1930, 51:1; 1931, 53:115.

RICE, T. B., and BEATTY, N. Am. J. Pub. Health, 1928, 18:421.

RIVERS, T. M. Infections of the Central Nervous System, Chap. II, p. 49 in Proc. Assoc. Research in Nervous & Mental Dis., Baltimore, 1931.

——— Arch. Neurol. & Psychiat., 1932, 28:757.

RIVERS, T. R., and SCOTT, T. F. McN. Science, 1935, 81:439.

——— J. Exp. M., 1936, 63:415.

ROSENOW, E. C. J. Infect. Dis., 1924, 34:329.

——— J. Am. M. Ass., 1924, 82:449.

ROSENOW, E. C., and WHEELER, G. W. J. Infect. Dis., 1918, 22:281; and series of papers in this Journal.

SABIN, A. B. J. Exper. M., 1931, 29:59.

SCHLEIFSTEIN, J. Am. J. Pub. Health, 1937, 27:1283.

SCHOENING, H. W. Am. J. Pub. Health, 1931, 21:637.

SCHULTZ, E. W. J. Pediatrics, 1932, 1:358; 1938, 13:38.

———, and GEBHARDT, L. P. J. Am. Ass., 1937, 108:2182.

SEMPLE. Indian J. M. Research, Calcutta, 1911, 44.

——— Lancet, 1911, 173.

SMADEL, J. E., BAIRD, R. D., and WALL, M. J. Proc. Soc. Exper. Biol. and M., 1939, 40:71.

SMITH, H. F. U. S. Pub. Health Rep., 1921, 36:207.

STALLYBRASS, C. O. Lancet, 1923, 2:922.

STRAUSS, I., and HUNTOON, F. M. N. York M. J., 1910, 91:64.

STRAUSS, I., HIRSCHFELD, S., and LOEWE, L. N. York M. J., 1919, 109:772.

——— J. Infect. Dis., 1919, 25:378; 1920, 27:250.

TAKAKI, I. Ztschr. f. Immunitätsforsch. u. exper. Therap., 1926, 47:456.

TISDALL, F. F., BROWN, A., DEFFRIES, R. D., ROSS, M. A., and SELLERS, A. H. Can. Pub. Health J., 1937, 28:523.

TOOMEY. Proc. Soc. Exper. Biol. and M., 1933-34, 31:680, 1015; 1934-35, 32:423.

——— Ann. Int. M., 1935, 8:854.

TRASK, J. P., VIGNEC, A. J., and PAUL, J. R. J. Am. M. Ass., 1938, 111:6.

TURNBULL, H. M., and McINTOSH, J. Brit. J. Exper. Path., 1926, 7:181.

UMENO and DOI. Kit. Arch. Exper. M., 1921, 5:89.

VAN GEHUCHTEN. Bull. Acad. de méd. et biol., 1900.

VON ECONOMO, C. Wien. klin. Wchnschr., 1917, 30:581.

VON WIESNER, R. R. Wien. klin. Wchnschr., 1917, 30:933.

WEBSTER, L. T., and FITE, G. L. Science, 1933, 78:463.

——— Proc. Soc. Exper. Biol. & Med., 1933, 31:344.

——— and CLOW, A. D. J. Exper. M., 1937, 66:125.

——— and DAWSON, J. R. Proc. Soc. Biol. and Exper. M., 1935, 32:570.

WEYER, E. R., PARK, W. H., and BANZHAF, E. J. Am. J. Pathol., 1929, 5:517.

——— J. Exper. M., 1931, 53:553.

WICKMAN, I., Beiträge zur Kenntniss der Heine-Medinischen Krankheit, Berlin, 1907.

WILLIAMS, A. W., and LOWDEN, M. M. J. Infect. Dis., 1906, 3:452.

WILSON, S. A. K. Lancet, 1918, 2:7.

WILSON, R. E., and FORD, F. R. Bull. Johns Hopkins Hosp., 1927, 40:337.

WITHINGTON and BIGELOW. Boston M. & S. J., 1925, 193:552.

ZINSSER, H. Report on poliomyelitis virus obtained from a case of Landry's Paralysis, California State Medical Society Meeting, Santa Barbara, 1912.

——— Arch. Pathol., 1928, 6:271.

ZINSSER, H., and TANG, F. J. Exper. M., 1926, 44:21.

CHAPTER LXIV

YELLOW FEVER, DENGUE, PAPPATACI FEVER AND PSITTACOSIS

YELLOW FEVER

Yellow fever is an acute infectious disease, due to a filtrable virus, which prevails endemically in the tropical countries of the Western Hemisphere and along the West Coast of Africa. In these places epidemic outbreaks also occur and the disease has appeared in epidemic invasions in the north temperate United States and Europe. The area of accidental epidemics extends from parallel 45° north latitude to 40° south latitude. The zone is defined by the range of occurrence of the chief vector, the mosquito *Aedes aegypti*. In the United States, severe epidemics occurred frequently in the years before 1906, in Louisiana, Mississippi, Alabama, and occasionally in Philadelphia and Baltimore. Students of the history of yellow fever, particularly Carter, are of the opinion that West Africa is the place of origin of the disease and that the infection was brought with Negro slaves, or by those engaged in the slave traffic, from Africa to the Western Hemisphere.

In man afflicted with the malady the clinical picture is one of a rapidly developing fever with severe gastro-intestinal symptoms, jaundice, vomiting of blood ("black vomit"), albuminuria, and often active delirium. The mortality is usually high, often reaching 80 per cent or more in severe epidemics.

For many years, no lower animal had been found susceptible to yellow fever. In 1927, *Macacus* monkeys, particularly *Macacus rhesus*, were discovered by Stokes, Bauer, and Hudson to be susceptible, and in 1930, Theiler showed that the white mouse could be infected by intracerebral injection. These discoveries have made possible great advances in the investigation of the disease.

Sawyer divides research in yellow fever into two epochs. The first commenced in 1900, when the Yellow Fever Commission under Major Walter Reed proved that the common stegomyia mosquito of the tropics, *Aedes aegypti,* is responsible for the transmission of yellow fever. The second epoch began in 1927, when Stokes, Bauer, and Hudson found out that *Macacus* monkeys are susceptible to yellow fever and are suitable experimental animals.

Mode of Transmission.—Until 1900 the mode of transmission of yellow fever was not understood and many erroneous theories were prevalent. It was supposed that yellow fever was contagious, and transmitted from person to person by direct or indirect contact with those afflicted or by fomites. The first to make the definite assertion that yellow fever was transmitted by the agency of mosquitoes was Carlos Finlay. Finlay, as early as 1881, advanced the theory that mosquitoes were responsible for transmission of this disease and, furthermore, recognized *Stegomyia fasciata* or *Stegomyia calopus* as the guilty species. Finlay's opinion, although later proved to be correct, was at first based only upon such circumstantial evidence as the correspondence of the yellow-fever zones with the distribution of this species of mosquito and the great prevalence of mosquitoes at times during which epidemics occurred. His theory was, therefore, received with much skepticism and was neglected by scientists until its revival in 1900, when the problem was extensively investigated by a commission of American Army surgeons.

Reed, Carroll, Agramonte, and Lazear were the members of this commission. The courage, self-sacrifice, and scientific accuracy which characterized the work of these men have made the chapter of yellow fever one of the most brilliant in the annals of American scientific achievement (Agramonte).

Their work was much facilitated by the experience of Gorgas and others, who had demonstrated the absolute failure of ordinary sanitary regulations to limit the spread of yellow fever.

They began their researches by investigating carefully the validity of Sanarelli's claims as to the etiological significance of his "*B. icteroides.*" The results of this work yielded absolutely no basis for confirmation.

They then proceeded to investigate the possibility of an intermediate host.

In August, 1900, the commission began its work on this subject by allowing mosquitoes, chiefly those of the stegomyia species, to suck blood from patients, later causing the same insects to feed upon normal susceptible individuals. The first nine experiments were negative. The tenth, of which Carroll was the subject, was successful. Four days after being bitten by the infected insect Carroll became severely ill with an attack of yellow fever, by which his life was endangered, and from the effects of which he died several years later.

On the 13th of September, Lazear, while working in the yellow-fever wards, noticed that a stegomyia had settled upon his hand, and deliberately allowed the insect to drink its fill. Five days later he became ill with yellow fever and died after a violent and short illness.

With these experiences as a working basis, the commission now decided upon a more systematic and thoroughly controlled plan of experimentation.

In November of the same year, 1900, an experiment station, "Camp Lazear," was established in the neighborhood of Havana, about a mile from the town of Quemados. The camp was surrounded by the strictest quarantine. Volunteers from the army of occupation were called for, and 12 individuals were selected for the camp, 3 immunes and 9 nonimmunes. Two of the latter were physicians. The immunes and the members of the commission only were allowed to go in and out. All nonimmunes who left the camp were prohibited from reentering and their places taken by other nonimmune volunteers. During December, 5 of the nonimmune inmates were successfully inoculated with yellow fever by means of infected mosquitoes. During January and February 5 further successful experiments were made. Clinical observations were made by experienced native physicians, Carlos Finlay among them, and the patients, as soon as they were unquestionably ill with yellow fever, were removed to a yellow-fever hospital. This was done to prevent the possibility of the disease spreading within the camp itself. The mosquitoes used for the experiments were all cultivated from the larvae and kept at a temperature of about 26.5° C.

A further important experiment was now made. A small house was erected and fitted with absolutely mosquito-proof windows and doors. The interior was divided by wire mosquito netting into two spaces. Within one of these spaces fifteen infected mosquitoes were liberated. Seven of these had fed upon yellow-fever patients four days previously; 4, eight days previously; 3, twelve days previously; and 1, twenty-four hours previously. A nonimmune person then entered this room and remained there about thirty minutes, allowing himself to be bitten by 7 mosquitoes. Twice after this the same person entered the room, remaining in it altogether sixty-four minutes and being bitten 15 times. After four days this individual came down with typical symptoms of yellow fever.

In the other room 2 nonimmunes slept for thirteen nights without any evil results whatever.

It now remained to show that mosquitoes were the sole means of transmission and to exclude the possibility of infection by contact with excreta, vomitus, or fomites. For this purpose another mosquito-proof house was constructed. By artificial heating its temperature was kept above 32.2° C. and the air was kept moist by the evaporation of water. Clothing and bedding, vessels, and eating utensils, soiled with vomitus, blood, and feces of yellow-fever patients were placed in this house and three nonimmune persons inhabited it for twenty days. During this time they were strictly quarantined and protected from mosquitoes. Each evening, before going to bed, they unpacked and thoroughly shook clothing and bedding of yellow-fever patients, and hung and scattered these materials about their beds. They slept, moreover, in contact with linen and blankets soiled by patients. None of these persons contracted yellow fever. The same experiment was twice repeated by other nonimmunes, in both cases with like negative results.

All of the nonimmunes taking part in these experiments were American soldiers. Four of them were later shown to be susceptible to yellow fever by the agencies of mosquito infection or blood injection.

The results obtained by the investigations of this commission may be summarized, therefore, as follows:

Yellow fever is acquired naturally only by the bite of the *Stegomyia fasciata* (*Aedes aegypti*). It is necessary that the infecting insect shall have sucked the blood of a yellow-fever patient during the first four or five days of the disease, and that an interval of at least twelve days shall have elapsed between the sucking of blood and the reinfection of another human being. Sucking of the blood of patients advanced beyond the fifth day of the disease does not seem to render the mosquito infectious, and at least twelve days are apparently required to allow the parasite to develop within the infected mosquito to a stage at which reinfection of the human being is possible.

The results of the American Commission were soon confirmed by Guiteras and by Marchoux, Salimbeni, and Simond. These latter observers, moreover, confirmed the fact that infection could be experimentally produced by injections of blood or blood serum taken from patients during the first three days of the disease. They showed that blood taken after the fourth day was no longer infectious, that 0.1 c.c. of serum sufficed for infection and finally that no infection could take place through excoriations upon the skin. They furthermore confirmed the observation of Carroll that the virus of the disease could pass through the coarser Berkefeld and Chamberland filters, passing through a Chamberland candle "F" but held back by the finer variety known as "B."

The fundamental factors of yellow-fever transmission thus discovered, we are in possession of logical means of defense. The most important feature of such preventive measures must naturally center upon the extermination of the transmitting species of mosquito.

Aedes aegypti (formerly called *Stegomyia fasciata* or *Stegomyia calopus*) is a member of the group of culicidae. It is more delicately built than most of the other members of the group culicidae, is of a dark gray color, and has peculiar thorax-markings which serve to distinguish it from other species. The more detailed points of differentiation upon which an exact zoological recognition depends are too technical to be entered into at this place. Briefly described, they consist of lyre-like markings of the back, unspotted wings, white stripes and spots on the abdomen, and band-like white markings about the metatarsi and tarsi of the third pair of legs. The peculiar power of transmitting yellow fever possessed by this species is explained by Marchoux and Simond by the fact that *Aedes aegypti* is unique among culicidae in that the female lives for prolonged periods after sucking blood. Among other species— *Culex fatigans, Culex confirmatus,* and most others—the female lays its eggs within from two to eight days after feeding on blood and rarely lives longer than the twelfth day—the time necessary for the development of the yellow-fever parasite.

The limitation of yellow fever to tropical countries is explained by the fact that *Aedes* develops only in places where high temperatures prevail. The optimum temperature for this species lies between 26° and 32° C. At 17° C. it no longer feeds, and becomes practically paralyzed at 15° C. In order to thrive, the species requires a temperature never going below 22° C. at night and rising regularly above 25° C. during the day. The females only are dangerous as sources of infection. The insect, like anopheles, has the peculiarity of feeding chiefly in the afternoon and at night.

Other species of *Aedes* mosquitoes and the mosquito *Eretmopodites chrysogaster* were shown by Bauer to be capable of transmitting the infection. But *Aedes aegypti* remains the most important insect vector.

Experiments done by Reed, Carroll, Agramonte, and Lazear, to ascertain whether the power of infecting was hereditarily transmissible from the mosquito to the next generation, were negative. Marchoux and Simond, however, reported that hereditary transmission of the virus occurred. Bauer and Hudson were unable to confirm this. Under natural and experimental conditions *Aedes aegypti* becomes infectious about 12 days after ingestion of the virus.

Accidental laboratory infections with yellow-fever virus have occurred relatively frequently, and some of these infections have been fatal. In the review (Sawyer) from which we have quoted so much, a tribute is paid to Adrian Stokes, Noguchi, Alexander Young, Paul Lewis, and Theodore Hayne, all of whom lost their lives by infection contracted in the course of their investigation of this disease. In 1921, our colleague, Howard Cross, died of yellow fever in Mexico from naturally acquired yellow fever at the start of his investigations.

The cases of seven others, who contracted the disease accidentally in the laboratory, have been reported in detail by Berry and Kitchen. Fortunately, all of these recovered.

Etiology.—Since the discovery of Carroll that the virus of yellow fever was filtrable was confirmed in 1903 by the members of the French Yellow Fever Commission and by Stokes, Bauer and Hudson, and others, no advantage, other than historical interest, would be gained by discussing the varieties of bacteria and protozoa which different investigators have isolated from the blood and lesions of yellow fever patients and to which they have attributed etiological importance. Two of these, however, call for special notice. The first was the *Bacillus icteroides,* of Sanarelli, which was soon disposed of by the Reed Commission in 1900. The second was *Leptospira icteroides,* considered by Noguchi to be the cause of yellow fever.

In 1918, Noguchi isolated *Leptospira icteroides* from the blood of a patient diagnosed as a case of yellow fever in Guayaquil. In a series of investigations during the following years he presented much bacteriological and immunological evidence to sustain the opinion that this spirochete caused the disease. Agramonte and other students of the natural history of yellow fever remained skeptical. The investigators who took up the research in yellow fever in West Africa (Sawyer) about 1926, were unable to obtain leptospirae by culture or inoculation of guinea-pigs with blood from patients with yellow fever, and failed to find lytic antibodies for leptospirae in the serum of persons who had recovered from yellow fever. Sellards also showed that *Leptospira icteroides* and *Leptospira icterohaemorrhagiae,* the cause of Weil's disease, were immunologically identical. The outcome of much investigation leads to the conclusion that Noguchi was misled by erroneous clinical diagnosis, that the cases diagnosed yellow fever from which he isolated the *Leptospira* were in reality cases of hemorrhagic jaundice, or Weil's disease, and that *Leptospira icteroides* has no etiological relation to yellow fever.

The Virus.—The virus from the blood and organs of infected man and animals and from the bodies of mosquitoes is filtrable through Berkefeld V and N candles. When suspended in 10 per cent serum, the virus passes readily through these filters, but when suspended in physiological sodium chloride solution it is often retained by the filter (Sawyer).

The virus is apparently capable of passing through the intact skin (Bauer and Hudson).

The virus is susceptible to slow desiccation at room temperature, and is relatively readily inactivated by heat and age and salt solution. Desiccation of frozen blood or liver mash *in vacuo,* according to the method of Harris and Shackell, was found by Sawyer to be an efficacious means of preserving the virus for several years.

Different strains of the virus vary in virulence, but are immunologically alike. The strains of virus from West Africa and Brazil are immunologically identical, and the sera of immune persons in North America, Central America, South America, and West Africa neutralize each strain of virus. From this, it is concluded that yellow fever in Africa and in North and South America is the same disease, having the same etiology.

Confirmatory evidence that the disease is due to a virus was provided by the discovery by Torres of *intranuclear inclusion bodies* in the cells of the livers of monkeys experimentally infected with yellow fever. These have been studied by the usual histological methods by Cowdry and Kitchen. By the microincineration method of investigation, Cowdry showed that these inclusion bodies differed from the nucleoli and basophilic chromatin in yielding little or no ash. Similar inclusion bodies were found in the liver cells of 10 of 39 persons who had died of yellow fever.

After passage through mice by intracerebral inoculation the virus gained neurotropic properties for monkeys, producing in monkeys a fatal encephalitis (Lloyd and Penna). The neurotropic virus was transmissible by mosquitoes (Davis, Lloyd and Frobisher).

Immunity.—Recovery from an attack of yellow fever protects against subsequent infection throughout life.

The disease in children is milder than in adults. Hence, in an endemic area, many become immunized by infections which do not result in clinically recognizable yellow fever. There is no fundamental difference between the susceptibility of the Negro and white races. Maturation phenomena do not play a part in the acquisition of immunity to yellow fever, as adults in areas in which the disease is not endemic (China and Canada) are not immune and do not have protective substances in their blood (Hughes and Sawyer).

Tests for immunity are based upon the usual "protection methods" carried out by making injections of mixtures of virus and the serum under examination. The discovery by Theiler that mice were susceptible to the virus by intracranial inoculation has made possible extended investigations of the incidence and persistence of immunity. The method has been described by Sawyer and Lloyd as follows:

In this test 0.03 cc. of sterile 2 per cent starch solution is injected intracerebrally into each of six anesthetized mice to localize the virus in the brain. Immediately thereafter the mouse is given an intraperitoneal injection of a mixture of 0.2 c.c. of a 10 per cent suspension of virus-containing mouse brain and 0.4 cc. of the serum to be tested. Control groups of mice are given injections in the same way, except that known normal and immune serums are substituted for the serum to be tested. Mice dying from five to ten days after inoculation are considered to have died of yellow fever encephalitis if the results with the control groups are satisfactory. At least five out of six mice must survive if the result is to be considered "protection," and likewise five out of six must succumb if the result is "no protection." Results falling outside these narrow limits are regarded as "inconclusive."

Complement fixation tests have been used by Frobisher and his associates as a measure of antibodies in serum, and hence as an index of the incidence of immunity among the people in any country.

Prophylactic vaccination has been improved constantly since 1930. The first effective method of immunization that was adapted to human use was based on the work of Theiler. This mouse-brain virus, injected with a small amount of immune serum, as in the method of Sawyer, Kitchin and Lloyd, was efficient, but cumbersome. Injected without protective serum the virus was dangerous. Various types of culture vaccine have been tried, with attention directed to variations in the neurotropic and viscerotropic properties of the strains. Finally a culture virus known as 17D derived from the Asibi strain was found to be suitable for making a safe and efficient vaccine. The material used by Smith, Penna and Paoliello for the vaccination of more than 59,000 persons in Brazil in 1937-38 was obtained from chick embryos inoculated at the 7th day within the shell and incubated for four days thereafter. Since 1938 many thousands of persons have been vaccinated against yellow fever.

Prevention.—The eradication of yellow fever from Havana and Panama by Gorgas and from Rio de Janeiro by Oswaldo Cruz seemed, by 1915 to show that quarantine, fumigation, screening of houses and cisterns, elimination of breeding places of *Aedes aegypti* and general anti-mosquito measures were sufficient to prevent the occurrence and spread of the disease. The "complete eradication" of the disease from the world was envisioned. However, these measures failed to control the disease in Brazil, where two previously unrecognized epidemiological types, rural yellow fever transmitted by *Aedes aegypti,* and jungle fever occurring in the absence of this mosquito, were recognized. Similar conditions appear to exist on the West Coast of Africa, in the great endemic region of yellow fever. Jungle fever, contracted in the forests, probably has its reservoir on monkeys and is transmitted by a variety of mosquitoes. The virus is identical with the virus of yellow fever. The problem of eradication of the disease has become vastly more complex and difficult. In addition to the older methods mentioned above the control of yellow fever in Brazil is now based on viscerotomy for diagnosis, anti-aegypti measures and prophylactic vaccination (Soper).

DENGUE FEVER

Dengue fever is a disease occurring chiefly in the tropics. Its onset is often sudden, followed by very characteristic severe pains in the extremities, with a rising fever. There is also severe headache and, occasionally, joint pains. There may be a catarrhal condition of the conjunctivae and pain in the eyeballs and considerable weakness. In typical cases there is usually a remission followed by a second attack, the first attack ending with a crisis-like fall of temperature. There is often a sore throat with some enlargement of the cervical glands and there is so often a skin rash that some writers classify it with the exanthemata. The leukocytes are depressed, often below four thousand. The disease is usually mild. There is no albuminuria and very few sequelae.

Etiology.—Dengue fever is caused by a filtrable virus (Ashburn and Craig) and is transmitted by mosquitoes *Aedes aegypti* (Siler, Hall and Hitchens) and *Aedes albopictus. Culex fatigans* and *Culex quinquefasciatus* (Cleland, Bradley and McDonald; Graham) formerly thought to be vectors, are incapable of transmitting the virus, except mechanically. The virus of dengue fever exists in the blood of patients during the first three days of the disease. The virus has not been seen and has not been cultivated on lifeless media. Characteristic cell inclusions have not been found.

It is necessary for the virus to remain more than eleven days in the mosquito before the mosquito can transmit the infection. It is probable that the mosquitoes remain infectious throughout their lives.

Dengue fever is followed by definite immunity, which, however, is not as complete as that of yellow fever.

This precise knowledge of the etiology, mode of transmission, and of many other facts relating to dengue fever has been gained by medical officers of the United States Army, Craig, Ashburn, Siler, Hall, Hitchens, Simmons, and their associates and many men who volunteered to submit themselves to experimental tests. The results of these investigations have been published in two large monographs.

PAPPATACI FEVER

This disease is also spoken of as sand-fly fever or three-day fever. It was formerly known to occur chiefly in countries bordering upon the Mediterranean, but has been since then described in many different parts of the world, especially in warm climates, occurring in summer epidemics. The fever is characteristically a short one, lasting rarely more than two or three days. During this time the temperature rises to 102°, 103°, or 104° F. There are muscle pains and considerable systemic symptoms. Occasionally there may be vomiting and severe intestinal symptoms. Recovery is followed by a lasting immunity. Although the disease has been known for a long time, it was not recognized as a separate entity until relatively recently, since its mold character, sudden onset and rapid defervescence led to its confusion with many conditions, such as early influenza, attacks of malaria, dengue fever, Malta fever, etc. Transmission is by an insect host, the *Phlebotomus papatassii* or the sand-fly. The disease was thoroughly studied by an Austrian commission (Doerr, Franz and Taussig), by which the chief facts now known were determined. The virus is present in the blood of the patients very soon after the onset of fever and can be transferred with the blood to normal subjects, symptoms appearing after an incubation of from four to eight days. The virus seems to disappear from the blood with the defervescence of the fever. It can be filtered through ordinary Berkefeld filters by properly diluting the blood, and in 1908 Doerr succeeded in transmitting the disease with the bite of the sand-fly. The flies were permitted to bite cases during the first twenty-four hours of the fever. When the infected insects were allowed to bite normal non-immunes, Doerr found that transfer of the disease was possible only after the infected blood has been in the body of the sand-fly for at least four to five days. Transfer through the medium of the fly earlier than this did not transmit the disease, a fact which proves that it is not a mere mechanical transfer of virus, but that, similar to malaria, yellow fever and some other insect transmitted diseases, a definite development in the intermediary host is necessary.

PSITTACOSIS

Psittacosis is primarily a disease of parrots, occurring naturally in these birds in Argentina and among parrots in aviaries. About 1890, it was noticed that persons having close contact with birds sick with this disease developed fever, pneumonia and paralysis of the extremities. Some of the human cases ended fatally. The spread of the infection from person to person took place only rarely. In 1893, Nocard isolated from the lesions in parrots a paratyphoid-like organism to which etiological importance was attached. This bacterium, called *Bacillus psittacosis*, later identified as *Bacillus aertrycke*, was isolated from time to time from birds and human beings suffering from psittacosis, but it was not constantly found in association with the disease (Thompson). It is now known that this bacillus is not the cause of the disease, since it has been proved that psittacosis is caused by a filtrable virus.

The exact knowledge of the etiology of psittacosis was gained through studies prompted by the widespread outbreak of the disease in the United States, England, and Europe in 1929–30. The first to show that the agent which causes psittacosis is a filtrable virus were Bedson, Western and Simpson, and Krumwiede, McGrath and

Oldenbusch. This discovery has been abundantly confirmed (Armstrong and McCoy).

The virus has the usual properties of a filtrable virus and has not been propagated in lifeless media. Minute coccoid bodies, 0.2 μ in diameter, are found in the exudates and in the cytoplasm of cells in the liver and spleen of infected birds and mice. These were first seen by Levinthal, who called them "psittacosis bodies." Their nature is not known. These small cocci have not been cultivated in artificial media, but as they appear to be in some way associated with the virus, they have diagnostic importance. A cycle of development of these "bodies" has been described by Bedson and Bland, who refer to the organism as *Microbacterium multiformepsittacosis* (Levinthal).

Rickettsia-like organisms (Lillie; Cole) have been described in the exudates and cells, but these may be identical with the "psittacosis bodies" of Levinthal.

There has been a high incidence of infection among the workers in laboratories where this disease is under experimental investigation. The experimentally infected parrots and parrakeets are particularly dangerous as sources of infection.

Krumwiede and his associates showed that mice are susceptible to the virus. Rivers and Berry, who made a most thorough investigation of the disease, confirmed this and studied the pathological effects of the virus upon mice, rabbits, guinea-pigs, and monkeys all of which, in addition to parrots, parrakeets, and man, are susceptible. Parrots are susceptible to intraoral, intranasal, and intramuscular inoculation. Mice are usually inoculated intracerebrally or intraperitoneally. Rabbits and guinea-pigs are susceptible to the virus introduced intracerebrally. The virus introduced intratracheally or intranasally in monkeys produces a pneumonia similar to that caused by the virus in man.

Man and animals, after recovery from an attack of psittacosis, are immune to subsequent infection and have virus-neutralizing and protective substances in their blood.

The secretions and exudates and diarrheal discharges of parrots are infectious. The sputum of human beings suffering from psittacotic pneumonia contains the virus. The lungs, liver, and spleen of all infected animals, including man, harbor the virus. The virus can be obtained from the blood of patients by injection of the blood into parrots or parrakeets, as shown by Bedson.

Rivers and Berry have found that the mouse is a relatively safe experimental animal. They have proved the value of a safe diagnostic procedure based upon the use of white mice, which is described in their words as follows:

Laboratory Diagnosis.—The patient's sputum to which 20 to 50 volumes of meat infusion broth, pH 7.8, and a small amount of alundum have been added is thoroughly ground in a mortar. The emulsion is centrifuged for 10 minutes at a speed of 3000 R.P.M. Then the supernatant fluid is filtered through a Berkefeld V candle at a pressure of 15 to 30 cm. of mercury. Each of 6 mice receives intraperitoneally on 3 successive days 2 c.c. of the filtrate. The animals are housed in screened battery jars placed in shallow baths of 5 per cent lysol solution in order to prevent the mechanical spread of the infection by insects. All animals are observed for a period of 30 days. Rivers has found that if streptococci and pneumococci are not present in the sputum, unfiltered sputum can be used for the inoculation of mice.

If a patient dies without a diagnosis having been established and if at the autopsy psittacosis is suspected of being the cause of death, confirmatory evidence frequently can be obtained by the injection of filtrates of lung, liver, and spleen into mice in a manner similar to that just described.

The criteria by which the presence of psittacosis in the inoculated mice is established are: (1) the development in some or all of the animals of illness which is usually fatal within 10–14 days, but occasionally not before 30; (2) the characteristic pathological picture consisting of focal necrotic lesions in the liver and spleen; (3) the absence of ordinary bacterial infections as determined from necropsy cultures; (4) the presence in liver and spleen impression smears of the "minute bodies" of psittacosis; (5) the establishment of serial passages of the virus in mice by means of liver and spleen emulsions from the animals receiving filtrates; (6) the demonstration that mice which have lived for 30 days following the inoculations of filtrates have developed an active immunity against a potent strain of psittacosis virus. All of these conditions obviously need not be fulfilled in each instance, sometimes one, sometimes another serves to establish the diagnosis.

For clinical accounts of the disease as it appeared in human beings in this country in 1929–30, the reader is referred to the papers of Rivers, Benjamin, and Berry, and Gorham and his associates. The encephalomyelitic phase of the disease, noted by these authors, has been studied also by Krichefski.

INFLUENZA

As it has been proved that influenza is caused by a virus it would be appropriate to consider the disease in this section. For convenience, however, we have discussed influenza in the portion of this book dealing with other respiratory diseases. The reader is referred to Chapter XXV.

REFERENCES

AGRAMONTE, A.   The Inside History of a Great Medical Discovery, Scientific Monthly, 1915, 1:209.
———— N. York Med. News, 1900.
ARMSTRONG, C., and McCoy, G. W.   U. S. Pub. Health Rep., 1930, 45:725.
ASHBURN, P. M., and CRAIG, C. F.   Philippine J. Sci., Sect. B., 1907, 2:93.
———— J. Infect. Dis., 1907, 4:440.
———— J. Am. M. Ass., 1907, 48:692.
BAUER, J. B.   Am. J. Trop. Med., 1928, 8:261.
BAUER, J. B., and HUDSON, N. P.   Am. J. Trop. Med., 1928, 8:371.
————, ———— J. Exper. M., 1928, 48:147.
BEDSON, S. P., and BLAND, J. O. W.   Brit. J. Exper. Pathol., 1932, 13:461.
BEDSON, S. P., WESTERN, G. T., and SIMPSON, S. L.   Lancet, 1930, 1:235, 345.
BERRY, G. P., and KITCHEN, S. F.   Am. J. Trop. Med., 1931, 11:365.
CARROLL.   J. Am. M. Ass., 1903, 40.
———— Yellow Fever in MENSE, Handbuch der Tropen-Krankheiten, p. 2.
CARTER, H. R.   Yellow Fever, An Epidemiological and Historical Study of Its Place of Origin, Ed by L. A. Carter and W. H. Frost, Baltimore, 1931.
CLELAND, J. B., BRADLEY, B., and McDONALD, W.   Med. J. Australia, 1916, 2:179, 200.
———— J. Hyg., 1916, 16:317; 1919, 18:217.
COLE, A. C.   Lancet, 1930, 1:1011.
COWDRY, E. V.   Am. J. Path., 1933, 9:149.

COWDRY, E. V., and KITCHEN, S. F. Am. J. Hyg., 1930, 11:227.
DAVIS, N. C., LLOYD, W., and FROBISHER, M. J. Exper. M., 1932, 56:853.
DOERR, R. Berl. klin. Wchnschr., 1908, 45:1847.
DOERR, R., FRANZ, K., and TAUSSIG, G. Wien. klin. Wchnschr., 1909, 22:609.
FINLAY. An. r. Acad. de cien. méd. de la Habana, 1881.
FROBISHER, M. J. Prev. Med., 1931, 5:65; and SOPER, F. L., FROBISHER, M., KERR, J. A., and
    DAVIS, N. C. J. Prevent. M., 1932, 6:341.
GORGAS, W. C. J. Trop. M., 1903.
GORHAM, L. W., CALDER, F. G., and VEDDER, J. D. J. Am. M. Ass., 1930, 94:1816.
GRAHAM, H. J. Trop. Med., 1903, 6:209.
GUITERAS, R. Rev. de méd. trop., Habana, Jan. 1901.
———— Am. Med., 1901, 11.
HARRIS, D. L., and SHACKELL, L. F. J. Am. Pub. Health Ass., 1911, 1:52.
HINDLE, E. Brit. M. J., 1928, 1:976.
———— Yellow Fever, in A System of Bacteriology in Relation to Medicine, London, 1930, 7:Chap.
    38, p. 449.
HUGHES, T. P., and SAWYER, W. A. J. Am. M. Ass., 1932, 99:978.
KRICHEFSKI, H. J. Brit. M. J., 1930, 1:1093.
KRUMWIEDE, C., McGRATH, M., and OLDENBUSCH, C. Science, 1930, 71:262.
LEVINTHAL, W. Klin. Wchnschr., 1930, 9:654.
LILLIE, R. D. U. S. Public Health Rep., 1930, 45:773.
LLOYD, W., and PENNA, H. A. Am. J. Trop. Med., 1933, 13:1.
MARCHOUX, E., and SIMOND, P. L. Compt. rend. Soc. de biol., 1905, 59.
MARCHOUX and SIMOND. Ann. de l'Inst. Pasteur, 1906, 20:16 et seq.
MARCHOUX, SALIMBENI, and SIMOND. Ann. de l'Inst. Pasteur, 1903.
NOCARD, E. Conseil d'Hyg. du Depart. de la Seine, 1893.
NOGUCHI, H. J. Exper. M., 1919, 29:547; 1920, 30:1, 9, 13, 87, 95, 401; 1920, 31:135.
REED. J. Hyg., Cambridge, 1902.
REED, CARROLL, and AGRAMONTE. Am. Med., July, 1901.
———— Boston M. & S. J., 1901, 14.
REED, W., CARROLL, J., AGRAMONTE, A., and LAZEAR, J., Phil. M. J., Oct., 1900. Am. Pub. Health
    Ass. Rep., 1903.
———— U. S. Senate Documents, 1911, 61:No. 822.
RIVERS, T. M., BENJAMIN, B., and BERRY, G. P. J. Am. M. Ass., 1930, 95:577.
RIVERS, T. M., and BERRY, G. P. J. Exper. M., 1931, 54:91, 105, 119, 129; 1935, 61:205.
———— Proc. Soc. Exper. Biol. & Med., 1932, 29:942.
SANARELLI, G. Ann. de l'Inst. Pasteur, 1897; Brit. M. J., 1897, 52:7.
SAWYER, W. A. Recent Progress in Yellow Fever Research, DE LAMAR Lecture, Johns Hopkins
    Univ. School of Hyg. and Pub. Health, Baltimore, 1930, Medicine, 1931, 10:509.
SAWYER, W. A., and FROBISHER, M. J. Exper. M., 1929, 50:713.
SAWYER, W. A., KITCHEN, S. F., and LLOYD, W. J. Exper. M., 1932, 55:945.
SAWYER, W. A., and LLOYD, W. J. Exper. M., 1931, 54:533.
SELLARDS, A. W. Am. J. Trop. M., 1927, 7:71.
SELLARDS, A. W., and THEILER, M., Am. J. Trop. M., 1927, 7:368.
SILER, J. H., HALL, M. W., and HITCHENS, A. P. J. Am. M. Ass., 1925, 84:1163; and Dengue,
    Monogr. No. 20, Bureau of Science, Manila, 1926.
SIMMONS, J. S. Am. J. Trop. M., 1931, 11:77.
SIMMONS, J. S., ST. JOHN, J. H., and REYNOLDS, F. H. K. Experimental Studies of Dengue,
    Monogr. No. 29, Bureau of Science, Manila, 1931.
SMITH, H. H., PENNA, H. A., and PAOLIELLO, A. Am. J. Trop. Dis., 1938, 18:437.
SOPER, F. L. Trans. Roy. Soc. Trop. M. and Hygiene, 1938, 32:297.
STOKES, A., BAUER, J. H., and HUDSON, N. P. Am. J. Trop. M., 1928, 8:103.
THEILER, M. Ann. Trop. M. & Parasit., 1930, 24:249.
THOMPSON, A. P. Lancet, 1929, 2:115.
TORRES, C. M. Compt. rend. Soc. de biol., 1928, 99:1344.

CHAPTER LXV

BACTERIOPHAGE

Bacteriophage is an agent or substance which causes transmissible lysis of bacteria. A small amount of bacteriophage, for example, one part in a billion, added to a young, actively growing broth culture of susceptible bacteria will, in the course of three or four hours, cause solution of all, or nearly all, of the cells. A billionth of a cubic centimeter of the clear solution, unfiltered or filtered through a Berkefeld candle, added to a new young culture of growing bacteria will again cause the lysis of the cells in a few hours. The active agent has multiplied or has been regenerated during the process. This experiment can be repeated in series indefinitely.

Lysis, solution of bacteria, is the most conspicuous feature of bacteriophage action. From it, the name, signifying "devourer of bacteria" was derived. But lysis is not the only effect of this remarkable material. Bacteriophage has an influence upon the morphology, metabolism, colony-form, pathogenicity and antigenic properties of bacteria. It is a powerful incitant of bacterial mutation or dissociation.

The transmissible lytic agent, now called bacteriophage, was discovered independently by Twort in 1915 and by d'Herelle in 1917. Twort, who was searching for vaccine virus, noticed that some colonies of micrococci on his plates became glassy and transparent and that a small amount of this clear material transferred to another colony brought about the same change. It is to be noted here that the lytic agent described by Twort, while resembling the d'Herelle bacteriophage in all other respects, had the peculiar ability to dissolve old bacteria. D'Herelle has stated that he first noticed the effect of a lytic agent in cultures in 1909 when he was working on a bacterial disease of locusts in Mexico. In 1917, however, he found that the filtrate of the fecal discharges of a patient recovering from baciliary dysentery dissolved young, growing cultures of Shiga bacilli and that this type of lysis was transmissible in series. There has been much useless controversial discussion of the claims for priority by these investigators. The discoveries were independent and priority appears of less consequence than subsequent research. Some writers refer to the phenomenon as the "Twort-d'Herelle phenomenon," others as the "d'Herelle phenomenon." Certainly d'Herelle's extensive and active investigation of bacteriophagy has identified the process with his name, and his insistence upon the opinion that the bacteriophage is an ultramicroscopic virus parasite of bacteria has had a most stimulating effect upon research in the virus diseases of animal and man.

The *analogies between bacteriophage and filtrable viruses* are numerous and close. Both appear to be minute particulate bodies, invisible under the microscope under ordinary illumination, measuring approximately 50 to 75 mμ for the larger bacteriophages and 8 to 12 mμ for the smaller races, filtrable, uncultivable upon lifeless media, propagated only in the presence of living cells, relatively specifically adapted to certain cells, bacterial or animal, resistant and sensitive to the same physical and chemical agents, and affecting cells by stimulating them or destroying them. Almost all general characteristics of the viruses of man and animals are exhibited by bacteriophage.

A staphylococcus *bacteriophage, concentrated and purified* by Northrop was a homogeneous nucleoprotein which in the ultracentrifuge had a sedimentation constant of 650, corresponding to a molecular weight of about 300,000,000. It was unstable, denatured by acidity greater than pH 5.0 and by temperature over 50° C. for 5 minutes. It was digested by chymo-trypsin but not by trypsin. Northrop in 1938 suggested that the formation of phage may be more simply explained by analogy with the autocatalytic formation of pepsin and trypsin than by analogy with the far more complicated system of living organisms.

In 1917 the generally accepted opinion was that viruses were undoubtedly living things. It was natural, therefore, that d'Herelle should find in these analogies grounds for his belief that bacteriophage was a living virus parasite of bacteria. As no one can say with certainty that the viruses are either dead or living material until they can be cultivated on lifeless media, separated completely from living cells, so no one can affirm positively at present that bacteriophage, which "multiplies" only in the presence of living cells, is animate or inanimate. The consensus of opinion is opposed to d'Herelle's view that the bacteriophage is living, but, as we have noted in our discussion of the nature of viruses, this is a definition which cannot be made with certainty at this time.

Twort suggested that the filtrable virus diseases of man and animals might be due to a *cytophage*, and Doerr and others have considered this possibility. The conception of an inanimate cytophage which could initiate autolytic processes in cells and be reproduced by the cells which degenerated because of its action does not appear to be incompatible with the facts known about viruses and bacteriophage (Zinsser). It is obvious that bacteriophage and viruses are closely linked and that knowledge gained concerning the one will remove some of the mysteries surrounding the other.

Origin.—According to d'Herelle, bacteriophage is an autonomous living agent. Its ultimate origin is undeterminable. Its immediate origin is in the intestinal contents, blood secretions and organs of animals recovering from bacterial infection and in materials contaminated with the excreta of animals (sewage especially).

According to Bordet and his associates, who from the first opposed the notion that bacteriophage is alive, the lytic principle is a substance derived from the bacterial cells as a result of some vitiated metabolic process. Such organisms were called "lysogenic."

Bail's theory was that autolysis of bacteria is due to fragments, "splitters" or chromosomes which have lost their anabolic functions and that these imperfect chromosomes (or genes?) are capable of initiating autolysis in other bacteria. Hadley's opinion is in general somewhat similar to this, in that he conceives of bacteriophage as a derivative, perhaps a filtrable form, of bacteria and related to the life cycles of bacteria.

The number of papers dealing with bacteriophage is enormous. Much of this literature to 1928 was reviewed by Bronfenbrenner in two comprehensive surveys, in which he included accounts of his own important investigations of this subject.

The reader is referred to them for general information. In the rest of this chapter we shall make brief statements of facts and describe a few of the methods of studying bacteriophage.

Methods of Studying.—Bacteriophage has a relatively specific action upon groups of related organisms, or a strict species or even race specificity. Some specimens of bacteriophage dissolve only one strain of a particular bacterium, others act on several species of related organisms, as for example members of the typhoid-dysentery group. The action of bacteriophage is detectable, therefore, only by the subjection of a suitable sensitive bacterial culture to its influence. Bacteriophages have been obtained for nearly all the main groups or genera of bacteria.

The general technic of studying bacteriophage is well described in the paper published by Asheshov and his associates in 1933. This contribution to studies on cholera bacteriophage contains observations on the classification of bacteriophage, its practical application, and on its virulence and development.

Isolation.—The usual source of bacteriophage is fecal material or sewage. Emulsions of feces or sewage are filtered through Berkefeld N or V candles and small amounts of these filtrates are added with bacteria to tubes of broth for observations on lysis. The primary lytic filtrate, obtained in this way, may not be very active. Its potency can be increased by successive "passages" upon susceptible bacterial cultures.

Tests of Lytic Action.—The ability of bacteriophage to dissolve bacteria can be demonstrated in liquid media, upon the surface of solid media, or in poured plates of bacteria, bacteriophage and nutrient media. These procedures and their use in the *titration* of bacteriophage are described in the following typical protocols:

Simple procedures for the demonstration of lytic action and for the *titration of bacteriophage* are as follows:

I. ACTION UPON A SLANT CULTURE.—With a platinum loop, spread an inoculum of a susceptible culture of *B. coli* over the surface of an agar slant. With a sterile pipet, place a small drop of the anti-coli bacteriophage at the top of the slant and allow it to run down across the area inoculated. Incubate the culture 24 hrs. at 37.5° C. Growth will occur in all regions not touched by the bacteriophage. A clear area through the growth will indicate the path taken by the drop of bacteriophage when it ran down across the inoculated area.

II. ACTION UPON COLONIES ON A PLATE.—From a 24 hr. broth culture of the sensitive *B. coli*, streak out a small loopful in the usual manner to obtain colonies. Flame the loop. Next streak a loopful of the anti-coli bacteriophage over the same area. Incubate the plate 24 hrs. at 37.5° C. Where there were large amounts of bacteriophage on the plate, no growth will occur. Other colonies and groups of colonies of *B. coli* will show ragged indented edges, and a moth eaten appearance as a result of the lytic action of the bacteriophage. In the midst of some of the clear areas there may appear later, small granular colonies of the resistant form of this organism.

III. LYSIS IN BROTH CULTURES. TITRATION OF POTENCY OF BACTERIOPHAGE.[1]

1. Place 10 tubes each containing 9 c.c. peptone water in a rack.

2. In a series of 9 tubes each containing 9 c.c. of sterile peptone water make the following dilutions of anti-coli bacteriophage, 1 : 100, 1 : 1000, 1 : 10,000, 1 : 100,000, 1 : 1,000,000, 1 : 10,-000,000, 1 : 100,000,000, 1 : 1,000,000,000, 1 : 10,000,000,000. Make the first dilution of 1 : 100 by adding 1 c.c. of bacteriophage diluted 1 : 10, to 9 c.c. of peptone water. Proceed through the series by adding 1 c.c. of the previous dilution to 9 c.c. of peptone water. A separate sterile pipet should be used for the transfer of fluid at each step in the dilution. This is necessary for accurate titra-

---

[1] A more precise method for the quantitative determination of bacteriophage has been described by A. P. Kreuger, *J. Gen. Physiol.*, 1929, 13:557.

tion. If approximate results only are required, the use of a separate pipet for each step in the dilution series may be omitted.

3. To all tubes add 0.1 c.c. of a 24 hr. peptone water culture of susceptible *B. coli*. The tenth tube in series, to which bacteriophage was *not* added will serve as a control.

4. Place the tubes in the incubator at 37.5° C. and observe them at half-hour intervals for at least 5 hrs.

The control tube No. 10 will become progressively turbid as growth increases.

The first 3 or 4 tubes may remain clear.

In the remaining tubes, turbidity indicating growth will increase progressively, usually for about 3½ to 4 hrs. After this, several of the tubes will become clear in a short time, indicating lysis of the bacteria. The last tube in which clearing takes place indicates the potency of the bacteriophage.

IV. ACTION IN POURED PLATES.—TITRATION OF BACTERIOPHAGE BY ENUMERATION OF PLAQUES.—When bacteriophage acts upon bacteria in a thickly sown poured plate, transparent, clear, round areas are produced in the midst of the denser translucent bacterial growth. These are called "plaques." On the assumption that the bacteriophage exists as a particle, each plaque may indicate the location of one bacteriophage particle, and resemble a "colony" of bacteriophage. The size and clearness of the plaques is partly dependent upon the concentration of the agar, and also upon the "race" of the bacteriophage. To demonstrate them most clearly, it is best to use a semi-solid agar, composed of the usual nutrient base with only 0.5 per cent agar.

PROCEDURE.—After adding 0.1 c.c. of the 24 hr. culture of the sensitive *B. coli* to the above series of dilutions of anti-coli bacteriophage in peptone water, transfer with sterile pipets 1 c.c. from each dilution to separate tubes containing 10 c.c. of 0.5 per cent nutrient agar, melted and at a temperature of about 40° C. Mix by rotating the tubes and pour the mixtures into the bottoms of Petri dishes. Allow the agar to cool. As this semisolid agar will not solidify stiffly, the Petri dishes should be moved with care and should not be inverted. Place these poured plates in the incubator at 37.5° C. for 24 hrs. After this incubation period, count the plaques. The number of plaques in a plate, multiplied by the dilution factor, indicates the potency or titer of the bacteriophage.

Mechanism of Lysis.—Many bacteria under the influence of bacteriophage swell to relatively enormous dimensions and burst (d'Herelle, Wollman). The terminal stage of bursting of *B. coli* occupies about one-half second. *B. megatherium,* a gram-positive bacillus, does not enlarge and dissolves slowly (Cowles). An amorphous residue is left behind by the lysed cells. D'Herelle attributes the enlargement and bursting to the multiplication of bacteriophage particles inside the bacterial cell. Hetler and Bronfenbrenner, on the basis of chemical analyses for the determination of amino nitrogen, assume that the bacteriophage activates an endocellular autolytic enzyme which decomposes the proteins of the cell. Increased osmotic pressure, according to this theory, causes water to enter the cell, producing bursting. One of us (Bayne-Jones and Sandholzer) who, like Bronfenbrenner, has studied this process by serial motion photomicrography, has expressed doubt as to the validity of both of these theories. The actual mechanism of lysis remains obscure.

Other effects exerted by bacteriophage on bacteria are shown in numerous mutational or dissociative changes. "Rough" variants, mucoid variants, and organisms with decreased and sometimes increased pathogenicity arise in cultures acted upon by bacteriophage (Hadley). The strains of bacteria resistant to bacteriophage, which appear as delayed or secondary growths in cultures of the lysis, "carry" bacteriophage, producing the lytic principle without undergoing lysis. This, no doubt, accounts for the occurrence of bacteriophage in stock cultures.

The sudden appearance of bacteriophage in stock cultures may be due also to air-infection. The resistance of bacteriophage to drying and its proved transportation through the air have been used by Colvin as a means of studying air-borne bacterial and virus infections.

Antigenic Properties.—The investigations of those who have studied this subject indicate that bacteriophages have antigenic specificities (Schultz, Quigly and Bullock). Animals injected with the lytic filtrates develop corresponding antibacterial antibodies, and *also* antibodies which annul the action of the related bacteriophage or cause its rapid disappearance from the blood of an immunized animal into which it is injected (Kendrick).

The antigenic individuality of bacteriophage is cited as evidence that the bacteriophage is an autonomous living thing. But this argument is not altogether conclusive, since the possibility that the bacterial protoplasm might be specifically altered under the influence of the lytic substance has not been excluded.

Therapy.—From the beginning of his investigations d'Herelle has believed that the bacteriophage was an exogenous factor leading to recovery from infection. He has attributed recovery from typhoid fever, dysentery, cholera and other diseases to the destruction of bacteria by bacteriophage or to the change of the infecting organisms from virulent to nonvirulent forms under the influence of this agent. There is a large literature of experimental and clinical reports on this subject which we cannot review in any detail here. Some of this has confirmed d'Herelle's observations.

Other investigators have shown that bacteriophage is inhibited by blood and exudates (Colvin, Evans), and on theoretical grounds would not expect bacteriophage to be active in the body. Many clinical reports have been unfavorable.

In this country various preparations of bacteriophage have been used by instillation into the bladder and kidney pelvis for the treatment of cystitis and pyelitis, by injection into infected areas, chiefly for the treatment of staphylococcus infections, and by subcutaneous or intravenous injection for the treatment of septicemias. We have reviewed a great many of the reports on the therapeutic uses of bacteriophage and are not convinced that the lytic principle has had anything to do with the beneficial action obtained in some cases.

These lytic filtrates contain solutions of bacterial substance which are effective antigens for the stimulation of antibacterial immune bodies. They are, in fact, excellent vaccines. Larkum, with whom we agree, has attributed the benefit derived from bacteriophage preparations to the immunizing properties of the dissolved bacterial protoplasm contained in them.

REFERENCES

ASHESHOV, I. N., ASHESHOV, I., KHAN, S., LAHIRI, M. N., and CHATTERJI, S. K. Indian J. M. Res., 1933, 20, 1101.
BAIL, O. Deutsche med. Wchnschr., 1925, 51:13.
BAYNE-JONES, S., and SANDHOLZER, L. A. J. Exper. M., 1933, 57:279.
BAYNE-JONES, S., and EATON, M. D. J. Am. M. Ass., 1934, 103:1853, 1934.
BORDET, J., and CIUCEA, M. Compt. rend. Soc. de biol., 1920, 83:1293.
BORDET, J., and RENAUX, E. Ann. de l'Inst. Pasteur, 1928, 42:1283.
BRONFENBRENNER, J. J. Virus Diseases of Bacteria-Bacteriophagy; Chap. X, p. 373, in Filterable Viruses, ed. by T. M. Rivers, Baltimore, 1928; and The Bacteriophage, Chap. XL, p. 525, in The Newer Knowledge of Bacteriology and Immunology, Chicago, 1928.

A complete manual of the technical methods of medical bacteriology, immunology, and serology is beyond the scope of this book. Furthermore, it has not seemed advisable to attempt to bring together in one section all the technical procedures described in this book. Special methods of isolation and study of a particular microorganism are more appropriately considered in the chapter relating to that organism than in a more remotely placed section on Technic. On the other hand, there are many methods, media, stains and reagents which are useful in the study of all microorganisms or groups of micro-organisms. Such methods, having relatively general application, are those which we have selected for description in this section. Reference to the index will, we hope, direct the reader to the information desired.

MICROSCOPIC STUDY OF BACTERIA

Bacteria may be studied microscopically, in the living and unstained state, and after the application of dyes, in colored preparations. For the manipulation of bacteria for such study, glass slides and cover-slips of various design are used. These must be perfectly clean if the preparations are to be of any value.

Glass slides should be cleaned thoroughly before use. This may be accomplished by a variety of methods. A simple one suitable for general application is as follows: (1) The slides and cover-slips are thrown singly into boiling water and left there for half an hour; (2) wash in 25 per cent sulphuric acid; (3) rinse in distilled water; (4) wash in 95 per cent alcohol; (5) wipe with a clean cloth. Another method convenient for routine use is to immerse, after thorough washing in soapsuds, in 95 per cent alcohol and to leave in this until the time of use.

In the Living State.—Living bacteria may be studied in what is spoken of as the "hanging-drop" preparation. For this purpose a so-called hollow slide is employed, in the center of which there is a circular concavity about three-quarters of a centimeter to one centimeter in diameter. The preparation is manipulated as follows: if the bacteria are growing in a fluid medium, a drop of the culture fluid is transferred to the center of a cover-slip. If taken from solid medium, an emulsion may be made in broth or in physiological salt solution, and a drop of this transferred to the cover-slip, or the bacteria may be emulsified in a drop of salt solution, or broth,

COLVIN, M. C. Am. J. Hyg., 1932, 15:247.
——— J. Infect. Dis., 1932, 51:527.
COWLES, P. B. J. Bacteriol., 1930, 20:15.
D'HERELLE, F. Compt. rend. Soc. de biol., 1917, 165:373.
——— The Bacteriophage and Its Behavior, Baltimore, 1926, esp. pp. 112–115, 130–135.
——— Internat. Clinics, 1929, 39th Ser., 1:36.
EVANS, A. C. Inhibition of Anti-Streptococcus Bacteriophage by Animal Fluids (to be published).
HADLEY, P. J. Infect. Dis., 1924, 34:260; 1927, 40:1; 1928, 42:263.
HETLER, D. M., and BRONFENBRENNER, J. J. Exper. M., 1928, 48:269.
KENDRICK, P. Am. J. Hyg., 1933, 17:297, 318.
LARKUM, N. W. Am. J. Pub. Health, 1929, 19:31.
——— J. Lab. & Clin. M., 1932, 17:675 (bibliography).
NORTHROP, J. H. J. Gen. Physiol., 1938, 21:335.
——— Crystalline Enzymes. The Chemistry of Pepsin, Trypsin and Bacteriophage. New York, Columbia Univ. Press, 1939.
SCHULTZ, E. W., QUIGLY, J. S., and BULLOCK, L. T. J. Immunol., 1929, 17:245; 1931, 20:149.
TWORT, F. W. Lancet, 1915, 2:1241; 1930, 2:1064.
——— Ann. de l'Inst. Pasteur, 1931, 47:459.
WOLLMAN, E. Ann. de l'Inst. Pasteur, 1925, 39:789.
ZINSSER, H. Arch. Path., 1928, 6:271.

directly upon the cover-slip. The concavity on the slide, having first been rimmed with vaselin or mineral oil, by means of a small glass rod or matchstick, the cover-slip is inverted over the slide in such a way that the drop hangs freely within the hollow space. The preparation is then ready for examination under the microscope.

Another method, known as the "hanging block method," devised by Hill, for the study of living bacteria in solid media is carried out as follows: nutrient agar is poured into a Petri dish and allowed to solidify. Out of this layer a piece about a

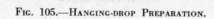

FIG. 105.—HANGING-DROP PREPARATION.

quarter of an inch square is cut. This is placed on a sterile slide. The upper surface of the agar block is then inoculated with bacteria by surface smearing, and the preparation covered with a sterile dish and allowed to dry for a few minutes in the incubator. A sterile cover-slip is then dropped upon the surface of the block and sealed about the edges with agar. Block and cover-slip are then taken from the slide and fastened over a moist chamber with paraffin. The entire preparation can be placed upon the stage of a microscope. This method is especially designed for the study of cell division.

Dark Field Illumination.—This is an important method for the study of living bacteria. It is particularly useful in examinations of materials for spirochetes, which are either difficult to stain or lose their characteristic morphology when fixed and stained. The use of the darkfield illumination should now be a part of elementary training in microscopy and a routine procedure in any medical bacteriological laboratories. For a detailed description of the instrument and its manipulation, reference should be made to the work of Gage.

Motion Photomicrography.—Motion photomicrography (Bayne-Jones and Tuttle) provides consecutive dynamic records of series of changes in the size and shapes of bacteria, movements of internal granules, development of spores, cell division and other visible phenomena of unstained bacteria.

Living bacteria may also be studied in stained preparations by the so-called "intravital" method of Nakanishi. Thoroughly cleaned slides are covered with a saturated aqueous solution of methylene blue. This is spread over the slide in an even film and allowed to dry. After drying, the slide should appear of a transparent sky-blue color. The micro-organisms which are to be examined are then emulsified in water, or are taken from a fluid medium and placed upon a cover-slip. This is dropped, face downward, upon the blue ground of the slide. In this way bacteria may be stained without being subjected to the often destructive processes of heat or chemical fixation. According to Nakanishi, cytoplasm is stained blue, while nuclear material assumes a reddish or purplish hue.

In Fixed Preparations.—Stained preparations of bacteria are best prepared upon glass slides, the process consisting of the following steps: (1) spreading on the slide; (2) drying in air; (3) fixing; (4) staining; (5) washing in water; (6) blotting; (7) mounting.

1. Bacteria from a fluid medium are transferred in a small drop of the fluid, with a platinum loop, to slide and carefully spread over the surface in a thin film.

If taken from a solid medium, a small drop of sterile water is first placed upon the cover-slip and the bacteria are then in very small quantity carefully emulsified in this drop with the platinum needle or loop and spread in an extremely thin film.

2. The film is allowed to dry in the air.

3. When thoroughly dried, fixation is carried out by passing the preparation, film side up, three times through a Bunsen flame, at about the rate of a pendulum swing. Fixation by heat in this manner is most convenient for routine work, but is not the most delicate method, in as much as the degree of heat applied cannot be accurately controlled. The other methods which may be employed are immersion in methyl alcohol, formalin, saturated aqueous bichloride of mercury, Zenker's fluid, or acetic acid. If chemical fixatives are used, they must be removed by washing in water before the stain is applied. If a preparation is made upon a slide instead of a cover-slip, passage through the flame should be repeated eight or nine times.

4. The dyes used for the staining of bacteria are, for the greater part, basic aniline dyes, such as methylene blue, gentian violet, and fuchsin. These may be applied for simple staining in 5 per cent aqueous solutions made up from filtered saturated alcoholic solutions, or directly by weight. They are conveniently kept in the laboratory as saturated alcoholic solutions. From these stock solutions, various mixtures are made to produce the staining solutions listed below.

The staining solution, in simple routine staining, is left upon the fixed bacterial film for from one-half to one and one-half minutes according to the efficiency of the stain used. Methylene blue is the weakest of the three stains mentioned; gentian violet the strongest.

5. The excess stain is removed by washing with water.

6. The preparation is thoroughly dried by a blotter or between layers of absorbent paper.

7. Stained films on slides are usually examined directly, without being covered with a cover-glass.

Solubilities of Dyes.—The solubilities [1] at 26° C. of the dyes commonly used in bacteriology are listed in the table on page 846.

The chemical principles which underlie the staining process are still more or less in doubt (Churchman). Suffice it to say here that most of the dyes in common use by bacteriologists and pathologists are coal-tar derivatives belonging to the aromatic series, all of them containing at least one "benzol ring" combined with what Michaelis terms a "chromophore group," chief among which are the nitro-group (NO_2), the nitroso-group (NO), and the azo-group $(N = N)$. Some authorities believe that the phenomenon is purely chemical, in which a salt is formed by the combination of the dye and the protoplasm of the cells, others that there is no such salt formation, and that the process takes place by purely physical means. To support the latter view it is argued that certain substances like cellulose are stainable without possessing the property of salt formation, and that staining may often be accomplished without there being a chemical disruption of the dye itself. Michaelis

[1] From *Pure Culture Study of Bacteria*, edited by Committee on Bacteriological Technic, Society of American Bacteriologists, H. J. Conn, Chairman, 1932, 1: No. 2, Leaflet IV, Geneva, New York. We are indebted to Dr. Conn for permission to quote from this publication and from *Biological Stains*, 2nd edition, Geneva, N. Y., 1929; published by Biological Stain Commission.

Color Index Number	Name of Dye	Per Cent*	
		Water	95 Per Cent Alcohol
381	Bismarck brown Y..............................	1.36	1.08
382	Bismarck brown R.............................	1.10	0.98
20	Chrysoidin Y..................................	0.86	2.21
21	Chrysoidin R..................................	0.23	0.99
370	Congo red.....................................	....	0.19
681	Crystal violet (chloride).......................	1.68	13.87
768	Eosin Y (Na salt)	44.20	2.18
678	Fuchsin, basic, new...........................	1.13	3.20
	Fuchsin, acid.................................	....	....
	Gentian violet, see methyl and crystal violet.......	....	....
133	Janus green...................................	5.18	1.12
657	Malachite green (oxalate)......................	7.60	7.52
680	Methyl violet.................................	2.93	15.21
922	Methylene blue (chloride)	3.55	1.48
825	Neutral red (chloride)	5.64	2.45
7	Picric acid...................................	1.18	8.96
739	Pyronin G....................................	8.96	0.60
676	Rosanilin.................................	0.39	8.16
	Pararosanilin	0.26	5.93
779	Rose bengal (Na salt)	36.25	7.53
841	Safranin......................................	5.45	3.41
248	Sudan III....................................	0	0.15
920	Thionin	0.25	0.25
925	Toluidin blue O...............................	3.82	0.57

* These figures are for grams per hundred cubic centimeters.

sums up his views by stating that probably both processes actually take place. A dye stuff, as a whole, may enter into and be deposited upon a tissue or cell by a process which he speaks of as "insorption." In such a case the coloring matter may be subsequently extracted by any chemically indifferent solvent. On the other hand, a dye after being thus deposited upon or within a cell, may become chemically united to the protoplasm by the formation of a salt, and in such a case the color can be removed only by agents which are capable of decomposing salts, such as free acids.

The staining power of any solution may be intensified either by heating while staining, by prolonging the staining process, or by the addition of alkalis, acids, aniline oil, and other substances which will be mentioned in the detailed descriptions of special staining methods.

STAINING METHODS [2]

CAPSULE STAINS

Welch's Method.—Cover-slips are prepared as usual but dried without heat.

Cover with glacial acetic acid for a few seconds. Pour off acetic acid and cover with aniline water gentian violet, renewing stain repeatedly until all acid is removed. This is done by pouring the stain on and off three or four times and then finally leaving it on for about three minutes.

Wash in 2 per cent salt solution and examine in this solution.

Hiss's Method.—*Copper Sulphate Method.*—Cover-slip preparations are made by smearing the organisms in a drop of animal serum, preferably beef-blood serum.

Dry in air and fix by heat.

Stain for a few seconds with—

Saturated alcoholic solution of fuchsin or gentian violet 5 c.c., in distilled water 95 c.c.

The cover-slip is flooded with the dye and the preparation held for a second over a free flame until it steams.

Wash off dye with 20 per cent aqueous sulphate solution.

Blot (do not wash).

Dry and mount.

By this method permanent preparations are obtained, the capsule appearing as a faint blue halo around a dark purple cell body.

Huntoon's Capsule Stain (applicable only to cultures, not to animal exudates).—This depends upon the precipitating action of lactic acid on nutrose. It requires two solutions.

1. *Diluent.*—Three per cent solution of nutrose in distilled water; place in Arnold steamer one hour, add a small amount of carbolic as preservative, and allow to settle.

2. *Stain and Fixative.*—Two per cent carbolic, 100 c.c.; concentrated lactic acid, 0.5 c.c.; 1 per cent acetic acid, 1 c.c.; saturated alcoholic solution basic fuchsin, 1 c.c.; carbol fuchsin, 1 c.c.

As to the dye employed, almost anything but methylene blue or Bismarck brown may be used. Methyl violet gives the most beautiful results but is not permanent. We have found the above mixture the best for classroom work.

Make a thin film, employing solution 1 as diluent. Dry in air. Do not fix. Cover with stain thirty seconds. Wash in water, dry, and examine.

Buerger's Method.—Cover-slip preparations are made by smearing in serum as in Hiss's method.

As the edges of the smear begin to dry, pour over it Zenker's fluid (without acetic acid) and warm in flame for three seconds.

(Zenker's fluid is composed of potassium bichromate 2.5 grams, sodium sulphate 1 gram, water 100 c.c., saturated with bichloride of mercury.)

Wash in water.

Flush with 95 per cent alcohol.

2 For history of staining in bacteriology, see Unna, *Centralbl. f. Bakteriol.*, I Abt., 1888, 3:22.

Cover with tincture of iodine, U. S. P., one to three minutes.

Wash with 95 per cent alcohol.

Dry in the air.

Stain with aniline water gentian violet two to five seconds.

Wash with 2 per cent salt solution.

Mount and examine in salt solution.

Wadsworth's Method.—Wadsworth has devised a method of staining capsules which depends upon the fixation of smears with formalin. After such fixation capsules may be demonstrated both with simple stains and by Gram's method. The technic is as follows:

Smear preparations, made as usual, are treated as follows:

Simple Stain

1. Formalin, 40 per cent, two to five minutes.
2. Wash in water, five seconds.
3. Ten per cent aqueous gentian violet.
4. Wash in water, five seconds.
5. Dry, mount in balsam.

Differential Stain (Gram's Method)

1. Formalin, 40 per cent, two to five minutes.
2. Wash in water, five seconds.
3. Aniline gentian violet, two minutes.
4. Gram's iodine solution, two minutes.
5. Alcohol, 95 per cent, decolorize.
6. Fuchsin, dilute aqueous solution.
7. Wash in water, two seconds.
8. Dry, mount in balsam.

It is important that the formalin be fresh and the exposure to water momentary. When decolorizing in the Gram method, strong alcohol only should be used. Wadsworth also found that encapsulated pneumococci could be demonstrated in celloidin sections of pneumonic lesions hardened in strong formalin. The lungs should be distended with the formalin or the lesions cut in very thin bits, hardened, dehydrated, embedded, and cut in the usual way. The celloidin sections may be fixed on the slides by partially dissolving the celloidin in alcohol and ether and setting the celloidin quickly in water before staining. Failure to obtain pneumococci encapsulated in such sections is usually due to improper or inadequate fixation in the formalin.

The differential method employed by Wadsworth for tissue staining is as follows:

1. Fix in formalin 40 per cent, two to five minutes.
2. Wash in water.
3. Aniline gentian violet, two minutes.
4. Iodine solution, two minutes.
5. Alcohol, 95 per cent, decolorize.
6. Eosin alcohol, counterstain.
7. Clear in oil of origanum.
8. Mount in balsam.

FLAGELLA STAINS

All flagella stains, in order to be successful, necessitate particularly clean coverslip preparations, best made from young agar cultures emulsified in sterile salt solution. Scrupulous care should be exercised in cleaning the glassware used.

Many methods have been proposed for the staining of flagella. We have obtained good results with the Casares-Gil stain and Shunk's stain.

Casares-Gil's Method

Solution A. Mordant: Tannic acid.. 10 gms.

Aluminum chloride ($Al_2Cl_6 \cdot 12H_2O$)........................ 18 gms.

Zinc chloride.. 10 gms.

Rosaniline hydrochloride.................................... 1.5 gms.

Alcohol (60%).. 40 c.c.

The solids are dissolved in the alcohol by trituration in a mortar, adding 10 c.c. of the alcohol first, and then the rest slowly. This alcoholic solution may be kept several years.

1. For use, dilute with two parts of distilled water, filter off the precipitate and collect the filtrate on the slide containing the smear of bacteria. Allow this to act 1–2 minutes. A precipitate and metallic sheen should form. Wash with distilled water.
2. Cover preparation with carbolfuchsin and allow to act 1–2 minutes. Wash in distilled water. Dry without blotting.
3. Slides and cover glasses must be free from grease and clean.
4. To make the preparation of bacteria: transfer 1 loopful of growth from an 18 hr. agar slant culture of the organism to 2 c.c. of sterile tap water. Incubate this suspension at 37° C. for 10–15 minutes. Transfer 1 loopful carefully to an absolutely clean slide. Tilt the slide so that the drop runs down, leaving a thin film, or the drop may be drawn out gently with paper. Allow to dry in air.

Shunk's Method

1. Mordant:

Solution A

Sat. aqu. solution of tannic acid..................................... 30 c.c.

Solution of ferric chloride (5 per cent in water)...................... 10 c.c.

Solution B

Aniline .... 1 c.c.

Ethyl alcohol (95 per cent)... 4 c.c.

Solution A is best prepared a week or more ahead of time and filtered before use. When using, place about eight drops of solution A on the slide and immediately add one drop of solution B; and there is then a precipitation on the slide. The excess mordant is carefully drained off, and the stain applied without previous washing.

2. Stain:

Carbolfuchsin, 1 per cent safranin in 50 per cent alcohol, aniline gentian violet, or Löffler's methylene blue may be used. Shunk recommends the following, however:

Löffler's methylene blue solution.................................... 30 c.c.

Solution B of Shunk's mordant .... 3 c.c.

This solution is immediately ready for use and keeps well.

Löffler's Method.—The preparation is dried in the air and fixed by heat. It is then treated with the following mordant solution:

20 per cent aqueous tannic acid.................................... 10 parts

Ferrous sulphate aqueous solution saturated at room temperature..... 5 parts

Saturated alcoholic fuchsin solution............................... 1 part

This solution, which should be freshly filtered before using, is poured over the cover-glass and allowed to remain there for one-half to one minute, during which time it should be gently heated, but not allowed to boil.

Wash thoroughly in water.

Stain with 5 per cent aniline water fuchsin or aniline water gentian violet made slightly alkaline by the addition of 0.1 per cent sodium hydroxide.

The stain should be filtered directly upon the cover-slip. Warm gently and leave on for 1 to 2 minutes. Wash in water. Mount in balsam.

Van Ermengen's Method.—This method requires the preparation of three solutions.

1.	20 per cent tannic acid solution	60 c.c.
	2 per cent osmic acid solution	30 c.c.
	Glacial acetic acid	4 to 5 drops

The cover-slip carrying the fixed preparation is placed in this solution for 1 hour at room temperature, or for 5 minutes at 100° C. (boiling).

Wash in water.

Wash in absolute alcohol.

Immerse the cover-slip for 1 to 3 seconds in

2. Silver nitrate, 0.25–0.5 per cent solution

Without washing, transfer to

3.	Gallic acid	5 gms.
	Tannic acid	3 gms.
	Fused potassium acetate	10 gms.
	Distilled water	350 c.c.

Immerse in this for a few minutes, moving the cover-slip about.

Return to the silver nitrate solution until the preparation turns black.

Wash thoroughly in water.

Blot and mount.

Gram's Stain.—The only dyes which are effective in this method are basic triphenyl methane compounds. By this method of staining, which is extremely important in bacterial differentiation, bacteria are divided into those which retain the initial stain and those which are subsequently decolorized and take the counterstain. The former are often spoken of as the gram-positive, the latter as gram-negative bacteria.

The mechanism of the Gram stain is not entirely clear. The theories proposed to account for the results are either physical, chemical, or physicochemical. Churchman has shown that certain organisms are gram-positive (*B. anthracis*) only in the cortical substance of the cell. In gram-positive bacteria the water soluble dye enters the cell. The iodine next either changes the permeability of the cell to the iodine-pararosaniline compound or forms an alcohol insoluble dye compound within the cell. There has been a large amount of investigation of the mechanism of the Gram stain. In this country the Stearns have reported numerous studies of this reaction. The subject has been reviewed at length by Smith and Churchman.

Many formulas and procedures for the Gram stain have been in use. The older procedures called for aniline gentian violet. These have been largely abandoned because aniline gentian violet deteriorates rapidly. Furthermore, gentian violet is an uncertain mixture of crystal and methyl violet. More dependable results are obtained by substituting crystal violet for gentian violet. Two modifications of Gram's stain, one by Hucker and one by Kopeloff and Beerman have given very satisfactory results, and are recommended by the Committee on Bacteriological Technic of the Society of American Bacteriologists. The directions for these procedures are quoted from *Pure Culture Study of Bacteria,* as follows:

HUCKER MODIFICATION [1]

AMMONIUM OXALATE CRYSTAL VIOLET

Solution A

Crystal violet (85% dye content) .... 4 gms.
Ethyl alcohol (95%) .... 20 c.c.

Solution B

Ammonium oxalate... 0.8 gm.
Water .... 80 c.c.

Mix solutions A and B, ordinarily in equal parts. It is sometimes found, however, that this gives so concentrated a stain that gram-negative organisms, such as the *Gonococcus,* do not properly decolorize. To avoid this, solution A may be diluted as much as ten times, and 20 c.c. of the diluted solution mixed with an equal quantity of solution B.

LUGOL'S IODINE SOLUTION

Iodine .... 1 gm.
Potassium iodide... 2 gms.
Water .... 300 c.c.

COUNTERSTAIN

Safranin (2.5% solution in 95% alcohol) .... 10 c.c.
Water .... 100 c.c.

Technic. Stain 1 minute with the gentian violet solution; wash in water; immerse in iodine solution for 1 minute; wash in water and blot dry; decolorize in 95 per cent ethyl alcohol for 30 seconds with gentle agitation; wash with water; cover with counterstain for 10 seconds. Then wash, dry, and examine with oil immersion objective.

KOPELOFF AND BEERMAN MODIFICATION [1]

ALKALINE GENTIAN VIOLET

Solution A

Gentian or crystal violet... 1 gm.
Distilled water... 100 c.c.

Solution B

Sodium bicarbonate... 1 gm.
Distilled water... 20 c.c.

Just before use, mix 30 drops of solution A with 8 drops of solution B.

IODINE SOLUTION

Iodine .... 2 gms.
Normal solution sodium hydroxide................................ 10 c.c.

After the iodine is dissolved make up to 100 c.c. with water.

COUNTERSTAIN

Basic fuchsin.. 0.1 gm.
Distilled water... 100 c.c.

Technic. Stain 5 minutes or more with the alkaline gentian violet solution; rinse with the iodine solution; add more iodine solution and allow to stand 2 minutes or longer; drain off iodine solution and blot dry (without washing); decolorize with 100 per cent acetone, adding drop by drop to the slide while tilted until no color is seen in drippings (generally less than 10 seconds); dry in air; counterstain for 10 to 30 seconds; wash in water, dry, and examine with oil immersion lens.

For decolorizing, 50 per cent acetone in ethyl alcohol may be used (Burke).

For routine bacteriological work, the following stains are very useful:

Löffler's Alkaline Methylene Blue [1]

ORIGINAL STATEMENT OF FORMULA

Conc. Sol. methylene blue in alcohol............................... 30 c.c.
Sol. KOH in distilled water (1 : 10,000)............................ 100 c.c.

EMENDED STATEMENT
Solution A

Methylene blue (90% dye content)............................... 0.3 gm.
Ethyl alcohol (95%)... 30 c.c.

Solution B

Dilute KOH (0.01% by weight).................................. 100 c.c.
Mix Solutions A and B.

Carbolfuchsin

Basic fuchsin.. 1 gm.
Alcohol, absolute... 10 c.c.
5 per cent aqueous carbolic acid................................. 90 c.c.

To make up this stain mix 90 c.c. of 5 per cent aqueous solution of carbolic acid with 10 c.c. saturated alcoholic basic fuchsin.
It can also be made up by weighing out:

Basic fuchsin.. 1 gm.
Carbolic acid... 5 gms.

Dissolve in distilled water, 90 c.c. filter and add absolute alcohol, 10 c.c.

Toluidine Blue Solution.—A very useful stain for general bacteriological work and for diphtheria bacilli.

Toluidine blue... 0.25 gm.
Glacial acetic acid.. 2.0 c.c
Absolute alcohol.. 5.0 c.c
Distilled water.. 100.0 c.c.

This can be used alone when it gives a stain like Löffler's methylene blue, but more clear, or else a counterstain of Bismarck brown can be used.

Pappenheim-Saathof Methyl-Green-Pyronine

Methyl green	0.15 gm.
Pyronine	0.5 gm.
95 per cent alcohol	5.0 c.c.
Glycerin	20.0 c.c.
2 per cent carbolic acid in water up to	100.0 c.c.

Stain one to two minutes, wash, blot. This is a splendid method of staining bacteria in general and it is particularly useful for the staining of phagocytes containing bacteria, as in gonococcus smears and in opsonic work.

Carbol Thionin

Thionin	1 gm.
Distilled water (hot)	1200 c.c.

Dissolve and filter; then add:

Glacial acetic acid	60 c.c.

Carbol Gentian Violet

FORMULA FROM EYRE, *2nd ed.*, p. 92

Sat. Alc. gentian violet	10 c.c.
1 per cent Aqu. Sol. Phenol	100 c.c.

EMENDED STATEMENT

Solution A

Crystal violet (85% dye content)	2.0 gms.
Ethyl alcohol (95%)	10 c.c.

Solution B

Phenol	1 gm.
Distilled water	100 c.c.

Mix solutions A and B.

Safranine

Safranine (sat. alc. sol.)	10 c.c.
Alcohol (95%)	90 c.c.

Stain for at least 1 minute.
Wash with water.
Blot dry.

Dorner's Nigrosin Solution

Nigrosin (nigrosin B Grübler recommended by Dorner; American nigrosins certified by Commission on Standardization of Biological stains ordinarily satisfactory)	10 gms.
Distilled water	100 c.c.

Boil 30 minutes in an Erlenmeyer flask; then add as preservative:

Formalin (40%)	0.5 c.c.

Filter twice through double filter paper and store in serological test tubes, about 5 c.c. to the tube.

This staining solution is used for the negative demonstration of bacteria, in place of the Burri India ink. A loopful of the bacterial suspension is mixed on the slide with the same quantity of the nigrosin solution. After drying, the slide can be examined without a cover glass. In the case of cultures on solid media, a smaller quantity of the bacterial suspension should be used.

SPORE STAINS

Dorner's Method (Recommended).

Solution:
A. Carbolfuchsin (freshly filtered).
B. Saturated aqueous solution of nigrosin.

Procedure:
1. Make a heavy suspension of the organism in 2 to 3 drops of distilled water in a small test tube. Use the growth of the culture on an agar slant for this emulsion.
2. Add an equal quantity of freshly filtered carbolfuchsin.
3. Allow the mixture to stand in a boiling water bath 10 to 12 minutes.
4. On a cover-slip or slide mix one loopful of the stained preparation with one loopful of a saturated aqueous solution of nigrosin.
5. Smear as thinly as possible and dry rapidly.

The spores are stained red, the bodies of the bacteria are almost colorless and stand out against the dark gray background of nigrosin.

Moeller's Method.—Cover-slips are prepared as usual and fixed in the flame.
Wash in chloroform for 2 minutes.
Wash in water.
Cover with 5 per cent chromic acid one-half to 2 minutes.
Wash in water. Invert and float cover-slip on carbolfuchsin solution in a small porcelain dish and heat gently with a flame until it steams; continue this for 3 to 5 minutes. (This step can also be done by covering the cover-glass with carbolfuchsin and holding over flame.)
Decolorize with 5 per cent sulphuric acid 5 to 10 seconds.
Wash in water.
Stain with aqueous methylene blue one-half to 1 minute. By this method spores will be stained red, the body blue.

STAINS FOR ACID-FAST BACTERIA

These methods of staining are chiefly useful in the demonstration of tubercle bacilli. These bacteria because of their waxy cell membranes are not easily stained by any but the most intense dyes, but when once stained, retain the color in spite of energetic decolorization with acid. For this reason they are known as acid-fast bacilli. However, some of the forms may not be acid-fast under all conditions.

Carbolfuchsin (Ziehl-Neelsen Method)

Solution A:
Basic fuchsin (sat. alc. solution) .... 10 c.c.
5 per cent aqueous phenol solution .... 90 c.c.

Solution B:
Decolorizing acid alcohol:
Hydrochloric acid (conc.) .... 3 c.c.
95 per cent alcohol .... 97 c.c.

Procedure:

1. Cover preparation with carbolfuchsin and steam this over a flame for 5 minutes. Renew the stain repeatedly to prevent its drying on the slide.
2. Wash with water.
3. Decolorize with acid alcohol until thin areas are colorless.
4. Wash with water.
5. Stain with methylene blue, 10 to 30 seconds.
6. Wash with water and blot dry.

Acid-fast organisms appear as red rods or bodies against a blue background. Bacteria which are not acid-fast are stained blue.

Gabbet's Method.—Gabbet has devised a rapid method in which the decolorization and counterstaining are accomplished by one solution. The specimen is prepared and stained with carbolfuchsin as in the preceding method. It is then immersed for one minute directly in the following solution:

Methylene blue.. 2 gms.
Sulphuric acid 25 per cent (sp. gr. 1.018)........ .... 100 c.c.

Then rinse in water, dry, and mount.
This method, while rapid and very convenient, is not so reliable as the Ziehl-Neelsen method.

Pappenheim's Method.—The method of Pappenheim is devised for the purpose of differentiating between the tubercle bacillus and the smegma bacillus. Confusion may occasionally arise between these two micro-organisms, especially in the examination of urine where smegma bacilli are derived from the genitals, and less frequently in the examination of sputum where smegma bacilli may occasionally be mixed with the secretions of the pharynx and throat.

Preparations are smeared and fixed by heat in the usual way.
Stain with hot carbolfuchsin solution for two minutes.
Pour off dye without washing and cover with the following mixture:

Corallin (rosolic acid).. 1 gm.
Absolute alcohol... 100 c.c.
Methylene blue added to saturation
Glycerin .... 20 c.c.

This mixture is poured on and drained off slowly, the procedure being repeated four or five times, and finally the preparation is washed in water. The combination of alcohol and rosolic acid decolorizes the smegma bacilli, but leaves the tubercle bacilli stained bright red.

STAINS FOR DIPHTHERIA BACILLI

Stains for diphtheria bacilli have been devised to demonstrate the polar and metachromatic granules in these organisms. For routine procedures, the commonly used stains are:

Löffler's alkaline methylene blue solution. The formula for this solution has been given above.

Toluidine blue (see under general stains).

Special differential stains for the demonstrations of deeply stained granules in sharp contrast with faintly stained bacterial bodies are:

Neisser's Stain

Solution No. 1

Methylene blue (dye content not specified).........................	1 gm.
Alcohol (*e.g.* 95%)	20 c.c.
Acetic acid (glacial)..	50 c.c.
Distilled water...	950 c.c.

Dissolve the dye in the alcohol and add the rest.

Solution No. 2

Crystal violet (dye content not specified)	1 gm.
Alcohol (*e.g.* 95%)	10 c.c.
Distilled water	300 c.c.

Solution No. 3

Chrysoidin	1 or 2 gms.
Distilled water	300 c.c.

Dried films are stained 10 seconds in a mixture of 2 parts of Solution No. 1 with 1 part of Solution No. 2. Wash Stain 10 seconds in Solution No. 3. Wash briefly in water, or not at all. Blot dry.

Ljubinsky's Stain

Solution A: Methyl Violet B

Methyl violet B...	2.5 gms.
Glacial acetic acid..	50 c.c.
Distilled water...	950 c.c.

B: Chrysoidin

Chrysoidin	5.6 gms.
Distilled water...	1000 c.c.

Dot not filter.

Procedure: 1. Stain the smear with solution A (methyl violet B), 1 minute.
2. Wash with water.
3. Stain with solution B (chrysoidin) 30 seconds.
4. Wash with water.
5. Dry in air or blot.

This is a differential stain for the polar granules in diphtheria bacilli. It also stains granules in other organisms. The granules should be dark blue or black, and the rest of the bacterial body reddish or yellowish. The time of application of the two solutions varies according to the age of the solutions and can be determined only by trial.

STAINS FOR SPIROCHETES

The Fontana-Tribondeau method depends upon the deposition of a silver salt in the organism and the reduction of the compound with formalin.

Solution A: Formalin

Acetic acid (glacial)	1 c.c.
40 per cent formalin..	10 c.c.
Distilled water...	100 c.c.

B: Tannic Acid

Tannic acid...	5 gms.
1 per cent phenol...	100 c.c.

C: Silver nitrate

5 per cent silver nitrate solution..................................	50 c.c.

Reserve a few c.c. of the silver nitrate solution. To the remainder add drop by drop concentrated ammonia solution until the sepia precipitate which forms redissolves. Shake and stir constantly during the addition of the ammonia. Then add, drop by drop, some of the reserved silver nitrate solution until there occurs a slight cloud, which persists on shaking. This solution will remain useful for several months. Occasionally pour it into a clean receptacle, and if it has become clear, add a few more drops of 5 per cent silver nitrate.

Procedure: 1. On a clean slide, make a film (thin) of fluid from a chancre or other material containing spirochetes, and let this dry in the air.
2. Cover the film with solution A for 1 minute.
3. Wash thoroughly with distilled water.
4. Cover with solution B and heat until the fluid steams.
5. Wash with distilled water.
6. Cover with solution C and heat until fluid steams. Let this act for 30 seconds.
7. Wash with water. Dry in air or blot.

The stained film should be of a dark maroon color. The spirochetes are stained dark brown or black.

Tunnicliff's Stain.

—This is a modified Gram's stain, omitting decolorization with alcohol. The method is useful also for staining gram-negative organisms. A modified procedure which we have found to be useful is as follows:

1. Make a thin smear of the material on a slide. Fix with heat.
2. Cover with carbol crystal violet, 30 seconds. (Sat. alc. sol. crystal violet, 10 c.c.; 5 per cent aqueous phenol sol. 90 c.c.)
3. Wash with water.
4. Cover with Lugol's iodine solution, 30 seconds.
5. Wash with water.
6. Cover with safranin, 30 seconds.
7. Wash with water.

Spirochetes and fusiform bacilli stain purplish black. Large bacterial forms are often granular. Capsules may be demonstrated by this method occasionally.

Noguchi's Stain

Formaldehyde buffer solution:
M/15 Na_2HPO_4 .... 88 parts
M/15 KH_2PO_4 .... 12 parts

The pH of this mixture is 7.6.
Add 9 parts of this buffer mixture to 1 part of 40 per cent formalin.

Procedure:

Put a drop of the formaldehyde buffer mixture on a slide and mix with this a drop of the fluid from a chancre or other lesion. Let stand 5 minutes. Then spread the mixture on the slide and dry in the air. To stain, flood the film with a saturated alcoholic solution of basic fuchsin or gentian violet. After 1 to 5 minutes, wash off the stain with water. Dry in air or blot gently.

Stain for Negri Bodies.

—Williams and Lowden applied Van Gieson's stain for the demonstration of Negri bodies in smears of brain tissue for the diagnosis of rabies. The procedure in use in New York State is as follows:

1. Dissect the brain of the dog, or other animal, and obtain material from the Rolandic area, the hippocampus (Ammon's horn), and cerebellum.
2. Make smears of small bits of brain tissue. Place the piece of nerve tissue on a clean slide. With a slide or cover slip used as a spreader, press evenly and firmly upon the tissue until it covers

almost the width of the slide. Then draw the spreader toward the opposite end of the slide, maintaining an even pressure.

3. Place the films immediately in the following fixative for ten seconds:

Methyl alcohol, c. p., neutral .... 1000 c.c.
Picric acid, 10 per cent sol. in neutral methyl alcohol.............. 1 c.c.

The alcohol is neutralized by adding 0.5 per cent of sodium carbonate, shaking, and allowing the excess to settle out. Add the picric acid just before use.

At the end of 10 seconds, remove the slide and blot dry.

4. Flood the film with modified Van Gieson's stain and gently heat it in a low flame to steaming. Wash the film in tap water and blot dry. The modified Van Gieson's stain is:

Basic fuchsin, sat. alc. sol. .... 0.5 to 1 c.c.
Methylene blue, sat. alc. sol. .... 10.0 c.c.
Distilled water.. 30.0 c.c.

Make up fresh before use. Keep on ice.

Rapid Demonstration of Negri Bodies in Sections.—The following method, developed at the Division of Laboratories and Research of the New York State Department of Health, is quoted from Schleifstein: [3]

Technic.—Fix blocks not more than 3 mm. in thickness of fresh tissue from the hippocampus major and the cerebellum in Zenker's solution for 4 hours at 37° C. Wash 30 minutes in running tap water. The tissue may be left in running water over night. For dehydration, use preferably a bottle with a tightly fitting ground glass stopper to prevent vapor from escaping, on the bottom of which anhydrous calcium chloride is put to a depth of about 1 cm. Add about 80 c.c. of dioxan containing a few flakes of iodine to assist in removing the mercury precipitate from the tissues. Place the blocks in the dioxan, supported well above the layer of calcium chloride. (A non-corrosive wire tripod with a fine mesh screen has been used.) Stopper the bottle tightly and keep the material at 37° C. for 1 hour.

Transfer the blocks to a mixture of equal parts of dioxan and paraffin and hold for 1 hour at 56° C. Care should be taken to have the blocks rest a few centimeters above the bottom of the bottle, since dioxan tends to settle.

Place the blocks in a paraffin bath at 56° C. for 1 hour; then embed in paraffin. Cut sections 4 μ in thickness and attach to slides with Mayer's albumin fixative. Heat slides carefully, section up, over a low Bunsen flame until the paraffin begins to melt. By that time, the water will have evaporated and the slides can be put in xylol. Remove paraffin in the usual manner and place slides in distilled water before staining sections.

Staining Method.—I. Stock solution
Rosanilin (Gruebler)... 1.80 gm.
Methylene blue (Nat. col.) .... 1.00 gm.
Glycerol (T. P.)... 100.00 c.c.
Methyl alcohol (T. P.) .... 100.00 c.c.

Shake for several minutes. The mixture keeps indefinitely.

II. Solution

1 : 40,000 aqueous solution of potassium hydroxide

For staining, add 1 drop of solution 1 to 2 c.c. of solution II. This mixture should be freshly prepared for each use.

Remove slides from the water; place on an electric plate; flood with freshly prepared stain and gently steam 5 minutes. Cool and wash quickly in tap water.

Decolorize and differentiate each section separately by gently swishing the slide in a jar of 90

3 From Schleifstein, J. Am. J. Pub. Health, 1937. 27, 1284.

per cent ethyl alcohol until the section assumes a faint violet color. This is a particularly important step.

Pass the sections rapidly through 95 per cent alcohol, absolute alcohol, and xylol. Mount in Canada balsam.

Negri bodies stain a deep magenta red and, under high magnification, the granular inclusions are dark blue. Nucleoli appear bluish black; cytoplasm, bluish violet; and red blood cells, a copper color.

Polychrome Stains.—The various polychrome stains are of value to the bacteriologist chiefly for the staining of pus and exudates where the relation of bacteria to cellular elements is to be demonstrated. They are also extremely useful in the study of fixed specimens of protozoan parasites. There is a large number of these stains in use; a few only, however, can be given here. In principle, all these stains depend upon a combination of eosin and methylene blue, these elements staining not only as units, but acting together in combination. One and the same solution, therefore, contains at least three elements which color the various structures of the preparation selectively.

The following brief directions for the preparation and use of Wright's stain, Giemsa's stain, and MacNeal's tetrachrome stain are quoted from the *Manual of Methods for Pure Culture Study*.[1] All of these stains can be purchased in powder form or in solution ready for use. The commercial preparations are often better than those made up in a bacteriological laboratory.

Wright's Stain

Methylene blue hydrochloride (90% dye content)	0.9 gm.
Sodium carbonate, 0.5 per cent aqu. sol.	100 c.c.

Heat in a steam sterilizer at 100° C. one hour, in containers in which the solution is not over 6 cm. deep. Cool and filter. To filtrate add:

Eosin Y (dye content about 85%)	1.0 gm.
Distilled water	500 c.c.

Mix thoroughly and filter. Save precipitate, and dissolve for use as follows:

Wright's stain (dry)	0.1 gm.
Methyl alcohol, absolute, neutral, acetone free	60 c.c.

Allow stain to stand a day or two; then filter. Always filter before using.

To stain, cover the dried preparation for 1 minute with the alcoholic solution of the stain. Dilute by dropping upon the stain an equal quantity of distilled water. A metallic film forms on the surface. Leave the diluted stain on for 3 to 15 minutes. Wash in distilled water by flooding the slide, taking care to float off the metallic film to prevent adherence of a precipitate to the slide.

Giemsa's Stain

	For Blood	For Tissue
Azure-II-eosin	3 gm.	3 gm.
Azure II	0.8 gm.	0.8 gm.
Glycerin, c.p.	250 c.c.	125 c.c.
Methyl alcohol, neutral, acetone free	250 c.c.	375 c.c.

Apply according to the directions for Wright's stain, or dilute 1 to 10 with water and place preparations, previously fixed in methyl alcohol, in the diluted Giemsa stain. Allow this diluted stain to act 6 to 18 hours.

Tetrachrome Stain, MacNeal

Eosin Y (dye content 80–85%) .... 1 gm.
Methylene blue hydrochloride (dye content about 90%) .... 1 gm.
Azure A .... 0.6 gm.
Methylene violet (Bernthsen) .... 0.2 gm.
Methyl alcohol, neutral, acetone free ....1000 cc.

Heat to 50° C., shake thoroughly and leave at 37° C. for a day or two; then filter and use filtrate. This stain can now be purchased either in dry form or in solution.

The staining procedure is the same as that outlined above for Wright's stain.

STAINING OF BACTERIA IN TISSUES

The preparation of tissue for bacterial staining is, in general, the same as that employed for purposes of cellular studies, in histology. For bacteriological studies the most useful fixatives are alcohol and Zenker's fluid. Other fixations, such as that by formalin, or Mueller's fluid, give less satisfaction. In other respects the details of dehydration and embedding are the same as those used in histological studies, except that it is desirable that the tissues should be handled rather more carefully than is necessary for ordinary pathological work, and the changes from the weaker to the stronger alcohols should be made less abruptly.[4]

Embedding in paraffin is preferable to celloidin, although the latter method is not unsuccessful if carefully carried out. The chief disadvantages of celloidin are the retention of color by the celloidin itself and the consequent unclearness of differentiation. It is also easier to cut thin sections from paraffin blocks, than from those prepared with celloidin.

When staining tissue sections for bacteria, it is most convenient to carry out the process with the section attached to a slide. For celloidin sections this may be accomplished by means of ether vapor. For paraffin sections it is necessary to cover the slide with an extremely thin layer of a filtered mixture of equal quantities of egg-albumin and glycerin, to which a small crystal of camphor or a drop or two of carbolic acid has been added. The sections are then floated upon a slide so prepared, and set away in the thermostat for four or five hours.

Gram-Weigert Method for Celloidin Sections.—Stain for one-half hour in the following freshly filtered solution:

Carmin .... 3–5 gms.
Saturated aqueous solution of lithium carbonate .... 100 c.c.

Dehydrate in 95 per cent alcohol.
Stick section to slide with ether vapor.
Stain in aniline water gentian violet for 5 to 15 minutes (or in a saturated solution of aqueous crystal diluted with water 1:10, 5 to 15 minutes).

Wash in physiological salt solution.
Cover with Gram's iodine solution 1 to 2 minutes.
Wash in water and blot.
Decolorize with aniline oil until no more color comes off.
This both decolorizes and dehydrates.
Treat with xylol. Mount in balsam.

[4] For details of such work reference should be made to the standard textbooks on pathological technic, notably the excellent one of Mallory and Wright.

Gram-Weigert Method for Paraffin Sections.—Preferably Zenker's fixation:

1. Stain sections lightly in alum-hematoxylin.
2. Wash in running water.
3. Four per cent aqueous solution of eosin, 5 minutes to ½ hour.
4. Wash in water.
5. Aniline methyl violet, ½ to 1 hour.
6. Wash off with water.
7. Lugol's solution, 1 to 2 minutes.
8. Wash off with water.
9. Blot with filter-paper and dehydrate and clear in several changes of aniline and xylol, equal parts, or in aniline oil alone.
10. Wash off with xylol.
11. Mount in xylol-colophonium.

Pappenheimer's Method for Gram-positive and Gram-negative Organisms in Tissues.— Fixation: Zenker preferred. Formalin or alcohol.

Paraffin sections 5 μ or less.

Staining:

1. Stirling's gentian violet—5 minutes.
2. Gram's iodine, 1 minute.
3. Aniline oil, or aniline oil, xylol. Decolorize to pale violet.
4. Absolute alcohol. Few seconds only.
5. Distilled water.
6. Aqueous safranin, ½ per cent 30 seconds.
7. Distilled water.
8. Blot. Absolute alcohol. Few seconds only.
9. Clear in xylol.

Differential Staining of Gram-positive and Gram-negative Bacteria in Tissue Sections.[5]

Paraffin sections are prepared as usual for staining.

1. Stain in freshly filtered alum-hematoxylin (Harris) for 2 to 5 minutes.
2. Wash in acid alcohol (3% HCl in 95% alcohol) until light pink.
3. Wash in ammonia water (1 c.c. of aqua ammoniae in 100 c.c. water) until blue.
4. Wash in water.
5. In a small vial mix 5 drops of 5 per cent aqueous solution of sodium bicarbonate (containing also 0.5 per cent phenol as a preservative) with about 0.75 c.c. of 1 per cent (by weight) aqueous solution of gentian violet. Immediately pour the mixture onto the slide and stain for 2 minutes.
6. Wash quickly with water.
7. Cover with Lugol's iodine solution for 1 minute.
8. Wash with water. Blot.
9. Decolorize in 1 part of ether plus 3 parts of acetone, dropping it onto the slide until no more color comes off.
10. Blot.
11. Stain with basic fuchsin (0.005 gm. of fuchsin per 100 c.c. water) for 5 minutes.
12. Wash in water. Blot but do not allow the section to dry.
13. Pass through acetone.
14. Decolorize and differentiate by dropping over the section a solution of 0.1 gm. picric acid in 100 c.c. of acetone until the section becomes a yellowish-pink. This is the most critical stage of the process and should be carried out by holding the slide over a white plate or dish. Most of the

5 Method of J. H. Brown and L. Brenn.

TUNNICLIFF, R. J. Am. M. Ass., 121, 78:191.
VAN ERMENGEN. Centralbl. f. Bakteriol., I Abt., 1894, 15.
WADSWORTH. J. Infect. Dis., 1906.
WELCH, W. H. Bull. Johns Hopkins Hosp., 1892, 3:81.
WILLIAMS, A. W., and LOWDEN. J. Infect. Dis., 1906, 3.
WRIGHT, J. H. J. Med. Research, 1902, 7:138.
ZIEHL, F. Deutsche med. Wchnschr., 1882, 8:451.

fuchsin should be decolorized from the tissue but the gram-negative bacteria should remain red.

15. Pass successively through acetone, equal parts of acetone and xylol, and xylol.

16. After clearing in xylol mount in balsam.

(Beginning with step 5 it is best to work with only one slide at a time.)

Cell nuclei should be stained dark reddish-brown; cytoplasm yellowish; gram-positive bacteria deep violet or almost black; gram-negative bacteria bright red. Leukocytes generally stand out plainly with a dusky yellowish cytoplasm. Basophilic granules stain red. Red blood cells may be yellow or red depending upon the degree of decolorization.

CHAPTER LXVII

THE PREPARATION OF CULTURE MEDIA

GENERAL TECHNIC

The successful cultivation of bacteria upon artificial media requires the establishment of an environment which shall be suitable in regard to the presence of assimilable nutritive material, moisture, and osmotic relations. These conditions are fulfilled in the composition of the nutrient media which are to some extent varied according to the special requirements of the bacteria which are to be cultivated. If cultivation, furthermore, is to have any value for scientific study of individual species, it is necessary to obtain these species free from other varieties of micro-organisms, that is, in pure culture, and to protect such cultures continuously from contamination with other innumerable species.

The technic which is employed for these purposes has been gradually evolved from the methods originally devised by Pasteur, Koch, Cohn, and others.

Bacterial cultivation is carried out in glassware of varied construction, the forms most commonly employed being test tubes of various sizes, Erlenmeyer flasks, the common Florence flasks, and Petri dishes. All glassware, of course, must be thoroughly cleansed before being used.

Preparation of Glassware.—The cleansing of glassware may be accomplished by any one of a number of methods. New glassware may be immersed in a 1 per cent solution of hydrochloric or nitric acid in order to remove the free alkali which is occasionally present on such glass. It is then transferred to a 1 per cent sodium hydrate solution for a few hours, and following this is washed in hot running water.

In the case of old glassware which has contained culture-media, sterilization in the autoclave is first carried out, then the glassware is boiled in 5 per cent soda solution or in soapsuds. After this, thorough mechanical cleansing is practised, and the glassware may be treated by acid and alkali followed by running water, as given above. These last steps, however, are not essential, thorough washing in hot water after the soapsuds or soda solution being usually sufficient to yield good results. Other workers have recommended immersion of the glassware after mechanical cleansing in 5 per cent to 10 per cent potassium bichromate solution in 25 per cent sulphuric acid. This is followed by thorough washing in hot running water, and drying.

Clean flasks and test tubes are then stoppered with cotton, which has been found to be a convenient and efficient seal against the bacteria of the air, catching them in the meshes of the fibers as in a filter. The technic of the stoppering or plugging of glass receptacles is important, in that, when poorly plugged, sterility is not safeguarded, and the purpose of culture study is defeated.

In almost all laboratories in this country nonabsorbent cotton or "cotton batting" is used for the plug. The absorbent variety may be employed. The disadvantages of the latter, especially in the case of fluid media, are obvious. The plugs should fit snugly, but not so tightly that force is necessary to remove them. Care should be taken, furthermore, that no creases are left between the surface of the glass and the periphery of the plug; for these, if present, may serve as channels for the entrance of bacteria. The plugging itself is carried out by tearing a small piece of cotton, about 2 by 2 inches, from the roll, folding over one of its corners, and, applying the smooth end of a glass rod to the folded portion, gently pushing it into the mouth of the tube.

After plugging and before media are introduced into the tubes and flasks, these should be sterilized. This is best done in one of the "hot-air sterilizers," by exposing the tubes for one hour to a temperature of 150° C. If greater speed is desired exposure to 180° to 190° C. for half an hour is usually safe. If by mistake, however, the temperature is allowed to rise above 200° C., a browning of the cotton plugs occurs and the glassware is apt to be stained by the burning of the fat and other organic material derived from the cotton. Petri dishes after cleansing are fitted together, and then sterilized in the hot-air chamber at 150° C. for one hour.

Glassware so prepared is ready for the reception of media.

Ingredients of Culture Media.—The food requirements of bacteria have been discussed in another section. It is apparent that artificial culture-media must, to a certain extent, be adjusted to the peculiarities of individual bacteria. In the cases of the more strictly parasitic micro-organisms growth can be obtained only by the most rigid observance of special requirements. For the large majority of pathogenic bacteria, however, routine or standard media may be employed, which, while slightly more favorable for one species than for another, are sufficiently general in their composition to permit the growth of all but the most fastidious varieties.

The basis of many of our common media is formed by the soluble constituents of meat. These substances are best obtained by macerating 500 grams of lean beef in 1000 c.c. of distilled water. The mixture is allowed to infuse in the ice chest over night, and then strained through cheesecloth. To this infusion are added the other required constituents in the manner given in the detailed instructions below. Some of the soluble constituents of meat, however, may also be procured in a simpler way by the use of the commercial meat extracts, such as that of Liebig. These extracts are dissolved in quantities of 5 grams to the liter, and other constituents are added to this nutrient basis. Though simpler to make, the meat-extract media are less favorable for the cultivation of the more delicate organisms than are the media made directly from fresh meat. Nevertheless, they suffice for the cultivation of the large majority of the more saprophytic pathogenic micro-organisms. The use of meat-extract is decreasing, as it is an unnecessary addition to bacteriological peptones.

The ingredients and methods used in various laboratories in the preparation of standard media should be, as much as possible, uniform, in order that confusion in results may be avoided; for, as is well known, the biological characteristics of one and the same bacterial species may vary considerably if grown on media differing in their composition.

Titration of Media.—Next in importance to the actual composition of media is the adjustment of their reaction. Bacteria are highly susceptible to variations in the acidity and alkalinity of media, excessive degrees of either may completely inhibit development or moderate variations may lead to marked modifications of cultural characteristics. It is necessary, therefore, to adjust the reaction both for the sake of favoring growth and in order to insure uniformity of growth characters.

Older Method of Titration.—The color indicator employed for the titration is a 0.5 per cent solution of phenolphthalein in 50 per cent alcohol. The chief advantage of this indicator over others is due to the fact that it indicates the presence of organic acid and acid compounds in its reaction. For actual titration N/20 (one-twentieth normal) solutions of sodium hydrate or of hydrochloric acid are used. Since media in the process of preparation are usually acid, the sodium hydrate solution is the one most frequently needed. Five c.c. of the medium to be tested is measured accurately in a carefully washed pipet and transferred into a porcelain evaporating dish. To this are added 45 c.c. of distilled water. The mixture is thoroughly boiled for three minutes over a free flame. The boiling drives off carbon dioxide, giving the true neutral point, and approximates the conditions prevailing during the further sterilization of the medium from which the 5 c.c. have been taken. After boiling, 1 c.c. of the phenolphthalein is added. If the medium is acid, no color is present; if alkaline, a pink or red color appears. The N/20 alkali or acid solution is allowed to drop into the dish from a graduated buret. When the neutral point is approached in an acid solution, each drop of sodium hydrate added brings forth at first a deep red, which, however, upon slight stirring with a clean rod, completely disappears. The end reaction is reached when a faint but clear and distinct pink color remains in the fluid after stirring.

This method has been practically abandoned because of its inaccuracy and is given only for use when for some reason or another the method for determining the hydrogen-ion concentration is not available.

Colorimetric Method of Titration.—*Determination of H-ion concentration and pH.*—The method given above is not an accurate one because, in the titration of culture media, we are dealing with solutions which contain considerable quantities of materials, such as peptone, proteins, phosphates, etc., which have an action which is spoken of technically as that of a "buffer." This term signifies the power of these substances to oppose changes in reaction. The degree of "buffer" action, as shown by a number of writers, but in connection with bacteriological work particularly by Clark and Lubs, is proportionate to the concentration of the constituents, and the consequence of the action is that volumetrically proportionate amounts of acid or alkali added to such solutions do not change the reaction in the same proportions. Curves found in the paper of Clark and Lubs, cited above, will make this sufficiently clear. In consequence, when we titrate 5 c.c. of the medium as in the old method, to the neutral point of phenolphthalein, we could bring the entire medium to this point by adding proportionate amounts of acid or alkali, but we cannot foretell the final hydrogen ion concentration attained in the medium by adding fractions of this total amount. It is plain, therefore, that to make an accurate adjustment of media it would be better to apply either an electrode method or a colorimetric method to the medium, adjusting to a standard of known hydrogen ion concentration. The potentiometer methods have been considerably simplified, and have been applied by many bacteriologists to the titration of media. For routine laboratory work colorimetric methods have been introduced which, as used by others and by us, have checked up quite accurately with potentiometer measurements.

Before describing the method at present in use, it will be best to say a few words about the nomenclature used at present for the expression of hydrogen ion concentrations.

The Meaning of pH.—The hydrogen ion concentration of pure water is approximately 0.0000001 gm. $H+$ per liter. This is more simply expressed as 1×-7. Since, in pure water, hydroxyl ions are equal in concentration to the hydrogen ions, and the hydroxyl ions are also 1×10^{-7}, and this is the neutral point. Solutions in which the hydrogen ion concentration is less than 1×10^{-7} (and the hydroxyl, therefore, more than 1×10^{-7}) are alkaline, and vice versa. This method of expression offers certain difficulties to the plotting of curves, and it has been found simpler for such purposes to plot curves according to the logarithms of the expressions used above. Sörensen initiated a method of doing this, by introducing the symbol pH which signifies the logarithm of the reciprocal of the hydrogen ion concentration. Expressed as above, thus,

$$pH \text{ equals log of } \frac{1}{[H]}$$

The following table indicates the relationships:

Hydrogen Ion Concentration	pH Value
1×10^{-1}	1
1×10^{-2}	2
1×10^{-3}	3
1×10^{-4}	4
1×10^{-5}	5
1×10^{-6}	6
1×10^{-7}	7
1×10^{-8}	8
1×10^{-9}	9
1×10^{-10}	10

Indicators are substances, usually weak organic acids or bases which change in color when subjected to changes of reaction, that is, to changes of hydrogen or hydroxyl ion concentrations. A table will give the color reactions at various pH measurements for a number of common indicators.

Clark and Lubs particularly have been responsible for introducing the method at present in use in bacteriological laboratories, based upon the preparation of solutions which can be used as standards for the colorimetric measurements of the pH of culture media. The solutions must be very carefully prepared, and should, whenever possible, be controlled by potentiometer measurements; however, with proper care and the use of pure substances by a reliable worker, this may, with reasonable safety, be omitted. The principle of making the dilutions is that carefully measured amounts of molecular solutions of acids and alkalies are mixed in series so that each successive tube shall contain a definite hydrogen ion concentration. These tubes are the standard. Clark and Lubs, in the first of the series of papers noted above, cite tables of mixtures for such purposes, with a range of pH extending from 1 to 10. For the exact composition of all of these mixtures, the reader is referred to the original paper pH RANGE OF INDICATORS [1]

Indicator	Concentration of Aqueous Stock Solution Per Cent	Color Change	pH Range
Thymol blue	0.04	Red → yellow	1.2– 2.8
Bromphenol blue	0.04	Yellow → blue	3.0– 4.6
Methyl red	0.02	Red → yellow	4.4– 6.0
Bromcresol green	0.04	Yellow → blue	3.8– 5.4
Bromcresol purple	0.04	Yellow → purple	5.2– 6.8
Bromthymol blue	0.04	Yellow → blue	6.0– 7.6
Phenol red	0.02	Yellow → red	6.8– 8.4
Cresol red	0.02	Yellow → red	7.2– 8.8
Thymol blue	0.04	Yellow → blue	8.0– 9.6
Cresol phthalein	0.02	Colorless → red	8.2– 9.8
Phenolphthalein	0.02	Colorless → red	8.5–10.5
Alizarine yellow	....	Colorless → yellow	10.0–12.0
Litmus	....	Red → blue	4.5– 8.3

of Clark and Lubs, page 25. For the routine of the ordinary laboratory bacteriology, only the fourth section of this table is necessary. This is as follows:

$$KH_2PO_4—NaOH$$

5.8	50 c.c. M/5 KH₂PO₄	3.72 c.c. M/5 NaOH	Dilute to 200 c.c.
5.8	50 c.c. $M/5$ KH_2PO_4	3.72 c.c. $M/5$ NaOH	Dilute to 200 c.c.
6.0	50 c.c. $M/5$ KH_2PO_4	5.70 c.c. $M/5$ NaOH	Dilute to 200 c.c.
6.2	50 c.c. $M/5$ KH_2PO_4	8.60 c.c. $M/5$ NaOH	Dilute to 200 c.c.
6.4	50 c.c. $M/5$ KH_2PO_4	12.60 c.c. $M/5$ NaOH	Dilute to 200 c.c.
6.6	50 c.c. $M/5$ KH_2PO_4	17.80 c.c. $M/5$ NaOH	Dilute to 200 c.c.
6.8	50 c.c. $M/5$ KH_2PO_4	23.65 c.c. $M/5$ NaOH	Dilute to 200 c.c.
7.0	50 c.c. $M/5$ KH_2PO_4	29.63 c.c. $M/5$ NaOH	Dilute to 200 c.c.
7.2	50 c.c. $M/5$ KH_2PO_4	35.00 c.c. $M/5$ NaOH	Dilute to 200 c.c.
7.4	50 c.c. $M/5$ KH_2PO_4	39.50 c.c. $M/5$ NaOH	Dilute to 200 c.c.
7.6	50 c.c. $M/5$ KH_2PO_4	42.80 c.c. $M/5$ NaOH	Dilute to 200 c.c.
7.8	50 c.c. $M/5$ KH_2PO_4	45.20 c.c. $M/5$ NaOH	Dilute to 200 c.c.
8.0	50 c.c. $M/5$ KH_2PO_4	46.80 c.c. $M/6$ NaOH	Dilute to 200 c.c.

The method of procedure in using these solutions is as follows:

From the solutions made above a colorimetric scale is prepared. All glassware must be very carefully cleansed, and it should be remembered that some of the cheaper glassware obtained in laboratories at the present time often seems to give off considerable amounts of alkali. Whatever method of cleaning is used, the final thorough rinsing must be done thoroughly with redistilled water. Ten c.c. each of the respective series of standard mixtures is placed into each test tube, and to it 10 drops of the indicator are added. For the range from 6.8 to 8.4, which is sufficient for all ordinary pathogenic work, the indicator used is phenolsulphonephthalein, or phenol red in concentration of 0.02 per cent aqueous solution. If ranges from 6 to 7.6 are desired, bromthymol blue in a concentration of 0.04 per cent may be used, and when ranges just above 8 are desired, cresol red in concentration of 0.02 per cent is recommended.

A series of tubes so prepared, each of which contains 10 c.c. of each of the graded mixtures, with indicator added, represents a colorimetric scale against which the media can be standardized.

[1] Clark and Lubs.

This standardization is now carried out as follows, and can be utilized for any media which are not too highly colored and not turbid: Into a thoroughly cleaned test tube 2 c.c. of the medium are measured and this diluted with 8 c.c. of redistilled water. Ten drops of indicator are then added, and after thoroughly mixing, a color reading is taken against the scale. If the reaction is too acid, as is usually the case, add N/20 sodium hydroxide from a buret or graduated pipet, a drop at a time, until the color matches that of the standard tube. By calculating from the amount of weak alkali added, the total quantity of media is then brought to the desired pH with N/1 sodium hydroxide. In the titration of agar, Clark and Lubs recommended that the broth be titrated and adjusted before the addition of the agar, in order to avoid possible colloidal changes between the agar and the indicator, and that the agar be added after the adjustment is made. It is possible, however, without excessive error, to carry out the titration of media containing agar in the same way as outlined above, adding cold water to the hot agar, and making the comparison at once at a temperature of 35° to 40° before the mixture has jellied. In solutions like bacterial media, which have a certain amount of color or some turbidity, a so-called "comparator" may be used in the form of a wooden box painted black with four holes for test tubes and a slit in front and behind, so that it can be looked through against a source of light. The arrangement of this is given in the following diagram.

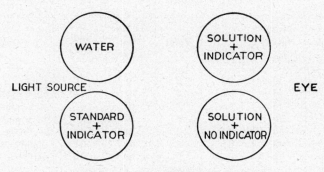

ARRANGEMENT FOR READING TITRATION.

A practical simplification of preparing color standards has been published by Medalia. This method is being successfully used in our laboratory and is recommended as a practical and simple routine procedure. It is based on the fact that Medalia noticed that in the ranges between the extreme acid and alkaline colors of each indicator there is a difference of pH 1.6. Dividing this sensitive range into eight equal parts, he obtains a range for each indicator of pH 0.2 intervals. He accomplishes this by adding 0.1 c.c. of the indicator solution to one test tube containing 10 c.c. of an alkaline solution and 0.7 c.c. of the same indicator to another test tube containing 10 c.c. of an acid solution, solutions which bring out the alkaline and acid colors of the indicator. Looking through the two test tubes, one behind the other, that is, superimposing the alkaline and acid colors of the indicators of the different strengths in this way, gives a full range of the indicator at intervals of pH 0.2. Stock alcoholic solutions of indicators are prepared by dissolving 0.1 gram of the respective indicators in pure form in 50 c.c. of 95 per cent ethyl alcohol. Five c.c. of these stock alcoholic solutions are added to 45 c.c. of distilled water in dark-colored bottles, and these solutions of 0.02 per cent sterilized in the autoclave. For the titration of media, bromthymol blue and phenol red are used. Two sets of tubes for each indicator are prepared as in the following tables:

COMPOSITION OF "STANDARD COLORS" PREPARED WITH BROMTHYMOL BLUE 0.02 PER CENT WATERY SOLUTION—RANGE pH 6.4 TO 7.6

Pair	Tube	N/20 NaOH, c.c.	Indicator c.c.	Tube	0.1 Per Cent HCl, c.c.	Indicator	Color	pH
1	1	10	0.1	2	10	0.7	yellow	6.4
2	1	10	0.2	2	10	0.6	lighter yellow	6.6
3	1	10	0.3	2	10	0.5	yellow-green	6.8
4	1	10	0.4	2	10	0.4	green	7.0
5	1	10	0.5	2	10	0.3	bluish green	7.2
6	1	10	0.6	2	10	0.2	greenish blue	7.4
7	1	10	0.7	2	10	0.1	blue	7.6

COMPOSITION OF "STANDARD COLORS" PREPARED WITH PHENOL RED 0.04 PER CENT WATERY SOLUTION—RANGE pH 7 to pH 8.2

Pair	Tube	N/20 NaOH, c.c.	Indicator c.c.	Tube	0.1 Per Cent HCl, c.c.	Indicator	Color	pH
1	1	10	0.1	2	10	0.7	yellow	7.0
2	1	10	0.2	2	10	0.6	lighter yellow	7.2
3	1	10	0.3	2	10	0.5	pink-yellow	7.4
4	1	10	0.4	2	10	0.4	more pink-yellow	7.6
5	1	10	0.5	2	10	0.3	beginning red	7.8
6	1	10	0.6	2	10	0.2	slightly more red	8.0
7	1	10	0.7	2	10	0.1	red	8.2

The seven pairs of tubes are set up in a rack, the tubes containing the acid solution in one row and those containing the alkaline solution behind them, so arranged that the acid tubes get, from left to right, 0.7, 0.6, etc., down to 0.1 c.c. of the 0.02 indicator solution, while the alkaline ones get, from left to right, 0.1 c.c. of the indicator solution, increasing by 0.1 c.c. for each tube up to 0.7 c.c. in the right-hand tube. A glance at the table will make this clear. Each pair of tubes then contains 0.8 c.c. of the indicator.

For the titration of culture media three test tubes similar to those used for the color standards are filled each with 2 c.c. of the filtered medium and 8 c.c. of distilled water. To one of these 0.8 c.c. of the 0.02 per cent of the bromthymol blue indicator is added and compared with the color standards. The other two tubes are used to offset the color of the medium, which is important. The tube to be titrated is placed between the two pairs of test tubes nearest to the pH required and in front of each pair is placed the tube containing 2 c.c. of the medium and 2 c.c. of distilled water, again to offset the color of the medium. If the amount of N/20 sodium hydroxide required to bring the titrated 2 c.c. to pH 7 is multiplied by 25, this will represent the amount of N/1 sodium hydroxide necessary to neutralize 1 liter of the medium.

INDICATORS USED IN CULTURE MEDIA

In order to detect the production of acid by bacteria growing in culture media, it is often convenient to add the indicator to the medium at the time of its preparation. The solutions commonly used for this purpose are:

Andrade's Indicator

0.5% aqueous sol. acid fuchsin... 100 c.c.
N/1 NaOH .... 16 c.c.

1. Mix acid fuchsin solution and N/1 NaOH.
2. Sterilize in autoclave at 15 lbs. for 15 min.
One c.c. of this indicator is added to 100 c.c. of the medium. The color of the mixture is pink when the medium is hot. This disappears when the medium is cold.
The medium with the indicator is colorless (or pale yellow) when alkaline and pink when acid. The indicator is colorless at pH 7.2.

Basic Fuchsin Decolorized with Sodium Sulfite.—This is the indicator used in Endo's medium. It is in reality Schiff's reagent and changes from colorless to deep red in the presence of both aldehydes and acids. The components are usually added directly to the agar-carbohydrate medium.

The formula for the solution is:
Basic fuchsin, 10 per cent sol. in 95 per cent alcohol..................... 0.3 c.c.
Sodium sulfite, 2.5 per cent aq. sol. .... 5–10 c.c.

Different samples of basic fuchsin vary in the ease with which they can be decolorized by sulfite.

Bromcresol Purple: Stock 1.6 per cent solution (alcohol).
To prepare: Add 1.6 gm. bromcresol purple to 100 c.c. 95% ethyl alcohol.

In our experience, this indicator serves all the purposes for which litmus was formerly used. It has replaced litmus as an indicator in milk and all carbohydrate broth media used for fermentation tests. Usually 5 to 10 c.c. of this stock solution added to a liter of the medium produces sufficient depth of color.

Methyl Red (For Methyl Red Test).
Dissolve 0.1 gm. methyl red in 300 c.c. 95% ethyl alcohol and dilute to 500 c.c. with distilled water.

METHODS OF CLEARING MEDIA

Clearing with Eggs.—When culture media are prepared from substances containing no coagulable protein, it is occasionally necessary, for purposes of clearing, to add the whites of eggs, and then to heat for forty-five minutes in the Arnold sterilizer. In the following detailed descriptions, the direction "clear with egg" has been given whenever such a step is deemed necessary. The exact technic of such a procedure is as follows:

In a small pot or pan, the whites of several eggs (one or two eggs to each liter of medium) are beaten up thoroughly with a little water (20 c.c.). This egg white is then poured into the medium, which, if hot, as in the case of melted agar or gelatin, must first be cooled to about 50° to 55° C. The mixture is then thoroughly shaken and steamed in the Arnold sterilizer for thirty minutes. At the end of this time, the flask containing the medium is removed from the sterilizer and thoroughly shaken so as completely to break up the coagulum which has formed. It is then replaced and allowed to steam for another fifteen minutes. At the end of this time the medium between the coagula should be clear. It is now ready for filtration through cotton.

Filtering Media through Cotton.—The filtration of medium after clearing, either by the addition of eggs or by the coagulation of the proteins originally contained in it, is best done through absorbent cotton. A small spiral, improvised of copper wire, is placed as a support in the bottom of a large glass funnel. A square piece of absorbent cotton is then split horizontally giving two squares of equal size. Ragged edges and incisures should be avoided. These two layers of cotton are then placed in the funnel, one piece above the other in such a way that the direction of the fibers of the two layers is at right angles one to the other. They are then gently depressed into the filter with the closed fist. The edges of the cotton are made to adhere to the sides of the funnel by allowing a thin stream of tap water to run over them, while smoothing them against the glass with the hand. A stronger filter is obtained by folding the cotton between layers of surgical gauze.

The medium, when poured into such a filter, should be poured along a glass rod at first, to avoid running down the sides or bursting the filter. After filtration has begun, the filter should be kept as full as possible. The first liter or so which comes through may not be clear, but the filter gains in efficiency as the coagulum settles into the fibers of the cotton, and the first yield may be sent through a second time. Filtration of agar or gelatin is best done in a warm room with windows and doors closed, and the filter covered with a lid, to avoid too rapid cooling. The funnel and filter should be warmed just before use.

Filtering through Paper.—Many media may be efficiently cleared by filtration through close filter-paper without the aid of coagula.

Bacterial Filtration.—Filtration is an important method of freeing fluid cultures of bacteria, both in the manufacture of toxins and in the sterilization of media, ascitic fluid, serum, etc. Berkefeld, Mandler, Chamberland or Seitz filters are used for this purpose.

Tubing of Media.—Most of the media described in the foregoing section are used in test tubes.

In order to fill these tubes, the media are best poured into a large glass funnel to which a glass discharging tube has been fitted by means of a short piece of rubber tubing. Upon this is placed a thumb cock. The plug is then removed from the test tube by catching it between the small and ring fingers of the right hand and the glass outlet is thrust deeply into the test tube, in order to prevent the medium from touching the upper portion of the test tube where the cotton plug will be lodged. About 7 to 8 c.c. are put in each test tube.

Sterilization of Media.—*By Heat.*—Many varieties of media may be sterilized in the autoclave at fifteen pounds pressure for fifteen minutes to half an hour. Media which contain carbohydrates, blood, proteins or other substances subject to injury from the high temperature, must be sterilized by the fractional method, *i.e.*, by twenty minutes' exposure in the live steam sterilizer on each of three consecutive days. During the intervals between sterilizations, they should be kept at room temperature or in the incubator, to permit the germination of spores which may be present. Media containing animal serum or other albuminous solutions which are to be sterilized without coagulation, may be sterilized in water-baths, or in hot-air chambers, at temperatures varying from 60° to 70° C., by the fractional method. In such cases five or six exposures of one hour on succeeding days should be employed. Serum media, coagulated in the inspissator, can be sterilized in the autoclave.

The destruction of bacteria by heat has been discussed in Chapter VII.

Composition and Preparation of Culture Media

The nutrient media used for the cultivation of bacteria have been numerous and varied. Levine and Schoenlein gathered from the literature formulae of about seven thousand culture media and have arranged and classified these into approximately twenty-five hundred distinct media. This valuable compilation, replete with specific directions and provided with a workable index and a large bibliography is an indispensable source of information on the subject of media for the cultivation of micro-organisms.

In this section, we shall describe the culture media commonly used in medical bacteriology.

Meat Extract Broth.—To 1 liter of distilled or clear tap water, add 5 grams or 0.5 per cent of Liebig's meat extract, 10 grams or 1 per cent of Witte or any other reliable brand of peptone, and 5 grams or 0.5 per cent of common salt, NaCl.

The ingredients are mixed together in a suitable vessel and heated with stirring over a free flame. When the peptone and meat extract are completely dissolved, the vessel is removed from the flame. The medium is titrated by the colorimetric method described above and adjusted to the desired reaction. It is advisable to make the reaction about two points (on the pH scale) more alkaline than the final reaction should be, since the heat of the autoclave usually increases the acidity of the medium. Using Liebig's meat extract and Digestive Ferment's peptone, we have found that the addition of 10–12 c.c. of normal sodium hydroxide to every liter of extract broth usually brings the reaction, before autoclaving, to pH 7.6, making it about pH 7.4 after autoclaving, which is the optimum for most pathogenic bacteria. After the addition of the alkali, the broth is boiled for thirty minutes. The medium is then filtered, the reaction checked and after tubing and sterilization, is ready for use. It is not necessary in most cases to add eggs to extract broth, since it is easy to clear it by filtration through paper.

Meat Extract Agar (Plain 2 per cent Agar)

Formula:		
Agar	20 gms.	
Peptone (Difco or Witte)	20 gms.	
Meat extract	3 gms.	
Sodium chloride	5 gms.	
Distilled water	1000 c.c.	

1. Mix these ingredients in a sauce pan and bring to boiling, stirring constantly. Keep boiling until all the agar is dissolved.
2. Add distilled water to restore volume.
3. Titrate and adjust reaction to pH 7.6–7.8.
4. Filter through absorbent cotton and gauze.
5. Place in tubes or flasks as desired. For slants, put about 8 c.c. in each tube.
6. Sterilize in autoclave at 15 lbs. for 15 min.
7. Allow the agar to harden in the tubes in a slanting position.

Meat Extract Gelatin

Formula:		
Gelatin	150 gms.	
Peptone (Difco)	20 gms.	
Meat extract	3 gms.	
NaCl	5 gms.	
Distilled water	1000 c.c.	

1. Put all the ingredients, except the gelatin, into a sauce pan or double boiler, heat until the peptone is dissolved and bring to boil.
2. Remove from the stove and add the gelatin.
3. Stir until the gelatin is almost entirely dissolved.
4. Place the pan again on the stove or in the Arnold sterilizer and heat only as long as required to dissolve all the gelatin. Stir frequently.
5. Add distilled water to restore volume.
6. Titrate and adjust reaction to pH 7.6–7.8.
7. Keep solution hot and filter through cotton.

8. Put 8–10 c.c. in each tube.
9. Sterilize in autoclave at 15 lbs. for 15 minutes, or in the Arnold sterilizer.
10. Let gelatin harden with tubes in upright position.

Meat Infusion Gelatin.—Meat infusion gelatin is made in the same way as the above except that fresh meat infusion is substituted for the meat extract broth.

Peptone Water, Dunham's Solution

Formula: Peptone (Difco) ....   20 gms.
Sodium chloride ....   5 gms.
Distilled water .... 1000 c.c.

1. Mix these ingredients in a sauce pan and boil for about 5 minutes.
2. Add distilled water to restore volume.
3. Titrate and adjust reaction to pH 7.6–7.8.
4. Cool to about 48–50° C.
5. Filter through paper.
6. Place in tubes or flasks as desired.
7. Sterilize in the autoclave at 15 lbs. for 15 minutes.

This peptone solution is used as a base for a number of different media.

Meat extract broth contains peptone water + 0.3 per cent meat extract.

Carbohydrate media for fermentation tests with organisms of the colon-typhoid-dysentery group are made by adding 1 per cent to 2 per cent of the various carbohydrates to peptone water.

Nitrate broth, used in testing for the reduction of nitrates to nitrites is peptone water + 0.1 per cent or + 0.02 per cent potassium nitrate.

Carbohydrate Media for Fermentation Tests

1. Mix in a saucepan and boil about 2 minutes.

Difco peptone ....   5 gms.
Beef extract ....   3 gms.
Distilled water .... 1000 c.c.

2. Add water to restore volume.
3. Titrate and adjust reaction to pH 7.4–7.8.
4. Add 1 c.c. of a 1.6 per cent alcoholic solution of bromcresol purple per liter.
5. Cool to about 50° C. and filter through paper.
6. Add 10 grams of the desired carbohydrate.

Glucose, in this laboratory, is distinguished by a blue cotton plug.
Lactose, in this laboratory, is distinguished by a pink cotton plug.
Sucrose, in this laboratory, is distinguished by a white cotton plug.
Mannite, in this laboratory, is distinguished by a yellow cotton plug.

7. Tube, placing 5 to 8 c.c. in tubes containing inverted ampules.
8. Sterilize in autoclave at 15 pounds for 15 min.

Note.—If it is found undesirable to autoclave the carbohydrate, the carbohydrate solution may be sterilized by filtration through a Berkefeld filter and added to the autoclaved base.

Nitrate Broth

Formula: Peptone (Difco) ....   10 gms.
Potassium nitrate (nitrite free) ....   0.2 gm.
Distilled water .... 1000 c.c.

1. Heat to dissolve ingredients.
2. Adjust reaction to pH 7.4–7.6.
3. Filter through paper.
4. Tube as desired.
5. Sterilize in autoclave at 15 pounds for 15 min.

Uschinsky's Protein-free Medium.—To 1 liter of distilled water add:

Asparagin	3.4 gms.
Ammonium lactate	10.0 gms.
Sodium chloride	5.0 gms.
Magnesium sulphate	0.2 gm.
Calcium chloride	0.1 gm.
Potassium phosphate	1.0 gm.

When these substances are thoroughly dissolved, add 40 c.c. of glycerin. Tube and sterilize by heat or Berkefeld filtration.

Meat Infusion Broth

1. Remove all fat from lean beef and grind meat finely.
2. To each 500 grams of meat add 1000 c.c. of distilled water.
3. Allow this mixture to infuse in the icebox for 12 to 18 hrs.
4. Skim off all fat.
5. Boil vigorously for ½ hr.
6. Restore volume with distilled water several times during the boiling.
7. Filter through gauze to remove meat particles.
8. Filter through paper.
9. Restore volume with distilled water.
10. To each 1000 c.c. of this infusion add:

Witte's peptone or any brand of good peptone	20 gms.
Sodium chloride	5 gms.

11. Heat to dissolve peptone.
12. Titrate and adjust reaction to pH 7.6–7.8.
13. Boil ½ hr.
14. Allow to cool to about 30° C.
15. Filter through paper.
16. Distribute in tubes and flasks.
17. Sterilize in the autoclave at 15 pounds for 15 min.

Meat Infusion Agar

Formula: Agar	20 gms.
Meat infusion broth	1000 c.c.

1. Add the agar to the broth, boil and stir constantly until the agar is dissolved.
2. Add distilled water to restore volume.
3. Filter through absorbent cotton.
4. Put required amounts in tubes or flasks.
5. Sterilize in the autoclave at 15 pounds for 15 min.
6. Place tubes in slanting position when agar is cooling, if slants are desired.

Northrop's Yeast Extract Medium. This medium contains less than 0.01 mgm. protein nitrogen per cc. It is suitable for the growth of streptococci, pneumococci and many other bacteria.

Directions:

1. Suspend 12.5 gm. brewer's yeast in a cheese-cloth bag in 1000 c.c. of distilled water.
2. Boil for 2½ hours.
3. Remove the yeast.
4. Adjust the reaction to pH 7.6.
5. Distribute the containers.
6. Sterilize in the Arnold sterilizer or in the autoclave at 15 lbs. of steam pressure for 15 minutes.

"Hormone Medium" (Cole and Lloyd, Huntoon).—The filtration of media removes from them certain substances which considerably enhance their nutritive value for bacteria.

These substances, for want of a better name, have been spoken of as hormones. The hormone media, which are used pretty generally, and which we have found to possess unusual advantages over ordinary culture media, are made as follows, the description given being published by Huntoon in 1918:

The basis for "hormone media" is beef heart instead of the customary beef or veal. It is important that the hearts be fairly fresh. The heart muscle is cut up in the usual way and after the removal of fat and large vessels, put through the meat grinder. The chopped meat is weighed and 1 liter of water added for every 500 grams of meat. One per cent peptone and 0.5 per cent salt are added directly, and 1 egg (whole) added for each liter of medium. If the bouillon is to be used for broth, 1 per cent gelatin is added immediately. If the bouillon is to be used as a basis for agar, it is not necessary to add the gelatin. The 3 per cent agar, finely cut up, is added to the other ingredients.

When all the ingredients have been placed in the same pot, the mixture is heated over the free flame until it reaches a temperature of about 70° C. and meat begins to turn brown. Twenty-five c.c. of normal sodium hydroxide are then added per liter. The pot is placed in the Arnold sterilizer and allowed to cook for one and one-half to two hours. At the end of this time, a firm clot has usually formed and the broth or agar can be decanted.

The medium is then titrated accurately and brought to the desired reaction. The medium usually gets slightly more acid on autoclaving, so that it is better to adjust to about two points more alkaline on the pH scale, than the final reaction desired. It is important, in making hormone media, never to filter in any way. Cotton, paper, and cheesecloth filters are equally undesirable. If a firm clot is obtained after the first heating, there is usually no difficulty in obtaining a clear medium. On the first autoclaving a second precipitate usually forms, from which the clear medium can easily be decanted. It is best to check up the reaction after the final sterilization. The hormone media can also be cleared with the Sharples centrifuge.

Sugar-free Broth.—Make 1 liter of infusion broth according to the directions given. The medium need not be filtered at the start of this procedure. Inoculate with a young culture of *B. coli communis*. Incubate for twenty-four to forty-eight hours. The bacteria will ferment and thus destroy any sugar (monosaccharide) which may be present in the broth, and thus render the medium sugar-free and acid. Arnold for one hour to kill the *B. coli*. Titrate and adjust. Arnold again for thirty minutes. Filter through paper until clear.

This sugar-free medium is used as a basis for fermentation reactions. The different sugars are added in 1 per cent concentrations and the medium is then sterilized for three successive days in the Arnold, since the higher temperatures of the autoclave tend to split the more complex sugars into the simpler ones.

Glycerin Broth.—To ordinary, slightly acid or neutral meat infusion broth, add 6 per cent of C. P. glycerin. Sterilize by fractional method.

Calcium Carbonate Broth.—This medium is designed for obtaining mass cultures of pneumococcus or streptococcus for purposes of immunization or agglutination.

To 100 c.c. of meat infusion broth in small flasks, add 1 per cent of powdered calcium carbonate, and 1 per cent of glucose. It is a wise precaution to sterilize the dried calcium carbonate in the hot-air chamber before using. Small pieces of marble may be used as suggested by Bolduan.

Buffer Broth for Streptococcus Agglutination.—One pound of *lean* chopped beef allowed to infuse in a liter of tap water over night in the refrigerator. The unfiltered meat infusion is then boiled for thirty minutes, filtered through paper, and the loss by evaporation made up by the addition of water. One per cent peptone (Fairchild) and 0.2 per cent sodium phosphate (Na_2HPO_4) are now added. The mixture is allowed to boil for twenty minutes and the reaction is adjusted to the desired pH. (About 0.2 of a pH is allowed for change in the reaction during sterilization. For pneumococcus work the optimum pH is 7.8; in the adjustment, therefore, before sterilization the reaction is set at pH 8.) The broth is sterilized in the Arnold sterilizer for twenty minutes on three successive days. For streptococcus work the final reaction should be pH 7.4.

Lactose-Agar (with Litmus or Andrade).—This is meat extract agar adjusted to pH 7.5 to 7.8, to which 1 per cent of lactose is added, and enough litmus to give it a bluish purple color when cooled. Instead of litmus, 1 per cent of the Andrade indicator can be used. If the latter indicator is used, the reaction of the medium must be brought down to pH 7.2. The medium containing 1 per cent of the indicator, if the reaction is correct, will be dark red when hot and colorless when cold. After the addition of the sugar and the indicator, it is best to sterilize by the intermittent method on three successive days.

Media Made by Digestion Methods (*Martin's Broth, Douglas' and Hartley's Broth*).—A great many media have been devised, the purpose of which was to furnish bacteria with the products of digestion, peptone, albumoses, amino-acids, etc. Many variations of these media have been described under the headings of "trypsin" or "pepsin" agar or broth, or with the name of the individual describing them attached, it will be sufficient to describe the principles with one or two examples.

Trypagar.—To 1 pound of chopped meat, free from fat, add 1 liter tap water and make faintly alkaline to litmus with 20 per cent sodium hydroxide solution. Heat in double boiler at 75° to 80° for five minutes. Cool to 37° and add 0.5 gram trypsin. Incubate for five to six hours. Test for peptone as follows: Take 5 c.c. of the liquid, add 5 c.c. N/1 sodium hydroxide and 1 c.c. dilute copper sulphate. A pink color indicates that trypsinization is complete, a bluish purple shade that it is incomplete. If test is satisfactory, slightly acidify the broth with glacial acetic acid and bring slowly to boiling point, boil gently for ten minutes and filter through paper. Add 2 per cent agar and 0.5 per cent salt, autoclave to dissolve agar, and proceed from this point as usual, clearing by filtration and adjusting the reaction to pH 7.5, or any desired reaction.

Douglas' Medium (Hartley Broth)

1. Mix 150 grams of minced lean beef or horse muscle with 250 c.c. distilled water.
2. Heat to 80° C.
3. Add 250 c.c. of 0.8 per cent solution of anhydrous sodium carbonate.
4. Cool to 45° C.
5. Add 5 c.c. Cole and Onslow's pancreatic extract and 5 c.c. chloroform.
6. Incubate mixture at 37.5° C. for 6 hrs. Stir frequently.
7. Add 40 c.c. N/1 HCl.
8. Boil the mixture for 1 hr.
9. Cool and filter through paper.
10. Adjust reaction to pH 7.6–7.9. Boil for 1 hr. Filter through paper after cooling to about 45° C.
11. Autoclave at 15 pounds for 15 min. or sterilize by the discontinuous method.

Douglas' Agar

1. To make Douglas' agar, add 20 grams of agar shreds to 1000 c.c. of Douglas' broth, pH 7.6–7.8.
2. Heat to boiling until all the agar is dissolved.
3. Filter through cotton.
4. Place required amounts in tubes or flasks.
5. Sterilize in autoclave at 15 pounds for 15 minutes.

Pancreatic Extract, Cole and Onslow.—The pancreatic extract used for the preparation of Douglas' broth is made as follows:

1. To 1000 grams of minced fresh pancreas from pigs (pancreas must be free from fat) add 3000 c.c. distilled water and 1000 c.c. of 95 per cent alcohol.
2. Place in large bottle, shake repeatedly and allow to stand 3 days at room temperature.
3. Strain through gauze and filter through paper.
4. The filtrate, which comes through very slowly, is measured and treated with 1 c.c. concentrated HCl for each liter. This causes a cloudy precipitate which settles in a few days and can be filtered off and discarded.

The liquid keeps for an indefinite period if placed in a stoppered bottle. No additional antiseptic needed.

Blood Clot Pepsin Digest.—A simple and very cheap way of obtaining an excellent base for broth and agar is one described to us by Ten Broeck as used in China. It has the advantage of cheapness. Obtain blood clot at slaughterhouse, mixing 2000 c.c. of the total clotted shed blood with six fresh pig stomachs. Grind them together and to three parts of this add two parts of water. Add concentrated hydrochloric acid to about 4 per cent, bringing the pH to between 2 and 3. Incubate from thirty-six to thirty-eight hours. Strain through gauze. To each part of this digest add 3 to 4 parts of water, heat to 85° to 100° C.; add concentrated sodium hydroxide up to pH 6. Filter, add 0.5 per cent dextrose and adjust reaction. Agar can be added to this to the desired percentage.

Casein Digest Agar (for Lactobacillus acidophilus)

Formula: Casein .... 15 gms.
Peptone (Difco) .... 15 gms.
Beef extract .... 3 gms.
Trypsin .... 10 c.c.
(Cole and Onslow's pancreatic extract)
Water .... 1000 c.c.

1. Make this mixture slightly alkaline and add 25 c.c. chloroform to prevent bacterial growth. Incubate at 37° C. for 48 hrs.
2. Boil several minutes to remove chloroform.
3. Add 15 grams of agar.
4. Adjust reaction to pH 7.0.
5. Add 15 grams lactose.
6. Add 50 c.c. of 2 per cent sodium oleate.
7. Filter through cotton.
8. Place in tubes or flasks and sterilize in autoclave at 15 pounds for 15 minutes.

Tomato Juice Agar (for Lactobacillus acidophilus)

Formula: Tomato juice (from canned tomatoes) .... 400 c.c.
Peptonized milk (Difco) .... 10 gms.
Peptone .... 5 gms.
Agar .... 11 gms.
Water (distilled) .... 600 c.c.

Procedure:

1. The tomato juice is obtained from commercial canned tomatoes. Pour the contents of the can into a large funnel with a coarse filter paper. Use the clear yellow juice filtrate.
2. Heat the mixture of tomato juice, peptonize milk and peptone to dissolve the ingredients.
3. Adjust the reaction of this mixture to pH 6.8 before adding the agar to it. Filter through paper. The final pH after sterilization will be about 6.6.
4. Add the agar to the water and boil or autoclave to dissolve the agar.
5. Combine these two mixtures while hot.
6. Filter through cotton.
7. Dispense in tubes or flasks and sterilize in the autoclave at 15 pounds pressure for 8 minutes. Remove the medium from the autoclave as soon as possible.

Potato Media.—Large potatoes are selected, washed in hot water, and scrubbed with a brush. They are peeled, considerably more than the cuticle being removed. The peeled potatoes are washed in running water, following which cylindrical pieces are removed with a large apple corer. The cylinders are cut into wedges.

Since the reaction of the potato is normally acid, this should be corrected by washing the pieces in running water over night, or, better, by immersing them in a 1 per cent solution of sodium carbonate for half an hour.

The pieces are then inserted into the large variety of test tubes known as "potato tubes." In the bottom of the tubes a small amount of water (about 1 c.c.) or a small quantity of moist absorbent cotton should be placed in order to retard drying out of the potato. The tubes are sterilized by fractional sterilization, twenty minutes to half an hour in the Arnold sterilizer on three successive days.

Potato Broth.—Petroff has used extract of potatoes in fluid media for the growth of tubercle bacilli. There are many different ways of preparing the potato extract. The best way is to finely grind thoroughly, or grate the potatoes and soak them in tap water for from twelve to twenty-four hours, using about 500 grams to a liter of water. This mixture can be filtered, or, better, heated before filtration. It may be used as an ingredient with or without glycerin in ordinary broth or agar, or can be used with peptone and salt added, as an independent culture-medium.

Milk Media.—Fresh milk is procured and is heated in a flask for fifteen minutes in an Arnold sterilizer. It is then set away in the ice chest for about twelve hours in order to allow the cream to rise. Milk and cream are then separated by siphoning the milk into another flask. It is rarely necessary to adjust the reaction of milk prepared in this way, since, if acid at all, it is usually but slightly so. If, however, it should prove acid, it should be discarded. The milk may then be tubed either with or without the addition of an indicator. Bromcresol purple is the most satisfactory indicator in milk. The Andrade indicator can be used also, but usually discolors the milk somewhat. However, if fractional sterilization is carefully carried out, the milk becomes yellowish, but acid production shows up clearly by a distinct reddening of the medium. If the milk is to be used for the differentiation of the anaerobic bacilli isolated from war wounds, it is best not to add any indicator, since the type of coagulum formed is a differential characteristic, and coagulation does not take place readily when Andrade's indicator is present.

Serum Media.—*Löffler's Medium.*—Beef blood is collected at the slaughterhouse in high cylindrical jars holding two quarts or more. It is desirable that attempts should be made to avoid contamination as much as is feasible by previously sterilizing the jars, keeping them covered, and exercising care in the collection of the blood.

The blood is allowed to coagulate in the jars, and should not be moved from the slaughterhouse until coagulated. All unnecessary shaking of jars should be avoided. As soon as the coagulum is fully formed, adhesions between the clot and the sides of the jar should be carefully separated with a sterile glass rod or wire. The jars are then set away in the ice chest for twenty-four to thirty-six hours. At the end of this time clear serum will be found over the top of the clot, and between the clot and the jar. This should be pipetted off, preferably with a large pipet of 50 to 100 c.c. capacity, or siphoned off with sterile glass tubing, and transferred to sterile flasks.

Formula: Serum (horse, beef or pig) .... 3 parts
Beef extract broth with glucose................................ 1 part

1. Preparation of beef extract broth with glucose

Beef extract .... 3 gms.
Glucose .... 10 gms.
Peptone (Difco or Witte).. 10 gms.
NaCl .... 5 gms.
Distilled water .... 1000 c.c.

2. Mix the ingredients and dissolve by warming over a flame. Do not adjust the reaction.
3. Filter through paper.
4. When the broth is cool add it to the clear serum in the proportions given above.
5. Tube, 3 to 5 c.c. per tube, and place tubes in a slanting position in a pan or rack. Take care to prevent the occurrence of bubbles and frothing. Cover tubes with newspaper.
6. Sterilize in autoclave at 15 pounds for 15 minutes. Bring steam pressure up gradually and let autoclave cool slowly after steam is turned off, or allow steam to blow off rapidly, according to action of autoclave.
7. Alternative methods of sterilization at lower temperatures: The tubes are placed in a slanting position in the apparatus known as an inspissator. This is a double-walled copper box covered by a glass lid, cased in asbestos, and surrounded by a water jacket. It is heated below by a Bunsen flame. Together with the tubes a small open vessel containing water should be placed in the inspissator to insure sufficient moisture. The temperature of the inspissator is now raised to 70° to 75° C., care being taken that the rise of temperature

takes place slowly. The temperature is maintained at this point for two hours, and the process is repeated, for the same length of time, at the same temperature, on six successive days, preferably without removing the tubes from the inspissator at any time. It is also possible to sterilize in the inspissator for one day, following this on the second and third days by exposure for 30 minutes to 100° C. in the Arnold steam sterilizer. In doing this, the Arnold should be very gradually heated, at first without outer jacket, this being lowered only after thorough heating has taken place.

Serum-water Media for Fermentation Tests.—For the determination of the fermentative powers of various micro-organisms for purposes of differentiation, Hiss has devised the following media in which the cleavage of any given carbohydrate is indicated, not only by the production of an acid reaction, but by the coagulation of the serum proteins.

Obtain clear beef serum by pipetting from clotted blood in the same way as this is obtained for the preparation of Löffler's blood-serum medium. Add to this two or three times its bulk of distilled water, making a mixture of serum and water in proportions of 1:2 or 1:3. Heat the mixture for fifteen minutes in an Arnold sterilizer at 100° C. to destroy any diastatic ferments present in the serum. Add 1 c.c. of a 1.6 per cent alcoholic solution of bromcresol purple. With many batches of serum, it will be found that the addition of two or three times its bulk of distilled water is not a sufficient dilution to prevent coagulation. It will often be found necessary to add four or five volumes of distilled water to one volume of serum. One per cent of the Andrade indicator may be substituted for the bromcresol purple. Add to the various fractions of the medium thus made 1 per cent respectively of the sugars which are to be used for the tests.

Inulin Serum Water

Formula: Distilled water .... 400 c.c.
Serum (horse, beef) .... 100 c.c.
Peptone (Difco or Witte) .... 2.5 gms.
Inulin .... 5 gms.

1. Dissolve the peptone in 25 c.c. distilled water, heating slightly.
2. Adjust reaction to pH 7.4 to 7.8.
3. Dissolve inulin in 25 c.c. distilled water, heating slightly.
4. Add 350 c.c. distilled water to 100 c.c. of serum.
5. Mix peptone and inulin solutions with the diluted serum.
6. Add sufficient saturated alcoholic solution of bromcresol purple to give the desired color.
7. Tube, placing about 3 c.c. in each serological tube.
8. Sterilize in Arnold sterilizer for 30 minutes on three successive days.

Ascitic Fluid Agar

1. Melt 100 c.c. of sterile Douglas' agar, pH 7.4 to 7.8, in a flask.
2. Cool to about 48–50° C.
3. With sterile pipet add 20 c.c. of sterile, bile free, ascitic fluid.
4. Pour into tubes or plates and allow to harden.

Ascitic Fluid Agar with Carbohydrates for Gonococcus-meningococcus Group

1. Melt 100 c.c. of sterile Douglas' agar, pH 7.4 to 7.8, in a flask.
2. Cool to about 48° to 50° C.
3. With sterile pipet add 20 c.c. of sterile, bile free, ascitic fluid.
4. With sterile pipet add 5 c.c. of a sterile 20 per cent aqueous solution of the carbohydrate.
5. With sterile pipet add 1 c.c. of sterile solution of Andrade's indicator.
6. Pour into test tubes and allow to harden in slanting position.
7. Incubate for twenty-four hours at 37° C. to test sterility.
8. The carbohydrates commonly used in this medium are glucose, maltose, sucrose and lactose. A 20 per cent solution of each sugar is made in distilled water and sterilized in the autoclave at 15 pounds for 15 minutes. In order to rule out hydrolysis of the disaccharides by autoclaving, the solutions may be sterilized by filtration through a Berkefeld filter.

Avery's Medium for Pneumococcus

90 c.c. meat infusion or Douglas' broth, pH 7.4 to 7.8.
  5 c.c. sterile 20 per cent solution of glucose.
  5 c.c. sterile rabbit's blood.

1. With sterile pipet add 5 c.c. of sterile 20 per cent solution of glucose.
2. With sterile pipet add 5 c.c. rabbit's blood.
3. Mix in flask.
4. With sterile pipet transfer 4 c.c. to each of a series of small sterile test tubes.

Blood Agar

1. Melt 100 c.c. of meat infusion or Douglas' agar (pH 7.4 to 7.8) in a flask.
2. Allow to cool to 45° to 50° C.
3. Add 5 c.c. of sterile defibrinated or citrated blood. Rabbit's blood is the most serviceable blood for use in this medium. Human blood may inhibit the growth of *B. influenzae*.
4. Mix and pour into tubes for slants, or into Petri dishes for plates as desired.
5. Incubate 24 hours at 37° C. to test for sterility.

Bordet-Gengou Medium for B. pertussis.—Modified by Lawson and Mueller.

Used in cough-plate method of isolating *B. pertussis*.

1. Pass 500 grams of peeled potato through meat grinder.
2. Add this to 1000 c.c. distilled water.
3. Add 40 c.c. glycerin.
4. Mix well in flask and place in Arnold sterilizer for 1 hour.
5. Press the extract through cheesecloth in a small press.
6. To each 500 c.c. of the fluid from the press add 1500 c.c. of 0.6 per cent NaCl solution and 50 grams agar.
7. Sterilize in Arnold sterilizer for 1 hour on three successive days.
8. Following the third heating in the Arnold sterilizer, cool the medium to 42° C. and add from 5 to 10 per cent fresh citrated horse blood. Rabbit blood defibrinated may be used in place of horse blood. Best results obtained with use of blood not more than seventy-two hours old.
9. Before the addition of the blood the pH ranges from 5.8 to 6.4. After the addition of the blood the reaction becomes pH 6.6 to 7.3. No other adjustment of the reaction is required.

Bradford's Medium for Gonococcus

100 c.c. 2 per cent Douglas' agar (pH 7.6–7.8) melted and cooled to 45° C.

To this add:

  25 c.c. sterile ascitic or hydrocele fluid
  5 c.c. sterile 20 per cent solution of glucose
  10 c.c. sterile defibrinated rabbit's blood

Mix and pour 20 c.c. in each of several sterile 100 c.c. centrifuge tubes, without lips, and 5 c.c. into each of several ordinary test tubes.

Slant the tubes and allow to harden. After agar has hardened, replace cotton plugs with well-fitting sterile rubber stoppers and incubate 24 hours to prove sterility of medium.

The rubber stoppers are sterilized by boiling 5 minutes. Their function is to prevent evaporation and to aid in maintaining reduced oxygen tension after inoculation of the medium. This lowered oxygen tension is obtained by heating the upper third of the tube in a flame and quickly inserting a rubber stopper. Take care not to heat the medium in this process.

Rabbit's Blood for Ducrey Bacillus Cultivation.—Rabbits are bled from the heart with a sterile syringe and about 1½ to 2 c.c. placed into small test tubes. The blood is allowed to clot and inactivated at 56° C. for one-half hour. This makes an excellent medium for the cultivation of the Ducrey bacillus, for streptococci and some other organisms. It is also excellent for the preservation of streptococci and pneumococci in a virulent condition.

Sodium Oleate Agar for Influenza Bacilli.—Avery found that sodium oleate will enhance the development of influenza bacilli, and at the same time inhibit many of the gram-positive organisms commonly found in sputum.

A neutral solution of Kalbaum's sodium oleate in water is prepared and sterilized in the autoclave. Human or rabbit blood is defibrinated, centrifuged, the serum removed, and the volume made up to the original with broth. One c.c. of the red blood-cell suspension and 5 c.c. of the 2 per cent sodium oleate solution are added to 94 c.c. of agar at 80° to 90° C. The agar is preferably a 2 per cent hormone agar with a reaction of pH 7.4.

Hemo-peptone Water for B. influenzae

To 1 liter of water add 20 grams peptone and 5 grams NaCl. Dissolve ingredients by heating. Titrate and adjust the reaction to pH 7.6. Add 10 c.c. washed red corpuscles or 20 c.c. of defibrinated blood (it is not necessary to use sterile blood). Heat to 95° C. or just bring to a boil. Filter through paper. Sterilize by filtration through a Berkefeld or Mandler filter. Tube in sterile test tubes. Incubate at least 48 hours to prove sterility before use.

Nitrate Hemo-peptone Water for B. influenzae:

This is made in the same manner as hemo-peptone water with the addition of 0.02 gm. KNO_3 per liter. The nitrate is added before the medium is sterilized. Sterilize by filtration through Berkefeld or Mandler filter. This is used to assist in the differentiation of influenza bacilli, from pertussis bacilli. The former reduce nitrates to nitrites, the latter do not.

Chocolate Media.—For the cultivation of organisms like the influenza bacillus, meningococcus, and a number of other bacteria, an excellent medium can be made up in the following way: Agar or broth is made up as usual, and to them added defibrinated rabbit, beef, horse or human blood in proportions of from 5 per cent to 10 per cent by volume. This mixture is then heated gradually up to about 75° C., until the blood begins to coagulate and assume a dark brown chocolate-like color. The broth or agar can first be adjusted to the desired reaction, but it is likely that any excess alkali or acidity is corrected by the proteins which are added.

As far as we can find out, the first mention of the so-called "chocolate" media is by Fleming in 1919. Fleming found that influenza bacilli grew very luxuriantly on media containing blood which had been digested with trypsin. In seeking for a simpler medium, he found that boiling 10 per cent mixtures of blood and agar and slanting so that the coagulum settled gave him a very luxurious growth of influenza. He obtained similar results when he boiled 10 to 20 per cent blood in slightly acidified water and added the fluid so obtained after the settling of the coagulum to agar or broth.

In the case of broth the medium can be filtered through paper while hot, and sterilized subsequently. Such filtrate consists of a clear brownish fluid on which influenza bacilli and other organisms grow easily.

Vedder Starch Agar.—Beef infusion agar is prepared without salt and peptone. This is adjusted to pH 6.8, 10 grams of cornstarch is added to each liter, and the mixture is heated in the autoclave for twenty minutes at fifteen pounds. It is tubed and sterilized. This medium has been recommended by Vedder for the cultivation of gonococcus.

Welch's Modification of Guarnieri's Medium.—This medium is made on a meat infusion basis according to the directions given for the preparation of meat infusion agar. It contains 5 grams of agar, 80 grams of gelatin, 5 grams of sodium chloride, and 10 grams of peptone to one liter. It should be adjusted to a neutral reaction. It is used for stab-cultures and is designed chiefly for pneumococcus cultivation and storage.

Media Useful in Cultivating Tubercle Bacilli.—Dorsett's Egg Medium.—1. Carefully break eggs and drop the contents into a wide-mouthed flask. Break up the yolk with a sterile platinum wire, and shake up the flask until the whites and yolks are thoroughly mixed.

2. Add 25 c.c. of distilled water to every four eggs; strain through sterile cloth.

3. Pour 10 c.c. each into sterile test tubes and slant in an inspissator and expose to 73° C. for four to five hours on two days.

4. On the third day, raise the temperature to 76° C.

5. The sterilization may be finished by a single exposure to 100° C. in the Arnold sterilizer for fifteen minutes. Before inoculation, add two or three drops of sterile water to each tube.

Lubenau's Glycerin-egg.—To 1 liter of veal broth containing 2 per cent peptone, 5 per cent of glycerin is added. Neutralize this to litmus, and to every 200 c.c. add ten fresh eggs. The mixture is thoroughly stirred, and when homogeneous, is tubed, slanted and inspissated, as in the case of other egg media.

Petroff's Medium.—1. Meat Juice. Five hundred grams of beef or veal are infused in 500 c.c. of a 15 per cent solution of glycerin in water, in a cool place. After twenty-four hours the meat is squeezed in a sterile press and the infusion collected in a sterile beaker.

2. Eggs. The shells of the eggs are sterilized by ten-minute immersion in 70 per cent alcohol. They are broken into a sterile beaker, well mixed and filtered through sterile gauze. One part of meat juice is added to two parts of egg by volume.

3. Gentian Violet. One per cent alcoholic solution of gentian violet is added to make a final proportion of 1:10,000.

The three ingredients are well mixed. The medium is tubed and inspissated as usual.

Petroff recommends for sputum the following technic: Equal parts of sputum and 3 per cent sodium hydroxide are shaken and incubated at 38° C. for fifteen to thirty minutes, the time depending on the consistency of the sputum. The mixture is neutralized with hydrochloric acid and centrifugalized. The sediment is inoculated into the medium described above. Pure cultures are obtained in a large proportion of cases.

Glycerin Potato.—In preparing glycerin potato the potato wedges are treated as above and are then soaked in a 10 to 25 per cent aqueous glycerin solution for one to three hours. A small quantity of a 10 per cent glycerin solution should be left in the tubes. In sterilizing these tubes, thirty minutes a day in the Arnold after the sterilizer is hot will sterilize without altering the glycerin.

Corper's Medium for Isolation of B. tuberculosis

1. From fresh potatoes, cut cylinders 3 inches long by ⅝ inch in diameter. Cut each cylinder in half longitudinally.
2. Soak the cylinders of potato in freshly prepared mixture of 0.0015 per cent crystal violet in 1 per cent sodium carbonate solution (prepared from pure anhydrous sodium carbonate). A faint blue tint acquired by the potato cylinder in an hour or less is sufficient.
3. Into each of the required number of sterile test tubes, 6 in. by ¾ in., place 1.5 c.c. of 6 per cent aqueous glycerin solution, pH 7.0 to 7.5.
4. Put a half-cylinder of the potato soaked with crystal violet into each tube of glycerin solution.
5. Plug tubes with cotton and sterilize in the autoclave at 15 pounds pressure for 15–30 minutes.

Synthetic Media.—A considerable number of synthetic media have been made for the growth of the tubercle bacillus. The purpose of these media is to omit complex protein substances as much as possible.

Long's Synthetic Medium

Asparagin	5	gms.
Ammonium citrate	5	gms.
Potassium acid phosphate	3	gms.
Sodium carbonate (anhydrous)	3	gms.
Sodium chloride	2	gms.
Magnesium sulphate	1	gm.
Ferric ammonium citrate	0.05	gm.
Glycerol	50	c.c.
Water	1000	c.c.

Place the desired quantities of this solution in tubes or flasks and sterilize in the autoclave at 15 pounds for 15 minutes.

Sauton's Medium

Sauton's medium adjusted to pH 7.2–7.4 just prior to inoculation.

Dipotassium phosphate	0.5 gm.
Magnesium sulphate	0.5 gm.
Citric acid	2.0 gm.
Asparagin	4.0 gm.
Iron citrate (ammoniacal)	0.05 gm.
Glycerol	35 c.c.
Distilled water to	1000 c.c.

Adjust the medium to pH 7.4 with sodium hydroxide. Autoclave at 15 pounds pressure for fifteen minutes.

Petroff's Synthetic Medium (Baldwin, Petroff and Gardner)

0.35 gm.	K_2HPO_4
4.93 gms.	$Mg\ HPO_4 2H_2O$
10 c.c.	normal H_2SO_4
20 c.c.	normal (1/3 molar) H_3PO_4
10 c.c.	3 times normal (molar) citric acid
5.29 gms.	asparagin
20 c.c.	glycerin
1000 c.c.	water

Add 10 c.c. normal NaOH.

Infusion-free Broth (for Diphtheria Toxin)

Wadsworth, Wheeler and Kirkbride have shown that it is not necessary to use a meat infusion base for the production of diphtheria toxin. One of us (Bayne-Jones) has been able to obtain routinely diphtheria toxin having more than 300 M.L.D. per c.c. and an L_F value of 15 or above by using this medium, prepared as follows:

1. Formula: Part I.

Sodium chloride	5	gms.
Dipotassium phosphate (K_2HPO_4)	1	gm.
Monopotassium phosphate (KH_2PO_4)	1	gm.
Magnesium sulphate	0.2	gm.
Calcium chloride	0.1	gm.
Proteose peptone (Difco)	20	gms.
Water, distilled, to make	1000	c.c.

Part II.

Sodium lactate	5	gms.
Dextrose	2	gms.

2. *Procedure.* Part I. Use c. p. chemicals and weigh accurately. Dissolve the NaCl in about one-half of the total volume of water. Then dissolve the proteose peptone in this NaCl solution. Next add the other salts, each dissolved separately in small amounts of water. Add distilled water to bring up the volume to the required total. Adjust the reaction to pH 7.8 with N/1 sodium hydroxide solution. Boil over a free flame for 15 minutes or heat in a steam sterilizer at 100° C. for 30 minutes, covered to prevent evaporation. Filter through paper until clear. Add distilled water to make up any loss of volume. Dispense in Erlenmeyer flasks in such amounts as will give a surface area to volume ratio of 0.58. Sterilize in the autoclave at 15 pounds pressure for 15 minutes.

Procedure. Part II. The sodium lactate and dextrose are added with sterile precautions in solution at the time when the medium is to be inoculated. For each 100 c.c. of medium, add 2 c.c. of a filter-sterilized solution composed of 25 per cent sodium lactate and 10 per cent dextrose.

3. *Preparation of sodium lactate-dextrose solution.* For each 100 c.c. of this solution required, neutralize 24 c.c. of U. S. P. (85 per cent) lactic acid with 40 per cent solution of sodium hydroxide, using phenol red as an indicator in the titration. Adjustment of this solution to pH 7.0 usually requires the addition of 23 to 5 c.c. of the 40 per cent sodium hydroxide solution to 24 c.c. of the

lactic acid. Add to this sodium lactate solution 10 grams of dextrose dissolved in a small amount of distilled water. Make up the total volume to 100 c.c. by the addition of distilled water. Sterilize by filtration through a Berkefeld N or Mandler filter. Test the filtrate for sterility before adding it to the medium.

Tellurite Medium for B. Diphtheriae.—This is a selective medium recommended by Horgan and Marshall.

To a tube containing 15 c.c. of nutrient agar, pH 7.6, melted and brought to 50° C. add 1.5 c.c. blood (defibrinated rabbit's blood) and 1.5 c.c. of 2 per cent solution of potassium tellurite. Mix and pour the mixture into a Petri dish. While the agar is hardening, place the cover of the dish at an angle, to avoid the condensation of water on the surface of the medium.

Mueller's Medium for Diphtheria Toxin.—Diphtheria toxin containing 60 Lf units per c.c. has been produced on this medium in eight days.

Measure an amount of a hydrochloric acid hydrolysate of casein equivalent to 300 g. of casein into a 6-liter Florence flask. Add a solution containing 20 g. each anhydrous Na_2HPO_4 and KH_2PO_4 in 300 or 400 c.c. of hot H_2O. Dilute to about 3.5 liters. Add strong NaOH (150 g. in 400 c.c.) with mixing until the maximum amount of precipitate has formed. The solution should then be slightly alkaline to litmus paper, about pH 8.0. Let the precipitate settle for a minute or two and test the clear supernatant with more NaOH to make sure no further precipitate forms. Filter through a pleated paper into another 6-liter Florence flask. The precipitate removes 90–95% of the Fe which was present.

Add concentrated HCl, 10 c.c., then 100 c.c. 1% $CaCl_2$. If a precipitate forms or much opalescence appears, add more HCl until clear, then add NaOH to pH 7.4–7.6. This procedure is followed in order to insure distribution of the Ca throughout the solution before precipitation takes place; otherwise not all of the iron will be exposed equally to adsorption and irregular results might occur. Heat just to boiling and filter. Should the precipitate not flocculate well, add more $CaCl_2$ solution until it does so.

Cool filtrate and test for Fe as follows: To 20 c.c. (of filtrate) in a pointed centrifuge tube, add 0.5 c.c. of 1% $CaCl_2$, and a drop or two of strong (0.2%) phenol red. Mix and adjust reaction if necessary to pH 7.4–7.6. Heat the tube in a beaker of boiling water until the precipitate flocculates well (3–4 minutes or less) and centrifuge. Discard supernatant. Add 5 c.c. water to precipitate and 0.1 c.c. of concentrated HNO_3, and either boil for a few seconds or place in a beaker of boiling water for 3 or 4 minutes. Cool, and add 1.0 c.c. of a 5% NH_4SCN or KSCN solution, and 1.0 c.c. amyl or isoamyl alcohol. Shake thoroughly and compare the color in the alcohol layer with that obtained from (1) the reagents alone, (2) 5.0γ $FeSO_4$, 7 H_2O, and (3) 10.0γ $FeSO_4$ similarly treated by heating in 5.0 c.c. H_2O with HNO_3, followed by NH_4SCN. If the batch of medium shows, at this stage, not more than 10γ $FeSO_4$ 7 H_2O per 20 c.c. (= about 100 c.c. completed medium) it is satisfactory. Otherwise a second precipitation with $CaCl_2$ and boiling must be carried out as above.

Pour the casein solution into a 20-liter bottle and dilute to about 18 liters. Add 40 c.c. of a concentrated solution containing the necessary amounts of $MgSO_4$, accessories and metals (except Fe), adjust the pH to 7.4–7.6 and mix. The composition of this solution is as follows:

(For 100 c.c. solution, enough for 50 liters of medium)

$MgSO_4.7H_2O$	22.5	gm.
Beta-alanine	0.115	gm.
Nicotinic acid *	0.115	gm.
Pimelic acid	0.0075	gm.
$CuSO_4.5H_2O$ (1%)	25.0	c.c.
$ZnSO_4.7H_2O$ (1%)	15.0	c.c.
$MnCl_2.4H_2O$ (1%)	2.0	c.c.
HCl	1.0	c.c.

* Dissolve separately in about 1 c.c. H_2O and a few drops of concentrated HCl.

This solution should be stable at room temperature for long periods, and can be prepared in any convenient quantity according to the same proportions.

Dissolve 8 gm. of cystine (reasonably free from Fe) in about 50 c.c. of water and approximately 10–11 c.c. concentrated HCl, and add this solution to the 18 liters in the bottle. Mix, dilute to final volume (20 liters) and mix very thoroughly.

Again test for Fe in this way: Nearly fill a 100 c.c. centrifuge tube with the medium, add 4–5 drops phenol red and 1.0 c.c. 1% $caCl_2$. Adjust reaction if necessary to pH 7.4–7.6 and heat in a beaker of boiling water. If a flocculent precipitate has not separated in 5 minutes, add a little NaOH, enough to raise the pH, perhaps, to 7.8. If a precipitate still does not form, add about 0.5 c.c. more $CaCl_2$, drop by drop. When the precipitate has separated, centrifuge it down and test for Fe as already described, using for comparison, this time, 10, 20 and 30 γ $FeSO_4.7H_2O$.

Assuming the optimal concentration for toxin production to be about 0.1 MgFe per liter (= 0.5 $mgFeSO_4.7H_2O$), add enough iron solution to give this value. Example:

Final test shows approximately 15. γ $FeSo_4.7H_2O$ per 100 c.c., = 0.150 mg per liter (0.03 mg Fe per liter).

$$\begin{array}{r} 0.50 \\ 0.15 \\ \hline 0.35 \end{array} \times 20 = 7.0 \text{ mg } FeSO_4/20 \text{ liters}$$
$$= 7.0 \text{ c.c. of a } 0.1\% \text{ solution}$$

A stock solution of ferrous sulfate containing 0.1 gm. of the salt in 99 c.c. water and 1.0 c.c. concentrated HCl should be kept on hand in a carefully stoppered bottle.

Finally, mix very thoroughly by stoppering the bottle and rolling on the table for three minutes. If possible, allow to stand for an hour or two, and mix again before distributing into flasks. The layer of medium in the flask should be 0.8 to 1.0 cm. deep for best results.

Because of the danger of introducing iron, sterilization by passing through a filter is best avoided, although a chromium plated Seitz can be used if necessary. If this is done, a solution of maltose containing $CaCl_2$ (see below) may be added to the *cold* medium before filtration.

Autoclaving of the medium is preferable to filtration but must be done carefully, since prolonged heating is injurious. Small flasks will safely withstand 10 minutes at 10 lbs. pressure (115° C.) and larger containers 15 minutes. The autoclave should be brought up to the specified pressure as rapidly as possible, and at the end of the period of sterilization, the steam vent should be opened slightly and the pressure relieved as rapidly as is consistent with preventing the cotton plugs from blowing out of the flasks.

The flasks should be at once removed from the autoclave and allowed to cool to room temperature. A 50% solution of maltose ("Merck's Purified" is a satisfactory grade) containing 0.5 gm. Baker's "Calcium Chloride, C. P. Cryst" ($CaCl_2.2H_2O$) per 100 c.c. and sterilized either by autoclaving at 10 lbs. for 10 or 15 minutes, or by filtering through a chromium plated Seitz filter is then added with a sterile pipette. A final concentration of 1.75% maltose is used. The maltose —$CaCl_2$ must not be added until the medium is *cold*, otherwise a precipitate of calcium phosphate forms.

It is well to check the Fe content of the maltose. Dilute a suitable amount (2.0 gm.) with water, 20 c.c., add Na_2HPO_4, 1.1 gm. and 0.5 c.c. of 1% $CaCl_2$ and heat in a beaker of water until the precipitate separates. Centrifuge at once, while still hot (some tendency for precipitate to redissolve on cooling) and proceed as already described. The grade of maltose specified above usually shows only a trace of Fe. If more is found, allowance must, of course, be made for it when adjusting the total Fe concentration of the medium. Maltose containing too great quantities of iron can be purified by forming a precipitate of calcium phosphate in a 50% solution of the sugar (addition of an excess of Na_2HPO_4 and a suitable amount of $CaCl_2$ and heating in a boiling water bath), and centrifuging while hot. In this case, however, the maltose and calcium chloride, which are to be added to the completed medium, must be sterilized and added separately.

Inoculation with a young, actively growing culture of *B. diphtheriae* (8–10 hrs. at 34°) gives best results, and the medium is best adapted to the Toronto strain of the Park 8 culture of *B. diphtheriae*. Other strains are likely to prove unsatisfactory.

Casein hydrolysate is prepared as follows: 500 gm. of commercial casein, contained in a 5 liter Pyrex boiling flask is mixed with 2 liters of concentrated HCl and 500 c.c. water. The flask is heated on a boiling water bath or in an Arnold sterilizer for an hour or two with occasional shaking, until the casein has dissolved, and is then fitted with a reflux condenser and boiled for 15–18 hours. The boiling need not be continuous. A few bits of anthracite coal added to the flask effectively prevent bumping.

The solution is cooled, and the excess HCl and water distilled off in vacuo until there remains a very thick, black syrup. This is dissolved in water and diluted to 5000 c.c, (= 10% concentration of original casein). It is decolorized by stirring (cold) with enough norit charcoal to fill a 150 c.c. beaker and filtering, repeating the process a second time with the same or a slightly greater quantity of norit. After the second filtration the solution should be pale yellow. It may be used at once, or kept on hand as a stock solution either as it is, or after again concentrating in vacuum to any desired strength, since the solution is sufficiently acid to prevent the growth of bacteria or moulds.

Hemolyzed Blood Glucose Agar for Meningococci:

1. Hemolyze 3 c.c. of sterile defibrinated rabbit's blood by adding 10 c.c. sterile distilled water or a few drops of ether.
2. Melt 100 c.c. of meat infusion agar or Douglas' agar in a flask, pH 7.4–7.8.
3. Cool the agar to about 45–50° C.
4. Add the hemolyzed blood to the agar.
5. Add 5 c.c. of a sterile 20 per cent solution of glucose in water (to give 1 per cent glucose in the agar).

Mix and pour into sterile Petri dishes.

Blood Glucose Cystine Agar for Bact. Tularense.[2]—Fresh beef infusion agar, containing

1.0 per cent peptone, 1.5 per cent agar, and 0.5 per cent sodium chloride, adjusted to a pH of 7.3, is kept on hand in stock. When needed, there is added to the stock agar 0.1 per cent of cystine and 1.0 per cent glucose, and this is heated in an Arnold steam sterilizer sufficiently long to melt the agar and to sterilize the cystine and glucose, after which it is cooled to 50° C., when 5 to 8 per cent defibrinated or whole rabbit is added.

The addition of cystine does not change the pH of the medium, but if the cystine hydrochloride is substituted for cystine, a correction may be necessary on account of acidity. Cystine is not very soluble in the beef infusion peptone agar, and for that reason it should be pulverized before being added; even then, visible particles settle in the medium. Complete solution of the cystine may be obtained by frequent shaking of the flask while in the Arnold sterilizer, followed, if necessary, by allowing the melted cystine agar to remain over night in a 56° C. water bath.

Rabbit blood is quickly obtained by syringe from the heart of an etherized rabbit by plunging the needle through the skin. During etherization from a cone, clip the hair with scissors from a three-inch area over the heart and disinfect the clipped area for three minutes by saturation with 95 per cent alcohol followed by full strength tincture of iodine. The whole blood is expelled from the syringe directly into the flask of cystine agar at about 50° C.

Sterility is promoted by heating the flask of blood-glucose-cystine agar in a water bath for two hours at 60° C., avoiding a higher temperature which will cause sedimentation. The medium is then tubed from a sterile funnel, slanted and incubated to insure sterility.

Tubes in which the water of condensation has evaporated are preferable. The organism scarcely grows in a liquid medium. Freshly prepared tubes with moist surface and with abundant water of condensation should be allowed to stand with cotton stoppers, in a slanted position, in the incubator at 37° C. for about one week, until almost free of water of condensation. They are then stood upright and plugged with cork stoppers soaked in a very hot mixture of equal parts of vaseline and paraffine, to prevent further evaporation; then they are stored in the cold room.

Stock cultures are kept in the cold room and transferred every two months. Cultures are stoppered with paraffined cotton or cork during two months in the cold room at 5 to 10° C., preferably 5° or even frozen.

A large loopful of growth is carried over when making transfers. A control tube of plain agar should show no growth.

2 Directions from Edward Francis, U. S. Public Health Service.

The blood in the medium conduces to luxuriance of growth and to longevity of life to the culture; 8 per cent is preferable to 5 per cent. Human blood might be more accessible than rabbit blood and might serve equally well.

Special Media for Colon-Typhoid-Dysentery Group Differentiation.—Endo's Medium:

3 per cent agar.. 100 c.c.

This agar contains:

2 per cent Witte's peptone
0.3 per cent meat extract
0.5 per cent NaCl
3 per cent agar (pH 7.6–7.8)

Lactose .... 1 gm.
10 per cent sol. basic fuchsin in 95 per cent alcohol...................... 0.3 c.c.
2.5 per cent sodium sulfite... 5–10 c.c.

1. Melt the agar.
2. Dissolve the lactose in about 10 c.c. distilled water and add this to the melted agar.
3. Add 0.3 c.c. of solution of basic fuchsin.
4. Add 2.5 per cent sodium sulfite until the hot mixture becomes pink. This requires about 5–10 c.c. of the sodium sulfite solution.
5. Pour into Petri dishes and allow to harden uncovered in order to obtain a dry surface.
6. As an alternative method the required amount of fuchsin solution may be mixed with distilled water and decolorized with sodium sulfite before adding it to the agar. Sometimes decolorization fails in this mixture but takes place satisfactorily in the agar.

Eosin-methylene Blue Agar

Formula: Agar .... 15 gms.
Peptone (Difco) .... 10 gms.
Dipotassium phosphate (K_2HPO_4)........................... 2 gms.
Distilled water .... 1000 c.c.

1. Boil until all ingredients are dissolved and add distilled water to make up any loss due to evaporation.
2. Adjustment of reaction not required. Preferable pH 6.2–7.0.
3. Filter through cotton.
4. Place measured quantities (100 or 200 c.c.) in flasks and sterilize in the autoclave at 15 pounds for 15 minutes.

Just before using:

Melt the stock agar and add:

Lactose, sterile 20 per cent solution................................. 5 c.c.
Eosin, yellowish, 2 per cent aqueous solution......................... 2 c.c.
Methylene blue 0.5 per cent aqueous solution......................... 2 c.c.

Mix thoroughly and pour into Petri dishes.
Allow to harden and inoculate by streaking on the surface.

It is allowable to add all the ingredients to the stock agar at the time of preparation, place in tubes or flasks and sterilize. Decolorization of the medium occurs during sterilization. The color returns after cooling. (From *Standard Methods of Water Analysis*, A.P.H.A., 1925.)

Brilliant Green Agar for Typhoid Isolation.—Krumwiede devised a brilliant green agar which has given excellent results.

The basis is an extract agar like that used for Endo's medium:

Beef Extract .... 0.3 per cent
Sodium chloride .... 0.5 per cent
Peptone (Domestic peptones are satisfactory)...................... 1.0 per cent
Agar .... 1.5 per cent

Dissolve in autoclave, clear and filter. A clear agar is essential. The final reaction of the medium is to be neutral to Andrade's indicator, which in terms of phenolphthalein is 0.6–0.7 per cent acid (normal HCl) or pH 7.2. It is more convenient to have the reaction set slightly alkaline at the time of preparation and to acidify each bottle as used. The agar is bottled in 100 c.c. amounts and autoclaved. When needed, the agar in the bottles is melted and the volume of each corrected (if necessary) to an approximate 100 c.c. Add to each bottle:

> 1 per cent Andrade indicator
> Acid to bring to neutral point of the indicator [3]
> 1 per cent lactose [4]
> 0.1 per cent glucose [4]
> Brilliant green in 0.1 per cent aqueous solution

Two dilutions of dye are used in routine plating, corresponding to 1:500,000 and 1:330,000 in terms of solid dye (0.2 c.c. and 0.3 c.c. of 0.1 per cent solution per 100 c.c. of agar). The sample of dye which Krumwiede used was from Bayer, but he also tested and found equally satisfactory samples from Gruebler and Hoechst. One-tenth gram of dye is accurately weighed on a foil, washed with boiling water into a 100 c.c. volumetric flask and made up to the mark when cool. The flask should be clean and neutral (by test). Fresh solutions vary in activity (see standardization tests); they keep about a month.

The contents of each bottle are mixed and poured into six plates only (a thick layer of agar gives the most characteristic colonies). Plates are left uncovered until agar has "jellied"; porous tops are used; dry plates are essential to avoid diffusion.

STANDARDIZATION.—The agar must have proper "balance." The reaction is important; sediment reduces the activity of the dye and light-colored media are better than darker ones. Different lots of agar with the same dye solution may act differently; a new batch or a new solution must be tested. Any variation in the composition of the medium necessitates a readjustment of dye concentration. Success in preparation of this medium is acquired by practice and by attention to details difficult to describe fully.

Brilliant green, in appropriate dilutions, not only inhibits all gram-positive and many gram-negative bacteria, but exhibits differential action on the colon-typhoid group. Paratyphoid and the *B. lactis aerogenes* are untouched, typhoid is restrained only at low dilutions, while dysentery and the other colon group are extremely susceptible. The typhoid colony on this medium is characteristic. Looking through the plate against a dark surface, in oblique light the colony has a snowflake appearance; the edge delicately serrate. With artificial light and a hand lens, the texture is that of a coarse woolen fabric. Acid production from the trace of glucose may tinge the colony. The colony is large.

In concluding the description of some of the most important typhoid isolation media, we would like to add that a great deal seems to depend upon the habit-acquired skill which the individual worker attains. None of these stool isolation media are ordinarily successful at once in the hands of any one, and a certain amount

---

[3] Andrade's indicator: 0.5 per cent aqueous acid fuchsin.............................100 c.c.
       Normal NaOH .... 16 c.c.
The dye is slowly (2 hours) alkalinized to the color-base; the red tint is restored by acids.
As agar is neutral to Andrade's indicator, when hot the color is a deep red, but fades completely on cooling. This is determined by cooling 3 or 4 c.c. of acidified hot agar in a serum tube under the tap and adjusting accordingly.
[4] These are conveniently added from one sterile solution containing 20 per cent lactose and 2 per cent dextrose, 5 c.c. to 100 of agar gives the requisite concentration.

The methods employed for the isolation of bacteria depend upon the use of streaked plates, and poured plates, of agar containing various nutritive substances. In pour plates the individual bacteria, distributed in the medium when liquid, are held apart and separate when the medium becomes stiff. The masses of growth or "colonies" which develop from these single isolated micro-organisms are discrete and are descendants of a single organism, and can be transferred, by means of a process known as "colony-fishing," to fresh sterile culture media. By spreading or "streaking" the material on the surface of solidified medium in plates separate colonies can be obtained. This is the most frequently used method for isolating bacteria.

Each Petri dish plate consists of two circular glass dishes; the smaller and bottom dish has an area of 63.6 square centimeters; the larger is used as a cover for the smaller, and forms a loosely fitting lid. The plates when fitted together are sterilized and thus form a closed cell which, if properly handled, may remain sterile indefinitely.

The *technic for making a pour plate* for the purpose of isolating bacteria from mixed culture is described in the following example:

The actual "pouring" of plates is preceded by the preparation of usually three graded dilutions of the material to be examined. For this purpose three agar or gelatin tubes are melted and, in the case of the agar, are cooled to a temperature of about 42° C. in a water-bath. A platinum loopful of the material to be examined is transferred to one of these tubes. The bacteria are then thoroughly distributed throughout the melted gelatin or agar by alternately depressing and raising the plugged end of the tube, giving it a rotary motion at the same time. This thoroughly distributes the bacteria throughout the medium without allowing the formation of air-bubbles. Two loopfuls of this mixture are then transferred to the second tube and a similar mixing process is repeated. This second tube contains the bacteria in much greater dilution than the first and the colonies

FIG. 108.—POURING MEDIUM INTO PETRI DISH.

which will form in the plate poured from this tube will be farther apart. A third dilution is then made by transferring five loopfuls of the mixture in the second tube to the third. This again is mixed as before. The contents of the tubes are then poured into three sterile Petri dishes. The pouring should be done with great care. The cover of the dish is raised along one margin simply far enough to permit the insertion of the end of the test tube, the plug of which has been removed and the lips passed, with a rotary movement, through the flame. The medium is poured into the dish without the lips of the tube being allowed to touch either the bottom or the cover of the dish. The cover is then replaced and the medium allowed to harden.

Any desired series of dilutions may be made and the materials transferred in measured amounts with sterile pipets.

When agar has been used, the dishes may be placed in an incubator at 37° C. It is well to place the plates upside down in the incubator. This prevents the condensation water, squeezed out of the agar during hardening, from collecting on its surface, and forming channels for the diffuse spreading of bacteria. The same end may be attained by the use of Petri plates provided with porous earthenware lids. Simple inversion of the plates, however, usually suffices.

Colonies in agar, kept at 37.5° C., usually develop in eighteen to twenty-four hours; those in gelatin or agar at room temperature in from twenty-four to forty-eight hours, depending upon the species of bacteria which are being studied. Often in the second dilution, more frequently in the third, the colonies will be found well apart and can then be "fished." The process of "colony-fishing" is one which requires practice and should always be done with care, for upon its success depends the purity of the subculture obtained. Colonies should never be fished under the naked eye, no matter how far apart and discrete they may appear, since not infrequently close to the edge of or just beneath a larger colony there may be a minute colony of another species which may be too small to be visible to the naked eye, but which, nevertheless, if touched by accident will contaminate the subculture.

For proper "fishing," the Petri plate with cover removed, should be placed upon the stage of the microscope and examined with a low power objective, such as Leitz No. 2 or Zeiss AA or a binocular dissecting microscope. The sterilized platinum needle, held in the right hand, is then carefully directed into the line of focus of the lens, while the small finger of the hand is steadied upon the edge of the microscope stage. When the point of the needle is clearly visible through the microscope, it is gently depressed until it is seen to touch the colony and to carry away a portion of it. The needle is then withdrawn without again touching the nutrient medium or the edges of the glass or the lens, and transferred to a tube of whatever medium is desired. In this way, individuals of one colony, descendants of a single bacterium of the original mixture—are carried over to the fresh medium.

Separation of Bacteria by Surface Streaking.—Upon surface streaked plates, if dilutions have been properly made, and this is only a question of judgment based upon an estimation of the numbers of bacteria in the original material, discrete colonies of the micro-organisms sought for may develop, and can be "fished" in the usual manner.

Barber Pipet Method for the Isolation of Single Micro-organisms.—We shall give no extensive description of the apparatus or the manner of using it, because both are too complicated to permit of satisfactory use from textbook description.

The principle of the method depends upon a specially prepared mechanical stage adjusted to a compound microscope on which there is a moist chamber closed with a large cover-glass, on the bottom of which drops of fluid containing bacteria can be placed. A very fine glass pipet, manipulated by a specially constructed pipet holder and with a rubber tubing attached, is governed by observation through the microscope and by means of it small drops of the fluid are taken up, an attempt being made to obtain a single micro-organism in each drop. These separate drops in which the individual bacteria can be seen are made to suspend from the bottom of the cover-slip, closing the top of the moist chamber.

The apparatus can be understood and worked only by practice and suitable instruction, together with a study of the description given by Barber in his article in the *Philippine Journal of Science*. A modification of the Barber method for the isolation of single cells has been described by Chambers and will be found precisely explained in his article.

India Ink Method of Isolating and Observing Single Cells.—A useful method originated and demonstrated to us by Otto Schubert for the observation of single cells is the following:

Dilutions of broth cultures or suspensions of the organism to be observed are made in series. A brand of evenly suspended India ink—the variety used for the India ink spirochete method is the best—is procured. Ordinary glass slides are sterilized and covered with a thin layer of agar, which is allowed to cool and harden on them, the agared slides being kept sterile inside of Petri dishes. On a glass plate or on slides a series of mixtures are now made in which one loopful of India ink is mixed with one drop of the respective suspensions, the dilutions used being those high enough to justify the hope of containing a few bacteria only. A sterile cambric needle is now dipped into each of the mixtures and the small amount of the mixture thus picked up is transferred lightly to a spot on the agared slide, about eight or ten such small drops from the respective dilutions being transferred to a single slide.

If this simple technic is successfully carried out, which is only a matter of a little practice, the agar will be covered with a series of small dark spots made by the spreading out of the mixture of India ink and bacterial suspension. With a low power, some one of the spots will be found to contain individual bacteria outlined by the India ink, and a high power can be focused upon this spot. Individual cells can thus be found and, the chief virtue of the method, can be observed to grow in the colonies on the agar, individual cell cleavages being followed. Schubert applied the method to the study of the development of bacteriophage colonies with many interesting results, but without obtaining anything fundamentally new.

Isolation of Single Cells by Direct Observation on Agar.—By far the simplest method of obtaining single cell strains of bacteria is the method of direct observation on agar as practised by Hort, Orskov, Reimann and others and practised with minor modifications and complete satisfaction by Grinnell in our laboratory.

Deep hollow ground slides are filled with a suitable agar and allowed to harden. A dilution of a young culture is made by adding one loopful of a twelve to twenty-four hour broth culture to about 5 c.c. of broth. These specifications must be adapted by trial to organisms of various growth capacities. One loopful of such a dilution is gently spread over the surface of the agar in the hollow of the slide and the organisms allowed to settle for about fifteen minutes. During this period the preparation may be covered with a cover-slip with vaseline. The entire preparation is now placed under a microscope upon a mechanical stage, the light properly adjusted and search made with a high dry lens for separate cells. We add a few drops of sterile blood to the dilution broth. This furnishes a few blood cells to the surface of the agar, a procedure which facilitates focusing at this stage. A number of individual cells are located and, for each of them, coordinated readings are made on the Vernier scales of the stage, and a rough drawing added of the relationship of the particular bacterial cell to blood cells or other landmarks on the agar. The preparation is then taken off, covered with the cover-slip and incubated. With sufficient care and practice the cells can later be found by the readings, without much difficulty. The cover-slips may be omitted and Grinnell prefers setting the slides into a Petri dish with moist filter-paper. Many of the cells so located will not grow. But those which develop can be fished with a fine platinum wire, under the microscope in from six to eight hours.

soluble starch in a solid nutrient medium, incubating the inoculated starch agar plate 24 to 48 hours and then flooding the plate with Lugol's iodine solution. If the starch has been split by the bacteria, the zone around the colony will be colorless or light brown. The unhydrolyzed starch will give a deep blue color due to its reaction with the iodine.

Inverting Ferments.—Inverting ferments are determined by a procedure similar to the above in principle. Dilute solutions of cane sugar are mixed with old cultures or culture filtrates of the respective bacteria and the mixture allowed to stand. It is then filtered, and the filtrate tested for glucose, preferably by Fehling's solution.

ANIMAL EXPERIMENTATION

In the study of pathogenic micro-organisms, animal experimentation is essential in many instances. The virulence of any given organism for a definite animal species and the nature of the lesions produced are characteristics often of great value in differentiation. Isolation, moreover, of many bacteria is greatly facilitated by the inoculation of susceptible animals and recovery of the pathogenic organism from the heart's blood or from the lesions produced in various organs. That investigations into the phenomena of immunity would be absolutely impossible without the use of animal inoculation is, of course, self-evident, for by this method only can the action of bacteria in relation to living tissues, cells, and body-fluids be observed.

The animals most commonly employed for such observations are guinea-pigs, white mice, white rats, and rabbits. The method of inoculation may be either subcutaneous, intrapleural, intraperitoneal, intravenous, or subdural, etc. It must be borne in mind always that the mode of inoculation may influence the course of an infection no less than does the virulence of the micro-organism or the size of the dose.

Inoculations are made with some form of hypodermic needle fitted to a syringe. The most convenient syringes are the all-glass Luer syringes. Any form of sterilizable syringe may be used. In making inoculations the hair of the animal should be clipped and shaved, and the skin disinfected with tincture of iodine or alcohol.

Subcutaneous inoculations are most conveniently made in the abdominal wall, where the skin is thin. After clipping, shaving and sterilizing, the skin is raised between the fingers and the needle is then plunged in obliquely so as to avoid penetrating the abdominal wall and entering the peritoneum.

In making intraperitoneal inoculations, great care must be exercised not to puncture the gut. This can be avoided by passing the needle first through the skin in an oblique direction, then turning it into a position more vertical to the abdomen and perforating the muscles and peritoneum by a very short and carefully executed stab.

Intravenous inoculations in rabbits are made into the veins running along the outer margins of the ears. The hair over the ear is shaved and the animal held for a short time head downward so that the vessels of the head may fill with blood. An assistant holds the animal firmly in a horizontal position, the operator grasps the tip of the ear with the left hand, and carefully passes his needle into the vein in the direction as nearly as possible parallel to its course.

Mice are usually inoculated under the skin near the base of the tail. They may be placed in a jar over which a cover of stiff wire-gauze is held. They are then grasped by the tail, by which they are drawn up between the side of the jar and the edge of the wire cover, so that the lower end of the back shall be easily accessible. The skin is then wiped with a piece of cotton dipped in carbolic solution and the needle is inserted. Great care must be exercised to avoid passing the needle too close to the vertebral column. Mice are extremely delicate, and any injury to the spine usually causes immediate death.

With proper care mice or rats may be easily injected intravenously if a sufficiently fine needle is used. There are four superficially placed veins running along the tail, which stand out prominently when rubbed with cotton moistened with xylol. Into these the injections are made.

When inoculating rats or guinea-pigs with *B. pestis* the Kolle vaccination method is used. The skin is merely shaved and a loopful of the culture vigorously rubbed into the shaven area.

The various forms of animal holders which have been devised are rarely necessary in bacteriological work unless working unassisted, immobilization of the animals being accomplished by the hands of a skilled assistant.

Autopsies upon infected animals must be carefully made. The animals are tied, back down, upon pans fitted in the corners with clamps for the strings. They are then moistened either with hot water or with a weak solution of carbolic acid, so that contamination by hair may be avoided. A median cut is made, the skin is carefully dissected back, and the body cavities are opened with sterile instruments. Cultures may then be taken from exudates, blood, or organs under precautions similar to those recommended below for similar procedures at autopsy upon man.

Inoculated animals should be, if possible, kept separate from healthy animals. Rabbits and guinea-pigs are best kept in galvanized iron-wire cages, which are fitted with floor-pans that can be taken out and cleaned and sterilized. Mice may be kept in battery jars fitted with perforated metal covers. The mice should be supplied with large pieces of cotton batting since they are delicately susceptible to cold.

The Bleeding of Animals.—Animals are bled for the purpose of obtaining either corpuscles, defibrinated blood or serum.

In order to obtain small amounts of blood, that is about 5 or 10 c.c. from rabbits, the ear is shaved and had best be immersed in warm water for a few moments in order to expand the vessels. Gentle rubbing with xylol is also advantageous. The rabbit is then held with head hanging downward, and a broad needle of the Hagedorn needle type is thrust into the vein and withdrawn. The drops can be caught directly in a centrifuge tube, or in the culture-media for which it is intended. All blood media should be incubated for twenty-four hours and the contaminated tubes discarded.

A better method is to take blood from rabbits and from guinea-pigs directly from the heart. If this is skillfully done the animals can be repeatedly bled without being killed. For taking blood for complement in Wassermann reactions, this is among the best methods since large guinea-pigs can be alternately bled and rested. Both in rabbits and guinea-pigs, bleeding directly from the heart is easily accomplished after a little practice. The anterior thorax of the animal is clipped and painted with tincture of iodine and the operator in feeling for the third interspace close to the sternum had best paint the tips of his fingers with iodine. A twenty-two gauge needle about two inches long is then attached to a syringe and passed downward in the third left interspace close to the sternum, slight suction being exercised at the same time. There is not much purpose in describing this in detail since it can be taught only by practice.

Both rabbits and guinea-pigs can be bled from the carotid. The animal is anesthetized as above, and the carotid laid bare. It is found very close to the trachea, in rabbits lying almost in contact with the trachea, and a little behind it. It is carefully separated from the vagus nerve, and tied off in its distal portion. The thread with which it is tied can be used to handle it thereafter. A sterile glass cannula can be thrust into the artery and the blood taken through this, or else, as we prefer to do it, the side of the artery is picked up with a very fine forceps and held with one hand while it is cut across with a sharp scissors. In this way the blood can be directed straight into a wide-mouth flask without being allowed to come in contact with anything until it hits the inside of the flask.

Larger animals, like sheep, goats, horses, are easily bled by plunging a sterile needle into the external jugular vein which runs in these animals from a line just behind the angle of the lower jaw to the sternoclavicular junction.

The blood can be, run directly into media as for blood agar, blood broth and chocolate medium.

If serum is desired, it can be run into containers of various kinds slanted and allowed to clot in the ice box.

If defibrinated blood is desired, the blood can be taken directly into sterile flasks containing pieces of broken glass or beads and defibrinated by shaking. Such blood can be kept in the ice chest and added to media subsequently.

Blood can be also preserved for culture purposes by the addition of just enough ether to hemolyze it, and added to media in this form. The ether is evaporated off.

The removal of hair from guinea-pigs, rabbits, rats and other animals is a necessary preparation for the performance of intradermal injections for skin-tests. The hair may be removed by clipping followed by shaving. This must be done with great care to avoid abrasions and cuts. It is often more satisfactory to apply a *depilatory*. The preparation generally used for depilation is a thin paste made by adding water to a mixture of equal parts of barium sulphide and cornstarch. Apply the paste with a sponge or piece of cloth held in forceps or with a wooden spatula. Allow the paste to remain three or four minutes, wash it off thoroughly in lukewarm water and dry the animal with a towel. Since this procedure may cause some irritation of the skin, it is advisable to remove the hair on the day before the injection or at least several hours in advance.

Carmichael has described a solution of barium sulfide which is said to be superior to the paste as a depilatory.

REFERENCES

CARMICHAEL, E. B.   Science, 1932, 75:136.
SIERAKOWSKI.   Biochem. Ztschr., 1924, 152:111.
VALLEY, G., and RETTGER, L. F.   J. Bacteriol., 1926, 11:78; 1927, 14:101.

CHAPTER LXX

FILTRATION AND MISCELLANEOUS METHODS

Filters used for the removal of bacteria from liquids are of three main types: (1) diatomaceous earth filters: (Berkefeld, Mandler), (2) unglazed porcelain filters: (Pasteur-Chamberland, Doulton, Massen), (3) asbestos filters: (Seitz).

In addition to filters of these types, collodion membranes are used occasionally to separate bacteria from liquids. They are used frequently for the separation of particles of sub-bacterial dimensions and for the study of the sizes of the particles of ultramicroscopic viruses, bacteriophage and colloids.

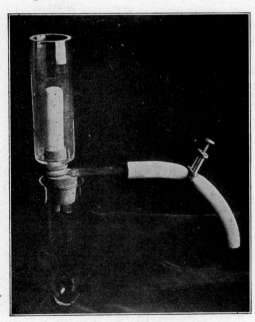

FIG. 114.—BERKEFELD FILTER.

The filters in the first group are called *bacterial filters,* those in the second, *ultra-filters.* Since we have discussed elsewhere the physics of filtration, we shall deal in this chapter with practical considerations of the preparation and use of filters.[1]

Suction is the most convenient method to use in drawing liquid through these filters. The air in a filter flask or filter system is withdrawn by aspiration through a water pump or electrically operated vacuum pump. With suitable attachments to a mercury manometer, the pressure during the filtration process can be observed and regulated. Indications of two varieties of attachments of filters to side-neck filter flasks for filtration by suction are shown in Fig. 114. Filtration should be carried out as rapidly and at as low a pressure as possible. It is best not to use a pressure greater than 35 to 50 cm. Hg.

The liquid may be forced through the filter by pressure exerted by compressed air or by a metal plunger. But this method is not as satisfactory as suction or aspiration for the usual bacterial filtrations.

Berkefeld filters are hollow candles of compressed diatomaceous earth cemented to a circular metal base. This joint is one of the places at which cracks or leaks may occur. The metal base is drawn out in a metal tube, by which the filter may be at-

1 For a clear presentation with excellent diagrams see J. McIntosh, and S. P. Bedson. Filtration, in A System of Bacteriology in Relation to Medicine, London, 1931, 9:Chap. IX, p. 118.

The membranes are prepared by impregnating Whatman No. 1 filter paper disks with acetic collodion solutions of various concentrations and gelling the collodion in water.

"Anthony's negative cotton" is dried in a desiccator to constant weight and solutions of the following collodion content are prepared in glacial acetic acid: 6.0, 5.5, 5.0, 4.5, 4.0, 3.5, 3.0, 2.5, 2.0, 1.5, 1 and 0.5 per cent. These solutions are best made in quantity and kept in large bottles, removing the amounts needed for current work from time to time.

The solutions for immediate use are placed in squat, covered cylindrical containers sufficiently large to receive the filter paper. The surface of the solution is scraped free from bubbles and a disk of filter paper is lowered into it, taking every precaution to avoid bringing air bubbles with the paper. When the paper has become thoroughly impregnated with collodion it is lifted up above the surface and slowly rotated in its own plane until the excess solution has completely run off. Flat, broad-billed cover-glass forceps are used in this manipulation.

The filter paper disk impregnated with collodion is now plunged into sterile distilled water, again avoiding bubbles, and is washed in successive changes until the wash water is free from acetic acid. Membranes prepared in this way can be stored in sterile water saturated with chloroform for two weeks without changing in permeability.

Krueger and Ritter state:[3] "No special precautions for sterilizing the membranes are necessary since the original acetic collodion solutions are sterile, and if aseptic technic is followed during the washing, contamination will not occur." Membranes from each batch should be tested for sterility.

The apparatus for holding these filter disks and for the filtration process is described and figured in the article of Krueger and Ritter.

Additional general information on ultrafiltration and membrane filters will be found in the papers of Bechhold, Zsigmondy, and Asheshov.

Semipermeable *collodion sacs* are useful in a number of bacteriological procedures when it is desired to interpose a filtration or diffusion barrier between an organism and its environment in a culture tube or in the body of an animal. A method of constructing these sacs upon a gelatin capsule has been described in detail by Gates. Collodion sacs constructed in this manner can be filled with infectious material and implanted in the peritoneal cavities or subcutaneous tissue of animals, used in studies of the relation of dialyzable nutritive constituents to bacterial growth or investigations of the dialyzable properties of bacterial products.

REFERENCES

Asheshov, I. J. Bacteriol., 1933, 25:323, 339.

Bechhold, H. Ultrafiltration and Electro-ultrafiltration, Colloid Chemistry, ed. by J. Alexander, New York, 1926, 1:820.

——— Ztschr. f. physik. Chem., 1907, 60:257; 1908, 64:328.

d'Herelle, F. The Bacteriophage and Its Behavior, Baltimore, 1926, pp. 21–22.

Elford, W. J. J. Path. & Bacteriol., 1931, 34:505.

Gates, F. L. J. Exper. M., 1921, 33:25.

Krueger, A. P., and Ritter, R. C. J. Gen. Physiol., 1929, 13:409.

Mudd, S. Proc. Soc. Exper. Biol. M., 1927, 25:60.

Zsigmondy, R. Membrane Filters and Their Uses. Colloid Chemistry, ed. by J. Alexander, New York, 1926, 1:994.

[3] A. P. Krueger and R. C. Ritter, *J. Gen. Physiol.*, 1929, 13:409.

CHAPTER LXXI

METHODS OF IMMUNOLOGY AND SEROLOGY

The principles underlying the procedures of immunology and serology have been discussed in the preceding sections of this book. Although these principles need not be restated here, the bare descriptions of the various methods would require more space than that available in this volume if we should attempt to include in it a manual of immunology and serology. Furthermore, much of that description would seem to be unprofitable, since the manipulations which are rapidly acquired correctly from the demonstration of one skilled in immunological technic are rarely learned from a printed description of reasonable length. Our object in this chapter, therefore, will be to describe the technic of a few methods having general application and a few special procedures which appear to us to have features of particular interest.

Serum Diagnosis of Syphilis.—The two types of methods used for the serological diagnosis of syphilis are: (1) Complement fixation tests with lipoidal antigens consisting of extracts of normal heart muscle. These tests are modifications of the Wassermann reaction. (2) Precipitation or flocculation tests with tissue extract antigens. The best and most reliable of these is the Kahn test.

As adequate descriptions of these methods cannot be presented in the space at our disposal, the reader is referred for details on the complement fixation or Wassermann tests to the manuals of Wadsworth and Kolmer and Boerner, and for the technic of the Kahn test to the manual of this method published by Kahn.

Bacterial Complement Fixation.—The procedure to be outlined here illustrates the method of demonstrating fixation of complement by a specific complex formed by the union of an antigen with its antibody. This is the fundamental Bordet-Gengou reaction which has been and can be modified in many ways to suit particular needs.

Materials Required

   Antigen: suspension of bacteria in salt solution
   Antiserum: antibacterial serum
   Complement: fresh serum from guinea-pig
   Amboceptor: specific immune hemolysin for sheep erythrocytes
   Sheep cells: 5 per cent suspension of washed RBC of sheep
   0.85 per cent NaCl solution
   Color standards
   Glassware: test tubes, 100 × 10 mm. Serological pipets: 10 and 5 c.c. graduated in 0.1 c.c.;
      1 c.c. pipets graduated in 0.1 c.c. to tip; 0.2 c.c. pipets graduated in 0.01 c.c.
   Copper racks

Preparation of Reagents

   (*a*) ANTIGEN.—With 0.85 per cent NaCl solution (Saline) wash off the growth from a twenty-four hour agar slant culture of the organism to be used. The amount of saline necessary to make a satisfactory emulsion varies between 5 and 10 c.c. depending upon the heaviness of the growth.

Shake well. Filter through cotton. Heat in water bath at 60° C. for one hour. Add sufficient phenol to make a 0.5 per cent solution.

For comparative work, the density of the emulsion should be standardized by nephelometric determinations or by a direct count of the number of organisms contained in 1 c.c., as it is important to use approximately similar suspensions. All cell suspensions, including suspensions of bacteria have the property of inhibiting the action of complement. This nonspecific property is known as their "anticomplementary action." The titration of the anticomplementary action of the antigen is given in a subsequent paragraph.

(b) IMMUNE SERUM (ANTIBODY).—Immunize an animal against the organism to be studied by repeated injections of the organism. Rabbits are especially suitable for this purpose. Injections may be made into the marginal veins of the ears, intraperitoneally, or subcutaneously. For the injections, use light suspensions of the organism in 0.85 per cent saline, made by washing off the culture from a 24-hr. agar slant. Washed broth cultures can be employed in cases where it is desired to use an organism which will not grow well on agar slants. Organisms requiring a carbohydrate for growth can be grown in sugar broth and then washed free of acid and used as antigen. Before the suspensions are injected, they should be heated for 1 hr. at 60° C. On the first injection, use 0.5 c.c. of this suspension. Increase the dose by increments of 0.5 c.c. at intervals of 5 to 7 days. If the organism is not too virulent and the animal has not lost weight, the last few injections may be made with unheated suspensions of living organisms. Seven to 9 days after the last injection, bleed the rabbit from the ear vein and obtain sufficient serum for a preliminary test to determine its potency. If this test shows that the serum contains antibodies in sufficiently high titer, bleed the rabbit from the heart or in some manner which will provide as large an amount of serum as possible. After the collection of the serum, heat it at 55° C. for ½ hr. to destroy complement, add 0.3 per cent tricresol as a preservative, and store in sealed ampules or bottles. The serum should be stored in a refrigerator.

(c) COMPLEMENT.—Guinea-pig serum furnishes an active and easily fixable complement. It is usually advisable to pool the sera from at least 3 guinea-pigs to obtain a sample of complement having average properties. Bleed the guinea-pigs from the heart, removing 5 to 10 c.c. of blood from each animal. Allow the blood to clot. Pipet off the serum and store in a sterile glass container in the ice box. The most potent complement can be obtained by allowing the clotted blood to stand over night in the ice box before separating the serum. Complement rarely retains its potency longer than three days. It is essential to titrate it daily. Keep the complement in the ice box as much as possible when not actually being used.

(d) AMBOCEPTOR (ANTI-SHEEP-RED-CELL HEMOLYSIN).—Very strong hemolysin may be obtained by the following method. Two strong rabbits are given intravenous injections of undiluted washed sheep's corpuscles according to the following schedule: 1st day, 0.5 c.c. packed erythrocytes; 3rd day, 1.0 c.c.; 5th day, 1.0 c.c.; 7th day, 1.0 c.c.; 11th day, 1.5 c.c.

Eight days after the last injection a trial bleeding is made from the marginal ear vein. If the serum is found sufficiently potent the rabbits are bled to death or as much blood is taken from the heart as is desired for stock hemolysin.

The serum is allowed to separate from the clot, pipetted off, and treated with 0.4 per cent phenol, 0.3 per cent tricresol, or an equal amount of 50 per cent glycerin. The potency will be retained for many months, when stored in the refrigerator. Titrations should be made, however, at intervals not exceeding three or four months.

The titration of hemolytic amboceptor, using a constant amount of complement, is discussed below. The amboceptor should have a titer sufficiently high to avoid interference by agglutinins.

(e) SHEEP CELLS.—Five per cent suspension of washed erythrocytes of sheep in 0.85 per cent solution of NaCl.

Sheep's blood obtained by puncture of jugular vein, is placed in a flask containing an equal amount of 2 per cent sodium citrate. To wash the cells, put 10 c.c. of citrated blood in a 50 c.c. conical centrifuge tube. Fill the tube with salt solution. Centrifuge at 1400 r.p.m. for fifteen minutes. Draw off the supernatant fluid, replace with salt solution and centrifuge as before. Repeat this process once more, centrifuging for fifteen minutes at 1800 r.p.m. to pack the cells. After the final washing, the supernatant fluid should be clear and colorless. If the fluid is tinged with hemoglobin, do not use these cells. To make a 5 per cent suspension of the cells add 5 c.c. of packed cells to 95 c.c. of salt solution. Filter through gauze to remove small clots. Shake well before using. Keep in ice box. Cells more than forty-eight hours old are unsatisfactory.

(f) SENSITIZED CELLS.—Mix thoroughly equal parts of 5 per cent suspension of sheep RBC and the proper dilution of amboceptor. Let this stand 10 minutes at room temperature before using. The amount of the amboceptor to be added will contain 2 units of amboceptor in each 0.2 c.c. of the mixture of amboceptor and cells.

That is: 0.2 c.c. of sensitized cells contains 0.1 c.c. of 5 per cent suspension of sheep cells and 0.1 c.c. of a dilution of the amboceptor providing 2 units of amboceptor.

(g) COLOR STANDARDS FOR ESTIMATING DEGREE OF FIXATION OF COMPLEMENT

1. Centrifuge 5 c.c. of 5 per cent suspension of sheep cells in a 15 c.c. graduated centrifuge tube for 10 min. at 1800 r.p.m.
2. Draw off the supernatant liquid.
3. Make up to 4.5 c.c. with distilled water and mix with pipet to lake the cells.
4. Add 0.5 c.c. of 8.5 per cent salt solution to make this hemoglobin solution isotonic.
5. Prepare color standards as follows:

Tube	Hemoglobin Solution	5 per cent Sheep RBC	Salt Solution, c.c.	Complement, c.c.	Antigen, c.c.	Indicates—Fixation Inhibition of Hemolysis
1	0.09 c.c.	0.01	0.2	0.1	0.1	$10 - 25\% = \pm$
2	0.075	0.025	0.2	0.1	0.1	$25 - 50\% = 1 +$
3	0.05	0.05	0.2	0.1	0.1	$50 - 75\% = 2 +$
4	0.025	0.075	0.2	0.1	0.1	$75 - 95\% = 3 +$
5	0.005	0.095	0.2	0.1	0.1	$95\% -$ up $= 4 +$

NOTE: The total volume in all the subsequent tests is approximately 0.5 c.c.

AMBOCEPTOR TITRATION, USING CONSTANT AMOUNT OF COMPLEMENT

Tube	Anti-sheep Amboceptor 1–800, c.c.	Complement 1–15 dil., c.c.	Sheep Cells 5 Per Cent c.c.	Salt Solution, c.c.	Incubation	Result
1	0.10	0.1	0.1	0.2	Incubate for fif-	
2	0.09	0.1	0.1	0.2	teen minutes in	
3	0.08	0.1	0.1	0.2	water bath at	
4	0.07	0.1	0.1	0.2	37° C., shaking	
5	0.06	0.1	0.1	0.2	repeatedly	
6	0.05	0.1	0.1	0.3		
7	0.04	0.1	0.1	0.3		
8	0.03	0.1	0.1	0.3		
9	0.02	0.1	0.1	0.3		
10	0.01	0.1	0.1	0.3		

The purpose of this titration is to find the lowest dilution of amboceptor which gives complete hemolysis in 0.05 c.c. in the presence of 0.1 c.c. of a 1–15 dilution of complement. Adopt this dilution as the amboceptor unit. In subsequent titrations it will be convenient to use a dilution of the amboceptor such that 0.1 c.c. contains 2 units. A 1–800 dilution is noted in the protocol. This may require a different dilution with amboceptors of higher titer.

Complement and amboceptor have a reciprocal relationship in producing hemolysis. The standard amboceptor unit is arbitrarily regarded as the least quantity required to give complete hemolysis of 0.1 c.c. of a 5 per cent suspension of sheep cells in the presence of 2 units of complement after incubation for 15 minutes in a water bath at 37° C.

COMPLEMENT TITRATIONS, TO TEST FOR HEMOLYTIC ACTIVITY OF INDIVIDUAL
GUINEA-PIG SERUM

Tube	Guinea-pig Serum, 1–10, c.c.	Salt Solution, c.c.	Sensitized Cells, c.c.	Incubation	Result
1	0.04	0.2	0.2	Incubate for fifteen minutes in water bath at 37° C., shake repeatedly	
2	0.03	0.3	0.2		
3	0.02	0.3	0.2		

Record the least amount of diluted serum which gives complete hemolysis.
Include in the pooled complement only the guinea-pig sera which give complete hemolysis in 0.04 c.c. or less of the 1–10 dilution.

TEST OF INDIVIDUAL GUINEA-PIG SERUM FOR NATURAL ANTI-SHEEP AMBOCEPTOR

Tube	Guinea-pig Serum, 1–10, c.c.	Sheep Cells 5 Per Cent, c.c.	Salt Solution, c.c.	Incubation	Result
1	0.1	0.1	0.3	Incubate for fifteen minutes in water bath at 37° C.	
2	none	0.1	0.4		

Centrifugalize each tube to deposit the cells and record the degree of hemolysis in each tube. If hemolysis occurs, it is due to natural antisheep amboceptor in the guinea-pig serum, provided the cell-control shows no hemolysis. Use only sera showing no hemolysis or a very slight amount.

TEST OF INDIVIDUAL GUINEA-PIG SERUM FOR NONSPECIFIC FIXABILITY

Tube	Guinea-pig Serum Dilution for Test, c.c.	Antigen Bacterial, c.c.	Fixation	Sensitized Cells, c.c.	Secondary Incubation	Result
1	0.1	0.2	2 hours in ice box	0.2	Incubate in water bath at 37° C., shaking tubes until hemolysis is complete.	
2	0.1	0.2	Water bath 37° C. for 30 min.	0.2		

Record the time required for complete hemolysis with each serum. Include in the pooled complement only the sera with which the sensitized cells are hemolyzed in seven minutes or less.

	ANTIGEN		SERUM UNDILUTED, c.c.	MENT 2 UNITS, c.c.	SOLUTION, c.c.	FIXATION	CELLS, c.c.	INCUBATION	RESULT
TUBE	Dilution	Amount, c.c.							
1	1– 5	0.1	0.05	0.1	0.1	Incubate for one hour in water bath at 37° C.	0.2	Incubate in water bath at 37° C. for fifteen minutes	
2	1– 10	0.1	0.05	0.1	0.1		0.2		
3	1– 20	0.1	0.05	0.1	0.1		0.2		
4	1– 40	0.1	0.05	0.1	0.1		0.2		
5	1– 80	0.1	0.05	0.1	0.1		0.2		
6	1–160	0.1	0.05	0.1	0.1		0.2		
7	1–320	0.1	...	0.1	0.1		0.2		
8	1– 5	0.1	...	0.1	0.1		0.2		
9	...	...	0.1	0.1	0.1				

COMPLEMENT TITRATION.—After these titrations of sera of individual guinea-pigs are made, the specimens found to be suitable are pooled. The pooled complement is diluted 1–40 and a titration of its activity is made in the presence of 2 units of amboceptor as follows:

Tube	Complement 1–40, c.c.	Salt Solution, c.c.	Sensitized Sheep Cells, c.c.	Incubation	Result
1	0.15	0.2	0.2	Incubate for fifteen minutes in the water bath at 37° C., shaking the tubes re-	
2	0.14	0.2	0.2		
3	0.13	0.2	0.2		

Tube 8 is the anticomplementary antigen control.

Tube 9 is the anticomplementary serum control.

Record the degree of hemolysis in all tubes. For subsequent use, select a dilution of the antigen which completely fixes complement with 0.05 c.c. of the immune serum. The fixing power of the antigen should be at least 10 times as great as its anticomplementary action.

TITRATIONS OF THE IMMUNE SERUM

Immune serum is inactivated at 55° C. for one-half hour.

The immune serum should not be hemolytic in any dilution. Some sera are anticomplementary. This property often increases with the age of the serum, with the formation of precipitates in it, and as a result of bacterial growth in contaminated specimens. Titrate the immune serum to determine its anticomplementary action as follows:

TITRATION OF ANTICOMPLEMENTARY ACTION OF IMMUNE SERUM

TUBE	SERUM Dilution	SERUM Amount, c.c.	COMPLEMENT 2 UNITS, c.c.	SALT SOLUTION, c.c.	FIXATION	SENSITIZED CELLS, c.c.	SECONDARY INCUBATION	RESULT
1	Undil.	0.1	0.1	0.1	Incubate for	0.2	Incubate for	
2	1– 5	0.1	0.1	0.1	one hour in	0.2	fifteen min-	
3	1–10	0.1	0.1	0.1	water bath	0.2	utes in	
4	1–20	0.1	0.1	0.1	at 37° C.	0.2	water bath at 37° C.	

TITRATION OF ANTIBODY CONTENT (BINDING POWER) OF IMMUNE SERUM

TUBE	IMMUNE SERUM Dilution	IMMUNE SERUM Amount, c.c.	BACTERIAL ANTIGEN DILUTION AS DETERMINED, c.c.	COMPLEMENT 2 UNITS, c.c.	SALT SOLUTION, c.c.	FIXATION	SENSITIZED CELLS, c.c.	SECONDARY INCUBATION	RESULT
1	Undil.	0.05	0.1	0.1	0.1	Incubate	0.2	Incubate	
2	1– 5	0.05	0.1	0.1	0.1	in water	0.2	in water	
3	1– 10	0.05	0.1	0.1	0.1	bath at	0.2	bath at	
4	1– 20	0.05	0.1	0.1	0.1	37° C. for	0.2	37° C. for	
5	1– 40	0.05	0.1	0.1	0.1	one hour	0.2	fifteen	
6	1– 80	0.05	0.1	0.1	0.1		0.2	minutes	
7	1– 160	0.05	0.1	0.1	0.1		0.2		
8	1– 320	0.05	0.1	0.1	0.1		0.2		
9	1– 640	0.05	0.1	0.1	0.1		0.2		
10	1–1280	0.05	0.1	0.1	0.1		0.2		

Record degree of hemolysis in all tubes. The results of this titration will show the smallest amount of the immune serum which will fix complement completely in the presence of a constant amount of the antigen. The amount of antigen to be used should be neither hemolytic nor anticomplementary, as shown by previous titrations.

COMPLEMENT FIXATION TEST WITH BACTERIAL ANTIGEN
FINAL TEST WITH CONTROLS
BASED UPON PREVIOUS TITRATIONS OF REAGENTS

TUBE	IMMUNE SERUM, c.c.	ANTIGEN BACTERIAL SUSPEN- SION, c.c.	COM- PLEMENT 2 UNITS, c.c.	SALT SOLU- TION, c.c.	FIXATION	SENSI- TIZED CELLS, c.c.	SECONDARY INCUBATION	RESULT
1	0.05	0.1	0.1	0.1	Incubate in water bath at 37° C. for one hour	0.2	Incubate in water bath at 37° C. for fifteen minutes	
2	0.02	0.1	0.1	0.1		0.2		
3	0.05	...	0.1	0.2		0.2		
4	...	0.1	0.1	0.1		0.2		

Record degree of hemolysis in all tubes using color standard.

This is a simplified form of the test using two quantities of the antiserum and anticomplementary serum and antigen controls. In the same manner additional tests for specificity can be added by using normal sera and other antigens.

Agglutination and Absorption of Agglutinins.—The following procedures are described in connection with the colon-typhoid-dysentery group, but may be used with appropriate modifications in dealing with any other group of bacteria.

Rapid Slide Agglutination:

1. Prepare a 1–50 dilution of the antiserum, and place a drop of this on a slide.
2. Place two drops of salt solution on the slide.
3. Emulsify a loopful of bacteria from an agar slant culture in one of these drops, and with the loop, transfer equal amounts of this emulsion to: (a) the drop of salt solution and (b) the diluted antiserum, mixing each in turn.
4. Observe under low power of the microscope for presence or absence of clumping in the mixture of bacteria and antiserum, and for smoothness of the emulsion (absence of clumps) in the salt solution control.

Microscopic Agglutination Test (Widal Reaction).

Dilute specimens of dried blood or blood serum which are to be used in making microscopic agglutination tests 1–10, 1–20, 1–40, 1–80, 1–160, etc., using 0.85 per cent salt solution.

Use for the test a culture of the *Bacillus typhosus* which agglutinates readily. Incubate this culture in broth at 37° C. for not more than 18 hours. Do not shake the culture and use only the growth in the upper part of the fluid for the test, or if the growth is too heavy it may be diluted to correspond to a turbidity standard. If a suspension in saline of a fresh agar culture after 18 hours' incubation at 37° C. is used, allow the clumps to settle. Test this culture or suspension with antityphoid serum to prove its agglutinability.

One loop of this culture and one loop of the 1–10, 1–20, 1–40, etc., dilutions of dried blood or of blood serum are mixed on the cover glass. Examine the hanging drops thus prepared, together with those of culture and salt solution or normal blood or blood serum for purposes of control, after an incubation period of 1 hour at 37° C. Then make the readings of the agglutination reactions in terms of the final dilutions of 1–20, 1–40 and 1–80. (Whenever the lytic action of a serum is so strong as to interfere with the agglutination, inactivate part of the serum by heating at 55° C. for 30 minutes and repeat the test.)

The reaction should not be considered significant unless there is definite clumping after 1 hour's incubation in the 1–40 dilution. History of the patient, with special reference to previous injections of typhoid vaccine, must be known before results of this test can be interpreted.

Macroscopic Agglutination Test.—The most satisfactory way to do an agglutination test is to

Absorption of agglutinin is used: (1)
bacteria, and (2) to prepare strictly specific monovalent agglutinating sera.

The minimal absorbing dose of the homologous bacterium should be determined in each case and two or three times this amount should be used in absorbing the agglutinin from the serum. Final titrations with absorbed sera should be made over the whole range of the titer. Prozone reactions may inhibit agglutination in tests with 1–10, 1–40 and even 1–100 dilutions of the absorbed serum. Time of contact, shaking of mixtures, temperature of incubation, dilution of serum and a number of other factors influence the results of agglutinin absorption. The technic must be varied to suit each problem. A satisfactory procedure for absorption of agglutinins with antisera and members of the colon-typhoid-paratyphoid group is as follows:

1. Calculate the amount of serum required for the final titration.
2. Dilute sufficient of the antiserum 1–10 with salt solution.
3. Wash off the growth of an 18 hour culture of *B. typhosus* (or other member of the group) on a plain agar slant. To do this add 2–3 c.c. of salt solution to the tube, emulsify the bacteria in this by scraping them off the agar with a platinum loop, taking care not to break the agar surface.

use measurable amounts of antigen and antiserum in quantities which give reaction visible to the eye.

With organisms of the colon-typhoid-dysentery group, the best antigen is a 24 hour culture in meat extract broth, killed by heat at 60° C. for 1 hour. 0.5 per cent formalin is added to this suspension. This can be prepared in large amounts, several liters at one time. The suspensions keep well. It is advantageous, for comparative determinations, to use the same antigen-suspension. Emulsions of the bacteria, made by taking up growth from agar cultures in 0.85 per cent sodium chloride solution, may be used. These emulsions should have a density of about 0.5 on the McFarland nephelometer scale and contain about 500 million bacteria per c.c. Kill organisms by heating at 60° C. for 1 hour and then add 0.5 per cent formaldehyde. (See paragraphs on H and O antigens.)

The antiserum may be kept sterile from the start, or may be filtered and preserved with 0.5 per cent phenol, 0.15 per cent tricresol or 50 per cent glycerin. A stock solution composed of a 1–5 dilution of the antiserum in saline containing 0.5 per cent phenol keeps well in the ice box. A

Place the emulsion of bacteria in a graduated tube and centrifuge this at 2000 r.p.m. until the volume of packed bacteria is constant. Pipet off the supernatant saline.

4. To 1 part of the bacterial mass in the centrifuge tube, add 9 parts of serum diluted 1–10. This gives an approximate 1–10 absorbing dose of bacteria. For exact method of computing this see Krumwiede's paper.

5. Shake the mixture of bacteria and serum and incubate in water bath for two hours at 37° C. Place mixtures in the ice box over night.

6. After incubation and standing in ice box, centrifuge to remove bacteria and pipet off the clear supernatant fluid.

7. Set up agglutination tests with the absorbed serum and broth culture antigens of colon-typhoid bacilli.

Example: Required: 2 c.c. of absorbed serum diluted 1–10. Absorbing dose equals 0.2 c.c. of packed bacteria. Then: to 0.2 c.c. of packed bacteria in a graduated centrifuge tube add 1.8 c.c. of serum diluted 1–10.

This gives approximate results. The formulae used by Krumwiede for this calculation, in which a correction factor is used for the saline included in the bacterial mass are as follows:

$$(\text{Mass}-10\%) \text{ x dose factor} = \text{total volume}$$

$$\frac{(\text{Mass}-10\%) \text{ x (dose factor}-1)}{\text{serum dilution factor}} = \text{amount undiluted serum required.}$$

PRECIPITIN TEST WITH PROTEINS

Production of Precipitin.—The rabbit is the most satisfactory animal to use for the production of precipitin. On account of individual variations, several rabbits should be immunized at the same time. A solution of foreign protein is injected intravenously at intervals in increasing amounts. For the production of precipitins against serum proteins, inject intravenously 1, 2, 3, 4, 8 and 10 c.c. of the serum at 3 day intervals. Bleed rabbit for preliminary test 4 to 8 days after the last injection. If the titer is not sufficiently high, increasing amounts of serum 15, 20 and 25 c.c. should be injected intravenously at 3 day intervals. Precipitins reach their highest concentration in the blood 8 to 12 days after the last injection. To collect serum at the end, bleed the rabbit from the heart, allow blood to clot and collect the serum. The bleeding and serum collection may be done with sterile technic, or a preservative may be added to the serum, or the serum may be sterilized by filtration. The serum used in these tests must be clear, free from all precipitate.

The Antigen.—Serum, hemolyzed blood, and other solutions of proteins cleared by filtration and suitably diluted are used in this test. Dilutions are made with 0.85 per cent salt solution.

The strength or titer of a precipitin serum is determined by finding the highest dilution of the antigen with which the precipitin serum forms a precipitate in 1 to 2 hrs. at room temperature. Note: In this titration the amount of the antiserum is kept constant and the antigen dilutions are varied. A good precipitin serum should give a precipitate with its antigen diluted 1–1000 almost at once at room temperature.

Procedure.—1. In ordinary test tubes, make up 1 to 10 c.c. of the following dilutions of the solution of protein (antigen) in saline : 1–10, 1–100, 1–500, 1–1000, 1–2000, 1–5000, 1–10000.

2. Use small tubes, about 3 mm. inside diameter.

3. With capillary pipet, place approximately 0.1 c.c. precipitin serum in bottom of each small tube in the series.

4. With capillary pipet layer approximately 0.1 c.c. of each dilution of the solution of protein carefully on the precipitin serum.

5. Note presence or absence of precipitate at the junction of the two fluids in 15 minutes, 1 hour and 2 hours at room temperature.

6. The fluids may be mixed and let stand in the ice box over night, when the precipitate settles to the bottom.

7. Set up controls to prove specificity as required.

Titration of Diphtheria Toxin and Antitoxin by Flocculation.—The Ramon method of flocculation titration, slightly modified, is as follows:

In a series of mixing of diphtheria toxin and antitoxin a precipitate forms *first* in the tube containing toxin and antitoxin in equivalent proportions. Advantage may be taken of this primary precipitin reaction occurring in a neutral mixture to nitrate diphtheria toxin and antitoxin in vitro. At present the symbol used to express the unitage on this basis is L_F. The L_F amount of toxin is that amount of toxin which precipitates first in a series of mixtures with differing amounts of antitoxin. It corresponds usually to approximately 1 unit of antitoxin as determined by the usual tests based upon results of injections into animals. The reaction seems to be due to the combination of the antigen portion of the toxin with an equivalent amount of antitoxin. Toxins deprived of toxicity by formaldehyde, etc., retain antigenicity and ability to "neutralize" antitoxin; *e.g.* to combine in equivalent proportions with antitoxin. Different toxins and different preparations of antitoxins require different times of incubation for flocculation. Some flocculate rapidly; some flocculate very slowly. The height of the column of liquid in the tubes influences the time of flocculation somewhat on account of varying convection currents. Flocculation will take place at room temperature. It is more convenient and time saving to carry out the reaction at 45–50° C. in a water bath. The tubes should be observed frequently in order to note the first appearance of flocculation. The small amounts of antitoxin used in the following series may be delivered from Trevan's micro-syringe or pipetted from diluted antitoxin with a 0.2 c.c. pipette graded in 0.01 c.c.

To Determine the Value of an Antitoxin:

Procedure.—1. Into a series of 10 test tubes place 2 c.c. of a standardized rapidly flocculating toxin. This toxin is standardized by repeated flocculation titrations against a standard antitoxin. The antitoxin was standardized originally by the usual tests on animals.

If a standard antitoxin is available, the flocculating value (L_F unit) of an unknown toxin can be determined. If a standardized toxin, of known L_F value is available, the equivalent value in units of an unknown antitoxin can be determined.

2. To each tube add a series of amounts of antitoxin, differing by 0.001 c.c. from tube to tube.

3. Place the tubes in a water bath at 45° to 50° C. and observe for the *first* appearance of flocculation.

Tube	1	2	3	4	5	6	7	8	9	10
Standard toxin	2 c.c.	2 c.c.	2 c.c.	2 c.c.	2 c.c.	2 c.c.	2 c.c.	2 c.c.	2 c.c.	2 c.c.
Unknown antitoxin	0.031	0.032	0.033	0.034	0.035	0.036	0.037	0.038	0.039	0.040
Time, Minutes										
15	..	C	C	C	C	C	C	C	C	C
30	..	..	P	P	P	P	P	P	..	..
67	..	..	..	..	F	..	..	..	..	..
80	..	..	F	F	F	F	F	F	..	..

C = Cloudy; P = finely granular precipitate; F = flocculation, flaky clumps. Here the L_F value of 1 c.c. of the toxin = 7.65 units of antitoxin.

Therefore: 2 c.c. of this toxin are equivalent to 15.3 units of antitoxin. From the above titration test, 0.035 c.c. of the antitoxin flocculated first with 2 c.c. of the toxin.

Therefore: 0.035 c.c. of antitoxin = 15.3 units of antitoxin and 1 c.c. of antitoxin = 436 units of antitoxin.

Test for Solubility in Bile (Pneumococcus and Streptococcus).—*Preparation of Ox Bile.*

1. Place ox bile in a flask and heat this in the autoclave at 15 pounds for 15 minutes.
2. Filter through paper to remove precipitate. The filtrate must be clear.
3. Distribute in tubes or flasks.
4. Sterilize in autoclave at 15 pounds for 15 minutes.

To test for solubility in bile, place 0.5 c.c. of the ox bile preparation in each of two serological tubes. To one tube add 0.5 c.c. of an 18- to 24-hour broth culture of the organism (pneumococcus or streptococcus). To the second tube of bile add 0.5 c.c. of the uninoculated broth. A second control should be made by placing in a tube 0.5 c.c. of the broth culture and 0.5 c.c. of sterile broth or saline. Incubate the tubes in the water bath at 37° C. for 2 hours or less, and note whether or not the mixture of bacteria and bile becomes clear.

Test for the Production of Hemolysin or Methemoglobin.—The test of the action of bacteria upon blood cells is sometimes more conclusive when made in test tubes than when carried out in plates of blood agar. The following procedure is especially useful for the differentiation of streptococci and pneumococci. It is essential to use young cultures, 12 to 18 hours old, in sugar free infusion or Douglas' broth.

Into each of two serological tubes place 0.5 c.c. of a 5 per cent suspension of washed sheep red corpuscles. To one tube add 0.5 c.c. of saline or sterile broth. This will serve as a control. Into the second tube place 0.5 c.c. of the broth culture of the organism. Incubate the tubes in a water bath at 37° C. for 2 hours, and note whether the blood cells in the mixture with the bacteria remain unchanged, are hemolyzed or become greenish without hemolysis.

Pneumococcus Typing.—The following methods are quoted, with permission, from *The Biology of Pneumococcus*, by B. White, E. S. Robinson and L. A. Barnes, published by the Commonwealth Fund in 1938.

Mouse Method.—One c.c. of a fresh sample of sputum is injected intraperitoneally into a mouse. From 3 to 4 hours later, some of the peritoneal fluid is obtained by puncture with a glass capillary. A glass slide is marked off into four parts, and a minute drop of the peritoneal fluid is expelled on each one of the four partitions. The first is smeared with saline solution for control, and the others with a loopful of 1:10 dilution of Type I and of Type II, and a 1:5 dilution of Type III diagnostic serums, respectively. These dilutions of serum are chosen largely to eliminate group agglutinins. Thin smears are made, allowed to dry, and fixed by passing the slide through a flame; they are then stained for from 20 to 30 seconds with a fuchsin solution (10 c.c. saturated alcoholic solution of basic fuchsin plus 90 c.c. of water) or any other available stain. The stain is washed off in water or 20 per cent copper sulfate solution, and the smears are examined with the oil immersion lens. If a specific agglutination reaction is observed in one of the smears with diagnostic serum, the organism is of that type. If no reaction occurs in any of the smears and numerous pneumococci are clearly seen, a diagnosis of Group IV is suggested. When it is desired to know whether the organism is one of the fixed types of Group IV (especially those for which concentrated antiserums are available) a similar procedure is carried out with the homologous immune serums.

Bacteria other than pneumococci in the sputum as well as avirulent forms of pneumococci may occur in clumps in the peritoneal exudate; but these differ in appearance from those produced by specific agglutination and can be distinguished further by their occurrence in the saline control smear. Unless a fresh sample of sputum is used, many of the organisms will have undergone autolysis, and therefore more time must be allowed for growth. Since the mouse is not killed, another type determination can be made if the first should show insufficient organisms, and then after the death of the mouse, the type may be confirmed.

In the case of Type III pneumococci, sufficient organisms are usually present even two hours after injection. The appearance of the specific reaction with Type III pneumococci, primarily on account of the larger size of the capsule, differs somewhat from that obtained with pneumococci of other types; the organisms are farther apart in the agglutinated clumps which occur in mucoid strands. When diagnostic serums for pneumococci of types formerly in Group IV are used, a dilution must be chosen that fails to show any cross-agglutination with any other type.

The peritoneal exudate may contain too many organisms four hours after inoculation or after death of the mouse, so that it may be necessary to dilute the fluid in the capillary tube with saline solution in order to obtain a correct typing. This method is illustrated in Chart 1.

Krumwiede Method.—A small amount of sputum (3 to 10 c.c.) is transferred to a test tube and placed in boiling water for a few minutes until coagulation occurs. The coagulum is broken up with a heavy platinum wire or glass rod and sufficient saline solution added to give just enough fluid after centrifuging. The suspension is again placed in boiling water for a few minutes to extract the soluble antigen from the coagulum, and is shaken several times during the heating process. The mixture is centrifuged and the clear supernatant fluid used for the test.

For the test, 0.2 c.c. amounts of undiluted typing serum are placed in narrow test tubes and the antigen carefully layered over the serum. The tubes are placed in a water-bath at 50° to 55° and examined after several minutes. A definite contact ring occurs in the tube containing homologous serum if the sputum is rich in antigen. The true ring is more or less opaque and in the majority of positive reactions is evident in less than 10 minutes. The success of the test depends upon the quality of the sputum. If coagulation does not occur, there is little use in continuing the test (see Chart 1).

Neufeld Quellung Method.—There are variations in the application of the Neufeld *Quellung* phenomenon to the determination of pneumococcal types in sputum samples. The one given here is the technique used in the Bacteriological Laboratory of the Massachusetts Department of Public Health.

Upon receipt of the sputum at the laboratory, stained liquid mounts of the specimen are mixed with undiluted rabbit antiserums (Types I to XXXII). Combinations of monovalent antiserums (rabbit) are used instead of making separate preparations of the sputum with each of the thirty-two monovalent serums. The combinations of serums used are:

> Type I
> A, Types II, IV, V and VII
> B, Types III and VIII
> C, Types IX, XI, XIII, and XV
> D, Types VIa, VIb, XVII, and XVIII
> E, Types XII, XIX, XVI, and XXVIII
> F, Types X, XIX, XX, and XXI
> G, Types XXII, XXIII, XXIV, and XXV
> H, Types XXVII, XXIX, XXX, XXXI, and XXXII

Nine loopfuls of sputum are placed approximately one inch apart on a 9 by 2 inch glass slide; to each drop are added 2 loopfuls of the antiserum, that is, the first drop is mixed with Type I antiserum, the second drop with combined serum A (II, IV, and VII), the third drop with B, et cetera. The preparations are stained with Loeffler's alkaline methylene blue (2 drops to each mixture) and are covered at once with cover-slips to prevent drying. Examination is made with the oil immersion lens, with the light dimmed. When a positive reaction occurs, which is usually within a few minutes, there is a decided swelling of the capsule of the pneumococcus present. The swollen capsule is of a light greenish-gray color, is much less translucent than one that is not swollen, and has a definite outline which is one of the most characteristic features of a positive reaction. In the preparations in which no reaction is evident, the capsule of the pneumococcus appears as a halo of refracted light. In all preparations the body of the pneumococcus stains a definite blue. If the reaction is observed in drop 1, then the pneumococcus present is Type I and can be reported immediately; if the reaction is observed in drop 3, for example, the test is repeated using 2 drops of the sputum mixed with Type III and Type VIII undiluted monovalent rabbit serums, respectively; if the reaction is observed in drop 9, five loopfuls of the sputum are mixed with Type XXVII, XXIX, XXX, XXXI, and XXXII undiluted monovalent serums, respectively. Should no reaction be seen on the first examination, the preparations are reëxamined at the end of 30 minutes.

When dealing with sputums containing many Type III organisms, it is necessary occasionally to dilute the sputum with salt solution before any *Quellung* of the pneumococcus capsule becomes evident. In such instances, when the regular Neufeld technique is used, the organisms form large masses surrounded by much precipitated material, and no definite swelling of the capsules can be seen. However, upon dilution of the sputum and repetition of the test, the individual diplococci will usually show a typical, positive reaction.

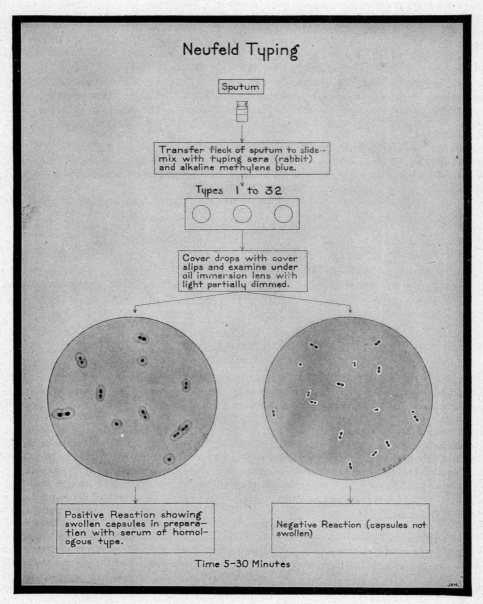

FIG. 116.—THE NEUFELD OR QUELLUNG METHOD OF TYPE DETERMINATION.
(Courtesy of Massachusetts Department of Public Health.)

The age of the specimen of sputum makes little difference in relation to the success with which the Neufeld method is applied. Positive reactions can be demonstrated on sputum 48 hours or more after collection from the patient. Figure 116 shows the steps in the technique.

The intensity of the reaction may vary from an almost imperceptible cloud to a heavy, flocculent precipitate. The reaction may occur in some instances immediately on mixing the urine and serum, or it may require incubation in the water-bath at 37° for one hour. Prolonged incubation, however, must be avoided, since bacterial growth may obscure the test. In the precipitin reaction it is essential that all the reagents used, including the immune serums, should be water-clear. In case the reaction is negative or so faint as to be indefinite with the whole urine, the following method of concentrating the urine may be employed:

Concentrated urine for precipitin test. Twenty-five c.c. or more of a 24-hour specimen of urine, with the addition of a few drops of acetic acid, are evaporated to a volume of about 5 c.c., filtered through paper to remove any precipitate of albumin that may occur, and the filtrate is added to 8 to 10 volumes of 95 per cent alcohol. The precipitate which forms is collected by centrifuging and rapidly dried to remove the excess of alcohol, and the residue extracted with 2 to 3 c.c. of salt solution, which redissolves the specific substance. Any undissolved material is removed by centrifuging, and the clear salt solution extract is used for the precipitin test. Chart 3 shows the procedure.

Isolation of Several Components of Pneumococcus.—MEDIUM FOR THE PRODUCTION OF CULTURE OF STANDARD MAXIMAL DENSITY, VIRULENCE, AND POLYSACCHARIDE CONTENT.

Witte peptone	10.0 grams
Difco proteose peptone, Fairchild, Parke-Davis, or Neopeptone	40.0 grams
Glucose	5.0 grams
Sodium chloride	5.0 grams
Sodium bicarbonate	5.0 grams
Potassium phosphate (K_2HPO_4)	2.0 grams
Thioglycollic acid	0.1 grams
Distilled water	to 1000.0 c.c.

The Witte peptone and sodium chloride are dissolved in water and the reaction of the solution adjusted to pH 8.0. The sodium bicarbonate, glucose, potassium phosphate, and extra peptone (usually Difco proteose) are then added and when they have dissolved the broth is clarified by passing through filter paper. Thioglycollic acid is finally added and the medium sterilized by candling. During the entire course of preparation the temperature of the medium is not allowed to rise above 50°.

Preparation of Bacterial Vaccine and Enumeration of Bacteria.—There are many methods for the preparation of suspensions of bacteria for use as vaccines and for the enumeration of the bacteria in these suspensions. In the following outlines we shall describe several useful and illustrative methods.

A bacterial vaccine is usually a suspension of dead bacteria in saline. An antiseptic is added to prevent growth of contaminating organisms.

1. Bacterial suspension may be made by emulsifying in saline, the growth of bacteria on any solid medium, or taking up in saline the sediment obtained by centrifuging broth cultures of bacteria. The stock emulsion is usually made more dense than the final suspension used as the vaccine.

Example: Take up twenty-four hour growth of *Staph. aureus* on an agar slant in 5 c.c. of saline. Place this in an ampule and seal in flame.

2. Shake up the emulsion and kill the bacteria by heat. The temperature usually used is 60° C. for 1 hour. Submerge the whole ampule containing the emulsion. After heating, open ampule and make transfers to prove sterility. Add 0.5 per cent phenol to the suspension.

3. Standardization. Dosage of vaccine is based upon the number of bacteria per c.c. Enumeration of bacteria may be made by:

(*a*) Direct count in a hemocytometer or best in a counting chamber especially constructed for counting bacteria (Petroff).

(*b*) Estimation of density of the suspension by method of Gates or McFarland (Nephelometry).

(*c*) Wright's method.

A Wright capillary pipet is prepared with a mark about 1 inch from the tip. A small puncture is made in the tip of the finger and a fresh drop of blood obtained. Three units of salt solution are then drawn up in the pipet, admitting a bubble of air between each two portions of salt solution. Blood from the finger tip is then drawn up to the mark, a bubble of air admitted and bacterial suspension drawn up to the mark. The mixture is then blown out on a clean slide and drawn in and out of the pipet several times to insure even mixing of the blood and bacteria. A drop of this mixture is placed on a second slide and carefully spread across the slide in the manner of making blood smears. It is important that the film be thin and even so that the red cells are not piled in masses in any portion of the film. This film is stained with Jenner's stain, or by any other simple method, and a differential count of the number of bacteria and red cells in a number of fields in different parts of the slide is made. For this a ruled scale to be inserted in the eyepiece of the microscope is very helpful. A number of fields are counted taken at random, until 200 red cells have been counted. The number of bacteria in the suspension may then be estimated from the number of bacteria counted, using the following formula (assuming that the blood of the worker contains 5,000,000 red cells per cubic mm.):

$$\frac{\text{Number of bacteria} \times 5,000,000 \times 1000}{\text{Number of red cells (200)}} = \text{Number of bacteria per c.c.}$$

3. Final dilution of vaccine. Dilute sufficient of the stock emulsion with saline containing 0.5 per cent phenol to give the required number of bacteria in the amount of vaccine required. Most bacterial vaccines contain about 500 million bacteria per c.c. Place this in a sterile ampule with special rubber stopper. Use aseptic technic throughout and make transfers of 0.1 c.c. of the final vaccine to 10 c.c. of broth to prove sterility. Incubate this test for forty-eight hours before deciding that no growth has occurred.

Barium Sulfate Standards (McFarland).—To prepare these standards, use 1 per cent sulphuric acid and 1 per cent solution of barium chloride. Combine the solutions as follows:

Standard	1 Per Cent $BaCl_2$, c.c.	1 Per Cent H_2SO_4, c.c.
No. 1	1	99
2	2	98
3	3	97
4	4	96
5	5	95
6	6	94
7	7	93
8	8	92
9	9	91
10	10	90

Select 10 tubes (150 × 19 mm.) of the same internal diameter. Put 10 c.c. of each suspension of barium sulfate in each tube and seal each tube over a flame. Prepare fresh suspensions at least once a year.

The calibration of these standards in terms of the number of bacteria per c.c. is accomplished by making direct counts of the organisms in suspensions matching in density several of the tubes in this series.

REFERENCES

GATES, F. L.   J. Exper. M., 1920, 31:105.

KAHN, R. L.   The Kahn Test, A Practical Guide, Baltimore, 1928.

NEUFELD, F.   Ztschr. f. Hyg. u. Infectionskrank., 1902, 40:54.

KOLMER, J. A., and BOERNER, F.   Approved Laboratory Technic, New York, 1931, p. 453.

KRUMWIEDE, C., COOPER, G., and PROVOST, D. J.   J. Immunol., 1925, 10:55.

SABIN, A. B.   J. Infect. Dis., 1930, 46:469.

——— J. Am. M. Ass., 1933, 100:1584.

TREVAN, J. W.   Lancet, 1922, 1:786.

VELDEE, M. V.   U. S. Pub. Health Rep., 1932, 47:1043; and special Memorandum, National Institute of Health, 1933.

WADSWORTH, A. B.   Standard Methods of the Division of Laboratories and Research of the New York State Department of Health, Baltimore, 1927, pp. 177–197.

WHITE, B., ROBINSON, E. S., and BARNES, L. A.   The Biology of Pneumococcus. Commonwealth Fund, New York, 1938.

CHAPTER LXXII

COLLECTION AND EXAMINATION OF MATERIAL FROM PATIENTS AND FROM CADAVERS

EXAMINATION OF SPECIMENS

Technical procedures for the examination of specimens of exudates, stools, sputum, etc., in various conditions are given in appropriate places in the text dealing with the individual diseases. In this chapter we wish to discuss briefly general principles of bacteriological examinations which will be useful in properly collecting and handling materials which are sent to the laboratory for diagnosis.

In making bacteriological examinations the validity of result is as fully dependent upon the technic by which the material is collected, as upon proper manipulation in the later stages of examination.

It is our opinion that hospital bacteriology is, as a rule, relatively inefficient because it is done as routine without sufficient reference to the case, specimens being sent to the laboratory by interns and nurses and handled as so much detached material. The study of pathogenic bacteria in its diagnostic and therapeutic bearing upon cases should always be combined with an understanding of the clinical problem. We encourage, wherever we can, the appointment in hospitals of experienced bacteriologists with clinical training who, by guiding the technical laboratory staff and seeing the cases with the clinicians, form the proper liaison for these purposes.

Material taken at autopsy should be, if possible, directly transferred from the cadaver to the proper culture media. If cultures are to be taken from the liver, spleen, or other organs, the surface of the organ should first be seared with a hot scalpel and an incision made through the capsule of the organ in the seared area, with the same instrument. The platinum needle can then be plunged through this incision. When blood is to be transferred from the heart, the heart muscle may be incised with a hot knife, or else the needle of a hypodermic syringe may be plunged through the previously seared heart muscle. In taking specimens of blood at autopsy it is safer to take them from the arm or leg, by allowing the blood to flow into a broad, deep cut made through the sterilized skin, than from the heart, since it has been found that postmortem contamination of the heart's blood takes place rapidly, probably through the large veins from the lungs. Exudates from the pleural cavities, the pericardium, or the peritoneum may be taken with a sterilized syringe or pipet. Under all circumstances it should be remembered that cultures taken from blood or tissues of the cadaver will be contaminated, unless cultures are taken within a few hours after death. Bacteria may get into the circulation and multiply throughout the body with astonishing speed after death.

Materials collected at the bedside or in the operating-room should be transferred

940

directly to the proper media or else into sterile test tubes and so sent to the laboratory. When the material is scanty, it may be collected upon a sterile cotton swab, which should be immediately replaced in the sterilized containing tube and sent to the laboratory.

Syringes, when used for the collection of exudates or blood, should be of some variety which is easily sterilizable by dry heat, or boiling. Most convenient of the forms in common use are the all-glass Luer type of syringe. Instruments which can be sterilized only by chemical disinfectants should not be used. When fluids are collected for bacteriological examination, such as spinal fluid, ascitic fluid, or pleural exudates, it is convenient to have them taken directly into sterilized centrifuge tubes, since it is often necessary to concentrate cellular elements by centrifugalization. By immediate collection in these tubes, exposure by transference to other tubes becomes unnecessary and the danger of contamination is avoided.

It should be remembered that the bacteriological examination of pus exudates should be combined with a cytological scrutiny of the type of cells present. The relation between polymorphonuclear leukocytes, lymphocytes and eosinophiles may furnish considerable evidence of bacteriological and prognostic import.

Pus.—Pus should first be examined morphologically by the Gram stain. It is convenient, also, to stain a specimen by one of the polychrome blood stains, in order to show clearly the relation of bacteria to the cells. Such morphological examination not only furnishes a guide to future manipulation, but supplies a control for the results obtained by cultural methods. Pus is then transferred to pour-plates or streaks made upon the surface of agar or serum-agar plates.

A guide to the choice of media is often found in the result of the morphological examination. It is well also to make anaerobic cultures by some simple method.

The colonies which develop upon the plates should be studied, and specimens from the colonies transferred to coverglasses or slides for morphological examination and to the various media for further growth and identification. Animal inoculation and agglutination tests must often also be resorted to. A knowledge of the source of the material may furnish considerable aid in making a bacteriological diagnosis, though great caution in depending upon such aid is recommended.

If the morphological examination shows gram-positive micrococci, as in staphylococcus boils, any ordinary properly made agar will suffice.

If streptococci are present in the Gram stain, it will be useful to employ blood agar plates without glucose.

When the pus is gonorrheal, ascitic agar plates with glucose should be used, and the pus transferred directly from the patient to the plate and incubated before it chills. In the case of pus from abrasions of the skin, furuncles or boils that arouse any suspicion of anthrax a careful search for gram-positive bacilli should be made with the Gram stain, and the characteristic colonies looked for on ordinary agar plates.

When plentiful leukocytes are present and the pus shows no organisms in smear, this should not discourage culture since it is not unusual to obtain colonies on culture when nothing can be found by smear.

Peritoneal, Pericardial or Pleural Exudates.—In the examination of peritoneal, pericardial, or pleural exudates it is often advantageous to use the sediment obtained by centrifugalization. A differential count of the cells present may be of

Pneumococci, streptococci, influenza bacilli, etc., may be cultivated by appropriate methods.

The cytological character of the fluid and the relationship of cells to bacteria should always be determined since this may have a certain amount of prognostic significance.

Examination of Sputum.—Sufficient emphasis cannot be placed upon the necessity of collecting the sputum in a proper way. The sputum collected by patients in the ordinary sputum cup consists to a very large extent of material obtained from the mouth and throat. If a successful examination of sputum is to be made, the patient should be taught to rinse out his mouth thoroughly, and the sputum collected directly after a cough. It is very little to ask for this amount of care, if the examination is really worth making at all. Sputum so collected should not be left in the ward, but should be sent to the laboratory immediately. Smears should be made on such sputum, with an intelligent idea of what is desired.

In the appropriate chapters we have described the procedures for the examination of sputum for pneumococci, streptococci, influenza bacilli and fungi. The examination of sputum for *tubercle bacilli* is one of the most important diagnostic procedures. The methods used are as follows:

aid in confirming the bacteriological findings. Morphological examination and cultural examination are made as in the case of pus. Specimens should also in these cases be stained for tubercle bacilli. Whenever morphological examinations of such fluids are negative, no bacteria being found, and especially when among the cellular elements the lymphocytes preponderate, the search for tubercle bacilli should be continued by means of animal inoculation. Guinea-pigs should be inoculated intraperitoneally with specimens of the fluid. The animals will usually die within six to eight weeks, but can be killed and examined at the end of about six weeks if they remain alive. The chances for a positive result are considerably increased if the fluid is set away in the ice chest until a clot has formed and the animals are inoculated with the material from the broken-up clot.

Spinal Fluid.—Normal spinal fluid is a clear, colorless fluid which contains not more than ten to twelve cells per cubic millimeter. Anything above this should be regarded as suspicious. When clear spinal fluid is brought to the laboratory it is always well to shake up the specimen and do a direct count. Both total and differential cell counts may be made at this time.

It is of value also to do a globulin reaction on such clear fluids, which is easily done by Noguchi's butyric acid method as follows:

Acid-fast Stain.—Pour the specimen of sputum from the sputum bottle or cup into a Petri dish and pick grayish-yellow particles or strands with the platinum loop. Make a thin smear on a slide, fix over the flame, stain with carbolfuchsin and decolorize with acid alcohol. Counter stain with methylene blue (see section on Stains: Carbolfuchsin, Ziehl-Neelsen Method).

Concentration of Tubercle Bacilli.—1. Mix equal parts of sputum and 4 per cent NaOH, and incubate one-half hour at 37.5° C. Tenacious sputum requires more shaking, longer incubation and more NaOH solution.

2. After complete homogenization, centrifuge the mixture at high speed and decant the supernatant fluid.

3. Add 2 to 3 drops of normal HCl to the sediment to neutralize it or make it slightly acid. This point can be determined when the sediment changes from transparent to white or opaque.

4. If the sediment is properly neutralized it will stick to a slide when dried in a thin film. If it does not stick, mix with serum or dilute egg white and make a thin smear of the mixture.

5. Dry film in the air and fix over the flame.

6. Stain as desired.

Isolation of B. tuberculosis from Sputum.—1. Digest sputum or other material with 4 per cent NaOH as described under Concentration of Tubercle Bacilli.

2. Centrifuge, decant supernatant fluid and neutralize the sediment with 1 to 2 drops of normal HCl.

3. Transfer neutralized sediment with sterile capillary pipet to Petroff's gentian violet egg medium. (See Petroff's gentian violet egg medium.)

Isolation of Tubercle Bacilli from Sputum by the Sulphuric Acid-potato Method (Corper's Method).—1. Transfer 1 c.c. of the specimen (sputum, urine, tissues, etc.) by means of a sterile 10. c.c. pipet into a previously stoppered and sterilized 15 c.c. centrifuge tube.

2. Add 1 c.c. sulphuric acid, 6 per cent. This is made by adding 17 c.c. of 96 per cent sulphuric acid, sp. gr. 1.84 to 500 c.c. of distilled water. 1 c.c. of 5 per cent pure oxalic acid (by weight) may be used in place of sulphuric acid. Using a sterile blunt-tipped stirring rod, beat the mixture into a homogeneous emulsion. Do not splash the mixture too near the top of the container. Flame the tube before replacing the sterile cork stopper.

3. Incubate for thirty minutes at 37° C., shaking the mixture occasionally.

4. Add 10 c.c. normal saline, replace the stopper tightly, mix well by carefully inverting several times, and centrifuge for five minutes. If the sediment is not well settled, centrifuge again at a higher speed. Decant the supernatant fluid, first carefully flaming the tube with stopper removed.

5. Seed the residue lightly on the surface of 3 to 6 of the tubes of crystal violet-potato medium, particularly in the lower half near the fluid level. (See Corper's Medium.)

6. Impregnate the cotton plug with hot paraffin, replace in tube, allow to cool, cap plugged tube with tinfoil, and incubate at 37° C. until growth appears (two to eight weeks). If contaminants, most commonly yeasts, are still present, they will appear usually within twenty-four to forty-eight hours and grow so rapidly as to overwhelm or prevent the detection of colonies of tubercle bacilli.

Throat Smears and Throat Examinations.—The bacteriologist, if possible, should take these specimens himself, or the physician taking them should take them only with a clear illumination of the throat, taking his specimen from the exact spot where the lesion is supposed to be located.

For diphtheria examination, the specimen is taken with a sterile swab, and plated directly upon Löffler's medium. This should be incubated without delay, and the swab sent to the laboratory with the culture. The method has been standardized and is described in the section on diphtheria.

For Vincent's angina examination, smears should be taken and stained, best by strong gentian-violet, such as used in the Gram stain, and the smear searched for the characteristic spirilla, and fusiform bacilli. If the patient is in the laboratory, it is best to make a dark field examination.

For the enumeration, or rough estimation of the numbers of hemolytic streptococci on swabs from the tonsils and pharynx, the following procedure, using poured plates of blood agar, is serviceable:

1. Place the swab, containing pus, secretions from throat, material from tonsillar crypts, etc., in a tube containing 10 c.c. of broth. Emulsify the material in the broth by gently rolling the swab along the side of the tube.

2. Make a series of dilutions of this emulsion. With sterile pipet, place 0.5 c.c. of the emulsion in a second tube containing 10 c.c. of broth. Mix this thoroughly and transfer 0.5 c.c. to a third tube containing 10 c.c. of broth.

3. From each of the 3 tubes transfer 0.1 c.c. to a sterile tube of 20 c.c. capacity.

4. Add about 15 to 18 c.c. of fluid 5 per cent blood agar at 45 to 48° C. to each of the three tubes containing 0.1 c.c. of the original diluted emulsion.

5. Mix the blood agar and bacterial emulsion by rotating or inverting the tube rapidly, and pour the contents into sterile Petri dishes.

6. Allow the agar to harden and incubate at 37° C.

7. Colonies are usually sufficiently developed to allow "picking" in twenty-four hours.

8. To obtain sufficient growth of pure cultures from single colonies, touch the colony with the tip of a sterile platinum wire and streak this on a blood agar slant or part of a blood agar plate. If properly spaced, about 10 pure culture transfers can be made on one blood agar plate. Incubate the plate at 37° C. for twenty-four hours or longer.

Examination of Lesions on the Genitalia.—Lesions suspicious of primary syphilitic nature should be gently washed, the superficial pus removed, and only exudate from the bottom of the lesion taken. If necessary, the lesion can be gently scraped and serum, mixed with as little blood as possible, used. No examination for *Treponema pallidum* is equal to the dark field examination. A drop of the exudate is placed on the slide and a cover-slip dropped on it. Then a drop of oil is placed on the bottom of the slide, over the preparation and on the top of the cover-slip, and the preparation is placed on the dark field condenser. In doing this, care should be taken to avoid air bubbles in the oil.

When suspicion of chancroid exists, the material should be inoculated immediately into tubes of coagulated and inactivated sterile rabbit's blood, and incubated according to the method of Teague.

Examination of Urine.—Bacteriological examination of the urine is of value only when specimens have been taken with sterile catheters, and care has been exercised in the disinfection of the external genitals. This is particularly important in the female. Many of the numerous finds of *B. coli* in urine are unquestionably due to defective methods. Urine should be centrifugalized or it may be precipitated with tannic acid solution in order to concentrate the bacteria. The resultant precipitate can be redissolved in small amounts of slightly alkaline fluid and then sufficiently diluted. If necessary, animal inoculation may be done. In examining urine for tubercle bacilli, special care should be taken in staining methods so as to differentiate from *B. smegmatis*. When the question is one of infection of one kidney alone the specimens must of course be obtained by ureteral catheterization.

Examine urine for tubercle bacilli as follows:

Take a twenty-four-hour specimen of urine and a sufficient amount of acetic acid to make the reaction slightly acid. To each 1000 c.c. of urine add 2 c.c. of 5 per cent tannic acid. Let this stand for a few hours. Collect the precipitate and centrifugalize. Dissolve the sediment in 4 per cent sodium hydroxide. Centrifugalize again. Decant the supernatant fluid and add a drop of hydrochloric acid. For cultivation inoculate this sediment in gentian violet medium or stain by the usual method.

Examination of Feces.—Human feces contain an enormous number of bacteria of many varieties. Klein, by special methods, estimated that there were about 75,000,000 bacteria in one milligram of feces. It has been a noticeable result of all the investigations upon the feces, that although enormous numbers can be counted in morphological specimens, only a disproportionately smaller number can be cultivated from the same specimen. This is explicable upon the ground that special culture media are necessary for many of the species found in intestinal contents and upon the consideration that many of the bacteria which are present in the morphological specimen are dead, showing that there are bactericidal processes going on in some parts of the intestinal tract, possibly through the agency of intestinal secretions, bile, and the action of the products of metabolism of the hardier species present. By far the greater part of the intestinal flora consists of members of the colon group, bacilli of the lactis aerogenes group, *B. faecalis alcaligenes, B. mesentericus,* and relatively smaller numbers of streptococci, staphylococci, and gram-positive anaerobes. Many other species, however, may be present without being necessarily considered of pathological significance. Certain writers have recently laid much stress upon a preponderance of gram-positive bacteria in specimens of feces, claiming that such preponderance signifies some form of intestinal disturbance. Herter advanced the opinion that the presence of *B. aerogenes capsulatus* in the intestinal canal is definitely associated with pernicious anemia. This is discussed in another section. The determination of these bacilli in the stools is made both by morphological examination by means of Gram stain and by isolation of the bacteria. Isolation of *B. welchii* is easily done by the method of Welch and Nuttall.

A suspension of small quantities of the feces in salt solution is made and 1 c.c. of the filtered suspension is injected into the ear vein of a rabbit. After a few minutes the rabbit is killed and placed in the incubator. After five hours of incubation, the rabbit is dissected, and if the Welch bacillus has been present in the feces, small bubbles of gas will have appeared in the liver from which the bacilli may be cultivated in anaerobic cultures.

Bacteriological examination of feces is most often undertaken for the isolation of *B. typhosus,* paratyphoid bacilli, dysentery bacilli and cholera vibrios. Details of the methods used are presented elsewhere.

The determination of tubercle bacilli in stools is difficult and of questionable significance, in that they may be present in people suffering from pulmonary tuberculosis as a consequence of swallowing sputum, and in that there may be other acid-fast bacilli, such as the timothy bacillus, present.

One method which is quite reliable for demonstration of tubercle bacilli in feces is to treat a feces dilution with 5 per cent antiformin and after sufficient solution has taken place, centrifugalize, wash and inject into guinea-pigs.

Another method is to dilute the stool with three or four parts of water, mix and filter through gauze, saturate with dry sodium chloride and allow to stand in a jar. Then collect the scum on the surface and add approximately four volumes of sodium hydroxide. Centrifugalize and add a few drops of hydrochloric acid to the sediment and stain for tubercle bacilli in the usual way (Petroff).

Blood Cultures.—The diagnosis of septicemia can be positively made during life only by the isolation of bacteria from the blood. Such examinations are of much value and are usually successful if the technic is properly carried out. A large number of methods are recommended, the writers giving, however, only the one which they have found successful and simple for general use.

The blood is taken by preference from the median basilic vein of the arm. If, for some reason (both forearms having been used for saline infusion), these veins are unavailable, blood may be taken from the internal saphenous vein as it turns over the internal malleolus of the ankle joint.

The skin over the vein should be prepared before the specimen is taken by painting with iodine, as for a surgical operation. The syringe which is used should be of some sterilizable variety (the most convenient is the Luer model), which is easily manipulated and does not draw with a jerky, irregular motion. Its capacity should be at least 10 c.c. It may be sterilized by boiling for half an hour, or preferably, when all-glass syringes are used, they may be inserted into potato-tubes and sterilized at high temperature in the hot-air chamber. Before drawing the blood, a linen bandage is wound tightly about the upper arm of the patient in order to cause the veins to stand out prominently. When the veins are plainly in view, the needle is plunged through the skin into the vein in a direction parallel to the vessel and in the direction of the blood stream. After perforation of the skin, the needle is passed into the vein. Great care should be exercised that the piston is not allowed to slip back, and air be, by accident, forced into the vessel. In most cases no strong suction is necessary, the pressure of the blood being sufficient to push up the piston. After the blood has been drawn, it should be immediately transferred to the proper media. Epstein has recently recommended the mixture of the blood with sterile 2 per cent ammonium oxalate solution in test tubes, by which means the clotting is prevented, and transfers can be made more leisurely to culture media. While this method is convenient in cases where blood must be taken at some distance from the laboratory, it is preferable, whenever possible, to make cultures from the blood immediately at the bedside.

The choice of culture media for blood cultures should, to a certain extent, be adapted to each individual case. For routine work it is best to employ hormone broth or agar, or Douglas' broth or agar.

At least six tubes of hormone agar or Douglas' agar medium should be melted and immersed in water at 45° C. Before blood is mixed with the medium, the agar should be cooled to about 41° C. in order that bacteria, if present, may not be injured by the heat. The blood is added to the tubes in varying quantities, ranging from 0.25 to 1 c.c. each, in order that different degrees of concentration may be obtained. Mixing is accomplished by the usual dipping and rotary motion, the formation of air-bubbles being thus avoided. The mouth of each test tube should be passed through the flame before pouring the contents into the plates. Three flasks of glucose broth, containing 100 to 150 c.c. of fluid each, should be inoculated with varying quantities of blood—at least one of the flasks containing the blood in high dilution. The most stringent care in the withdrawal and replacement of the cotton stoppers should be exercised. The writers have found it convenient to use, in place of one of these flasks, one containing, in addition to the glucose, 1 gram of powdered calcium carbonate. This insures neutrality, permitting pneumococci or streptococci, which are sensitive to acid, to develop and retain their vitality.

In making blood cultures from typhoid patients, Buxton and Coleman have obtained excellent results by the use of pure ox bile containing 10 per cent of glycerin and 2 per cent of peptone in flasks. The writers have had no difficulty in obtaining typhoid cultures by the use of slightly acid meat-extract broth in flasks containing 200 or more c.c. to which comparatively little blood has been transferred. The failure of a proper blood culture service in most hospitals is due, we believe, to the fact that blood cultures are taken by the intern staff, and worked out by the bacteriologist. It is of the utmost importance, in our opinion, that a single individual should be responsible for the entire examination from beginning to end. This is to avoid the great possibility of contamination in blood culture work.

Anaerobic Blood Cultures.—These cultures may be taken by mixing blood in deep tubes with glucose-ascitic fluid agar, covering with albolene and putting into Novy jars or any other form of anaerobic apparatus.

In estimating the results of a blood culture, the exclusion of contamination usually offers little difficulty. If the same micro-organism appears in several of the plates and flasks, if colonies upon the plates are well distributed within the center and under the surface of the medium, and if the micro-organisms themselves belong to species which commonly cause septicemia, such as streptococcus and pneumococcus, it is usually safe to assume that they emanated from the patient's circulation. When colonies are present in one plate or in one flask only, when they are situated only near the edges of a plate or upon the surface of the medium, and when they belong to varieties which are often found saprophytic upon skin or in air, they must be looked upon with suspicion. It is a good rule to look upon all *Staphylococcus albus* cultures skeptically.

Autopsy Bacteriology.—Cultures from the blood, exudates, secretions and tissues of cadavers at autopsy are important for the light they shed upon the etiology of infectious disease, for the study of the distribution of bacteria in the tissues of the body and for the isolation of numerous rare varieties of bacteria. Many notes and reports have been published on the bacteriological phases of the examinations of the dead bodies of animals and men, but the first systematic study of the postmortem bacteriology of human tissues was conducted by Burn [1] at the Yale Medical School. The results of his studies, published in 1934, contain important new contributions to this field of knowledge. Burn has shown that postmortem invasion by bacteria is not as common as previously believed. A large group of pathogenic and nonpathogenic bacteria failed to invade the tissues after death, even though ample opportunity was given for invasion to occur. Cultures from the lungs at autopsy often consist of the bacterial flora of the oral cavity. *B. welchii, B. coli* and staphylococci are capable of invading the tissues of animals within from 5 to 48 hours after death when the bodies are kept at 25° C. But a temperature of 10° C. restrains this invasion for as long as 96 hours. In the organs and body fluids of human cadavers Burn found a high incidence of bacteria. He found that while cultures of the heart's blood at autopsy do not represent the true bacterial flora of the tissues, the lungs, kidneys, liver, and spleen yielded bacterial growth in an order of frequency as thus listed. For details of technic and the relation of the bacteriological findings antemortem to those disclosed by postmortem examination in various diseases the reader is referred to the publications of Burn.

1 Burn, C. G. *J. Infect. Dis.*, 1934, 54:388 and 395.

CHAPTER LXXIII

THE TESTING OF ANTISEPTICS AND DISINFECTANTS

Many *in vitro* methods have been proposed for the testing of antiseptics and disinfectants. The results of these methods permit the comparison of one disinfectant with another in terms of their effects upon bacteria in culture media, but give no reliable index of the antibacterial efficacy of the substances when applied to infected tissues. The test tube tests have reached a considerable degree of precision. The actual chemotherapeutic and chemoprophylactic tests are far more difficult to perform —and more difficult still to evaluate. The testing and rating of antiseptics and disinfectants is in an unsatisfactory state. Nevertheless, as something may be learned from test-tube tests, we produce here the methods used for testing disinfectants by the U. S. Food and Drug Administration. The material is quoted almost verbatim, with permission, from Circular No. 198, U. S. Dept of Agriculture, issued in December, 1931.[1] All disinfectants and antiseptics in inter-state commerce must be submitted to these tests.

The standardization of disinfectants and antiseptics is based upon the determination of their activities in comparison with phenol. Their ratio is known as the *phenol coefficient,* which is defined as follows:

The phenol coefficient is a figure expressing the ratio of the killing efficiency of a disinfectant as compared with that of phenol tested under identical conditions. The sample to be tested is diluted and the dilutions arranged in a series of decreasing concentrations (increasing dilutions). To these a specified amount of the test organism in broth culture is added. At the end of fixed periods of time a small definite portion of the mixture of diluted disinfectant and test organism is transferred to a nutrient culture medium and incubated. No growth in the subculture indicates that the organism has been killed. The greatest dilution (weakest concentration) of the disinfectant killing in a definite time period is divided by the greatest dilution of phenol killing in the same time period. This ratio is the phenol coefficient. It should be noted that the phenol coefficient is not based on a comparison of different time intervals but on a comparison of different concentrations acting for specified time periods, under specified conditions.

At present, there are in general use three methods of determining the phenol coefficient: the U. S. Hygienic Laboratory (H.L.) method,[2] the Rideal-Walker (R.W.) method, and the method described below, of the Food and Drug Administration (F.D.A.).

---

1 Quotation marks are omitted. Reference should be made directly to this Circular for the actual phraseology of official statements.

2 *Disinfectant Testing by the Hygienic Laboratory Method.* Reprint No. 675, *U. S. Pub. Health Rep.,* 1921, 36:1559.

The F.D.A. method, based upon the R.W. and H.L. methods, was designed by Shippen and Reddish to overcome the handicaps and minor deficiencies in both of the older procedures for determining the phenol coefficient. Special features of the F.D.A. method are the use of cultures of *B. typhosus* (*Eberthella typhi*) and *Staphylococcus aureus* of known resistance to phenol and provisions for the use of other organisms.

The phenol coefficients of a large number of substances chemically related to phenol (the only type of disinfectants for which the H.L. method is accepted) are, in most cases, practically the same, whether tested by the F.D.A. or the H.L. method (Brewer and Reddish).

DIFFERENCES IN MEDIA AND MANIPULATION OF THE THREE METHODS OF DETERMINING PHENOL COEFFICIENT

Item	F.D.A. Method	R.W. Method	H.L. Method
Composition of medium.	Peptone*, 10 gm.... Liebig's beef extract, 5 gm. Salt, 5 gm.......... Water, 1,000 c.c.... Boil 20 minutes.....	Peptone,† 20 gm...... Liebig's beef extract, 10 gm. Salt, 10 gm.......... Water, 1,000 c.c....... Boil 30 minutes......	Peptone,* 10 gm. Liebig's beef extract, 3 gm. Salt, 5 gm. Water, 1,000 c.c. Boil 15 minutes.
Acidity of medium.....	pH 6.8............	+ 1.5. No definite pH..	Unadjusted but pH between 6.0 and 7.0.
Amount of culture medium in tube	10 c.c.............	5 c.c.	10 c.c.
Amount of culture added to diluted disinfectant.	0.5 c.c. to 5.0 c.c....	0.5 c.c. to 5.0 c.c......	0.1 c.c. to 5.0 c.c.
Resistance of test culture to phenol (dilutions killing in 10 minutes but not in 5 minutes)	1–90.............	1–90 to 1–110.......	No limits stated.
Condition of tube in test.	Plugged with cotton.	Plugged with cotton....	Open tubes.
Temperature of test	20° C.............	15–18° C.	20° C.
Time intervals of the test	5, 10, and 15 minutes	2½, 5, 7½, and 10 minutes.	5, 7½, 10, 12½, and 15 minutes.
Amount of medication mixture transferred (size of loop).	4 mm. loop (of No. 23 B. and S. gage wire).	4 mm. loop (of No. 27 Imperial gage wire).	Spiral loop (four spirals wrapped around a No. 13 B. and S. gage wire. Made of No. 23 B. and S. gage wire).
Calculation of phenol coefficient.	Highest dilution not killing in 5 minutes but killing in 10 minutes divided by same for phenol.	Highest dilution not killing in 5 minutes but killing in 7½ minutes divided by same for phenol.	Mathematical mean of highest dilutions showing no growth in 5, 10, and 15 minutes divided by same for phenol.

* Armour's. Special bath set aside for disinfectant testing.   † Allen and Hanbury's.

The curtailment in labor, time, and material through the use of the F.D.A. method renders it particularly valuable where a large number of samples are involved. The F.D.A. method is considerably superior to the R.W. method in producing consistent results. The medium employed is better adapted to bacterial growth, and the technic is not restricted to the use of one test organism (*Eberthella typhi*) as is the case in the R.W. and H.L. methods. Moreover, the stock cultures of *E. typhi* and *Staphylococcus aureus*, the organisms principally used in germicidal testing, remain sufficiently constant in their resistance to phenol, when grown on an adjusted medium, to necessitate but one phenol control, though two controls are used frequently as an additional check. This allows the use of 9 dilutions of the unknown with 30-second intervals between transfers, or 14 when 20-second intervals are used. With a little practice, 20-second intervals allow sufficient time.

Food and Drug Administration Method

APPARATUS AND TECHNIC

Test Organism and Culture Medium

The test organism is a 22–26-hour culture of *Eberthella typhi* (Hopkins strain) incubated and grown in nutrient broth at 37° C. The broth contains the following ingredients: 5 gm. of Liebig's beef extract, 5 gm. of chemically pure sodium chloride, and 10 gm. of Armour's peptone (for disinfectant testing) in 1000 c.c. of distilled water. The mixture is boiled for 20 minutes, made up to original weight (or volume) with distilled water, and adjusted with NaOH to pH 6.8 using the colorimetric method. It is then filtered through paper, tubed (10 c.c. to each tube), and the tubes plugged with cotton and sterilized at 15 pounds pressure for 40 minutes. The test culture is transferred daily in this medium for not more than one month. At the end of each month, a fresh transfer is made from the stock culture. The stock culture is carried on agar slants of the same composition as the broth medium plus 1½ per cent Bacto-Agar (Difco), adjusted to pH 7.2 to 7.4. This medium is also filtered, tubed, plugged with cotton, sterilized, and slanted. The stock culture is transferred once a month, and the test organism is taken from the month-old stock culture. When the test organism has not been transferred daily, it is advisable to make four or five consecutive daily transfers in broth before using it for testing purposes, to be reasonably sure of its conforming to the phenol resistance requirements. When only one transfer has been skipped the following transfer from the 48-hour culture is usually satisfactory for use after 24 hours. Transfers are made with the platinum loop used in the test. Only cultures giving readings within the following limits are considered satisfactory:

	5 Minutes	10 Minutes	15 Minutes
Phenol:			
1–90	+	+	0
1–100	+	+	+
Or			
1–90	0	0	0
1–100	+	+	0

The following reading is that most usually obtained and is the most convenient:

	5 Minutes	10 Minutes	15 Minutes
Phenol:			
1–90	+	0	0
1–100	+	+	+

Phenol

The phenol used must meet the requirements of the United States Pharmacopoeia, and in addition the congealing point must not be below 40° C. A 5 per cent solution may be used as a stock solution if kept in a relatively cool place in well-stoppered amber-colored bottles protected from the light. This 5 per cent solution should be standardized with decinormal bromine, or with sodium bromide and bromate solution.

Apparatus

Besides a number of accurately graduated pipets, 100-c.c. glass-stoppered graduates or volumetric flasks are almost essential for the making of correct dilutions. All pipets and graduates should be standardized. The test tubes for containing the dilutions should be large enough to permit transfers being made without touching the sides with the transfer needle. Lipped pyrex (to withstand constant flaming) test tubes 25 by 150 mm. serve very well as these seeding or medication tubes. A water bath for holding the dilutions at the desired temperature must be provided. To maintain the temperature practically constant during the period of the test, the bath should be made so as to contain a relatively large volume per surface area, and should be insulated. The lid is made with well-spaced holes admitting the 25-mm. tube, but not the lip. The most convenient form of subculture tubes (tubes containing medium for incubating the tested organisms, as well as for growing the test culture) are ordinary nonlipped bacteriological test tubes 20 by 150 mm. The racks for holding the subculture tubes may be any convenient style. Blocks of wood with a series of holes bored in them are quite satisfactory. Dimensions depend somewhat on the size of the incubator, but the holes should be well spaced to insure quick selection and easy manipulation during the test. It is an added convenience to have the holes large enough to admit the medication tubes while dilutions are being made. The transfers are made with a 4-mm. (inside diameter) single loop of number 23 B. & S. gage platinum wire, 1½ to 3 inches long, set in a suitable holder such as an aluminum or glass rod approximately 0.5 cm. in diameter.

Procedure

One per cent stock dilutions of the substance to be tested (or any other convenient dilution of the disinfectant, depending on the strength) are made up, usually in the glass-stoppered cylinders or volumetric flasks from which the individual dilutions are then prepared. For rapid routine work, the final dilutions may be made directly in the medication tubes. In this case all excess over 5 c.c. must be removed. For more precise work and when high dilutions are required or volatile substances are dealt with, it is preferable to make up all of the dilutions in volumetric flasks and then transfer 5 c.c. of the final dilution to the medication tubes. These tubes containing 5 c.c. of each dilution (including the phenol control) are placed in the water bath at 20° C. for five minutes until the temperature of the bath is reached. Even slight variations in temperature may affect the results. The dilutions should cover the range of the killing limits of the disinfectant within 5 and 15-minute periods and should at the same time be spaced sufficiently close together to insure the desired accuracy. Five-tenths of a cubic centimeter of the test culture is then added to each of the dilutions at a time interval corresponding to the interval at which the transfers are to be made. Thus by the time 10 tubes have been seeded at 30-second intervals, four and one-half minutes will have elapsed and a 30-second interval intervenes before the transference to the subcultures is commenced. The culture is added from a graduated pipet holding sufficient culture to seed all the tubes in any one set. The pipet may be loosely plugged with cotton at the mouth end before sterilizing, as a precautionary measure. Unfiltered culture is used, but it should be thoroughly shaken 15 minutes before use and allowed to settle. The temperature of the culture should be practically that of the water bath before being added.

In inoculating the medication tubes they should be held in a slanting position, after removal from the bath, and the culture run in without the tip of the pipet touching the disinfectant. The tip may be allowed to rest against the side of the tube just above the surface of the liquid. The tubes are agitated gently but thoroughly after the addition of the culture to insure even distribution of the bacteria. Five minutes from the time of seeding the first medication tube, transfer 1 loopful of the mixture of culture and diluted disinfectant from the medication tube to the corresponding subculture tube. To facilitate transfer of uniform drops of the medication mixture, the loop is bent to form a slight angle with the stem and the medication tube is held at an angle of 60°. In other words, as the loop is withdrawn, its plane should be parallel with the surface of the liquid. At the end of 30 seconds, a loopful is transferred from the second medication tube to the second subculture tube and the process continued for each successive dilution. Five minutes from the time of making the first transfer, a second set of transfers is begun for the 10-minute period and finally repeated for the 15-minute period. Before each transfer the loop is heated to red heat in the Bunsen flame and the mouth of every tube is flamed. Sterilization of the loop is effected immediately after making the previous transfer (before replugging the tubes) to allow time for sufficient cooling. Time does not permit flaming the tubes after making the transfer. For this reason, care in transferring and seeding is necessary. Due caution is observed to prevent either the seeding pipet or the transfer needle from touching the sides or mouth of the medication tube; neither should cotton threads be found adhering to the sides or mouth of these. After completion of the transferring, the subculture tubes are incubated at 37° C. for 48 hours and results read. Macroscopic examination usually suffices for this, but occasionally agglutination with antityphoid serum will aid in reading doubtful results. A 3-day incubation period of agar streak or microscopic examination may be resorted to in determining feeble growth, especially when organisms other than *Eberthella typhi* are used.

There are certain types of germicidal agents, such as many of the mercury compounds, which give very high results by phenol coefficient tests. Due to the high inhibitory value of such substances in preventing growth in the subcultures these figures are frequently misleading. For germicides used in the disinfection of such objects as surgical instruments, this is of particular importance and must be taken into account. Failure to appreciate this characteristic of certain compounds is much more likely to lead to error when *Staphylococcus aureus* is used rather than *Eberthella typhi* as the test organism. That false values may not be obtained for products of this type, or for any other disinfectant giving suspiciously high results, the subcultures should contain very large amounts of medium (not less than 200 c.c.) or they should be retransferred by carrying at least 4 loopfuls from the first subculture to a second tube of broth, as recommended by Shippen.

Other groups of disinfectants in common use, for which the phenol coefficient method of testing is not well adapted, are those compounds containing chlorine as the active agent as well as oxidizing agents in general. These are affected so materially by the presence of organic matter that a phenol coefficient statement may grossly misrepresent their value under practical conditions of use and is very apt to be misleading to the consumer when placed on the label.

CALCULATION OF THE PHENOL COEFFICIENT

The results of the test are expressed in terms of the phenol coefficient. This represents the germicidal value of the diluted disinfectant as compared with the diluted phenol control. It is a figure obtained by dividing the numerical value of the greatest dilution (the denominator of the fraction expressing the dilution) of the disinfectant capable of killing *Eberthella typhi* in 10 minutes but not in 5 minutes, by the greatest dilution of phenol showing the same results; that is, by the phenol control. Thus, if the results were as follows:

	5 Minutes	10 Minutes	15 Minutes
Disinfectant (X):			
1–300	0	0	0
1–325	+	0	0
1–350	+	0	0
1–375	+	+	0
1–400	+	+	+
Phenol:			
1–90	+	0	0
1–100	+	+	+

The phenol coefficient would be $\dfrac{350}{90} = 3.89$.

If none of the dilutions shows growth in 5 minutes and killing in 10 minutes, the hypothetical dilution may be estimated in certain cases. This may be done only when any three consecutive dilutions show the following results:

The first, no growth in 5 minutes; the second, growth in 10 minutes but not in 15 minutes; and the third, growth in 15 minutes; for example:

If the results were as follows:

	5 Minutes	10 Minutes	15 Minutes
Disinfectant (X):			
1–300	0	0	0
1–350	+	+	0
1–400	+	+	+
Phenol:			
1–90	0	0	0
1–100	+	+	0

the estimated phenol coefficient would be $\dfrac{325}{95} = 3.42$.

To avoid giving an impression of fictitious accuracy, the phenol coefficient is calculated to the nearest 0.1 unless the coefficient is less than 1.0. Thus, in the examples cited above, the phenol coefficients would be reported as 3.9 and 3.4 instead of 3.89 and 3.42.

In the preceding description, *Eberthella typhi* has been mentioned as the test organism. Wherever any expression of phenol coefficient occurs in literature, on labels, etc., it is assumed to mean the *E. typhi* phenol coefficient, unless otherwise stated. It is, however, the distinct intention not to limit the test to the use of one organism. In fact, the test has been found adaptable to the use of a wide variety of bacterial species in the determination of phenol coefficients. In cases where some of the more strictly parasitic bacteria are used, modifications in media are necessitated, and, of course, a change in the phenol dilutions. The writers are not in a position at this time to prescribe the limits of resistance for many of the organisms that might be used. Therefore discussion of the exact technic is here omitted, with the exception of that for *Staphylococcus aureus*. Suggestions for the use of certain representative types may, however, be found in a paper by Reddish. When any test organism other than *E. typhi* is used it should be distinctly designated when stating the phenol coefficient.

S. aureus has been found to be an extremely useful organism for testing disinfectants and antiseptics and has been used for this purpose for a number of years. When substituted in the above test the technic remains exactly the same. The phenol dilutions, however, must be changed. The resistance of any strain of *S. aureus* used in this test must come within the following limits: At 20° C. it must survive a 1:60 dilution of phenol for 5 minutes and a 1:70 dilution for 15 minutes. The following is the minimal resistance that would be acceptable:

	5 Minutes	10 Minutes	15 Minutes
Phenol:			
1–60	+	0	0
1–70	+	+	+

In the bacteriological examination of disinfectants, the *Eberthella typhi* and the *S. aureus* phenol coefficients give, in general, sufficient information to render tests with other organisms unnecessary, except in special instances. The commonly accepted criterion that disinfectants for general use be employed at a dilution equivalent to the germicidal efficiency of 5 per cent phenol against *E. typhi* (that is, 20 times the *E. typhi* phenol coefficient) allows a reasonable margin of safety for the destruction of infective agents likely to be the object of general disinfection about premises with the possible exception of *Mycobacterium tuberculosis*. *S. aureus*, due to its ubiquity, resistance and ever-ready tendency to cause infection, should always be employed in testing those substances recommended for personal use or as applications for wounds. If the disinfectant is recommended for use externally the temperature of test should be 20° C., but where such substances are recommended for use in the body cavities, such as for mouth washes, gargles, douches, etc., this test should be conducted at 37° C. In such case the test should be designated "The F.D.A. method (special) *S. aureus*, 37° C." At body temperature the *S. aureus* should show the following resistance to phenol:

	5 Minutes	10 Minutes	15 Minutes
1–80	+	0	0
1–90	+	+	+

Or

	5 Minutes	10 Minutes	15 Minutes
1–80	+	0	0
1–90	+	+	0

The previous description of this method (Reddish) differed from this only in allowing a slightly wider latitude in the resistance of the test organism against phenol.

Other Tests for Germicides and Antiseptics [3]

The limitations of the phenol coefficient make it necessary in some cases to judge the germicidal preparation by other tests or by additional tests. This is particularly true of preparations that are not completely soluble or miscible in water. It is also true of certain preparations designated as antiseptics.

Soluble antiseptics or antiseptics completely miscible with water can be tested, of course, by the procedure already described as the F.D.A. *Staphylococcus aureus* phenol coefficient method. In the testing of these substances, however, the phenol coefficient is not obtained necessarily, the phenol figure being used merely as a check of the resistance of the test organism. The information desired is the concentration which will kill in five minutes.

In an effort to simulate practical conditions, it is frequently advisable to conduct the tests in the presence of blood serum. Sterile horse serum in a concentration of 10 per cent is ordinarily used, both in the germicidal and inhibitory tests. Special claims and uses of a product, however, frequently indicate the desirability of a higher concentration of this organic enrichment.

The following methods designed for the testing of insoluble and immiscible products are in use in this laboratory at the present time. Some of them have been used for years and have been described previously (Brewer and Reddish). Laboratory tests, of course, can not duplicate the exact conditions found in practice. The procedures here outlined, however, are as close an approach to practical conditions as is feasible in routine laboratory tests, and reveal the obviously useless preparations. It should be noted that inhibitory tests are considered along with other facts in interpreting whether or not the substance will be of value in practical use. It must be remembered that not only bacteriological but physiological and pharmacological facts frequently must be taken into consideration in judging many substances.

THE WET FILTER-PAPER METHOD

The wet filter-paper method is a germicidal test rather than a test of inhibitory properties. It is used when the substance to be tested is not soluble or completely miscible with water, or for substances that are to be used in high concentration, such as soaps, tooth pastes, suppositories, dyes,

---

3 According to current usage the word "antiseptic" has two meanings: to kill bacteria or to prevent their growth, depending upon the use of the product. Products such as salves, ointments, and dressings that remain in contact with the body for long periods of time, may be designated properly as antiseptics if they inhibit the growth of bacteria. On the other hand, mouth washes, douches, gargles, and preparations of like nature are in contact with the body for but brief periods of time and exert negligible inhibitory action. These may be described properly as antiseptics only if they will destroy bacteria under the conditions of use; that is, in the dilutions recommended and in a period of time comparable to that in which they would have an opportunity to act when used as directed.

dusting powders, salves, and ointments. If the substance is to be used in the body cavities the test is carried out at 37° C.; if not, the test is carried at 20° C., or at room temperature, and the temperature is recorded.

No. 2 Whatman filter paper is cut into pieces about 0.5 cm. square, and sterilized in a plugged test tube at temperatures below 170° C. to prevent charring. A suitable number of the paper squares are then impregnated with *Staphylococcus aureus*, or other test organisms, by immersion in a 24-hour broth culture of the organism. The culture must have the standard resistance required for phenol coefficient testing. The wet inoculated squares are then placed in the liquid or solid substance to be tested in such a way as to be completely covered and in intimate contact. At the end of 5 minutes, 10 minutes, 15 minutes, or 1 hour, or any other desired length of time, the wet papers are removed with a sterilized, stiff, platinum wire bent at a sharp angle to form a hook and placed in 10 c.c. of sterile broth. After as much of the disinfectant as possible has been removed (in the case of sticky substances, the needle must be used to aid in freezing the squares of adherent germicide) the squares are retransferred to a fresh tube of sterile broth (10 c.c.) and the tubes incubated at 37° C. for 48 hours, when they are observed for evidence of growth.

It will be noted that in this test resubcultures are always required, since the first tube of broth to which the filter-paper squares have been added frequently contains sufficient antiseptic to exhibit inhibition of growth. Both tubes of broth are usually incubated.

The Dry Filter-paper Method

The dry filter-paper method is used in tests of fumigants and of oils that are to be used where moisture is absent. It is similar to the wet filter-paper test, squares of paper being used that have been impregnated as described under the test above, except the squares are dried for two days in a sterile Petri dish in the 37° C. incubator. This test can be used successfully only with organisms capable of resisting the drying. *Eberthella typhi* will not withstand the drying. In the writers' work *Staphylococcus aureus* is the usual test organism. The inoculated dried paper squares may be used at any time after drying up to 30 days, but the resistance of the organism at no time should fall so low that it is incapable of withstanding a 1–80 dilution of phenol for five minutes at 20° C. It should be noted that control tests with nonmedicated squares should always be carried out to test the viability of the test organism. As in the wet filter-paper method, resubcultures are always necessary.

The Agar-plate Method

The agar-plate method is a test for inhibitory properties and is used for substances remaining in contact with the body in the absence of serous body fluids. Examples of substances which may be tested by this method are salves, dusting powders, creams, plasters, pads, adhesive tape, catgut, and suppositories. The test organism ordinarily used is *Staphylococcus aureus*, but for special purposes the test may be used with any organism capable of growing on agar. The agar is of the same composition as that previously described for carrying stock cultures of the test organism.

Fifteen to twenty cubic centimeters of agar are melted and cooled to 42° to 45° C. To this is added 0.1 c.c. of a 24-hour broth culture of the test organism. The inoculated agar is then poured into a sterile Petri plate and allowed to harden. As soon as the agar has hardened, the test substance is placed in intimate contact with the surface of the agar. If a salve, it is first warmed just sufficiently to soften it and thus secure a complete peripheral contact. As a control, warmed sterile petrolatum may be placed on another portion of the plate. The plates are incubated 24 to 48 hours under unglazed porcelain tops at 37° C. and then are examined for evidence of inhibition. If the preparation is antiseptic or inhibitory, a zone of clear agar will be noted around the place where the substance has been in contact and the width of the zone will indicate the diffusibility of the inhibitory (antiseptic) agent. If there is no inhibition, growth of the test organism will be observed adjacent to and even under the test substance.

The Serum Agar-plate Method

Preparations recommended for use on open wounds, cuts, etc. will be effective only if they exhibit activity in the presence of serous fluids. In testing such preparations the agar-plate method is modified by the addition of 10 per cent sterile horse serum to the agar.

THE AGAR CUP-PLATE METHOD [4]

The agar cup-plate method is merely a variation of the agar-plate method. It is to be used on products liquid at the temperature of the test. The agar or serum agar is inoculated as in the agar-plate method. Before the agar cools, a depression or cup is made in the medium by standing a sterile flat-bottomed glass tube, 1.5 c.m. in diameter, in the liquefied agar. On hardening, the glass tube is removed by slightly twisting and pulling at the same time. Insertion of a sterile wire down the side of the tube for the introduction of air will eliminate much of the cracking of the agar. Another method of preparing the agar-cup plate is to allow the medium to harden and then cut out a disk in the agar, by means of a cork borer, 1.5 cm. in diameter. One or two drops of melted agar are placed in the cup to seal cracks or crevices. After the agar cup plate is prepared, 6 drops of the liquid to be tested are placed in the cup and the plate incubated under an unglazed porcelain top for 24 to 48 hours. If there is a clear zone about the cup, the substance under test has inhibitory properties. Here, as well as in the agar-plate test, the agar in the clear zone may be tested for growth by subculture in broth to indicate whether the action is germicidal or merely inhibitory.

REFERENCES

BREWER, C. M., and REDDISH, G. F.   J. Bacteriol., 1929, 17:44.

COWLES, P. B.   Yale J. Biol. and M., 1938, 11:127.

REDDISH, G. F.   Am. J. Pub. Health, 1927, 17:320; J. Lab. and Clin. Med., 1929, 14:649.

RIDEAL, S., and WALKER, J. T. A.   Approved Technique of the Rideal-Walker Test, London, 1921.

RUEHLE, G. L. A., and BREWER, C. M.   Circular No. 198, U. S. Dept. of Agriculture, 1921.

SHIPPEN, L. P.   Am. J. Pub. Health, 1928, 18:1231.

[4] The authors are indebted to L. C. Himebaugh for this method.

INDEX

Bacteria (cont'd)   Bacteria (cont'd)

Pneumonia (cont'd)
— epidemiology of, 338
— Friedländer's bacillus causing, 482, 486
— lobar, 313
— mortality in, 330
— primary, 338
— prophylactic vaccination against, 343
— resistance to, 255
— secondary, 341
— septicemia and, 329
— serum therapy of, 332
— susceptibility to, 340
— tularemic, 577
— vaccine therapy of, 344
Pneumosintes, 136
Pneumonic plague, 584, 585, 586
Pneumonic tularemia, 577
Poisons, bacterial, 152
— mode of attack by, 154
Polar bodies, 21
Polarized light, effect of, on bacteria, 94
Poliomyelitis, 136, 159, 256, 260, 771, 801
— anterior, 801
— carriers of, 805
— epidemiology of, 805
— etiology of, 802
— immunity in, 803
— serum therapy of, 804
— spinal fluid in, 942
— virus of, 803
Polychrome stains, 859
Polymorphism, 130
Polyplax spinulosus, 663, 666
Polysaccharides, bacterial, 44, 45
Potassium permanganate, 105
Poultry diseases. See Chicken diseases.
Precipitation, 203
— phenomena of, 189, 204
Precipitins, 165
— test of, with proteins, 932
— typhoid bacillus and, 519
Pressure, effects of, on bacteria, 93, 95
Primates, tuberculin test in, 454
Proflavine, 110
Prontosil, 111, 307
Prontylin, 307
Protargin, 108
Protargol, 108
Protein therapy, nonspecific, 216
Proteins, bacterial, 42, 43
Proteolytic enzymes, 68
Proteus bacilli, 680
— characteristics of, 496
— gram-negative, 147
Proteus mirabilis, 496
Proteus vulgaris, 496, 497
Proteus zenkeri, 496
Protoplasm, bacterial, 51
— changes in, 53
Protozoa, 144
Prozones, 200

Pseudo-influenza bacilli, 359, 362
Pseudomonas, 144
Pseudomonas aeruginosa, 561. See Bacillus pyocyaneus.
Pseudo-rabies, 780
Pseudo-tuberculosis ovis bacilli, 432
Psittacosis, 826, 833
— bacillus of, 504, 833
— laboratory diagnosis of, 834
— virus of, 504, 833-834
Psychrophilic bacteria, 85
Ptomaine poisoning, Proteus vulgaris and, 497
Ptomaines, 70, 153
Puerperal sepsis, 304
Pulmonary tuberculosis, 443
Pus, specimen of, examination of, 941
Putrefaction, 69
Pyemia, 152
Pyocyanine, bacterial, 48

"Quarter-evil," 634

Rabbits, encephalitis of, 780
Rabbits, filtrable virus of Rivers in, 779
— infectious myxomatosis in, 779
Rabies, 254, 780, 801, 815
— immunization of dogs, against, 822
— inoculation of mice with, 818
— lower animal or human hosts of, 119
— negri bodies in, 817
— specific therapy of, 15, 819-822
— virus of, 818
Radiations produced by bacteria, 57
Radium, effect of, on bacteria, 94
Ramon test, 182
Rat bite fever, 254, 715-716
— diagnosis of, 717
Rat leprosy, 471
Rat-proofing in prevention of plague, 592
Rauschbrand, 634
Reagin, 234
Receptors, double, in bacteria, 521
Refractive index of bacteria, 51
Relapsing fever, 699
— immunity in, 702
— spirochetes of, 699, 700, 701
— — cultivation of, 700
— — pathogenicity of, 701
— types of, 702
Reproduction of bacteria, 27-30
— asexual, 28
— sexual, 30
Reptiles, tubercle bacillus in, 458
Resistance, defensive factors and, 157-170
Respiration, bacterial, 62
Respiratory pigments, bacterial, 47
Respiratory tract infections, 355
Reticulo-endothelial system, 209
— immunity and, 209